DESIGN OF BRUSHLESS PERMANENT-MAGNET MACHINES

Safety barrier at a railway level-crossing in Tsuruoka, Japan, operated by a brushless DC motor designed by M. Saito (pictured).

This photograph somehow symbolizes the quiet and lowly work done by millions of motors in everyday applications. It also symbolizes the gateway to a fascinating revolution in motor technology which we have tried to address in this book.

See page 208 for more railway action . . .

Design of Brushless Permanent-Magnet Machines

J.R. Hendershot Jr.
T.J.E. Miller

DESIGN OF BRUSHLESS PERMANENT-MAGNET MACHINES

Published in the USA by Motor Design Books LLC
102 Triano Circle, Venice, Florida, 34292, USA

This is an entirely re-written successor to
Design of Brushless Permanent-Magnet Motors
J.R. Hendershot and T.J.E. Miller
published in 1994 by
Magna Physics Publishing & Oxford University Press
(ISBN 1-88155-03-1 and 0-19-859389-9)
[Errata for that book available from the Authors]

J.R. Hendershot : hendershot@ieee.org

T.J.E. Miller : tjemiller@ieee.org

ISBN 978-0-9840687-0-8

Preface

There are now many more books on brushless permanent-magnet machines than when we wrote *Design of Brushless Permanent-Magnet Motors* in 1994. Not only books, but academic and trade publications by the thousand have emerged in the last 16 years. Yet this is nothing compared to the expansion in the range and number of products using brushless permanent-magnet machines.

We have tried to catch up with the progress of engineering theory and practice in this important and growing field. Almost the entire work is the direct result of intensive consulting by the authors, in collaborating with many of the leading producers of brushless permanent-magnet machine products worldwide. This work has included the formulation, writing, documentation, teaching, application, and technical support of the *SPEED* software, particularly the *PC-BDC* program which is widely used throughout the industry for design and analysis of brushless permanent-magnet machines. Much of the theoretical material can be used as a guide to the basic algorithms of that program, and even the structure of the book reflects the different components of *PC-BDC* and its calculations. However, the book is independent of the program and can be understood without reference to it. It was written with a focus on actual engineering practice and tries to deal with many of the questions that arise on a daily basis in design.

The book is written for practising engineers, many of whom have used the 1994 book heavily (and deserve something better!). It has many more worked examples than the earlier book. In writing it we have held Veinott as the model of what we wanted to achieve, (increasing our reverence for Veinott in the process). Should anyone wish to use it for undergraduate teaching, some problems and solutions are available and may be obtained from TJEM; but the book is too narrow and too detailed for undergraduates.

The authors' partnership is a long-standing and sometimes orthogonal combination of the practical and the academic. Engineering is a practical art with just enough theory. When the archaeologists dig up our civilization in a couple of thousand years' time, they will marvel at how many sophisticated things we made, using only a few simple calculations.

Chapter 1 begins with a definition of the synchronous machine, sufficiently broad to include the squarewave and sinewave drive systems which are linked by the process of commutation. The Chapter develops the essential theory of the squarewave brushless DC motor as far as the torque/speed characteristic, keeping as close as possible to the theory of the classical DC commutator motor. This is important not only because of its historical significance, but because it introduces key concepts such as the torque and EMF constants, and even field weakening. The ideal energy-conversion equation of the DC commutator motor is also at the root of the *dq*-axis theory which underlies the theory of the brushless AC machine. Sinewave motors and drives are introduced using the phasor diagram.

Chapter 2 is a review of the main types of brushless PM machine, and is essentially a gallery of examples with brief explanations of essential features and characteristics.

Chapter 3 addresses the most important technical approaches to the design of brushless PM machines. Starting from such basic questions as the number of slots and poles, the choice of interior or exterior rotor etc., the design decisions are examined systematically. Practical details are treated alongside theoretical principles, and there is a systematic section on windings with several detailed examples. Chapter 3 includes treatment of dimensioning, cogging, winding manufacture, AC resistance, and magnet retention.

Chapter 4 covers the basic electromagnetic theory of motors and generators, including squarewave and sinewave operation. It begins with the open-circuit flux produced by the magnets, and the operating point of the magnet on its demagnetization curve. It then derives the EMF waveform, with reference to the properties of windings and the "BLV" and "Tooth-flux waveform" methods. Torque is introduced in this Chapter, with a detailed treatment of instantaneous and average torque in squarewave and sinewave systems, leading to the *dq* transformation and Park's equations for salient-pole machines. With current flowing, the effect of inductance is also important, and this is incorporated into the torque calculation partly by classical theory and partly by means of the flux-MMF diagram or energy-conversion loop, also known as the i-ψ diagram. This diagram follows naturally from the EMF and current waveforms, and leads to a powerful method for analyzing the effect of saturation.

Chapter 5 presents a thorough analysis of inductance, including all its components: airgap, slot-leakage, end-turn, differential, and synchronous inductance. The practical effects of inductance are described (without mathematics). The theoretical basis of the measurement of inductance is laid down. There is a discussion of the limitations of the concept of inductance and the strength of methods that are based purely on flux-linkage. This includes a description of the magnetization curves of the brushless permanent-magnet machine. Finally the effect of saturation is described, along with means to deal with it especially in sinewave machines.

Chapters 6 and 7 give detailed accounts of the principles of electronic drive and control, Chapter 6 for squarewave systems and Chapter 7 for sinewave systems.

Chapter 6 covers the commutation sequence and the current regulation using several different algorithms for three-phase, two-phase, and unipolar drives. Phase advance, regeneration, dwell control, and back-EMF sensing are all treated in this Chapter.

Chapter 7 is a complete account of the theory of sinusoidal drive control, starting with the phasor diagram for motoring and generating, and proceeding to the analysis of voltage and current limits, firstly through the voltage locus diagram. Then the voltage-limited circle (for nonsalient-pole) and ellipse (for salient-pole) machines are developed in detail, including an exhaustive treatment of the torque/speed characteristics for surface-magnet, IPM and synchronous reluctance machines. The effects of saturation are discussed also. The treatment of the torque/speed characteristics is unique and uses normalization (per-unit) to a greater degree than anywhere else in the literature, achieving a compact and powerful analysis that has the necessary equations in their irreducibly simplest form. All this forms the first part of Chapter 7.

The second part of Chapter 7 is a comprehensive treatment of current regulation and control in sinewave systems, beginning with six-step, progressing through simple controllers such as the hysteresis-band and the sine/triangle modulator, and then moving to more sophisticated systems such as the synchronous regulator, the space-vector modulated controller, and direct torque control (DTC). This section is organized more or less historically because this makes a convenient structure for introducing successive levels of sophistication. Included in this section is a detailed description of the dq_VV_CR controller used in the *PC-BDC* program as a form of primitive DTC that is very convenient for system simulation because of the small number of parameters needed to control it.

Chapter 7 will also be found to be a good introduction to space vectors, especially from the point of view of unifying the world of the machine designer with the world of the control engineer.

Chapter 8 is by far the most comprehensive and rigorous study of the EMF and torque constants k_E and k_T yet published. For both sinewave and squarewave systems and mixed combinations of motor and controller, and for both 3-phase and 2-phase systems, the relationships between k_T and k_E are rigorously developed from first principles based on the ideal commutator motor. This Chapter is important for the servo-motor industry which uses k_T and k_E in catalogue data for matching motors to controllers. In this context the correct conversion factors are essential. The Chapter is also of interest from a theoretical point of view, as it is closely related to the theory of reference-frame transformations and power-invariance, although these heavyweight mathematical constructs do not intrude on the essentially practical analysis which is based on simple well-known electrical engineering principles. Chapter 8 also offers the reader (as it offered the writer) a sharp test in precise understanding of the meaning of *peak*, *mean rectified*, and *RMS* quantities.

Chapter 9 deals with generators. Quite simply treating the permanent-magnet generator as a motor with the power flow reversed, it progresses through the whole range of possible *loads*, from open- and short-circuit conditions to passive and active loads including the infinite bus, the rectifier, and the transistor inverter.

Chapter 10 is a specialist treatment of multiple-phase machines, specifically *multiplex* machines of 6 or 9 phases. The main element of this Chapter is the derivation of the steady-state phasor diagram, but the matrix analysis leading up to it is an interesting exercise in extended *dq*-axis theory.

Chapter 11 is about the line-start motor, which is one of the oldest brushless permanent-magnet machines, yet is now enjoying a resurgence of interest as a result of pressure to improve energy efficiency. The treatment includes the history, the steady-state and transient operation of both three-phase and single-phase line-start motors. Advanced analysis methods are used including symmetrical components with successive reference frame transformations to deal with unbalanced windings and external impedances. Detailed methods for calculating simulation models are also included. The Chapter ends with a discussion of circuits used for controlling line-start motors.

Chapter 12 is a detailed treatment of losses and cooling. It covers iron loss in the stator in rather general terms, but it has a very detailed analysis of rotor eddy-current loss in both surface-magnet and IPM type machines by analytical methods, and can take its place alongside many of the most advanced recent works in this important field. Finite-length effects (end-effects) and segmentation are treated approximately. For both types of machine the presence of conducting circuits on the rotor leads to a subtransient regime during short-circuits, and Chapter 12 shows how to calculate the subtransient reactance and time-constant for use in short-circuit studies. The analysis of a symmetrical three-phase short-circuit is included.

Chapter 12 includes a discussion of cooling and heat-transfer at a basic level, with details of thermal equivalent circuits and main cooling methods. The analysis of intermittent operation extends the 2-parameter model that has long been in use, and much practical data is included.

Chapter 13 is about testing. It covers the measurement of resistance, inductance, inertia, torque, power, current, efficiency, cogging, and has many specialized details not found elsewhere, especially on the measurement of inductance and the use of the FC-4 "flexible controller" for electromagnetic and system measurements.

In the very last days of writing, we put together a FAQ section (frequently asked questions), thinking that we really hadn't done enough in 700 pages to answer the designer's real questions. This is lodged at the beginning of Chapter 14, which ends with a few "nuggets" on *saliency*, *half turns*, *series and parallel inductances*, *gearing*, *units of inertia*, and the *calculation of inertia*. These are all topics on which debate can rage in design offices, but which would clutter the main text.

The methods described in this book are not all suitable for immediate calculation using a slide-rule or a pocket-calculator, even though a quick glance at the text seems to reveal "lots of formulas". Many of the methods were designed for the *PC-BDC* computer program of the *SPEED* Laboratory, which executes them rapidly and has been tested in hundreds if not thousands of product designs.

Perhaps we should say a word about what we have *not* covered, to save the reader the trouble of searching in vain:

Codes and standards — these tend to change, and in many cases they are local rather than universal. They often relate to particular classes of product, whereas the scope of this book is rather general. They are also steeped in trade politics and specialist issues on which we are not expert. Articles on codes and standards appear regularly in trade magazines and competent web-sites.

Safety — Safety is of paramount importance in all engineering work. It is a matter of attitude, habit, and procedure; and standards are important in defining procedure. Safety procedures for handling magnets are particularly important; as are those associated with electrical equipment and rotating machinery. However, this is a book about design and the theory of design, and it contains no procedural information on practical safety issues.

Materials — Material properties are mentioned and used throughout the text, but the chemistry, metallurgy, processing, and general properties of specific materials are not covered; neither is the magnetization of magnets. Basic information on materials is readily available on the Internet, and specialist information on particular materials should be obtained first-hand from suppliers.

Heat transfer — Although there is a basic section on cooling in Chapter 12, this important subject really needs another book.

Insulation systems; **Failure modes**; **Bearings** — these are specialized topics outside the scope, but some practical comments are offered in §14.1. **Protection** is not addressed at all.

Finite-element analysis is not treated in detail, although *PC-FEA* is used in places for illustration or to strengthen some technical arguments. This book is mainly about traditional analytical methods, in which the theory of electrical machines resides.

Unusual or specialty machines — There is a huge variety, sufficient to make a complete book. We have concentrated on the mainstream machines.

Electronic control at the circuit-board level; **EMI/EMC**; **factory automation**; **databus protocols**; and **encoders and resolvers** — these subjects are outside our scope.

We have not written much about **computer simulation**; we have left that to the *SPEED* documentation.

Acknowledgements

This book was really "written" by the people who make electric machines.[1]

JRH writes : "I have been greatly influenced and extremely grateful to several motor design teachers & practitioners of the past as well as many of our contemporaries. (Some I knew personally and others only by their writings.) From the past I would like to mention Dr. Michael Liwschitz-Garik, Polytechnic Institute of New York University; Gene Fisher, IBM Fellow; Dr. Cyril Veinott, Westinghouse and Reliance; Marlin Walmer, founder of Electron Energy Corp.; M.G. Say, Heriot-Watt University; and Herbert C. Roters. Among contemporaries I would like to mention Dr. T.J.E. Miller; Gene Aha, Clifton Precision (MOOG); Dr. Takashi Kenjo; Erland Persson, Electro-Craft Corp (EAD); Dr. Tony Davis, Saminco Inc.; Clyde Hancock, MicroMo Electronics Inc.; James Gollhardt, Allen-Bradley, (Rockwell); Homer Lazar, Pacific Scientific, (Danaher Motion); Victor Aronovich, MTS Systems; Dr. Duane Hanselman, University of Maine; Dr. Peter Campbell; Clark E. Johnson Jr.; Dr. Jacob Tal, Galil Motion Control; and Professor Benjamin C. Kuo, University of Illinois at Urbana-Champaign."

TJEM writes : "The companies of the *SPEED Consortium* together with the *SPEED* Distributors and their customers have given me immense support and education, much of it attained through joint work on common problems, and through the formulation of the *SPEED* software and all its documentation and training materials. I would like to thank all the *SPEED* community for this privilege, including J.R. Hendershot (Motorsoft); Professor E.M. Freeman and Dr. Richard Ashen (Infolytica Ltd.); Ted Hopper and Dr. Markus Anders (Maccon GmbH); Dr. David Staton (*SPEED* Laboratory and later Motor Design Ltd.); Morihiro Saito (MS-TECH, Japan) and colleagues at J-SOL (J-MAG), Japan, together with Dr. Keith Klontz (Advanced MotorTech LLC); and colleagues at Magsoft (USA) and Cedrat (France). Like Jim I would like to add my appreciation of several from my early years in engineering who gave me instruction and guidance: Dr. Tony Appleton, Dr. Austin Hughes, Dr. Antony Anderson and Bob MacNab of International Research and

---

[1] "I didn't want to make a description, I wanted to offer a mirror" — Alexis de Tocqueville, to his friend Jean-Jacques Ampère.

Development Co. Ltd. (now Rolls-Royce); Dr. T.R. Foord and P.G. Ross (formerly of AEI), both of the University of Glasgow; Professor Peter Lawrenson and Dr. J. M. Stephenson, SRDL (Emerson) and University of Leeds; Professor M.R. Harris; Dr. Eike Richter, D.W. Jones, V.B. Honsinger, Dr. G.B. Kliman, Tom Neumann and many others from my years at General Electric Co. (USA); and Dr. H.L. Thanawala of GEC (Stafford, UK). I would also like to thank and acknowledge my close colleagues in the *SPEED* Laboratory, Malcolm McGilp, Calum Cossar, Saffron Pearce, Peter Miller and Ian Young; including former colleagues Dr. Dan Ionel (A.O. Smith, USA); Dr. Mircea Popescu (Motor Design Ltd.); and M. Olaru, the author of the *PC-FEA* finite-element software that is part of the *SPEED* system."

Particular thanks are due to those companies who helped us with photographs and technical data: Günsu Çirpanlı Albaş and Cihad Ekin, Arçelik; Victor Aronovich, MTS; Morihiro Saito, MS-TECH; Scott Omori, Oriental Motor; Henrik Ørskov Pedersen, Grundfos; Jim Shoemaker, John Deere; Andrew Druszba and Evgeni Ganev, Honeywell; Dr. Rich Schiferl, Baldor Advanced Technology; Maxon; Pacific Scientific (Danaher Motion); Toyota Motor Company; Dr. H. Murakami, Matsushita/Panasonic; REA Magnet Wire Co.; Fabrico Division of EIS Inc.; Dr. Dan Ionel, A.O. Smith; David Watkins, Overview Ltd.; Omar Benzaid, SEM Ltd.; Carlos E.G. Martins and Sebastian Nau, WEG; Yuhito Doi, Shin-Etsu Chemical Co. Ltd.; Dr. J.A.T. Taufiq of Alstom Transport (p. 208); and finally to Dr. Mircea Popescu who proof-read much of the manuscript. TJEM is also indebted to Mel Amato of Maxim Electronic Sales in California, who helped untiringly to check the details of Chapter 8 for three-phase systems, and brought many practical issues to light.

J.R. Hendershot — Florida, January 15, 2010

T.J.E. Miller — Glasgow, 15 January 2010

Design of Brushless Permanent-Magnet Machines was written in a total of 8 months using Corel WordPerfect 8®. Most of the line diagrams were made with Visual CADD 5.0® and Corel Presentations 8®. It must be said, however, that it has taken us nearly 90 man-years of study to get to the point where we could do this. A great deal of material has been adapted from the *SPEED* documentation, particularly *SPEED's Electric Machines, Chapter 2.*

We would also re-emphasize what engineers already know — that technical books are always incomplete and seldom free from error. In spite of our best efforts to present the most reliable account we're capable of, we humbly ask our readers to notify us of any errors or omissions.

Contents

1 GENERAL INTRODUCTION 1

1.1 Definitions and types of brushless motor 1

1.2 Commutation 4

1.3 Operation of 3-phase brushless DC motor 5

1.3.1 EMF waveform 7
1.3.2 Torque and EMF constants 10
1.3.3 Speed/torque characteristic 11

1.4 Sinewave motors and generators 16

1.4.1 Phasor representation 19
1.4.2 Voltage 22

1.5 Practical considerations 23

2 MACHINE TYPES and APPLICATIONS 25

2.1 Machine configuration 25

2.1.1 Reasons for variety 25
2.1.2 Classification 27

2.2 Radial-flux machines 30

2.2.1 Interior-rotor surface-magnet machines 30
2.2.2 Interior-rotor interior-magnet machines (IPM) 32
2.2.3 Exterior-rotor machines 35

2.3 Axial-flux, linear and other machines 37

2.4 Gallery 43

3 BASIC DESIGN CHOICES 65

3.1 Machine and drive configuration 67

3.1.1 Squarewave and sinewave drives 67
- 3.1.1.1 Squarewave drive 67
- 3.1.1.2 Sinewave drive 68

3.1.2 Salient-pole and nonsalient-pole machines 68
- 3.1.2.1 Nonsalient-pole machines 68
- 3.1.2.2 Salient-pole machines 69

3.2 Number of phases, poles and slots 71

3.2.1 Number of phases 71
- 3.2.1.1 Practical considerations 71
- 3.2.1.2 Number of phases in electrical systems 72
- 3.2.1.3 Number of phases in electrical machines 75
- 3.2.1.4 Distribution of coils between phases 77
- 3.2.1.5 Number of phases in inverters and rectifiers 80

3.2.2 Numbers of slots and poles 82

3.3 Sizing — the ABC of electric machine design 87

3.3.1 The output equation 87

3.4 Rotor design 92

3.4.1 Length/diameter ratio 92
3.4.2 Airgap length 92
3.4.3 First estimate of magnet dimensions 93
3.4.4 Exploratory selection of magnet grade 94
3.4.5 Magnet overhang 95
3.4.6 Rotor yoke dimensions 96

3.5 Stator design 97

3.5.1 Cutting the laminations 97
3.5.2 Choice of core plate 97
3.5.3 Stacking 98
3.5.4 Insulating the slots 100
3.5.5 Slot-fill factor 101
3.5.6 Winding and inserting the phase coils 103
3.5.7 Varnishing 104
3.5.8 Winding with multiple-strand conductors 104

3.5.9 Number of stator slots 105
3.5.10 Stator core dimensions 105
3.5.11 Stator tooth-tips 106
3.5.12 Cogging and skew 107
3.5.13 Management of end-turns 109

3.6 Electrical design of windings 110

3.6.1 Definitions 110
3.6.2 Integral-slot windings 111
3.6.3 Windings for squarewave drive 115
3.6.4 Fractional-slot windings 118
3.6.4.1 A rule and two examples 118
3.6.4.2 The 12/10 motor; alternative windings 124
3.6.4.3 Pitch factor 128
3.6.4.4 Sinewave and squarewave motors 130
3.6.5 Irregular slotting 131
3.6.6 Systematic analysis of slot/pole ratio and windings 133
3.6.7 Winding resistance 139
3.6.7.1 Resistance calculation 139
3.6.7.2 Relationship between resistance and copper weight 140
3.6.7.3 Variation of resistance with temperature 140
3.6.7.4 AC resistance 143

3.7 Magnet retention 153

4 FLUX, EMF, AND TORQUE 157

4.1 Permanent magnets and magnetic circuits 157

4.1.1 Magnetic equivalent circuits 158
4.1.1.1 Airgap flux distribution 164
4.1.1.2 Clearance gap and equivalent magnet 165
4.1.1.3 Magnet divided by thin bracing bridges 167
4.1.2 Direct solution of Laplace / Poisson equations 169
4.1.3 Finite-element method 174

4.2 EMF 178

4.2.1 Formula 179
4.2.1.1 EMF constant of squarewave motors 179
4.2.1.2 EMF constant of sinewave motors 180

4.2.2 **BLV waveform method** 181
4.2.3 **Toothflux waveform method** 183

4.3 Torque 185

4.3.1 **Torque constants** 186
4.3.1.1 Three-phase squarewave motor 186
4.3.1.2 Sinewave motors 187

4.4 Torque and inductance 190

4.4.1 **Salient-pole machines in phase variables** 190
4.4.2 **Salient-pole machines in dq axes** 193

4.5 i-psi loop 197

4.6 Properties of the elliptical i-psi loop 203

5 INDUCTANCE 209

5.1 Definition of inductance and flux-linkage 210

5.1.1 **Alternative definitions** 211
5.1.1.1 di/dt 211
5.1.1.2 Flux times turns 211
5.1.2 **Other necessary laws of electromagnetism** 211
5.1.3 **Turns squared** 212

5.2 Important practical effects of inductance 213

5.3 Inductance components 214

5.4 Airgap inductance of surface-magnet machines 215

5.4.1 **Airgap Self** 215
5.4.2 **Airgap mutual** 217
5.4.3 **Examples of airgap inductance calculation** 217
5.4.4 **General case of airgap inductance** 221

5.5 Slot-leakage inductance 226

5.6 End-winding leakage inductance 233

5.7 Inductances of slotless (airgap) windings 238
5.7.1 Helical windings 241
5.7.2 Lawrenson's method 241

5.8 Equivalent sine-distributed windings 242

5.9 Synchronous inductance 243
5.9.1 Static measurement of synchronous inductance 246

5.10 Inductances of salient-pole machines 247
5.10.1 dq-axis inductances from Park's transform 248
5.10.2 Synchronous inductance coefficients 252
5.10.3 Direct calculation of synchronous inductance 253
5.10.4 Differential leakage inductance 258
5.10.5 Static measurement again 260

5.11 Inductance from finite-element calculations 262

5.12 Magnetization curves — beyond inductance 263
5.12.1 Magnetization curves in *dq*-axes 266

5.13 Saturation in the *dq*-axis model 267

5.14 Demagnetization 268

6 SQUAREWAVE DRIVE 273

Introduction 273

6.1 Three-phase bipolar drives 274
6.1.1 Waveforms and commutation sequences 274
6.1.2 Current regulation 279
6.1.3 Commutation 282
6.1.4 3-phase squarewave control strategies 286
6.1.5 Accumulations for mean and RMS currents 288
6.1.6 Selection of appropriate switching strategy 289

6.2 Transient analysis of 3-phase drives 291

6.2.0.1 Wye connection 293
6.2.0.2 Delta connection 296
6.2.0.3 Regeneration (over-running); no-load speed 301
6.2.0.4 Phase advance 304
6.2.0.5 Dwell control 306

6.2.1 Salient-pole machines with squarewave drive 309
6.2.2 Back-EMF sensing 312

6.3 1- and 2-phase unipolar drives 315

6.4 Controller architecture 321

7 SINEWAVE DRIVE 325

Introduction 325

7.1 The phasor diagram — motor operation 327

7.1.1 Torque/angle curves 332
7.1.2 The voltage locus diagram 336
7.1.3 The circle and ellipse diagrams 338
7.1.4 Calculation of the torque/speed characteristic 349
7.1.5 The synchronous reluctance motor 361
7.1.6 Summary — calculated characteristics 367

7.2 Electronic control 368

7.2.1 The need for current regulation 369
7.2.2 Historical development 371
7.2.3 Overview of controllers 373
7.2.4 Switching representation by voltage vectors 374
7.2.5 Six-step 375
7.2.6 Hysteresis-band current regulator 377
7.2.7 dq_VV_CR 381
7.2.8 Sine/triangle ramp comparison 383
7.2.9 Voltage PWM (sine/triangle) 385
7.2.10 The synchronous regulator 389
7.2.11 Space-vector controller 391
7.2.12 Direct torque control (DTC) 396
7.2.13 Summary of voltage capabilities 404

8 kT AND kE, AND FIGURES-OF-MERIT 405

8.1 Introduction 405

8.2 kT & kE of squarewave and sinewave motor/drives 407

8.2.1 DC commutator motor and drive 407
8.2.2 3-phase squarewave motor and drive 411
8.2.3 3-phase sinewave motor and drive 415
8.2.4 3-phase sinewave motor with squarewave drive 417
8.2.5 3-phase squarewave motor with sinewave drive 419
8.2.6 3-phase squarewave & sinewave systems compared 422
8.2.7 Example calculations (3-phase) 424
8.2.8 2-phase squarewave motor and drive 426
8.2.9 2-phase sinewave motor and drive 428
8.2.10 2-phase sinewave motor with squarewave drive 430
8.2.11 2-phase squarewave motor with sinewave drive 432
8.2.12 2-phase squarewave & sinewave systems compared 435

8.3 Figures of merit 436

8.3.1 kT and kE 436
8.3.2 Efficiency and power factor 436
8.3.3 Torque/Inertia ratio 437
8.3.4 Power rate 437
8.3.5 Speed rate and mechanical time-constant 439
8.3.6 Motor constant 440

8.4 The brushless PM motor in control systems 442

8.4.1 Classical transfer function between voltage & speed 443
8.4.2 Brushless DC motor model including inductance 445
8.4.3 Closed-loop feedback system 446
8.4.4 Response of generic second-order system 448
8.4.5 Dynamic braking 449

9 GENERATING 451

9.1 Introduction 451

9.2 Configurations and loads 454

9.2.1 No-load (open-circuit) 455
9.2.2 Steady-state short-circuit 456
9.2.3 Passive impedance load 457
9.2.4 Voltage regulation curves 459
9.2.5 Connection to an infinite bus 462
9.2.6 Diode rectifier load 464
9.2.7 Active rectification 467

9.3 Short-circuit faults 468

9.3.1 Classical analysis 468
9.3.2 Transient Magnetic Field by Fourier Transform 472

10 MULTIPLE-PHASE MACHINES 475

Introduction 475

10.1 Polyphase machines 475

10.2 Multiplex windings 478

10.2.1 Reasons for using multiplex windings 479
10.2.2 Fault-tolerant machines 480

10.3 Analysis of multiplex windings 481

10.3.1 Balance 484

10.4 Matrix analysis of the inductances 485

10.5 Torque 491

10.6 Steady-state operation : phasor diagram 493

10.7 Solution method — transient 495

10.8 Finite-element analysis 496

11 LINE-START MOTORS 497

11.1 Introduction 497

11.2 History 500

11.3 Analysis of polyphase line-start motors 503

11.3.1 Steady state 503
11.3.2 Asynchronous operation and starting 506
11.3.3 Analysis of synchronization 510

11.4 Analysis of single-phase line-start motors 517

11.4.1 Steady state; no rotor cage 517
11.4.2 Symmetrical components 519
11.4.3 Asynchronous and starting performance 537

11.5 Advanced topics 542

11.5.1 Winding harmonics 542
11.5.2 Bar-pair-by-bar-pair model of the rotor cage 543
11.5.3 Connection circuits 550

12 LOSSES and COOLING 553

12.1 Introduction 553

12.2 Joule losses in stator conductors 554

12.3 Core losses 555

12.3.1 The nature of core losses 555
12.3.2 Core loss properties of practical materials 556
12.3.3 Calculation of core losses 559

12.4 Rotor eddy-current losses 561

12.4.1 Causes of rotor loss 561
12.4.1.1 Loss mechanisms in the magnets themselves 563
12.4.1.2 Resistance- or inductance-limited eddy-currents? 564
12.4.1.3 Hysteresis loss in magnets 566
12.4.2 Harmonic losses in surface-magnet machines 568
12.4.2.1 Solution of the Complex Diffusion Equation 570

12.4.2.2 Exterior-rotor machine; 2-region model 574
12.4.2.3 Evaluation of the Exciting Harmonic Current Sheets 580
12.4.2.4 Balanced operation of 3-phase machines 586
12.4.2.5 Unbalanced operation of 3-phase machines 589
12.4.3 Segmented magnets and finite-length effects 602
12.4.3.1 Circumferential segmentation 604
12.4.3.2 Simplified analysis of double segmentation 610
12.4.3.3 End-effect; segmentation in the axial direction 611
12.4.3.4 Russell and Norsworthy's method 616
12.4.3.5 Alternative analysis of segmented magnets 618
12.4.4 Slot ripple 620
12.4.4.1 Flux-dip-sweeping analysis of losses in thin can 624
12.4.4.2 Rotor can losses 626
12.4.5 Harmonic losses in the IPM 628
12.4.5.1 Losses caused by time-harmonics in the current 628
12.4.5.2 Losses caused by flux-pulsations (slotting) 629
12.4.6 Subtransient inductance and time-constant 631
12.4.6.1 Effect of segmentation on subtransient reactance 635
12.4.6.2 Coupling coefficient of the IPM 638
12.4.6.3 Rotor time-constant 642
12.4.7 Finite-element calculation of losses 644

12.5 Windage, friction and bearing losses 647

12.6 Thermal analysis and cooling 648

12.6.1 The need for cooling 648
12.6.2 Cooling and efficiency 649
12.6.3 Responsibility for temperature rise 650
12.6.4 Heat removal 650
12.6.5 Detailed analysis of cooling 652
12.6.5.1 Conduction 652
12.6.5.2 Radiation 653
12.6.5.3 Convection 654
12.6.5.4 Some rules of thumb 655
12.6.5.5 Internal temperature distribution 656
12.6.5.6 Thermal equivalent circuit 657
12.6.5.7 Some useful tables 658
12.6.6 Intermittent operation 660

13 TESTING 667

13.1 Introduction 667

13.2 Objectives of testing 667

13.3 Basic tests and measurements 668

13.3.1 Inertia 668

13.4 Resistance 669

13.5 EMF Testing 670

13.6 Generator load testing 671

13.7 Motor load testing 672

13.8 Torque Testing 672

13.8.1 Torque constant kT 672
13.8.2 Cogging torque 673
13.8.3 On-line estimation of torque using the i-psi loop 674

13.9 Thermal Testing 675

13.9.1 Thermal equivalent-circuit parameters 675

13.10 Inductance Testing 676

14 APPENDIX 681

14.1 Frequently asked questions 681

14.1.1 Machine Design Questions 681
14.1.1.1 How do I decide the shape and size of the machine? 681
14.1.1.2 How do I choose the number of slots and poles? 682
14.1.1.3 How do I design the stator teeth and slots? 682
14.1.1.4 How do I decide the number of turns? 684
14.1.1.5 How do I decide the type of stator winding? 685
14.1.1.6 How can I get a fractional number of turns/coil? 685
14.1.1.7 How can I reduce the wire size? 685
14.1.1.8 How can I reduce the inductance? 686
14.1.1.9 How can I increase the inductance? 686
14.1.1.10 How do I choose between SPM and IPM? 686

14.1.1.11 How do I choose between exterior or interior rotor? 688
14.1.1.12 When should I consider an axial-flux machine? 688
14.1.1.13 How do I decide the rotor geometry? 689
14.1.1.14 How can I reduce the inertia? 691
14.1.1.15 How can I improve the torque linearity? 692
14.1.1.16 How can I reduce torque ripple? 692
14.1.1.17 How do I design a PM synchronous generator? 692
14.1.1.18 How do I test a PM synchronous machine? 692
14.1.1.19 Why isn't my measured kE equal to kT? 692
14.1.1.20 How do I calculate the machine temperature? 692
14.1.1.21 What are the main effects of temperature? 693
14.1.1.22 How can I prevent demagnetization? 694
14.1.1.23 How can I reduce the noise level? 695
14.1.1.24 How can I reduce the motor cost? 695
14.1.1.25 How about EMF ripple? 696
14.1.1.26 How about a sine-EMF motor with squarewave drive? 696

14.1.2 Performance and Control Questions 697

14.1.2.1 How can I increase efficiency? 697
14.1.2.2 How can I increase power-factor? 698
14.1.2.3 How can I get smooth rotation at low speed? 698
14.1.2.4 How can I make the motor go faster? 699
14.1.2.5 How can I get a more sinusoidal EMF waveform? 700
14.1.2.6 How can I get a more sinusoidal current waveform? 700
14.1.2.7 How do I avoid first-turn insulation failure? 700
14.1.2.8 How do I avoid bearing currents? 702
14.1.2.9 What causes machines to fail? 702

14.2 Saliency 703

14.3 Half turns 706

14.4 Series and parallel inductances 709

14.5 Gearing 714

14.6 Units of inertia 716

14.7 Calculation of inertia 721

Symbols, Abbreviations, and Explanatory Notes 723

Bibliography 737

Index 755

1 GENERAL INTRODUCTION

1.1 Definitions and types of brushless motor

A brushless motor or generator has no brushes, no slip-rings, and no mechanical commutator.

Several types of machine satisfy this basic definition, but the machines in this book are all *synchronous* machines, in that the speed N is related to the supply frequency f and the number of pole-pairs p by the equation

$$N = \frac{f \times 60}{p} \quad \text{RPM}. \tag{1.1}$$

It is worth expressing eqn. (1.1) in the form

$$f = \frac{N}{60} \times p = \frac{N}{60} \times \frac{\text{Poles}}{2} \tag{1.2}$$

because this emphasizes the fact that a rotating magnetized rotor generates an EMF whose frequency is fixed by the speed and the number of poles. N is called the **synchronous speed**.

The **brushless DC motor** is essentially a set of permanent magnets rotating past a set of conductors that carry DC current during a fixed angle of rotation, typically 60 "electrical" degrees. It is equivalent to an inverted DC commutator motor, in that the magnet rotates while the conductors remain stationary. In both cases, the current must reverse polarity (or direction) every time a magnet pole passes by, to ensure that the torque is unidirectional. This polarity-switching is called *commutation*. The commutation processes are similar in the two cases, as are the performance equations and speed/torque curves.

In the DC motor, the polarity reversal is performed by the commutator and brushes. Since the commutator is fixed to the rotor, the reversals are automatically synchronized with the alternating polarity of the flux through which the conductors are passing. In the brushless DC motor, the polarity of the current is reversed by transistors that are switched in synchronism with the rotor position.

The current in any phase reverses polarity twice in every cycle of the fundamental frequency f. In brushless DC motors with so-called **squarewave** drive, the EMF waveform is approximately trapezoidal, and the DC current is kept constant throughout a fixed *commutation interval*, through which the torque remains constant. At the end of each commutation interval, the current *commutates* or switches to another phase to sustain the torque.

In motors with **sinewave** drive, the current is regulated by PWM to have a sinusoidal waveform, while the motor is designed to have a sinusoidal EMF waveform. With two or more phases and a suitable phase-shift between their currents and EMFs, it is again possible to produce constant torque. Polarity reversal at twice the fundamental frequency is a natural property of the alternating current.

The **brushless PM generator** also requires commutation in the same way as the motor. When it is connected to a diode rectifier, commutation is automatic, and is the same process as natural commutation in a conventional rectifier. Brushless PM generators may also be operated with active rectifiers using the same power electronic circuit as a transistor inverter. In this case commutation and current control are the same as in the sinewave motor drive, except for the phase relationship between the current and the EMF.

Brushless DC and **brushless AC** motors are physically similar: both have rotating magnets and both commonly have 3-phase stator windings. The main difference is that in the "AC" machine the stator ampere-conductor distribution is distributed sinusoidally and rotates continuously at synchronous speed, whereas in the "brushless DC" machine its axis remains fixed in space for intervals of 60°elec., and jumps through 60°elec. at commutation. The brushless AC motor is a pure synchronous AC motor; but the brushless DC motor is akin to a DC brush motor with a small number of commutator segments.

The brushless motor is sometimes called "self-synchronous" or "auto-synchronous": as the commutation is synchronized to the rotor position, the machine cannot lose synchronism in the same way as a classical synchronous machine when the so-called pull-out torque is exceeded. The torque capability is determined only by the current, so if the motor is forced to slow, the drive frequency will slow with it.

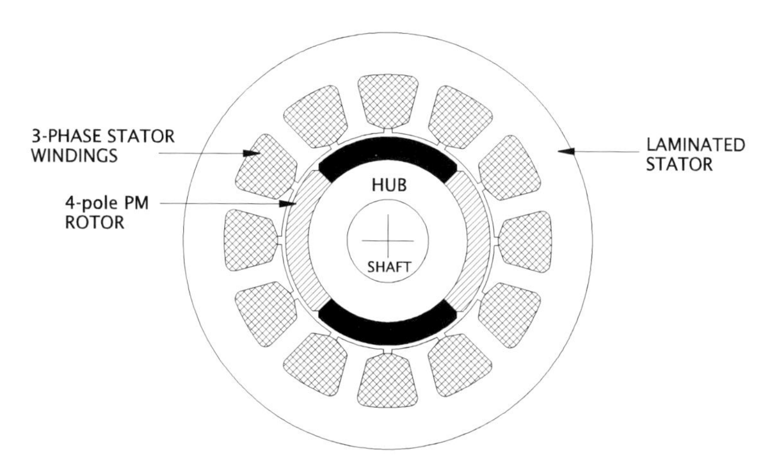

Fig. 1.1 Cross-section of interior-rotor brushless machine

Fig. 1.1 shows the cross-section of a typical **interior-rotor** brushless PM machine. Here we will simply note a few main features before studying its principle of operation as a brushless DC motor.

There are four magnets affixed to the rotor, with alternating polarity NSNS; that is, two pole-pairs: $p = 2$. For low peripheral speeds the magnets may be bonded to a solid hub of soft magnetic steel, but at higher speeds a retaining sleeve is used. The shaft may be integral with the hub; or it may be separate, in which case it can be magnetic or non-magnetic. With so-called Halbach magnets the hub can be made non-magnetic. The small rotor diameter reduces the inertia compared to that of the exterior-rotor motor, and this configuration is common in servo-motors.

The stator windings are usually housed in slots punched in a laminated core. Between the slots are the teeth which carry the flux through the winding region. Although the flux is predominantly confined to the teeth, it is important to understand that it *links* the coils of the winding. The concept of flux-linkage is arguably more fundamental than either EMF or inductance.

Brushes and commutator are not necessary because the windings are stationary. However, the EMF generated by the rotating magnets is alternating (AC), and therefore the current must also alternate. In the next section we shall see the simplest means of ensuring alternating current by means of electronic commutation.

1.2 Commutation

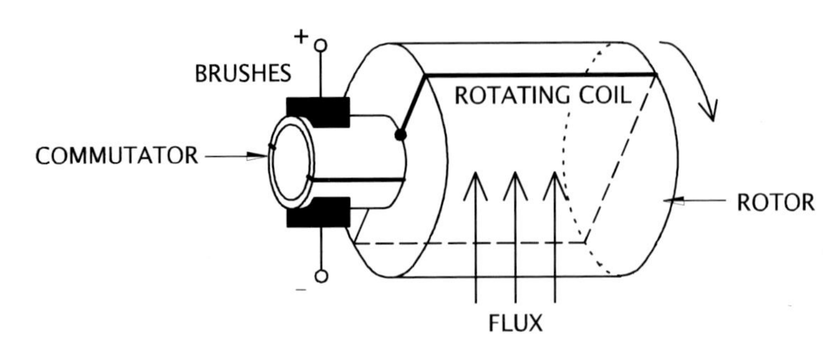

Fig. 1.2 A coil rotating in a magnetic field, with a mechanical commutator

The process of commutation is fundamental in brushless DC motors. It is explained here in terms of the commutation of a simple DC commutator motor. From this we will see that the performance characteristics of the two machines are fundamentally identical.

The rotor of an elementary PM DC commutator motor is shown in Fig. 1.2. It rotates through a magnetic field that is excited by stationary magnets fixed inside the stator frame (not shown). It carries the rotating winding or *armature*, which consists of a single coil whose ends are brought out to a 2-segment commutator, that is, a copper ring divided into two segments insulated from each other.

The magnetic field in Fig. 1.2 is a 2-pole field, which means that each conductor or coil-side passes under one N pole and one S pole in each complete revolution of the rotor. The EMF generated in the coil is therefore alternating in polarity. It is connected to the outside world by two brushes that bear on the commutator. The brushes are diametrically opposite, and switch the polarity of the connection twice per revolution, or every 180°. As a result, the EMF communicated to the outside world is unidirectional — that is, DC. The terminals are accordingly labelled + and –.

DC current fed to the brushes is switched to the armature conductors by the commutator. The switching action of the commutator causes the current in the armature conductors to alternate (change direction) at the same frequency as the EMF. As a result, the torque and power are unidirectional.

1.3 Operation of 3-phase brushless DC motor

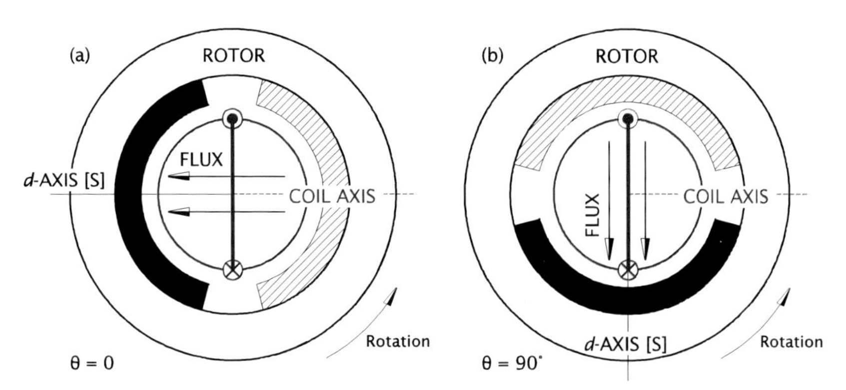

Fig. 1.3 A permanent magnet rotor and a single stator coil

The motor of Fig. 1.2 is represented again in Fig. 1.3, but now the *magnets* are rotating while the coil remains stationary. The motor is brushless, and its operation will be explained in terms of the relative motion of the rotating magnets and the stationary coil.

Each magnet has a d-axis or *direct* axis, coinciding with its centre-line. The d-axis is the reference axis of the rotor, so the position in Fig. 1.3(a) is the reference position, $\theta = 0$. The coil also has an axis of symmetry, which is along the x-axis in Fig. 1.3. Assume that the coil is open-circuited. Its flux-linkage ψ_1 is the product of flux and turns, and is a negative maximum when its axis is aligned with a magnet d-axis and the coil is facing a south pole, as in Fig. 1.3(a). This flux-linkage is *magnet* flux-linkage, since there is no current in the coil.

Fig. 1.3(b) shows the position of the rotor 90° later. The coil axis is aligned with a q-axis or *interpolar* axis of the rotor, and the coil flux-linkage is zero. Maximum positive flux-linkage follows after a further 90° of rotation, at $\theta = 180°$. The variation of the coil flux-linkage ψ_1 is shown in Fig. 1.4(a) over a whole electrical cycle.

The waveform $\psi_1(\theta)$ is shown idealized as a trapezoid. For brushless DC motors the straight slopes are the most important characteristic, but sinewave machines are designed to have a sinusoidal flux-linkage waveform. The shape of the waveform depends partly on the winding layout, and partly on the shape and magnetization pattern of the magnets, as we shall see in Chapter 4.

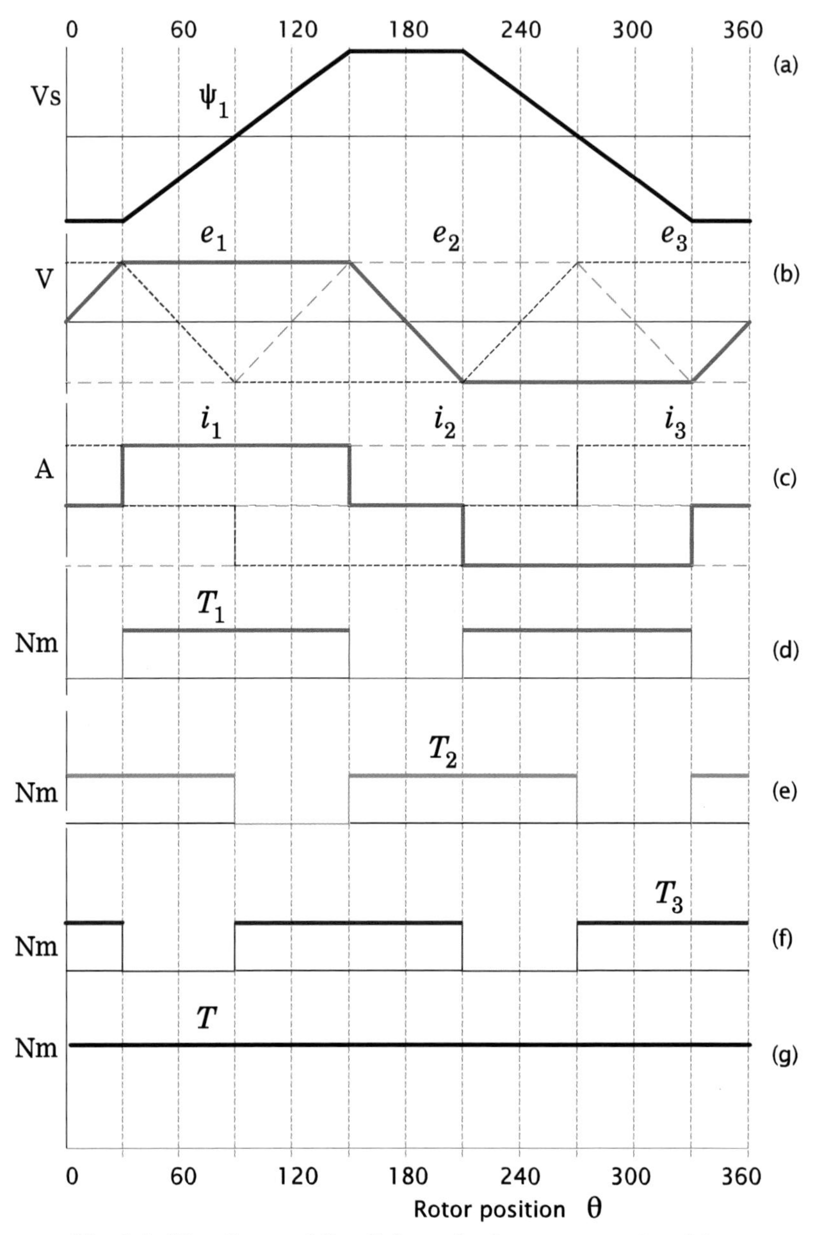

Fig. 1.4 Waveforms of flux-linkage, back-EMF, current and torque

1.3.1 EMF waveform

Of primary interest is the waveform of the EMF in the coil as the magnet rotates past it. By Faraday's Law, the EMF is

$$e_1 = \frac{d\psi_1}{dt}. \tag{1.3}$$

This can be expressed as

$$e_1 = \frac{\partial\psi_1}{\partial\theta}\cdot\frac{d\theta}{dt} = \omega_m\frac{\partial\psi_1}{\partial\theta}, \tag{1.4}$$

where ω_m is the angular velocity,

$$\omega_m = N \times \frac{2\pi}{60} \quad \text{rad/s}. \tag{1.5}$$

We already have the flux-linkage waveform $\psi_1(\theta)$ in Fig. 1.4(a), so the derivative $\partial\psi_1/\partial\theta$ is simply the gradient of this waveform at any angle θ. The coil EMF follows immediately by multiplying the derivative by ω_m, Fig. 1.4(b). It is an alternating quantity, that is, AC.

When a current i_1 is forced through coil 1, the product $e_1 i_1$ represents power that is converted into mechanical power; thus

$$e_1 i_1 = T_1\omega_m \tag{1.6}$$

where T_1 is the electromagnetic torque produced by the current in the coil; thus

$$T_1 = \frac{e_1 i_1}{\omega_m} \quad \text{N m}. \tag{1.7}$$

Since e_1 is alternating, i_1 must also be alternating to ensure that the torque is always positive, as shown in Fig. 1.4(c) and (d). When e_1 is positive, i_1 is positive; and when e_1 is negative, i_1 is negative.

In the brushless DC motor the current is supplied from a DC source *via* a transistor inverter. Fig. 1.5(a) shows the states of the transistors in the 60° commutation period when $i_1 > 0$ and $i_2 < 0$, that is, from 30° to 90°. The DC current is routed through transistors Q_1 and Q_6. Only two transistors and two phases are conducting. The DC current is positive in one and negative in the other.

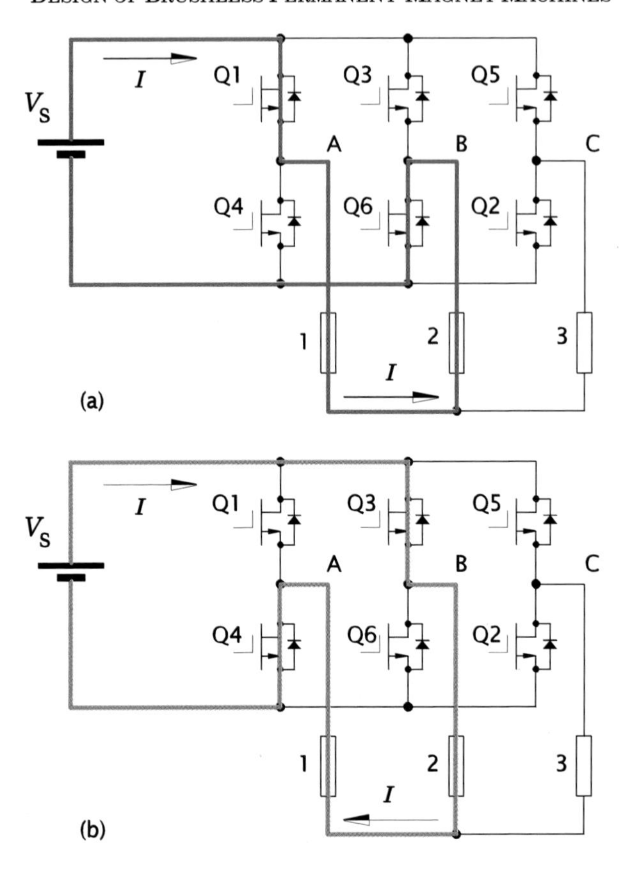

Fig. 1.5 Brushless DC motor drive

When $e_1 < 0$, in the interval 210°— 330°, the current flows in the opposite direction through transistors Q_3 and Q_4, as in Fig. 1.5(b). It is clear from Fig. 1.5 that the *supply* current I is unidirectional — that is, DC. By switching it is routed through the windings so that its polarity is always matched to that of the EMF.

Fig. 1.5 contains much more than the operation of a single coil. It represents the operation of an entire 3-phase machine. The phase windings, shown as circuit elements 1,2,3, may contain *many* coils similar to the original coil in Fig. 1.3, all of which have essentially the same generated EMF, connected in a series/parallel arrangement in each phase. It is advantageous for each phase to have a multiplicity of coils, to make full utilization of the stator periphery.

Although commutation makes the torque produced by one coil unidirectional, there remain periods of zero torque which can be traced back to the flat top in the flux-linkage waveform. Although 2 phases are theoretically sufficient to fill the gaps in the torque waveform, it is more common to use 3 phases as shown in Fig. 1.5.

Figs. 1.4 and 1.5 show that two of the three lines are conducting at any instant, while the third line is idle for a period of 60°. The wye connection ensures that the current in one phase is positive $(+I)$ while the current in the other is negative $(-I)$; this connection persists for one commutation period and can be called "series opposing". If the phases are connected in delta, there is no difference in the *line* current waveforms, but the current divides naturally between the three phases of the delta. $2I/3$ goes through one phase, while $I/3$ goes through the series combination of the other two, (in each of which it is negative). In both cases the total electromagnetic torque is $2e_1I/\omega_m$ and not $3e_1I/\omega_m$. The detailed analysis of square-wave drive is given in Chapter 6.

Fig. 1.6 shows schematically the operation of a DC motor with three commutator segments equivalent to the 3-phase brushless motor of Fig. 1.5. The *coils* in the commutator motor are the *phases* in the brushless motor. The brushes and commutator are equivalent to the transistor inverter in Fig. 1.5, and Fig. 1.4 applies equally to both motors. The torque waveforms produced by coils 2 and 3 are identical to T_1, but displaced in phase by 120° and 240° respectively, as in Figs. 1.4(e) and (f). The total torque T is the sum of $T_1 + T_2 + T_3$, as shown in Fig. 1.4(g). This torque is *constant*.

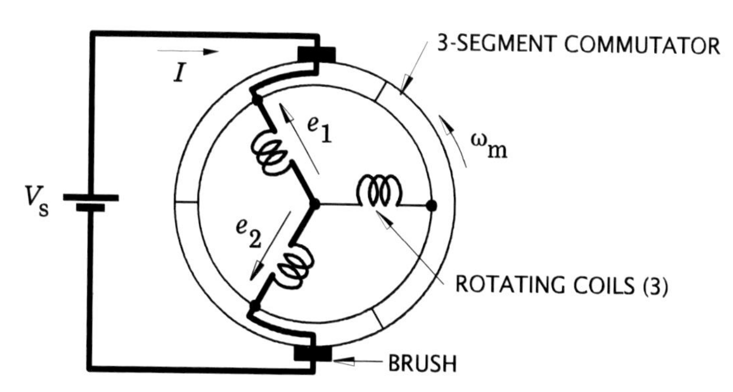

Fig. 1.6 DC motor with 3 commutator segments and 2 brushes

1.3.2 Torque and EMF constants

The line current waveform is a so-called "120° squarewave" with a peak flat-top value equal to the DC supply current I. With two phases conducting in the wye connection, the line-line EMF E is the difference of the two phase EMFs.

At constant speed, the electromechanical energy conversion is governed by the equation

$$EI = T\omega_m . \tag{1.8}$$

T is the electromagnetic torque, not the shaft torque. The difference is ascribed to mechanical losses such as friction and windage, but certain other loss components may be added to the mechanical loss to account for iron loss and other parasitic losses that are difficult to represent in the electrical equivalent circuit.

Eqn. (1.8) could be said to be the most fundamental equation in electrical machine theory. It represents lossless energy conversion from electrical to mechanical form, or *vice versa*. In DC or brushless DC machines operating in the steady-state the quantities in eqn. (1.8) are all constant, so their average values are equal to their instantaneous values. The energy conversion proceeds at a constant rate; the torque is constant; and there is no question of energy storage or reactive power.

Referring to equation (1.4), if the rate of change of flux-linkage $\partial\psi/\partial\theta$ remains constant in each phase through each 120° interval, the line-line EMF E will be flat-topped for successive intervals of 60°. It follows that E, can be written

$$E = k_E \omega_m \tag{1.9}$$

where k_E is a constant called the **EMF constant**. This equation expresses the important principle that *EMF is proportional to speed.*

It follows immediately from eqns. (1.8) and (1.9) that

$$T = k_T I, \tag{1.10}$$

where k_T is the **torque constant** and $k_T = k_E$. This equation expresses the principle that *torque is proportional to current.*

The equality $k_T = k_E$ is valid only when these constants are expressed in consistent units, such as Nm/A and V/(rad/s). In other systems of units k_T and k_R are not numerically equal, but differ by a constant multiplying factor. It must also be emphasized that the underlying equality is an ideal that is not exactly met in practice. k_E can be measured only under open-circuit conditions, whereas k_T can only be measured with current flowing. The magnetic and electric conditions are therefore not the same when k_T and k_E are measured, and this leads to differences in their values.

The relationship between k_T and k_E also depends on the current and EMF waveforms, as analyzed in detail in Chapter 8. Here we will simply note that whenever these constants are used or quoted they need to be defined with great care and precision.

Eqn. (1.10) embodies the essential linearity and simplicity of the DC motor from a control viewpoint, and is the basis of the feedforward component of the classical feedback control system on which DC servo systems and variable-speed drives have been based for many decades. In its ideal form the brushless DC motor has exactly the same characteristics. We shall see that the same is true of the brushless AC motor, although AC controllers tend to be rather more sophisticated.

By contrast, the natural linear relationship between torque and current does not apply to the AC induction motor, or to any kind of reluctance motor. To achieve servo-quality control with these machines, mathematical transformations and other compensating functions are required; and in the case of the switched reluctance motor, current-profiling as well. While these techniques are quite feasible and indeed in production, the contrast remains.

1.3.3 Speed/torque characteristic

The best way to gain an understanding of the performance characteristics of a brushless DC motor is to study the speed vs. torque curve. This curve represents the capability of the motor in driving various types of loads. Its importance stems from the fact that the speed/torque curve of the motor should be compatible with the speed/torque characteristic of the load. Certain loads, for example, compressors, hoists, and conveyors, have a more-or-less constant torque that does not vary with speed, Fig. 1.7.

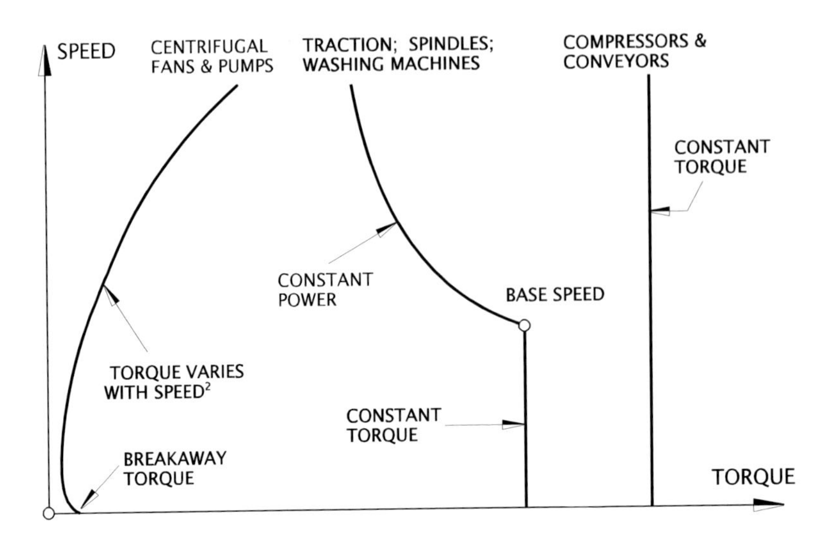

Fig. 1.7 Speed/torque characteristics of various loads

Some loads have a torque that increases in proportion to the square of the speed: this is typical of centrifugal pumps, fans and blowers. Others require a constant-torque drive up to a certain *base speed*, and a constant-power drive at higher speeds. This is typical of traction loads, as in electric vehicles; and it is also found in washing machines and machine-tool spindles.

The main function of the speed/torque curve is to ensure that the motor has enough torque to accelerate the load from standstill and maintain full speed without exceeding any thermal or electrical limits. The thermal and electrical limits appear as boundaries of regions on the speed/torque curve, as we shall see.

Voltage-limited speed/torque curve — Referring to the circuit of Fig. 1.5 or 1.6, if V_s is the DC voltage, I is the DC supply current, and E is the line-line EMF of the motor,

$$V_s = E + RI, \tag{1.11}$$

where R is the resistance of two coils (phases) in series. The voltage drop in the power transistors is neglected for the present, but it can be very significant in low-voltage systems such as automotive auxiliaries and battery-powered equipment.

By substituting E from eqn. (1.9) and I from eqn. (1.10), with a little manipulation the speed/torque equation can be derived in the following form:

$$\frac{\omega_m}{\omega_{NL}} = 1 - \frac{T}{T_{LR}} = 1 - \frac{I}{I_{LR}}, \qquad (1.12)$$

where ω_{NL} is the *no-load speed*,

$$\omega_{NL} = \frac{V_s}{k_E} \quad \text{rad/s}, \qquad (1.13)$$

and T_{LR} is the locked-rotor torque or *stall* torque,

$$T_{LR} = k_T I_{LR} = k_T \frac{V_s}{R} \quad \text{Nm}. \qquad (1.14)$$

I_{LR} is the locked-rotor current or *stall* current, limited only by the winding resistance.

According to eqn. (1.12), the voltage-limited speed/torque curve is a straight line as shown in Fig. 1.8. The equation is normalized: the angular velocity is normalized to the no-load value, while the torque and current are normalized to their locked-rotor values.

If the motor is operating at no load, the torque is zero and no current is drawn from the supply. There is no volt-drop in the resistance R and therefore E must be equal to V_s. This occurs, by definition, at the no-load speed. Eqn. (1.13) shows that the *no-load speed* is *proportional to the supply voltage*. This is precisely the characteristic of DC motors that made them the mainstay of adjustable speed drives, even in the early days of power electronics, because variable-*voltage* drives (in the form of phase-controlled rectifiers and choppers) were available and cost-effective long before variable-*frequency* converters.

When load torque is applied, current is drawn from the supply, resulting in a volt-drop RI in the motor resistance. This volt-drop causes E to fall to the value $V_s - RI$, and so the speed must fall. The drop in E is proportional to the current, and therefore to the torque; consequently the speed/torque curve at constant voltage is linear.

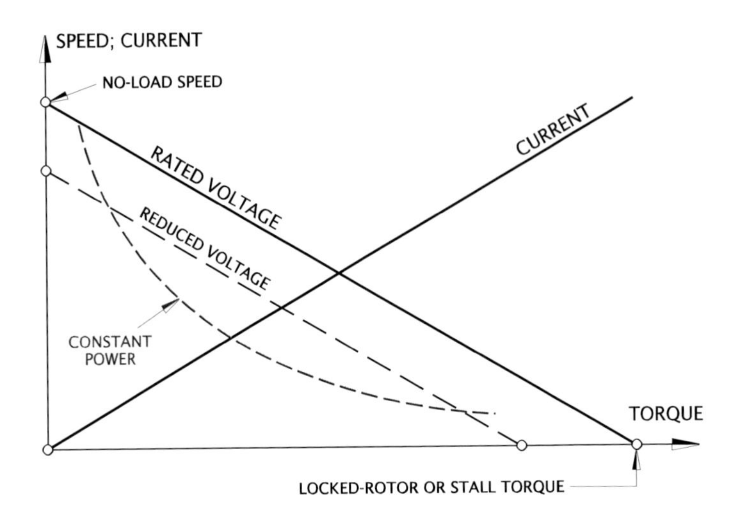

Fig. 1.8 Speed/torque and current/torque characteristics of brushless DC motor

If sufficient load torque is applied, the speed falls to zero and the motor is then *stalled*, i.e., in the locked-rotor condition. Then $E = 0$ and all the supply voltage is dropped across the motor resistance R. Since R is usually a very small resistance, the resulting stall current is extremely large. It is not normally permissible to allow the full locked-rotor current to flow, even for a short time, because it would either demagnetize the magnets or destroy the power transistors, or burn the winding insulation. Normal operation is generally confined to the left-hand region of Fig. 1.8. Typically, up to 30% of the locked-rotor torque (and current) may be obtained continuously, and perhaps 50-60% for short periods, although these percentages vary widely among different designs. A motor that is designed to operate for extended periods at stall is called a *torque motor*.

The speed/torque characteristic is often presented with the axes interchanged, that is, as a torque/speed characteristic. In that case the ratio of stall torque to no-load speed is sometimes called the *steepness*, and it is given by

$$S = \frac{T_{\mathrm{LR}}}{\omega_{\mathrm{NL}}} = \frac{k_{\mathrm{T}} k_{\mathrm{E}}}{R}. \tag{1.15}$$

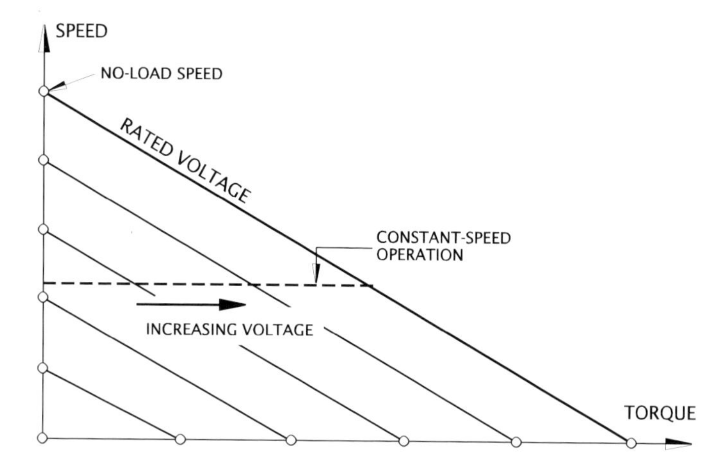

Fig. 1.9 Constant-speed operation of a brushless DC motor, showing that the effective supply voltage must vary

Figs. 1.8 and 1.9 include additional speed/torque curves at different voltages, showing the linear relationship between voltage and no-load speed. The torque constant is not affected by the voltage or the speed, so there is only one graph of torque vs. current. Also shown in Fig. 1.8 is a constant-power curve. Mechanical power is the product of torque and speed, so this curve is a rectangular hyperbola.

To operate at constant speed, it is evident from the dotted line in Fig. 1.9 that the voltage must respond to any change in the torque. As the torque increases, the voltage at the motor terminals must increase at the same rate as the RI volt-drop, so that E remains constant and therefore the speed remains constant. The operating point thus finds itself on a continuous *series* of speed/torque curves corresponding to the variable voltage. In a practical drive the adjustment of the motor terminal voltage to track the RI volt-drop is automatically achieved by speed feedback control. (See §8.4).

Constant-speed operation is only one of several possible modes of operation. The operating point can track any of the load curves in Fig. 1.7 provided that it lies within the capability of the motor and its drive. If the operating point is changing dynamically, additional torque will be necessary for acceleration and braking. This torque does not appear in the ordinary torque/speed diagram of the load, and is usually calculated by computer simulation.

1.4 Sinewave motors and generators

Suppose we replace the phase currents in Fig. 1.4 by sinewaves,

$$\begin{aligned} i_1 &= i_{pk} \sin p\theta; \\ i_2 &= i_{pk} \sin(p\theta - 2\pi/3); \\ i_3 &= i_{pk} \sin(p\theta + 2\pi/3). \end{aligned} \qquad (1.16)$$

and suppose that the phase EMFs are also sinusoidal:[1]

$$\begin{aligned} e_1 &= e_{pk} \sin p\theta; \\ e_2 &= e_{pk} \sin(p\theta - 2\pi/3); \\ e_3 &= e_{pk} \sin(p\theta + 2\pi/3). \end{aligned} \qquad (1.17)$$

The angle θ represents the rotor position in mechanical radians, defined in Fig. 1.3. Eqns. (1.16–17) express the fact that the current and EMF are AC quantities synchronized with the rotor position. In both equations the argument $p\theta$ ensures that there are p electrical cycles of current and EMF in every mechanical revolution, with

$$\theta = \omega_m t. \qquad (1.18)$$

The total instantaneous torque is obtained in the same way as it was for the squarewave motor:

$$T_0 = T_1 + T_2 + T_3 = \frac{1}{\omega_m}\left[e_1 i_1 + e_2 i_2 + e_3 i_3\right]. \qquad (1.19)$$

When eqns. (1.16) and (1.17) are substituted in this equation, the result (after some algebraic simplification) is the ripple-free torque

$$T_0 = \frac{3}{2}\frac{e_{pk} i_{pk}}{\omega_m}. \qquad (1.20)$$

As in the squarewave motor, ripple-free torque is obtained only with balanced conduction in all three phases, as in Fig. 1.10.

---

[1] It is not unhelpful to think of these sinewaves as the fundamental components of their squarewave counterparts. One of the interesting properties of the squarewave motor/drive is that it produces torque from all the harmonics that are common to both the current and the EMF, whereas the sinewave motor/drive produces torque only from the fundamental components. For further discussion see Chapter 8.

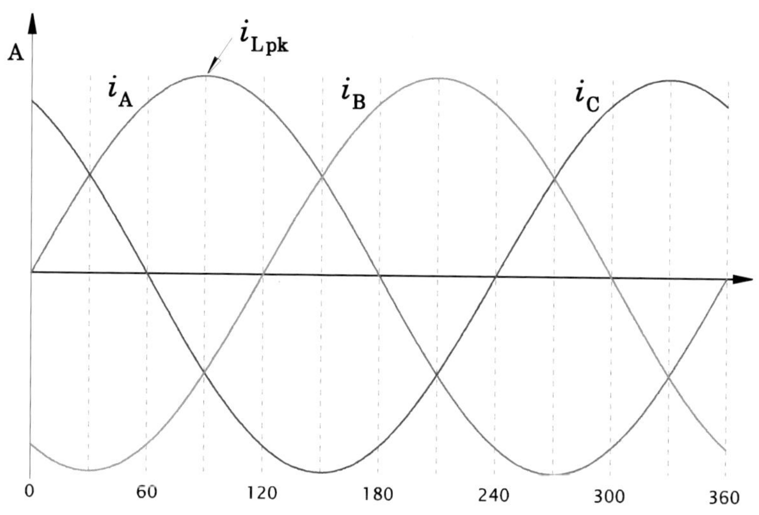

Fig. 1.10 3-phase sinewave currents (balanced)

The sinusoidal EMFs and currents have the RMS values

$$E_{LN\,rms} = \frac{e_1}{\sqrt{2}}; \quad I_{L\,rms} = \frac{i_1}{\sqrt{2}}; \tag{1.21}$$

and if these are substituted in eqn. (1.20) we get

$$T_0 = 3\,\frac{E_{LN\,rms} I_{L\,rms}}{\omega_m}. \tag{1.22}$$

The notation identifies E_{LN} as the line-neutral EMF, assuming wye connection; the current I_L is then the line current, which is the same as the phase current for the wye connection.

The line-line EMF is

$$E_{LL\,rms} = \sqrt{3}\,E_{LN\,rms}, \tag{1.23}$$

and if this is substituted in eqn. (1.22) we get

$$T_0 = \sqrt{3}\,\frac{E_{LL\,rms} I_{L\,rms}}{\omega_m}. \tag{1.24}$$

This equation holds for delta connection as well as wye.

It is worth noting the effect of a **phase advance** γ in the current, such that eqn. (1.16) for i_1 becomes

$$i_1 = i_{pk} \sin (p\theta + \gamma), \tag{1.25}$$

while γ is added to the phase of i_2 and i_3 as well. If the equations deriving the torque are worked again, the result will be found to be

$$T = T_0 \cos \gamma, \tag{1.26}$$

where T_0 is calculated from eqn. (1.20), (1.22) or (1.24) with $\gamma = 0$. The torque is therefore a cosine function of the phase-advance angle. If $\gamma > 90°$ the torque becomes negative, implying that the power flow is negative; the machine is then **generating** or regenerating.

The sinewave currents are produced by the same drive circuit as in Fig. 1.5, but with different switching control. It is clear from Fig. 1.10 that *three* lines are normally conducting at any instant, except at the zero-crossings. This is fundamentally different from the 3-phase squarewave system, in which only two lines are normally conducting. When the machine is acting as a generator loaded with a diode rectifier, the operation becomes closer to the squarewave system in reverse, as it were, with conduction in two lines (and two diodes) at any instant.

We have already noted on p. 2 that in the sinewave motor, the ampere-conductor distribution does not jump suddenly through 60°at the end of each commutation period, but rotates continuously at the synchronous speed. This can now be demonstrated mathematically. Suppose the conductors of phases 1, 2 and 3 are distributed sinusoidally:

$$\begin{aligned} C_1(\xi) &= C \cos p\xi; \\ C_2(\xi) &= C \cos (p\xi - 2\pi/3); \\ C_3(\xi) &= C \cos (p\xi + 2\pi/3); \end{aligned} \tag{1.27}$$

where ξ is the angle measured around the stator periphery. If we multiply these functions by the respective currents from eqns. (1.16), we get expressions for the *ampere*-conductor distributions, and when these are added together the result is

$$i_1 C_1 + i_2 C_2 + i_3 C_3 = \frac{3}{2} i_{pk} C \sin p(\theta - \xi). \tag{1.28}$$

In synchronous operation the electrical angle $p\theta$ is given by

$$p\theta = \omega t + \alpha, \tag{1.29}$$

where $\omega = 2\pi f$ and α is a phase angle, which we can set to 0 without loss of generality if i_1 is taken as the "reference" current. Then

$$i_1 C_1 + i_2 C_2 + i_3 C_3 = \frac{3}{2} C i_{pk} \sin(\omega t - p\xi), \tag{1.30}$$

and this represents an ampere-conductor distribution that *rotates* at synchronous speed ω/p mechanical rad/s. Its peak value is 3/2 times the peak value of the ampere-conductor distribution of one phase.

1.4.1 Phasor representation

The natural next step is to represent the EMF and current as phasors.[2] In setting up a system of phasors it is useful to start with the rotating flux of the magnet. This flux produces a sinusoidally varying flux-linkage in each phase: for example, in phase 1,

$$\psi_1 = \sqrt{2}\,\Psi_{1Md} \cos(\omega t). \tag{1.31}$$

If we express this flux-linkage as a phasor $\mathbf{\Psi}_{1Md}$, the fundamental EMF generated in phase 1 by the rotating magnet flux is[3]

$$\mathbf{E}_{q1} = j\omega \mathbf{\Psi}_{1Md} \tag{1.32}$$

It is natural to draw the flux-linkage phasor $\mathbf{\Psi}_{1Md}$ along the real or x-axis and to define this as the d-axis of the phasor diagram, since it is aligned with the magnet flux. By virtue of the $j\omega$ multiplier the EMF phasor $\mathbf{E}_{q1}$ leads the flux-linkage by 90°. We can also write

$$\mathbf{E}_{q1} = jE_{q1}, \tag{1.33}$$

where E_{q1} is measured in RMS volts. In the subscript, q means that $\mathbf{E}_{q1}$ is drawn along the imaginary or q-axis, as in Fig. 1.11, while *1* means the fundamental component.

---

[2] A phasor $\mathbf{I}$ is here defined as a complex number $Ie^{j\beta}$ such that the instantaneous quantity $\sqrt{2}\, I \sin(\omega t)$ is equal to Re $\{-j\sqrt{2}\,\mathbf{I}\, e^{j(\omega t+\beta)}\}$. By convention, phasors use RMS values; hence the appearance of the $\sqrt{2}$ factor. See footnote on p. 20.

[3] In the subscript, *1M* means the fundamental component of the magnet flux distribution, and d means that the orientation of the magnet flux defines the d-axis of the rotor. As the magnet rotates in space, the phasors rotate in synchronism.

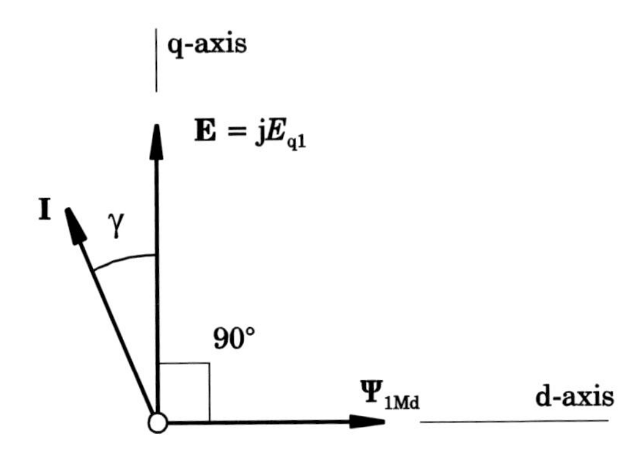

Fig. 1.11 Phasor diagram showing $\mathbf{E}_{q1}$ and **I**

The current phasor is a complex number

$$\mathbf{I} = I\, e^{\mathrm{j}(\gamma + \pi/2)} \tag{1.34}$$

where I is the RMS value of the phase current. With the flux-linkage Ψ_{1Md} as reference phasor, the phase of **I** is $\gamma + \pi/2$, not γ.[4]

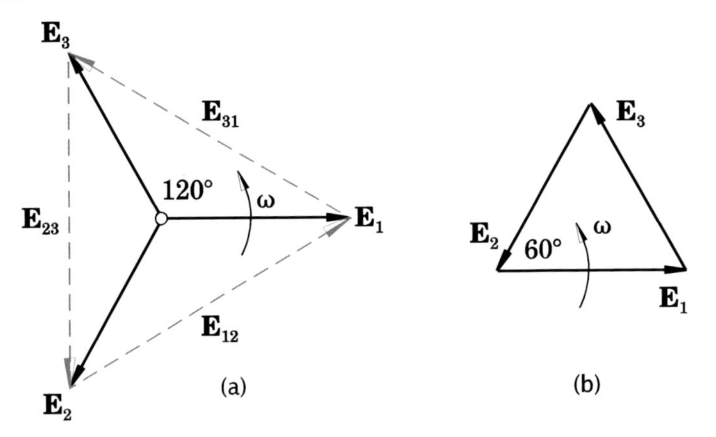

Fig. 1.12 Three-phase system of EMFs

[4] The reference axes in Fig. 1.11 are arguably the natural choice for a PM AC motor, while sin ωt is regarded as a natural choice for the reference of the current waveform of phase 1 in Fig. 1.10. However, these are not mathematically consistent unless we define "phasors" with $-\mathrm{j}e^{\mathrm{j}\omega t}$ instead of $e^{\mathrm{j}\omega t}$; see footnote on p. 19. In normal calculations this subtlety will never be noticed, but in programming these equations it can catch you out. The choice of reference axes is free, so we take full advantage of it.

A full set of EMF phasors for the three phases is shown in Fig. 1.12, with a further change of reference phasor — this time $\mathbf{E}_1$ is drawn on the reference axis and the subscript 1 refers to phase 1. In (a) the phasors are drawn in a star, while in (b) they are drawn in a closed triangle.[5] The closed triangle expresses the relationship

$$\mathbf{E}_1 + \mathbf{E}_2 + \mathbf{E}_3 = 0, \tag{1.35}$$

which is a necessary (but not sufficient) condition for balanced operation.[6] The star, on the other hand, shows the difference phasors

$$\mathbf{E}_{12} = \mathbf{E}_1 - \mathbf{E}_2; \quad \mathbf{E}_{23} = \mathbf{E}_2 - \mathbf{E}_3; \quad \mathbf{E}_{31} = \mathbf{E}_3 - \mathbf{E}_1. \tag{1.36}$$

which in a wye connection are the phasors of the line-line EMFs. It is noted that $\mathbf{E}_{12}$ leads $\mathbf{E}_1$ by $30°$ in a balanced system, and for balanced operation it is often written in terms of RMS values as $E_{LL} = \surd 3 E_{LN}$ or $E_{LL} = \surd 3 E_{ph}$, with no mention of the phase difference.

In a delta connection, an equation similar to eqn. (1.36) applies to the currents, so for the one in Fig. (6.2) we have[7]

$$\mathbf{I}_A = \mathbf{I}_1 - \mathbf{I}_3; \quad \mathbf{I}_B = \mathbf{I}_2 - \mathbf{I}_1; \quad \mathbf{I}_C = \mathbf{I}_3 - \mathbf{I}_2. \tag{1.37}$$

For the wye connection the equation

$$\mathbf{I}_1 + \mathbf{I}_2 + \mathbf{I}_3 = 0 \tag{1.38}$$

expresses Kirchhoff's first law at the star point, when there is no neutral connection; it applies also in terms of the instantaneous currents. Again, eqn. (1.38) is necessary (but not sufficient)[6] for balanced operation, and we can observe that it is automatically satisfied with a 3-wire wye connection. For the delta connection or for a 4-wire wye connection with the neutral connected, eqn. (1.38) is still necessary for balanced operation, but it is not automatic.

---

[5] The position of an isolated phasor on the page is arbitrary: as long as its value as a complex number remains unchanged, it can be drawn anywhere. However, with respect to the relationships between different phasors, their positions are critical.

[6] Eqns. (1.35) and (1.38) mean that the zero sequence component is zero, but for balanced operation the negative-sequence component must also be zero. Imbalance and sequence components (symmetrical components) are considered in Chapter 10.

[7] There is an alternative way to connect the delta, such that $\mathbf{I}_A = \mathbf{I}_1 - \mathbf{I}_2$ etc.

The phasor diagram (Fig. 7.) is a powerful tool for calculating the relationship between voltage and current, including the effect of inductance and phase advance. It works naturally with the *dq*-axis model of the machine, so that salient-pole machines (like the IPM) can be readily calculated, even under saturated conditions, without resort to complex nonlinear simulations. It also forms the basis for the **voltage locus diagram** which represents the capability of the drive in relation to the available voltage; and the **ellipse diagram** which forms the basis of the speed/torque characteristic. These subjects are covered in Chapter 7. Systems with 2,4,5,6 and more phases are also considered in Chapters 4 and 7.

1.4.2 Voltage

We have mentioned on p. 18 that the current (and therefore the voltage) can be supplied to the motor by the same transistor bridge circuit as for the squarewave drive, Fig. 1.5. We have also mentioned that when the machine is a generator, it will commonly be connected to a rectifier whose load either fixes or strongly influences the terminal voltage. A third possibility is to connect the machine to a sinewave voltage source such as the mains, as is the case with the line-start PM motors discussed in Chapter 11. In all these cases the phasor diagram plays an important practical and theoretical part in design and analysis, even though it represents only the fundamental components of the currents and voltages.

In the case of inverter-fed machines the voltage waveform at the terminals is obtained from the DC supply by switching between the three levels $+V_s$, 0 and $-V_s$ at high frequency. On an oscilloscope it looks noisy and nothing like a sinewave. With a suitable PWM switching algorithm, sufficient inductance, and a sinusoidal EMF waveform, the *current* waveform can be made almost perfectly sinusoidal, and then the phasor diagram can be used for the basic calculation of torque and *fundamental* voltage. Chapter 7 describes various PWM algorithms including the use of **space vectors** that can be used even when the current is not sinusoidal in the case of *sinewound* machines. PWM control algorithms are also used in squarewave drives (Chapter 6), but in that case the phasor diagram cannot be used even for the most basic calculations.

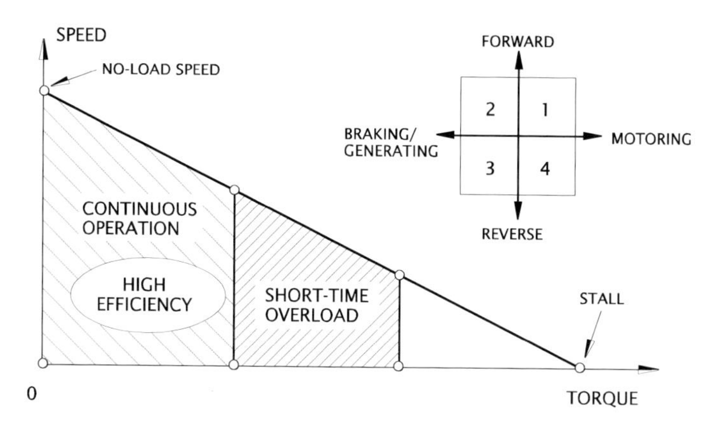

Fig. 1.13 Typical continuous and short-time operating regions

1.5 Practical considerations

The most important factor limiting the power output is the temperature of conductors and magnets in the machine, and of transistors and other components in the drive. The temperature rise depends on the load, on the efficiency, and on the effectiveness of the cooling arrangements.

Fig. 1.13 shows how the continuous and short-time operating regions of a brushless DC motor are often identified on the speed/torque diagram. Over a long period, the average operating point must remain within the continuous operating range. Short excursions into the overload range are permitted, as frequently as demanded by the load, provided that the accumulated heating effect does not cause the motor temperature rise to exceed the short-term rated value. Thermal calculations are described in Chapter 9. They are very important in rating and selecting brushless DC motors.

Maximum efficiency is usually achieved within the continuous operating range, and it is common to show efficiency contours on the operating diagram as indicated in Fig. 1.13.

The effect of temperature on the magnet characteristics is also important. At high temperatures the magnets provide less flux, so there is a reduction in the torque constant k_T. At the same time k_E is reduced, so the no-load speed is increased.

The ideal analysis presented so far has ignored the effect of all losses except the I^2R losses in the stator windings. Additional losses include core losses (hysteresis and eddy currents) in the lamination iron, bearing friction, and windage. In addition, there may be eddy currents in the retaining can if one is fitted; or even in the magnets themselves in cases where the resistivity is low enough. These additional losses are caused or increased by variations in magnetic flux-density due to the stator slotting, or by ripple in the phase currents due to chopping or pulse-width modulation.

Extreme currents and temperatures give rise to concern about demagnetization of the magnets. In principle it should be possible to avoid demagnetization through overcurrent in a current-regulated drive. However, even when the motor is fitted with temperature sensors, it is difficult to measure *magnet* temperature, and so it is necessary to design to minimize the likelihood of demagnetization. Even partial demagnetization is unacceptable in the great majority of cases, because it ruins the normal operating characteristics.

The speed/torque "curves" in Figs. 1.8–13 are all straight lines described by the ideal equation (1.12). In practice the curve is not straight because of the effects of winding **inductance**, which causes distortion at high speed; and because of magnetic **saturation**, coupled with the demagnetizing effect of the phase currents at high torque. These effects are addressed in later chapters.

Fig. 1.13 also shows the four **quadrants** of operation: motoring or braking/generating, and forward or reverse. Most brushless PM *machines* are inherently capable of operating in all four quadrants, but this is not true of their *drives* and controls. In general, four-quadrant operation is more expensive than single- or two-quadrant operation, especially if full regeneration of kinetic energy is required.

The perfectly smooth torque indicated in Fig. 1.4 cannot be obtained in a practical motor, although it can be closely approached. Torque variations during one revolution arise from imperfect commutation of the phase currents; from ripple in the current waveform caused by chopping; and from variations in the reluctance of the magnetic circuit due to slotting, as the rotor rotates. This last effect is sometimes called **cogging**. It is detectable when the shaft is slowly rotated by hand.

2 MACHINE TYPES and APPLICATIONS

2.1 Machine configuration

There are several different configurations of brushless motors and generators which use rotating permanent magnets and stationary phase coils. The variety has evolved enormously in the last 20 years and it is interesting to consider why.

2.1.1 Reasons for variety

Ultimately the *application* determines the viability of a particular machine configuration. In general the increase in the variety of applications has been driven partly by demand for increased functionality, precision, and automation in motion control; and partly by demand for increased energy efficiency and better utilization of primary energy sources. Individual products often have special circumstances behind the choice of a particular machine. It is often said that the motor business is a "niche" business; nowhere is this truer than in the brushless permanent-magnet motor business. Products in this field often have a high research and development content, while standardization is not found to the same extent as, for example, in induction motors. These considerations have little to do with the production *volumes*: at one end of the scale, some brushless motor products (such as muffin fans, disk drives) are produced at the rate of millions per month. At the other end, there are plenty of examples of single-digit production volumes.

Invention is another powerful "variety driver".[1] Indeed the expansion in applications for brushless permanent-magnet machines can be compared to the expansive development of electrical machine technology and applications 100 years earlier, but with the addition of power electronics and high-coercivity magnets. While some inventions appear to come "out of the blue", others are the result of attempts to avoid patents taken out to protect earlier inventions. Often the resulting alternative configurations are patented themselves in turn, and so the process continues.

---

[1] We have often seen the invention of gadgets that, once invented, become "must have" possessions. Sometimes invention is the mother of necessity.

The development of new and/or improved *materials* is a third and most important "variety driver". For example the development of ferrite magnets revolutionized the technology of low-voltage DC motors and paved the way for the introduction of brushless motors (particularly in the form of muffin fans). The development of Samarium-Cobalt magnets (in the late 1960s) extended the range of applicability of brushless permanent-magnet machines to higher power levels. Then in the early 1980s, Neodymium-Iron-Boron magnets increased the cost-effectiveness of high-energy magnets, precipitating a prolonged expansion in the application of brushless permanent-magnet machines.

Improvements in soft iron materials have also contributed significantly in the development of brushless permanent-magnet machines. Reduced losses in electrical lamination steels have been achieved through metallurgical and process development, including thin gauges, improved chemical composition and heat-treatment, and improved core-plate insulation. Although these improvements have benefited other types of machine, the brushless permanent-magnet machine has benefited greatly, especially in high-speed applications. Brushless permanent-magnet motors are often designed for high power density, to work in small spaces, and the high-quality steels can be as important as the magnets themselves. Further, powdered-metal materials permit the manufacture of cores with shapes and features that are not easily obtainable with laminated construction.[2]

Insulating and encapsulating materials also contribute. For example, inverter-grade magnet-wire insulation is important in connection with fast-switching power transistors. Thermally conductive encapsulating compounds improve heat transfer, permitting the use of higher power densities.

High-strength non-magnetic materials such as Inconel® and carbon-fibre are also important in the design of high-speed brushless permanent-magnet machines, where they are used in retaining sleeves that extend the range of operation to much higher speeds than would otherwise be possible.

---

[2] These are also known as *soft magnetic composite* materials, as developed particularly by the Höganäs company in Sweden. SMC cores are related to sintered components but are specially developed for their magnetic and electrical properties.

Most brushless permanent-magnet motor and generator systems require an electronic drive or rectifier. Developments in power electronics have been significant in several important respects, resulting in higher PWM switching frequencies (for improved torque control, reduced acoustic noise, and reduced core loss); higher voltage and current levels; more advanced sensors and control; and generally improved power density, efficiency, and reliability. With all these advances, the cost of the drive has also decreased in relative terms, permitting a wider range of affordable applications.

These technical developments have been part of a more general process in which sophisticated technical solutions have become more affordable and more widespread than they were, say, 20 years ago. Indeed the relentless demand for cost reduction has itself resulted in technical innovation and product development, leading in some cases to designs or "varieties" that might seem less than optimal from a purely engineering point of view.

2.1.2 Classification

Many electrical-machine texts attempt to group machines into families, as a means of organizing and classifying them to improve understanding of their similarities and differences. In this text we are already concerned with a specialized group of machines, all of which have rotating permanent-magnet excitation and stationary armature windings.[3] The process of extending the classification is further specialized, and we have chosen to organize the machines mainly according to the physical configuration of their stationary and rotating parts: radial-flux, surface-magnet, interior-rotor, etc.

The classification could be refined by introducing sub-divisions according to the type of drive: squarewave, sinewave, etc. However, we have stopped short of doing this, on the grounds that this book is mainly about machines. Although both types of drive are treated in detail in Chapters 6 and 7, and generators in Chapter 9, there is no merit in making the classification more complicated.

---

[3] The term "armature" here refers to the winding that handles the main electrical power. In brushless permanent-magnet machines it is always stationary. By contrast, the electrical "power winding" in DC machines is always rotating. In relays, the armature has no winding at all.

Terminology is inextricably linked with classification. The terms used with brushless permanent-magnet machines are not rigidly standardized, and in some cases there is even a lack of clarity in definition that can be confusing. While we would not want to be dogmatic in our use of terms, it is worth discussing some of the terminology in order to make our own descriptions clear.

The terms "brushless AC" and "brushless DC" merit some discussion in this context. "Brushless DC" usually refers to the original brushless permanent-magnet motor that uses electronic commutation of an essentially direct current, with low-resolution shaft-position sensors to synchronize the switching of the drive transistors with the rotor position. The terms "brushless AC" and "PM AC synchronous" usually refer to systems with sinewave drive.

Fig. 2.1 is a chart of machine configurations, some of which are described in more detail in the remaining sections of this chapter.

1 Surface-magnet machine with arc magnets bonded to the rotor yoke. This drawing is similar to that of a motor with ring-arc magnets, fitted as a complete ring.

2 Surface-magnet machine with "bread-loaf" magnets. The magnets have profiled surface at the airgap, and are bonded to flats on the rotor yoke.

3 Inset magnets, developed by Sebastian and by Schiferl to achieve better protection against demagnetization and a wider speed range using flux-weakening.

4 Exterior-rotor motor. Popular in fan drives and disk drives, this machine also has a wide range of applications in motion control, such as in Figs. 2.43 and 2.44.

5 Spoke-type interior-magnet rotor. Developed to increase the airgap flux-density by the flux-concentration principle, this machine was used as an aircraft generator [Richter, 1979] and in servo-motors by Fanuc and by Pacific Scientific.

6 The IPM or "interior permanent-magnet" motor comes in a wide variety of shapes and sizes, and is used for applications as diverse as washing-machines, compressors for air-conditioning, and hybrid vehicle traction.

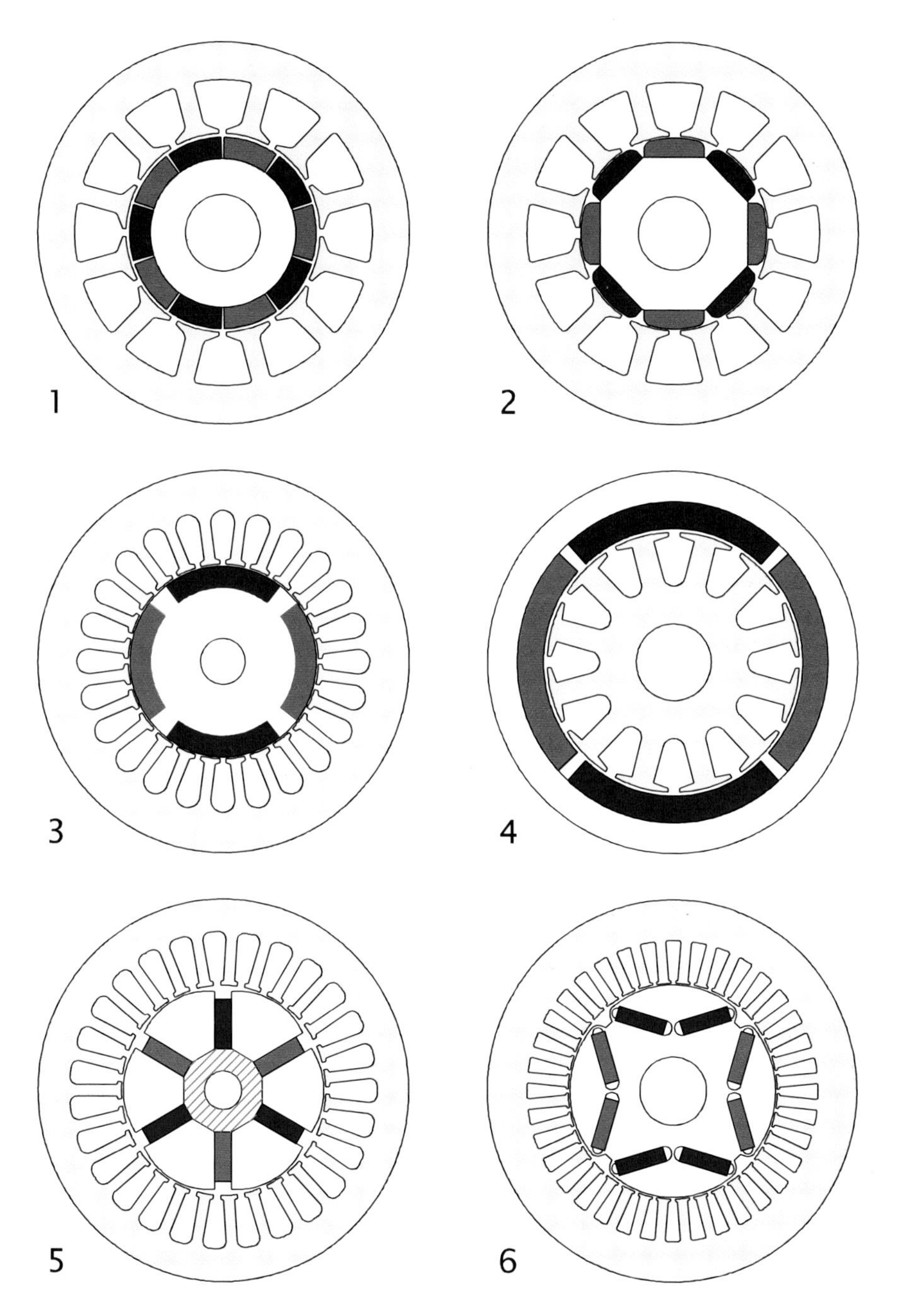

Fig. 2.1 Motor chart

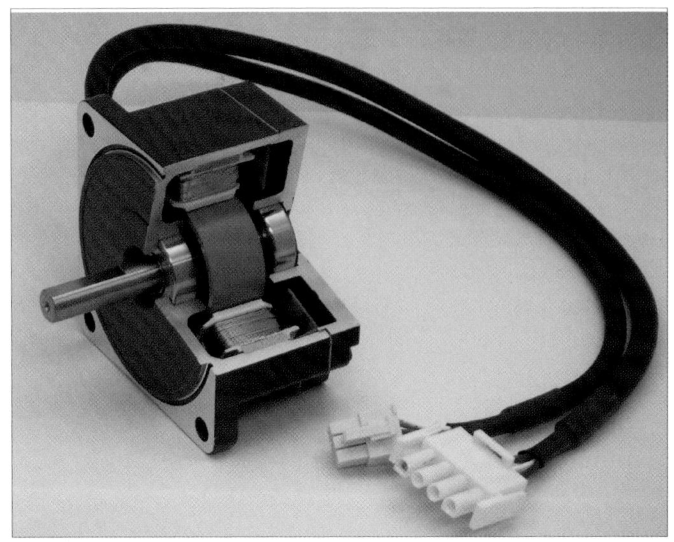

Fig. 2.2 Surface-magnet PM brushless motor used in motion-control applications. *Oriental Motor Co. Ltd., Japan*

2.2 Radial-flux machines

2.2.1 Interior-rotor surface-magnet machines

A cutaway of a surface-magnet interior-rotor motor is shown in Fig. 2.2. Several important features are evident in this figure. Most obvious are the compactness and the exquisite manufacturing finish and precision. These are not just superficial observations, but stem from the mechanical design which is optimized to achieve excellent concentricity and alignment of the bearings, the stator, and the rotor.

Fig. 2.2 also shows the specialized connecting leads for both the motor phases and the shaft-position sensor, which is mounted on a printed-circuit board inside the housing. Large bearings mounted very close to the PM rotor make the assembly rugged and precise — important features especially in gearmotors, or when there is a significant radial load on the shaft.

The totally-enclosed aluminium frame is typical of brushless PM machines, ensuring good heat extraction, cleanliness, and low noise. The apparent simplicity of the components, the general proportions, and the overall finish combine to present what can only be described as an elegant example of a successful PM brushless motor product.

Radial-flux machines have advantages relating to manufacturing and magnetic configuration, that help to explain why these machines are the most common type of brushless PM machine. They can use standardized parts, tooling, materials, winding methods and other processes available and long established for other motor types (especially induction motors and stepping motors).

For most slot/pole combinations the radial magnetic forces are balanced, as are the axial centering forces, so that virtually all the electromagnetic forces contribute to the torque.[4] This is good for bearing life and helps to minimize acoustic noise.

The torque/inertia ratio is inherently high, and the torque is closely proportional to the current. Both of these features are essential in many motion-control applications.

Interior-rotor radial-flux machines can easily be manufactured with different core lengths for different ratings, using the same laminations and even the same magnets. Laminated construction permits the rotor and stator cores to be punched at the same time from a single blank, reducing material cost. Especially with higher pole-numbers, the rotor weight and inertia can be reduced by including holes in the rotor punching. (See Fig. 14.2)

Most of the heat in brushless PM machines arises in the stator winding and the stator core. As these components are stationary and in close thermal proximity to the frame, the heat is easily removed by any one of several different methods, or combinations thereof: for example, natural or forced air convection, conduction to mountings or heatsinks, and radiation. In highly rated machines, liquid coolants (water, oil etc.) can be used in a simple and accessible jacket integrated as part of the frame. All of these heat-removal methods can be applied without disturbing the totally-enclosed construction.

In the interior-rotor surface magnet machine, the mechanical retention of the magnets can be achieved by different methods including self-support (ring magnets); dovetailing; adhesive; or a separate high-strength nonmagnetic banding or sleeving (which also helps during rotor insertion at the point of assembly).

---

[4] This is in marked contrast to single-sided linear machines or axial-flux machines.

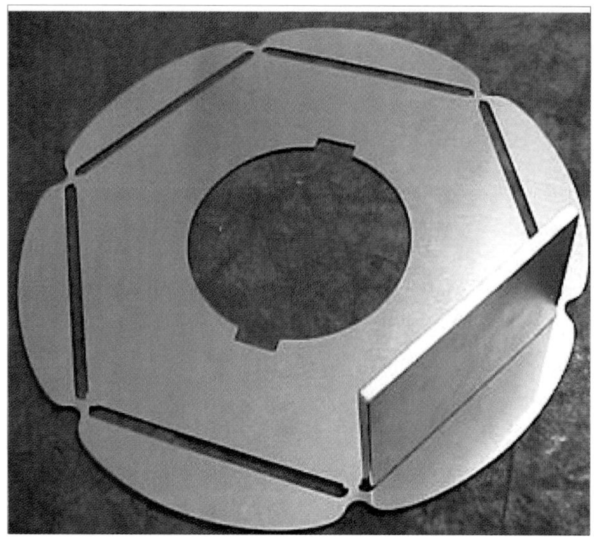

Fig. 2.3 Lamination and magnet of a 6-pole IPM rotor
WEG, Brazil

2.2.2 Interior-rotor interior-magnet machines (IPM)

Fig. 2.3 shows the essential features of an interior permanent-magnet (IPM) rotor. It uses a stack of unitary laminations with simple rectangular magnets, which are less expensive than arc magnets, and which can be inserted before or after magnetization. The punching can be inexpensively profiled, to improve the EMF waveform. No special tooling is required, and there is generally no need for a retaining sleeve. The structure can be strengthened for high-speed operation by means of webs or internal bridges, as in Fig. 4.6. The magnet pole area and the flux/pole can also be increased by using two magnets per pole, inclined in a V, Fig. 2.1(6).

The IPM is a salient-pole machine. This means that it has a component of torque — the *reluctance* torque — that comes from the shape of the steel lamination and not from the magnets. The total torque is the combination of reluctance torque and "magnet alignment" torque. In practice the reluctance torque is but a modest fraction of the total torque (perhaps no more than 30%), although it can be increased by constructing the rotor with more than one *layer* of magnets as in Fig. 2.50 or Fig. 14.1. This idea is derived from the theory of the synchronous reluctance machine.

The IPM is usually designed with an airgap comparable to that of an induction motor of the same size, and generally smaller than that of a surface-magnet motor. While this tends to increase the flux/pole and the reluctance torque, it also increases the inductance.

Higher inductance confers some benefit in current regulation, because it reduces the current ripple for a given PWM switching frequency. However, the voltage drop across the inductance tends to limit the maximum speed attainable with a given supply voltage. At the same time inductance is what makes flux-weakening possible, by which the speed range can be extended as explained in Chapter 7. The IPM is generally regarded as having greater flux-weakening capability than the surface-magnet machine. Moreover, the inductive voltage drop in the IPM is associated with the production of reluctance torque, whereas in the surface-magnet machine it is not.

Equally important to the control engineer is the fact that the IPM has a nonlinear relationship between the torque and the current. To obtain maximum torque the current must be phase-shifted by an angle that is not fixed but depends on the load, even without magnetic saturation. Saturation exacerbates the nonlinearity, as we shall see in detail later.

While the manufacturing and other advantages of the IPM were recognized long ago (and actually realized in line-start motors as long ago as the 1970s), it has taken a long time for the IPM to come to the forefront of modern electronically controlled applications. Probably the control complexity arising from the nonlinearity has been the main factor in this slow evolution. The availability of low-cost digital signal processing has facilitated the wider application of the IPM. At the same time, there is a wider range of applications requiring a wide speed range at constant power, and the flux-weakening capability of the IPM is seen as a means of achieving it. Particularly in electric vehicle traction, the combination of this capability with the prospect of low manufacturing cost makes the IPM attractive.

IPM rotors are less susceptible to demagnetization than surface-magnet rotors. This is partly due to the rotor leakage paths which divert the armature-reaction flux away from the magnets, and partly due to the higher inductance which limits the current under fault conditions.

Fig. 2.4 Complete electromechanical transmission system of the 2010 Toyota Prius. Both the motor (on the right) and the generator (on the left) are IPM machines. *Toyota Motor Company, Japan*

Another advantage of the IPM is that the magnets are less susceptible to eddy-current losses, partly because they are removed from the rotor surface and partly because the space-harmonic fields produced at the airgap are attenuated by the soft iron pole-caps.

Flux concentration is possible in the IPM. It was mentioned earlier in connection with a V-shaped divided magnet.[5] A disadvantage of flux concentration is the reduction in the permeance coefficient, which reduces the open-circuit flux-density in the magnet. So although it permits the use of a magnet with a lower remanent flux-density, it also requires the magnet to have adequate coercivity and thickness. A subtle but useful advantage of the V configuration is that it reduces the effect of saturation on the q-axis inductance and the reluctance torque.

[5] Even greater flux-concentration is obtained with the "spoke" geometry, Fig. 2.1. Examples include servo-motors manufactured by Fanuc and Pacific Scientific.

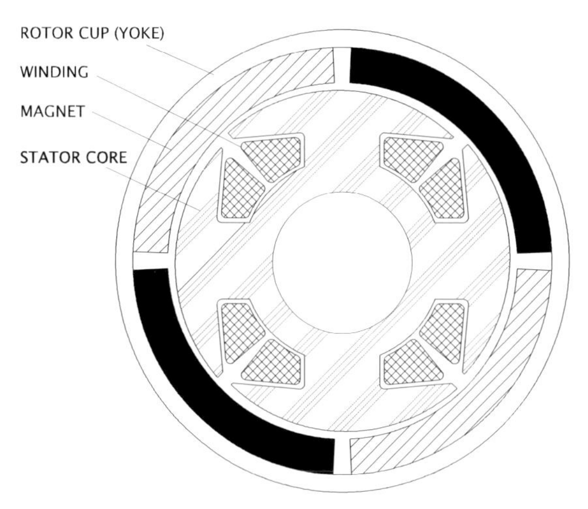

Fig. 2.5 Exterior-rotor surface-magnet machine

2.2.3 Exterior-rotor machines

These machines have long been common in low-power constant-speed applications that run in a single direction, including fans, certain types of pumps, blowers, disk drives, and mirror scanners. Early examples often used 2-phase or single-phase bifilar windings with squarewave drive, but 3-phase versions are now widely used to obtain increased power density, bidirectional operation, and other characteristics of precision motion control systems; see p. 60.

The torque is produced at a radius that is quite large relative to the outside diameter of the machine, implying that the same torque can be obtained with lower electric and magnetic loadings than would be required in an interior-rotor machine; this advantage may well be realisable in very large ring-type designs with high pole number and a large central aperture.

Typically the magnets are retained with adhesive inside a deep-drawn rotor cup that also provides a return flux path, and requires little machining. In small machines the cup is staked to a sintered hub which in turn is fixed to the shaft. The single-ended mounting of the cup imposes limits on the axial length of the motor and the speed, thus limiting the maximum power and the power density. Higher power can be obtained with a back-to-back dual configuration.

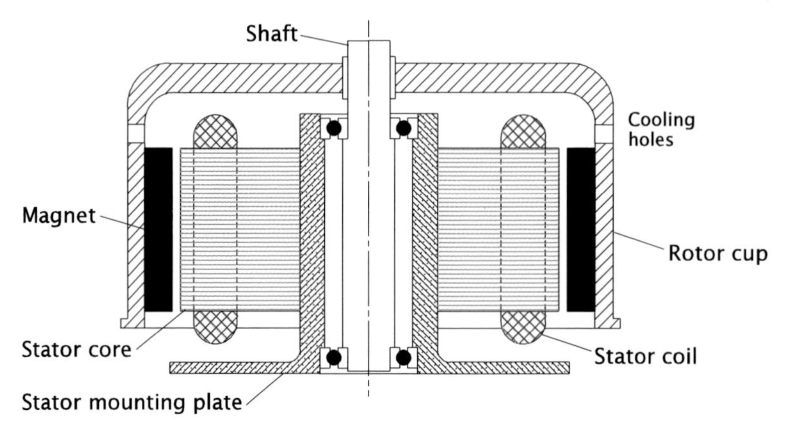

Fig. 2.6 Axial cross section of exterior-rotor surface-magnet machine

The inertia is relatively high because of the large rotor diameter. These machines are not used for highly dynamic servo applications, so the torque/inertia ratio is usually unimportant; in constant-speed applications the inertia is beneficial as it helps to mitigate the effects of torque ripple (including cogging torque).

The axial length of the soft magnetic rotor cup is generally greater than the axial length of the magnets, permitting the "yoke flux" to spread out beyond the ends of the magnets, into the overhanging regions of the cup. This amounts to an increase in the effective magnetic cross-section of the rotor yoke, permitting the cup to be made of a thinner material than would otherwise be the case. A degree of flux concentration is obtained from the fact that the inside radius of the magnets is greater than the outside radius of the stator, and with a large magnet surface area, low-cost ceramic or bonded NDFEB magnets can be used, usually with radial magnetization. The pole-to-pole flux-leakage is also minimal in this configuration.

The stator coils are wound in slots on the outside of the stator core, using automatic winding machinery (fly-winders) that can wind one, two or three phases at a time to minimize cost. Because the axial length is typically quite short, the end-winding resistance and inductance may be significant fractions of the total phase resistance and inductance. Furthermore, the inductance may be increased by the need for a large number of turns when ceramic or bonded NDFEB magnets are used, especially if the voltage is high.

It is sometimes held against the exterior-rotor motor that it is difficult to cool, given that the heat arises mainly in the stator which is almost completely enclosed by the rotor. However, the rotor cup can be provided with holes to promote the flow of cooling air through the stator. Certain high-power designs have used a reservoir of cooling oil circulating inside the cylindrical stator support member, which may even be internally finned. Although the heat transfer coefficient on this interior cooling surface can be as high as in an interior-rotor machine, its area is inevitably smaller.

The exterior-rotor machine is almost always a surface-magnet machine, although interior-magnet configurations are possible.

2.3 Axial-flux, linear, and other machines

The main incentive to use an axial-flux configuration is to make a flat machine with short overall length. Nowhere has this been more effectively demonstrated than in floppy-disk drives and other disk drives, millions of which have been manufactured.

The short length/diameter ratio or *aspect ratio* of the machine envelope stems from the topology of a flat disk of magnets rotating past an array of flat coils (sometimes called *pancake coils*) which may themselves be laid on a flat disk (in a slotless configuration) or in slots in a laminated or powdered-metal core. Fig. 2.7 shows an example of a rotor magnet plate, and Fig. 2.8 shows an array of stator coils.

The conformation of the stator coils presents the designer with certain difficulties. It can be seen in Fig. 2.8 that there is much less space for the inner "end turns" than for the outer end-turns. The extent to which the inner end-turns can be compacted is limited by problems of assembly and also by the need to cool them. Practical designs include the capstan construction in Fig. 2.9 and the Gramme ring construction in Fig. 2.10. Fig. 2.11 shows a historical example of an axial-flux alternator with electrical excitation, in which many of the design questions (and some answers) can be seen. This example actually combines the "capstan" construction for the stationary coils with the flat-coil construction (similar to Fig. 2.8) for the rotating coils, which almost makes them look like magnets.

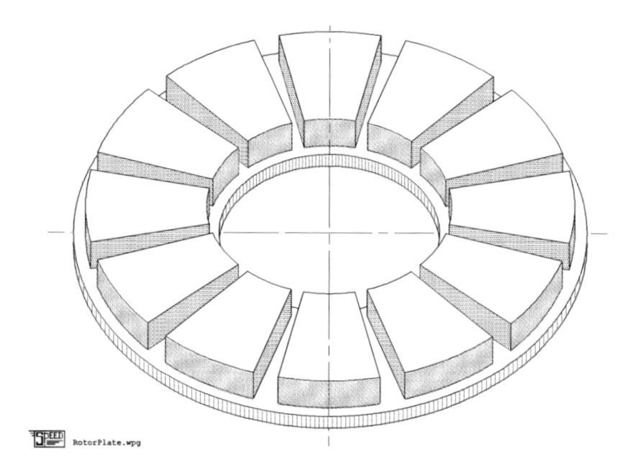

Fig. 2.7 Rotor magnet plate with 12 magnet poles

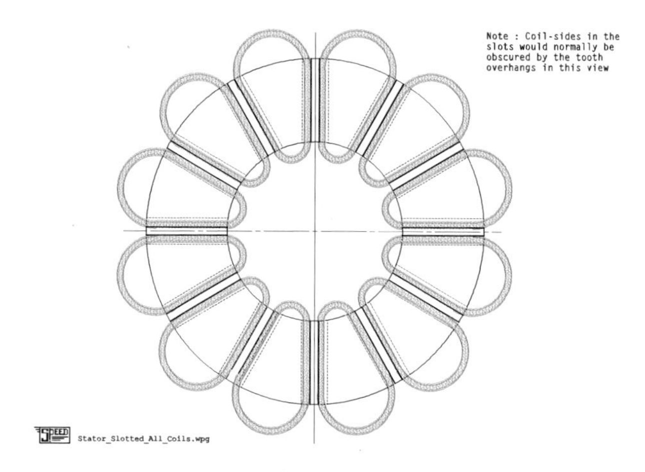

Fig. 2.8 Array of stator coils (one phase only)

The magnets in Fig. 2.7 are retained by adhesive, but additional support can be in the form of a nonmagnetic retaining ring forming a rim around the outside of the magnets. Although standard magnet shapes (such as disks or rectangles) have been used, it is preferable to design the magnet shape to maximize the flux/pole, to minimize cogging torque, and to control the EMF waveform. It is noted that large magnet blocks may be susceptible to eddy-current losses and may need to be subdivided into smaller segments.

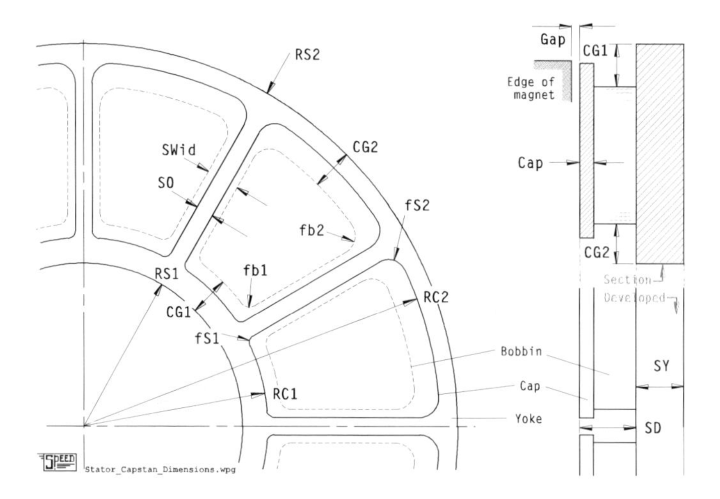

Fig. 2.9 "Capstan" construction of stator

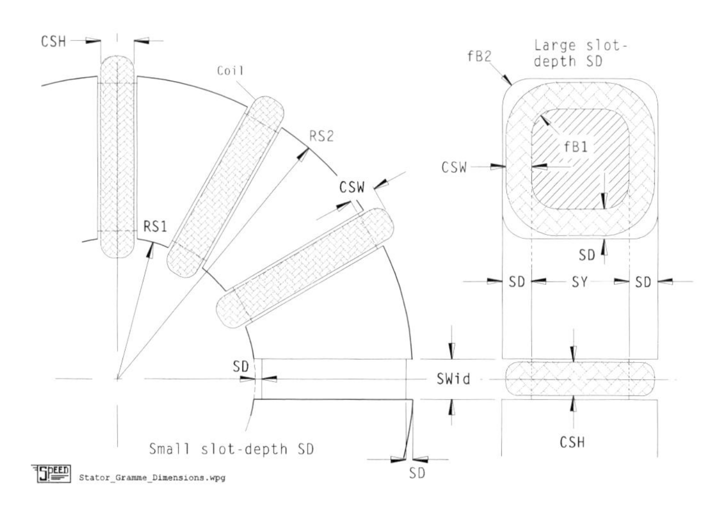

Fig. 2.10 "Gramme ring" construction of stator

Winding the "capstan" is a bobbin-winding operation, but the Gramme ring winding requires specialized winding machinery. The stator cores are open to a variety of construction methods including powdered-metal core and other fabricated forms, except that solid components are precluded by the need to suppress eddy-currents.

Fig. 2.11 Axial-flux alternator. From R.M. Walmsley, *Electricity in the Service of Man*, Cassell, London, 1904

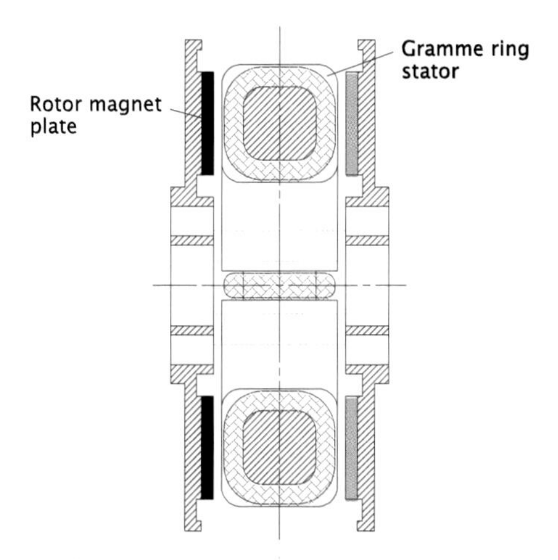

Fig. 2.12 Double-sided PM axial-flux machine with Gramme-ring stator

The "flat-pack" aspect of the entire assembly is apparent in Fig. 2.12, even in a double-sided configuration with two rotor magnet plates. In the double-sided machine the axial magnetic forces are balanced; the magnetic circuit is symmetrical, and no backplate is required to complete the flux path.

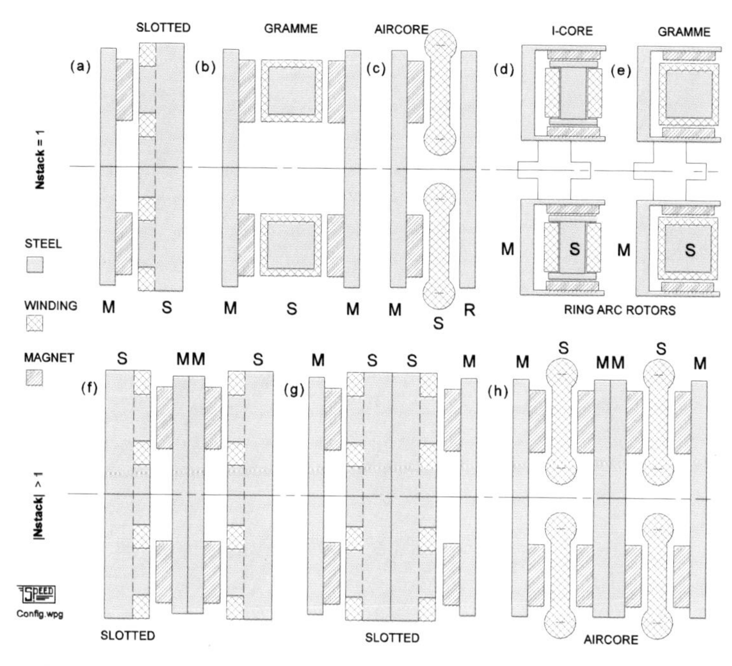

Fig. 2.13 Configurations of axial-flux and ring-arc machines

Fig. 2.13 shows a number of configurations of axial-flux machines together with two "ring-arc" machines described later.[6] Fig. 2.13(a) shows a single-sided machine with a stator of "capstan" construction. The same rotor magnet plate is used twice in the double-sided machine in Fig. 2.13(b), which has a Gramme-ring stator (also known as a toroidal stator). It is used again in Fig. 2.13(c), which has a slotless or "air-core" stator.

Fig. 2.13(f) is a double-sided version of Fig. 2.13(a), with back-to-back rotor plates sandwiched between two separate "capstan"-type stators. Fig. 2.13(g) is also a double-sided version of Fig. 2.13(a), but with back-to-back stators sandwiched between two separate rotors.

Multiple-stack machines can be built with a greater number of rotor and stator sections, although the "flat-pack" aspect is quickly lost when this is done.

[6] A detailed treatment of axial-flux machines is given in Gieras J.F., Wang R.J., and Kamper M.J., *Axial Flux Permanent Magnet Brushless Machines*, Kluwer Academic Publishers, 2004.

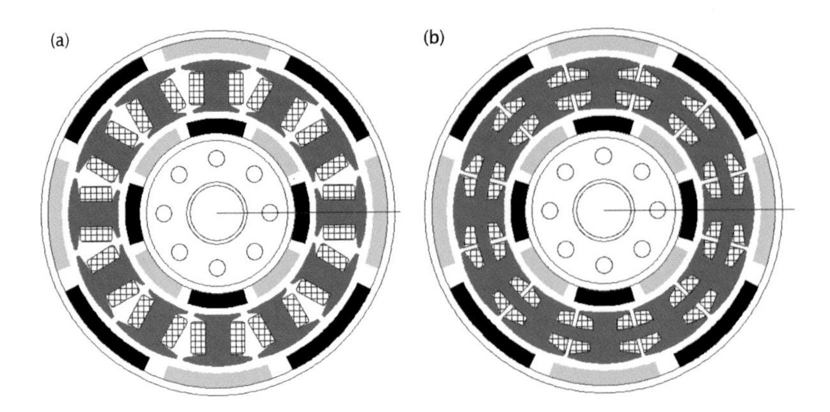

Fig. 2.15 "Ring-arc" machines (dual-rotor radial-flux machines)

Fig. 2.15 shows two variants of a so-called "ring-arc" motor, also known as a dual-gap radial-flux motor.[7] This machine has a short overall length/diameter ratio, with high torque produced by the two rows of magnets. Many different stator winding configurations are possible.

Fig. 2.14 shows the general configuration of a double-sided linear motor; (the stator winding is not shown). Such machines are used in specialized motion-control applications where mechanical gears and linkages are precluded. They generally have very rapid response and good control characteristics, and they sometimes use special linear precision encoders for position feedback. Either the stator or the magnet track can be the moveable part.

Fig. 2.14 Double-sided linear motor

[7] Qu and Lipo, [2003] and [2004]; Yoshikawa, Li and Murakami, [2006]

2.4 Gallery

This section presents some examples of engineered products using brushless permanent-magnet machines, chosen from graphic images kindly supplied by a number of the authors' collaborators. The images are accompanied by brief comments mainly supplied by the manufacturing companies themselves, to explain the distinctive features of the machines and their applications.

Fig. 2.16 is a 3D CAD exploded view of a typical high-quality industrial servomotor with surface-mounted magnets and integral shaft position sensor (which may be a resolver, encoder, or Hall sensor depending on the application and customer requirements). The mounting flange has standard dimensions (IEC, NEMA etc.), for interchangeability. Such motors are supplied for use with sinewave and squarewave controllers, and they have substantially replaced the DC commutator servo motor.

Fig. 2.17 is a photograph of the components of an "integrated motor controller assembly" (IMCA), a rotary actuator manufactured by Honeywell (USA) for use on the Space Station. The applications are listed to show the versatility and functionality of this brushless permanent-magnet motor drive:[8] *Segment-to-Segment Attach System*; *Unpressurized Logistics Carrier*; *Propulsion Module Attach System*; *Unpressurized Berthing System*; *Thermal Radiator Deployment System*; *Iso-Valve Actuation System; Mobile Transporter System*.

The IMCA receives power from a remote control module to drive a three-phase brushless DC motor which transmits torque to an internal speed-reduction gear drive with a clutched-output spline. Its operational parameters are downloaded interactively from a Space Station computer to provide closed-loop motion control, specific to each application, with controlled slewing rate, jerk limitation, and a certain degree of fault tolerance.

Fig. 2.17 shows not only the motor but also the immediate accessories including the power electronic drive, together with the output gear and a clutch. The IMCA controller utilizes multiple custom microcircuits.

---

[8] Apologies for the buzzwords, but it really is quite a list by anybody's standards.

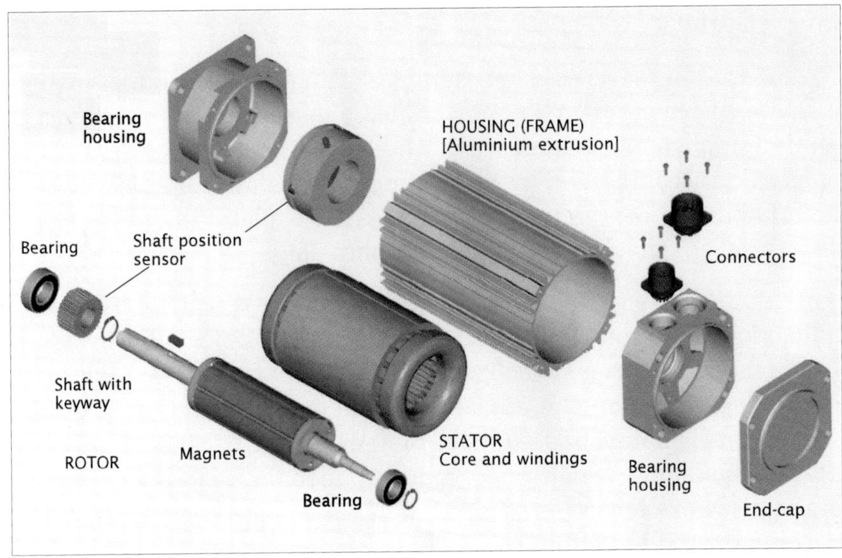

Fig. 2.16 Exploded 3D CAD view of brushless permanent-magnet servo motor
SEM, UK

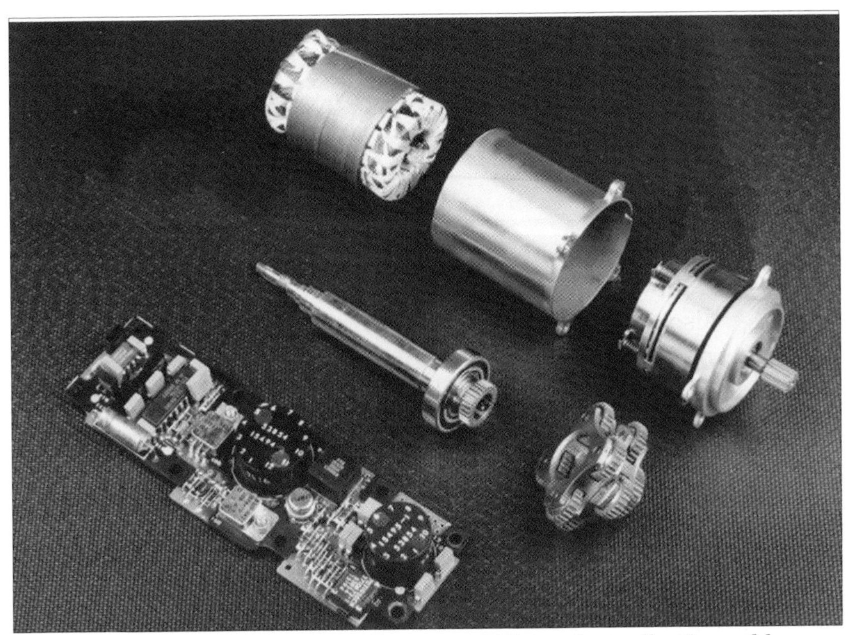

Fig. 2.17 Components of Integrated Motor Controller Assembly
Honeywell, USA

Fig. 2.18 Stator from ALPHA2 circulator pump
Grundfos, Denmark

Fig. 2.18 shows the stator of an ALPHA2 circulator pump, designed and manufactured by Grundfos A/s, Bjerringbro, Denmark. The core of this 2-pole, 4-slot, 2-phase stator is fully segmented. To facilitate high-speed automatic coil winding, each segment carries a moulded bobbin or coil form with winding shields on each end. The coil form also insulates the winding from the stator core.

Fig. 2.19 shows a circulator pump widely used in central heating systems, also designed and manufactured by Grundfos A/s, Bjerringbro, Denmark. The rotor uses polymer-bonded NDFEB magnets, hermetically encapsulated in a laser-welded stainless steel rotor can. The stator in this figure uses a traditional inserted winding. The integrated frequency converter supplies sinusoidal 3-phase currents. Fig. 2.20 shows an exploded view of a circulator pump from the same series with a single-tooth (concentrated) winding. The motor is known as a "wet runner". Fig. 2.21 shows the stationary steel can that separates the wet rotor from the dry stator. The complete rotor unit includes the impeller. Fig. 2.22 shows the stator and rotor, together with the ceramic water-lubricated shaft.

Fig. 2.19 Grundfos MAGNA circulator pump
Grundfos, Denmark

Fig. 2.20 Exploded view of Grundfos MAGNA series circulator pump
Grundfos, Denmark

Fig. 2.21 MAGNA circulator pump components
Grundfos, Denmark

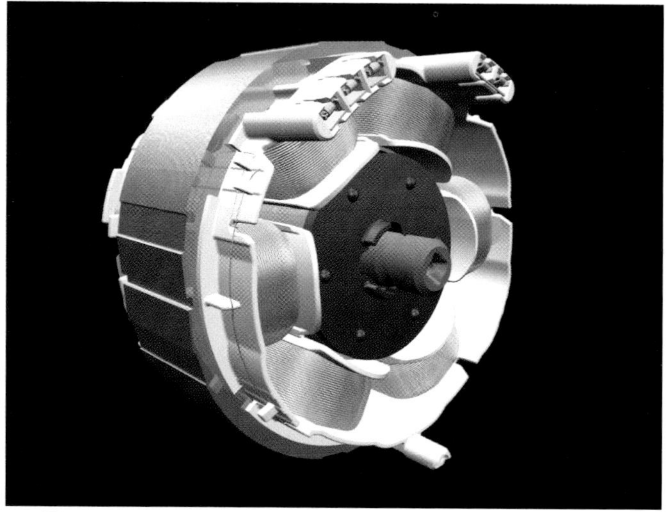

Fig. 2.22 MAGNA circulator pump — rotor and stator
Grundfos, Denmark

Fig. 2.23 V8 Dynamometer machine used for testing F1 transmissions
MTS Systems Corporation, USA

Fig. 2.24 Dynamometer for testing F1 transmissions
MTS Systems Corporation Inc., USA

Fig. 2.23 shows a brushless permanent-magnet machine used as the main dynamometer machine for simulating F1 racing engines during the testing of the transmission system. It has the same inertia as an actual F1 engine, while the dynamic performance (control torque bandwidth) is sufficiently high to emulate the dynamics of the engine crankshaft, including individual cylinder firing pulses. Fig. 2.24 shows the complete test bench. The main dynamometer machine has a rated torque of 330 Nm at a speed of 20,000 rpm. The motor inertia with MTS torque transducer is 0·012 kg m^2, and the torque response is from −100% to +100% of rated torque in 1 ms. The maximum acceleration rate is nearly 40,000 rad/s^2. The duty-cycle is continuous, as it must be to simulate actual race conditions. The two electric machines connected to the half-shafts are dynamometers for simulating the torques and speeds at the drive axles. These "load machines" are low-inertia brushless permanent-magnet motors with less demanding specification.

Fig. 2.25 shows the rotor of a much smaller high-speed brushless permanent-magnet motor (100 kW at 40,000 rpm) used in high-speed machining of aircraft wing spars. It has all the features required in high-speed machinery including magnet retention and high lateral and torsional stiffness that results from the integral construction.

Fig. 2.25 High-speed rotor with carbon retaining sleeve
J.R. Hendershot, USA

Fig. 2.26 John Deere Hybrid Tri-Plex Greens Mower
John Deere, USA

Fig. 2.27 Motor of John Deere Greens Mower
John Deere, USA

Fig. 2.26 shows the John Deere Hybrid Greens Mower that uses a traditional engine to drive an alternator which powers electric "reel motors" to drive the cutting units, "eliminating more than 90% of the potential leak points while also reducing sound levels and increasing fuel efficiency". Because the mower is not dependent on battery power levels, it can keep the same "frequency of clip" on every green.

This product is a convincing example of the effectiveness of purpose-designed brushless permanent-magnet motor drive technology in a demanding application that meets stringent environmental requirements with high efficiency and low noise.

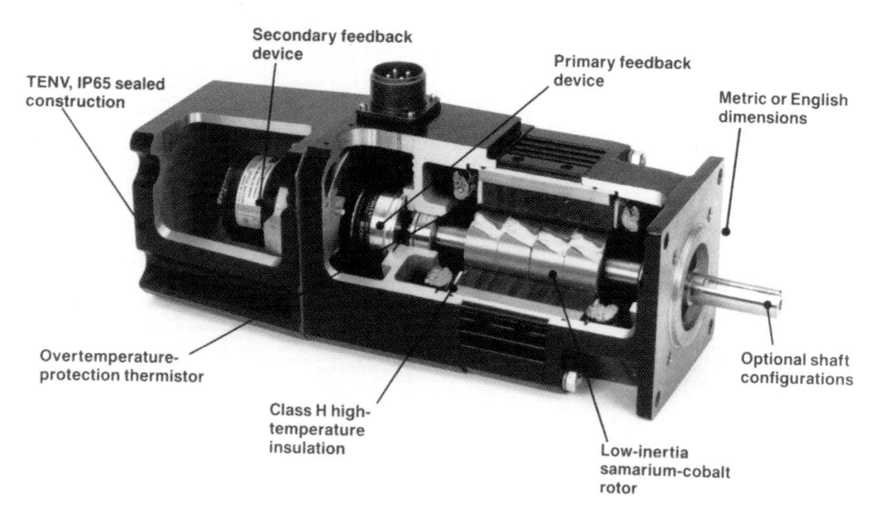

Fig. 2.28 Cutaway of a Samarium-Cobalt Servo-Motor showing "step-skewed" magnets to reduce cogging torque.
Pacific Scientific, USA

Fig. 2.29 Example of stepped magnets to reduce cogging torque and improve EMF waveform
Baldor Advanced Technology, USA

The 1985 servo-motor in Fig. 2.28 is included mainly for historical interest; new models benefit from better magnet materials and are more compact, with higher torque density. The staggered magnets in Fig. 2.29 have less expensive shapes than those in Fig. 2.28, and the step can be adjusted for different core lengths.

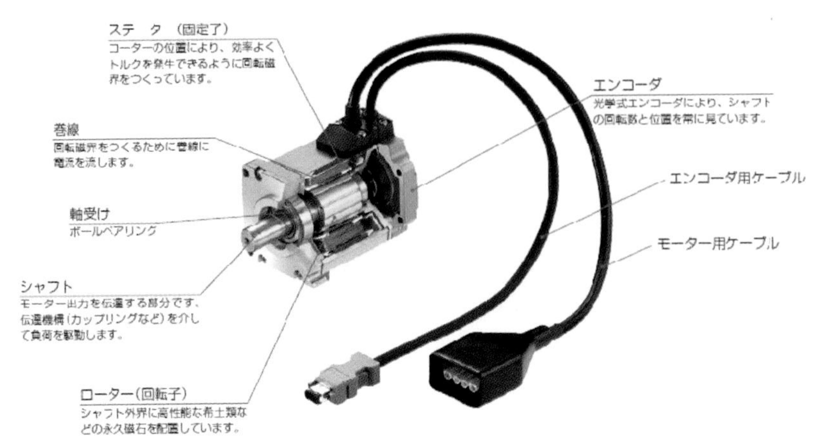

Fig. 2.30 Cutaway of NX-series high-performance servo-motor
Oriental Motor, Japan

Fig. 2.31 Servo-motor with integral brake and planetary gearbox
Oriental Motor, Japan

Fig. 2.32 Hollow-shaft flat gearhead with integral servo-motor
Oriental Motor, Japan

Figs. 2.30-32 are further examples of radial-flux interior-rotor motors discussed in §2.2. The motor in Fig. 2.30 is a high-performance servo-motor with low cogging torque and high torque density. In Fig. 2.31 this motor is coupled to a planetary gear and a brake unit. Fig. 2.32 shows a multiple-stage reduction gearbox with a hollow shaft, suitable for use with roll drives and linear motion.

Fig. 2.33 IPM rotor with 2 magnets/pole in a V-shaped flux-concentrating arrangement
MS-TECH, Japan

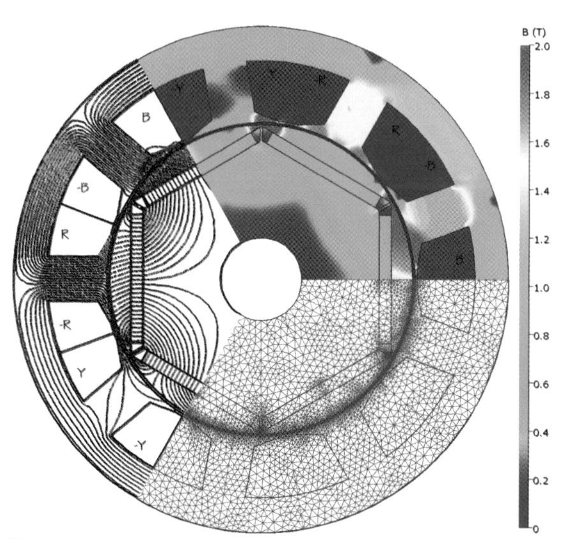

Fig. 2.34 Finite-element graphics: mesh, flux plot, and lines of flux
A.O. Smith, USA

Fig. 2.33 shows a typical IPM configuration for a fairly large machine, with 8 poles and 2 magnets per pole. The magnets and the poles are marked with fibre-tip pen to assist in assembly: it is obviously essential to insert the magnets with the correct polarity. Some means of testing the polarity is almost always used at the point of assembly — for example, a proofing magnet can be used to detect for attraction or repulsion.[9]

The arrangement of the two pole-magnets in a V-shape increases the total magnet pole area and the resulting flux, thus compensating for the loss of area that results with a simple chord configuration using one magnet per pole (as in Fig. 2.35).

Fig. 2.34 is a composite figure showing three views of finite-element analysis.[10] This figure is included to underline the importance of numerical analysis in connection with IPM machines. While unsaturated values of EMF and reactances can be calculated with surprising accuracy by the methods described in this book, even for quite complex geometries, the effect of saturation cannot be calculated with certainty without using the finite-element method. Most of the necessary analysis can be done with a 2D magnetostatic solver, but speed of execution is of the utmost importance in a design environment. In recent times, eddy-current calculations have come to the fore, particularly in connection with rotor heating; these calculations are much more sophisticated and may require 3D time-stepping solutions.

Fig. 2.35 shows a partially disassembled view of an integral-hp variable-speed IPM motor for inverter operation with very high energy efficiency. Fig. 2.36 shows a cast rotor end-plate fitted to a very large IPM machine of 1000 hp rating. The end-plate clamps the rotor together and prevents the magnets from moving.

---

[9] The magnet that is about to be inserted is offered up to the proofing magnet. Care must be taken to protect against uncontrolled movement of the magnets under their magnetic forces of attraction or repulsion. The proofing magnet must also be strong enough to prevent it from being demagnetized or remagnetized in the opposite direction by the magnet that is being tested. It can be difficult to remove magnets after assembly, especially if end-plates are welded to the rotor.

[10] The figure was made up by Malcolm McGilp of the *SPEED* Laboratory for Dr. D.M. Ionel of A.O. Smith. The finite-element program is *SPEED*'s *PC-FEA*, developed by M. Olaru together with M. McGilp, M. Popescu and D.M. Ionel.

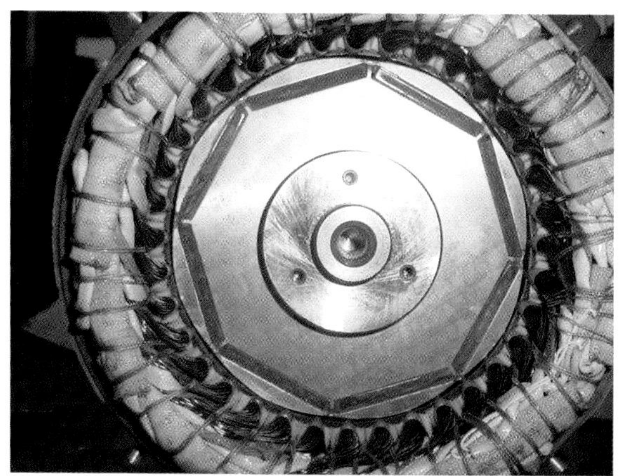

Fig. 2.35 IPM machine with end-plate, shaft, and bearing housing removed to show detail
WEG, Brazil

Fig. 2.36 Rotor end-plate of a 1000-hp IPM during initial assembly. Note the lifting eyebolts.
Baldor Advanced Technology, USA

Fig. 2.37 shows two variable-speed IPM motors developed for electric washing machines. The one on the left uses ferrite magnets, while the one on the right uses NdFeB and achieves a noticeable reduction in size and weight. These machines are high-speed machines that drive the drum through belts and pulleys.

Fig. 2.37 IPM washing-machine motors with ferrite and NDFEB magnets
Arçelik, Turkey

Fig. 2.38 Direct-drive brushless DC washing-machine motor with exterior rotor
Arçelik, Turkey

Fig. 2.38 shows a completely different type of washing-machine motor — a *direct-drive* type with a much larger number of poles and an exterior-rotor configuration. This machine has a large airgap diameter to achieve high torque with a short axial length while using inexpensive magnets. It is noted that the "flat-pack" aspect ratio is achieved with this radial-flux machine at least as well as could be achieved with an axial-flux machine. It uses moulded plastic components in both the stator and the rotor, and is highly engineered for the application. The exterior rotor configuration lends itself to automation of the stator winding.

Fig. 2.39 shows a development of the large-diameter direct-drive washing-machine motor to a double-airgap configuration. A high torque with a "flat-pack" aspect is again achieved, while the stator is fabricated with double-sided coils and pole-pieces rolled up from a segmented assembly as shown in Fig. 2.40. Design for automation is clearly evident in these figures.

The idea of a "roll-up" stator has been implemented in many forms, of which Fig. 2.40 is a good example. Strip-on-edge-wound cores are another example. Many of these ideas are very old.

The "roll-up" stator shown in Fig. 2.40 requires steel strip that is much narrower than the strip used to punch conventional unitary laminations. It shares this property with many other forms of segmented core. The narrow strip requires lighter handling facilities in the factory, and the punching operation requires less expensive tooling with a small footprint and quieter operation.

The stator shown in Fig. 2.41 at first sight has similarities with Figs. 2.38 and 2.40, but it comes from a very different application — the hybrid electric vehicle transmission system of Fig. 2.4.[11] The stator teeth have no overhanging tips, so that the pre-wound coils can be placed over them.

---

[11] It also has superficial similarities with the alternator stator of a well-known British motorcycle (the *Triumph Bonneville*) from the 1960s. The motorcycle alternator used a 6-pole Alnico magnet that was susceptible to demagnetization on disassemblywithout a keeper; (see also Chapter 9). No such concerns should trouble the owners of the drives systems of Fig. 2.4. This anecdote underlines the importance of new materials which can completely transform the applications and commercial prospects of electrical machines whose pedigree is often very old.

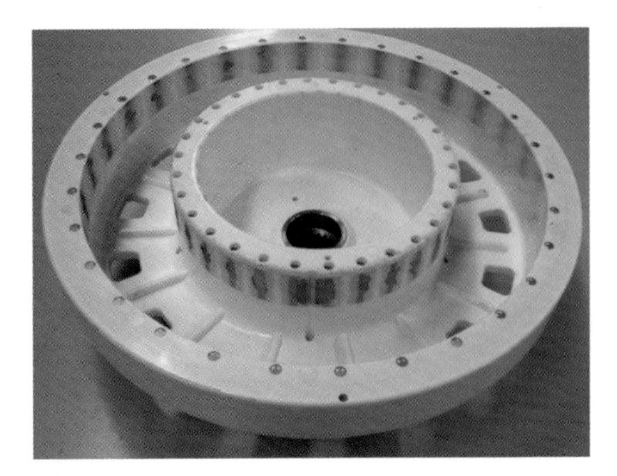

Fig. 2.39 "Dual rotor" for direct-drive washing-machine motor
Panasonic, Japan

Fig. 2.40 (a) Stator sector and (b) Roll-up stator of "Armadillo" Moulded motor
Panasonic, Japan

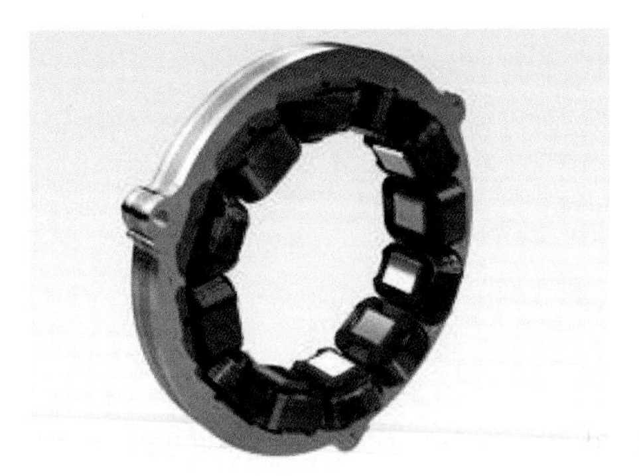

Fig. 2.41 Stator of 2010 *Prius* IPM generator
Toyota, Japan

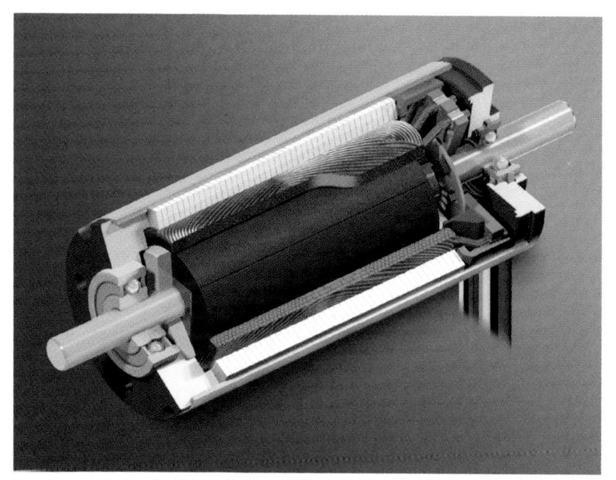

Fig. 2.42 Slotless brushless PM motor
Maxon, Switzerland

Fig. 2.42 shows an example of a brushless permanent-magnet motor with a *slotless* stator winding, also known as an "air-cored" winding or "airgap winding". The stator core is generally a set of laminated rings, but a spiral edge-wound strip was used by Lai and Abu-Sharkh [2006] in a "rim-thruster" for a marine application, to avoid the difficulties of manufacturing a slotted core in a ring-type machine with a small ratio of outside to inside diameter.

Slotless machines are manufactured by several companies for hand-held surgical tools requiring a very small diameter (often less than 0·5 in); a low temperature rise; high speed (up to 100,000 rpm); high torque; negligible vibration and cogging torque; low noise, and the ability to withstand hundreds of autoclave cycles for sterilization. The windings may be straight or highly skewed (as in the configuration invented by Dr. Faulhaber in the 1940s). The slotless core has reduced iron losses, which helps to limit the temperature rise at high speed. Ceramic ball bearings are used in some designs.

It is possible to achieve a strong sinusoidally-distributed flux by means of a Halbach magnet. There is an optimal radial thickness of winding to maximize the torque per unit of copper loss, [Jang et al, 2001]. The ThinGap Motor Technologies company of Ventura, CA, uses a precision-machined copper sheet to make the stator winding with a very high effective slot-fill factor.

Fig. 2.43 Side view of exterior-rotor motor
Overview Ltd, UK

Fig. 2.44 Exterior-rotor motor with rotor removed
Overview Ltd, UK

Figs. 2.43 and 44 show details of an exterior-rotor motor designed for a precision pan-and-tilt mechanism for camera positioning. All the features discussed in §2.2.3 are evident, many of which are intended to achieve low manufacturing cost. The motor has concentrated single-tooth windings and 0·75 slots/pole, while the magnet is in the form of a ring of bonded NDFEB. In spite of the relatively large slot-openings the cogging torque is reduced to a negligible level by means of skew in the magnetization pattern of the magnet.

The exterior-rotor motor makes it possible to drive the pan-and-tilt mechanism directly without gearing, permitting an extremely compact assembly including the drive and control electronics; the entire drive is DSP controlled and has only a 4-wire connection to the main system. The drive operates with a 9V DC bus voltage.

2.5 Factory and Workshop Snapshots

Fig. 2.45 Manual insertion of coils in a prototype stator; note the variety of hand-tools
MS-TECH, Japan

This Chapter closes with a small number of photographs from the development shop and the factory floor, underlining the unity of the products and the means of manufacturing them.

Fig. 2.45 shows the highly skilled process of manual winding insertion. Entire books have been written on the design and manufacture of windings, but Fig. 2.45 shows at a glance that no matter how much theory lies behind the winding, it requires equal skill to make it. The hand tools look simple, but in the hands of the craftsman they produce a remarkable result; without them the winding simply could not be inserted. The complexity of the connections is also apparent in Fig. 2.45, with multiple coils, multiple strands, and multiple parallel paths.

The end result is *production*, illustrated by the factory images in Figs. 2.46 and 2.47.

Fig. 2.46 Laced end-turns, blocked for compactness
WEG, Brazil

Fig. 2.47 Finished stators waiting to be varnished
WEG, Brazil

Fig. 2.48 shows a method of stator core construction designed for pre-winding concentrated coils to achieve a high slot-fill factor with narrow slot-openings to reduce cogging.

Fig. 2.49 shows a frozen PM rotor just before fitting a retaining sleeve in the development workshop.

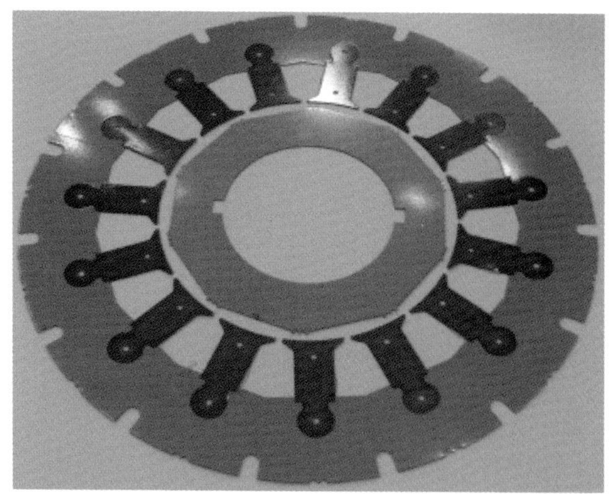

Fig. 2.48 Segmented stator core construction
J.R. Hendershot, USA

Fig. 2.49 A frozen rotor before fitting a retaining sleeve
MS Tech, Japan

The large rotor in Fig. 2.50 is an axially-laminated PM-assisted synchronous reluctance motor, a form of IPM designed to have the maximum possible saliency ratio. (See Chapter 7). [12]

---

[12] Soong W.L., Staton D.A. and Miller T.J.E., *Design of a new axially-laminated interior permanent-magnet motor*. IEEE Transactions on Industry Applications, Vol.31, No.2, March/April 1995, pp.358-367.

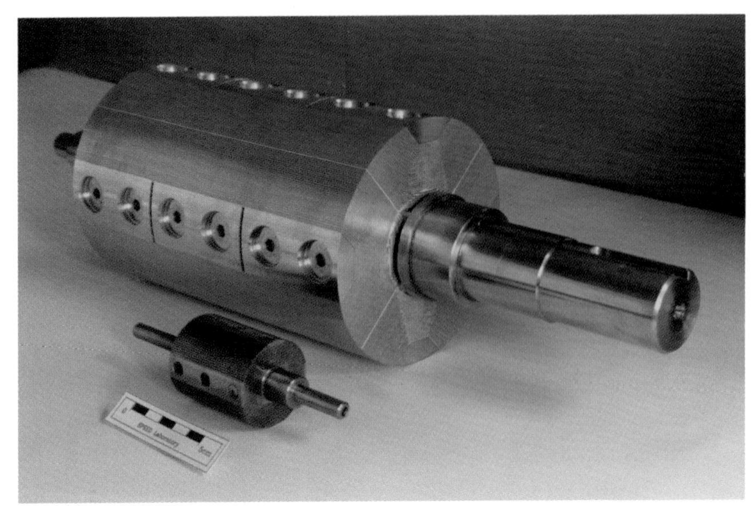

Fig. 2.50 Axially-laminated PM-assisted synchronous reluctance motor
SPEED Laboratory, 1990

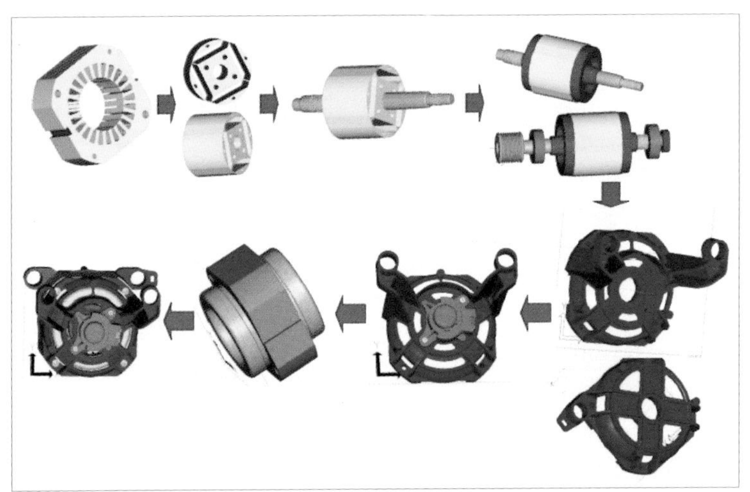

Fig. 2.51 An example of CAD used to describe an assembly process
Arçelik, Turkey

The examples in this Chapter are only a small sample of the vast range of brushless permanent-magnet machines in production. The remaining theoretical Chapters serve only to mirror the creativity that lies behind them, while Fig. 2.51 provides a fine and final illustration of the close link between the practical and the conceptual.

3 BASIC DESIGN CHOICES

Introduction

This chapter is concerned with practical design choices, which have to do with the configuration, sizing, and main features of the machine, considered as far as possible with regard to the most appropriate manufacturing methods. The intention is to provide a practical foundation on which we can build the theoretical analysis and methods of calculation in subsequent chapters.

In view of the wide variety of machine types, materials, and methods of control, it is obvious that several important decisions must be made at an early stage in the design of a brushless motor or generator. No single step-by-step procedure exists to suit all cases, but the following list covers most aspects of most cases:

1. Decide the configuration of the machine and its control.
2. Select numbers of phases, poles and slots.
3. Estimate main dimensions and choose materials.
4. Design rotor.
5. Design stator lamination and core pack.
6. Design stator winding.

Step 3 is sometimes called *sizing*. Decisions taken here will determine the ultimate temperature rise of the machine, and therefore its operating capability. Although all steps are important, it is essential to keep this aspect in mind from the start.

The six steps are essentially practical steps. They can be carried out with a minimum of calculation, and in the early days they *were* carried out with a minimum of calculation. But today's market requires the technology to be driven to its limits, and this calls for more analysis, the basis of which is developed in later chapters.

The machine design is always performed in the context of a wider range of constraints and requirements, and a checklist of these is offered in Table 3.1, without further discussion.

1	Appropriate national, US, EC, international & industry standards
2	Continuous power or torque requirement
3	Peak power or torque requirement
4	Maximum speed
5	Forward/reverse operation
6	Motoring/braking operation
7	Supply voltage , including upper and lower limits
8	Supply frequency: AC or DC
9	Type of control required : torque, velocity, position
10	Precision and bandwidth required in closed-loop control
11	Programmability : motion profiles, start/stop ramps etc.
12	Soft-starting requirements (inrush limitation)
13	Interface with PLC's, RS232, RS485, Fieldbus systems, IEEE488, remote controllers, communication protocols, etc.
	Front-panel control requirements
14	Dynamic requirements: torque/inertia ratio, accel/decel capability
15	Gearbox or direct drive
16	Inlet & outlet temperature of available coolant; air/oil/water flow rate
17	Environmental factors : dust, hazardous chemicals, explosive gases. Compatibility with insulation, magnets & other motor materials.
18	Maximum level of acoustic noise
19	Compliance with regulations on EMI/EMC and harmonics
20	Warranty requirements
21	Maintenance; spares
22	Operator's manual and repair manual
23	Vibration withstand levels
24	Fault protection: type of protection required. (Overcurrent, overvoltage, undervoltage, overtemperature, winding faults, vibration sensors)

TABLE 3.1 CHECKLIST OF APPLICATION REQUIREMENTS

For more up-to-date information see *The Control Techniques Drives and Controls Handbook*, W. Drury, IET, 2009.

3.1 Machine and drive configuration

It is very much the case that new designs either evolve from existing ones, or they come "out of the blue". In the first case, the discussion of the features and properties of the main types of brushless PM machine in Chapter 2 should be helpful at least in explaining what has already been invented. In the second case, no book can provide a prescription for what has not yet been invented. For these reasons the choice of machine configuration will not be discussed any further, but we have yet to classify the characteristics of different **drives**, and that subject will be dealt with here, so that we have a sensible grasp of the power electronics before embarking on the design and analysis of machines and systems. We will also consider **saliency** before addressing the question of sizing.

3.1.1 Squarewave and sinewave drives

The two main drive systems are the **squarewave** drive and the **sinewave** drive, and their characteristics are summarized here.

3.1.1.1 Squarewave drive

This is the original "brushless DC" system; its iconic current waveform is shown in Fig. 3.1. It is equivalent to a DC motor with electronic commutation. The current is regulated by chopping (PWM). Phase advance can be used to increase speed, but at the expense of torque ripple and power factor.

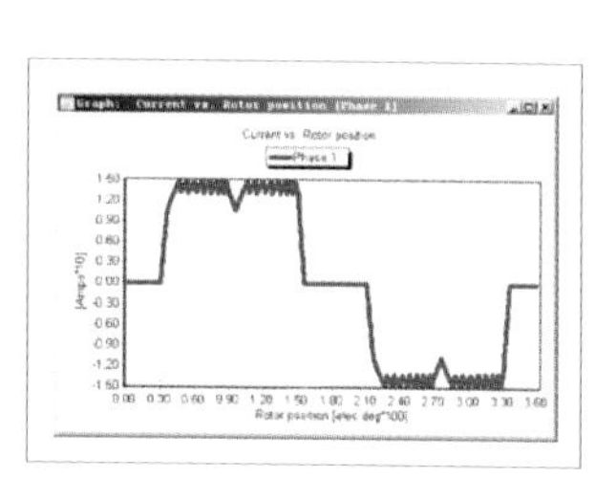

Fig. 3.1 Square wave

The motor should have a flat-topped (trapezoidal) EMF waveform. We shall see later that this tends toward the use of **concentrated windings**. Salient-pole motors such as the IPM should not be used with square-wave drive, because of torque ripple, but in practice there are cases where this rule is broken. Fractional slots/pole can be used with non-overlapping windings (single-tooth coils), while reducing cogging torque.

The AC phasor diagram does not work with squarewave drive: neither does vector control (field-oriented control). All except the simplest control calculations must be done by computer simulation.

3.1.1.2 Sinewave drive

Ideally, the current and EMF are both sinusoidal. The current in Fig. 3.2 is of course just as iconic as the square wave!

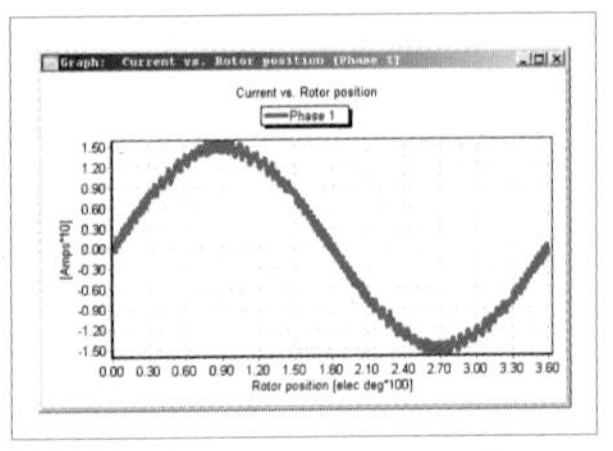

Fig. 3.2 Sine waveform

Controllability and low torque ripple are associated with the sinewave drive. Continuous position feedback is assumed, although sensorless drives are common.

The power electronic inverter circuit is the same as for the squarewave drive, but 3 of the 6 transistors are normally conducting at any time, whereas only 2 are conducting in the squarewave drive.

The sinewave drive can employ salient-pole motors such as the IPM, and it can use the reluctance torque available from these machines. The higher inductance of salient-pole motors makes it possible to use flux-weakening to extend the speed range. This is useful in vehicle drives that require a constant-power characteristic at higher speeds. The basic theory is the phasor diagram of classical synchronous machines, but digital controllers generally use field-oriented control principles.

Surface-magnet motors may have Halbach or ring magnets to achieve a sinusoidal EMF waveform. Distributed and concentrated windings are both used, with integral or fractional slots/pole.

3.1.2 Salient-pole and nonsalient-pole machines

An electrical machine is said to possess **saliency** if its winding inductances vary as a function of rotor position. Saliency has far-reaching consequences as we will see from the comparison of nonsalient-pole and salient-pole machines.

3.1.2.1 Nonsalient-pole machines

Fig. 3.3 shows a simple nonsalient-pole motor in which the rotor is rotationally symmetric. Another way of saying this is that if the magnets are removed, the rotor has no tendency to align itself with the stator when current is flowing. The technical expression of this property is that there is no reluctance torque, and winding inductances do not vary with rotor position.

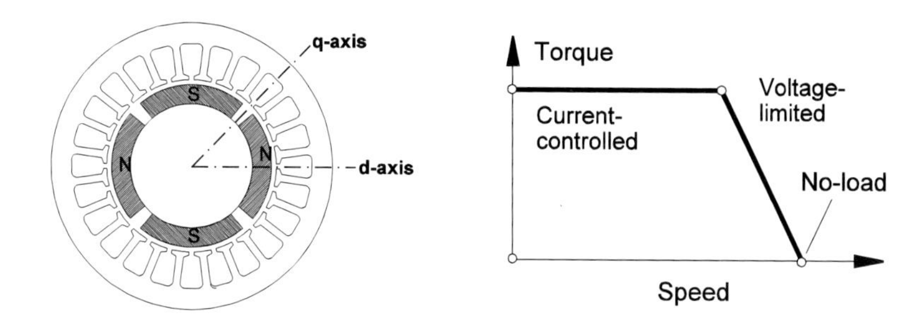

Fig. 3.3 Nonsalient-pole motor and torque/speed characteristic

The winding inductance of the nonsalient-pole (surface-magnet) machine is usually quite low, which means that a relatively high chopping frequency is needed to minimize current ripple. Low inductance limits the extent to which flux-weakening can be used, and tends to produces a rapid collapse in the torque/speed curve at speeds above the base speed (at which the EMF becomes comparable to the DC source voltage).

The low inductance may be of concern in the event of a short-circuit fault. Although this is obviously relevant for generators, it may also be important in motors especially when the load has a significant kinetic energy.

Square-wave drive is possible, including unipolar. These offer cost savings, and sensorless operation by back-EMF sensing is common. Sinewave drive is also possible (including vector control) and many high-grade motion control systems use this type of motor.

3.1.2.2 Salient-pole machines

The best known example of a salient-pole PM brushless machine is the interior PM motor or IPM, Fig. 3.4. If the magnets are removed, the rotor tends to align itself with the ampere-conductor distribution on the stator when current is flowing; it thus has reluctance torque, and passes the test for saliency, (p. 704). The winding inductances vary with rotor position, as we shall see in detail in Chapter 5.

The properties of salient-pole machines are associated with the axes of symmetry: the direct or d-axis, and the quadrature or q-axis. The d-axis is the magnet axis, and is usually the low-inductance axis. The q-axis (interpolar axis) is usually the high-inductance axis.

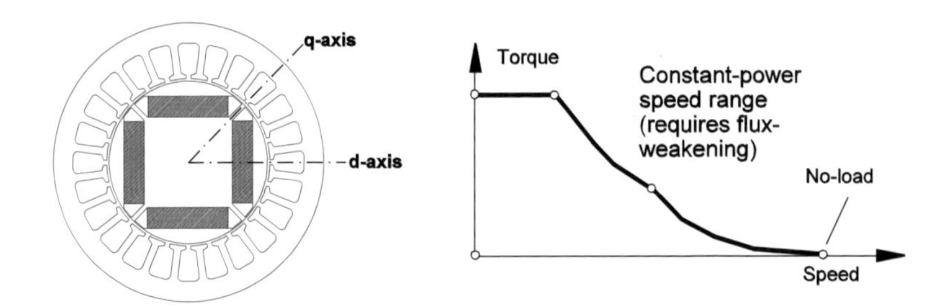

Fig. 3.4 Salient-pole motor (IPM) and torque/speed characteristic

Saliency is required to produce reluctance torque, but it requires the current to be advanced in phase relative to the back-EMF. Phase advance depletes the so-called "magnet-alignment" torque, so there is a trade-off and an optimum phase-advance angle to maximize the total torque. The optimum angle is not fixed, but depends on the current. Moreover, the torque is not linearly proportional to the current as it is in the surface-magnet motor. Consequently the control of the IPM is more complicated.

Phase advance also weakens the d-axis flux, making higher speeds possible with a given drive voltage. This is the essence of flux-weakening, which helps in the evolution of the constant-power characteristic needed in traction drives and high-speed spindles.

The basic operating theory is the phasor diagram of classical synchronous machines, and digital controllers are usually based on vector (field-oriented) principles, although there are many varieties. All of them are based on the assumption of sinusoidal EMF, and considerable effort is expended to achieve this in practice. The current is sinusoidal at low and medium speeds, but at high speeds harmonics appear as the current regulator saturates or "runs out of voltage".

The salient-pole machine typically experiences a large reduction in its inductances as the current increases, particularly in the q-axis. This variation is primarily due to saturation of the soft-iron magnetic paths in the rotor, but it can be exacerbated by saturation of the stator teeth. Finite-element analysis is essential for calculating these machines, even at normal load levels.

3.2 Number of phases, poles and slots

3.2.1 Number of phases

3.2.1.1 Practical considerations

Brushless PM motors are often assumed to have three phases but this is not always the case. 4-phase motors are rare but are sometimes considered for fault-tolerance, while 5, 6, and 9 phases can be considered for large machines (Chapter 11). 4-phase brushless motors are rare today, as are 2-phase motors. However, 2-phase brushless fan motors have been made with 2 phases bifilar-wound, and the term *single-phase bifilar* is often used to describe it. It requires only one Hall-effect sensor for commutation, and only two power transistors are needed. This makes it cost-effective for light-duty fan applications. The phase axes are displaced by 180° elec.

The problem with the simple single-phase bifilar motor is that the torque passes through zero every 180° elec. If by chance the rotor comes to rest at a position of zero torque, the motor would fail to start the next time it was turned on; moreover, the direction of rotation is indeterminate if the magnets and stator laminations are symmetrical. To solve this problem various designs have emerged which typically use space-harmonic fluxes that may vary with saturation of the iron, producing enough of a shift in the zero-torque position to get the motor started. The methods include tapered airgaps, auxiliary teeth, and "parking" techniques, and in general they introduce asymmetry so that the motor rotates in a preferred direction and is no longer bi-directional.

Unipolar and bifilar motors and drives with 1, 2, 3, and 4 phases are analyzed in detail in Chapter 6. Until then we will concentrate on pure polyphase motors (both squarewave and sinewave), in which the minimum number of phases is two.

Three-phase motors are by far the most common choice for all but the lowest power levels. In common with AC motors generally, they have extremely good utilization of copper, iron, magnet, insulating materials, connecting cables and power-electronic devices, in terms of the quantity of these materials and the number of components required for a given output power. The most important circuit is the three-phase bridge inverter, Fig. 3.11(c).

Three-phase motors have the flexibility afforded by wye- or delta-connected windings. They can operate with only three connecting leads with no loss of control flexibility. They have excellent starting characteristics, with smooth rotation in either direction, and low torque ripple. They can work with a wide range of winding layouts, and magnet arrangements, and can operate with either squarewave or sinewave drive. They are also well adapted to the development of "sensorless" controls that require no physical shaft position sensor.

3.2.1.2 Number of phases in electrical systems

The number of phases is a fundamental attribute of AC systems, and in this section we will consider it first in terms of a general AC system without regard to the field rotation that must be produced in motors and generators.

Fig. 3.5 shows a variety of circuits having different numbers of phases m. The simplest is (a), in which $m = 1$. Assuming a power-factor of 1, the power is equal to EI, where E is the RMS phase voltage and I is the RMS phase current. Two conductors are required. If we define one *unit of conductor area* as that which is required to carry the current I, then the total conductor area for circuit (a) is 2 units. These parameters are summarized in Table 3.2.

		Power	Total conductor area	No. of conductors	Max line-line voltage
		($EI = 1$)	($I = 1$)		($E = 1$)
(a)	1 phase	1	2	2	1
(b)	2 phases	2	4	4	1
(c)	2-phase quadrature	2	$2 + \surd 2 = 3{\cdot}41$	3	$\surd 2$
(d)	3 phases	3	6	6	1
(e)	3-phase star	3	3	3 or 4	$\surd 3$
(f)	4 phases	4	8	8	1
(g)	4-phase star	4	4	4 or 5	2

TABLE 3.2 COMPARISON OF 2-, 3- AND 4-PHASE CONNECTIONS

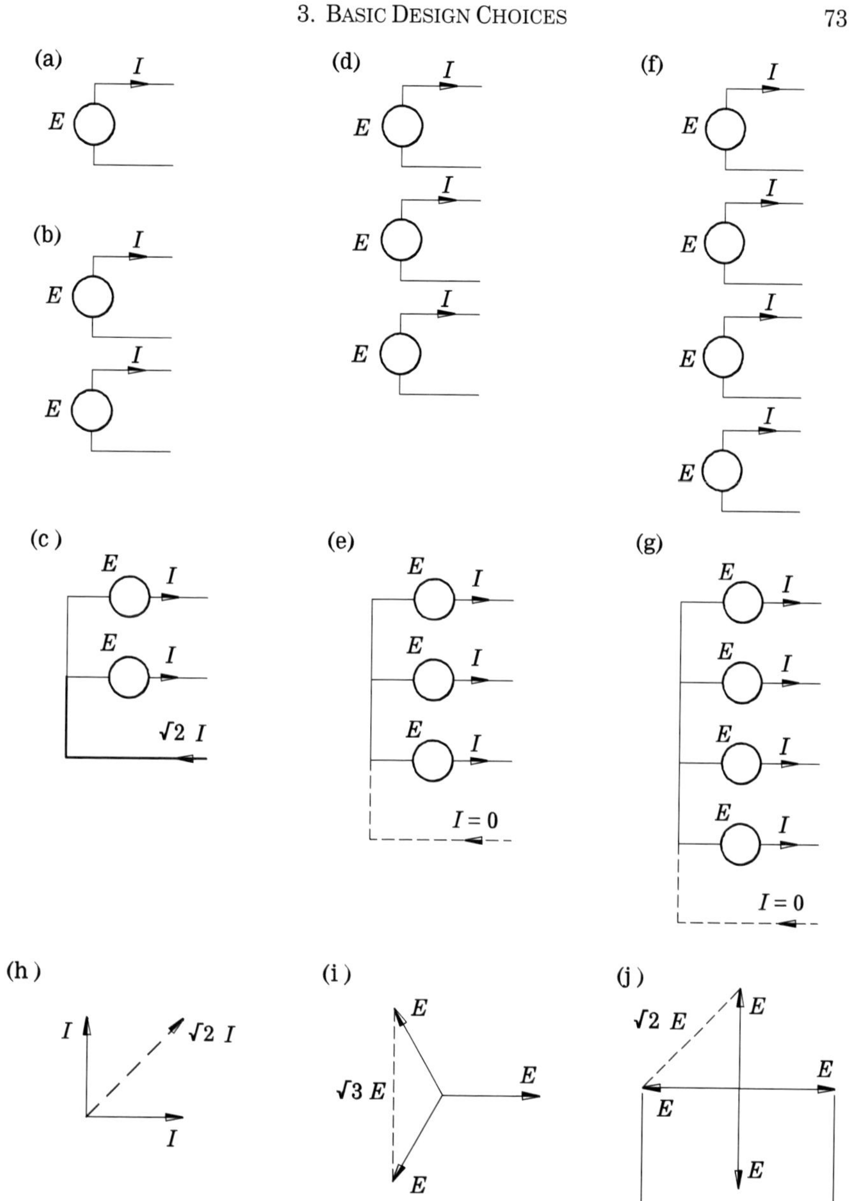

Fig. 3.5 Circuits and phasor diagrams with different numbers of phases

Circuit (b) has two phases, $m = 2$, with no connection between them. Likewise circuit (d) has $m = 3$ and circuit (f) has $m = 4$. All these circuits are simply m-multiples of circuit (a), so the total power, the total conductor area, and the total number of conductors are all m times the corresponding value in circuit (a).

In circuit (c) a common return conductor is shared between the two phases of circuit (b). If the phases are balanced and in phase quadrature as in Fig. 3.5(h), the current in the common conductor is $\sqrt{2}I$, requiring 41·4% more conductor area. The total conductor area is therefore $(2 + 2 + \sqrt{2}) = 3{\cdot}41$ units, a reduction of 14·6% relative to Fig. 3.5(b), for the same power. Although the number of conductors is reduced from 4 to 3, the three conductors must differ in size if they are to have the same current-densities.

Circuit (e) is obtained by sharing a common return conductor between the three phases of circuit (d). If the phases are balanced and phased at 120° from each other, the current phasor diagram forms a star similar to the EMF phasor diagram in Fig. 3.5(i), and the return line carries *zero current*, so it can be left out, leaving a 3-wire connection. The total conductor area is only 3 units. Compared with circuit (d) the same power is conveyed with only half the total conductor area and half the number of conductors.

Compared with the combined 2-phase circuit (c), the 3-phase 3-wire connection conveys 50% more power with only 87·9% of the conductor. The star can be used with 4 or more phases, as in Figs. 3.5(f) and (g) for $m = 4$. But the number of conductors cannot be reduced further: for $m > 2$, the minimum number is m.

Another consideration is the maximum voltage between any two lines, because this can add to the cost of insulation. The combined circuits (c), (e) and (g) all have a maximum line-line voltage greater than E, as can be seen from the phasor diagrams in Fig. 3.5(i) and (j), and as summarized in Table 3.2. The 3-phase circuit has a maximum of $\sqrt{3}E$, while the 4-phase circuit has $2E$.

The 3-phase 3-wire connection is so much more effective than the 2-phase circuit in terms of the total conductor area per unit of power conveyed, as to put the 2-phase quadrature system out of contention in most cases. There is also no advantage in having $m = 4$, because although the conductor area per unit of power conveyed is equal to that of the 3-phase 3-wire connection, the number of conductors is 33·3% higher and the maximum line-line voltage is 15·5% higher.

The 3-phase delta connection has the same advantages as the 3-phase star. Both require only three conductors between the source and the load. The only difference is the relationship between the phase voltages and currents, and the line-line voltages and currents:

$$\begin{aligned} \text{STAR}: \quad & E_L = \sqrt{3}E; \quad I_L = I \\ \text{DELTA}: \quad & E_L = E; \quad I_L = \sqrt{3}I \end{aligned} \tag{3.1}$$

3.2.1.3 Number of phases in electrical machines

In AC electrical machines the flux rotates, and so do the patterns or distributions of ampere-conductors and generated EMFs. Consider the flux produced by a single phase-winding, represented in Fig. 3.6. If the conductors are sine-distributed around the stator with p pole-pairs, the flux-density at any instant can be written $B_m \cos p\theta$, where B_m is the peak value and θ is the angle measured around the airgap.

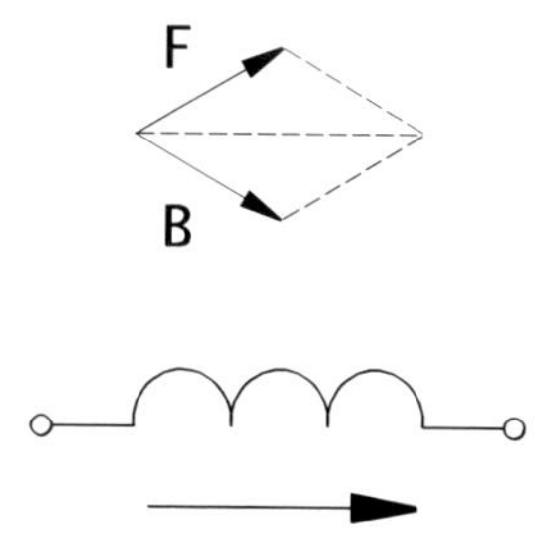

Fig. 3.6 Pulsating field

If the winding is fed with sinusoidal current, the flux varies sinusoidally in phase with the current, so the flux-density is written $B_m \cos p\theta \cos \omega t$. Now this expression can be split into two parts:

$$B_m \cos p\theta \cos \omega t = \frac{B_m}{2}\cos(p\theta - \omega t) + \frac{B_m}{2}\cos(p\theta + \omega t). \tag{3.2}$$

The first term on the RHS denotes a **backward**-rotating component of the flux, and the second term a **forward**-rotating component.

In a pure single-phase machine, the **F** and **B** components are equal and combine to produce a field that pulsates in time, but remains fixed in space, and there is no vestige of rotation. But consider what happens if a second phase is added, with its magnetic axis displaced 90°elec. from that of the first phase, and its current displaced 90° in time from that of the first phase: Fig. 3.7.

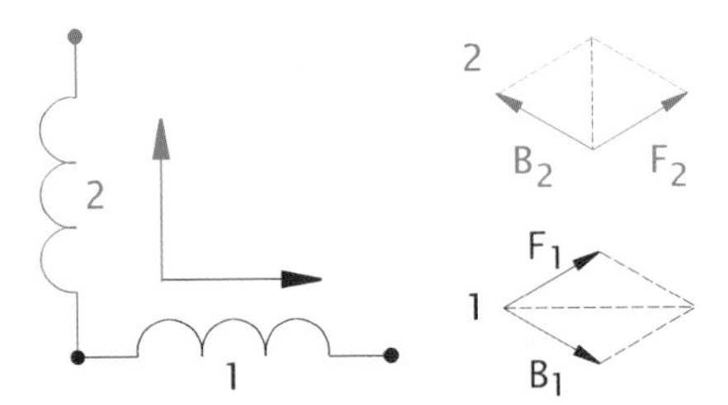

Fig. 3.7 Combination of pulsating fields to produce a rotating field

The **F** and **B** components from the second phase are obtained from

$$B_m \sin p\theta \sin \omega t \;=\; \frac{B_m}{2}\cos(p\theta - \omega t) \;-\; \frac{B_m}{2}\cos(p\theta + \omega t). \qquad (3.3)$$

When these are added to those of the first phase, eqn. (3.2), the backward components cancel while the forward components add to produce a resultant $B_m \cos(p\theta - \omega t)$. The amplitude of the rotating resultant is the same as the amplitude of one pulsating component.

The process can be explained graphically. Arrows labelled **F** and **B** are **space vectors** representing the forward and backward components of the flux distribution. In Fig. 3.7 $\mathbf{F}_2$ is displaced forwards by 90° in space, but backwards 90° in time, so it remains in phase with the $\mathbf{F}_1$. It is important to note the physical position of phase 2. As the flux rotates in the forward direction (anticlockwise), its axis passes the axis of phase 1 90° before it passes the axis of phase 2. The $\mathbf{B}_2$ vector is also displaced forwards by 90° in space, and again 90° backwards in time, but since it is rotating backwards it ends up 180° displaced from $\mathbf{B}_1$, and the two cancel. The in-phase combination of the **F** components, and the cancellation of the **B** components, is continuous if the phases are balanced.

At least two phases are needed to produce a pure forward-rotating field with no backward field component, and a few servo motors are made with two phases. The phases are as nearly as possible sine-distributed, and their axes are orthogonal. The phase currents are sinusoidal and in phase quadrature. It can be shown that any number of phases can be combined to produce a pure forward-rotating field. Later we will study this for 3-phase machines and also for multiplex machines (multiples of 2- and 3-phase machines).

Although we have used flux-density to explain the principle of the rotating field, the same equations apply to the ampere-conductor distribution and to the distribution of conductor EMFs. That is what underlies the definition of space-vectors for the phase current, EMF, and terminal voltage. The B in eqns. (3.2) and (3.3) actually refers to the "armature reaction" flux produced by the stator current. The total flux is the combination of the magnet flux and the armature-reaction flux, but of course the magnet produces only a forward component. Under balanced conditions the forward component of armature reaction combines vectorially with the magnet field. Any backward component due to imbalance is asynchronous, and rotates backwards at twice the synchronous speed relative to the rotor.

3.2.1.4 Distribution of coils between phases

Each of Figs. 3.9(a), (b) and (c) shows a succession of 18 phasors representing the EMFs in 18 coils connected in series in a 36-slot stator, shown in Fig. 3.10. The number of poles is 2.

The 18 coils constitute half of one phase of a lap winding. Since successive coil-sides are distributed over 180°, the winding is said to have a *phase spread* of 180°. In Fig. 3.10 each slot contains only one coil-side, but when the remaining 18 coils are added, there will be two coil-sides in each slot and the winding will have two *layers*.

Since all the coils are connected in series, their EMFs add. The result is the vector sum which is a diameter of the circle, labelled E in Fig. 3.9. This is considerably less than the *arithmetic* sum of the phasor amplitudes of the individual coil EMFs, which is represented very nearly by half the *circumference* of the circle.

For any phase group, the chord-to-arc ratio of the voltages is defined as the **distribution factor** (also known as the **spread factor**). From Fig. 3.8, if q is the number of coils per group, and γ is the slot angle, the distribution factor for any harmonic is given by

$$k_{\mathrm{dn}} = \frac{\sin(nq\gamma/2)}{q\sin(n\gamma/2)}. \tag{3.4}$$

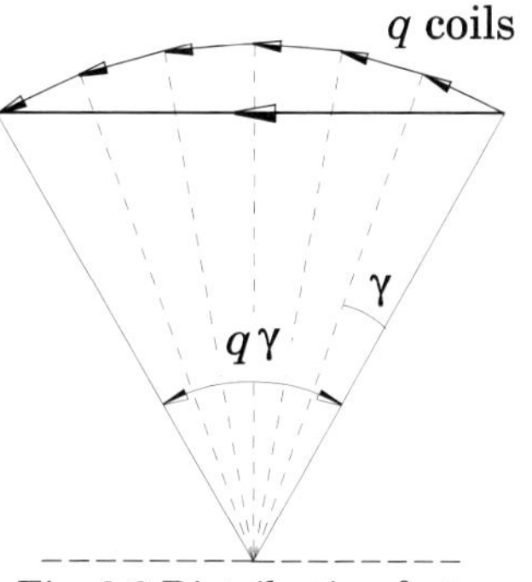

Fig. 3.8 Distribution factor

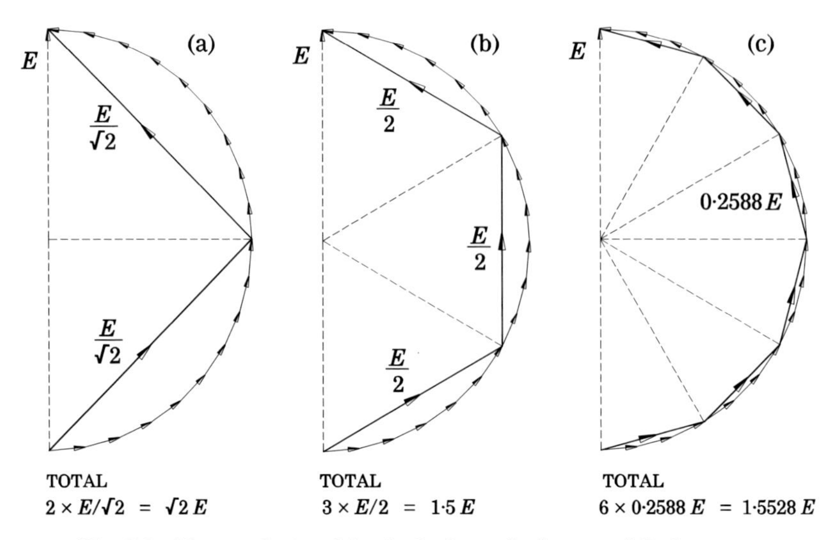

Fig. 3.9 Phase relationships in 2-phase, 3-phase and 6-phase systems

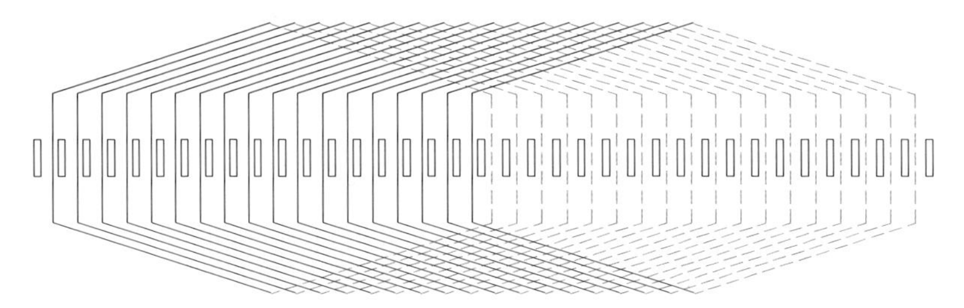

Fig. 3.10 18 coils of a 2-pole lap winding in 36 slots

For the single-phase grouping in Fig. 3.9 the chord-to-arc ratio (spread factor) is approximately $2/\pi = 0{\cdot}637$. Only 63·7% of the total voltage-generating capacity of the winding is being utilized. The EMF in each coil is very nearly equal to $\pi E/36$, and with $q = 18$, $\gamma = 10°$, eqn. (3.4) also gives $k_{d1} = \sin(18 \times 5°)/(18 \times \sin 5°) = 0{\cdot}637$.

Fig. 3.9(a) shows the effect of segregating the winding into two equal phases of 9 coils each. Each phase EMF is now $E/\surd 2$. The utilization(spread) factor becomes $(E/\surd 2)/(9 \times \pi E/36) = 0{\cdot}900$. We can say that the total usable voltage now being taken from the machine is $2 \times E/\surd 2 = \surd 2 E$, counting both phases; this total is labelled in Fig. 3.9(a). It exceeds the total for the single-phase winding by $\surd 2$ — a huge increase.

By a similar argument, if the winding is divided into 3 phases as in Fig. 3.9(b), the winding utilization increases to $(E/2)/(6 \times \pi E/36) = 3/\pi = 0{\cdot}955$. The three EMF phasors in Fig. 3.9(b) are equivalent to those in Fig. 3.5(i), after the points of connection are re-arranged.

If we divide the 1-phase winding into 6 phases, as in Fig. 3.9(c), each phase EMF becomes $2 \times E/2 \sin 15^\circ = 0{\cdot}2588E$, and the winding utilization increases to $(0{\cdot}2588E)/(3 \times \pi E/36) = 0{\cdot}9886$, a further increase of 3·5% over the 3-phase winding.

As in the case of the connections in Fig. 3.5, the 3-phase configuration confers most of the available benefits of a multi-phase system, and in most cases the additional 3·5% obtainable from 6 phases would not be justified in view of the increase in the number of terminals, leads, and conductors. Even so, the subject of multi-phase drives is still of interest for other reasons, and later it is discussed in detail, with an analysis of multiplex windings using dq-axis theory.

We can now consider the second half of the winding in Fig. 3.9. Physically it is constructed by continuing the series of lap-wound coils from No. 19 to No. 36. The second half is identical to the first half except that the polarity of the EMFs is reversed, as the concatenation of EMFs completes the circle. The two halves of the winding provide two **paths** which can be connected either in series or in parallel.

The phasor diagrams in Figs. 3.5 and 3.9 are drawn on the assumption that the flux-distribution in the airgap is sinusoidal. If it is not sinusoidal, they refer only to the fundamental component. In squarewave drives the currents and EMFs are not sinusoidal, and the flux distribution in the machine is also not sinusoidal; all these quantities are rich in harmonics. Nevertheless, the conclusions about the utilization of material remain the same.

With squarewave drives there is an additional reason for considering more than 2 phases, and that is the reduction of torque ripple. The argument is practically the same as the reduction of voltage ripple in a 12-pulse or 24-pulse rectifier, and is not developed in detail here because it almost never justifies a choice of more than three phases. The cost and utilization arguments take precedence, and if very smooth torque delivery is required, sinewave systems are in any case now the natural choice.

3.2.1.5 Number of phases in inverters and rectifiers

The number of phases suitable for inversion or rectification is treated in detail in power-electronics textbooks, and we have already mentioned the reduction of ripple obtained with a 12-pulse or 24-pulse rectifier compared with the standard 6-pulse 3-phase rectifier. The reduction of "ripple" as a function of the number of phases applies not only to the voltage and current, but also to the torque. However, PWM inverters are now so sophisticated that an argument for more than three phases cannot be made on the basis of reducing torque ripple. Instances of more than three phases are now much more likely to be based on the subdivision of very large power levels between multiple inverters, for reasons of cost or fault tolerance.

At the other end of the scale, where component count and cost reduction appear to put pressure on the number of phases, it should first be noted that a 2-phase drive with full control flexibility does not automatically provide a cost saving. If each phase is fed from a full-bridge inverter, that is, a duplex configuration with two circuits of the form of Fig. 3.11(a), there will be 8 transistors and diodes instead of the 6 that are required with a 3-phase drive, Fig. 3.11(c). It is possible to reduce the number of transistors and diodes to 4, using a circuit of the form of Fig. 3.11(b); but because this circuit employs a split DC link, it affords only half the peak-to-peak line voltage compared with Fig. 3.11(c), and if the power level is to remain the same, the currents and therefore the ratings of the semiconductors must double. In addition, two large electrolytic capacitors are required, compared with only one in Fig. 3.11(c) (not shown). Several variants of this type of circuit have been studied, but they are uncommon in production.

For control flexibility and good utilization of the available DC voltage, the 6-transistor bridge circuit of Fig. 3.11(c) is by far the commonest in production. At lower power levels the power devices are often packaged in a single module, while the protection and control techniques are so far advanced that it is hard to see it being displaced in mainstream drives. Similar considerations apply to rectifiers used with PM generating systems. Even so, there is a wealth of research in multi-level and multi-phase converters, and even cycloconverters for special applications.

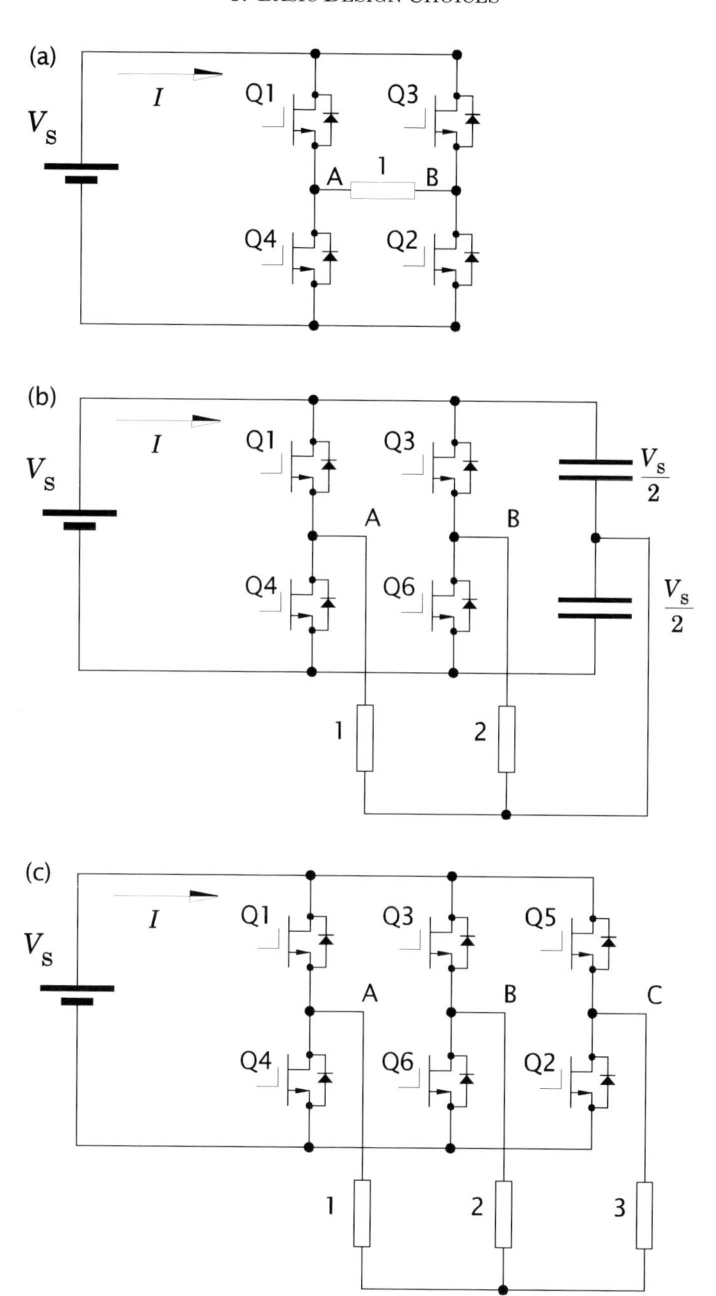

Fig. 3.11 1-, 2- and 3-phase drive circuits

3.2.2 Numbers of slots and poles

The numbers of slots S and poles $2p$ cannot be considered separately from one another, because of the importance of the **slots/pole ratio** $S/2p$, which has a profound effect not only on the winding layout but also on the space-harmonics of the resulting ampere-conductor distribution, which in turn influence the rotor eddy-current losses and the inductance. The slots-per-pole ratio has an equally important (but separate) effect on the cogging torque. Over the last decade its importance has become better understood, and it can be used as a basis for classification of machine types.

We will consider the choice of S and $2p$ first from a practical point of view, because many design decisions are tied more to one than to the other. Later the ratio $S/2p$ will be analyzed systematically.

The number of poles depends upon many factors, some of which are as follows:

1. Magnet material and grade
2. Interior-rotor vs. exterior-rotor vs. axial-flux configuration
3. Mechanical assembly of the rotor and magnets
4. Speed of rotation
5. Inertia requirements

We have already seen that the frequency of the generated EMF is proportional to the speed and the number of poles. It follows that for very high speeds, two- and four-pole machines are preferred. Two-pole motors tend to have bulky end-windings and they also have the greatest susceptibility to magnetic unbalance which can lead to shaft flux and induced currents in the bearings. For these reasons the 4-pole machine may be preferred even though it requires a higher magnetic frequency, provided that the iron losses can be limited.

Every time the number of poles is doubled the required thickness of the rotor yoke or back-iron inside the magnets is reduced by one half, as is the thickness of the stator yoke. When the pole number is very large, the machine approximates a linear machine that is rolled up into a pair of concentric rings with a large central hole. Such machines are used for very high torque applications.

2-phase											
Slots	8	12	16	20	24	28	32	36	40	44	48
Poles	2	2	2	2	2	2	2	2	2	2	2
	6	10	4	6	4	6	4	6	4	6	4
			6	14	6	10	6	10	6	10	6
			10		10	18	8	14	10	14	8
			12		18	22	10	22	12	18	10
			14		20		12	26	14	30	12
							14	30	26	34	14
							20		28	38	18
							22		30		20
							24		34		30
							26				34
							28				36
											38
											40
											42

TABLE 3.3 SOME SLOT/POLE COMBINATIONS FOR 2-PHASE MOTORS

As the number of poles increases, the stator ampere-conductors per pole decrease in inverse proportion, so that the inductance and synchronous reactance decrease in machines of higher pole-number.

Another important point regarding the number of poles has to do with cost. If a bonded ring magnet is used, it is easy to magnetize any number of poles desired on the outside diameter or inside diameter of the ring. In fact, it does not cost any more to magnetize two poles than it does a hundred poles once the magnetizing fixture is paid for. On the other hand, if the motor uses arcs or blocks of Samarium-Cobalt, the greater the number of poles the greater is the cost in magnets and fabrication.

3-phase																
Slots	3	6	9	12	15	18	21	24	27	30	33	36	39	42	45	48
Poles	2	2	2	2	2	2	2	2	2	2	2	2	2	2	2	2
	4	4	4	4	4	4	4	4	4	4	4	4	4	4	4	4
		8	6	8	8	6	8	8	6	8	8	6	8	8	6	8
		10	8	10	10	8	10	10	8	10	10	8	10	10	8	10
			10	14	14	10	14	14	10	14	14	10	14	14	10	14
			12	16	16	12	16	16	12	16	16	12	16	16	12	16
			14	20	20	14	20	20	14	20	20	14	20	20	14	20
			16	22	22	16	22	22	16	22	22	16	22	22	16	22
					26	20	26	26	18	26	26	20	26	26	20	26
					28	22	28	28	20	28	28	22	28	28	22	28
						24	32	32	22	32	32	24	32	32	24	32
						26	34	34	24	34	34	26	34	34	26	34
						30	38	38	26	38	38	28	38	38	28	38
						32	40	40	28	40	40	30	40	40	30	40
						34		44	30	44	44	32	44	44	32	44

TABLE 3.4 SLOT/POLE COMBINATIONS FOR 3-PHASE MOTORS

Table 3.3 shows a selection of slot/pole combinations for 2-phase motors, which are relatively rare; and Table 3.4 for 3-phase motors for which a balanced winding is possible. These tables are far from exhaustive. In contrast with classical polyphase AC machines, where sinusoidal operation is often synonymous with a large number of slots/pole, brushless PM motor design practice has converged more and more towards very low ratios, including some that are less than 1. (See Tables 3.14 and 3.15).

Theoretically the lowest permissible value of slots/pole is 0·5. The shortest possible coil-span is 1 slot-pitch, so with such a low value there would be 2 poles per slot-pitch, and no net flux-linkage with the coils, so the EMF would be zero.

0·75		0·8571		0·875	
Slots	Poles	Slots	Poles	Slots	Poles
3	4	12	14	21	24
6	8	24	28	42	48
9	12	36	42		
12	16				
15	20				
21	28				
1·125		1·2		1·5	
Slots	Poles	Slots	Poles	Slots	Poles
9	8	12	10	3	2
18	36	24	20	6	4
36	32	36	30	9	6
				12	8
				15	10
				21	14
2·25		3		3·75	
Slots	Poles	Slots	Poles	Slots	Poles
9	4	6	2	15	4
18	8	12	4	30	8
27	12	18	6	45	12
4·5		5·25		6	
Slots	Poles	Slots	Poles	Slots	Poles
9	2	21	4	12	2
18	4	42	8	24	4
27	6			36	6

TABLE 3.5 SLOT/POLE RATIOS FOR 3-PHASE MOTORS

Examples of slot/pole ratios are shown in Table 3.5. Again, the list is far from exhaustive. (See Tables 3.14 and 3.15).

Slots/pole	Coil-span in slot-pitches
≤ 1·5	1
2·25	2
3	3
3·75	3
4·5	4
5·25	5
6	5

TABLE 3.6 COIL-SPAN OR PITCH FOR DIFFERENT SLOTS/POLE

A value of slots/pole close to 1 implies that a single-tooth coil will link almost all the flux from one pole, as reflected in the high winding factors to be found in Table 3.14. The slots/pole cannot be 1 in a self-starting motor, because there would be no phase difference between the EMFs of different phases, and the cogging torque would be extremely high. This is analyzed more systematically in §3.6. The coil-span is determined by rounding the slots/pole down to the next integer not less than 1, as summarized in Table 3.6 for the slot/pole ratios in Table 3.5. A coil-span of 1 slot-pitch gives the shortest possible end turns and permits a **non-overlapping** winding, as noted by Croft in 1924 and shown in Fig. 3.12.

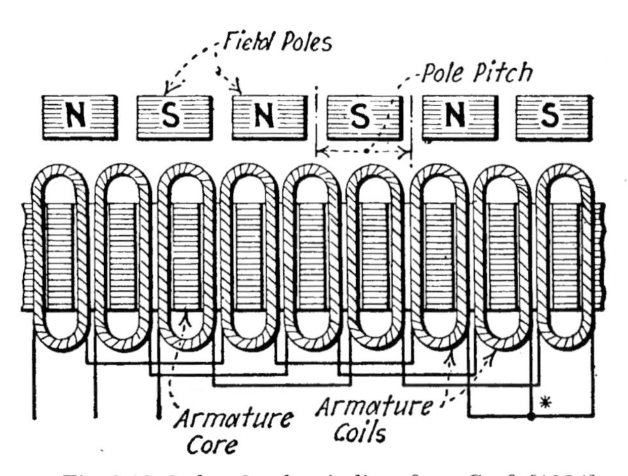

Fig. 3.12 9-slot, 6-pole winding; from Croft [1924]

3.3 Sizing — the ABC of electric machine design

3.3.1 The output equation

The size of electrical machines is generally characterized by the *torque per unit of rotor volume* (TRV), which in turn depends directly on the product of the *electric loading* A and the *magnetic loading* B. We will define these terms precisely, but we should start out with the underlying idea that "torque equals current × flux", which helps to explain why the product AB is important. Both A and B are limited by the properties of materials; but even when the best materials are used, they are also limited by the *temperature rise* and the available cooling. So it is handy to describe this topic as the *ABC* of electric machine design — "*A*, *B*, *C*ooling."

In many cases, new machine designs are evolved by modifying existing components to minimize the cost of changes. During any "re-design", the A, B, C parameters will be in the forefront of the engineer's mind.

The **electric loading** A is defined as the linear current density around the airgap circumference, that is, the number of ampere-conductors per metre around the stator surface that faces the airgap.

$$A = \frac{\text{Total ampere–conductors}}{\text{Airgap circumference}} = \frac{2mT_{ph}I}{\pi D} \quad \text{A/m} \qquad (3.5)$$

where I is the RMS phase current, m is the number of phases, T_{ph} is the number of turns in series per phase, and D is the diameter of the airgap. The airgap is assumed to be small compared to the rotor diameter, so that no distinction is made between the rotor diameter and the stator diameter. The RMS current is used because it determines the I^2R heating, which is what limits the electric loading.

The **magnetic loading** B is defined as the average flux-density over the rotor surface. In AC motors the flux-density is distributed sinusoidally and the fundamental flux/pole is

$$\Phi_1 = B \times \frac{\pi D L_{stk}}{2p} \quad \text{Wb} \qquad (3.6)$$

where p is the number of pole-pairs and L_{stk} is the *stack length*.

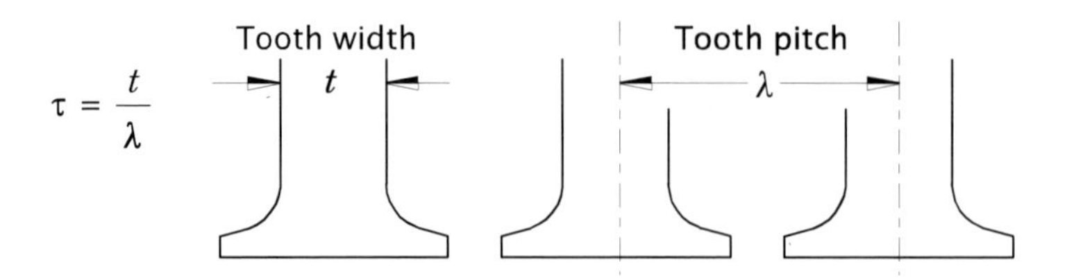

Fig. 3.13 Definition of tooth pitch and τ

In a slotted stator, the flux density in the teeth $B_{t(pk)}$ must be limited to about 1·6T, otherwise the iron losses may be excessive. The peak flux-density $B_{g(pk)}$ in the airgap is therefore $B_{g(pk)} \approx \tau B_{t(pk)}$, where τ is the ratio of tooth width to slot-pitch; see Fig. 3.13. A typical value of τ might be 0·5. If the flux is sine-distributed, the *average* is $B = 2/\pi \times B_{g(pk)} = 2\tau B_{t(pk)}/\pi$, or $2 \times 0{\cdot}5 \times 1{\cdot}6/\pi \approx 0{\cdot}5$T roughly.

The generated EMF per phase is given by the standard equation

$$E = \frac{2\pi}{\sqrt{2}} k_{w1} T_{ph} \Phi_1 f = \frac{\pi^2}{\sqrt{2}} \frac{k_{w1} T_{ph} B D L_{stk} f}{p} \quad \text{V}. \tag{3.7}$$

where f is the fundamental frequency, k_{w1} is the fundamental harmonic winding factor. The maximum available electromagnetic power at the airgap is mEI, and if all of this is converted into mechanical power $T\omega_m$, we get

$$\text{TRV} = \frac{T}{V_r} = \frac{\pi}{\sqrt{2}} k_{w1} A B \quad \text{Nm/m}^3. \tag{3.8}$$

where $\omega_m = 2\pi/60 \times N = 2\pi f/p$ is the speed in rad/sec, V_r is the rotor volume $\pi D^2 L_{stk}/4$; and eqns. (3.5)–(3.7) have been substituted.

Eqn. (3.8) embodies the expected flux-current product in the form AB. The coefficient $\pi k_{w1}/\sqrt{2}$ depends on the type of machine, and in this case is specific to a machine with sine-wave current and sine-distributed flux. Note that TRV is proportional to the fundamental winding factor k_{w1}.

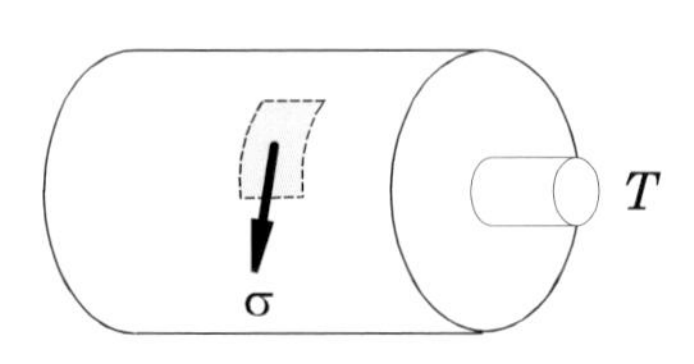

Fig. 3.14 Airgap shear stress

The TRV is also related to the **airgap shear stress** σ, which is the tangential (torque-producing) force per unit of swept rotor surface area; see Figs. 3.14 and 3.15. For every unit of surface area, the torque is $\sigma r = \sigma D/2$, so the total is $T = \pi D L_{stk} \times \sigma D/2 = 2\sigma \times (\pi/4) D^2 L_{stk}$, that is,

$$\text{TRV} = \frac{T}{V_r} = 2\sigma \quad \text{kNm/m}^3. \qquad (3.9)$$

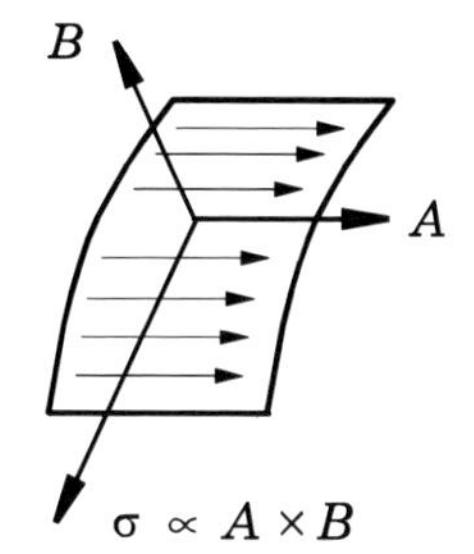

Fig. 3.15 Airgap shear stress

Typical values are given in Table 3.7.[8] If winding factor k_{w1} is 0·9, TRV $\approx 2\,BA$ and $\sigma \approx BA$. For example, if A = 20 A/mm and B = 0·5 T, $\sigma \approx 0{\cdot}5 \times 20 \times 10^3 = 10$ kNm/m³. For totally-enclosed motors with no fan, lower values of σ and TRV would apply, while higher values would apply with forced-air cooling supplied by an external fan.

Class of machine	TRV kNm/m³	σ lbf/in²
Small totally-enclosed motors (Ferrite magnets)	7 - 14	0·5 - 1
Totally-enclosed motors (Rare Earth magnets)	14 - 42	1 - 3
Totally-enclosed motors (Bonded NDFEB magnets)	20	1·5
Integral-hp industrial motors	7 - 30	0·5 - 2
High-performance servomotors	15 - 50	2 - 4
Aerospace machines	30 - 75	2 - 5
Large liquid-cooled machines (e.g. turbogenerators)	100 - 250	7 - 18

TABLE 3.7
TYPICAL VALUES FOR TRV AND σ (CONTINUOUS OPERATION)

The electric loading A is limited by the slot-fill factor, the depth of slot, and the cooling. It is also related to the current density J in the conductors. Suppose the area of one slot is A_{slot}. Let d = slot-depth, t = tooth width, w = slot width, and λ = slot pitch = $\pi D/N_s$, where N_s is the number of slots. Also let $\tau = t/\lambda$. Then $t + w = \lambda$ and $A_{slot} = wd = (1 - \tau)\lambda d$. If the slot-fill factor F_{slot} is defined as fraction of A_{slot} occupied by copper [as in eqn. (3.14) on p. 102], we can write

[8] If σ is in [lbf/in²], TRV = $13{\cdot}8\sigma$ kNm/m³.

$$J = \frac{A\lambda}{F_{\text{slot}} A_{\text{slot}}} = \frac{A}{F_{\text{slot}} d(1 - \tau)}. \tag{3.10}$$

For example, if the slot depth is d = 15mm, F_{slot} = 0·4, τ = 0·5, and A = 20 A/mm, the current density is

$$J = \frac{20}{0{\cdot}4 \times 15 \times (1 - 0.5)} = 6{\cdot}7 \text{ A/mm}^2. \tag{3.11}$$

Typical values of current density for use in AC or brushless machines for different applications are given in Table 3.8. Note that in machines operated from electronic drives there are usually time-harmonics in the current which increase the current-density without increasing the torque-producing value of A, and it may be necessary to allow for this by multiplying J by a form factor k_f. In AC machines this will be the ratio of the true RMS current to the RMS value of its fundamental component.

Condition	A/mm²	A/in²
Totally enclosed	1·5 – 5	1000 – 3000
Air-over, fan-cooled	5 – 10	3000 – 6000
Liquid-cooled	10 – 30	6000 – 20000

TABLE 3.8
TYPICAL CURRENT DENSITIES (CONTINUOUS OPERATION)

These values assume that the windings are varnished and tightly packed for good heat transfer. In air-cooled machines, the fan is often mounted on the rear of the motor outside the frame with a shroud which trains the air over the outside of the motor. Liquid-cooled motors may have a passageway or jacket around the stator with a cooling fluid circulating to remove the heat. The highest values are obtained with coolant flowing through hollow conductors. Peak (short-time) values may exceed the table values by 2 – 3 times.

It might seem strange to define the magnetic loading as the *average* flux-density in the airgap rather than the peak or RMS value, but the idea is to indicate how well the airgap area is being utilized. Its value is limited by the available MMF of the excitation source, and by core losses which increase at high flux-density and high speed.

It is interesting to see why it is the rotor volume and not its surface area that primarily determines the torque capability or "specific output". As the diameter is increased, both the current and the flux increase if the electric and magnetic loadings are kept the same. Hence the diameter appears squared in any expression for specific output. On the other hand, if the length is increased, only the flux increases, not the current. Therefore the length appears linearly in the specific output. Thus the specific output is proportional to $D^2 L_{stk}$, or rotor volume. Large machines tend to use more intense cooling, so the electric loading tends to increase as the diameter is increased, and the TRV increases faster than the rotor volume.

Stator volume — So far we have restricted attention to the torque per unit rotor volume, a natural consequence of the fact that the torque appears at the rotor surface. For a rough estimation of overall size including the stator, we can use a typical value of "split ratio", that is, the rotor diameter/stator diameter. Thus

$$\text{Stator volume} = \frac{\text{Rotor volume}}{\text{Split ratio}^2}. \tag{3.12}$$

For interior-rotor machines the split ratio is typically about 0·6, suggesting that the active volume is approximately 3 times greater than the rotor volume. When end-windings are included, the total space required is still greater, and it depends on the number of poles. So although the simple sizing rules are quite informative for rotor volume, they are less reliable for predicting the overall size of the machine, and more detailed calculations are required.

So far the discussion has been confined to interior-rotor machines. For exterior-rotor machines the split ratio must be redefined as the ratio of the rotor diameter at the airgap to its outermost diameter, and values up to at least 0·8 are typical. Coupled with the fact that exterior-rotor machines are often designed with a larger number of poles and short end-windings, this suggests that the exterior-rotor machine has an advantage in overall volume, provided that sufficient cooling is available to maintain the level of electric loading.

The best way to acquire practical values of σ or TRV is of course by testing family of products, or a prototype, and *always* with reference to the temperature rise and the cooling arrangements.

3.4 Rotor design

3.4.1 Length/diameter ratio

The TRV determines the volume of the rotor but not its shape. To estimate the rotor diameter and length separately, a length/diameter ratio should be decided. A value around 1 is common; however, it is also common to design motors of different ratings using the same laminations but with different stack lengths. The length/diameter ratio may then vary over a range of 3:1 or more. Very large length/diameter ratios are undesirable because of inadequate lateral stiffness, but may be used where a high torque/inertia ratio is desired, or in special cases where the motor has to fit into a narrow space.

A short length/diameter ratio tends to reduce the efficiency because it increases the fraction of copper that is in the end-windings, producing I^2R loss but not contributing to the torque. This issue is much less acute in machines with a high pole number, and even less in machines with a small number of slots/pole. Consequently it is possible to design radial-flux machines with quite low overall length/diameter ratio — so-called pancake machines — without recourse to the axial-flux configuration.

3.4.2 Airgap length

A short airgap length g maximizes the flux for a given thickness of magnet, but it also requires closer mechanical tolerances, increases cogging torque, and increases inductance. It is one of the advantages of surface-magnet brushless motors that they can tolerate an airgap length at least two or three times greater than in a comparable induction motor or switched reluctance motor, due to the high coercivity of modern magnets. At the same time, however, a greater airgap may be necessary to accommodate a retaining bandage or can, especially in high-speed machines. The interior-magnet motor generally has an airgap length comparable to that of an induction motor, especially when it is desired to make the most of the reluctance torque or to maximize the inductance for flux-weakening purposes at high speed.

With these factors in mind, it is unusual to find brushless motors with extremely small airgap lengths, and 0·5 – 1 mm is common in small motors. In larger machines of course it scales up.

3.4.3 First estimate of magnet dimensions

It is common to speak of the magnet length as the length in the direction of magnetization, (D.o.M.), even though this is usually the smallest dimension of a magnet block. A rough-and-ready first estimate of magnet length is about 5 – 10 times the airgap length. (If there are two airgaps per magnet, add them together). This method of first approximation applies to the use of high-coercivity magnets such as the ferrites and the rare-earth magnets. As we will see in Chapter 4, the ratio L_m/g determines the permeance coefficient and the operating point of the magnet on open-circuit, but it is also necessary to consider the worst-case conditions for demagnetization under load and during faults. To reduce the risk of demagnetization it is sometimes necessary to increase the ratio L_m/g, leading to values nearer 10 in extreme cases. Lower values, even as low as 3, can be used if demagnetizing conditions are not severe, for example, in lightly loaded machines in which the inverter drive is considered to provide adequate protection against overcurrent.

Ideally the magnet arc should be as large as possible to maximize the flux/pole, but shorter arcs may be used to reduce EMF harmonics. See also p. 689.

Magnet thickness is also very much a manufacturing question. Very thin magnets (less than 2 – 3 mm) are difficult to manufacture and to handle, as are very thick magnets (> 20 mm or so). It is possible to build stacks of thinner magnets, especially for use in interior-magnet machines, and they may be bonded together.

As for the width of the magnet in the two directions orthogonal to the D.o.M., "square" shapes are common because of the ease of handling and assembly, remembering that magnet materials are relatively brittle. A rotor with segmented magnets is shown in Fig. 3.16, suitable for a large PM rotor. Segmentation helps to reduce eddy-current losses (Chapter 12), and provides space for cooling channels and mechanical retaining fixtures.

Effective dimensions of arc magnets — If a radially-magnetized arc-shaped magnet is used, the magnet pole area A_m should be calculated using the length of an arc that is close to the inside radius of the magnet, and not the mean radius of the magnet.

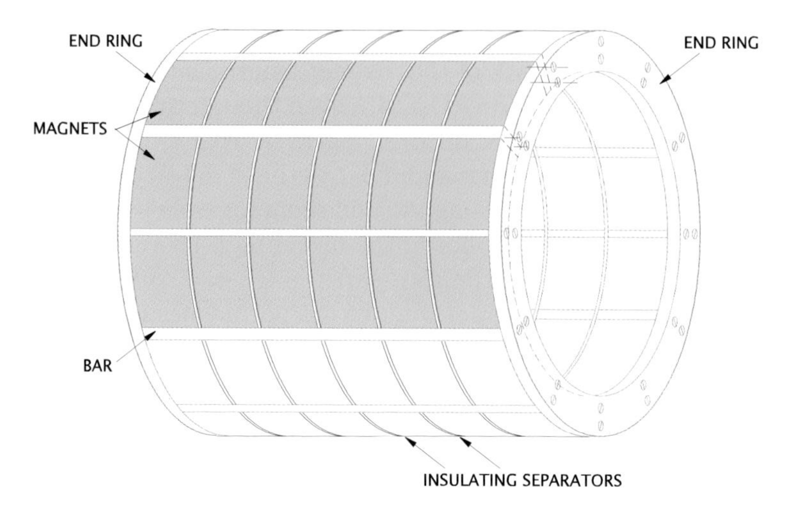

Fig. 3.16 Segmented magnets in a large PM rotor

3.4.4 Exploratory selection of magnet grade

Magnets are often named and ranked according to their energy product, but this property is almost useless in selecting a magnet for an electrical machine, other than as a general guide to its "strength". It is much more important to achieve the correct balance between high remanence and high coercivity, taking into account the worst-case conditions of temperature and demagnetizing MMF. Recoil permeability is generally of little significance, although it might be interesting to note in some very precise designs that it can impart a very small degree of saliency (and therefore reluctance torque) to a surface-magnet motor that is normally considered to have none.

The magnetic properties are by no means the only ones to be considered. Price, of course, is just as important. Corrosion can be a problem with metallic magnets, requiring coatings or even encapsulation. Electrical conductivity is important in considering eddy-current losses.

It is worth remembering that although the remanence is the primary property of interest in open-circuit calculations, those calculations are the easiest ones. The "business end" is at the *other* end of the BH characteristic, when the temperature is high, the demagnetizing MMF is high, and the BH characteristic is collapsing.

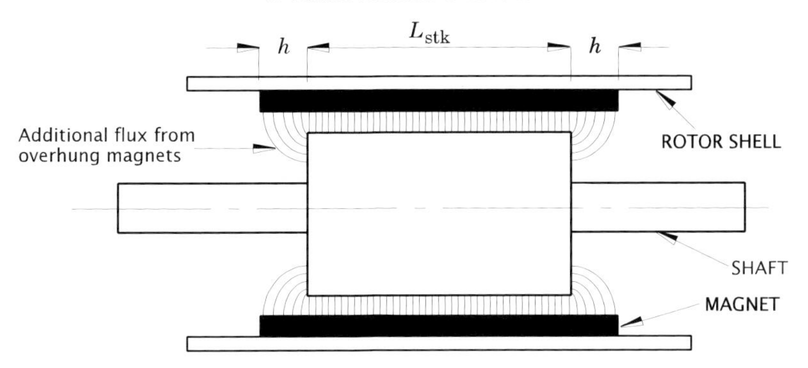

Fig. 3.17 Additional flux obtained from overhung magnets

3.4.5 Magnet overhang

In DC PM motors with ferrite magnets the magnet is often made longer than the rotor, as shown for an exterior-rotor PM brushless motor in Fig. 3.17, which has similar topology. Usually the overhang h at each end is less than the magnet thickness. Overhang is not used with rare-earth magnets because it would quickly saturate the stator teeth. In any case the method is justified only when the cost of magnet material is low enough to permit an "excess" of magnet; it is not an efficient way of using magnets but just a means of augmenting the relatively weak flux of ferrite magnets. The percentage increase in flux given by Williams [1983] is shown in Fig. 3.18 as a function of the overhang h and the rotor diameter D.

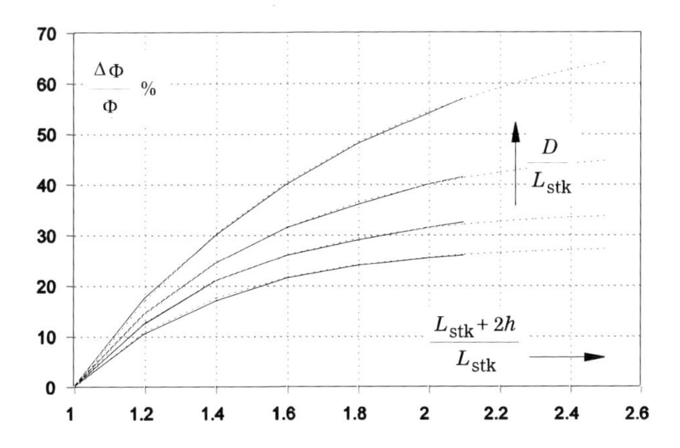

Fig. 3.18 Effect of magnet overhang

3.4.6 Rotor yoke dimensions

The yoke is also known as the back iron. Its magnetic function is to carry the flux from one pole to the next, or more correctly, from one *half*-pole to the next, since the flux emerging from the magnets usually splits into two, with one half going through each yoke section.

Fig. 3.25 shows the effect of pole-number on the rotor yoke flux. Two motors are shown, identical in all respects except that the one on the left has 4 poles, while the one on the right has 10. The yoke flux is much greater in the 4-pole motor, and it also spreads into the shaft, which is magnetic in the example. If the shaft were non-magnetic, the flux would be confined to the rotor yoke: its density would be greater, and so would the MMF drop. The 10-pole motor, in contrast, could use a thinner rotor yoke, allowing space for a greater shaft diameter, or even for holes to reduce the weight and inertia.

The rotor yoke is stationary relative to the main flux, and it can be made of solid steel provided that there is no risk of excessive rotor eddy-current loss arising from imbalance or harmonics. A solid steel rotor yoke forms a stiff hub that is invaluable in high-speed machines to prevent lateral deflection and whirling.

In rotors with Halbach magnets the rotor yoke can be nonmagnetic or removed altogether; (see Chapter 4). In other cases a magnetic stainless steel can be used, if high flux-densities are not required.

In exterior-rotor machines the rotor yoke is an integral part of the shell or cup that houses the rotating magnet. This shell invariably overhangs the magnet in the axial direction at one or both ends, and in doing so it provides extra cross-sectional area for the flux return path, as a result of which the shell can be made considerably thinner. Even the end-flange of the rotor shell contributes to this extra area.

If carbon steel is used for a rotor cup or any other form of magnet return path, it is advisable to keep the flux density under 1·5 T. In extreme cases 1·7 or 1·8 T is used if absolutely necessary, but saturation of the rotor yoke is undesirable because it limits the flux/pole available from the magnet. Laminating the exterior rotor shell is not practical as it is in interior rotors, so the flux-density should be kept below 1·2 T for these applications.

3.5 Stator design

3.5.1 Cutting the laminations

The stator consists of a stack of soft iron laminations, an insulation system, coils of "magnet wire", connectors and terminals. Prototype laminations are often cut by numerically-controlled laser cutting or wire-EDM (electro-discharge machining), also known as wire-slotting or wire-erosion. Both methods are capable of giving accurate dimensions with tolerances as good as ± 0.01 mm, with a square edge that is free from burrs. For production motors the laminations are stamped from core plate using a progressive die and an automatic press. For low volume production, the progressive dies are made to punch a single set of laminations per stroke (one stator punching and one rotor punching). The result is that the material used is not the area of the lamination cross section, but the square of a number slightly larger than the maximum lamination outside diameter. If round punchings are used, about 21% of the material is waste. If the volume is expected to be high, a quotation on a progressive die that will punch three at a time is recommended. This will greatly reduce the price of the laminations, partly because the punch press utilization is tripled, and partly because of material savings due to nesting of three rows of punches in the die, using a strip which is not as wide as three times the stator diameter.

3.5.2 Choice of core plate

In general, a high-performance motor (one with high efficiency and/or high operating speed) will require thinner laminations of materials that have low specific core losses. If the volume is low and cost is not as important as performance, the use of M-19 of either #29 gauge or #26 gauge is recommended; in metric steels this means alloy steels with typically 3% Si content and thickness of 0·35 or 0·5 mm. Ultra-high speed motors will require laminations as thin as 0·1 mm, while the highest power-densities will be obtained with cobalt-iron laminations; typically these are confined to aerospace applications. [JRH writes: Most other brushless motors can use either #26 or #24 gage M-36 or M-43 laminations]. For high-volume competitive applications, tests should ideally be conducted with different materials, thicknesses, heat treatments, core plates, and insulating coatings to determine the most cost-effective solution.

In recent times there has been much turmoil not only in the price of steel but even in the availability and the sources of supply. What is most important, if possible, is to characterize the steel as accurately and as throughly as possible in terms of its BH characteristics and its loss characteristics, and to use this data as carefully as possible in design calculations to understand not only the commercial margins but also the effect of material property changes on the performance of the product.

3.5.3 Stacking

There are six main ways to hold a lamination stack together before winding for the stator:

1. Bonding with epoxy or Loctite®
2. Riveting
3. Welding
4. Self-cleating (interlocking)
5. Slot liners
6. Segmented core

The bonding method is usually used only for prototypes or small quantities. A thin spray coating of epoxy is applied to one or both sides of every lamination before they are stacked in a fixture, clamped, and heated to cure the epoxy. Another method is to align, clamp, preheat and apply Loctite® which penetrates between the laminations and bonds them together.

For riveting, holes may be provided in the stamping die to accept through-rivets which are staked in place. The holes must be located at points in the magnetic circuit such that the electrical circuits formed by shorting the laminations to the rivets will not have significant induced currents in them. Thus the holes are usually near the outside of the lamination. Rivets or long bolts can be fitted outside the lamination stack, and in some cases they serve the additional function of helping to hold the end-bells in position.

Another common procedure is automatic TIG (tungsten/inert gas) welding. This can be used on an automatic assembly line for low-cost, high-volume production. Laser welding and electron-beam (EB) welding is also sometimes used.

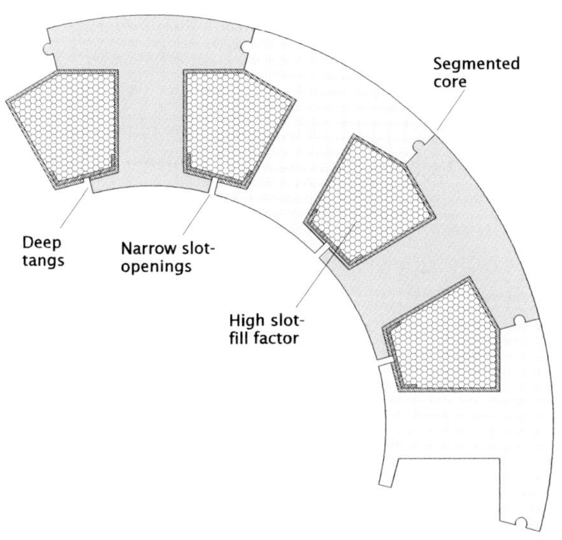

Fig. 3.19 Segmented core with compacted coils

A popular method of stacking and retaining laminations into packs that does not require welding is to use a progressive punching die with a station at the end of the stamping process which makes a small indentation in each lamination. The indentations protrude on the other side of each lamination, providing a self-cleating action when they are nested together under pressure. The indentations are usually located in the neighbourhood of the teeth.

Stacks can also be held together by cuffed slot-liners before winding. The method is common in the production of induction motors and can be used for brushless PM motors with similar stator laminations. The slot liners are automatically inserted into the stator slot openings, and the cuffs are folded back to hold the stack together quite snugly until it is wound and varnished. This is an excellent method for high-speed automatic stator production. Skewed packs can be made after winding using this system.

Fig. 3.19 shows the concept of a **segmented stator core**, pioneered in the Panasonic MINAS® servo-motor and also seen in Fig. 2.18; (also see Figs. 2.40 and 2.48). With pre-wound teeth the slot-fill factor can be substantially increased, and this also reduces the thermal resistance of the winding. Both of these lead to a higher torque per unit volume.

Fig. 3.19 also shows the use of closed or almost-closed stator slots, which help to reduce cogging torque. The almost-closed stator slots have a high slot-leakage inductance, and an interesting example of such a machine was built by Professor Jack [1996] with 6 phases to demonstrate "fault tolerance", which comes partly through the "impedance protection" of the high inductance and partly through the use of a "modular" winding in which no slot contains more than one coilside, thereby ensuring a high degree of isolation between phases. A similar machine was built by Professor Jack [2000] with a powdered-iron core and "prepressed" windings compacted before assembly. This machine was reported to have a slot-fill factor of 78% and a thermal resistance 46% lower than for a conventionally constructed machine, permitting a large increase in torque density.

3.5.4 Insulating the slots

Once the lamination stack is in a pack form, it must be insulated before winding. There are several common ways that this is accomplished. For prototypes either hand-cut slot-liners and end insulators are used (Fig. 2.45); or if the equipment is available, a 3M® fluidized-bed epoxy coating system can be used. (See Figs. 2.43 and 2.44). This method requires careful process control.

For high-volume production, a separate insulation system is commonly used for small brushless machines in the form of moulded plastic insulators, one at each end of the pack; (see Figs. 2.18 and 2.22). Various connectors or terminal posts can be incorporated in the moulding to facilitate the automatic connection of leads, Hall switches, thermal protectors, or printed-circuit boards together with the attachment of the magnet wire from the coil windings.

For larger motors a more common method is the cuffed slot liner as used in high-volume AC induction motors; (see Figs. 2.46 and 2.47). Fig. 3.20 shows a detailed annotated example. The height of the cuff at each end is made high enough to ensure that the cross-over of the coil end-turns cannot be shorted on the edges of the laminations.

Very large motors with open slots use form-wound coils which are taped and laid up in lap windings. Rectangular strap conductors are often used to obtain a high slot-fill factor, Figs. 3.22 and 3.23.

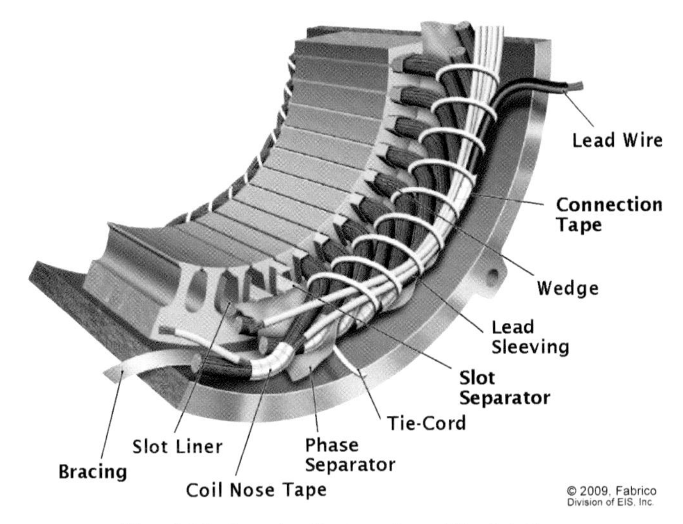

Fig. 3.20 Lamination packs with slot liners
Fabrico Division of EIS Inc., USA

3.5.5 Slot-fill factor

Slot-fill factor is a measure of how much copper is packed into the stator slot. Given the cost of copper and the difficulty of squeezing unruly wires into such an awkward space, one might ask why engineers strive to achieve a high slot-fill. The answer is clearly demonstrated by the Panasonic MINAS® motor and by Jack's example mentioned on p. 100: a high slot-fill reduces the resistance, the I^2R loss, the thermal resistance, and the temperature rise.

There is no standard definition for slot-fill factor, but a common formulation used in factories is the "net" slot-fill factor

$$\mathrm{SFn} = \frac{n d^2}{A_{\mathrm{slotLL}}}, \tag{3.13}$$

where n is the number of strands per slot, d is the OD of one strand (measured across the wire enamel), and A_{slotLL} is the available winding area, equal to the slot area A_{slot} *less the liner* and any other pieces of insulation (top-sticks, phase separators, etc). A_{slot} is shown in Fig. 3.21(a) as the gross punched area less the slot-opening area (hatched). In Fig. 3.21(b) and (c), A_{slotLL} is equal to A_{slot} less the areas of the slot-liner and the "closure" at the top of the slot.

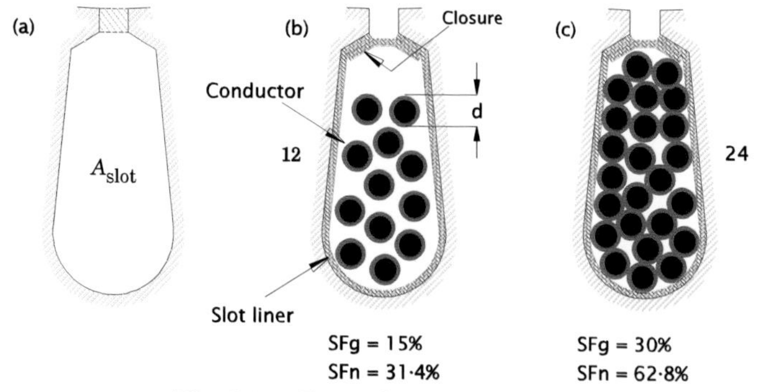

Fig. 3.21 Examples of slot-fill factors

An alternative definition is the "gross" slot-fill factor

$$\mathrm{SFg} \quad = \quad \frac{\text{Total copper area per slot}}{A_{\text{slot}}}. \tag{3.14}$$

SFn is generally much higher than SFg, and Figs. 3.21(b) and (c) show two examples roughly to scale, in which one slot has twice the amount of copper in the other. A value of SFn approaching 70–75% (or SFg approaching 40–45%) would normally be regarded as high with "random-wound" coils, but much higher values can be obtained with rectangular wire in open slots, as illustrated in Fig. 3.22. A practical example of a coilside with rectangular conductors is shown in Fig. 3.23. The Roebel transposition needed to minimize proximity losses is clearly shown; see §3.6.7.4.

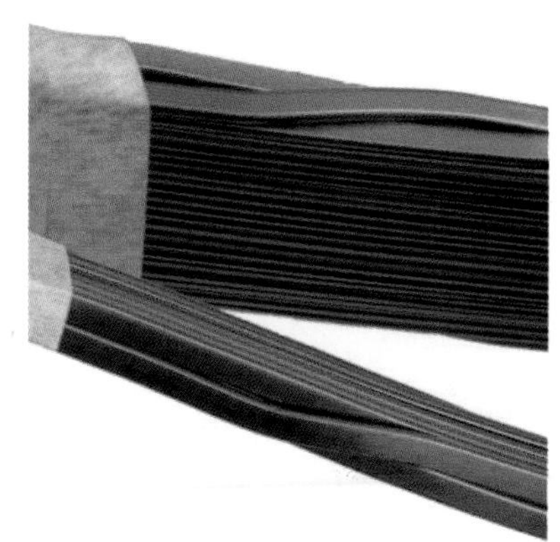

Fig. 3.23 Roebel transposition
REA Magnet Wire Co., USA

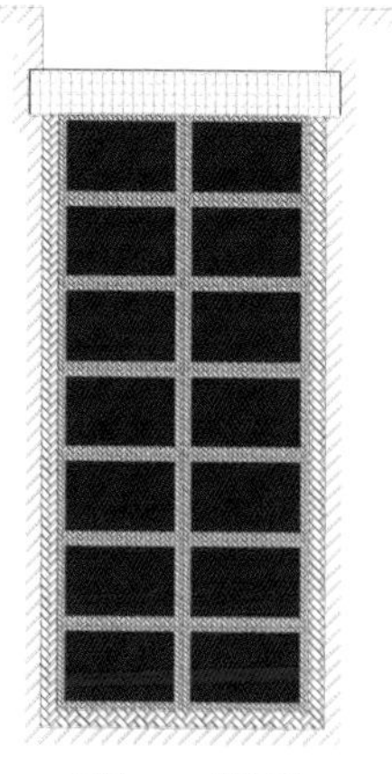

Fig. 3.22 Open slot

3.5.6 Winding and inserting the phase coils

The phase coils can be placed into the insulated lamination pack in several ways. The method used for prototypes is to make a coil form of the approximate size, hand-wind the coils, and hand-insert them into the correct slots; see Fig. 2.45. Usually the coils in a set or phase are wound continuously, with the finish lead of the first coil continuous with the start lead of the second coil and so on, to minimize the number of interconnections.

For production manufacturing of brushless motor stators, if the **throw** or the distance between the start side of a coil and the finish side of a coil is not more than one or two slots, needle winders can be used to wind the coils in place, as in the manufacture of stepping motors and universal motors. It is also possible to use a three-needle machine to wind all three phases simultaneously, indexing after each coil is completed to the next coil rotation with continuous interconnections of magnet wire. This type of winding machinery can even make automatic terminations, as seen in Fig. 2.22. We have also seen that single-tooth coils can be pre-wound on individual core segments that are subsequently assembled into a complete stator, Figs. 2.18 and 2.48.

Fig. 3.24 Impregnation of stator end-windings
WEG, Brazil

The other automatic method of winding is to use AC induction motor winding equipment. Usually the coils of the phases are wound separately and laid in slots of tooling which fits the particular lamination pack. Either hand loading a stator pack or automatic loading of a stator pack to a second station permits automatic insertion of the finished coils into the insulated slots of the pack. This process is sometimes called "coil-shooting" and is commonly used to make "concentric" windings, as in Fig. 2.46 and 2.47. Lap windings used in larger machines are normally inserted by hand into open slots. Several other examples can be seen in Chapter 2.

3.5.7 Varnishing

The end turns are usually formed and tied or laced before varnishing the entire wound completed stator assembly; see Fig. 3.24. Varnishing or encapsulating is necessary to provide a heat conduction path from the inner copper turns to the lamination stack. A second reason for varnishing is to eliminate movement of adjacent turns as current is switched on and off. Over a long period of time if the conductors are not held by varnish, the motion between them caused by electro-magnetic forces would eventually wear through the varnish insulation on the wires and cause electrical shorted turns; this wear process is known as "fretting". A third reason for varnishing is to provide a higher dielectric strength than that of the air which would otherwise lie between the turns of insulated magnet wire. Finally, the varnish excludes moisture, dust and chemicals which could have a deleterious effect on the integrity of the insulation.

3.5.8 Winding with multiple-strand conductors

Sometimes when the final number of turns is calculated for a specific machine, the size of the copper conductor is too large to wind by one of the above methods. It is not uncommon to wind several **strands-in-hand** of insulated magnet wire to make up the same cross-section area as the original single conductor. The composite conductor has the same resistance as the single conductor, but is more flexible and is less susceptible to high-frequency eddy-current loss, especially if the strands are twisted. One of the problems with multiple-strand conductors is the attachment of lead wires. It is difficult to strip and solder a multiple-strand conductor to a heavy lead wire. The best way to make this attachment for a good electrical joint without voltage drops, is to fuse or weld the multiple-strand magnet wire to the lead wire. Many brushless servo motors use MS connectors for power leads and commutation signal leads. By utilizing these heavy connectors for power leads it is possible to eliminate the lead wire and bring the ends of the magnet wire from the phase windings directly to the back of the MS connectors and solder or weld them in place. There is a considerable amount of controversy over which is the best method, but each one should be carefully analyzed and the correct one selected for a given manufacturing operation.

3.5.9 Number of stator slots

The required number of stator slots S is obviously proportional to the required number of coils C. As we have already seen, a **single-layer** winding has one coil-side per slot, and $S = 2C$. In a **double-layer** winding, there are two coil-sides per slot, and $S = C$. S is also influenced by the number of slots/pole, $S/2p$, which has been discussed in detail earlier.

In addition to the theoretical considerations discussed earlier, both S and C are constrained by the availability of laminations and winding machinery, so it is not always possible to make a free choice. In larger machines it is advantageous to use a larger number of slots and coils so that individual coils are of manageable size and flexibility. Moreover, with a larger number of slots the winding is subdivided into smaller units, and this reduces the thermal diffusion distance between hot-spots in the conductors and the cooler surface of the slot walls. The hot-spot temperature rise is thereby reduced.

In very large machines it is also an advantage to use form-wound coils in parallel-sided slots. The stator teeth are therefore tapered, and a large number of slots helps to reduce the taper angle, which in turn improves the utilization of the stator steel.

3.5.10 Stator core dimensions

The radial thickness of the stator yoke must be sufficient to limit the flux-density, typically to a value below 1·5 T, to minimize the MMF drop that would otherwise deplete the flux, and to avoid excessive iron loss. In high-speed machines, especially those designed to work at higher-than-normal frequencies, a lower value may be necessary.

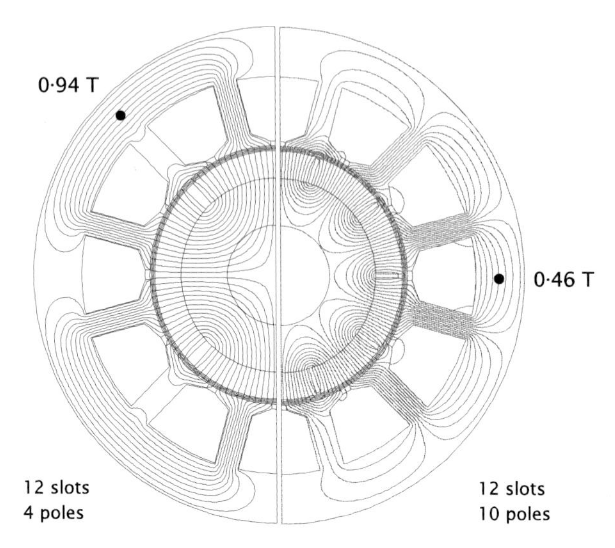

Fig. 3.25 Effect of pole-number on yoke flux-densities

With a given outside diameter and inside diameter of the stator, the stator yoke competes with the slots for radial space. If the yoke is thicker, the slot-depth must be smaller, and *vice versa*. Sometimes it helpful to consider a change in the pole number to achieve this compromise.

Fig. 3.25 illustrates several of these points by example. On the left is the open-circuit flux-plot for a motor with 12 slots and 4 poles. The motor on the right has the same stator, but the number of poles is 10. All other dimensions are unchanged. In the 12/4 motor, the peak flux-density in the stator yoke is twice as high as in the 12/10. It appears that the radial thickness of the stator yoke could be reduced, possibly by as much as 50% — or more, if a higher flux-density can be tolerated. Alternatively, the slots in the 12/10 motor could be made deeper, or the split ratio could be increased.

3.5.11 Stator tooth-tips

Although the stator is similar to that of an induction motor, it is subject to different electromagnetic requirements. In surface-magnet machines there is no slotted iron rotor on the other side of the airgap. This tends to reduce the so-called "zig-zag" leakage inductance and the modulation of the airgap flux wave by slotting ("slot-ripple").

If the stator tooth-tips are too thin, or if they are excessively tapered, they are liable to saturate, and the effect is similar to that of an increase in the slot-opening : the slot-ripple increases, and this in turn increases the cogging and the rotor eddy-current loss.

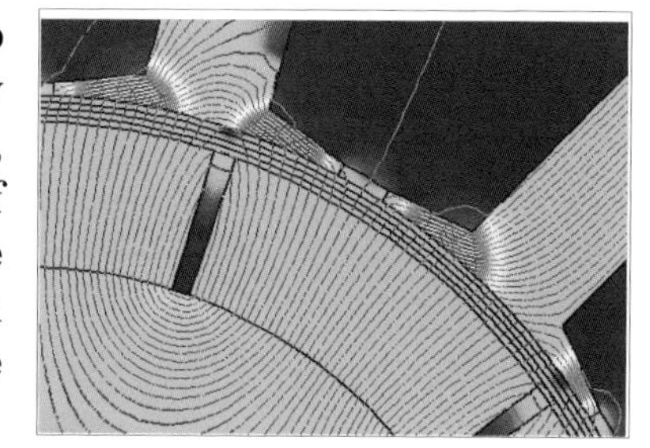

Fig. 3.26 Saturated tooth-tips

3.5.12 Cogging and skew

The use of integral slots/pole causes extensive cogging or detent torque, as every pole-edge aligns with a stator slot-opening at the same time. This is one of the reasons to use fractional slots/pole. Cogging is not simply a problem in smooth running. It can cause difficulties in starting, and it is associated with ripple in the EMF.

Cogging torque is a reluctance torque attributable to the interaction of the magnet MMF with the variable reluctance of the slotted stator as the magnet rotates past the slot-openings. The calculation of cogging requires the finite-element method, and extreme care must be taken to refine the mesh to achieve accurate results. When the cogging torque is nearly zero, the calculation becomes sensitive to "discretization noise". Analytical methods are not adequate for the design calculations need to minimize cogging.

It is helpful to use small slot-openings and a large airgap, but an effective way to reduce the cogging torque is to skew the stack of laminations by up to one slot-pitch. It is possible to wind the stator on a loose lamination stack held in place by cuffed slot liners, skew the stack mechanically after winding, and finally weld in three places on the OD to hold the stack in the skewed position. The method has the advantage that the coils are wound into straight, unskewed slots.

An alternative is to skew the rotor. With a full-ring magnet this can be done by imposing a skewed magnetization pattern, using a magnetizing fixture with skewed poles. With arrays of magnets such as shown in Figs. 2.29 or 3.16, a similar effect can be obtained by staggering one row of magnets relative to the next, or by skewing the individual magnet blocks into a rhombic shape.

Whether it is applied to the stator or the rotor, skewing reduces the winding factor and the fundamental EMF by the so-called skew factor, $k_{\sigma n}$. If σ is the skew angle, then for the nth harmonic EMF

$$k_{\sigma n} = \frac{\sin (n\sigma/2)}{n\sigma/2}. \tag{3.15}$$

For the fundamental, $n = 1$. For example in a 12-slot 4-pole motor with $p = 2$, a skew of 1 slot-pitch means that one end of the stator (or rotor) is rotated by $360/12 = 30°$ relative to the other end, so $\sigma = \pi/3$ elec. rad., and $k_{\sigma 1} = \sin(\pi/6)/(\pi/6) = 0{\cdot}9549$. In a sinewave motor this means a loss of fundamental EMF (and torque) of the order of 4·5%, the price paid to reduce the cogging torque to a low level.

Skewing also helps to remove the ripple in the EMF caused by so-called **permeance harmonics**, which refer to the variation in the overall magnetic circuit permeance cause by slotting. The permeance variation modulates the airgap flux at the slot-passing frequency, and since the EMF ripple is proportional to the rate of change of the flux, there is an amplification factor proportional to the speed.

In fractional-slot motors with a small slot/pole ratio, skewing by 1 slot-pitch can cause an excessive loss of EMF as explained on p. 134. Other methods for cogging torque reduction have therefore been developed, including shifting some of the magnets from their regular positions, or profiling the magnets or the magnetization pattern, or even using closed stator slots. Very low cogging torque ($< 1\%$) can be achieved with such methods without using skew.

Another technique is to use dummy slots, Fig. 3.27, which double the cogging-torque frequency while reducing its amplitude. (See also the irregular slotting on p. 132).

The ultimate in cogging-torque reduction is to use a slotless stator and an airgap winding, as in the motor in Fig. 2.42. In such motors the cogging torque is nearly zero.

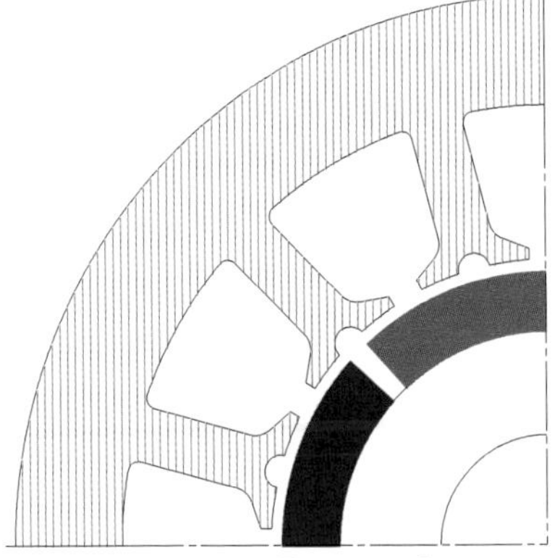

Fig. 3.27 Dummy slots

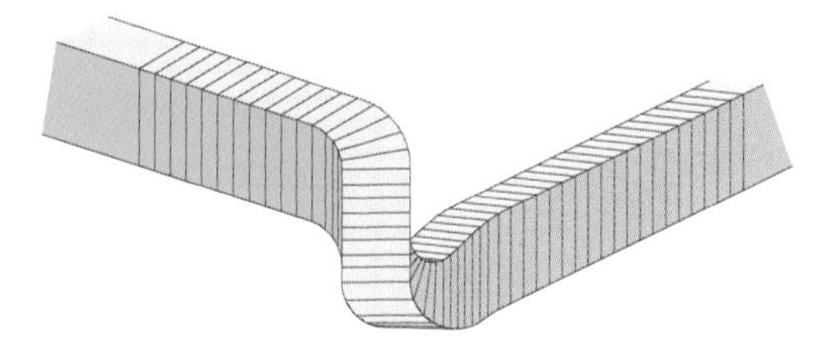

Fig. 3.28 Knuckle at the end of a form-wound coil

3.5.13 Management of end-turns

Many brushless stator configurations, especially those evolved from AC induction motor products, have large end-turns from slot to slot on each end of the stack. In order to contain these end-turns, it is necessary to lace them with string before varnishing, Figs. 2.46 and 3.20. This can be done by hand for small quantities, or the use of automatic lacing machines can be employed if they are available. It is necessary to make the end-turns fast before varnishing to ensure that their location is controlled and does not result in any shorting situations caused by wear of the varnish insulation.

Before the end-turns are laced it is sometimes desirable to interleave sheets of woven fiberglass between the end-turns of the coils of different phases, to help protect against so-called "first-turn" failure. This failure mode is an insulation breakdown attributed to steep-fronted voltage waveforms or standing waves arising from the switching of very fast IGBTs in the drive; see §14.1.2.7. Finally, the bulk of the end-turns can be reduced by a process known as "blocking" or "forming" in a set of blocking dies.

In large machines the entire coil may be pressed into shape after winding on a coil form, so that it can be fitted into an open slot in a lap winding. Fig. 3.28 shows the "knuckle" at the end of such a coil, and it should be noted that the top side of the "go" coilside turns over and becomes the bottom side of the "return" coilside. One of the reasons for this is to reduce the proximity losses as explained in §3.6.7.4. Coils of this type often use rectangular strap conductors, and they can achieve very high slot-fill factors as shown in Fig. 3.22.

3.6 Electrical design of windings

In this section we change our focus of attention from the physical design to the theoretical electrical properties of windings, in preparation for the calculation of EMF, torque, and inductance in Chapters 4 and 5. We begin with a definition of all the necessary terms, and proceed to the study of winding layouts and diagrams. The properties of windings that make them suitable for squarewave or sinewave drive are identified, and examples are given.

3.6.1 Definitions

Winding is a general term for the totality of coils in the machine. The winding is generally divided into m phases, usually 3 or 2. Phase windings are usually separated by $360°/m$ around the stator.

A **coil** is a loop of wire with T_c **turns**. Every coil has two coilsides, a "go" coilside and a "return" coilside. The two coilsides are generally in different slots displaced from one another by an integral number of slot-pitches, called the **span**. In most cases the span and turns are the same for all coils. When the coil-span is less than $S/2p$, the coils are said to be "short-pitched" or "chorded".

A **turn** has 2 **conductors**, a "go" conductor and a "return" conductor. If all coils in a phase are in series, each conductor carries the phase current: $I_{cond} = I_{ph}$. But if the coils of a phase are connected in a parallel paths, the conductor current is $I_{cond} = I_{ph}/a$.

A conductor may be wound as a single wire or it may be divided into n **strands**-in-hand. The current in one strand is $I_{strand} = I_{cond}/n$.

If the number of **coilsides** in the winding exceeds the number of slots, then at least one slot will have more than one coilside. If, for instance, every slot contains 2 coilsides, the winding is said to have two **layers**. With lap windings, one coilside will be in the bottom and one in the top layer, giving a uniform winding. For good utilization it is desirable to have equal numbers of coilsides in every slot.

A **balanced** m-phase winding has identical phase windings displaced by $360/m°$, $m \geq 3$, with equal resistances and inductances and EMF waveforms that have the same waveshape and are displaced in phase by $360/m°$ at the fundamental frequency. Ideally such windings should be supplied by balanced currents.

3.6.2 Integral-slot windings

Integral-slot windings are used where the slots/pole is an integer, and the coils of each phase are found in **pole-groups**, each group having the same number of **coils per pole**. Usually this type of winding is to be found in machines where the slots/pole is larger than 2 or 3. There are two main types : the **concentric** winding (Fig. 3.30) and the **lap** winding (Fig. 3.31). In both of these figures, only one phase is shown. Both windings have 2 coils/pole, so the total number of coils/phase is $6 \times 2 = 12$, and the total number of coils in the whole machine is $3 \times 12 = 36$. There are 36×2 coil-sides, so the number of layers is 2, and every slot holds two coil-sides.

The concentric winding is common in AC induction motors and is usually wound and inserted by automatic machinery, whereas the lap winding is more often found in large machines that use form-wound coils, hand-inserted. Very high slot-fill factors can be achieved by this method, especially when rectangular wire is used.

As a rule of thumb, the coil-span should be equal to the next integer less than the slots/pole, in this case $36/6 - 1 = 5$. This is in accordance with Table 3.6 on p. 86.

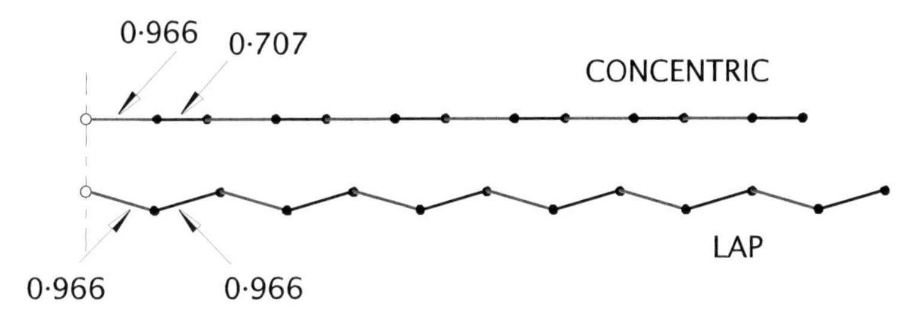

Fig. 3.29 EMF diagram for the two windings in Figs. 3.30 and 3.31

Fig. 3.29 shows the EMF phasor diagram for one phase of each winding. The individual coil EMFs are shown, and it can be seen that in the lap winding the coil EMFs all have the same magnitude (0·966), but are displaced in phase from one another by one slot-pitch, which is $360/36 \times p = 30^\circ$ elec. 0·966 is the cosine of the phase angle (15°) between each EMF phasor and the resultant, and this is equal to the so-called **spread factor** or **distribution factor**. We might also note in passing that 15° is also half the slot-pitch angle in $^\circ$ elec.

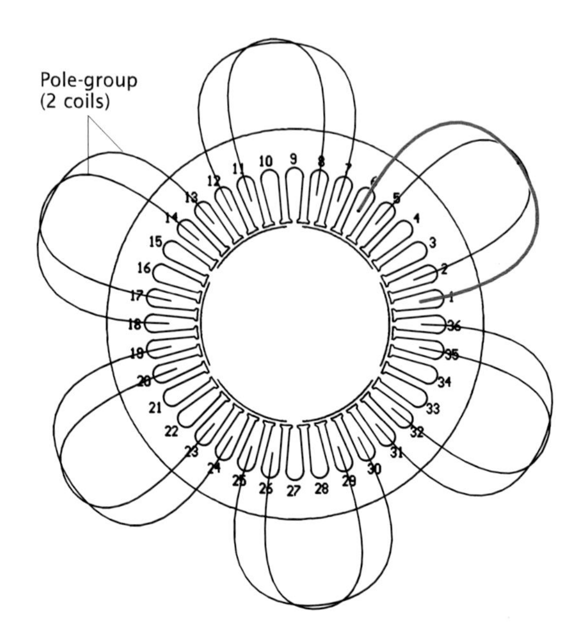

Fig. 3.30 Concentric winding with 6 poles, 2 coils/pole

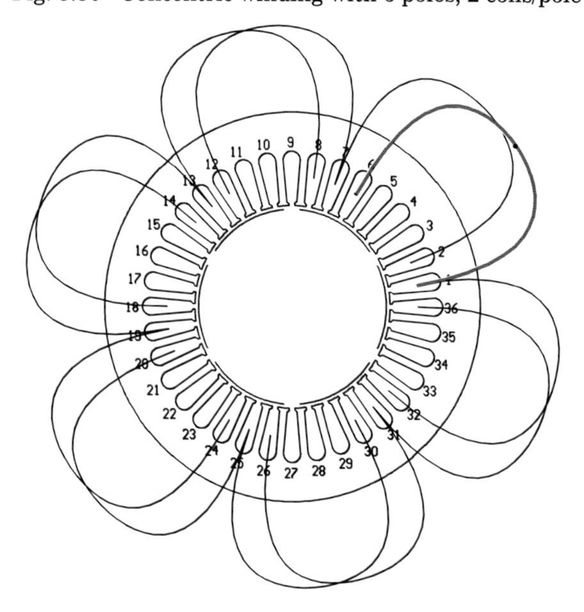

Fig. 3.31 Lap winding with 6 poles, 2 coils/pole

In the concentric winding all the coil EMFs are in phase with one another, so the distribution factor is 1. There is no loss of EMF due to phase-shifts between neighbouring coils. However, each pole-group has two coils of different span; the outer coil links more flux than the inner one, so its EMF is greater in the ratio 0·966/0·707. The value 0·966 is the **pitch factor** of the outermost coil, which has a span of $\alpha = 5/6 \times 180^\circ = 150^\circ$elec. As we will see later, the pitch factor of a single coil for the fundamental flux is $k_{p1} = \sin(\alpha/2) = \sin(75^\circ) = 0{\cdot}966$. The inner coil has a span of $3/6 \times 180^\circ = 90^\circ$elec., so its pitch factor is $\sin(45^\circ) = 0{\cdot}707$. The EMFs are in the same proportion as the pitch factors since all coils have the same numbers of turns.

The total phase EMF for the lap winding is $6 \times 2 \times \cos(15^\circ) = 11{\cdot}59$ V, while for the concentric winding it is $6 \times [\sin(75^\circ) + \sin(45^\circ)] = 10{\cdot}04$ V. The lap winding EMF is therefore 1·15 times that of the concentric winding. Other things being equal, the lap winding will produce 15% more output power for the same *sinewave* current, the same number of turns, and the same conductor size.

This is not a general conclusion about lap and concentric windings. For one thing, the lap winding in this example is likely to have more copper in the end-turns, which will decrease its efficiency slightly. The importance of the example is that it introduces the winding factors. Here we have calculated them on an *ad hoc* basis for a particular example, but later we will formulate them in more general terms. The above calculations relate to the fundamental component of EMF which is generated by the fundamental space-harmonic of the flux, but later we will be concerned with higher-order harmonics.

Next consider the suitability of these windings for sinewave or squarewave operation. Taking the lap winding, Fig. 3.32 shows the ideal calculated line-line EMF with a rectangular flux-distribution having a pole-arc of fully 180°. It appears that the required 60° flat-top is just achieved. However, fringing and pole-to-pole leakage cause the flux distribution to have rounded edges, so the actual EMF waveform is more like Fig. 3.33. The flat top is lost, and the EMF waveform begins to look more sinusoidal. If this motor is run with squarewave current, there will be about 15% torque ripple. If a skew of 1 slot-pitch is applied, the EMF waveform of Fig. 3.34 is obtained, which is clearly suitable for sinewave drive.

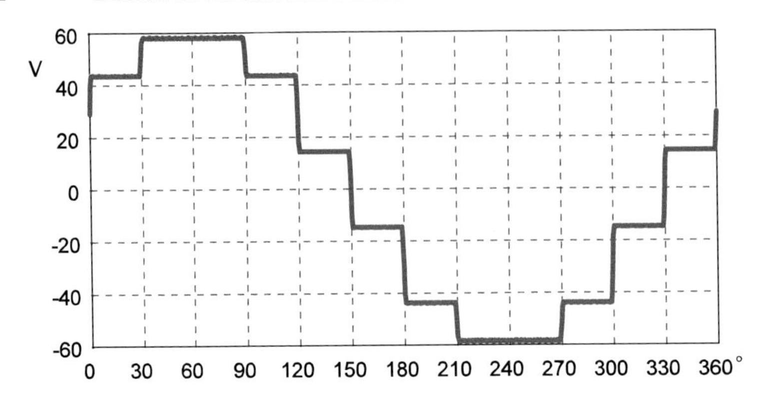

Fig. 3.32 EMF of winding of Fig. 3.31; 180° square flux wave

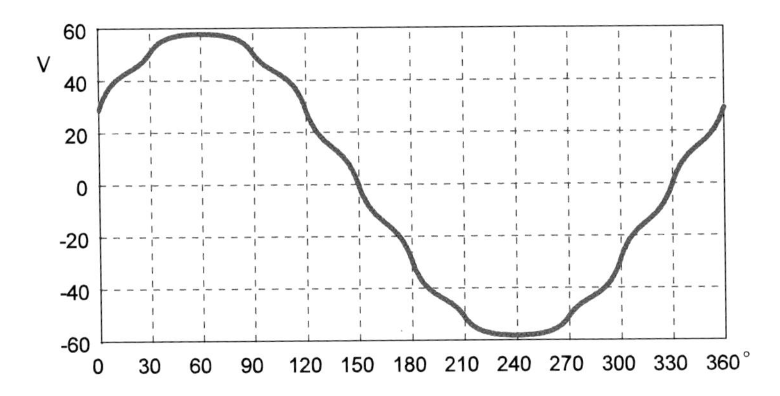

Fig. 3.33 EMF of winding of Fig. 3.31; 180° magnet arc, actual flux wave

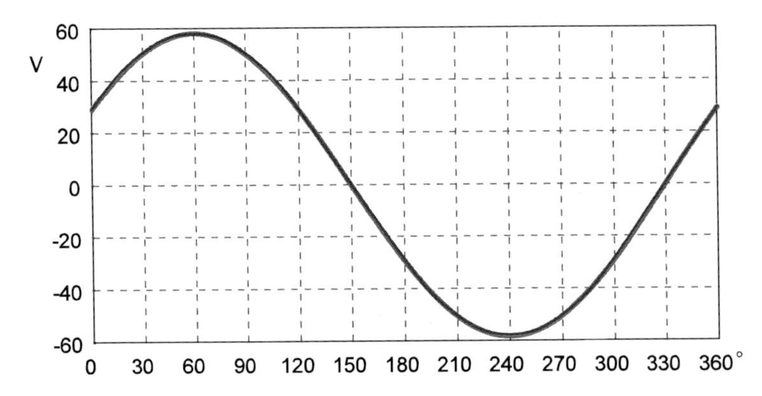

Fig. 3.34 EMF of winding of Fig 3.31; 180° magnet arc; skew = 1 slot

3.6.3 Windings for squarewave drive

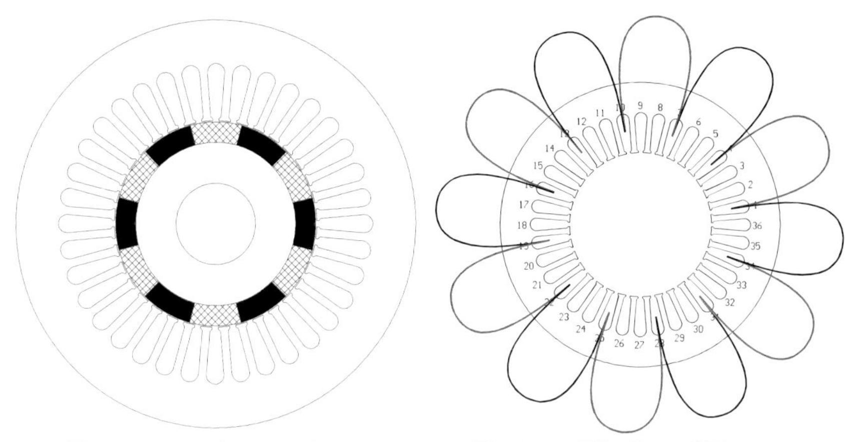

Fig. 3.35 36-slot 12-pole motor

Fig. 3.36 Winding of Fig. 3.35

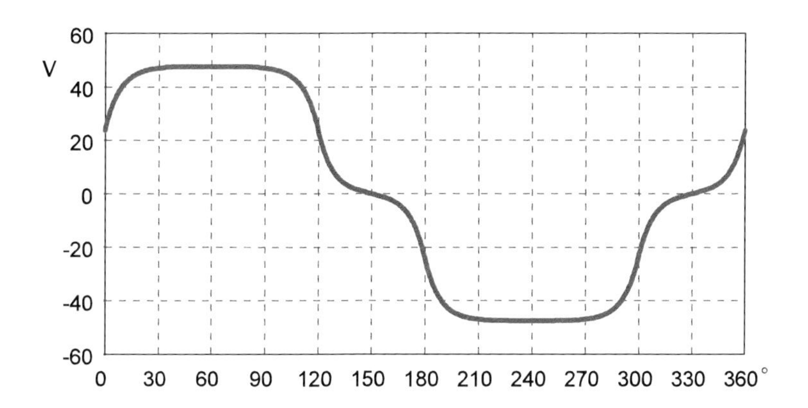

Fig. 3.37 EMF waveform of the motor in Fig. 3.35

Although the winding in Fig. 3.31 would work with squarewave drive, a better result is obtained by changing the rotor to 12 poles and using a full-pitch winding with 1 coil per pole, Figs. 3.35 and 3.36. The EMF waveform is shown in Fig. 3.37. Another modification in producing this result was to reduce the airgap from 1·0 mm to 0·3 mm; the rotor diameter being 50 mm. This "sharpens" the flux wave and flattens the top of the EMF waveform, but it sacrifices valuable radial space that could be used for a retaining can in the 6-pole motor.

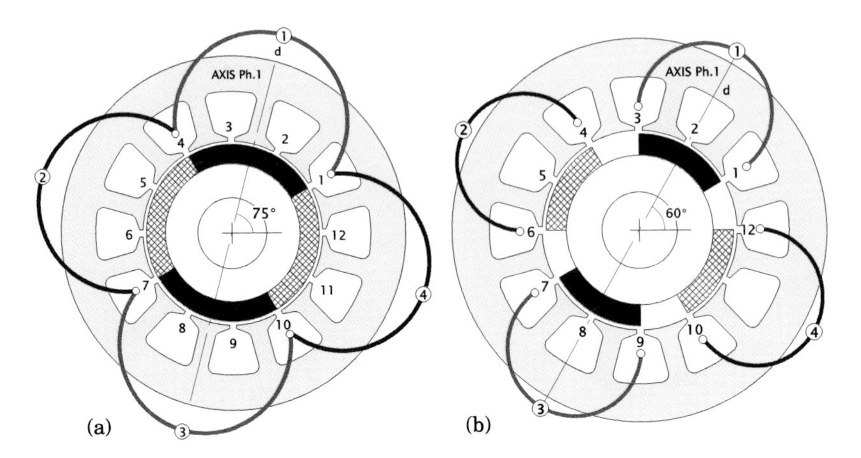

Fig. 3.38 12-slot 4-pole motors : only one phase shown

Example — Fig. 3.38(a) shows a 12-slot 4-pole motor with a 180° magnet pole-arc and a single-layer winding with a coil-span of 3 slots: that is, a pitch of 180° or "full pitch." The idealized EMF waveforms are shown in Fig. 3.39, drawn on the assumption of no fringing; in other words, the flux crosses the airgap in the radial direction, with no slotting effect and no leakage from pole to pole.

The flux-linkage waveforms are shown at the top. Because there is no fringing they are composed of straight-line segments. The slopes of these segments depend on the disposition of the conductors and the magnet pole-arc itself. With 180° pole arc and a full-pitch winding, maximum flux-linkage is reached at a single point when a south d-axis of the rotor is aligned with the axis of phase 1, and there is no "dwell" or "flat spot" around this position. Of course the maximum flux-linkage is repeated with alternating polarity every 180° elec.

The phase EMF waveform is a 180° squarewave, the derivative of the flux-linkage waveform. Even when its corners are rounded off by fringing, it is wider than the 120° needed in a wye-connected squarewave motor, (although if the airgap is widened it quickly loses its square shape and eventually becomes nearly sinusoidal).

The squarewave is rich in harmonics, and contains triplen harmonics. There is no possibility of satisfying the condition $e_1 + e_2 + e_3 = 0$ that is necessary to eliminate circulating current in a delta connection.

In principle it should be possible to eliminate all triplen harmonics by changing the magnet pole-arc to 120°. However, it is not possible to make and magnetize magnets with such precise magnetization patterns as to make this a practical method. Moreover, with a reduced magnet pole-arc the full-pitch coils are wider than necessary to link all the flux/pole, so they might as well be shortened to save copper in the end-windings.

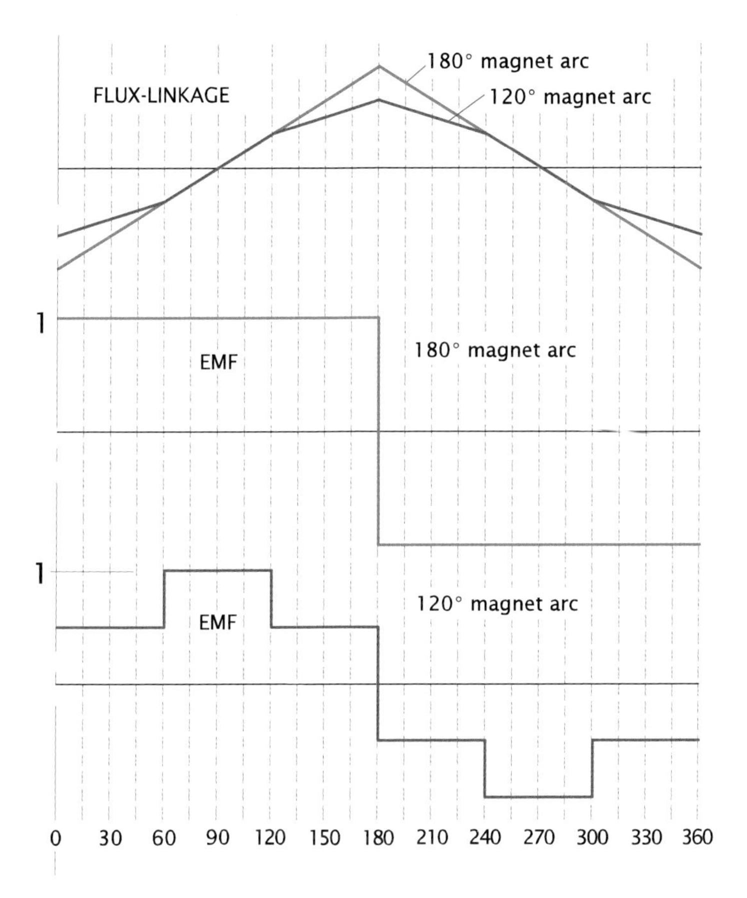

Fig. 3.39 Waveforms for Fig. 3.38 with 180° and 120° magnet arcs

If the coils are shortened to 2/3 pitch, as in Fig. 3.38(b), the triplen harmonic winding factors all become zero, while at the same time the coils are just wide enough to link all the flux/pole.

The EMF now has a double-step waveform due to the way in which the flux-linkage changes with rotor position. The flat top is ideally 60°, and slightly less when fringing is taken into account. It can be widened by increasing the pole-arc: as long as the winding pitch is 2/3, there is no risk of circulating current. Therefore a pole-arc of 130-140° works well with this configuration in delta.

The motor of Fig. 3.38(b) uses only 2/3 the magnet material compared with the motor of Fig. 3.38(a), yet its EMF, EMF constant k_E, torque and current are all unchanged. Moreover the flux/pole is only about 2/3 the value obtained with the 180° magnet, so that larger slots can be used, with consequent gain in efficiency.

3.6.4 Fractional-slot windings

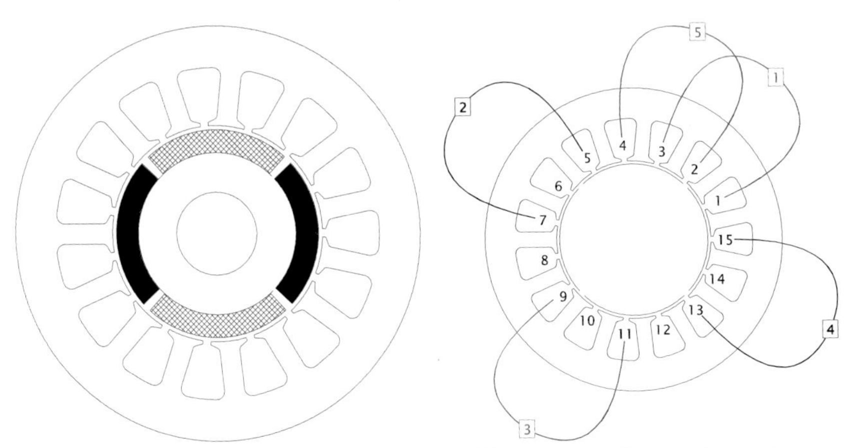

Fig. 3.40 15-slot 4-pole motor

Fig. 3.41 15-slot 4-pole winding

A *fractional-slot* winding is used when the stator has a non-integral number of slots per pole. The example in Figs. 3.40 and 3.41 is of a 3-phase 4-pole motor with 15 slots. The slots/pole is 3·75 and there is no winding with identical groups of coils disposed symmetrically with respect to the poles.

Rules for building fractional-slot windings are less regular, and possibly more ingenious than those for integral-slot windings. No single rule produces optimum windings for all slot/pole ratios, but the following procedure gives good results for double-layer windings.

3.6.4.1 A rule and two examples

Find the maximum coil-span σ_{max} as the next integer less than the slots/pole, in this case Int(15/4) − 1 = 3, in accordance with Table 3.6 on p. 86. σ_{max} is an integral number of slot-pitches, and the remainder ε is a fractional number of slot-pitches between 0 and 1: thus

$$\frac{S}{2p} = \sigma_{max} + \varepsilon \tag{3.16}$$

For the 15/4 motor, $\varepsilon = 0{\cdot}75$. The actual coil-span used can be less than 3 slots, and in the example Fig. 3.41 the coil-span is $\sigma = 2$ slots.

The first coil in Fig. 3.41 is wound in slots 1 & 3, so the position of its axis can be characterized as (1 + 3)/2 = 2, i.e. 2 slot-pitches from the origin (the x-axis), or aligned with the centreline of slot 2.

The rule for locating subsequent coils is expressed in terms of S_F, that is, the number of *slots forward* from the "return" coilside of the previous coil to the "go" coilside of the next coil to be inserted. The value of S_F is given by

$$S_F = \begin{cases} \sigma_{max} + 1, & \text{if } \varepsilon > 0.5 \\ S_1 - \sigma_{max}, & \text{if } \varepsilon < 0.5 \end{cases} \tag{3.17}$$

where S_1 is the number of slots per *section*. The winding is divided into sections if the number of coils per phase C is divisible by the number of pole-pairs p. The total number of sections N_S is equal to the highest common factor of C and pole-pairs p, and

$$S_1 = \frac{S}{N_S} = \frac{\text{Slots}}{\text{HCF}[C,p]}. \tag{3.18}$$

The rule expressed by eqns. (3.17) and (3.18) tends to minimize the build-up of *phase displacement* between successive coils. When $S_F = \sigma_{max} + 1$ the winding is said to be *progressive*, in the sense that successive coils follow one another in the positive (anticlockwise) direction. When $S_F = S_1 - \sigma_{max}$, the winding is *retrogressive* in the sense that successive coils follow one another in the negative (clockwise) direction.

In Fig. 3.41 a double-layer winding will have 15/3 = 5 coils per phase, so $C = 5$. With 4 poles $p = 2$ and since HCF (15,4) = 1 there is only one *section* : $N_S = 1$. Hence the number of slots per section is $S_1 = 15/1 = 15$, and with $\sigma_{max} = 3$ and $\varepsilon = 0{\cdot}75 > 0.5$, $S_F = 3 + 1 =$ 4 slots. Since the "return" coilside of coil 1 is in slot 3, the "go" coilside of coil 2 will be in slot 3 + 4 = 7. The polarity of successive coils is alternated so that coil 2 has a span of −2 rather than +2, and its "return" coilside is therefore in slot 7 − 2 = 5. Note that the axis of coil 2 is at (7 + 5)/2 = 6, and this is 4 slots further on than the axis of coil 1. Since the pole-pitch is 3·75 slots, the axis of coil 2 is displaced 1/4 of a slot clockwise from the position it would need to have in order for the EMFs in coils 1 and 2 to be in phase. It can be said that the phase displacement between coil 2 and coil 1 is +1/4 slot. This does not sound much, but in electrical degrees 1 slot is equivalent to $1/15 \times 2 \times 360 = 48°$, so the phase displacement of coil 2 is 12° relative to coil 1.

Proceeding with the winding, coil 3 is in slots (5 + 4) = 9 and (9 + 2) = 11. Its axis is at (9 + 11)/2 = 10, that is, 8 slot-pitches further on than the axis of coil 1. The nearest integral number of pole-pitches from the axis of phase 1 is at 7·5 slot-pitches from the axis of phase 1, and therefore coil 3 has a phase displacement of 1/2 slot or 24° relative to coil 1.

The winding can be completed by continuing in the same fashion: coil 4 is in slots 15 & 13 with a phase displacement of 36°, and coil 5 is in slots 2 & 4 with a phase displacement of 48° or one complete slot. The resulting coil list is summarized in Table 3.9. (See p. 123).

Coil No.	Turns	Go slot	Return slot	Span
1	12	1	3	2
2	12	7	5	-2
3	12	9	11	2
4	12	15	13	-2
5	12	2	4	2

TABLE 3.9 COIL LIST FOR 3-PHASE 15-SLOT 4-POLE MOTOR

The phase displacement accumulates in a regular fashion from each coil to the next, producing the same effect as in a distributed lap winding. There is therefore no difficulty developing appropriate winding factors for windings built by this procedure.

If the number of sections N_S is greater than 1, the winding algorithm expressed in eqns. (3.17) and (3.18) is applied only until one *sequence* of coils is completed. The first *sequence* is the first C/N_S coils generated by the winding algorithm, and these do not necessarily belong in the same *section*. A sequence is a logical grouping of coils, whereas a section is a physical sector of the stator.

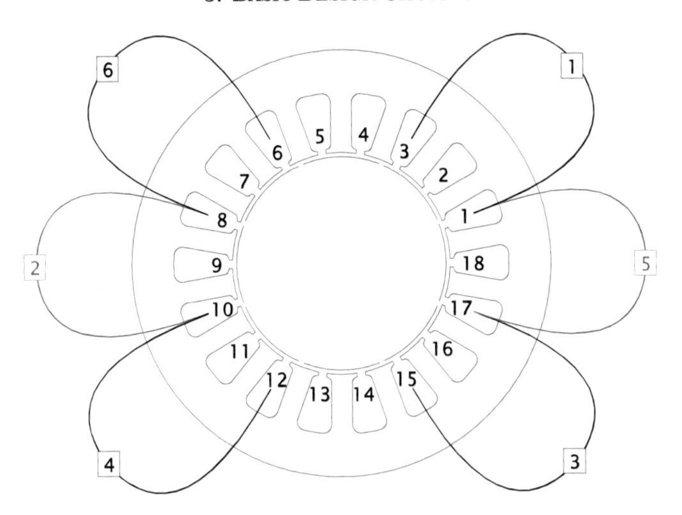

Fig. 3.42 18-slot 8-pole fractional-slot winding with 2 sections

The second example should make this more clear. The 3-phase motor in Fig. 3.42 has $S = 18$ slots and $2p = 8$ poles, so $C = 18/3 = 6$ coils per phase. With $p = 4$, the highest common factor of C and p is 2, and therefore there will be $N_S = \text{HCF}(6,4) = 2$ sections *and* two sequences, each containing 3 coils. Each section will have 4 poles and $S_1 = 9$ slots.

The number of slots/pole is $18/8 = 2{\cdot}25$, so $\sigma_{max} = 2$ and $\varepsilon = 0{\cdot}25 < 0{\cdot}5$. Therefore, from equation (3.11), $S_F = S_1 - \sigma_{max} = 9 - 2 = 7$. These parameters define the winding pattern shown in Fig. 3.42 for the first three coils only, forming the first sequence. Thus coil 1 in slots 1 & 3 is followed by coil 2 in slots $(3 + 7) = 10$ and $(10 - 2) = 8$, and the first sequence is completed by coil 3 in slots $(8 + 7) = 15$ and $15 + 2 = 17$.

The second sequence is obtained by copying the first sequence coilside-for-coilside, S_1 slots further on. Thus coil 1 is copied to coil 4, 9 slots further on in slots $(1 + 9) = 10$ and $(3 + 9) = 12$. Coil 5 is a copy of coil 2 in slots $(10 + 9) = 19 \bmod 18 = 1$ and $(8 + 9) = 17$, and coil 6 is a copy of coil 3 in slots $(15 + 9) = 24 \bmod 18 = 6$ and $(17 + 9) = 26 \bmod 18 = 8$. This naturally produces a winding in two sections, the first containing the odd-numbered coils 1,3 and 5 and the second the even-numbered coils 2,4 and 6.

Coil No	Turns	Go slot	Return slot	Span
1	12	1	3	2
2	12	10	8	-2
3	12	15	17	2
4	12	10	12	2
5	12	1	17	-2
6	12	6	8	2

TABLE 3.10 THEORETICAL COIL LIST FOR 18-SLOTS 8-POLE MOTOR

The resulting coil list is summarized in Table 3.10, with the two coil sequences separated by a double line.

The axis of coil 1 is at slot $(1 + 3)/2 = 2$ and the axis of coil 2 is at slot $(10 + 8)/2 = 9$, i.e. displaced from the axis of coil 1 by 7 slots. With 2·25 slots/pole the nearest integer number of pole-pitches subtending an arc close to 7 slots is 3, i.e. $3 \times 2{\cdot}25 = 6{\cdot}75$ slots. Therefore the phase displacement between coil 2 and coil 1 is 0·25 slots or $0{\cdot}25/18 \times 4 \times 360 = 20^\circ$ elec. With reference to the theory given later, Fig. 3.47, the effective distribution factor of this winding for the fundamental is $k_{d1} = \sin(3 \times 20/2)/3 \sin(20/2) = 0{\cdot}960$. The 5th-harmonic distribution factor is $k_{d5} = \sin(5 \times 3 \times 20/2)/3 \sin(5 \times 20/2) = 0{\cdot}218$. The fundamental pitch factor (see below) is $k_{p1} = \cos(\varepsilon/2)$ and with $\varepsilon = 0{\cdot}25$ slots $= 20^\circ$ elec, $k_{p1} = 0{\cdot}985$. Similarly $k_{p5} = \cos(5 \times 20/2^\circ) = 0{\cdot}643$. Thus the overall winding factors are $k_{w1} = k_{d1}k_{p1} = 0{\cdot}946$ for the fundamental, and $k_{w5} = k_{d5}k_{p5} = 0{\cdot}140$ for the 5th harmonic, suggesting the possibility of a fairly good sinewave back-EMF, as can be seen in Fig. 3.44. The winding factors for higher-order harmonics can be worked out in a similar manner.

Note that this winding has a non-zero third-harmonic winding factor, so it should not be connected in delta. The same is true of the 15/4 winding in Fig. 3.41.

The winding algorithm expressed by eqns. (3.17) and (3.18) works equally well for integral-slot windings, the number of sections being generally equal to the number of pole-pairs.

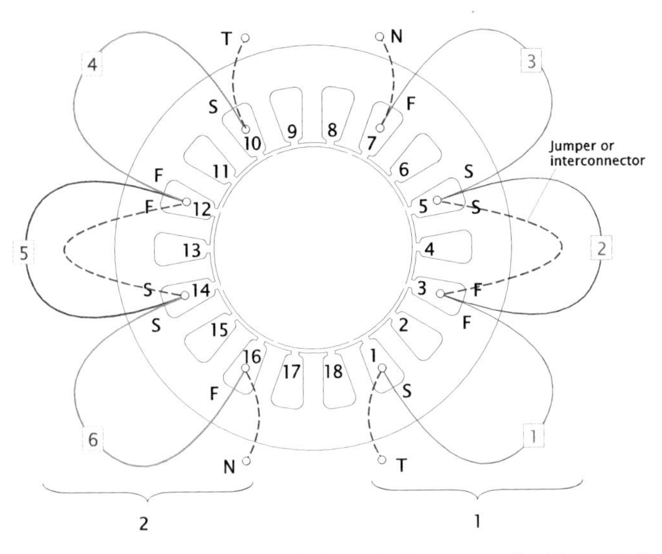

Fig. 3.43 18-slot 8-pole fractional-slot winding : practical layout diagram

Coil No	Turns	Go slot	Return slot	Span
1	12	1	3	2
2	12	3	3	-2
3	12	5	7	2
4	12	10	12	2
5	12	14	12	-2
6	12	14	16	2

TABLE 3.11 PRACTICAL COIL LIST FOR 18-SLOTS 8-POLE MOTOR

Practical considerations — The winding layout shown in Fig. 3.42 and Table 3.10 comes straight from the coil-placement algorithm which is based on the purely "electrical" placement of the coils without regard to the practicalities of winding. Fig. 3.43 and Table 3.11 go some way towards a more practical representation by numbering and grouping the coils as they would be wound. Fig. 3.43 also shows the interconnectors needed to reverse the polarity of the middle coil in each section, as well as the completely separate sections 1 and 2 that can be connected in parallel or series.

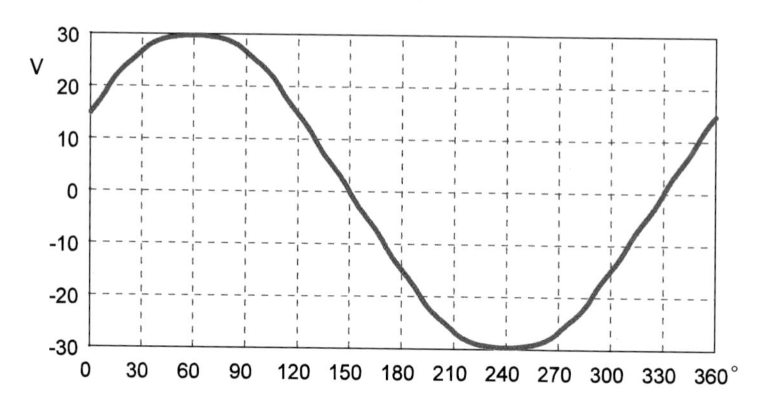

Fig. 3.44 EMF of winding of Fig. 3.42 with 18 slots and 8 poles

3.6.4.2 The 12/10 motor; alternative windings

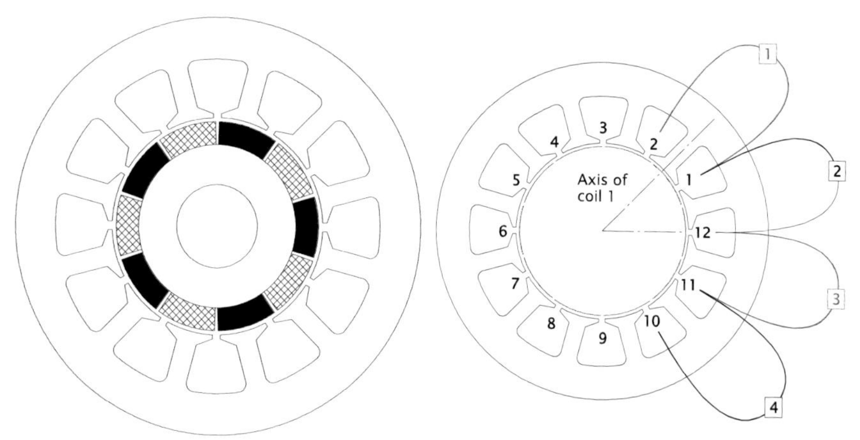

Fig. 3.45 12-slot 10-pole motor

Fig. 3.46 15-slot 4-pole winding

Fig. 3.45 shows a 12-slot 10-pole motor; that is, $S = 12, p = 5$. The winding in Fig. 3.46 was generated using the algorithm in the previous section, as follows. With $S/2p = 1{\cdot}2$ we have $\sigma_{max} = 1$ and $\varepsilon = 0{\cdot}2$. For a double-layer 3-phase winding there will be 12 coils and $12/3 = 4$ coils per phase, so $C = 4$. With $p = 5$ the number of sections $N_S = \text{HCF}(4,5) = 1$. The number of slots per section is $S_1 = S/N_S = 12$, and from eqn. (3.17) the *slots forward* is $S_F = 12 - 1 = 11$.

Coil No.	Turns	Go slot	Return slot	Span
1	12	1	2	1
2	12	1	12	-1
3	12	11	12	2
4	12	1	12	-2

TABLE 3.12 COIL LIST FOR 3-PHASE 12-SLOT 10-POLE MOTOR

This is an example of a retrogressive winding pattern. Coil 1 goes in slot 1 and returns in slot 2, with a span of 1. Coil 2 goes in slot 2 + S_F = 1 + 11 = 13 which is the same as slot 1. It returns in slot 1 − σ_{max} = 1 − 1 = 0 which is the same as slot 12. Note that the polarity is reversed compared with coil 1. Coil 3 goes in slot 12 + S_F = 12 + 11 = 23 which is the same as slot 11; it returns in slot 11 + σ_{max} = 11 + 1 = 12. Finally coil 4 goes in slot 12 + S_F = 12 + 11 = 23 which again is the same as slot 11; it returns in slot 11 − 1 = 10. The coil list is summarized in Table 3.12; all coils have 12 turns.

The axis of coil 1 is at the centre of tooth 1 between slots 1 and 2; i.e., $\alpha_1 = 1½ \times 360/S \times p = 225°$ elec from the x-axis. The axis of coil 2 is at the centre of tooth 12, between slots 12 and 1, giving $\alpha_2 = ½ \times 30p = 75°$ elec from the x-axis; but because of the reverse polarity relative to that of coil 1, α_2 should be taken as 75 + 180 = 255° elec or 75 − 180 = −105° elec. from the x-axis. The phase shift between coils 1 and 2 for the fundamental space-harmonic is therefore 255 − 225 = 30°, or −105 −(225) = −330°, which is the same. In this way a diagram of coil axes builds up for the whole phase winding, Fig. 3.47. Correctly scaled, this diagram represents the coil EMF phasors.

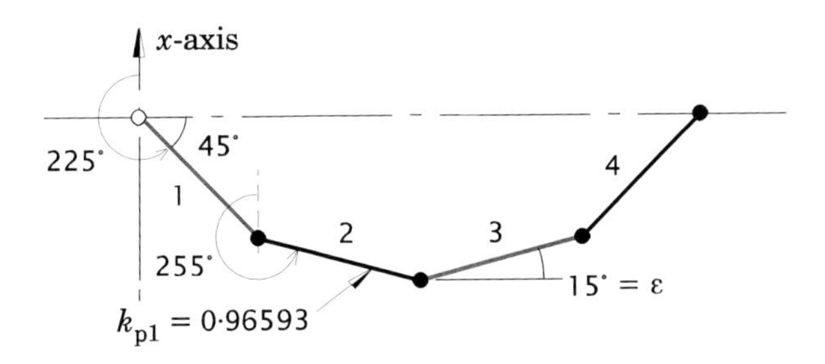

Fig. 3.47 EMF diagram for one phase of the winding in Fig. 3.46

We can calculate the fundamental winding factor from Fig. 3.47. First, the distribution factor k_{d1} is given by the ratio of the resultant chord to the arithmetic sum of the individual elements, and this is

$$k_{d1} = \frac{2 \times \cos 45° + 2 \times 15°}{4} = 0{\cdot}83652 \tag{3.19}$$

The span of each coil is 1 slot-pitch, so the pitch is 360/12 × 5 = 150° elec., and the pitch factor is sin 150°/2 = cos (ε/2) = 0·96593. The overall winding factor is $k_{w1} = k_{p1} k_{d1} = 0{\cdot}96593 \times 0{\cdot}83652 = 0{\cdot}80801$.

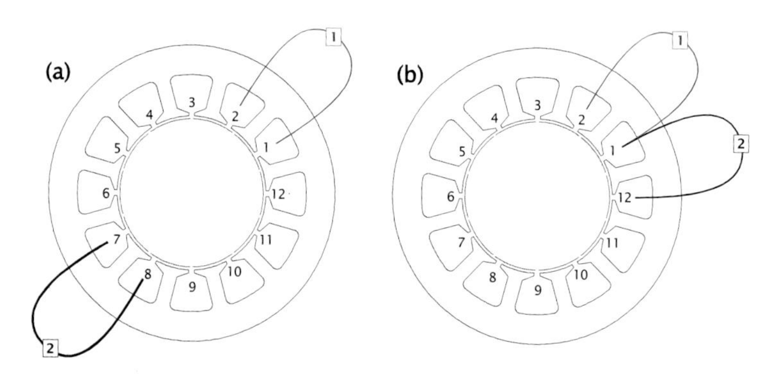

Fig. 3.48 12-slot 10-pole winding (single-layer)

Coil No.	Turns	Go slot	Return slot	Span
1	12	1	2	1
2	12	8	7	-1

TABLE 3.13 COIL LIST FOR 3-PHASE 12-SLOT 10-POLE MOTOR (a)

A better winding factor is achieved with the single-layer windings shown in Fig. 3.48. Winding (a) can be obtained from Fig. 3.46 by deleting coils 2,3 and 4, and inserting a copy of coil 1 diametrically opposite, but with reversed polarity because of the odd number of pole-pairs, giving the coil list in Table 3.13. The EMFs of coils 1 and 2 are in phase, so the winding factor is the same as the pitch factor, Fig. 3.49. Winding (b) is obtained by deleting coils 3 and 4. The EMFs of coils 1 and 2 are not in phase, so the winding factor is lower. Winding (b) also results from eqns. (3.17) and (3.18) with $C = 6$.

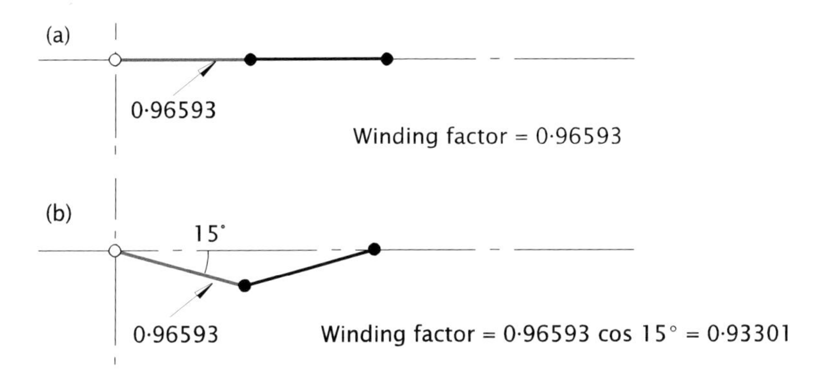

Fig. 3.49 EMF diagrams corresponding to Fig. 3.48

Where to start winding the second and third phases — In a 3-phase motor the axes of the phase windings should be displaced from one another by 120° elec. If phase 1 starts in slot 1, the start of phase 2 should be in slot 1 + *Offset*, where *Offset* is the number of slot-pitches in 2/3 of a pole-pitch, or $2/3 \times S/2p$. If this number is not an integer, it is necessary to search for alternative starts using the formula

$$Offset = \frac{2}{3} \times \frac{S}{2p} + k \times \frac{S}{p}, \qquad k = 1,2,3... \tag{3.20}$$

With integer values of k, the second term merely advances the start of phase 2 by $360k°$ elec.

For example, in the 15-slot 4-pole winding of Fig. 3.41, $S = 15$ and $2p = 4$; $2/3 \times S/2p = 5/2$ which is not an integer. But with $k = 1$ we find $2/3 \times S/2p + 1 \times 15/2 = 5/2 + 15/2 = 10$, which is a correct value. In the 18-slot 8-pole motor of Fig. 3.42, $S = 18$ and $2p = 8$, so $2/3 \times S/2p = 3/2$ which is not an integer. But with $k = 1$ we find $2/3 \times S/2p + 1 \times 18/4 = 3/2 + 9/2 = 6$, which is a correct value.

If no integral value of *Offset* can be found from eqn. (3.20), it is impossible to wind a balanced three-phase winding in the given number of slots and poles. For example, with 15 slots and 6 poles *Offset* is nonintegral for all integer values of k. Very occasionally a motor will be manufactured with a slightly incorrect *Offset* to make do with an existing lamination. This is risky and is not advised.

3.6.4.3 Pitch factor

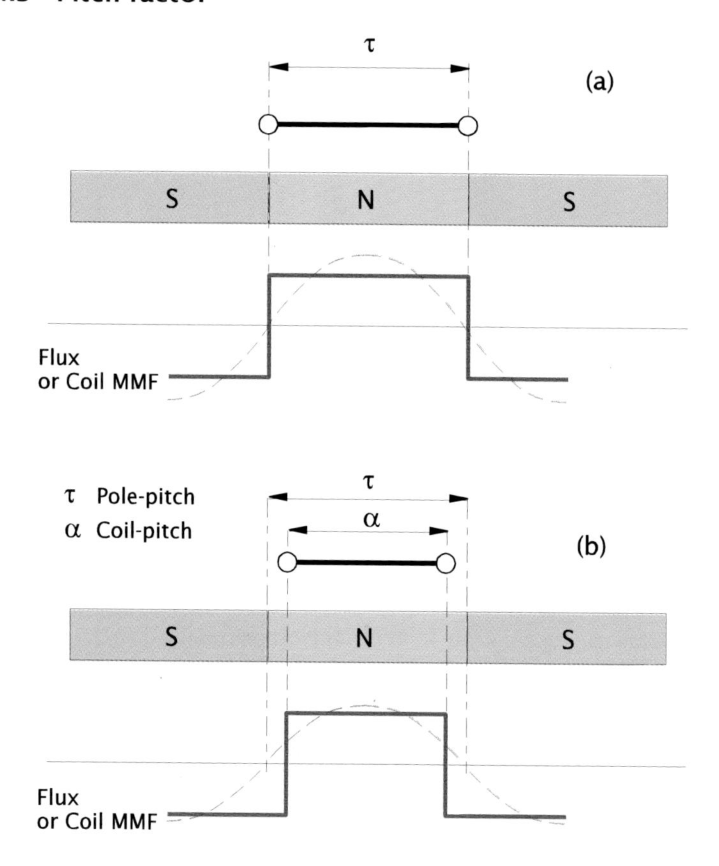

Fig. 3.50 Pitch factor

Fig. 3.50(a) shows a full-pitch coil and an array of full-pitch magnets which are included to define the pole-pitch: each magnet spans exactly 180° elec. The coil has a span $\tau = 180°$ and produces the MMF distribution shown by the solid line. The fundamental of this MMF wave is shown by the dashed line; by the well-known Fourier analysis of a square wave, its amplitude is $4/\pi$ times the amplitude of the rectangular wave.

The basic idea of "pitch factor" is to measure the effectiveness of a coil or winding in producing or linking flux, relative to that of a "full-pitch" coil. The fundamental pitch factor of a coil is the ratio

$$k_{p1} = \frac{\text{Fund. MMF produced by coil}}{\text{Fund. MMF produced by full–pitch coil}} \tag{3.21}$$

This definition can be shown to be identical to

$$k_{p1} = \frac{\text{Fund. flux linked by coil}}{\text{Fund. flux linked by a full–pitch coil}} \tag{3.22}$$

Fig. 3.50(b) shows a *short-pitched* coil having a span $\alpha < \tau$, together with its MMF and the fundamental component of MMF. The fundamental pitch factor is

$$k_{p1} = \frac{\int_{-\alpha/2}^{\alpha/2} 1 \cdot \cos\,\theta d\theta}{\int_{-\tau/2}^{\tau/2} 1 \cdot \cos\,\theta d\theta} = \sin\frac{\alpha}{2}. \tag{3.23}$$

For example, a coil with a span of $\alpha = 150°$ has a fundamental pitch factor $k_{p1} = \sin 75° = 0{\cdot}966$. We have already seen an example on p. 113.

The pitch factor can be extended to include harmonics. For the n'th harmonic we have

$$k_{pn} = \frac{\int_{-\alpha/2}^{\alpha/2} 1 \cdot \cos\,n\theta d\theta}{\int_{-\tau/2}^{\tau/2} 1 \cdot \cos\,n\theta d\theta} = \sin\frac{n\alpha}{2}. \tag{3.24}$$

Note that $k_{pn} = 0$ if $n\alpha/2 = 180k°$, where k is an integer. For example, if $\alpha = 144°$ and $n = 5$, $k_{p5} = 0$. A coil with a pitch of $(1 - 1/5) \times 180° = 144°$ produces no 5th harmonic MMF and no 5th harmonic flux; it also links no 5th harmonic flux produced by the magnet. Similarly a coil with a span of $(1 - 1/3) \times 180° = 120°$ produces no 3rd harmonic MMF and links no 3rd harmonic flux.

For a winding made up of many coils, the *winding factor* for any harmonic can be computed as the weighted sum of the pitch-factors of the individual coils, taking into account the direction of the MMF axis of each coil: thus with coils of N_1, N_2, ...turns with spans α_1, α_2, ... oriented at angles ϕ_1, ϕ_2, ... relative to a reference axis,

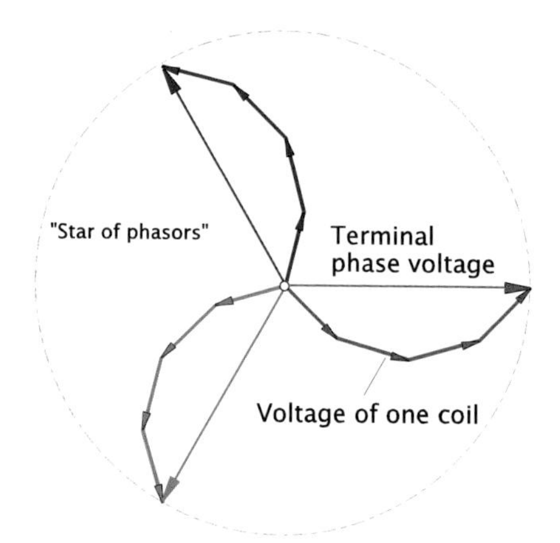

Fig. 3.51 Addition of coil MMFs or EMFs, showing the composition of the winding factor for any harmonic. (Simplified Görges diagram)

$$k_{pn} = \frac{N_1 \sin n\alpha_1 \cos n\phi_1 + N_2 \sin n\alpha_2 \cos n\phi_2 + \ldots}{N_1 + N_2 + \ldots} \tag{3.25}$$

The denominator of this expression represents the pitch-factor that would result if all the coils had a span of 180° and were aligned with the same MMF axis. Fig. 3.51 shows the addition of harmonic MMFs (or EMFs) in a winding of this type, having three phases.

3.6.4.4 Sinewave and squarewave motors

With squarewave motors it seems logical to design the winding to maximize the winding factors for all harmonics — in other words, to make the winding behave as nearly as possible to a full-pitch winding with coilsides concentrated exactly at intervals of 180° elec. With sinewave motors, on the other hand, it seems logical to design the winding to maximize the fundamental winding factor and, as far as possible, to minimize the winding factors for all other harmonics. In both cases, practicalities interfere with the idealized objectives.

In the case of sinewave machines, the most rigorous way to eliminate all the harmonic winding factors except the fundamental would be to design a winding with a perfectly sinusoidal distribution of conductors. This cannot be contemplated, since it would need an infinite number of slots filled with infinitesimally small conductors.

A satisfactory practical arrangement is to design for relatively small 5th and 7th harmonic winding factors, while leaving the 3rd harmonic to be suppressed by a 3-wire star connection. Although this is far from the perfect winding, the back EMF will be nearly sinusoidal if the rotor is designed with low flux harmonics, such as, for example, with a profiled rotor surface or a Halbach-type magnet. Higher-order harmonics are often ignored on the basis that their magnitudes decrease with increasing harmonic order, although we must be careful with that idea because the EMF ripple resulting from flux harmonics is amplified by differentiation (Faraday's Law) in proportional to the harmonic order.

Harmonic components of MMF contribute to the so-called differential leakage inductance, which will be analyzed in Chapter 5. In some cases it may be desirable to design for a higher inductance, in which case the combination of a winding with high MMF harmonics with a sinusoidally-magnetized rotor will produce a sinusoidal EMF yet have a relatively high inductance.

3.6.5 Irregular slotting

In recent years there has been much interest in motors with a small number of slots/pole having single-layer windings and even **irregular slotting** to maximize the winding factor at the same time as reducing cost by minimizing the number of coils.[9] An example is shown in Fig. 3.52, in which almost all the magnet flux passes through the tooth at the centre. A coil wound around this tooth links 100% of the magnet flux, so by definition its winding factor is unity. Only the wide teeth are wound, giving a single-layer winding. The narrow teeth serve merely to help in providing a flux-return path.

At first sight it is not obvious how the tooth-arcs and other proportions in Fig. 3.52 are determined, but there is a systematic procedure. Consider Fig. 3.53 in which the wide tooth-arc is $m\sigma$ and the "auxiliary" tooth-arc is $a\sigma$, σ being the slot-pitch. The effective "collecting" arc of the wide tooth is approximately equal to $(1 + m - a)\sigma/2$, and the idea is to make this equal to the pole-pitch.

[9] See Koch Th. and Binder A., *Permanent Magnet Machines with Fractional Slot Winding For Electric Traction*, International Conference on Electric Machines, Brugge, Belgium, 2002.

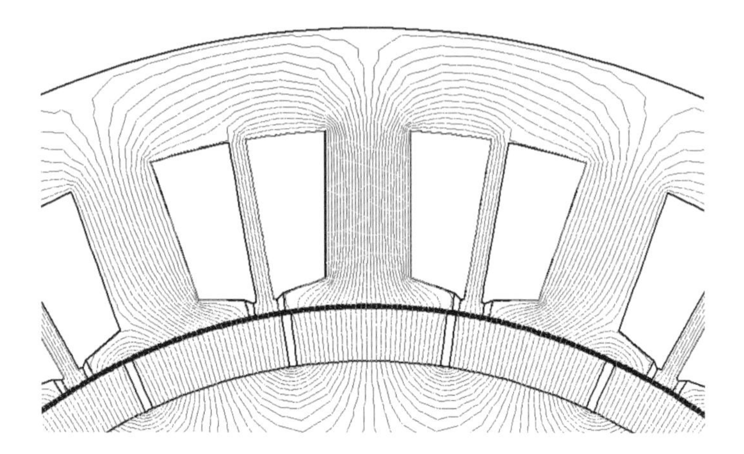

Fig. 3.52 Irregular slotting used to increase the winding factor

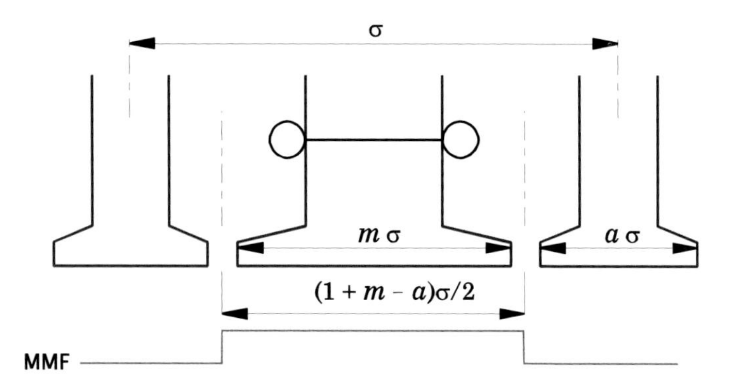

Fig. 3.53 Irregular slotting

For example, in an 18-slot 22-pole machine, $\sigma = 360/18 = 20^\circ$ while the pole-pitch is $\tau = 360/22 = 16{\cdot}364^\circ$. Therefore we need $(1 + m - a) \times 20/2 = 16{\cdot}364$, which implies that $m - a = 0{\cdot}636$. Only the difference between m and a is controlled by this requirement. Another constraint is required to define them separately, and this comes from the slot-opening. Suppose the slot-opening is $y\sigma$; then in general we have $(m + a + 2y) = 1$. In the example, if $y = 0{\cdot}1$, we get $m = 0{\cdot}7182$ and $a = 0{\cdot}0818$. The resulting tooth-arcs are $14{\cdot}36^\circ$ and $1{\cdot}636^\circ$, making a ratio of $8{\cdot}778$.

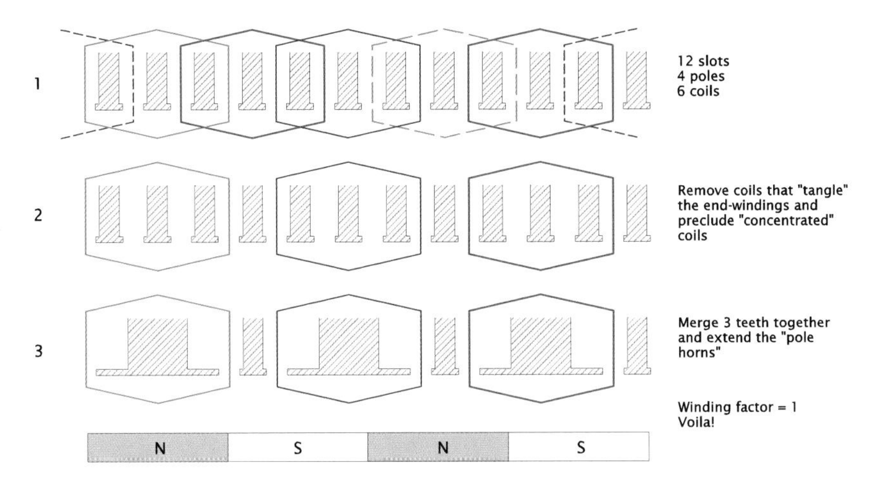

Fig. 3.54 Systematic development of irregular slotting (Cros & Viarouge)

The subject of irregular slotting was systematically expounded in more general terms by Cros and Viarouge, who gave the example shown in Fig. 3.54, showing the steps involved in reducing the number of coils and determining the basic relationships between the widths of wound and unwound teeth. Cros and Viarouge extended the concept to cases with as many as three different tooth-arcs.[10]

3.6.6 Systematic analysis of slot/pole ratio and windings

The advantages of concentrated windings with relatively high pole numbers, with regular or irregular slotting, are not limited to the possibility of a high winding factor. All such windings, with coils wound around single teeth, have short end-windings, and this is an advantage in minimizing the cost, the overall length, the winding resistance and therefore the losses. Since the end-windings do not overlap one another, the probability of a phase-to-phase fault is reduced, and so there is an advantage in reliability. Winding the coils on alternate teeth has the advantage of reducing the number of coils, and it also tends to isolate the coils from one another magnetically and thermally, suggesting the possibility of fault tolerance.

---

[10] Cros J. and Viarouge P., *Synthesis of High Performance PM Motors with Concentrated Windings*, IEEE Transactions on Energy Conversion, Vol. 17, No. 2, June 2002, pp. 248-253.

The term **modular winding** was used by Ishak, Zhu and Howe[11] to describe a winding with coils wound on alternate teeth, as in Figs. 3.53 and 3.54. The phase self-inductance can be increased by designing the slot-opening to give a high slot-permeance coefficient, and the differential (harmonic) leakage inductance can also be high (depending on the slot/pole ratio). Consequently these machines have a low short-circuit current and good flux-weakening properties.

A further advantage of a fractional slot/pole ratio is the **reduction of cogging torque**. The cogging-torque frequency is a multiple of the rotational speed, and increases in proportion to the least common multiple of the slots and poles, LCM(S,2p); see Table 3.14.

This table is a useful starting-point when surveying the complex subject of slot/pole ratios. Initially it serves as a guide to the choice of slot/pole ratio in terms of the cogging torque that would be obtained even before the windings have been determined. One can say that a satisfactory machine cannot be obtained *unless* a suitable slot/pole ratio has been selected to minimize the cogging torque. This is particularly true when the application requires low cogging, as is frequently the case. When using single-tooth coils with a slot/pole ratio close to 1, it is not satisfactory to dismiss the cogging torque on the grounds that skew will remove it. The skew required to remove it is 1 slot-pitch, and with 1·2 slots/pole, for example, that gives a fundamental skew factor of

$$k_{\sigma 1} = \frac{\sin \frac{5}{6} \times \frac{\pi}{2}}{\frac{5}{6} \times \frac{\pi}{2}} = 0{\cdot}738. \qquad (3.26)$$

The resulting 26·2% loss of EMF is more than enough to negate the high pitch factor of the concentrated winding.

Table 3.14 is compiled for pole-numbers 2p from 2 to 26, and for slot-numbers from 3 to 30. Only slot-numbers divisible by 3 are considered, restricting the table to balanced 3-phase machines.

[11] Ishak D., Zhu Z.Q.. and Howe D., *Permanent-Magnet Brushless Machines with Unequal Tooth Widths and Similar Slot and Pole Numbers*, IEEE Transactions on Industry Applications, Vol. 41, No. 2, March/April 2005, pp. 584-590.

	No. of poles, $2p$												
S	2	4	6	8	10	12	14	16	18	20	22	24	26
3	6	12											
6	*6*	12		24	30								
9	*18*	*36*	18	*72*	*90*	36	126	144					
12	*12*	*12*	~~*12*~~	24	60		84	48	~~36~~	60	132		
15	*30*	*60*	~~*30*~~	*120*	30	~~60~~	210	240	~~90~~	60	330	~~120~~	390
18	*18*	*36*	*18*	*72*	*90*	36	126	144		180	198	72	234
21	*42*	*84*	~~*42*~~	*168*	*210*	~~*84*~~	42	336	~~126~~	420	462	~~168~~	546
24	*24*	*24*	~~*24*~~	*24*	*120*	~~*24*~~	*168*	48	~~72~~	120	264		312
27	*54*	*108*	*54*	*216*	*270*	*108*	*378*	*432*	54	540	594	216	702
30	*30*	*60*	~~*30*~~	*120*	*30*	~~*60*~~	*210*	*240*	~~*270*~~	60	330	~~120~~	390

TABLE 3.14 LEAST COMMON MULTIPLE OF SLOTS AND POLES

It is helpful to line up the cases with slots/pole = 1·5, such as 3s2p, 9s6p, 12s8p, ..., where the abbreviation 12s8p means 12 slots and 8 poles (not 16 poles), etc. Not only is the "1·5 family" historically important;[12] it also represents, more or less definitively, the highest slot/pole ratio for which single-tooth windings would normally be considered.

Combinations below the "1·5 line" are more likely to be wound with a winding pitch greater than 1, following the guideline in Table 3.6 on p. 86; these are marked italic. Some of them have been considered already: for example, 36s6p on p. 112, the 36s12p on p. 115, the 12s2p on p. 116, the 15s4p on p. 118, and the 18s8p on p. 121, and no further discussion of them will be found in this section.

For any given number of slots, it appears that as we move to the right of the "1·5 line" the LCM increases. This suggests that the motors on the "1·5 line" have the lowest cogging-torque frequency of any feasible motor with that slot-number. It is likely, though not certain, that these motors will have the highest cogging torque.

[12] See Croft T., *Alternating-Current Armature Winding*, McGraw-Hill, New York, 1924, p. 37. Also von der Heide *et al*, U.S. Patent No. Re. 36,168, March 30, 1999 and No. 5,652,470, July 29, 1997.

As we move further to the right of the "1·5 line", the slot/pole ratio decreases until it falls to 0·5, which is impractically low for the reason explained on p. 84.

The 12-slot machine is an instructive example, not only because 12-slot machines are quite popular in products and in the technical literature, but also because it forms a starting point for designing machines with much larger numbers of slots. The 12s8p has an LCM of 24 cogging-torque cycles per revolution, and the winding pitch of a single-tooth coil is 120°elec, giving a pitch factor of 0·866; this pitch factor is normally also the winding factor of the entire winding. The 12s10p, on the other hand, has 60 cogs/rev, and a single-tooth coil has a pitch-factor of 0·966; the winding factor of the whole winding can then be as high as 0·933 as we saw in Fig. 3.49 on p. 127.

The 12s14p can use the same winding Fig. 3.48 on p. 126, and it has the same winding factors.[13] With 84 cogs/rev it would be expected to have lower cogging torque. Whether or not it is "better" than the 12s10p is not at all obvious from these considerations, because many other factors must be taken into account.

We can perhaps summarise the argument so far by saying that motors to the right of the "1·5 line" can be expected to have lower cogging torque and higher winding factors. Moving too far to the right results in a reduction in the winding factor, not only because of the reduction in the coil-span relative to the pole arc, but also because of the increase in tooth-tip leakage (also known sometimes as zig-zag leakage). Combinations with slot/pole ratios 0·5 or less are therefore blanked out in Table 3.14.

Cells with a diagonal bar indicate combinations where S and $2p$ have no common factor. They all have a relatively high value of cogs/rev but there is no symmetry — no repetition of the slot/pole pattern — and this can lead to an unbalanced radial force and noisy operation, even though the cogging torque may be very low. The 9s8p motor is an interesting example, manufactured in large numbers for computer disc drives.

---

[13] This arises from the identity $\sin(\pi/2 + \varepsilon) = \sin(\pi/2 - \varepsilon)$; see eqn. (23) on p. 129. The single-tooth coil in the 12s14p motor is over-pitched by the same amount $\varepsilon = 30°$ elec. as it is under-pitched in the 12s10p.

Unbalanced radial force is not the only "mechanical" concern.[14] Motors with different slot/pole combinations vary significantly in their sensitivity to eccentricity or run-out.[15] For example, the 9s8p might have a lower value of detent torque (cogging torque) than other slot/pole combinations when the rotor is exactly centred, but a greater rate of increase with eccentricity.

The cogging-torque frequency is closely correlated with the production of rotor losses, even on open-circuit. This is discussed further in Chapter 12.

Windings — so far in this section, almost the entire discussion has been about the motor without any windings. Supposing that we have a well-chosen slot/pole combination, the task of finding a suitable winding can begin.

We have already seen in §3.6.4 examples of fractional-slot windings, with one or two simple algorithms for formulating the process of laying out the winding. Here we will confine our discussion to a few important points not covered in earlier sections.[16]

In order to achieve a balanced 3-phase winding the slots can be considered to be divided into $3n$ repeating segments, each of which must contain an integer number of slots *and* poles: thus

$$\frac{S}{3n} = \mathrm{HCF}(S, 2p). \tag{3.27}$$

---

[14] Magnussen F. and Lendenmann H., *Parasitic effects in PM machines With Concentrated Windings*, Transactions IEEE, Vol. 43, No. 5, September/October 2007, pp. 1123-1232.

[15] See Cassat A. and Williams M.W., *Eccentricity Analysis in Brushless DC Motors*, Proceedings of the 23rd Annual Symposium, Incremental Motion Control Systems and Devices, 14 June 1994, pp. 201-216. Also Williams M.W. and MacLeod D.J., *Performance Characteristics of Brushless Motor Slot/Pole Configurations*, *ibid.*, pp. 145-153.

[16] Much more complex algorithms are known, and the scope for custom windings is almost unlimited. See Cros and Viarouge, *op. cit.*; also Libert F. and Soulard J., *Investigation of the Pole-Slot Combinations for Permanent-Magnet Machines with Concentrated Windings*, International Conference on Electrical Machines, September 2004; also Magnussen F. and Sadarangani C., *Winding Factors and Joule Losses of Permanent Magnet Machines with Concentrated Windings*, Proceedings IEMDC Conference , Madison, WI, June 1-4, 2003, pp. 333-339.

	No. of poles, $2p$												
S	2	4	6	8	10	12	14	16	18	20	22	24	26
3	·866												
6		·866											
9			·866										
12				·866	·933		·933						
15					·866								
18						·866	·902	·945		·945	·902		
21							·866						
24								·866		·933	·950		·950
27									·866		·915	·945	·954
30										·866			·936

TABLE 3.15 WINDING FACTORS OF "PROMISING" SLOT/POLE COMBINATIONS

This requirement excludes some of the slot/pole combinations in Table 3.14. Curiously the 18-pole case fails this test with almost any number of slots, the only valid result being 27 slots in the range of slot numbers that would give a concentrated winding with either one or two layers. Combinations that are precluded by failure to satisfy eqn. (3.27) are impaled on a "strikeout" line in Table 3.14.

Winding factors of windings compiled for the feasible slot/pole combinations in Table 3.14 were presented in the separate papers of Cros, Magnussen, and Libert referenced in the footnote on p. 137, with a greater range and more detail than can be presented here.

However, by way of a summary, winding factors for some of the more promising combinations are given in Table 3.15 in the green-shaded cells. The values on the "1·5 line" are all 0·866 and are included by way of reference, but all the others are greater than 0·9. The factors for the 12s10p and the 12s14p have already been developed earlier in detail, but the remaining values are quoted from Libert and Soulard, *op. cit.*

Without detracting in any way from the excellence of the cited works, it must be said that this is only the start of a performance comparison, for all the practical reasons we have studied earlier.

3.6.7 Winding resistance

3.6.7.1 Resistance calculation

The resistance of one *coil* is

$$R_{\text{coil}} = T_{\text{c}} \frac{\rho L}{n A} \tag{3.28}$$

where L is the mean turn length, T_{c} is the number of turns in the coil, A is the cross-sectional area of one strand, and n is the number of parallel strands in each conductor. If the machine has N_{c} coils per phase, connected in a parallel paths, the phase resistance is

$$R_{\text{ph}} = \frac{N_{\text{c}}}{a^2} R_{\text{coil}} \tag{3.29}$$

The number of turns in series per phase, $T_{\text{ph}} = N_{\text{c}} \times T_{\text{c}}/a$, so

$$R_{\text{ph}} = \frac{T_{\text{ph}}}{a} \frac{\rho L}{n A}. \tag{3.30}$$

Example — A phase winding has a mean turn length $L = 192$ mm and each conductor is wound with $n = 2$ strands-in-hand. The bare wire diameter is 1·4 mm. The number of turns in series per phase is $T_{\text{ph}} = 24$, and the number of parallel paths is $a = 2$. Calculate the phase resistance at 20°C.

The cross-sectional area of one strand is

$$A = \pi/4 \times (1{\cdot}4 \times 10^{-3})^2 = 1{\cdot}5394 \times 10^{-6} \text{ m}^2.$$

The resistivity of copper at 20°C is $1{\cdot}724 \times 10^{-8}$ ohm-m. Hence from eqn. (3.30) the resistance is

$$R_{\text{ph}} = \frac{24}{2} \times \frac{1{\cdot}724 \times 10^{-8} \times 192 \times 10^{-3}}{2 \times 1{\cdot}5394 \times 10^{-6}} = 0{\cdot}0129 \text{ [ohm]}$$

Practical difficulties — The length of wire is generally impossible to calculate accurately from the geometric dimensions of the motor, mainly because the shape of the end-windings is not mathematically known. For this reason it is often obtained empirically from the winding process, or from calculations on the coil-forms used to wind the coils. A further correction might be made to account for linear expansion of the length of wire, but this is unusual.

The wire (strand) diameter d can vary over the length, even from the same bale of wire; and it is liable to stretching during the winding process. Since A depends on d^2 this can lead to small but annoying uncertainties. For this reason the wire resistance is often specified (for a given wire gauge) as ohms per km or ohms per 1000ft length, effectively grouping ρ/A into a single parameter.

3.6.7.2 Relationship between resistance and copper weight

In design calculations it is important to get accurate values for both these parameters. If δ is the mass density of the wire, the ratio of resistance to copper weight is given by

$$\frac{R}{W_{\mathrm{Cu}}} = \frac{16\rho}{\delta\pi^2 d^4} \quad \text{[ohm/kg]}. \tag{3.31}$$

Since this depends on d^4, it is better to use the engineer's data for "ohms per 1000ft" and "lb per 1000ft" than the scientific formula (3.28), because it is not practical to measure d with sufficient accuracy over the entire length of wire. Even a small variation from the nominal gauge diameter d makes it impossible to calculate the resistance and the copper weight correctly at the same time.

3.6.7.3 Variation of resistance with temperature

Fig. 3.55 shows the resistivity of copper, ρ, which can be taken to vary linearly with temperature T:

$$\rho = \rho_0 [1 + \alpha(T - T_0)]. \tag{3.32}$$

As with any straight line ($y = mx + c$) we need only two parameters to define it, but eqn. (3.32) has three parameters: the reference temperature T_0, the resistivity ρ_0 at the temperature T_0, and the coefficient α. These parameters are not independent.

Evidently the slope of ρ vs. T is $m = \alpha\rho_0$, which we can get by differentiation:

$$m = \frac{d\rho}{dT} = \rho_0 \alpha. \tag{3.33}$$

The abscissa c is obtained with $y = 0$. From eqn. (3.32), with $\rho = 0$,

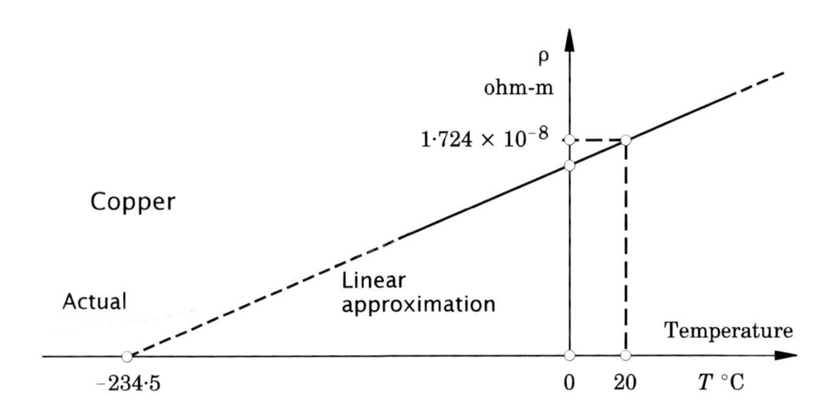

Fig. 3.55 Variation of resistivity of copper vs. temperature in °C

$$c = T_{\rho=0} = T_0 - \frac{1}{\alpha}. \tag{3.34}$$

If we know $T_{\rho=0}$ we can use this to calculate α :

$$\alpha = \frac{1}{T_0 - T_{\rho=0}}. \tag{3.35}$$

For copper, $T_{\rho=0} = -234{\cdot}5$ °C. So for example if $T_0 = 20$°C, $\alpha = 1/(20 + 234{\cdot}5) = 0{\cdot}003929$. If $T_0 = 25$°C, $\alpha = 0{\cdot}00385$. If $T_0 = 0$°C, $\alpha = 0{\cdot}00426$. These values are summarized in Table 3.16.[17]

In Fahrenheit, $T_{\rho=0} = -390$ °F, and the value of α must be recalculated from eqn. (3.35).

[17] Also note that

$$\alpha = \frac{d}{dT}\left[\frac{\rho}{\rho_0}\right] \tag{3.36}$$

This means that α is the temperature coefficient of the resistivity *ratio*, not the temperature coefficient of the resistivity itself. The resistivity ratio is the ratio of the resistivity at temperature T to the resistivity at the reference temperature. α is not independent of the reference temperature and is not a material property. However, the temperature coefficient of the resistivity itself is $\rho_0\alpha$, and this *is* a fixed property of the material: for copper it is $6{\cdot}774 \times 10^{-11}$ C^{-1}. (It can be obtained from $\rho_0 = 1{\cdot}724 \times 10^{-8}$ ohm-m at 20°C and $\alpha = 0{\cdot}003929$).

T_0 °C	ρ_0			α
	ohm-m	ohm-in	ohm-circ mil/ft	
0	$1{\cdot}589 \times 10^{-8}$	$0{\cdot}625 \times 10^{-6}$	9·56	0·00426
20	$\mathbf{1{\cdot}724 \times 10^{-8}}$	$0{\cdot}679 \times 10^{-6}$	10·37	**0·00393**
25	$1{\cdot}759 \times 10^{-8}$	$0{\cdot}693 \times 10^{-6}$	10·58	0·00385

TABLE 3.16[18]

TEMPERATURE COEFFICIENTS FOR USE WITH COPPER (TEMPERATURE IN °C)

Ratio formula — Eqn. (3.32) can be used for resistance as well as resistivity. Suppose we have a resistivity of R_1 at temperature T_1, and R_2 at temperature T_2. From eqn. (3.32),

$$\frac{R_2}{R_1} = \frac{1 + \alpha(T_2 - T_0)}{1 + \alpha(T_1 - T_0)} = \frac{(1 - \alpha T_0)/\alpha + T_2}{(1 - \alpha T_0)/\alpha + T_1}. \tag{3.36}$$

If we set $T_0 = 20$°C, then $\alpha = 0{\cdot}00393$ and $(1 - \alpha T_0)/\alpha = 234{\cdot}5$. Thus

$$\frac{R_2}{R_1} = \frac{234{\cdot}5 + T_2}{234{\cdot}5 + T_1} \quad [\mathrm{C}]. \tag{3.37}$$

This widely used formula is general, and does not depend on the choice of reference temperature T_0 or the coefficient α. If the temperatures are in Fahrenheit, 234·5 should be replaced by 390:

$$\frac{R_2}{R_1} = \frac{390 + T_2}{390 + T_1} \quad [\mathrm{F}]. \tag{3.38}$$

For example, the ratio of the resistances at 0°C and 20°C now becomes the ratio of the resistances at 32°F and 68°F, which is (390+32)/(390+68) = 0·921, the same as (234·5+0)/(234·5+20).

[18] These values are not certified or qualified. They are presented without reference to original sources, without tolerances, and with no details of the composition of the metal. In practice the resistivity of "copper" can vary approximately in the range 95–101% of what is known as international standard oxygen-free high-conductivity copper (OFHC). The boldface values Table 3.16 are used in the *SPEED* software as practical workaday engineering values.

3.6.7.4 AC resistance

It is well known that the apparent resistance of windings in AC machines increases with frequency. The effect is usually neglected in small machines below a few kW rating, but in large machines it is necessary to estimate the increase and to adopt measures to minimize it. The effect is amplified at the frequencies of PWM harmonics, so it becomes significant in inverter-fed machines of relatively small rating, even down to a few kW.

There are three separate causes of increased AC resistance: the **skin effect**, the **proximity effect**, and **circulating currents**. In general they are all active at the same time in conductors in the slots of an electrical machine. All of them increase the Joule losses in the conductors, but if all conductors carry the same current, it is possible to express the overall effect in terms of a factor K by which the winding resistance is increased over its DC value. Thus if K_s is the factor attributable to skin effect, K_p to the proximity effect, and K_c to the effect of circulating currents, we can write

$$K = K_s K_p K_c, \tag{3.39}$$

and then

$$\frac{R_{ac}}{R_{dc}} = K. \tag{3.40}$$

The Joule loss per phase is then calculated using $I^2 R_{ac}$ instead of $I^2 R_{dc}$. The additional loss due to the combination of skin-effect and proximity effect is sometimes called **strand loss**, while the additional loss due to circulating current is called **circulating current loss**.

Skin effect means the tendency of AC current to crowd into a "skin" just beneath the surface of the conductor. The redistribution of current due to skin effect is caused by the H-field *of the current in the conductor itself*. With DC the current density is uniform over the conductor cross-section, but with AC it decreases from the surface towards the centre. At high frequencies there is little current left in the centre, which could be hollowed out with no effect on the loss.

Fig. 3.56 shows the concept of skin effect in an isolated round conductor and separately in an isolated square conductor, sufficiently separated so that neither affects the other.

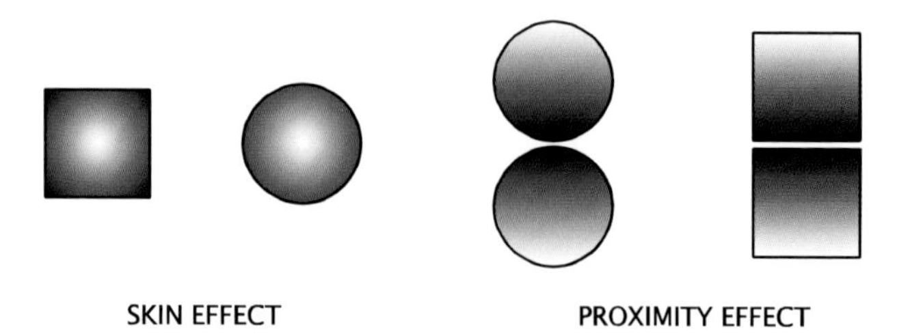

Fig. 3.56 Skin effect and proximity effect

Proximity effect is also a redistribution of current-density within a conductor, but it is caused by the H-field of *neighbouring* conductors; Fig. 3.56 shows the proximity effect between two *isolated* conductors with the currents flowing in the same direction. The redistribution is more complex in slot-conductors.

Both the skin effect and the proximity effect are governed by the so-called **skin depth**

$$\delta = \sqrt{\frac{2\rho}{\omega\mu}} = \sqrt{\frac{\rho}{\pi f \mu}}, \tag{3.41}$$

where ρ is the resistivity of the conductor, μ is its permeability, f is the frequency, and $\omega = 2\pi f$. For copper at 50 Hz at, say, 40°C,

$$\delta = \sqrt{\frac{1{\cdot}86 \times 10^{-8}}{\pi \times 50 \times 4\pi \times 10^{-7}}} = 9{\cdot}7 \text{ mm}. \tag{3.42}$$

At 5 kHz (a typical PWM frequency), $\delta = 0{\cdot}97$ mm. It is characteristic of both skin effect and proximity effect, that the redistribution of current starts to cause a significant increase in AC resistance when the skin depth is comparable to the diameter or thickness of the conductor. This explains why the AC resistance can be reduced or limited by using **stranded conductors**, in which the strand diameter is much smaller than the skin depth even though the total conductor area (made up of multiple strands) may be much larger than δ. As the strands are eventually connected together, they must be twisted to prevent redistribution of current among them. Even winding 2 or 3 "strands-in-hand" may be sufficient to limit the AC resistance; but for very high frequencies Litz wire can be used, manufactured with a large number of roved, insulated strands.

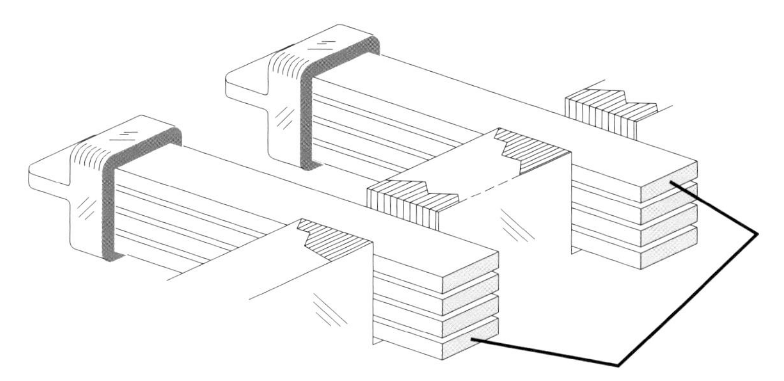

Fig. 3.57 Laminated conductors transposed at the end-turns

Circulating currents arise as a result of unequal currents in parallel paths. An example is shown in Fig. 3.57, in which a single turn of a rectangular conductor is laminated into four flat strands or layers. In any one slot the layers are in parallel, and the current tends to become unevenly distributed, as a result of the cross-slot H-field caused by currents in the layers below.

Unlike the redistribution in an isolated pair of conductors in Fig. 3.56, the current tends to crowd towards the top of each strand, but not to the same extent. The crowding is greater in the layers near the top of the slot.

Without transpositions, the disposition of the layers is the same in the go and return slots, and the current will be unevenly distributed in both. Fig. 3.57 shows the idea of a transposition in which the whole stack is inverted. This can be accomplished by means of the "knuckle" shown in Fig. 3.28. As a result of the transposition, layer 1 at the bottom of the left-hand slot occupies the top position in the right-hand slot, and so on, so that the tendency for unequal currents is cancelled and all strands carry equal current. This reduces the losses and the effective AC resistance. A much greater frequency of transposition is obtained in the Roebel coil in Fig. 3.23.

The "circulating" currents can be seen as fictitious currents between the parallel paths, superimposed on the load current, and adding or subtracting to the strand currents to give the actual unequal distribution.

The balancing of parallel paths is necessary not only for laminated conductors, but in any winding that has parallel paths. Where laminated conductors are used, balance must be observed in each individual path of each phase.

The circulating current in any layer depends on the current below that layer in the slot. In general in a 2-layer winding the coil-sides may be from the same phase or from another phase, giving rise to the terms "mixed" slots and "unmixed" slots. For perfect balance each strand must occupy each position an equal number of times in both types of slot. According to Tampion [1992] the number of mixed slots should be either an integral multiple or a factor of the number of unmixed slots, and the number of laminations (layers) should be a factor of the number of mixed or unmixed slots in the entire path, whichever is smaller.

The circulating-current loss factor K_c can be computed from a solution of the currents in the individual layers, which in turn requires a knowledge of the AC impedance of each parallel path. The simplest solution is obtained using only the AC resistances of the parallel paths, which will be discussed next.

Redistribution of current in a slot — The distribution of current-density within conductors in a single slot was analysed by A.B. Field in 1905, but the following treatment follows Lammeraner and Štafl.[19]

Fig. 3.58 shows the model for analysis of the current distribution in a single slot. It is assumed that the H-field is entirely parallel to the slot bottom. At any level x the cross-slot H-field is excited by the current below that level, and is unaffected by the current above. Only two conductors are shown. The H-field in the upper conductor is affected by the current $\mathbf{I}_s$ in the lower conductor, but the H-field in the lower conductor is not affected by the current $\mathbf{I}$ in the upper one. Attention is therefore focussed on the upper conductor and the origin of coordinates is set at the bottom of this conductor.

---

[19] Field A.B., *Eddy Currents in Large Slot-Wound Conductors*, 22nd AIEE Annual Convention, Asheville, N.C., U.S.A., June 19-23, 1905, pp. 761-788. Although Field established the method of analysis used by almost all subsequent authors, his paper concentrates on examples and his treatment is not easily formulated for general use. This facilitation was added by various later authors, notably Lyon [1921] and Lammeraner and Štafl [1966].

The conductors of width $b < w$ are represented by fictitious conductors of width w and conductivity $\sigma' = \sigma b/w$, so that a one-dimensional analysis can be used, σ being the conductivity of the actual conductors. The dimensionless parameter ξ is defined as

$$\xi = \frac{h}{\delta'} \tag{3.43}$$

where δ' is the effective skin-depth

$$\delta' = \sqrt{\frac{2}{\omega\mu\sigma'}}. \tag{3.44}$$

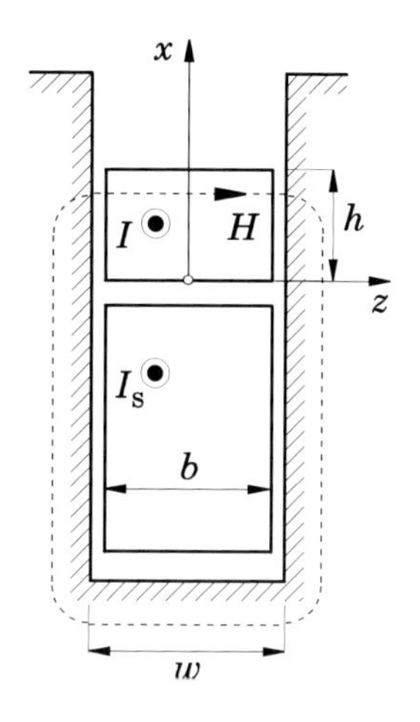

Fig. 3.58 Slot conductors

The solution of the complex diffusion eqn. (see Chapter 12) is given in detail by Lammeraner and Štafl. The main result is quoted here in the form of the resistivity ratio R_{ac}/R_{dc} for the upper conductor alone. Since this is computed for a single slot with different currents $\mathbf{I}$ and $\mathbf{I}_s$ in the upper and lower conductors, it includes the skin effect factor K_s and the proximity effect factor K_p, and is still sufficiently general to include the circulating current factor K_c, although the value of K_c averaged for the whole winding requires the determination of $\mathbf{I}$ and $\mathbf{I}_s$ which will be constrained by any transpositions. Thus for the upper conductor we can write

$$\mathbf{K} = \mathbf{I}\mathbf{I}^* \left[\phi(\xi) + j\phi_j(\xi)\right] + \left[\mathbf{I}_s\mathbf{I}_s^* + \frac{\mathbf{I}\mathbf{I}_s^* + \mathbf{I}^*\mathbf{I}_s}{2}\right]\left[\psi(\xi) + j\psi_j(\xi)\right] \tag{3.45}$$

where the real functions $\phi(\xi)$ and $\phi_j(\xi)$ are given by

$$\phi(\xi) = \xi\frac{\sinh 2\xi + \sin 2\xi}{\cosh 2\xi - \cos 2\xi}; \quad \phi_j(\xi) = \xi\frac{\sinh 2\xi - \sin 2\xi}{\cosh 2\xi - \cos 2\xi}; \tag{3.46}$$

and $\psi(\xi)$ and $\psi_j(\xi)$ are given by

$$\psi(\xi) = 2\xi\frac{\sinh \xi - \sin \xi}{\cosh \xi + \cos \xi}; \quad \psi_j(\xi) = 2\xi\frac{\sinh \xi + \sin \xi}{\cosh \xi + \cos \xi}. \tag{3.47}$$

The coefficient **K** in eqn. (3.45) is complex because the eddy-currents affect both the resistance and the reactance of the conductor. The resistance ratio R_{ac}/R_{dc} is taken as the real part and we can write $K = \mathrm{Re}\{\mathbf{K}\}$, while the reactance ratio is taken as $\mathrm{Im}\{\mathbf{K}\}$.

For small values of $\xi < 1$, Lammeraner and Štafl give the approximations

$$\phi(\xi) = 1 + \frac{4}{45}\xi^4; \qquad \phi_j(\xi) = \frac{2}{3}\xi^2;$$
$$\psi(\xi) = \frac{1}{3}\xi^4; \qquad \psi_j(\xi) = 2\xi^2. \tag{3.48}$$

For large values $\xi > 4$ they give

$$\phi(\xi) = \phi_j(\xi) = \xi; \quad \psi(\xi) = \psi_j(\xi) = 2\xi. \tag{3.49}$$

Two important special cases are given by Lammeraner and Štafl, the first of which arises for an m-layer winding in two halves with $\mathbf{I}_s = \mathbf{I}e^{j\gamma}$; i.e., the currents in the two halves are equal in magnitude but displaced in phase by γ, which is typically 60°. In this case we get

$$K = \phi(\xi) + \left[\frac{m^2 - 1}{3} - \frac{m^2}{4}\sin^2\frac{\gamma}{2}\right]\psi(\xi) \tag{3.50}$$

and if $\gamma = 60°$ this becomes

$$K = \phi(\xi) + \frac{0{\cdot}8125m^2 - 1}{3}\psi(\xi). \tag{3.51}$$

These values of K represent the average resistance ratio for the whole slot, and they apply directly in cases where there is no possibility of circulating currents, implying that $K = K_s K_p$ and $K_c = 1$.

The second special case arises when $\gamma = 0$, so that the currents in all conductors in the slot are identical, as in a single-layer winding:

$$K = \phi(\xi) + \frac{m^2 - 1}{3}\psi(\xi). \tag{3.52}$$

Lammeraner and Štafl provide many more details of interest for multi-layer windings including the effect on slot reactance and the effect of short-pitching, all of which are calculated from eqn. (3.45).

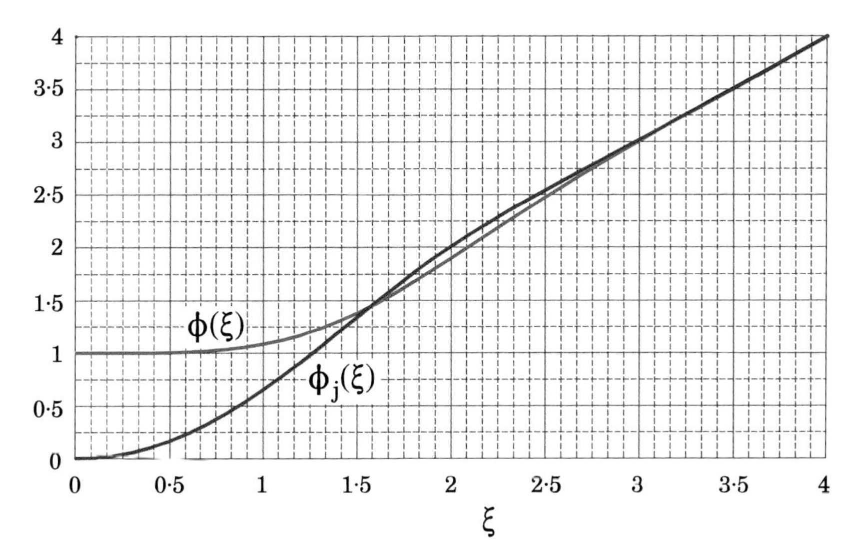

Fig. 3.59 $\phi(\xi)$ and $\phi_j(\xi)$ vs. ξ

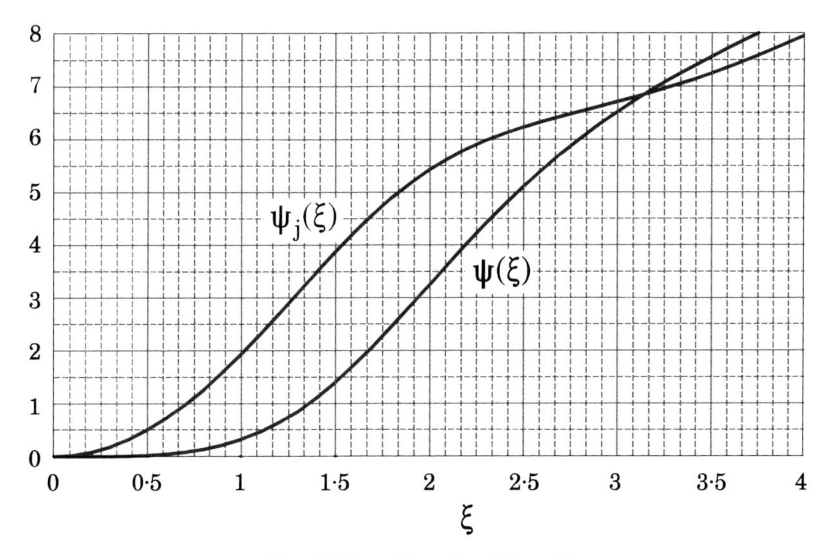

Fig. 3.60 $\psi(\xi)$ and $\psi_j(\xi)$ vs. ξ

Fig. 3.59 shows the $\phi(\xi)$ and $\phi_j(\xi)$ functions over the range 0–4, and Fig. 3.60 the $\psi(\xi)$ and $\psi_j(\xi)$ functions over the same range. At higher values of ξ the approximations in eqn. (3.49) can be used.

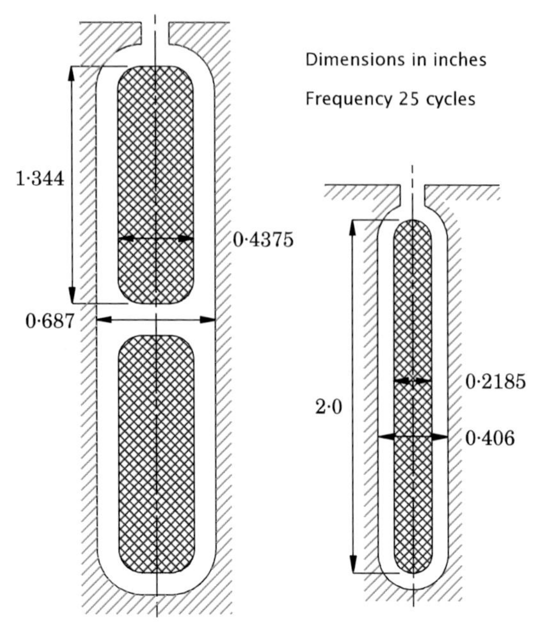

Fig. 3.61 Examples taken from Field [1905]

Example — Fig. 3.61 shows two examples from Field's original 1904 paper. For the double-layer winding, assuming copper conductors at 20°C we have $\sigma = 53{\cdot}763 \times 10^6$ S/m and $\sigma' = \sigma \times 0{\cdot}4375/0{\cdot}687 = 34{\cdot}238 \times 10^6$ S/m. At 25 cycles the skin-depth is $\delta' = \sqrt{(2/2\pi \times 25 \times \mu_0 \times 34{\cdot}238 \times 10^6)} = 0{\cdot}017$ m $= 0{\cdot}677$ in, so $\xi = h/\delta' = 1{\cdot}344/0{\cdot}677 = 1{\cdot}984$ or very nearly 2. From eqns. (3.46) and (3.47) we get $\phi(\xi) = 1{\cdot}8$ and $\psi(\xi) = 3{\cdot}2$. Assuming there is 60° phase-shift between the currents in the two layers, with $m = 2$ eqn. (3.51) gives $K = \phi(\xi) + 0{\cdot}75 \times \psi(\xi) = 1{\cdot}88 + 0{\cdot}75 \times 3{\cdot}2 = 4{\cdot}3$. Field quotes $K = 6{\cdot}6$ for the upper conductor and 1·7 for the lower one, giving an average of 4·15.

For the single-layer winding we have $\sigma' = \sigma \times 0{\cdot}2185/0{\cdot}406 = 28{\cdot}93 \times 10^6$ S/m and $\delta' = \sqrt{[2/(2\pi \times 25 \times \mu_0 \times 28{\cdot}93 \times 10^6)]} = 0{\cdot}019$ m $= 0{\cdot}737$ in, so $\xi = h/\delta' = 2{\cdot}0/0{\cdot}737 = 2{\cdot}715$. From eqn. (3.46) we get $\phi(\xi) = 2{\cdot}7$ and from eqn. (3.52) with $m = 1$ we get $K = \phi(\xi) = 2{\cdot}7$. Field's value is 2·5.

The AC resistance factor K_e in the end-windings is not the same as it is in the slots, and Lammeraner and Štafl give a formula for modifying K to the value $(K + K_e\lambda)/(1 + \lambda)$, where λ is the ratio of the end-turn length (including both ends) to the mean turn length. They point out that K_e often set equal to 1, on the grounds that proximity effect is weaker in the end-windings than in the slots.

Finally Lammeraner and Štafl give formulas for the resistance coefficient of individual layers, pointing out the importance of this for the layer at the top of the slot where the eddy-current effect is greatest. For an m-layer winding the coefficient for the mth layer is

$$k_2 = \phi(\xi) + m(m-1)\cos^2\frac{\gamma}{2}\,\psi(\xi), \tag{3.53}$$

and with $\gamma = 0$ it is simply

$$k_1 = \phi(\xi) + m(m-1)\,\psi(\xi). \tag{3.54}$$

In the double-layer example in Fig. 3.61, the values are $k_2 = 6{\cdot}68$ for the upper layer (cf. Field's value of 6·6); and $k_1 = 1{\cdot}88$ for the lower layer (cf. Field's value of 1·7). The values in Field's examples are undoubtedly exaggerated, as few machines will have conductors of the dimensions in Fig. 3.61. If the frequency was 250 Hz instead of 25, ξ would be $\sqrt{10}$ times greater and the same values of $\phi(\xi)$ and $\psi(\xi)$ would be obtained with conductors of $1/\sqrt{10}$ times the dimensions. Even these would be unusually large conductors in most permanent magnet machines. Nevertheless, even when K_s and K_p are close to unity, it does not follow that the circulating current loss is small or zero; it must be checked independently especially if the winding has parallel paths which are not perfectly balanced.

Practical considerations — The rather mathematical analysis of AC resistance can be summarized in practical terms. The inductance of strands near the top of the slot is considerably lower than that of strands near the bottom. Consequently if the strands are in parallel, more current flows in the upper strands near the slot-opening, and they are liable to experience a greater temperature rise. Also the overall Joule loss in the slot is increased, compared with the value it would have if the current was uniformly distributed between the strands. The increase in the apparent AC resistance has been the focus of the foregoing analysis, but the underlying phenomenon is inductive in nature.

Single-layer windings should never be used in stators of high-speed machines; the same goes for machines with high pole numbers. In practice double-layer windings have less than half the increase in AC resistance. Note that the use of Litz wire does not by itself eliminate the problem of imbalance between parallel paths.

Parallel paths must be used in many designs to get the required effective turns per coil. If a design requires 1·25 turns per coil the way to achieve this is to wind 5 turns per coil and connect with 4 parallel paths. However the flux linkage must be identical in each parallel path, or circulating currents will result. If 1·5 turns are required, then 3 turns per coil can be wound with two parallel paths. The choice depends upon the number of poles and slots.

Another good practice is that each parallel path should have a separate neutral connection that is insulated. This is good for two reasons. First, it eliminates the possibility of circulating currents between the paths if they are not balanced. Secondly the bundle or size of the connection is halved for two paths and quartered for 4 paths, etc. This can be important in large machines like vehicle traction motors or generators, to minimize the end-winding height with the neutral connections laced on top of the end-windings. The diffusion of the ohmic heat in the neutrals is better with more than one neutral spread around the end-windings.

A practical example that can be cited is a permanent-magnet generator rated over 250 kW running at over 50 krpm, initially designed with 240 strands of wire and one turn per coil with all coils in series per phase. An improved design, better for manufacturing and with a better chance of obtaining a balanced winding, is to connect the coils with 4 parallel paths with 4 turns per coil, enabling the number of strands in hand to be reduced to 80 per turn. In addition, a separate neutral connection is used for each parallel path. This is a safer design but care still must be taken to balance the 80 strands per turn. The lamination has a semi-closed slot, so Litz wire cannot be inserted.

The quality of the neutral and hook-up wire connections is important. Obviously it is essential to avoid defective solder joints caused by poor wire stripping or cold solder joints. For small motors with small wire gauges, silver soldering is fine if the wire is properly stripped. However for larger machines with many parallel strands the connections should be either induction fused in a special machine that works like a DC commutator bar fuser; or a copper sleeve should be used over the connection and crimped using the hand or power tool for that purpose. These practical points are every bit as important as the theory.

3.7 Magnet retention

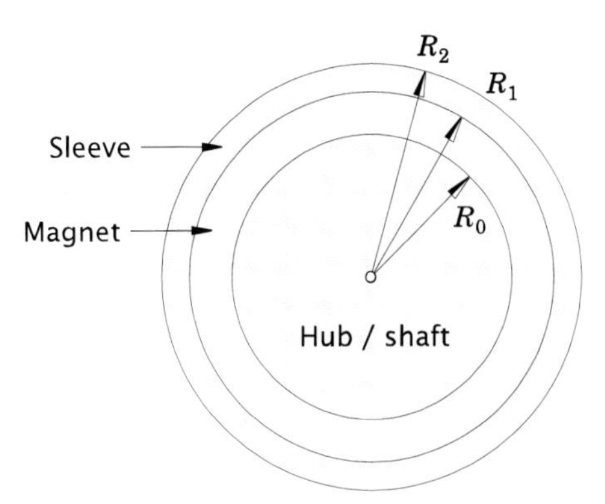

Fig. 3.62 Retaining sleeve

For a rotating cylinder with inner radius R_1 and outer radius R_2, the most important stress is the tangential or hoop stress σ_t, which is derived by Morley[20] as

$$\sigma_t = \frac{\delta \omega^2}{8 \times 10^{12}} \left\{ \frac{3m-2}{m-1} \left[R_1^2 + R_2^2 + \frac{R_1^2 R_2^2}{R^2} \right] - \frac{m+2}{m-1} R^2 \right\} \qquad (3.55)$$

in N/mm^2 (i.e., MPa}. δ is the mass density in kg/m^3; R_1, R_2 and R are in mm, Fig. 3.62; ω is the mechanical angular velocity in rad/s; and $1/m$ is Poisson's ratio. R is any radius between R_1 and R_2. For steel, m can be taken as 4, although 3 gives a more conservative result. The result in lbf/in^2 is obtained by multiplying σ_t by 145. For very detailed calculations Morley gives formulas for the radial and axial stresses and strains, as well as the circumferential strain.

The maximum value of σ_t is at the inner radius $R = R_1$, and if m is taken as 3 this is

$$\sigma_{t[max]} = \frac{\delta \omega^2}{8} [R_1^2 + 7R_2^2] \times 10^{-12} \quad \text{N/mm}^2. \qquad (3.56)$$

When the thickness of the sleeve is small relative to its radius, R_1 and R_2 become nearly equal, and if $v = \omega R/10^3$ is the peripheral velocity in m/s this formula reduces to

---

[20] Morley A., *Strength of Materials*, Longmans, Green and Co., London, 1940.

$$\sigma_t = \delta v^2 \times 10^{-6} \quad \text{N/mm}^2. \tag{3.57}$$

The hoop stress thus depends only on the peripheral velocity and the density, and not on the radius or the thickness of the sleeve.

Example — A steel ring has an inner diameter of 35 mm and an outer diameter of 37 mm, and rotates at 20,000 rpm. Calculate the maximum hoop stress if the density is 7800 kg/m^3 (0·28 lb/in^3). Assume Poisson's ratio is 1/3. From eqn. (3.55) with $\omega = 20 \times 10^3 \times \pi/30 = 2{,}094$ rad/s,

$$\sigma_t = \frac{7800 \times 2094^2}{8}\left\{\frac{7}{2}\left[17{\cdot}5^2 + 18{\cdot}5^2 + \frac{17{\cdot}5^2 \times 18{\cdot}5^2}{17{\cdot}5^2}\right] - \frac{5}{2}17{\cdot}5^2\right\} \times 10^{-12}$$

$$= 11{\cdot}55 \quad \text{N/mm}^2 = 1{,}675 \quad \text{lbf/in}^2.$$

Using the approximate formula (3.56)

$$\sigma_{t[max]} = \frac{7800 \times 2094^2}{8}[17{\cdot}5^2 + 7 \times 18{\cdot}5^2] \times 10^{-12} \quad \text{N/mm}^2$$

$$= 11{\cdot}55 \quad \text{N/mm}^2 = 1{,}675 \quad \text{lbf/in}^2.$$

Using the thin-cylinder formula (3.57), with $v = 18/10^3 \times \omega = 37{\cdot}7$ m/s,

$$\sigma_t = 7800 \times 37{\cdot}7^2 \times 10^{-6} = 11{\cdot}1 \quad \text{N/mm}^2 = 1{,}607 \quad \text{lbf/in}^2.$$

So far we have considered only the inertial hoop stress of the sleeve itself. The sleeve exerts the necessary centrifugal restraining pressure on the magnet. If the magnet is cylindrical with inner radius R_0, and density δ_m, we have

$$P = \frac{\delta_m \omega^2}{3R_1}\left[R_1^3 - R_0^3\right] \times 10^{-12} \quad \text{N/mm}^2. \tag{3.61}$$

The additional hoop stress in the sleeve is PR_1/t, where t is the sleeve thickness $R_2 - R_1$. Hence the additional hoop stress is

$$\sigma_m = \frac{\delta_m \omega^2}{3t}\left[R_1^3 - R_0^3\right] \times 10^{-12} \quad \text{N/mm}^2. \tag{3.62}$$

The total hoop stress is

$$\sigma = \sigma_t + \sigma_m. \tag{3.63}$$

Example — The retaining sleeve of the previous example supports a magnet of density 7800 kg/m^3 and thickness 5 mm. Calculate the additional hoop stress due to the centrifugal load on the magnet, and the total hoop stress.

From eqn. (3.62) with $t = 18{\cdot}5 - 17{\cdot}5 = 1{\cdot}0$ mm and $R_0 = R_1 - 5 = 12{\cdot}5$ mm,

$$\sigma_m = \frac{7800 \times 2094^2}{3 \times 1{\cdot}0 \times 10^{12}}\left[17{\cdot}5^3 - 12{\cdot}5^3\right] = 38{\cdot}8 \text{ N/mm}^2 = 5{,}630 \text{ lbf/in}^2.$$

From eqn. (3.63) the total hoop stress is

$$\sigma = 11{\cdot}55 + 38{\cdot}8 = 50{\cdot}4 \text{ N/mm}^2 = 7{,}300 \text{ lbf/in}^2.$$

Effect of temperature — If α is the coefficient of linear thermal expansion, a temperature change of ΔT causes a strain $\varepsilon = \alpha\,\Delta T$, and if E is the Young's Modulus the stress required to annul this strain is

$$\sigma_{\Delta T} = E\varepsilon = E\alpha\Delta T. \tag{3.66}$$

For example in steel with $E = 2{\cdot}07 \times 10^5$ N/mm^2 and $\alpha = 1{\cdot}1 \times 10^{-5}$ C^{-1}, a temperature change of $\Delta T = 130\,^\circ$C produces a stress of

$$\begin{aligned}\sigma_{\Delta T} &= 2{\cdot}07 \times 10^5 \times 1{\cdot}1 \times 10^{-5} \times 130 \\ &= 296 \text{ N/mm}^2 = 42{,}920 \text{ lbf/in}^2.\end{aligned} \tag{3.67}$$

This stress can easily exceed the centrifugal stress, as is the case in the numerical examples.

The sleeve is normally designed with an interference fit such that at maximum speed and maximum temperature it is on the point of "lift-off". A safety factor is built in by calculating at a higher speed than the quoted maximum speed, for example 120% higher. At this lift-off speed $\omega_0 = 1{\cdot}2\ \omega_{max}$, and maximum temperature, the enlargement of the sleeve due to the combined effect of centrifugal stress and thermal expansion is just sufficient to reduce the interference between the sleeve and the magnet to zero. This principle is used to determine the interference fit at the fitting temperature (usually room temperature).

An example will show the process. If the thermal expansion of the magnet and the rotor hub are both ignored, a temperature rise of $130\,^\circ$C will cause a strain of $\varepsilon = 1{\cdot}1 \times 10^{-5} \times 130 = 0{\cdot}00143$, and this is the per-unit increase in the sleeve diameter. We have already calculated that the total stress due to rotation at 20,000 rpm is $\sigma = 50{\cdot}4$ N/mm^2 or 7,300 lbf/in^2, but at 120% speed this will be 72·6 N/mm^2 or 10,500 lbf/in^2, and this will produce a further strain of $\varepsilon = \sigma/E = 72{\cdot}6/(2{\cdot}07 \times 10^5) = 0{\cdot}000351$.

The total strain is therefore 0·00143 + 0·000351 = 0·00178. On an internal sleeve diameter of 2 × 18·5 = 37mm, the interference is therefore 0·00178 × 37 = 0·066 mm, and this means that the magnet surface must be ground to a diameter of 37 − 0·066 = 36·934 mm or 1·4541 in — if possible with micron precision.

The strain ε = 0·00178 induces a cold stress of $E\varepsilon$ = 2·07 × 10^5 × 0·00178 = 368 N/mm^2 = 53,400 lbf/in^2, and this is the stress in the sleeve at the lowest temperature when it is not rotating. At the lift-off speed ω_0 at the lowest temperature, the rotation induces an additional stress of 72·6 N/mm^2, making a worst-case total of 441 N/mm^2 or 64,000 lbf/in^2.

Retaining sleeve materials — In some cases magnets are bonded to the rotor with no external means of retention. Thanks to the excellent bonding properties of modern adhesives, this is adequate for many applications; (see Price and Fakley, [2002]) and p. 690. Mylar® HS film spiral tubing can be shrunk over the magnets as an effective retaining sleeve that has no effect whatsoever on the electromagnetic performance and does not experience any eddy-current loss; (Polifibra S.p.A., Italy). For high-speed machines a range of metallic, glass-fibre, and carbon-fibre materials is discussed on p. 690.

4 FLUX, EMF, AND TORQUE

Introduction

This chapter is concerned with electromagnetic design, starting with the magnet flux at no-load (open-circuit). The EMF constant k_E is introduced for both squarewave and sinewave machines, together with simple essential formulas for calculating it. More advanced methods of calculating the EMF and its waveform from the magnet flux distribution are presented in detail.

Once we know the EMF waveform, we can impose current in the windings and calculate the torque and the torque constant k_T. Torque is always analysed in detail in electrical machines, and this Chapter describes a range of methods for instantaneous and average torque, including dq-axis methods and the role of inductance. Of equal importance for brushless permanent-magnet machines is the i-ψ loop introduced in §§4.5 and 4.6.

An understanding of flux, EMF, current, and torque provides the basis for studying the drive and control in Chapters 6–7. Losses are discussed in §3.6 and in Chapter 12.

4.1 Permanent magnets and magnetic circuits

The most basic magnetic calculation in brushless permanent-magnet machines is to determine the flux produced by the magnets. An important result of this calculation is the "operating point" of the magnets and the general saturation level of the iron, firstly on open-circuit with no current flowing in the stator. Together with the winding layout (Chapter 3), the *distribution* of the flux around the airgap determines the EMF *waveform*.

The methods for calculating the flux fall into three main classes:

1. Magnetic equivalent-circuit methods.
2. Analytical solution of the Laplace/Poisson equations.
3. Finite-element methods.

All three of these methods are important, and they all give different insights. The first two are fast and closely related to the classical theory of machines, including the circuit theory. Finite-element methods are slower, but essential in cases where saturation is important, or where the geometry is complex.

4.1.1 Magnetic equivalent circuits

The simplest form of the magnetic equivalent circuit is circuit 3 in Fig. 4.1. The airgap flux per pole Φ_g is driven through the airgap reluctance R_g by a Norton equivalent circuit that represents the magnet by its remanent flux $\Phi_r = B_r A_m$, and a parallel permeance P_m. All these parameters are calculated from dimensions and material properties. Some of the magnetic potential is lost in the stator and rotor steel, and some of the flux leaks from one pole to the next without crossing the airgap. These effects are represented by additional elements appearing in circuit 1.

The method is to reduce the equivalent circuit as far as possible by means of series/parallel connections and conversions between Thévenin and Norton equivalents, and then to "work back up the chain" to extract the required branch fluxes. Thus circuit 2 is an intermediate step in reducing circuit 1 to circuit 3. When the magnetic circuit is saturated the nonlinear reluctances can be calculated recursively, updating them by means of the BH curve together with the appropriate geometric dimensions.

Under open-circuit conditions it is usually sufficient to consider only one pole, and to make use of symmetry. Thus in Fig. 4.1 the quadrature or interpolar axes qq can be assigned zero magnetic potential.

From Fig. 4.1, the flux through the magnet is, in general,

$$\begin{aligned}\Phi_m = \Phi_g + \Phi_L &= \Phi_g + \frac{P_L}{P_{m0} + P_L}(\Phi_r - \Phi_g) \\ &= \Phi_g + \frac{p_{rl}}{1 + p_{rl}}(\Phi_r - \Phi_g).\end{aligned} \tag{4.1}$$

where P_{m0} is the internal magnet permeance $\mu_0 \mu_{rec} A_m / L_m$ and P_L is the leakage permeance per pole.

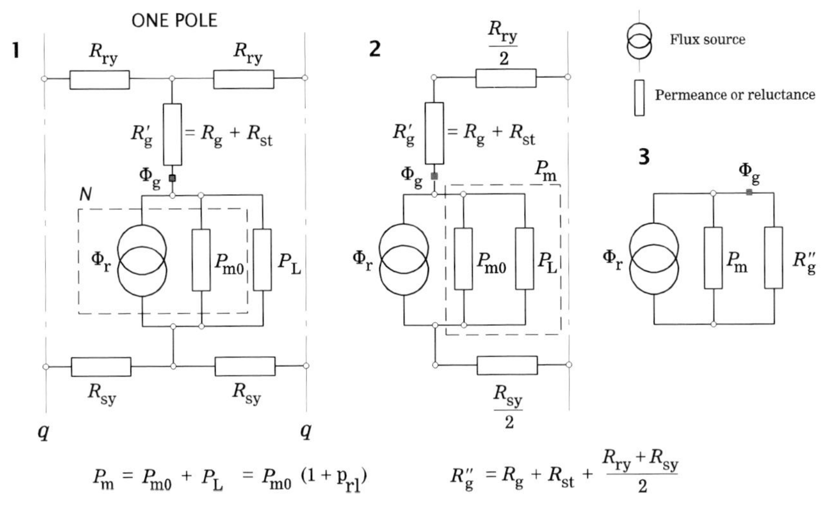

Fig. 4.1 Simple magnetic circuit for one pole

The leakage permeance P_L is often not clearly defined and it sometimes helps to express it as a fraction of the magnet internal permeance : thus p_{rl} is the normalized leakage permeance

$$p_{rl} = \frac{P_L}{P_{m0}}. \tag{4.2}$$

and

$$P_m = P_{m0} + P_L = P_{m0}(1 + p_{rl}). \tag{4.3}$$

When the airgap and the rest of the magnetic circuit can be represented by a single external reluctance R_g, the airgap flux is given by any of the following expressions:

$$\begin{aligned} \Phi_g &= \frac{1/R_g}{1/R_g + P_{m0} + P_L}\Phi_r \\ &= \frac{1/R_g}{1/R_g + P_m}\Phi_r \\ &= \frac{1}{1 + P_m R_g}\Phi_r \\ &= \frac{1}{1 + (1 + p_{rl})P_{m0}R_g}\Phi_r. \end{aligned} \tag{4.4}$$

If Φ_g from eqn. (4.4) is substituted in eqn. (4.1), we obtain also an expression for the magnet flux Φ_m in terms of Φ_r:

$$\Phi_m = \frac{1 + P_L R_g}{1 + P_m R_g}\Phi_r = \frac{1 + p_{rl} P_{m0} R_g}{1 + (1 + p_{rl}) P_{m0} R_g}\Phi_r. \tag{4.5}$$

The **leakage factor** is defined in general as the ratio of airgap flux to magnet flux:

$$f_{LKG} = \frac{\Phi_g}{\Phi_m} = \frac{\Phi_g}{\Phi_g + \Phi_L} < 1, \tag{4.6}$$

and if Φ_g and Φ_m are substituted from eqns. (4.4) and (4.5) we get

$$f_{LKG} = \frac{1}{1 + P_L R_g} = \frac{1}{1 + p_{rl} P_{m0} R_g}. \tag{4.7}$$

for the particular case of a single external reluctance R_g. This can be rearranged to give

$$p_{rl} = \frac{1/f_{LKG} - 1}{P_{m0} R_g}. \tag{4.8}$$

Eqn. (4.8) can be substituted in eqn. (4.5) to give

$$\Phi_m = \frac{1}{1 + f_{LKG} P_{m0} R_g}\Phi_r, \tag{4.9}$$

and in eqn. (4.4) to give

$$\Phi_g = \frac{f_{LKG}}{1 + f_{LKG} P_{m0} R_g}\Phi_r. \tag{4.10}$$

We now have several interchangeable equations for Φ_g and Φ_m. For surface-magnet motors it is usually more convenient to use eqns. (4.9) and (4.10) which characterize the leakage in terms of f_{LKG}, which typically has a value in the range 0·85 to 0·95. For interior-magnet motors eqns. (4.4) and (4.5) may be preferable: the leakage path represented by P_L in Fig. 4.1 usually includes a saturable magnetic bridge, which increases p_{rl} and makes it variable, but its position in the magnetic circuit is defined, and it can be replaced by a flux-source if the bridge is permanently saturated.

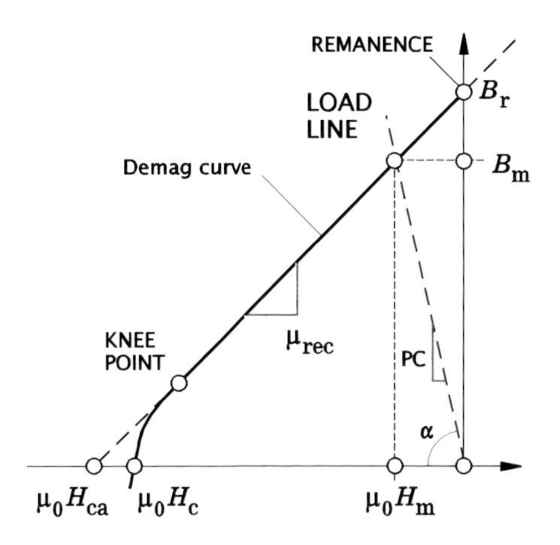

Fig. 4.2 Permeance coefficient

Finally, given that $\Phi_g = B_g A_g$ and $\Phi_r = B_r A_m$, eqn. (4.10) gives another convenient formula for B_g:

$$B_g = \frac{f_{LKG}}{1 + f_{LKG} P_{m0} R_g} \times \frac{A_m}{A_g} B_r. \tag{4.11}$$

B_g is the average airgap flux-density across the airgap area A_g, and A_m is the magnet pole area, both being calculated for one pole.

The **permeance coefficient** is defined as the slope or tangent of the **load line**, that is, tan α in Fig. 4.2. (See pp. 93 and 694). Since

$$B_m = B_r + \mu_0 \mu_{rec} H_m, \tag{4.12}$$

it follows that

$$\mathrm{PC} = \frac{B_m}{\mu_0 |H_m|} = \frac{\mu_{rec} B_m / B_r}{1 - B_m / B_r} = \frac{\mu_{rec}}{f_{LKG} P_{m0} R_g} = \frac{1}{f_{LKG}} \times \frac{L_m}{g'} \times \frac{A_g}{A_m}. \tag{4.13}$$

This can be arranged to give another formula for B_m:

$$B_m = \frac{\mathrm{PC}}{\mu_{rec} + \mathrm{PC}} B_r. \tag{4.14}$$

Eqn. (4.13) shows that the permeance coefficient is reduced if $A_m/A_g > 1$ ("flux-concentration"); but increased if L_m is increased.

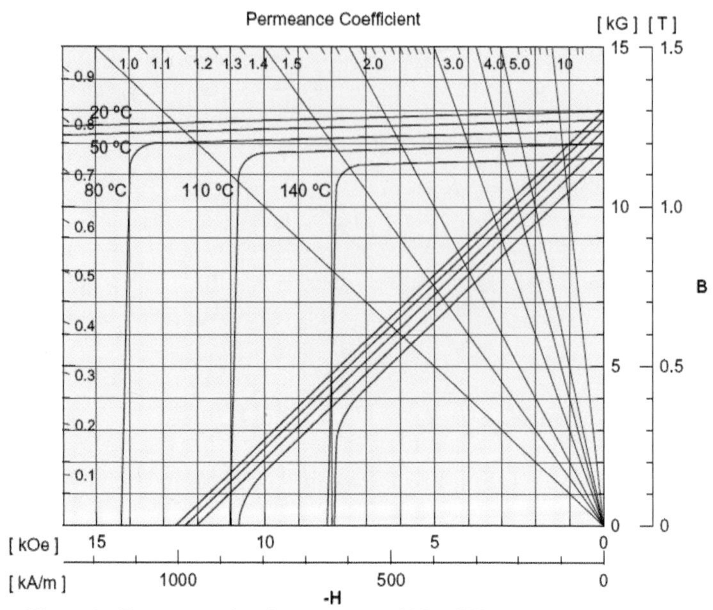

Fig. 4.3 Demagnetization curves of N42SH magnet
Shin-Estu Chemical Co. Ltd., JAPAN

Fig. 4.3 shows an example of a typical set of demagnetization curves, for a high-energy NdFeB magnet — the N42SH grade produced by Shin-Etsu Chemical Co. Ltd., Japan.

The "normal" BH curves are shown together with the corresponding "intrinsic" JH curves of magnetization J versus magnetizing force H. The intrinsic curves are almost right-angled. Different permeance coefficients are also marked on the chart.

In machine design the normal curve is the one most used, as it is in all the theoretical calculations in this book. However, the knee-point is much better defined in the intrinsic curve; this is the point at which irreversible demagnetization begins, as it might if the demagnetizing field of armature reaction (i.e., stator current) becomes too large. (See also Fig. 14.4).

The curves are presented at several different temperatures. It is essential to do all design calculations for the worst-case temperature. Usually with NdFeB magnets this is the highest temperature expected in service (including abnormal conditions).

Example — Consider a magnet with pole-face area $A_m = 625\ \text{mm}^2$ and length $L_m = 8$ mm. Suppose $B_r = 1{\cdot}1$ T and $\mu_{rec} = 1{\cdot}05$. Then

$$\Phi_r = 1{\cdot}1 \times 625 \times 10^{-6} = 687{\cdot}5\ \mu\text{Wb}$$

and the internal magnet permeance is

$$P_{m0} = \frac{\mu_0 \mu_{rec} A_m}{L_m} = \frac{4\pi \times 10^{-7} \times 1{\cdot}05 \times 625 \times 10^{-6}}{8 \times 10^{-3}} = 1{\cdot}03084 \times 10^{-7}\ \text{Wb/A}.$$

Suppose the airgap area is $A_g = 700\ \text{mm}^2$ with effective gap length $g' = 0{\cdot}7$ mm, giving $L_m/g = 11{\cdot}4$ (quite a high value). The airgap reluctance is

$$R_g = \frac{g'}{\mu_0 A_g} = \frac{0{\cdot}7 \times 10^{-3}}{4\pi \times 10^{-7} \times 700 \times 10^{-6}} = 0{\cdot}7958 \times 10^6\ \text{A/Wb},$$

giving

$$P_{m0} R_g = 0{\cdot}08203.$$

Suppose $f_{LKG} = 0{\cdot}95$, (typical for a surface-magnet motor). From eqn. (4.10),

$$\Phi_g = \frac{0{\cdot}95}{1 + 0{\cdot}95 \times 0{\cdot}08023} \Phi_r = 0{\cdot}88272\,\Phi_r.$$

From eqn. (4.8), $p_{rl} = 0{\cdot}6416$. From eqn. (4.6) the flux in the magnet is

$$\Phi_m = \frac{\Phi_g}{f_{LKG}} = \frac{0{\cdot}88272}{0{\cdot}95} \Phi_r = 0{\cdot}92918\,\Phi_r.$$

The airgap flux-density is

$$B_g = \frac{\Phi_g}{A_g} = \frac{0{\cdot}88272 \times 687{\cdot}5 \times 10^{-6}}{700 \times 10^{-6}} = 0{\cdot}86696\ \text{T},$$

The flux-density in the magnet is

$$B_m = \frac{\Phi_m}{A_m} = \frac{0{\cdot}92918 \times 687{\cdot}5 \times 10^{-6}}{625 \times 10^{-6}} = 1{\cdot}0221\ \text{T}.$$

In the example, $B_m/B_r = 1{\cdot}02221/1{\cdot}1 = 0{\cdot}92918$, so from eqn. (4.13)

$$\text{PC} = \frac{1{\cdot}05 \times 0{\cdot}92918}{1 - 0{\cdot}92918} = 13{\cdot}776.$$

The large ratio L_m/g' makes PC rather high, but this is desirable to allow for temperature effects and the demagnetizing influence of the current, as well as the MMF expended in the steel components, all of which have been ignored here.

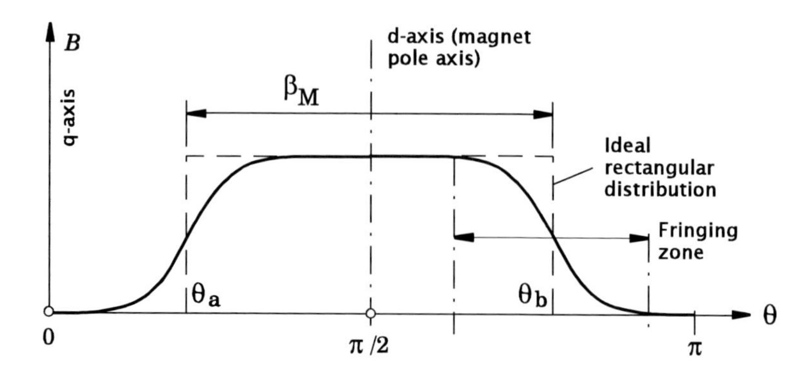

Fig. 4.4 Airgap flux distribution

4.1.1.1 Airgap flux distribution

It has already been pointed out that the magnetic equivalent-circuit method does not recognize the spatial distribution of flux. To maintain the simplicity and speed of the method, and extend its use to the calculation of the EMF waveform, it is possible to impose a distribution function of arbitrary shape, which can subsequently be modified or corrected by comparison with test or finite-element data. Such a distribution function is shown in Fig. 4.4, in which b is the normalized value of the airgap flux-density

$$\begin{aligned} b &= \frac{1}{2}\left[1 - e^{-(\theta - \theta_a)/a}\right], \quad \theta_a < \theta < \frac{\pi}{2}; \\ b &= \frac{1}{2} e^{(\theta - \theta_a)/a}, \quad 0 < \theta < \theta_a . \end{aligned} \tag{4.24}$$

and a is an empirical coefficient given by

$$a = \frac{1}{2}\sqrt{g[g + L_m/\mu_{rec}]}. \tag{4.25}$$

Similar functions are used on the right half of the distribution, symmetrical about θ_b. The fringing function is scaled so that the flux/pole is consistent with the magnetic equivalent circuit. It is then a straightforward matter to calculate the fundamental space-harmonic component $B_1(\theta)$ and from this the fundamental magnet flux/pole Φ_{M1} and the peak fundamental open-circuit airgap flux density, $B_{g1}^{(oc)}$. The function can also be modified for skew.

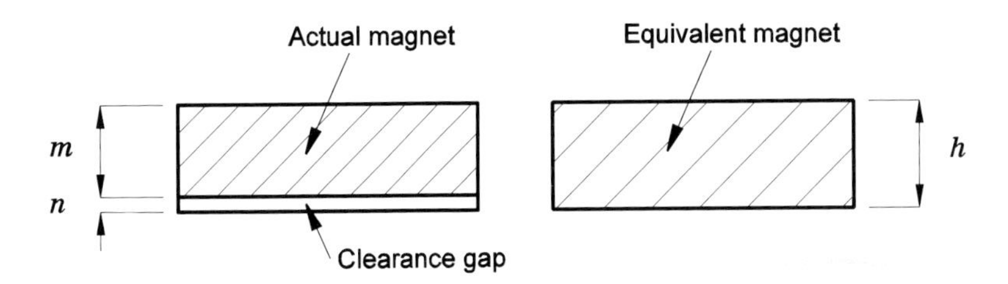

Fig. 4.5 Clearance gap and equivalent magnet

4.1.1.2 Clearance gap and equivalent magnet

Fig. 4.5 shows an actual magnet of length m in the direction of magnetization (vertical), with a clearance gap n. On the right is shown an equivalent magnet whose length is

$$h = m + n. \tag{4.26}$$

In the actual magnet,

$$B_{\mathrm{m}} = B_{\mathrm{r}} + \mu_{\mathrm{rec}}\mu_0 H_{\mathrm{m}}. \tag{4.27}$$

In the clearance gap,

$$B_{\mathrm{n}} = \mu_0 H_{\mathrm{n}}. \tag{4.28}$$

Assuming that the flux lines are all vertical,

$$B_{\mathrm{m}} = B_{\mathrm{n}} = B, \text{ say.} \tag{4.29}$$

To maintain the same magnetic potential difference between the upper and lower faces of the equivalent magnet, by Ampere's Law we have

$$H_{\mathrm{n}} n + H_{\mathrm{m}} m = H(m + n) = Hh. \tag{4.30}$$

i.e.,

$$\frac{B}{\mu_0} n + \frac{B - B_{\mathrm{r}}}{\mu_{\mathrm{rec}}\mu_0} m = Hh. \tag{4.31}$$

Rearranging and collecting terms in B,

$$B = \frac{1}{1 + \mu_{\mathrm{rec}} n/m} B_{\mathrm{r}} + \mu_{\mathrm{rec}}\mu_0 \frac{h/m}{1 + \mu_{\mathrm{rec}} n/m} H. \tag{4.32}$$

This can be written

$$B = B_{\text{r}\nu} + \mu_{\text{rec}\,\nu}\mu_0 H, \qquad (4.33)$$

where $B_{\text{r}\nu}$ is the remanence of the equivalent magnet and $\mu_{\text{rec}\,\nu}$ is its recoil permeability:

$$B_{\text{r}\nu} = \frac{B_\text{r}}{1 + \mu_{\text{rec}} n/m}; \qquad \mu_{\text{rec}\,\nu} = \frac{h/m}{1 + \mu_{\text{rec}} n/m}\mu_{\text{rec}}. \qquad (4.34)$$

In terms of a single parameter, let

$$\nu = n/m; \qquad (4.35)$$

then

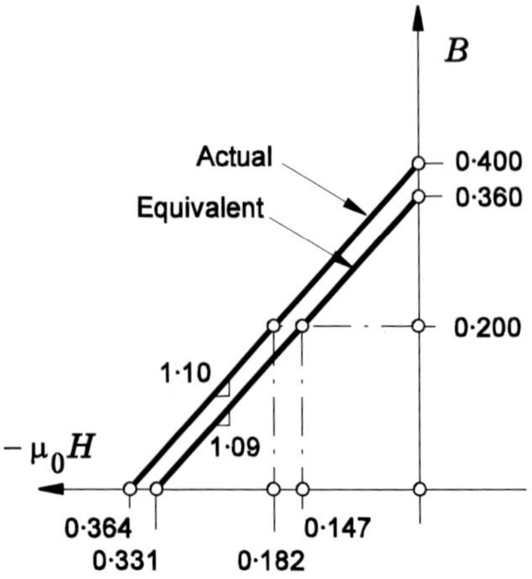

$$B_{\text{r}\nu} = \frac{B_\text{r}}{1 + \mu_{\text{rec}}\nu} \quad \text{and} \quad \mu_{\text{rec}\,\nu} = \frac{1 + \nu}{1 + \mu_{\text{rec}}\nu}\mu_{\text{rec}}. \qquad (4.36)$$

Fig. 4.6 Clearance gap; example

Note that once we have a solution for H, the magnetizing force in the actual magnet can be recovered by substituting eqn. (4.28) in eqn. (4.30) and rearranging:

$$H_\text{m} = \frac{1}{m}\left[Hh - \frac{B}{\mu_0}n\right] = (1 + \nu)H - \frac{B}{\mu_0}\nu. \qquad (4.37)$$

Example — Suppose $\mu_{\text{rec}} = 1{\cdot}1$, $B_\text{r} = 0{\cdot}4$ T, $m = 5$ mm, and $n = 0{\cdot}5$ mm; then $\nu = 0{\cdot}1$, $B_{\text{r}\nu} = 0{\cdot}901\ B_\text{r} = 0{\cdot}360$ T, and $\mu_{\text{rec}\,\nu} = 0{\cdot}991 \times \mu_{\text{rec}} = 1{\cdot}090$. The demagnetization curves of the actual and equivalent magnets are shown in Fig. 4.6.

In the example, suppose $B = 0{\cdot}2$ T. Then eqn. (4.33) gives

$$\mu_0 H = \frac{0{\cdot}2 - 0{\cdot}360}{1{\cdot}090} = -0{\cdot}147\,\text{T}, \qquad (4.38)$$

which implies that $H = -117$ kA/m in the *equivalent* magnet. But eqn. (4.37) gives

$$\mu_0 H_\text{m} = 1{\cdot}1 \times (-0{\cdot}147) - 0{\cdot}2 \times 0{\cdot}1 = -0{\cdot}182\ \text{T}, \qquad (4.39)$$

which shows that $H_\text{m} = -145$ kA/m in the *actual* magnet.

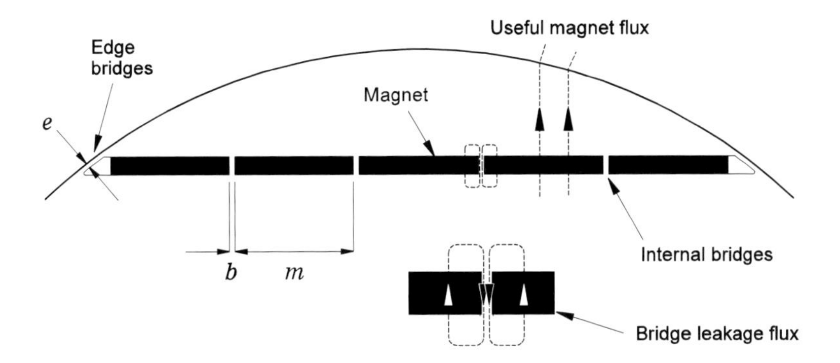

Fig. 4.7 Magnet divided by thin bridges

4.1.1.3 Magnet divided by thin bracing bridges

Fig. 4.7 shows an interior magnet divided by thin bridges which provide bracing or support against mechanical forces, not only when the motor is running but also during assembly. The detail shows the leakage flux in the bridges, which depletes the useful magnet flux. Generally the bridges will be dimensioned so that they saturate, and it is the saturation that limits the loss of useful magnet flux.

For the purposes of magnetic circuit analysis each unit can be represented by an equivalent magnet of width w, having an effective remanence $B_r{}'$ and recoil permeability $\mu_{rec}{}'$. Let m be the width of one magnet block, and b the width of one bridge. Then one "unit" of the array of magnets and bridges can be taken to comprise one magnet and one bridge. The width of one unit is $w = b + m$, and we can define a "bracing index" β to characterize the amount of bracing:

$$\beta = \frac{b}{w} = \frac{b}{b+m} \tag{4.40}$$

With five magnets and four bridges, Fig. 4.7 suggests a slight refinement of the form $\beta = 4b/(4b + 5m)$, or $(4b + 2e)/(4b + 2e + 5m)$ if the edge bridges are included in the equivalent magnet.

If $B_m{}'$ is the average flux-density produced over the width w, B_m the flux-density in the actual magnet, and B_s the saturation flux-density in the bridges (typically 2.1T), then

$$B_m{}'w = B_m m - B_s b. \tag{4.41}$$

But

$$B_m = B_r + \mu_{rec}\mu_0 H_m, \tag{4.42}$$

and if we substitute eqns. (4.40) and (4.41) in eqn. (4.42), after some rearrangement we get

$$B_m{}' = B_r{}' + \mu_{rec}{}'\mu_0 H_m \tag{4.43}$$

where

$$B_r{}' = (1 - \beta)B_r - \beta B_s \quad \text{and} \quad \mu_{rec}{}' = (1 - \beta)\mu_{rec} \tag{4.44}$$

are respectively the remanence and recoil permeability of the equivalent magnet of width w. The equivalent magnet produces the same useful magnet flux as the combination of one actual magnet and one bridge, provided that the bridge remains saturated. Moreover, if it does remain saturated, the linearity of eqn. (4.43) in H_m can be taken to imply that the equivalent magnet and its properties should be used in the calculation of the synchronous inductance L_d.

The equivalent magnet provides a simplified representation of fine details such as the bracing bridges and the clearance gap, which otherwise would need finite-element analysis with fine meshing.

The magnetic equivalent circuit method is fast and robust, and is a good starting point. Its main weakness is the use of lumped parameters for components in which the field may be far from uniform. Armature reaction is not easily incorporated, and although a separate inductance calculation can be used to model the circuit effects of armature reaction, this approach ignores the modification of the flux distribution by the stator current. The magnetic equivalent circuit ignores the spatial *distribution* of the flux, so it becomes necessary to impose a semi-empirical distribution function in the airgap, and to make gross simplifying assumptions elsewhere. The integral of the distribution function and its peak value must be consistent with the magnetic equivalent circuit.

Because of these limitations we turn our attention next to the solution of the field equations by analytical and numerical methods.

4.1.2 Direct solution of Laplace / Poisson equations

The second class of methods for calculating the magnet flux distribution is based on the analytical solution of Laplace's equation in the airgap and Poisson's equation in the magnet, which is the source of magnetization. Bernard Hague [1929],[21] published this solution comprehensively for the field between two concentric iron cylinders having smooth surfaces at the airgap, with an arbitrary distribution of current-carrying filaments in the airgap or on the surfaces of the cylinders. Hughes and Miller [1977] extended the solution to allow for finite permeability in the stator and rotor iron. They used harmonic current-sheets rather than current filaments, but both sets of solutions are interchangeable and both are used in this book. These original works were concerned with conventional wound-field machines; in particular, Hughes and Miller applied the theory to superconducting machines which are closely related to the permanent-magnet machine.

It was Boules [1984] who adapted Hague's solutions for permanent-magnet machines, by replacing the magnet with an equivalent distribution of ampere-conductors. This distribution of ampere-conductors can be determined rigorously when the rotor and stator iron have smooth surfaces, and the magnet lies on the rotor surface with a simple geometric shape and a certain direction of magnetization. Boules developed solutions for certain basic shapes of magnet with radial and parallel magnetization.

Equivalent ampere-conductor distributions — The magnet is replaced by a current sheet $\boldsymbol{K} = \boldsymbol{M} \times \boldsymbol{n}$ [A/m] on its edges, where $\boldsymbol{M}$ is the magnetization vector inside the magnet and $\boldsymbol{n}$ is the unit vector normal to the magnet surface. Since $\boldsymbol{M}$ and $\boldsymbol{n}$ are both always in the x,y plane, transverse to the axis of rotation, $\boldsymbol{K}$ is always in the z direction along the axis of rotation, i.e. $\boldsymbol{K} = (0,0,K)$. $\boldsymbol{M}$ is the actual magnetization of the magnet, which includes an induced component due to the demagnetizing field of the external magnetic circuit. Unfortunately this is not known *a priori*. However, if the recoil permeability is near 1, the susceptibility χ_m of the magnet is nearly

[21] Hague's work was done at the University of Glasgow in the 1920's. It was considerably extended by Zhu et al [1993] and Rasmussen et al [1999], using a harmonic series representation of the magnetization vector.

zero, and the induced magnetization is small.[22] Boules points out that on open-circuit the magnets are normally worked between $B_r/2$ and B_r, and he uses the average magnetization over this range, i.e., $M = k_m M_0 = k_m B_r/\mu_0$ where $k_m = (1 + 0{\cdot}75\,\chi_m)/(1 + \chi_m)$. Note that M is equivalent to the "apparent coercivity" H_{ca}, i.e. the coercivity that the magnet would have if its recoil line was straight throughout the second quadrant with relative permeability μ_r, Fig. 4.2. The value of the susceptibility χ_m and the constant k_m can be seen in Table 4.1 for typical values of μ_r. For most magnets μ_r does not exceed 1.1, so the maximum error from this approximation is less than 2·5%.

μ_{rec}	χ_m	k_m
1	0	1
1·05	0·05	0·988
1·1	0·1	0·977
1·2	0·2	0·958

TABLE 4.1 EFFECT OF RECOIL PERMEABILITY ON k_m

Examples are shown in Fig. 4.8. (a) For radially-magnetized arc magnets whose edges lie along radii, $K = 0$ on the curved surfaces and $K = \pm M$ on the edges. (b) For parallel-magnetized magnets whose edges lie along radii, $K = \pm M \sin\theta$ on the curved surfaces and $K = \pm M \cos\beta/2$ on the edges, where β is the magnet pole arc. (c) For parallel-magnetized magnets with parallel edges, along the curved surfaces $K = \pm M \sin\theta$ and $K = \pm M$ on the edges. (d) For the full-ring solid 2-pole magnet, on the curved surfaces $K = \pm M \sin\theta$; and $K = \pm M$ on the flat chamfers.

The magnetic field is built up from Hague's solution for the field of a set of filaments distributed in the airgap between two concentric cylinders of radii a and b. Fig. 4.9 shows one set of filaments for a 4-pole radially-magnetized magnet ($2p = 4$). Each filament has radius c and span 2ξ, and the field produced at the point (r, θ) by the set of $2p$ filamentary "coils" is given by

[22] Susceptibility is defined as $\chi_m = \mu_{rec} - 1$.

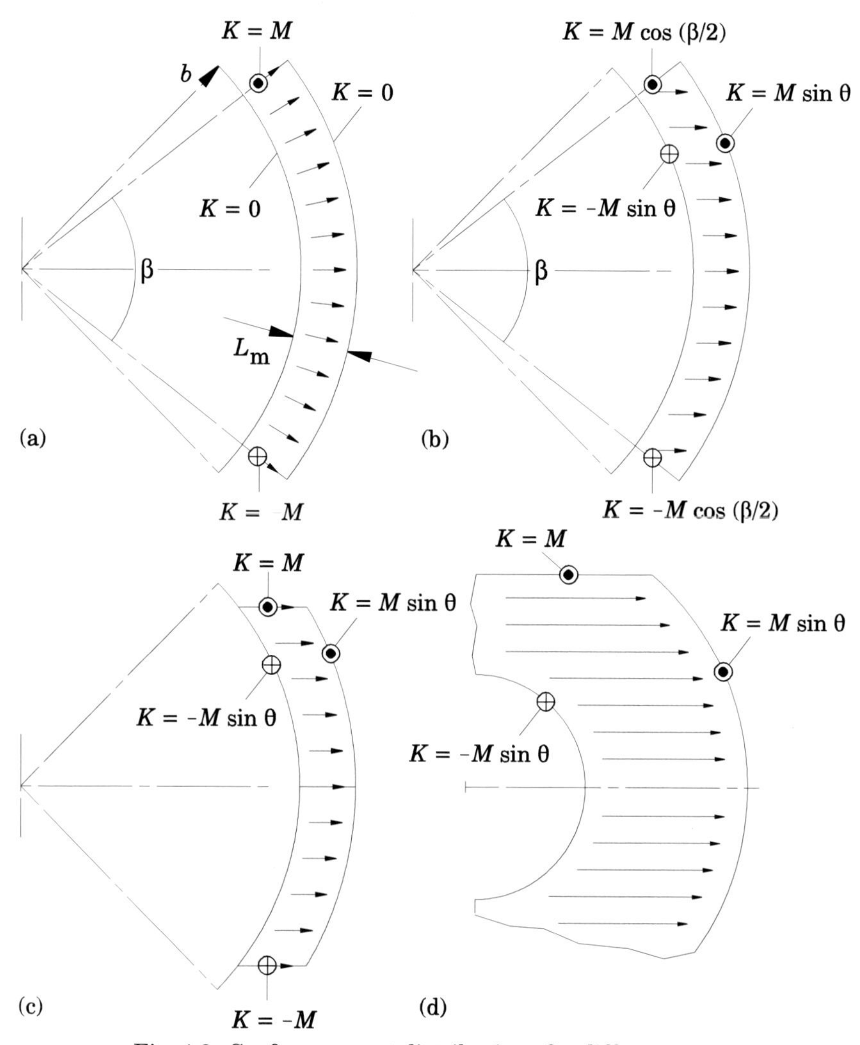

Fig. 4.8 Surface current distributions for different magnets

$$B_r = \frac{2p\mu_0 i}{\pi r} \sum_n^{\infty} \frac{a^n}{c^n} \cdot \frac{c^{2n}+b^{2n}}{a^{2n}-b^{2n}} \cdot \left[\frac{r^n}{a^n} + \frac{a^n}{r^n} \right] \cdot k_{\sigma n} \sin n\xi \cos n\theta \quad (4.45)$$

where i is the current in each filament. When the magnets are symmetrical the sum is taken over all odd electrical harmonics, i.e., $n = (2j - 1)$, $j = 1,2,3....$ For any distribution of ampere-conductors (Fig. 4.8), eqn. (4.45) must be integrated over each surface.

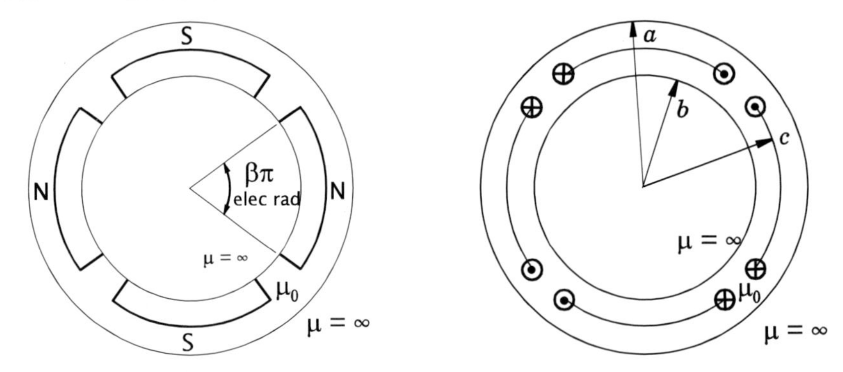

Fig. 4.9 Current filaments representing magnetized magnets

However it is just as easy to approximate the continuous distribution of ampere-conductors by discrete sets of filaments. For example, in Fig. 4.8(a) we can place m sets of filaments between the radii b and $b + L_m$, and each one will carry a current $i = KL_m/m$ A. Then eqn. (4.45) is evaluated m times with $c = b + (k - ½)L_m/m$, $k = 1,2,...m$. Because of the rapid attenuation of higher-order space-harmonic components away from the edges, the number of filament sets m does not have to be particularly large; a value of 10 is typically enough.

The factor $k_{\sigma n}$ in eqn. (4.45) is the n'th harmonic skew factor, which is equal to sin $(n\sigma/2)$ /$(n\sigma/2)$, where σ is the skew angle in electrical radians.

Later solutions developed by Rasmussen [1999] and by Zhu et al [1993] go beyond the Hague-Boules method just described, by using a direct scalar potential solution that relies on a harmonic series representation of the magnetization vector. The airgap field is given by expressions of the form

$$B_r = \sum_n \frac{q(M_n H_n + N_n K_n)}{\mu_r(q^2 - 1)} [r^{q-1} + a^{2q} r^{-q-1}] c^{-q+1} H_n \cos q\theta \qquad (4.46)$$

where $q = np$, M_n and N_n are the n'th harmonic components of the radial and tangential components of magnetization, and H_n and K_n are functions of q, μ_r and the various radii given in Rasmussen [*op cit.*]. Again for symmetrical magnets the sum is taken over all odd electrical harmonics, i.e. $n = (2j - 1)$, $j = 1,2,3...$ and similar expressions are given for B_θ and for the field in the magnet itself.

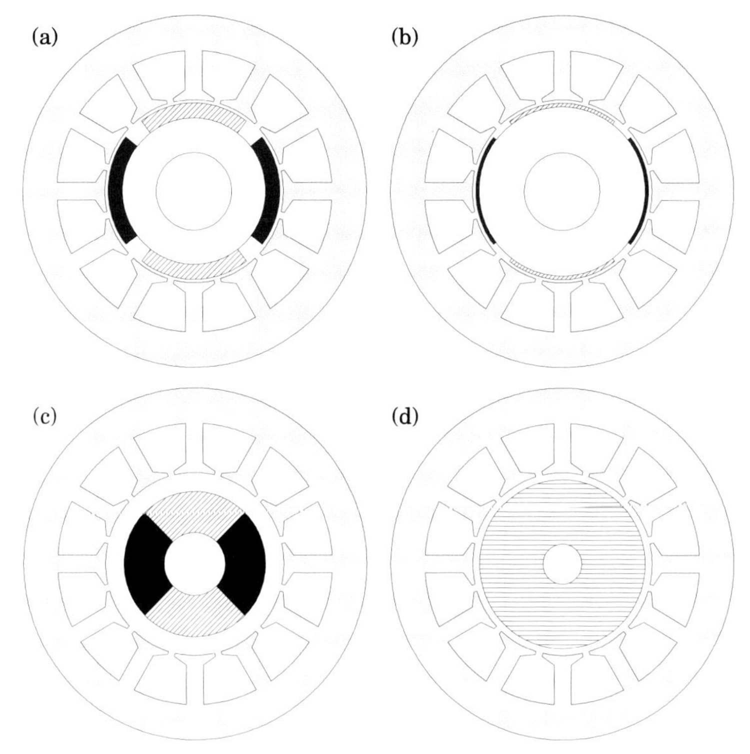

Fig. 4.10 Four rotors capable of accurate calculation with Hague-Boules method. Rotors (a) and (b) can also be calculated accurately with the magnetic equivalent circuit method.

These methods are useful for modelling Halbach-type magnets with sine-distributed magnetization, for example

$$\begin{aligned} M_1 &= B_r; \quad M_n = 0, \; n = 3,5,7,\ldots; \\ N_1 &= -B_r; \quad N_n = 0, \; n = 3,5,7,\ldots. \end{aligned} \tag{4.47}$$

The relative recoil permeability is incorporated formally in the solution, and so these methods do not require Boules' correction k_m.

In Fig. 4.10 (c) and (d) the large airgap makes it less likely that the steel will be saturated, while the field will have more "free shape"; the Hague-Boules method is appropriate in these cases. In cases (a) and (b) the field shape is more constrained, and the steel is more likely to be saturated; the magnetic equivalent-circuit method may be preferable in these cases.

4.1.3 Finite-element method

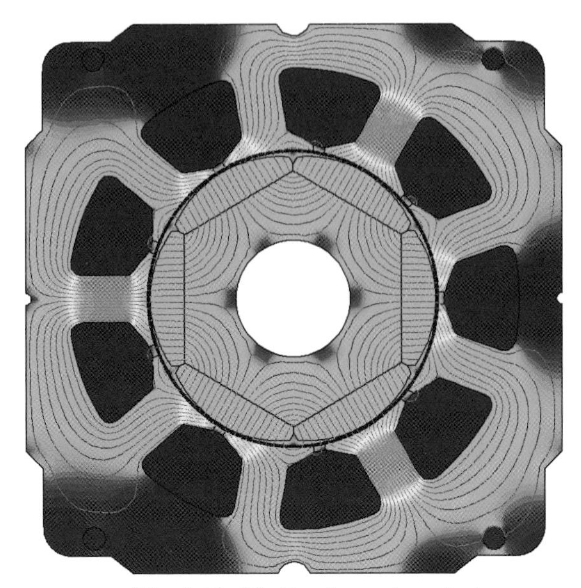

Fig. 4.11 Finite-element analysis

For thorough analysis of the magnetic field the finite-element method is by far the most powerful method. Although it may be slower than analytical methods, it is generally expected to reach an accurate result at the first attempt, so that less time needs to be spent on interpretation and validation.

The finite-element method is particularly effective in computing the details of local geometric features and the effects of arbitrary distributions of ampere-conductors and magnetization patterns. In the example in Fig. 4.11, it would be impossible to calculate the detailed effects of the irregular outside shape, or the effects of local saturation in narrow sections of the stator lamination. The profiled airgap could in principle be accommodated by the Hague-Boules method, but not with the flat-bottomed magnets. These details continually increase in importance, partly because of competitive pressure to improve performance and to reduce torque ripple and acoustic noise. Excellence in design ultimately comes down to the fine details, and at that level the finite-element method is an indispensable tool.

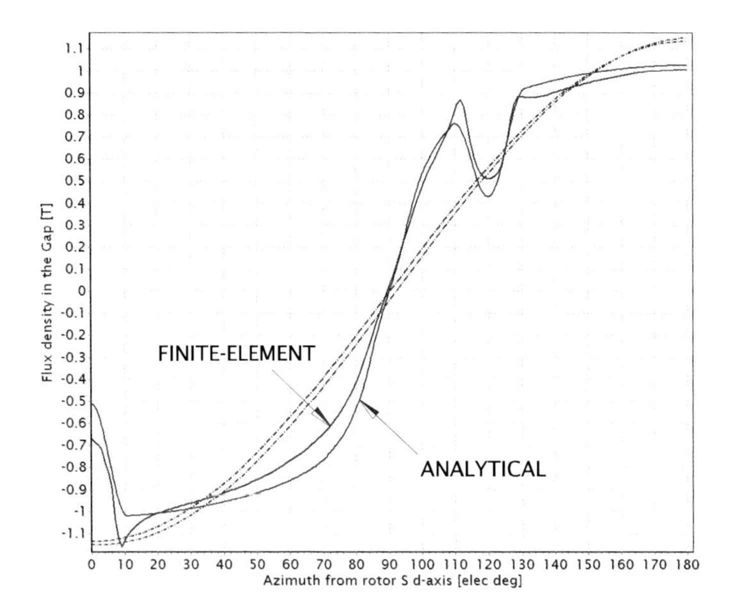

Fig. 4.12 Comparison of finite-element and analytical results for airgap flux distribution at the middle of the gap

Fig. 4.12 shows the comparison of the airgap flux-density distribution obtained by the finite-element and magnetic-circuit methods. The finite-element solution naturally includes the effect of the slot-openings, which is absent from the analytical solution obtained by the magnetic circuit method or the Hague-Boules method. The analytical distribution is obtained from Fig. 4.4 modulated by the slotting function described in Chapter 9.

Fig. 4.12 includes the fundamental harmonic component of the flux distribution, which is obtained from the actual distribution by

$$B_{g1} = -\frac{2}{\pi}\int_0^{\pi} B_g(\theta)\cos\theta\, d\theta . \tag{4.48}$$

The negative sign arises because the graph in Fig. 4.12 is plotted with a south (negative) pole at $\theta = 0$. It is important to note that this value of B_{g1} is peculiar to one radius and one rotor position. When the rotor moves, the slot-dips remain fixed in position, while the pole flux moves with the rotor; consequently the shape of $B_g(\theta)$ changes.

The fundamental flux per pole can be calculated from B_{g1} by

$$\Phi_{m1} = \frac{2}{\pi} \times B_{g1} \times \frac{\pi D}{2p} L = \frac{B_{g1} D L}{p}, \tag{4.49}$$

where D is the diameter of a cylinder at the middle of the airgap and L is the active length of the machine. The subscript m denotes the fact that this is magnet flux, on open-circuit, and the subscript 1 refers to the fundamental component.

The fundamental components in Fig. 4.12 can be made as close as desired by means of simple adjustments to the magnetic circuit calculation, but even when they are identical the result is far from satisfactory for the purposes of EMF calculation, as we shall see later.

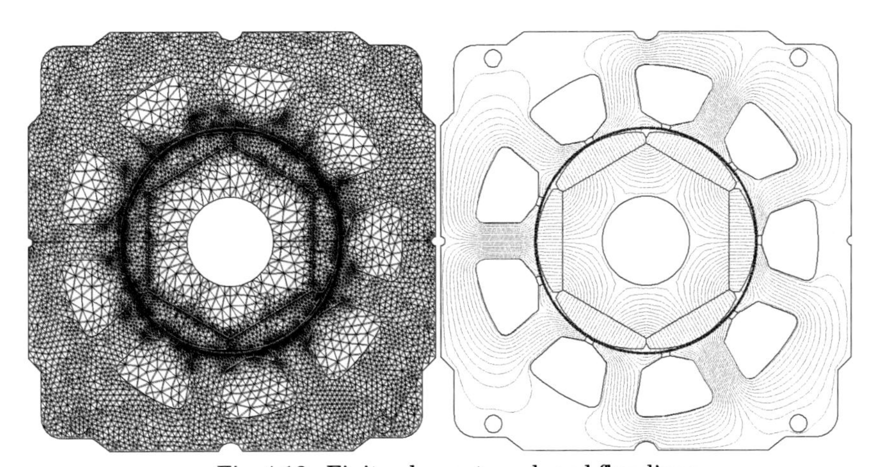

Fig. 4.13 Finite-element mesh and flux-lines

Fig. 4.13 shows the finite-element mesh and the flux-lines for the example in Figs. 4.11 and 4.12. The mesh has 23,555 elements and takes a few seconds to solve. Smaller elements are used in the neighbourhood of fine details such as corners or narrow sections (including the airgap). No matter how many elements are used, the division of the solution domain into triangles introduces discontinuities that do not exist in physical reality. The field is *approximated* within each element by shape functions which are not themselves solutions of the Maxwell equations. Collectively they converge to a solution, constrained by boundary conditions which are themselves approximations to physical reality. The convergence is driven by the minimization of an "energy functional", a process that requires the iterative solution of a large number of nonlinear algebraic equations. Convergence does not guarantee that the field value is correct at every single point. Parameters that arise from integrals, such as flux and flux-linkage, can be treated with more confidence than those that arise from derivatives, such as torque, EMF, and eddy-current loss. , and therefore the results should always be viewed critically and compared with physical test.

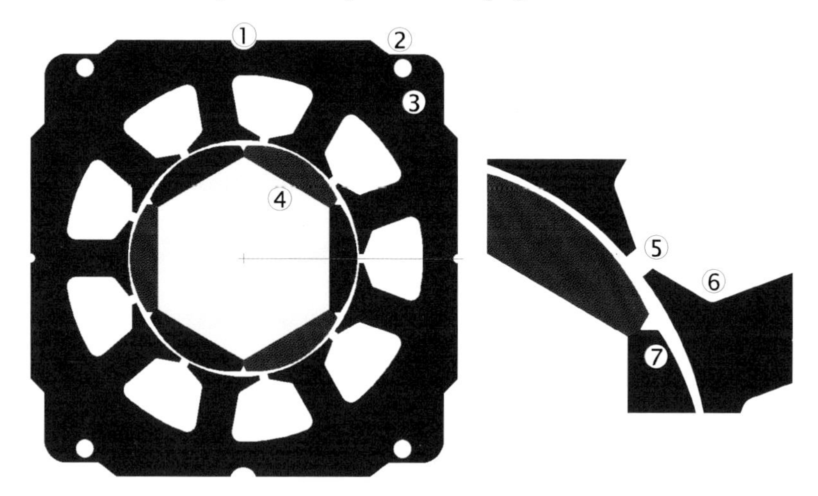

Fig. 4.14 Features that require finite-element analysis

But in spite of these cautions, Fig. 4.14 shows particular features of the example motor that are beyond the normal capacity of analytical methods and require finite-element analysis.

1. Notches and holes in the laminations.
2. Complicated outer edge of stator lamination.
3. Highly variable field distribution in the steel.
4. Non-circular shape of rotor hub.
5. Detailed geometry of slot-openings.
6. Detailed geometry of slots.
7. Profiled airgap and shape of magnet edges.

4.2 EMF

EMF is an "open-circuit" concept: we think of it as the induced voltage when the current is zero. We attribute it to the rotation of the magnets and write

$$e = \frac{\partial \psi}{\partial t} = \frac{\partial \psi}{\partial \theta} \cdot \frac{d\theta}{dt} = \omega \frac{\partial \psi}{\partial \theta} \quad [\mathrm{V}], \tag{4.50}$$

where ω is the angular velocity, θ is the rotor position, and ψ is the flux-linkage of the winding. The first expression $\partial\psi/\partial t$ is Faraday's law, which is not only incontrovertible but is also the basis on which flux-linkage is defined, that is,

$$\psi = \int e\,dt \quad [\mathrm{V{-}s}]. \tag{4.51}$$

Here ψ is the flux-linkage of the winding in which the EMF is induced, and since we have postulated that there is no current, it is the flux-linkage produced in the winding by the magnet. We have already seen in Chapter 1 how the rotation of the magnet causes the flux-linkage of the windings to alternate and so generate an alternating EMF, and we have seen in Fig. 1.4 that a trapezoidal flux-linkage waveform generates a rectangular EMF waveform.

Before considering further useful expressions and methods for calculating EMF, it is well to repeat that EMF is an open-circuit concept, and prepare ourselves to discover later that when current is flowing, the EMF can no longer be measured because the voltage at the terminals of the winding includes the resistive and inductive voltage drops due to the current. Moreover, when current is flowing it distorts the flux and the nonlinearity of the steel renders the magnet flux "unobservable": in other words, it cannot be separated from the total flux without making arbitrary assumptions. This is the problem of nonlinear armature reaction. It is not a new problem and it is not specific to permanent-magnet machines.

The methods in the following sections are all heavily used in different circumstances. The formula and BLV methods are more suitable for the classical methods of field calculation, while the tooth flux method is better with the finite-element method.

4.2.1 Formula

The formula

$$E = k_E \omega_m \tag{4.52}$$

is the primary formula for EMF in application engineering, and even when a drive system is being designed. The EMF constant k_E is closely related to the torque constant and appears in catalogue data.

Eqn. (4.52) is meaningful only when it is clear where the EMF E is measured. For three-phase motors it is often assumed to be the line-line value, but in many calculations (including most of those this book) it is better to use the phase value.

For DC motors the waveform of E is rarely mentioned because it is simply a horizontal line, normally with negligible ripple. Although the waveforms of individual coil EMFs are alternating and rich in features, the relatively large number of commutator segments and the smoothing effect of the collection process at the brushes remove all these features so that they are not observable at the terminals.

For *brushless* permanent-magnet machines the waveform $e(t)$ is alternating and its features are extremely important. The EMF of each phase is communicated to the DC terminals of the drive through large angles of rotation, without the smoothing effect of a commutator. In defining k_E it therefore becomes necessary to specify what measure of the EMF waveform is being used.

4.2.1.1 EMF constant of squarewave motors

Referring to Fig. 1.3 and 1.4, the peak flux-linkage per phase is

$$\psi_{pk} = k_w T_{ph} \Phi_g \tag{4.53}$$

where T_{ph} is the number of turns in series per phase, Φ_g is the airgap flux/pole due to the magnet, and k_w is a winding factor representing the fact that not all the flux links all of the turns. In Fig. 1.3 the flux-linkage of a full-pitch coil changes from $-\psi_{pk}$ to $+\psi_{pk}$ in just $\alpha\pi$ radians of rotation, where α is the per-unit pole arc. This takes

$$\Delta t = \frac{\alpha \pi}{p \omega_m} \ \text{s}. \tag{4.54}$$

The average phase EMF during this 120° rotation is

$$e_{\mathrm{ph}} = \frac{2\psi_{\mathrm{pk}}}{\Delta t} = \frac{2}{\pi}\frac{k_{\mathrm{w}} T_{\mathrm{ph}} \Phi_{\mathrm{g}} p\, \omega_{\mathrm{m}}}{\alpha}. \tag{4.55}$$

If there are two phases in series during any 60° interval, as in a wye connection, both having the same flat-topped EMF, the EMF constant appears as

$$k_{\mathrm{E}} = \frac{e_{\mathrm{LLpk}}}{\omega_{\mathrm{m}}} = \frac{4}{\pi}\frac{k_{\mathrm{w}} T_{\mathrm{ph}} \Phi_{\mathrm{g}} p}{\alpha} \quad [\mathrm{V\,s/rad}]. \tag{4.56}$$

This is sometimes written in terms of the total number of conductors $Z = 3 \times 2 \times T_{\mathrm{ph}} a$, where a is the number of parallel paths; thus

$$k_{\mathrm{E}} = \frac{e_{\mathrm{LLpk}}}{\omega_{\mathrm{m}}} = \frac{2}{3}\frac{k_{\mathrm{w}} Z \Phi_{\mathrm{g}} p}{a\,\alpha\,\pi} \quad [\mathrm{V s/rad}]. \tag{4.57}$$

For delta connection, the 2/3 factor is replaced by 1/3. For a 1-phase or 2-phase motor, k_{E} would be defined simply as $e_{\mathrm{ph}}/\omega_{\mathrm{m}}$. It cannot be emphasized too strongly that the k_{E} formula applies to the peak EMF and says nothing about the waveform. In particular it says nothing about the effect of the per-unit pole-arc α on the EMF waveform, yet this can be crucial as we will see later. Also the winding factor k_{w} is important for squarewave motors in representing the fact that not all the turns link all the flux. If the coils are sufficiently concentrated with a span nearly equal to full-pitch, k_{w} will be nearly 1; but if the coils are short-pitched or skewed, k_{w} will be less than 1.

4.2.1.2 EMF constant of sinewave motors

The fundamental EMF in a sinewave motor is deduced from the fact that the fundamental flux-linkage in each phase is sinusoidal with peak value

$$\Psi_{\mathrm{m1}} = k_{\mathrm{w1}} T_{\mathrm{ph}} \Phi_{\mathrm{m1}} \quad [\mathrm{V\,s}] \tag{4.58}$$

and frequency $f = \omega/2\pi = p \times \mathrm{RPM} \times \pi/30$ Hz. The fundamental EMF per phase is therefore

$$E_{\mathrm{ph}} = \frac{\omega \Psi_{\mathrm{m1}}}{\sqrt{2}} \quad [\mathrm{V\,rms}] \tag{4.59}$$

and this is written

$$E_{\mathrm{ph}} = \frac{\omega_{\mathrm{m}} p k_{\mathrm{w1}} T_{\mathrm{ph}} \Phi_{\mathrm{m1}}}{\sqrt{2}} \quad [\mathrm{V}]. \tag{4.60}$$

The peak value is √2 times greater, and for a wye connection the peak line-line EMF is √3 times greater again; hence the EMF constant is

$$k_{\mathrm{E}} = \frac{e_{\mathrm{LLpk}}}{\omega_{\mathrm{m}}} = \frac{\sqrt{3}\,E_{\mathrm{ph}} \times \sqrt{2}}{\omega_{\mathrm{m}}} = \sqrt{3} p k_{\mathrm{w1}} T_{\mathrm{ph}} \Phi_{\mathrm{m1}} \quad [\mathrm{V\ s/rad}]. \tag{4.61}$$

For a delta connection the √3 factor is omitted, and the same for 1-phase or 2-phase motors.

The fundamental flux/pole can be substituted from eqn. (4.49) on p. 176 to give the alternative expression for wye-connected motors:

$$k_{\mathrm{E}} = \frac{e_{\mathrm{LLpk}}}{\omega_{\mathrm{m}}} = = \frac{\sqrt{3} p k_{\mathrm{w1}} T_{\mathrm{ph}} B_{\mathrm{g1}} D L}{p} \quad [\mathrm{V\ s/rad}]. \tag{4.62}$$

The fundamental EMF/phase E_{q1} is also given by

$$E_{\mathrm{q1}} = \frac{e_{\mathrm{LL\,pk}}}{\sqrt{3} \times \sqrt{2}} = \frac{p k_{\mathrm{w1}} T_{\mathrm{ph}} \Phi_{\mathrm{m1}}}{\sqrt{2}} \omega_{\mathrm{m}} \quad [\mathrm{V\ rms}]. \tag{4.63}$$

The significance of the subscript q1 will appear later.

4.2.2 BLV waveform method

All the formula methods of EMF calculation are derived from the theory of classical DC and AC machines operating from pure DC or pure sinusoidal AC supplies. The brushless PM machine can operate with a flat-topped trapezoidal EMF waveform or a sinusoidal EMF waveform, but in all cases the actual EMF waveform is critical in defining its operation, particularly in relation to the current control and the torque ripple. The remainder of §4.2 is therefore concerned with the calculation of the whole EMF waveform, and not merely its peak or RMS value. Following classical principles, we begin with the idea of EMF in individual conductors and accumulate the EMF of the entire winding.

The BLV method is based on the notion that the EMF generated along the length of a conductor moving in a magnetic field is equal to the flux-density B times the length L times the velocity V, under the tacit assumption that these three quantities are pointing in mutually orthogonal directions. An alternative expression is that the induced electric field is $\mathbf{E}$ is equal to the vector product $\mathbf{V} \times \mathbf{B}$, which is useful for helping to remember the direction of the EMF.

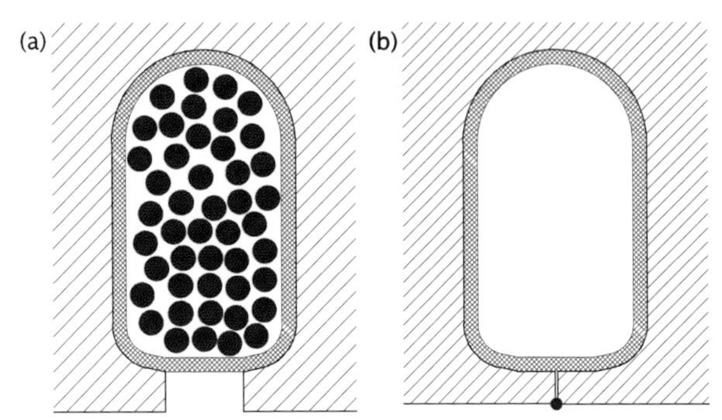

Fig. 4.15 Filament representing slot conductors

It is obvious from Figs. 4.11 and 4.13 that conductors laid in slots are not only not moving, but they are also located in a magnetic field that is practically zero. The BLV formula clearly does not apply. In order to render it usable the slot conductors in (a) are represented by a single filament located at the centre-line of a fictitious slot-opening of zero width, while the airgap is enlarged by Carter's coefficient to take account of the slotting, (b).

When the EMF in the filament is calculated by the BLV formula, B is notionally the B_{gap} distribution in Fig. 4.12 but *without slot-modulation*, because the "slot-dips" are not moving relative to the stator. The B_{gap} distribution without slot-modulation can of course be calculated by classical analytical methods if the stator surface is considered smooth and the airgap is modified by Carter's coefficient. However, it is impossible to remove the slot-dips from the finite-element B_{gap} distribution, so the BLV method cannot sensibly be used with the finite-element method in machines with slots.

If the conductors are located in the airgap (for example, in slotless machines), the BLV method can be used with the finite-element B_{gap} distribution, although B_{gap} will be different for each conductor.

4.2.3 Toothflux waveform method

Referring to Fig. 4.16, the EMF induced in a coil wound around one tooth is

$$e_T = N \omega_m \frac{\partial \phi_T}{\partial \theta}, \qquad (4.64)$$

where N is the number of turns and ϕ_T is the flux in the tooth. Slot flux is generally very small and is therefore neglected.

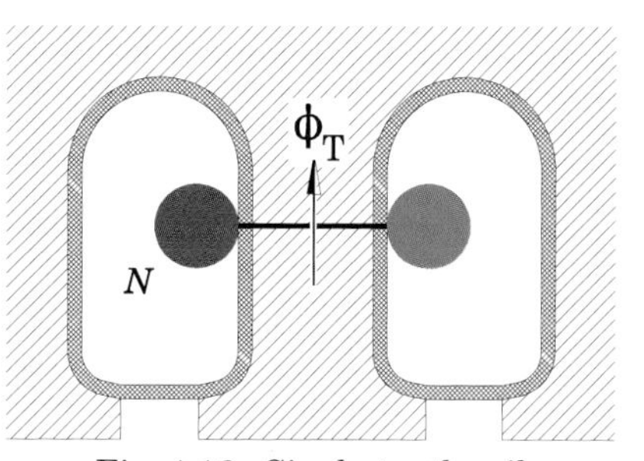

Fig. 4.16 Single-tooth coil

It is relatively straightforward to calculate the waveform of $\phi_T(\theta)$ as a function of rotor position θ by means of a series of finite-element solutions at discrete rotor positions over 180°elec. Then e_T can be computed by differencing.

When the field is calculated by the magnetic circuit method or by the Hague-Boules method, the waveform ϕ_T can be calculated from the integral of the B_{gap} distribution over the tooth arc τ as shown in Fig. 4.17. The B_{gap} distribution should be the one without slot modulation. The integral must be repeated over a sequence of angles covering 180° elec.; thereafter the EMF is calculated by differencing, as above.

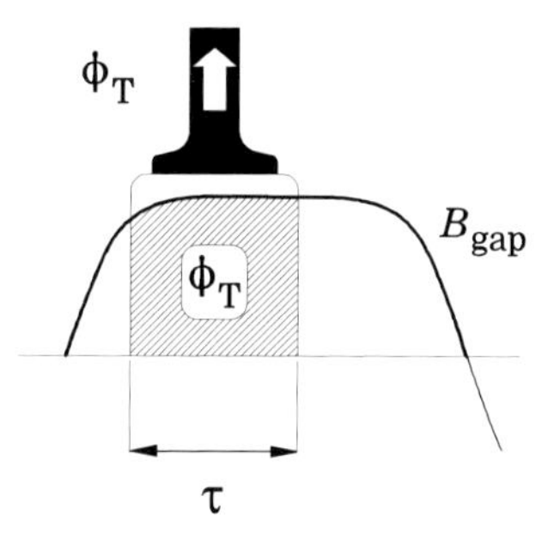

Fig. 4.17 Calculating tooth flux

When the slots/pole is small, the integration in Fig. 4.17 becomes unsafe because of leakage from pole to pole, as can be seen under tooth 2 in Fig. 4.18. There is no exact solution to this problem and it is necessary to use the finite-element method.

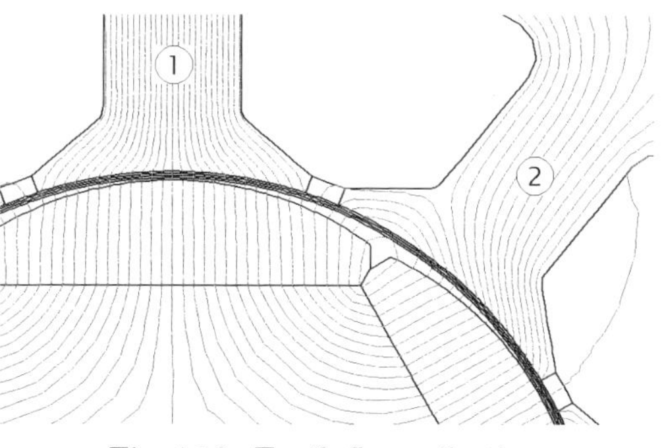

Fig. 4.18 Tooth flux collection

The phase EMF can be constructed from a summation of single-tooth coil EMFs even when the coil-span is more than one tooth. A coil wound in slots 1–10 is magnetically equivalent to a set of nine single-tooth coils in slots 1–2, 2–3, . . . , 9–10. The e_T waveforms are similar, but shifted in phase by one slot-pitch from one another. The summation must be done for every sample of the waveforms.

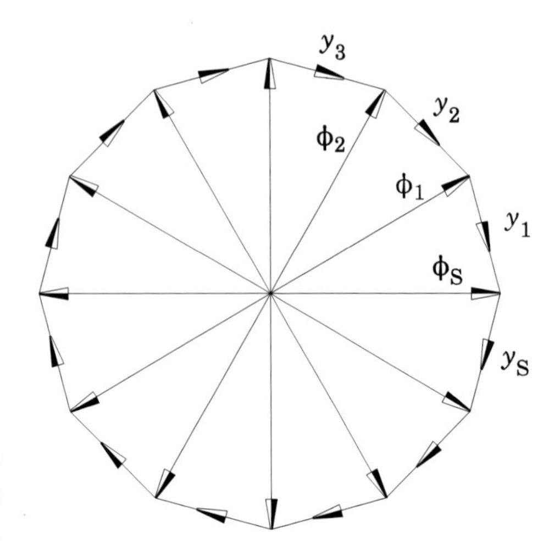

Fig. 4.19 Yoke flux construction

Development of yoke flux waveform — The yoke fluxes y_j are shown together with the tooth fluxes ϕ_j in Fig. 4.19. Evidently

$$\phi_j = y_j - y_{j+1}, \quad j = 1,2, \ldots S, \tag{4.65}$$

where S is the number of teeth, and

$$y_1 + y_2 + \ldots \; y_S = 0. \tag{4.66}$$

Then

$$\begin{aligned} y_2 &= y_1 - \phi_1 \\ y_3 &= y_2 - \phi_2 = y_1 - \phi_1 - \phi_2 \\ &\cdots \\ y_S &= y_1 - \phi_1 - \phi_2 - \ldots - \phi_{S-1} \end{aligned} \tag{4.67}$$

Adding these together with y_1,

$$\begin{aligned} & y_1 + (y_1 - \phi_1) + (y_1 - \phi_1 - \phi_2) + \ldots \\ & \ldots + (y_1 - \phi_1 - \phi_2 - \ldots - \phi_{S-1}) = 0, \end{aligned} \tag{4.68}$$

from which

$$y_1 = \frac{1}{S} \sum_{j=1}^{S-1} (S - j) \phi_j . \tag{4.69}$$

Then $y_2, y_3, \ldots, y_S$ follow from eqns. (4.67). Again the summation must be executed sample-by-sample over 180° elec.

4.3 Torque

It is important to distinguish between instantaneous torque and average torque. Consider first a rotary machine with only one winding, having a flux-linkage ψ produced by a magnet that can rotate. The coenergy is defined as

$$W_c = \int_0^i \psi di \quad [\mathrm{J}], \qquad (4.70)$$

and this is the hatched area labelled W_c in Fig. 4.20. The dimensions of coenergy are those of energy.

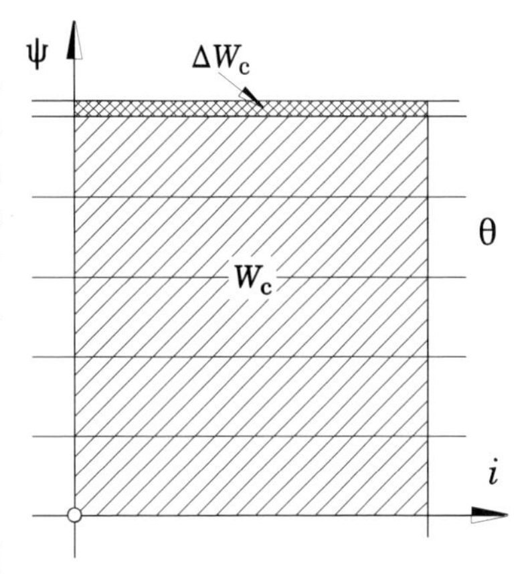

Fig. 4.20 Torque from coenergy

The flux linkage ψ here is entirely due to the magnet. Additional flux-linkage due to the self-inductance of the winding can be left out of consideration as long as the self-inductance remains constant.

When the rotor moves through an angle $\Delta\theta$, the flux-linkage changes by $\Delta\psi$ and the coenergy changes by ΔW_c. If the current remains constant there is no possibility of a change in stored energy, so the mechanical work exerted is $T_e\Delta\theta = \Delta W_c$, where T_e is the instantaneous torque, and from Fig. 4.20 this is equal to $i\Delta\psi$. In the limit as $\Delta\theta \to 0$, this can be expressed in differential form

$$T_e = \left.\frac{\partial W_c}{\partial \theta}\right|_{i=\mathrm{const}} = i\frac{\partial \psi}{\partial \theta}. \qquad (4.71)$$

We have already seen from eqn. (1.4) that the EMF generated by rotation of the magnet flux is

$$e = \omega_m \frac{\partial \psi}{\partial \theta}. \qquad (4.72)$$

It follows from these equations that

$$T_e \omega_m = ei. \qquad (4.73)$$

which is the same as eqn. (1.6). The derivation of this equation is practically the same as that on p. 7.

4.3.1 Torque constants

4.3.1.1 Three-phase squarewave motor

In a three-phase brushless permanent-magnet motor with wye-connected windings and constant inductances, the instantaneous torque is the sum of contributions from all three phases, that is,

$$T_e \omega_m = e_a i_a + e_b i_b + e_c i_c. \tag{4.74}$$

With "two-phase-on" operation one of the currents is always zero while the other two phases carry the DC current I, for example,

$$i_a = -i_b = I; \quad i_c = 0. \tag{4.75}$$

Then

$$T_e \omega_m = (e_a - e_b) I = e_{ab} I, \tag{4.76}$$

where e_{ab} is the line-line EMF between phases a and b. This condition persists for 60° elec before it is replaced by commutation, and another pair of phases behaves in the same way for the next 60°. If the line-line EMF is flat-topped during the 60° interval, and if the current I is also constant, then the torque will be constant (assuming the speed is also constant).

We can now define the **torque constant** k_T as

$$k_T = \frac{T_e}{I} = \frac{e_{LL}}{\omega_m} = k_E \quad [\mathrm{Nm/A}]. \tag{4.77}$$

The **average torque** is given by

$$T_{e\,avg} = \frac{1}{2\pi} \int_0^{2\pi} T_e(\theta)\, d\theta. \tag{4.78}$$

and if the instantaneous torque is constant, the average torque will be equal to the instantaneous torque, in this case $k_T I$. Usually when we speak of the torque, we mean the average torque.

If the windings are reconnected in delta without changing the turns, k_T and k_E will both be halved. This is evident from the fact that e_{LL} is equal to the phase voltage, which is half the line voltage in any 60° period. Also $e_b + e_c = -e_a$, while $i_a = 2I/3$ and $i_b = i_c = -I/3$, so $T_e = e_a \times 2I/3 + (e_b + e_c) \times (-I/3) = e_a I$ instead of $e_{ab} I$.

4.3.1.2 Sinewave motors

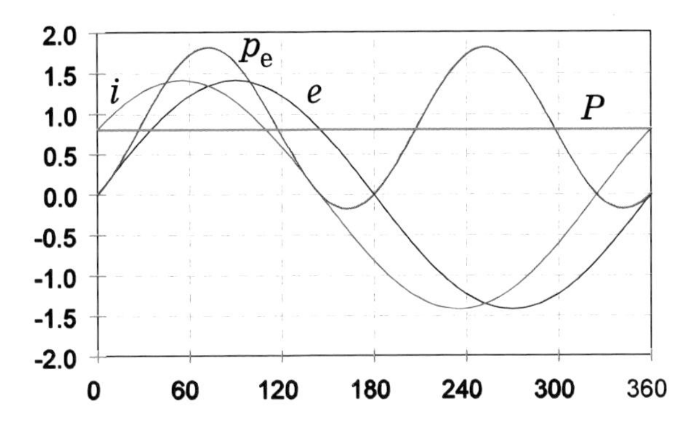

Fig. 4.21 Single-phase power

Consider a **single-phase machine** with a sinusoidal EMF:

$$e = \sqrt{2}E \sin \omega t \tag{4.79}$$

and suppose that the current waveform is also sinusoidal:

$$i = \sqrt{2}I \sin (\omega t + \gamma). \tag{4.80}$$

The EMF and current are not in phase unless $\gamma = 0$. A positive value of γ means that the current is leading the EMF. For the moment we will ignore the resistance and inductance of the windings.

The instantaneous power p_e is the product ei, which is

$$p_e = ei = EI[\cos \gamma - \cos (2\omega t + \gamma)]. \tag{4.81}$$

The sin-sin product becomes the sum of two cosine terms, one of which is *oscillatory* with a frequency 2ω, and the other is *constant* with a value $\cos \gamma$, which is effectively the power-factor angle between E and I. The constant term $P = EI \cos \gamma$ is the average power. The double-frequency oscillatory power has a constant amplitude EI.

If the power $p_e = ei$ is applied to the ideal energy-converter represented by eqn. (4.73), we get the electromagnetic torque

$$T_e = \frac{ei}{\omega_m} = \frac{EI}{\omega_m}[\cos \gamma - \cos (2\omega t + \gamma)]. \tag{4.82}$$

The nearest approach to this in practice would be a single-phase permanent-magnet machine with a sinusoidal EMF, negligible resistance and inductance, and no losses, operating at constant speed ω_m. The average torque is proportional to cos γ, but the double-frequency ripple has a constant amplitude.

Now consider a **2-phase machine** with balanced EMFs:

$$e_a = \sqrt{2}E \sin \omega t; \quad e_b = -\sqrt{2}E \cos \omega t. \tag{4.83}$$

Suppose the currents are slightly unbalanced:

$$i_a = \sqrt{2}I \sin(\omega t+\gamma); \quad i_b = -\sqrt{2}I(1+\varepsilon) \cos(\omega t+\gamma). \tag{4.84}$$

The currents are in phase quadrature, but i_b exceeds i_a by the factor $(1+\varepsilon)$. The power is

$$p_e = e_a i_a + e_b i_b = EI\,[(2+\varepsilon) \cos \gamma + \varepsilon \cos(2\omega t+\gamma)] \tag{4.85}$$

When the phases are balanced $\varepsilon = 0$ and the double-frequency oscillatory component vanishes, while the average component is exactly doubled (—in effect, multiplied by the number of phases). Again invoking the ideal energy-conversion process of eqn. (4.73), the instantaneous torque at constant speed is

$$T = \frac{p_e}{\omega_m} = \frac{2EI}{\omega_m} \cos \gamma, \tag{4.86}$$

which is constant. The elimination of the oscillatory or "pulsating" torque constitutes an enormous advantage of the balanced 2-phase motor over the 1-phase motor.

In a balanced **3-phase machine** the ripple torque is again eliminated, and

$$T = \frac{p_e}{\omega_m} = 3\frac{EI}{\omega_m} \cos \gamma \tag{4.87}$$

Balanced operation means that the EMFs are balanced,

$$\begin{aligned} e_a &= \sqrt{2}E \sin \omega t \\ e_b &= \sqrt{2}E \sin(\omega t - 2\pi/3) \\ e_c &= \sqrt{2}E \sin(\omega t + 2\pi/3) \end{aligned} \tag{4.88}$$

and the currents are also balanced:

$$\begin{aligned} i_a &= \sqrt{2}I \sin(\omega t + \gamma) \\ i_b &= \sqrt{2}I \sin(\omega t + \gamma - 2\pi/3) \\ i_c &= \sqrt{2}I \sin(\omega t + \gamma + 2\pi/3). \end{aligned} \tag{4.89}$$

The EMFs and currents are substituted in the equation

$$T_e = e_a i_a + e_b i_b + e_c i_c \tag{4.90}$$

to get the result in eqn. (4.87).

Torque constant — In eqns. (4.86) and (4.87), E is the RMS EMF per phase and I is the RMS phase current. Earlier in defining k_T for squarewave motors we used the peak *line* current with the same symbol I; but in the case of a 3-phase wye-connected motor the peak line current is $i_{L\,pk} = \sqrt{2}I$. Moreover the EMF constant was defined using the peak line-line EMF $e_{LL\,pk}$, which in the case of a 3-phase wye-connected motor is $\sqrt{3} \times \sqrt{2}E$. Putting $i_{L\,pk}$ and $e_{LL\,pk}$ into eqn. (4.87),

$$T = 3 \times \frac{e_{LLpk}/\omega_m}{\sqrt{3} \times \sqrt{2}} \times \frac{i_{Lpk}}{\sqrt{2}} \cos\gamma \tag{4.91}$$

and if we continue to define k_E as $e_{LL\,pk}/\omega_m$ this gives

$$k_T = \frac{T_e}{i_{Lpk}} = \frac{\sqrt{3}}{2} k_E \cos\gamma. \tag{4.92}$$

The $\sqrt{3}/2$ factor shows that it is not sufficient to quote the values of k_T and k_E without definition. We have used the same definitions as for squarewave motors, defining k_E as the ratio of peak line-line EMF and angular velocity, and k_T as the ratio of electromagnetic torque to peak line current. The $\sqrt{3}/2$ factor can be seen as an irksome consequence. However, k_T now also contains an equally "irksome" factor $\cos\gamma$, which is fundamentally meaningful and cannot be eliminated. When k_T is quoted, the phase angle γ should be quoted too. Phase-shift affects k_T in squarewave motors also, but it cannot be represented by such a simple factor as $\cos\gamma$, and is often ignored.

If a wye-connected motor is reconnected in delta, k_E and k_T both decrease by the factor $1/\sqrt{3}$. The $\sqrt{3}/2$ factor does not arise for 2-phase motors.

4.4 Torque and inductance

The addition of resistance and inductance in series with the EMFs makes no difference to the foregoing arguments provided that the inductance is constant and the current remains the same. In this section we consider machines with variable inductance, first in terms of phase variables and then in terms of dq-axis variables. The effect of harmonics in both the EMF and the current will be taken into account, but the effect of saturation is left to the i-ψ diagram in §4.5.

4.4.1 Salient-pole machines in phase variables

Saliency is the term used to describe the variation of inductance with rotor position θ. A machine in which the inductance varies with θ is described as a salient-pole machine, and a typical example is the interior-magnet machine or IPM.

So far we have developed the torque for the ideal energy-converter of eqn. (4.73), in which the inductance was assumed to be constant. The ideal energy-converter of eqn. (4.73) is therefore a nonsalient-pole machine, and in practice it is approximated by surface-magnet machines with low inductance and minimal saturation. Although the stored field energy is finite in such machines, and although it varies when the current varies, it plays no part in the generation of torque.

In magnetically linear machines the torque equation can be derived from power-balance considerations in terms of an equivalent circuit containing EMF, resistance, and inductance. In a single-phase machine the formula for instantaneous electromagnetic torque is

$$T_e = ei + \frac{1}{2} i^2 \frac{dL}{d\theta} = T_{ei} + T_{rel}. \tag{4.93}$$

The ei term is the **alignment torque** of eqn. (4.73). The second term is the **reluctance torque**, which is proportional to the rate of change of inductance with rotor position. It must be the case that the variation of inductance is periodic, with p cycles per revolution. If the machine is symmetric, there will be equal intervals of positive and negative $dL/d\theta$. Since the reluctance torque is proportional to i^2, there will be equal intervals of positive and negative reluctance torque, and no contribution to the average torque. Moreover, the instantaneous torque is no longer proportional to the current.

Eqn. (4.93) can be generalized for more phases. For example, with three phases a,b,c

$$
\begin{aligned}
T_e &= \frac{1}{\omega_m}\left[e_a i_a + e_b i_b + e_c i_c\right] \\
&+ \frac{1}{2}\left[i_a^2 \frac{dL_a}{d\theta} + i_b^2 \frac{dL_b}{d\theta} + i_c^2 \frac{dL_c}{d\theta}\right] \\
&+ i_a i_b \frac{dL_{ab}}{d\theta} + i_b i_c \frac{dL_{bc}}{d\theta} + i_c i_a \frac{dL_{ca}}{d\theta}.
\end{aligned}
\tag{4.94}
$$

In Chapter 5 we will see that in a 3-phase machine the phase self-inductances L_{aa}, L_{bb}, L_{cc} and the phase-to-phase mutual inductances L_{ab}, L_{bc}, L_{ca} can be written in the form

$$
\begin{aligned}
L_{aa}(\theta) &= L_0 + L_2 \cos 2\theta \\
L_{bb}(\theta) &= L_0 + L_2 \cos(2\theta + 2\pi/3) \\
L_{cc}(\theta) &= L_0 + L_2 \cos(2\theta - 2\pi/3) \\
L_{ab}(\theta) &= L_{ba} = M_0 + M_2 \cos(2\theta - 2\pi/3) \\
L_{bc}(\theta) &= L_{cb} = M_0 + M_2 \cos(2\theta) \\
L_{ca}(\theta) &= L_{ac} = M_0 + M_2 \cos(2\theta + 2\pi/3).
\end{aligned}
\tag{4.95}
$$

The variation of inductance with rotor position is restricted to a single term in θ, representing a double-frequency harmonic variation of inductance. In other words, the self-inductance of any phase will have two maxima and two minima in one electrical cycle of rotation. The mutual inductance between any two phases behaves similarly.

The reluctance torque is calculated from the $dL/d\theta$ terms in eqn. (4.94), and for sinewave operation it can be evaluated by substituting eqns. (4.89) and (4.95) into eqn. (4.94). For this purpose we can write

$$\theta = \omega t + \gamma \tag{4.96}$$

without loss of generality, where γ is constant at synchronous speed. The phase of the current relative to the rotor position is defined by γ. Then eqn. (4.94) gives

$$T_{rel} = 3I^2\left[\frac{L_2}{2} + M_2\right] \sin 2\gamma. \tag{4.97}$$

In Chapter 5 we will see that normally $L_2 = M_2$, so this becomes[23]

$$T_{\mathrm{rel}} = 3I^2 \times \frac{3}{2} L_2 \sin 2\gamma . \tag{4.98}$$

which is constant. With balanced operation there is no torque ripple: The same is true in a balanced 2-phase motor.

If $i_b = i_c = 0$, we have single-phase operation, which is highly unbalanced, and eqn. (4.94) gives

$$T_{\mathrm{rel}} = L_2 I^2 \left[\frac{1}{2} \sin \gamma - \sin 2\theta + \frac{1}{2} \sin (4\theta - 2\gamma) \right] \tag{4.99}$$

which shows that the single-phase reluctance motor has both a 2nd and a 4th harmonic torque ripple at synchronous speed. The average is only 1/9 of that of the 3-phase machine. A reduction of 1/3 is attributable to the two absent self-inductance terms, but even with all three currents flowing the self-inductance terms contribute only 1/3 of the total, so the overall reduction is by a factor of 9.

In the application of eqn. (4.94), eqn. (4.98) is an example of the derivation of a constant steady-state torque component, while eqn. (4.99) is an example of the computation of a torque component that varies with rotor position. Much algebraic manipulation is needed in both cases, which makes the method slow and error-prone.

Moreover, the computation of inductance derivatives is fraught with difficulty. If the finite-element method is used, differentiation is subject to discretization error, and it is unclear whether total or incremental inductance should be being used. Indeed any analysis that relies on inductance is strictly limited to magnetically linear machines, because the magnet flux and the armature reaction flux do not combine linearly in the general case.

The circuit-based equations do provide more useful physical insight than the direct use of eqn. (4.71), and in the next section we will continue it by using the *dq*-axis transformation to simplify the form of the equations and prepare the ground for the i-ψ loop which can deal with saturation and harmonics at the same time.

---

[23]This is consistent with the reluctance torque obtained using *dq*-axis theory in eqn. (7.18), where $L_2 = (L_d - L_q)/3$.

4.4.2 Salient-pole machines in dq axes

The dq transformation was developed to avoid the complexity of eqn. (4.94). The following exposition of the dq-axis transformation leads to a compact equation for instantaneous torque in dq axes.

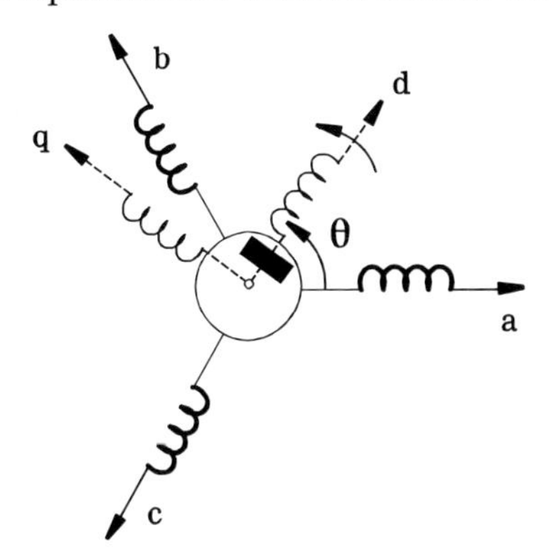

Fig. 4.22 dq axis reference

The dq-axis transformation (*Park's transformation*) is

$$\begin{aligned}\psi_d &= \frac{2}{3}[\psi_a \cos\theta + \psi_b \cos(\theta - 2\pi/3) + \psi_c \cos(\theta + 2\pi/3)];\\ \psi_q &= -\frac{2}{3}[\psi_a \sin\theta + \psi_b \sin(\theta - 2\pi/3) + \psi_c \sin(\theta + 2\pi/3)].\end{aligned} \tag{4.100}$$

It is the same for voltages, flux-linkages, and currents. θ is defined in Fig. 4.22 as the angle between the d-axis and the axis of phase a in electrical radians. The transformation appears in the literature in various forms with different coefficients; but its aim is always the same: namely to project the actual phase quantities from the stationary reference frame a,b,c to the rotating frame dq which is fixed to the rotor. If we apply the transform to the sinewave currents from eqn. (4.89), with $\theta = \omega t - \pi$, we get

$$i_d = -\sqrt{2}I \sin\gamma; \quad i_q = \sqrt{2}I \cos\gamma; \tag{4.101}$$

and these currents are **constant**. Similarly the EMFs, flux-linkages, and voltages are constant in dq axes in the steady-state. The choice of reference axis $\theta = \omega t - \pi$ means that a south pole is aligned with the axis of phase a at $t = 0$, and is consistent with the conventions used later in the phasor diagram.

The inverse transformation is given by

$$\begin{aligned}\psi_a &= \psi_d \cos\theta - \psi_q \sin\theta \\ \psi_b &= \psi_d \cos(\theta - 2\pi/3) - \psi_q \sin(\theta - 2\pi/3) \\ \psi_c &= \psi_d \cos(\theta + 2\pi/3) - \psi_q \sin(\theta + 2\pi/3).\end{aligned} \tag{4.102}$$

The dq transformation can be written as a matrix operator **T**,

$$\mathbf{T} = \frac{2}{3}\begin{bmatrix} C & C_- & C_+ \\ -S & -S_- & -S_+ \\ \frac{1}{2} & \frac{1}{2} & \frac{1}{2} \end{bmatrix}; \quad \text{Park's transform} \tag{4.103}$$

and its inverse $\mathbf{T}^{-1}$ is

$$\mathbf{T}^{-1} = \frac{3}{2}\mathbf{T}' = \begin{bmatrix} C & -S & 1 \\ C_- & -S_- & 1 \\ C_+ & -S_+ & 1 \end{bmatrix} \tag{4.104}$$

where $C = \cos\theta$, $C_- = \cos(\theta - 2\pi/3)$, $C_+ = \cos(\theta + 2\pi/3)$, and $S = \sin\theta$, $S_- = \sin(\theta - 2\pi/3)$, $S_+ = \sin(\theta + 2\pi/3)$. The zero-sequence component is included, because in general three independent *abc* variables must be transformed into three $dq0$ variables. With a 3-wire connection only two of the three *abc* variables are independent and the zero-sequence components are generally ignored; in any case the zero-sequence component plays no part in the torque equation.

If $\mathbf{v}_{abc}$ is the column vector of instantaneous voltages $[v_a, v_b, v_c]$, $[i_a, i_b, i_c]$ the column vector of instantaneous phase currents, etc., the transformations can be written in the concise form

$$\mathbf{v}_{dq0} = \mathbf{T}\mathbf{v}_{abc} \tag{4.105}$$

and their inverses similarly. The instantaneous power is

$$\begin{aligned} p_{abc} &= \mathbf{v}_{abc}{}'\,\mathbf{i}_{abc} = \{\mathbf{T}^{-1}\mathbf{v}_{dq0}\}'\{\mathbf{T}^{-1}\mathbf{i}_{dq0}\} \\ &= \mathbf{v}_{dq0}{}'\,\frac{3}{2}\mathbf{T}\mathbf{T}^{-1}\mathbf{i}_{dq0} = \frac{3}{2}\mathbf{v}_{dq0}{}'\,\mathbf{i}_{dq0} = p_{dq0}. \end{aligned} \tag{4.106}$$

Note that $\mathbf{T}^{-1} = (3/2)\mathbf{T}'$, i.e., the transformation is nearly orthogonal, but not quite, because of the 3/2 factor. The power is "not invariant under the transformation" — fancy language to remind us to use the 3/2 factor when we are calculating power (or torque) in *dq* coordinates.

If we write **p** for the operator *d*/*dt*, the voltage equations of the individual phases are:

$$\begin{aligned} v_a &= Ri_a + \mathbf{p}\psi_a; \\ v_b &= Ri_b + \mathbf{p}\psi_b; \\ v_c &= Ri_c + \mathbf{p}\psi_c. \end{aligned} \qquad (4.107)$$

If we write eqns. (4.100) for voltages, and substitute eqns. (4.107) with **p** as a live operator (*d*/*dt*), and $\mathbf{p}\theta = \omega$, we get

$$\begin{aligned} v_d &= Ri_d + \mathbf{p}\psi_d - \omega\psi_q; \\ v_q &= Ri_q + \mathbf{p}\psi_q + \omega\psi_d. \end{aligned} \qquad (4.108)$$

Eqns. (4.108) appear to be *independent of the winding distribution*, since no assumption about the winding was needed to derive them.

The derivation of v_d is as follows:

$$\begin{aligned} v_d = {} & \frac{2}{3}[(Ri_a + \mathbf{p}\psi_a)\cos\theta \\ & \quad + (Ri_b + \mathbf{p}\psi_b)\cos(\theta - 2\pi/3) \\ & \quad + (Ri_c + \mathbf{p}\psi_c)\cos(\theta + 2\pi/3)] \\ = {} & \frac{2}{3}R[i_a\cos\theta + i_b\cos(\theta - 2\pi/3) + i_c\cos(\theta + 2\pi/3)] \\ & + \frac{2}{3}\left[\mathbf{p}\psi_a\cos\theta + \psi_a\sin\theta\cdot\mathbf{p}\theta\right] \\ & + \frac{2}{3}\left[\mathbf{p}\psi_b\cos(\theta - 2\pi/3) + \psi_b\sin(\theta - 2\pi/3)\cdot\mathbf{p}\theta\right] \\ & + \frac{2}{3}\left[\mathbf{p}\psi_c\cos(\theta + 2\pi/3) + \psi_c\sin(\theta + 2\pi/3)\cdot\mathbf{p}\theta\right] \\ = {} & Ri_d + \mathbf{p}\psi_d - \omega\psi_q. \end{aligned} \qquad (4.109)$$

and similarly for v_q. An expression for the instantaneous torque can be deduced from the power balance in the steady-state at constant speed. Under these conditions $\mathbf{p}\psi_d = \mathbf{p}\psi_q = 0$, and if resistance is ignored we get

$$v_d = -\omega\psi_q; \quad v_q = \omega\psi_d. \tag{4.110}$$

If these are substituted in eqn. (4.106) we get

$$p_e = p_{abc} = \frac{3}{2}(v_d i_d + v_q i_q) = \frac{3}{2}\omega(-\psi_q i_d + \psi_d i_q). \tag{4.111}$$

It follows that

$$T_e = \frac{p_e}{\omega/p} = \frac{3}{2}p(\psi_d i_q - \psi_q i_d), \tag{4.112}$$

where p is, of course, the number of pole-pairs and not the derivative operator d/dt. Under steady-state sinusoidal conditions,

$$\psi_d = \sqrt{2}\,\Psi_d;\ \psi_q = \sqrt{2}\,\Psi_q \quad \text{and} \quad i_q = \sqrt{2}\,I_q;\ i_d = \sqrt{2}\,I_d, \tag{4.113}$$

where Ψ_d, Ψ_q and I_d, I_q are RMS values. The torque is constant and can be written in terms of RMS quantities as

$$T_e = mp(\Psi_d I_q - \Psi_q I_d). \tag{4.114}$$

The number of phases m has been substituted in place of 3 in this equation, to permit the expression to be used for 2-phase motors.

The torque in eqn. (4.114) can be evaluated using flux-linkages computed by the finite-element method. For any pair of values I and γ the computed B_{gap} distribution is Fourier-analysed to give B_{1d} and B_{1q}, where B_{1d} is the peak value of the d-axis component and B_{1q} is the peak value of the q-axis component. Then Ψ_{d1} and Ψ_{q1} are obtained using

$$\Psi_{1d} = \frac{k_{w1}T_{ph}}{\sqrt{2}}\frac{B_{1d}DL_{stk}}{p}; \quad \Psi_{1q} = \frac{k_{w1}T_{ph}}{\sqrt{2}}\frac{B_{1q}DL_{stk}}{p}. \tag{4.115}$$

Then Ψ_{1d} and Ψ_{1q} are substituted for Ψ_d and Ψ_q respectively in eqn. (4.114). The method has the advantage that multiple solutions covering a range of I and γ can be obtained quickly without rotating the rotor and therefore without re-meshing. It can thus be used to produce a set of torque curves [sometimes called "T-gamma curves"], $T_e(I,\gamma)$, relatively quickly.

If the leakage reactance is saturable, the i-ψ loop should be used instead (see below).

4.5 i-psi loop

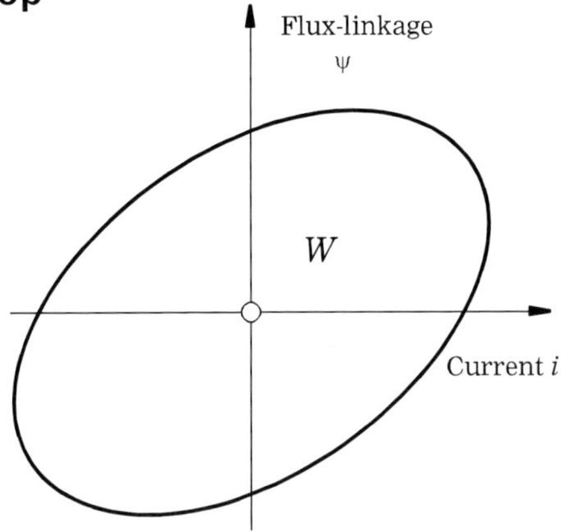

Fig. 4.23 i-psi loop for sinewave motor

In one electrical cycle the electromechanical energy conversion per phase is equal to the area W of a closed loop traced by the point whose coordinates are (i,ψ), the phase current and phase flux-linkage. With m phases and p electrical cycles per revolution, the average torque (including reluctance torque as well as alignment torque) is therefore

$$T_e = \frac{mp}{2\pi} \times W. \tag{4.116}$$

Fig. 4.23 shows an example for a sinewave machine. Suppose this machine has a sinusoidal airgap voltage and a sinusoidal current. In one phase,

$$v = \sqrt{2}\,V \cos \omega t; \quad i = \sqrt{2}\,I \cos (\omega t - \phi). \tag{4.117}$$

By Faraday's law the airgap voltage v is the time derivative of the flux-linkage ψ in the winding, so

$$\psi = \frac{\sqrt{2}\,V}{\omega} \sin \omega t = \sqrt{2}\,\Psi \sin \omega t, \tag{4.118}$$

where Ψ is the RMS flux-linkage, V/ω. Now the work done in one cycle by the vi product is given by

$$\begin{aligned} \int_0^T v i dt &= \frac{1}{\omega}\int_0^{2\pi} v\, i\, d\theta = \int_0^{2\pi} 2\,\Psi I \cos\theta \cos(\theta - \phi) d\theta \\ &= 2\pi \Psi I \cos\phi = W. \end{aligned} \tag{4.119}$$

This is the area of the loop formed by plotting ψ vs. i, Fig. 4.23. The mean electromagnetic torque is given by $W/(2\pi/p)$ where p is the number of pole-pairs. If there are m phases balanced, then

$$T_e = mp\Psi I \cos\phi = \frac{mp}{\omega} VI \cos\phi. \tag{4.120}$$

The induced voltage v includes not only the rotational EMF produced by the rotation of the magnet, but also the EMF induced by any variation in the phase self-inductance *and* the mutual inductance between phases. Consequently T_e includes the reluctance torque.

Now suppose the induced voltage and the current contain harmonics. It is enough to consider just one representative harmonic — the nth — by adding it to the fundamental: thus

$$\begin{aligned} v &= \sqrt{2}V_1 \cos\omega t + \sqrt{2}V_n \cos n\omega t; \\ i &= \sqrt{2}I_1 \cos(\omega t - \phi_1) + \sqrt{2}I_n \cos(n\omega t - \phi_n). \end{aligned} \tag{4.121}$$

The integral in eqn. (4.119) results in

$$W = 2\pi(\Psi_1 I_1 \cos\phi_1 + n\Psi_n I_n \cos\phi_n), \tag{4.122}$$

where $\Psi_n = V_n/n\omega$. Because of the othogonality of the harmonic functions, there are no cross-products involving V_n and I_1 or V_1 and I_n. This means that if the current is purely sinusoidal, harmonics in the voltage contribute no mean torque; conversely, if the voltage is purely sinusoidal, harmonics in the current contribute no mean torque. However, if the nth harmonic exists in *both* the voltage and the current, it will, in general, contribute to the mean torque.

Eqn. (4.122) can be written for the electromagnetic torque,

$$T_e = \frac{mp}{2\pi} W = \frac{mp}{\omega}\left[V_1 I_1 \cos\phi_1 + V_n I_n \cos\phi_n\right]. \tag{4.123}$$

In this equation V_1, I_1, V_n and I_n are all RMS quantities.

Eqn. (4.116) is not sensitive to the waveshape of the current or the flux-linkage, so the i-ψ loop can be used to calculate the torque for square-wave drives, as in Fig. 4.24, in which the current is regulated to follow a 120° squarewave by chopping.

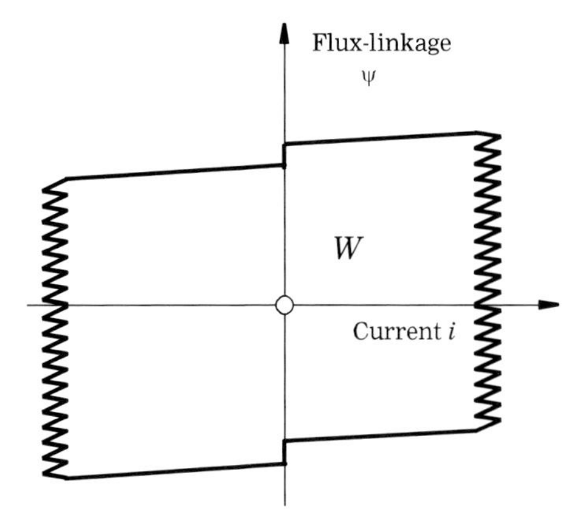

Fig. 4.24 i-psi loop for squarewave motor

In a 3-phase machine the *average* electromagnetic torque taken over one electrical cycle is given by

$$T_{e\,[avg]} = \frac{1}{2\pi} \times \frac{\text{Poles}}{2} \left[W_a + W_b + W_c \right] \tag{4.124}$$

where W_a is the "i-psi loop" area

$$W_a = \frac{1}{2} \oint (\psi_a \, di_a - i_a \, d\psi_a) \tag{4.125}$$

evaluated over one electrical cycle, and similarly for W_b and W_c. In normal balanced operation we can assume that $W_a = W_b = W_c$, so that only one i-psi loop need be evaluated (and multiplied by 3). Eqns. (4.124) and (4.125) are, in effect, the integral form of eqn. (4.71).

The i-ψ loop method requires the waveforms of current and flux-linkage in each phase. When the current waveform is known, it lends itself well to the finite-element method. The calculation proceeds in stepwise manner, creating a series of field solutions, one for each rotor position covering a complete electrical cycle. At each rotor position θ the phase flux-linkages in phase k are recovered using to a relationship of the form

$$\psi_k(\theta) = \sum_{q=1}^{N_k} T_{qk} \times [A_{gqk}(\theta) - A_{rqk}(\theta)] \tag{4.126}$$

where N_k is the number of coils in phase k, T_{qk} is the number of turns in the q'th coil of phase k, and $A_{gqk}(\theta)$ and $A_{rqk}(\theta)$ are the average vector potentials over the coil-sides of the go and return conductors of the q'th coil of phase k. At each step, the instantaneous phase currents i_1, i_2 and i_3 are assumed known, and the ampere-conductors in each slot are obtained from the conductor distribution according to a relationship of the form

$$AC[j] = \sum_{k=1}^{m} C[j,k] \times i[k] \tag{4.127}$$

where $AC[j]$ is the signed number of ampere-conductors in slot j, $C[j,k]$ is the signed number of conductors in slot j belonging to phase k, $i[k]$ is the instantaneous current in phase k, and m is the number of phases.

Examples — Figs. 4.25-36 show examples of i-ψ loops for different current and flux-linkage waveforms. The pure sinewaves in Fig. 4.25 give a perfectly elliptical loop, Fig. 4.26. Fig. 4.27 has −30% of 5th harmonic in the EMF, but no harmonics in the current. Consequently the loop area in Fig. 4.28 is the same as in Fig. 4.26. Fig. 4.29 has the converse: no harmonics in the EMF, but −30% of 5th harmonic in the current. Again the loop area, Fig. 4.30, is unchanged from Fig. 4.26. Fig. 4.31 has 30% of 5th harmonic in both the voltage and the current, and accordingly the loop area, Fig. 4.32, has changed.

Fig. 4.33 shows the interesting theoretical case of a pure squarewave current and triangular flux-linkage. The EMF waveform is rectangular and the i-ψ loop is a perfect rectangle, Fig. 4.34.

With 10% inductance and a phase advance as shown in Fig. 4.35, the loop is distorted in an interesting way, Fig. 4.36. The inductance adds a component of flux-linkage proportional to the current. The effect of phase-shift is to move the right-hand parallelogram vertically in the opposite direction to the left-hand parallelogram.

The i-psi loop is a practical method of calculating average torque in a saturated machine, especially when the flux-linkage waveform is obtained by finite-element analysis from a known current. Cogging torque is not included in the formulation described here, but in any case it has no average value over one cycle.

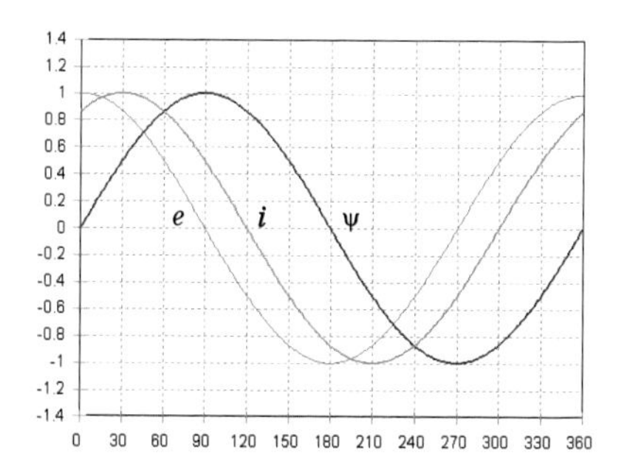

Fig. 4.25 $\phi_1 = 30°$; no harmonics

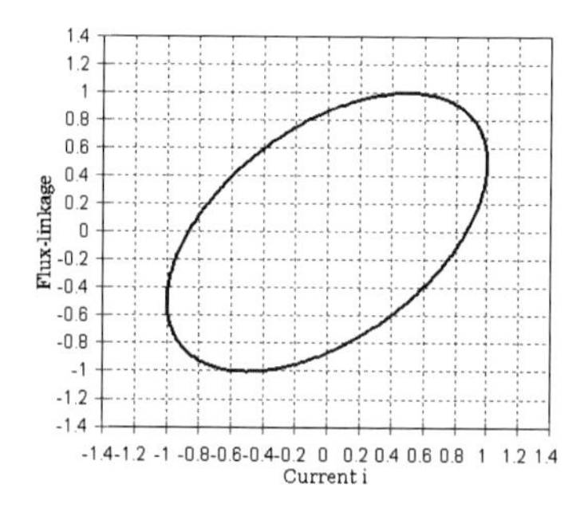

Fig. 4.26 $\phi_1 = 30°$; no harmonics

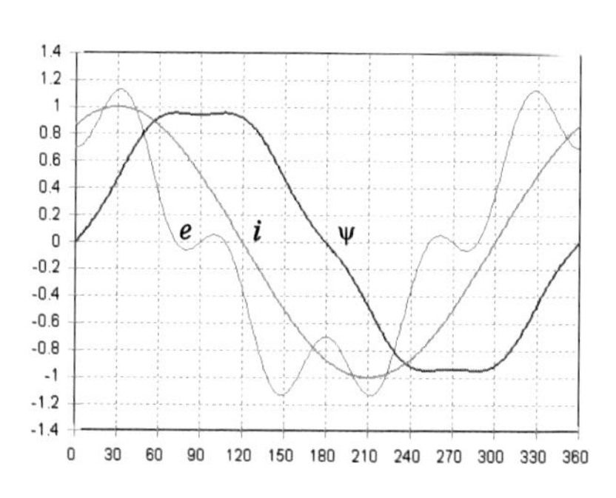

Fig. 4.27 $\phi_1 = 30°$; -30% 5th EMF

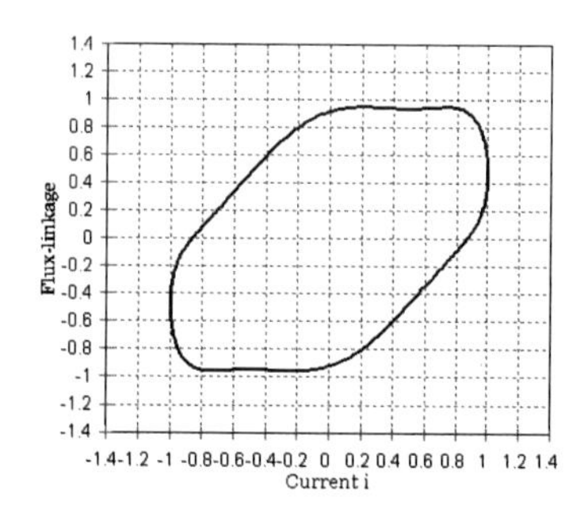

Fig. 4.28 $\phi_1 = 30°$; -30% 5th EMF

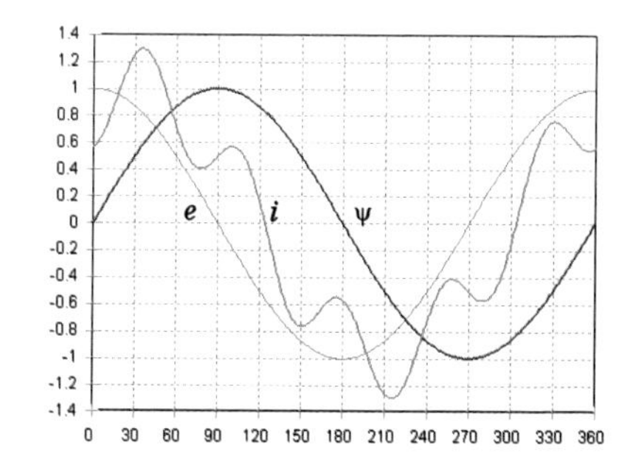

Fig. 4.29 $\phi_1 = 30°$; -30% 5th current

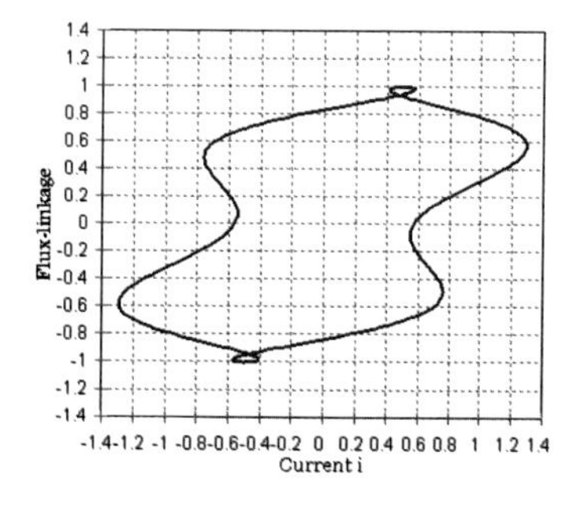

Fig. 4.30 $\phi_1 = 30°$; -30% 5th current

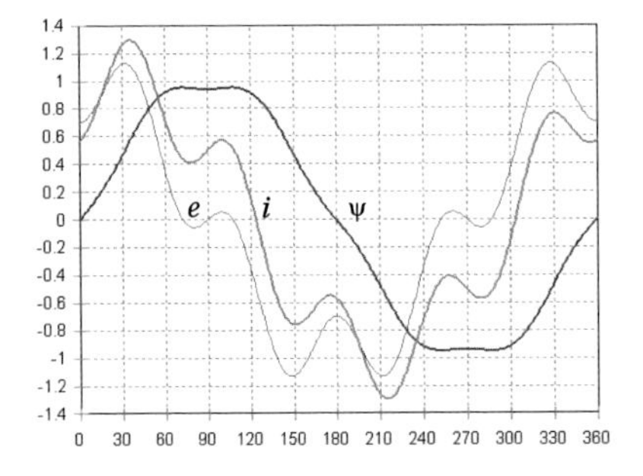

Fig. 4.31 −30% 5th current and EMF

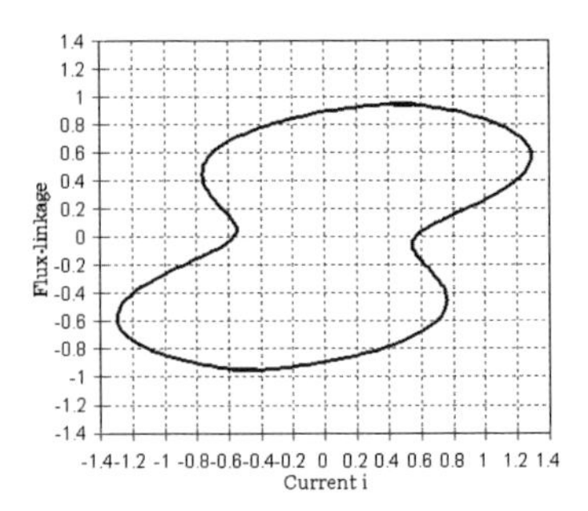

Fig. 4.32 −30% 5th current and EMF

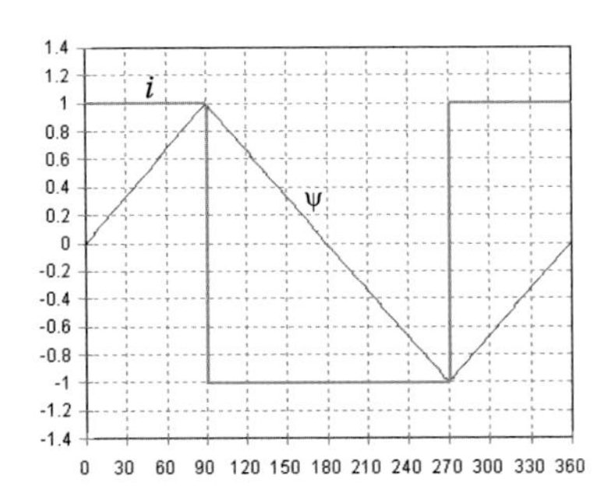

Fig. 4.33 180° square current

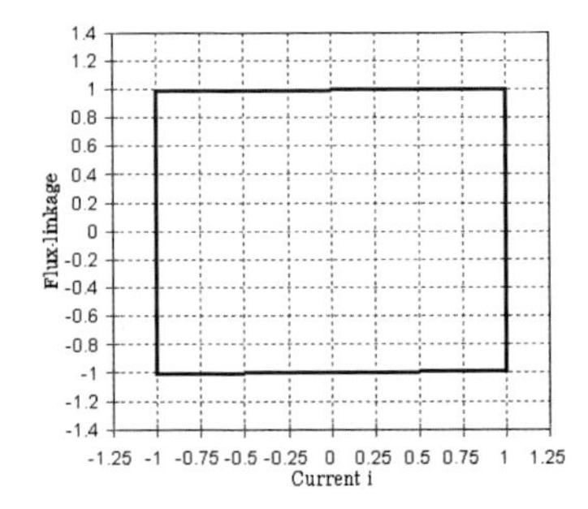

Fig. 4.34 180° square current

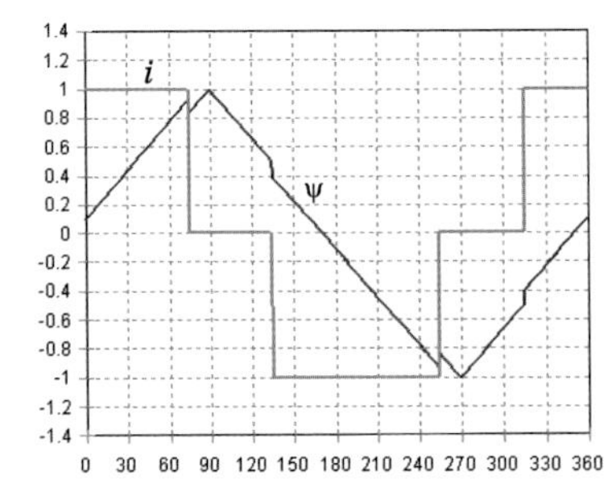

Fig. 4.35 120° current,10% inductance

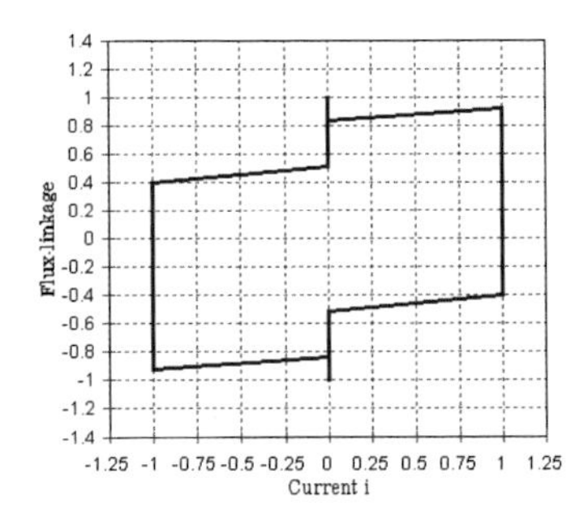

Fig. 4.36 120° current,10% inductance

4.6 Properties of the elliptical i-psi loop

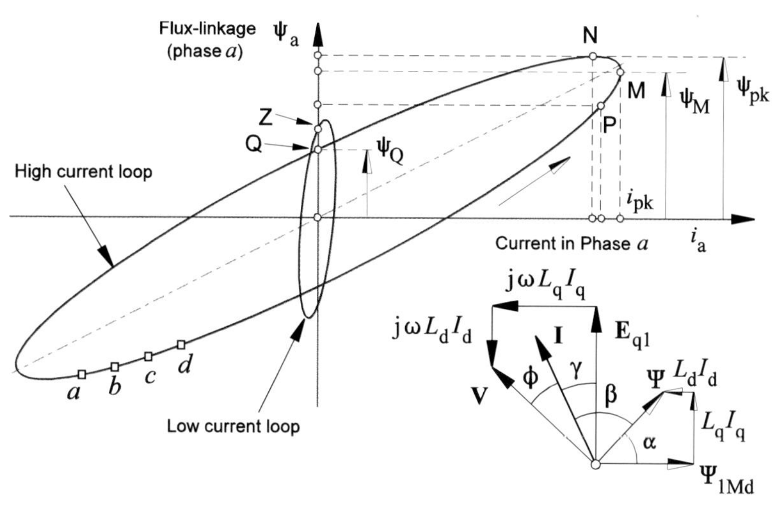

Fig. 4.37 i-ψ diagram or energy-conversion loop

Two elliptical i-ψ loops are shown in Fig. 4.37, for two operating conditions, one at high current and one at low current. The general form of the phasor diagram is also shown, together with the space phasor diagram of flux-linkages, in which Ψ_{1Md} is the notional "open-circuit" flux-linkage due to the magnet. $L_d I_d$ and $L_q I_q$ are the flux-linkages of armature reaction in the d- and q-axes respectively. The rotating fluxes associated with these flux-linkages generate the respective induced voltages: thus Ψ_{1Md} generates E_{q1}, $L_d I_d$ generates $j\omega L_d I_d$, $L_q I_q$ generates $j\omega L_q I_q$, and the resultant flux-linkage Ψ generates the total induced voltage V. Resistance is omitted.

Under ideal conditions the i-ψ loop is elliptical, which implies that both the current and the flux-linkage waveforms are sinusoidal in all three phases, and this in turn implies that L_d, L_q, Ψ_{1Md}, i_d and i_q are all constant throughout the cycle.

For the high-current loop, the current reaches its maximum positive value at **M**, and passes through a negative-going zero at **Q**. The flux-linkage ψ_a reaches its maximum value at **N**. Since the loop is traversed counterclockwise, **M** precedes **N**. This is consistent with the fact that **I** leads **Ψ**.

The phasor diagram tells us that the angle of rotation between **M** and **N** is β, which is the phase angle between the current **I** and the flux-linkage $\boldsymbol{\Psi}$. If we take the "open-circuit" flux-linkage Ψ_{1Md} as reference, we can use the phasor diagram to write the following equations for the instantaneous currents, with $\theta = \omega t$:

$$\begin{aligned} i_a &= i_{pk} \cos(\pi/2 + \gamma + \theta) &&= -i_{pk} \sin(\gamma + \theta); \\ i_b &= i_{pk} \cos(\pi/2 + \gamma + \theta - 2\pi/3) &&= -i_{pk} \sin(\gamma + \theta - 2\pi/3); \\ i_c &= i_{pk} \cos(\pi/2 + \gamma + \theta + 2\pi/3) &&= -i_{pk} \sin(\gamma + \theta + 2\pi/3). \end{aligned} \tag{4.128}$$

Note that i_{pk} is the abscissa at point **M**. If these equations are transformed into dq-axes [eqn. (4.100)], we get

$$i_d = -i_{pk} \sin \gamma; \quad i_q = +i_{pk} \cos \gamma. \tag{4.129}$$

in which i_d and i_q are constant. The corresponding equations for the instantaneous flux-linkages are

$$\begin{aligned} \psi_a &= -\psi_{pk} \sin(\gamma - \beta + \theta); \\ \psi_b &= -\psi_{pk} \sin(\gamma - \beta + \theta - 2\pi/3); \\ \psi_c &= -\psi_{pk} \sin(\gamma - \beta + \theta + 2\pi/3). \end{aligned} \tag{4.130}$$

Note that ψ_{pk} is the ordinate at point **N**. Again from the dq transformation, we get

$$\begin{aligned} \psi_d &= -\psi_{pk} \sin(\gamma - \beta) = \psi_{pk} \cos \alpha; \\ \psi_q &= +\psi_{pk} \cos(\gamma - \beta) = \psi_{pk} \sin \alpha. \end{aligned} \tag{4.131}$$

Like i_d and i_q, these are *constant*; they do not appear in Fig. 4.37.

When $i_a = 0$, we have $i_b = +(\sqrt{3}/2) i_{pk}$ and $i_c = -(\sqrt{3}/2) i_{pk}$, and this represents a negative-going zero of i_a at the instant **Q** defined by $\gamma + \theta = 0$, or $\omega t = -\gamma$. To determine the value of ψ_a at **Q**, we can use eqn. (4.130), which gives

$$\psi_a = \psi_{pk} \sin \beta = \psi_Q. \tag{4.132}$$

Thus when $i_a = 0$, the flux-linkage ψ_a in phase a at point **Q** is not simply the open-circuit value, but depends on the inductances L_d and L_q and the phase angle β. The true open-circuit flux-linkage is not observable in Fig. 4.37 unless the i-ψ loop is drawn for zero current, for which the i-ψ loop degenerates into a vertical straight line.

The maximum value of ψ_a is then equal to the peak open-circuit flux-linkage $\sqrt{2}\Psi_{1Md}$. The low-current loop in Fig. 4.37 shows this point very nearly at **Z**. There is no simple relationship between **Z** and **Q**, but note that the ψ-values at **Q** and **N** are in the ratio sin β.

When $\gamma = 0$, the current is in the q-axis and ψ_Q is then equal to the peak value of "magnet flux-linkage" in phase a, since $\beta = \pi/2 - \alpha$ and $\Psi \cos \alpha = \Psi \sin \beta = \Psi_{1Md}$. If the magnetic circuit is linear, this is equal to the open-circuit value of the magnet flux-linkage in phase a, because although i_b and i_c are not zero at point **Q**, they produce a transverse flux which does not link phase a. In that case points **Q** and **Z** are coincident. But if I_q is sufficient to cause appreciable saturation of the magnetic circuit, then sin β and ψ_Q can both be affected. In that case point **Q** deviates from point **Z**.

Another point of interest on the ellipse diagram is **M**, where $i_a = i_{pk}$. At this point, $\sin(\gamma + \theta) = -1$, so $\theta = \gamma + \pi/2$ and if this is substituted in eqn. (4.130) we get

$$\psi_a = \psi_{pk} \cos \beta = \psi_M . \tag{4.133}$$

Note the ratio

$$\frac{\psi_Q}{\psi_M} = \tan \beta . \tag{4.134}$$

Now β can be written as $\pi/2 - \phi$, where ϕ is the "internal power-factor angle", that is, the phase angle between the "internal" or "airgap" voltage **V** and the current **I**. Then

$$\tan \phi = \frac{\psi_M}{\psi_Q} , \tag{4.135}$$

from which the internal power factor cos ϕ can be determined. When $\cos \beta = 0$, $\beta = \pi/2$ and the current **I** is in quadrature with the flux-linkage Ψ. In this case **M** lies on the horizontal axis and the ellipse is not tilted; the internal power-factor is then 1. Although this condition represents the maximum possible internal power-factor, it does not give the maximum torque per ampere unless $L_d = L_q$. The greater the tilt angle, the lower the internal power-factor.

Torque — The electromagnetic torque can be calculated from eqn. (4.114) or eqn. (4.112), using d,q values for flux-linkage and current.

The instantaneous d,q values can be determined using the following expressions, which follow from eqns. (4.129) and (4.131): first,

$$\Psi_d = \frac{1}{\sqrt{2}}\psi_{pk}\cos\alpha; \quad \Psi_q = \frac{1}{\sqrt{2}}\psi_{pk}\sin\alpha;$$
$$I_d = -\frac{1}{\sqrt{2}}i_{pk}\sin\gamma; \quad I_q = \frac{1}{\sqrt{2}}i_{pk}\cos\gamma. \tag{4.136}$$

Substituting in eqn. (4.114),

$$\begin{aligned} T_e &= \frac{mp}{2}\psi_{pk}i_{pk}(\cos\alpha\cos\gamma + \sin\alpha\sin\gamma) \\ &= \frac{mp}{2}\psi_{pk}i_{pk}\cos(\alpha - \gamma). \end{aligned} \tag{4.137}$$

But from Fig. 4.37,

$$\alpha - \gamma = \frac{\pi}{2} - \beta. \tag{4.138}$$

Therefore

$$T_e = mp\frac{\psi_{pk}i_{pk}}{2}\cos\left(\frac{\pi}{2} - \beta\right) = mp\frac{\psi_{pk}i_{pk}}{2}\sin\beta. \tag{4.139}$$

If $\psi_{pk}\sin\beta$ is now substituted from eqn. (4.132), we get

$$T_e = \frac{mp}{2}i_{pk}\psi_Q. \tag{4.140}$$

Eqn. (4.140) shows that the *average* electromagnetic torque can be computed from a *single* finite-element computation in which ψ_Q is computed. If the current and flux-linkage waveforms are both sinusoidal, the result will be independent of the rotor position. If they are not sinusoidal, the i-ψ loop is not perfectly elliptical, and it is unsafe to rely on a single point.

Torque per ampere — Eqn. (4.140) also shows that ψ_Q is a direct measure of the torque per ampere. If $\gamma = 0$ and the current is in the q-axis, $I_d = 0$ and $L_dI_d = 0$, and the phasor diagram then shows that if the magnetic circuit is linear, point **Q** is independent of the current and the torque per ampere is also constant. But if I_q is sufficient to saturate the magnetic circuit, point **Q** moves downwards and the torque per ampere decreases.

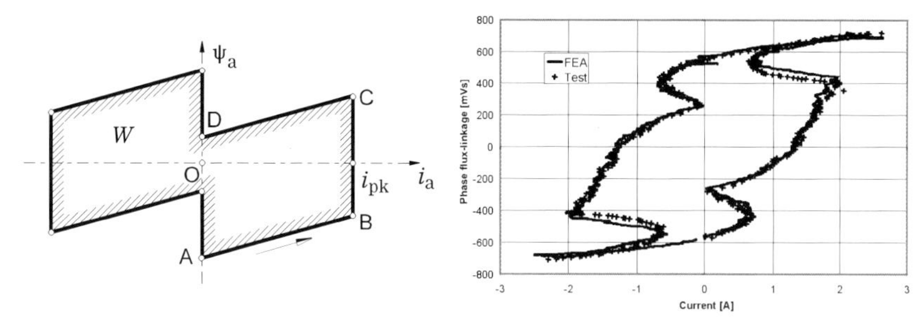

Fig. 4.38 i-ψ loop : squarewave drive Fig. 4.39 i-ψ loop for six-step operation

Squarewave and six-step drives — Fig. 4.38 shows the ideal form of the i-ψ loop for a squarewave drive in a motor which has a trapezoidal EMF waveform, as in Fig. 1.4. When the current waveform is phase-advanced relative to the flux-linkage waveform, the right-hand paralellogram **ABCD** moves vertically downward, while the left-hand parallelogram moves upward. The loop area W is twice the area of parallelogram **ABCD**, and if **AD** = $2\psi_{pk}$, then from eqn. (4.116) we get

$$T_e = \psi_{pk} i_{pk} \times \frac{2mp}{\pi}, \tag{4.141}$$

where m is normally equal to 2 for a three-phase drive, since only 2 phases are on at any time. p is the number of pole-pairs, and the torque constant given by this equation is identical to k_E in eqn. (4.56).

The same process using eqn. (4.116) can also be used to derive eqn. (4.140) for the sinewave motor with sinewave drive, since the area W of the ellipse in Fig. 4.37 is simply $\pi \psi_{pk} i_{pk}$.

When the shape of the i-ψ loop is regular, as in Figs. 4.37 and 4.38, the loop area W in eqn. (4.116) can be evaluated very simply, and it may well be sufficient to use only a few finite-element computations. The accuracy will depend on the degree to which the shape of the loop is affected by saturation, winding harmonics, or harmonics in the waveforms of the current and/or flux-linkage.

Fig. 4.39 shows the i-ψ loop of a three-phase motor with six-step drive. Because of the irregular shape of the loop, it is clear that many finite-element computations may be needed to get an accurate value for the area W and hence the electromagnetic torque.

Fig. 4.40 Alstom's 574·8 km/h record-breaking very high-speed train, with a bogie and 750 kW permanent-magnet brushless motor rotor. *Alstom, France*

Where flux, EMF and torque meet — On April 3, 2007, the Alstom V150 train tested in partnership with SNCF and RFF reached a speed of 574·8 km/h on the new East European high-speed line in France. The V150 trainset consisted of 2 TGV power cars, 3 TGV Duplex coaches and 2 AGV motorized bogies and traction units. The new AGV bogie design demonstrated excellent stability in extreme performance conditions. The AGV permanent-magnet motors (PMMs), pantographs, traction units and transformer were also fully validated. The world record was the culmination of thousands of hours of testing involving over 300 engineers and technicians.

Mounted directly in the AGV bogie, the permanent-magnet motors allow a simplified drive transmission to the wheels compared to the TGV. With the number of drive bogies reduced and optimized, significant gains were achieved in reliability and train weight.

The permanent-magnet motors have 1/3 less weight and volume than previous asynchronous motors, with a power-to-weight ratio of over 1kW/kg. The ventilation circuits are simplified and, most importantly, energy consumption is reduced. The traction inverter uses 6·5kV IGBT power modules and a 3600 V power bus.

Designed for high efficiency, interoperability, reliability and recyclability, with low emissions, the AGV is a leading example of advanced motor drive technology using permanent-magnet motors.

5 INDUCTANCE

Introduction

We have met inductance throughout Chapters 3 and 4. It arises in so many aspects of machine behaviour as to make it difficult to describe its effects systematically. So far we have not even defined it precisely, neither have we determined how to calculate it.

In this chapter we set out a definition of inductance and the related concept of flux-linkage: clarity in these definitions is vital, especially in the context of finite-element calculations. We then summarize some of the key effects and properties of inductance in purely practical terms. Finally the calculation of inductance is covered in detail, by analytical and numerical methods.

So far, in considering the equivalent circuit, the EMF, and the torque, we have tacitly assumed ideal current waveforms, either sinusoidal or squarewave. In the next chapter we will consider the *actual* current waveforms obtained with real drive circuits and controls. These waveforms are constrained principally by the EMF, the supply voltage, and the inductance. Inductance is not merely another element in the equivalent circuit but is the crucial link between the *static* domain of torque production with ideal current waveforms, and the *dynamic* domain of drive circuit operation with fixed supply voltage. The static torque calculation is essentially current-sourced, and largely ignores the real-life voltage limitation; although this calculation is important and valuable, the *actual* current waveforms and the torque achievable with a limited supply voltage (and with practical semiconductor switches) cannot be determined without taking inductance into account.

In three-phase machines we are typically concerned with three self-inductances and six mutual inductances. Symmetry reduces the number of distinct inductances to one self inductance L_{ph}, and one mutual inductance M_{ph}. For nonsalient-pole machines we shall see that the combination $L_{ph} - M_{ph}$ can often be regarded as the single characteristic inductance of the machine; in sinewave machines, this will turn out to be the **synchronous inductance**, L_d.

5.1 Definition of inductance and flux-linkage

Inductance begins with a definition of flux-linkage ψ, and this comes from Faraday's law

$$v = \frac{\partial \psi}{\partial t}, \tag{5.1}$$

where v is the induced voltage attributable to motion or to a varying current. Flux-linkage is therefore the time-integral of the induced voltage, in [V s].[24]

By writing flux-linkage as $\psi = Li$, we define inductance as "flux-linkage per ampere". If the flux-linkage ψ and current i are in the same circuit, L is **self-inductance**; if they are in different circuits, it is **mutual inductance**. Eqn. (5.1) then gives

$$v = L\frac{di}{dt} + i\frac{dL}{dt}. \tag{5.2}$$

When L is constant — that is, unaffected by motion or by current —

$$v = L\frac{di}{dt}. \tag{5.3}$$

This formula is often mistaken for Faraday's law. It is a *special case* of Faraday's law. The assumption that inductance is "unaffected by motion or by current" is rarely satisfied in electrical machines. Whenever eqn. (5.3) is used in machine calculations, or in computer simulations of power-electronic circuits and controls involving electrical machines, we should consider whether it is actually safe to do so. The theory of electrical machines is intricately constructed so that inductance *can* be used in specific roles without too much checking. But it is not automatic, and it should be noted that finite-element and computer simulation software do nothing to protect the unwary from the misuse and misinterpretation of inductance.

---

[24] By this definition, the voltage-time integral is the only way that flux-linkage can be detected, or its existence proven. All practical measurements of flux-linkage, and therefore of inductance, ultimately rely on this principle. It is an example of the marvellous imagination of engineers, that they regard flux and flux-linkage as saleable commodities, when the cruel truth is that they are nothing more than mathematical artifices contrived to coordinate the observed laws of electromagnetism.

5.1.1 Alternative definitions

5.1.1.1 di/dt

A definition of inductance as "induced voltage divided by di/dt" is predicated on the assumption that it is constant. This is too narrow for use with electrical machines. Even so, it is often used as a basis for measuring inductance in certain simple cases.

5.1.1.2 Flux times turns

The definition of flux-linkage in terms of a voltage-time integral is not tangible enough for practical engineers, in spite of the fact that it is ultimately the basis of all measurement of inductance. A more common practical definition is

$$\text{Flux-linkage} = \text{Flux} \times \text{Turns}$$

or

$$\psi = N\Phi, \tag{5.4}$$

where N is the number of turns linking or encircling the flux Φ. However, practically any finite-element flux-plot of an electrical machine will show that *not all the turns link all the flux*, and this imperfection is the start of the division between main flux and leakage flux. In this chapter we will follow these precepts, as we must, because they are part and parcel of the classical theory of electrical machines.[25]

5.1.2 Other necessary laws of electromagnetism

In spite of all that has been said so far, in order to calculate inductance we will need to calculate the flux Φ established by currents in conductors, and in simple cases this will be found as the integral of flux-density B over a collection area or gathering area. Later we will see how the vector potential is used with the finite-element method, for the same purpose.

---

[25] This definition is not rigorously derived from Faraday's law. So while $v = d\psi/dt$ implies that $v = Nd\Phi/dt$, there is uncertainty about the values of N and Φ, if the turns do not all link all of the flux. This question is ultimately unanswerable, because flux cannot be measured independently of the induced voltage in a circuit, which provides a measure of flux-*linkage*, not of flux.

5.1.3 Turns squared

The flux excited by a current is essentially proportional to the current × turns, Ni, which is often called MMF, F. This relationship is often written $\Phi = FP$, where P is a constant known as the *permeance* of the magnetic circuit in which the flux is established. From this we get a simple relationship for self-inductance,

$$L = \frac{\text{Flux} \times \text{Turns}}{\text{Current}} = \frac{N\Phi}{i} = \frac{NFP}{i} = N^2 P, \tag{5.5}$$

which establishes the principle that self-inductance is proportional to turns squared.

"Turns squared" has important consequences in brushless permanent-magnet motors. If the drive is operating from a fixed supply voltage, a motor with ceramic magnets will need more turns than one with rare-earth magnets to achieve a comparable EMF. The required increase in EMF is proportional to the turns, but the inductance increases with turns squared, so the motor with ceramic magnets will tend to have a higher inductance.

In this example the torque, power, current, EMF, speed, and voltage will be the same in both machines; but in the motor with ceramic magnets the flux will be lower, and the stator ampere-turns higher, than in the motor with rare-earth magnets.

We could take this a stage further by noting that the per-unit inductance of the motor with ceramic magnets is inherently higher than that of the motor with rare-earth magnets, because its excitation flux is lower and its armature reaction higher. Its weak flux must be compensated by an excess of ampere-turns, which is a characteristic feature of machines with a high per-unit inductance, regardless of the actual numbers of turns.

For mutual inductance the "turns squared" rule is modified. If one circuit has N_1 turns and the other N_2 turns, the mutual inductance will be generally proportional to $N_1 N_2$.

The turns squared rule applies even when the magnetic circuit is saturated, provided that the ampere-turn levels are such as to maintain the same level of saturation (i.e., the same flux).

5.2 Important practical effects of inductance

The most important aspects of inductance are as follows:

1. The inductive **voltage drop** absorbs a fraction of the supply voltage, tending to **limit the maximum speed** that can be attained with any given current (or torque).

2. In sinewave machines, inductance affects the **power factor** and is closely associated with **reactive power**. These effects are manifested in phase shift of the current and a reduction in power per volt-ampere, both of which are observed also in squarewave motors.

3. The flux associated with the inductance is superimposed on the excitation flux of the magnets, and tends to distort it. When the magnetic circuit is nonlinear, this produces a change in the torque constant. The general effect of stator current on the flux is sometimes called **armature reaction**.

4. Inductance determines di/dt, the rate of rise and fall of current when the power electronic drive circuit is chopping. Together with the EMF, it determines the relationship between **current ripple** and **chopping frequency**.

5. During **short-circuit faults** the current is both limited and *sustained* by the inductance, an important factor in the use of protection systems using overcurrent circuit-breakers.

Machines that are intended to operate over a very wide speed range present particular problems in relation to inductance. Low inductance ensures that most of the available drive voltage can be expended in overcoming the EMF, but motoring speed cannot then exceed the speed at which the EMF becomes equal to the available drive voltage. This speed is called the **base speed**. If the machine has sufficient inductance, the armature-reaction flux can be used to suppress the magnet flux to some degree, reducing the induced voltage and permitting the motor to run faster. The phase shift in the current required to achieve this **flux-weakening** causes a reduction in the torque constant, so this mode of operation is often associated with the search for a constant-*power* operating characteristic, rather than constant torque (versus speed).

5.3 Inductance components

Unlike resistance, inductance is made complicated by two facts:[26]

1. Any analysis of inductance seems to have a great many components.
2. Inductance is not constant, but varies with current and/or rotor position to a greater or lesser degree, depending on the details of the electromagnetic design.

The phase self-inductance L_{ph} can be considered to have three components: the airgap component L_g, the slot-leakage component L_{slot}, and the end-turn component L_{end} : thus

$$L_{ph} = L_g + L_{slot} + L_{end}. \tag{5.6}$$

Likewise the mutual inductance between two phases has three components

$$M_{ph} = M_g + M_{slot} + M_{end}. \tag{5.7}$$

If we have three components of self-inductance, we must have three components of flux-linkage. The airgap component relates to the flux that crosses the airgap, with the slotted stator represented by an equivalent smooth surface as in Chapter 4. The slot-leakage component relates to flux that crosses the slots, excited by all the ampere-conductors in the slot. It is considered to be independent of the airgap flux. End-turn leakage is associated with flux that encircles the end-turns, outside the active region altogether. All these components are excited by the stator current.

All components of inductance are subject to saturation, and in some cases they may be affected by eddy-currents; but the analysis ignores these effects and treats the steel as infinitely permeable.

The so-called differential or harmonic leakage inductance can be seen as part of L_g for the present, and is considered later.

---

[26] The whole concept of inductance could be abandoned if engineers would only be content to use flux-linkage instead. Indeed if all calculations were done with the finite-element method, this would be possible and it would represent a fantastic simplification. However, it would also mean throwing away a large section of the theory of electrical machines. Since most engineers would lose their right arm sooner than give up inductance, the status quo is unlikely to change.

5.4 Airgap inductance of surface-magnet machines

5.4.1 Airgap Self

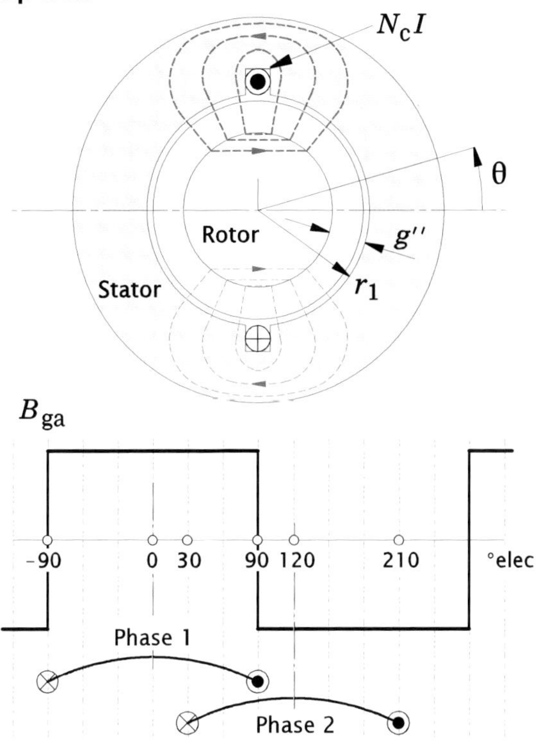

Fig. 5.1 Calculation of airgap inductance

The basis for calculating the airgap self-inductance L_g of a single coil is shown for a full-pitch coil in Fig. 5.1. In a 2-pole machine with 1 slot/pole/phase, this could be a complete phase winding. The total MMF around a complete flux path is equal to $N_c i$, where N_c is the number turns in the coil (or conductors in each coilside) and i is the current. If the steel in the rotor and stator is assumed to be infinitely permeable, then the MMF is concentrated across two effective airgaps, so the MMF drop across each airgap is $F_g = N_c i/2$. If we write $N_p = N_c/2$ as the number of turns per pole, then $F_g = N_p i$. In a surface-magnet machine, each *effective* airgap g'' includes the thickness of the magnet L_m as well as the airgap itself, modified by Carter's coefficient, k_c. If the flux is assumed to cross the gap in the radial direction, the magnetizing force H in each gap is

$$H = \frac{F_g}{g''} = \frac{N_p i}{g''} = \frac{N_c i}{2g''} \tag{5.8}$$

where the effective airgap g'' is given by

$$g'' = k_c g + \frac{L_m}{\mu_{rec}}. \tag{5.9}$$

Following Veinott, an approximation for Carter's coefficient is

$$k_c = \frac{5 + s}{5 + s - s^2/\lambda}, \tag{5.10}$$

where s is the ratio (slot-opening)/g', and λ is the ratio (slot-pitch)/g'. For surface-magnet machines, g' is taken as the total gap between steel surfaces $g + L_m$; otherwise it is just equal to the actual gap g.

The flux-density produced by H at the mean airgap diameter D is

$$B_{ga} = \mu_0 H = \frac{\mu_0 N_p i}{g''}. \tag{5.11}$$

The ideal flux distribution around the airgap is plotted in Fig. 5.1. If p is the number of pole-pairs, the flux per pole is

$$\Phi_p = B_{ga} \times \frac{\pi D}{2p} L_{stk}. \tag{5.12}$$

The flux-linkage of the entire phase winding is equal to Φ_p times the **number of turns in series per phase**,

$$T_{ph} = \frac{N_p \times 2p}{a}, \tag{5.13}$$

where a is the **number of parallel paths**. It follows that the airgap component of self-inductance is

$$L_g = \frac{\Phi_p \times T_{ph}}{i} = \frac{\pi}{4} \frac{\mu_0 T_{ph}^2 L_{stk} D}{p^2 g''} \tag{5.14}$$

The use of T_{ph}^2 in eqn. (5.14) automatically accounts for the fact that the inductance is inversely proportional to the square of the number of parallel paths. T_{ph} is common in electrical machine theory.

5.4.2 Airgap mutual

The mutual inductance between phases can be calculated in a similar way, by adding up the flux-linkages of a second coil placed in the field of the first one, Fig. 5.1. The coil of phase 2 is offset from phase 1 by 120°elec, so its coilsides are in slots at -90 + 120 = 30° and +90 + 120 = 210°. Its flux-linkage due to current in coil 1 is

$$\psi_{21} = N_c \times B_{ga} \times \frac{D}{2p} L_{stk} \times \left[-\left(\frac{7\pi}{6} - \frac{\pi}{2} \right) + \left(\frac{\pi}{2} - \frac{\pi}{6} \right) \right] \tag{5.15}$$

from which we get the airgap component of mutual inductance

$$M_g = -\frac{L_g}{3}. \tag{5.16}$$

This result is not general; it depends on the disposition of the windings. In this special case, each phase comprises just one full-pitch coil, and it is noteworthy because it includes all harmonics. It is interesting to compare this ratio −1/3 with the value -1/2 that is obtained with sine-distributed windings having only one harmonic.

Once L_g has been calculated, equation (5.16) can be used for M_g, provided that the flux distribution is a squarewave as shown in Fig. 5.1. Physically this result can be explained as follows: if the second coil was aligned with the first, the self and mutual would be equal. If the second coil was displaced 90°elec from the first, the mutual would be zero. With a rectangular flux distribution produced by current in the first coil, and with concentrated windings of one slot per pole per phase, the flux-linkage of the second one varies linearly with the angle between their axes. When the second coil is rotated to a position one-third of a right-angle past the 90° position, it picks up or links one-third of the flux, but in the negative direction relative to its own positive axis.

5.4.3 Examples of airgap inductance calculation

Consider a lap winding with 2 slots per pole per phase, as shown in Fig. 5.2. The conductors of a second, unexcited phase are shown in their correct positions for calculating the mutual inductance between phases. Again by adding together the flux-linkages of the individual coils, the self inductance is found to be

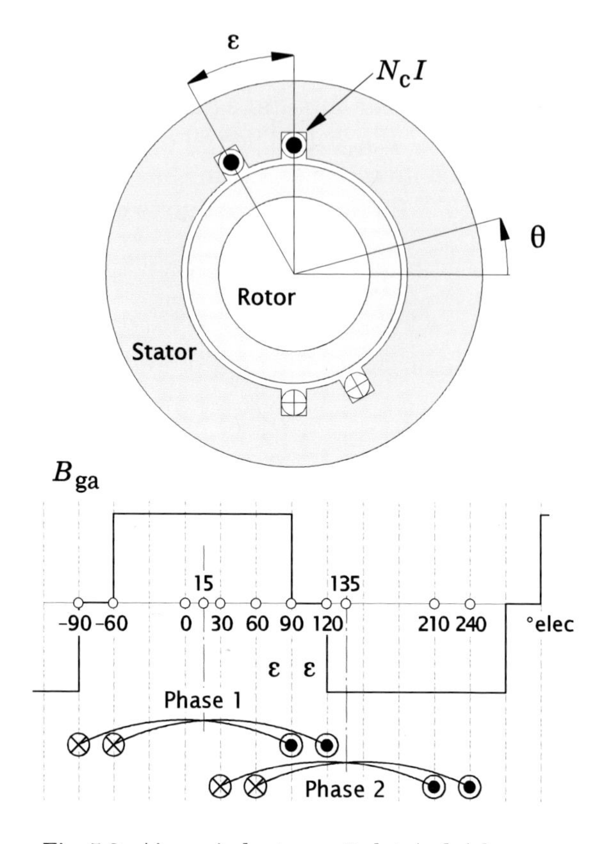

Fig. 5.2 Airgap inductance; 2 slots/pole/phase

$$L_g = \frac{\pi}{4} \frac{\mu_0 T_{ph}^2 D L_{stk}}{p^2 g''} k_w \qquad (5.17)$$

where

$$k_w = 1 - \frac{1}{3q} \qquad (5.18)$$

is the winding factor for $q = 2$ slots per pole per phase, i.e. 0·833. The self-inductance is thus only 83·3% of the value which would be obtained with the same number of turns concentrated in one slot per pole per phase. This is consistent with the general rule that the inductance of a coil is increased when its conductors are bunched or concentrated together.

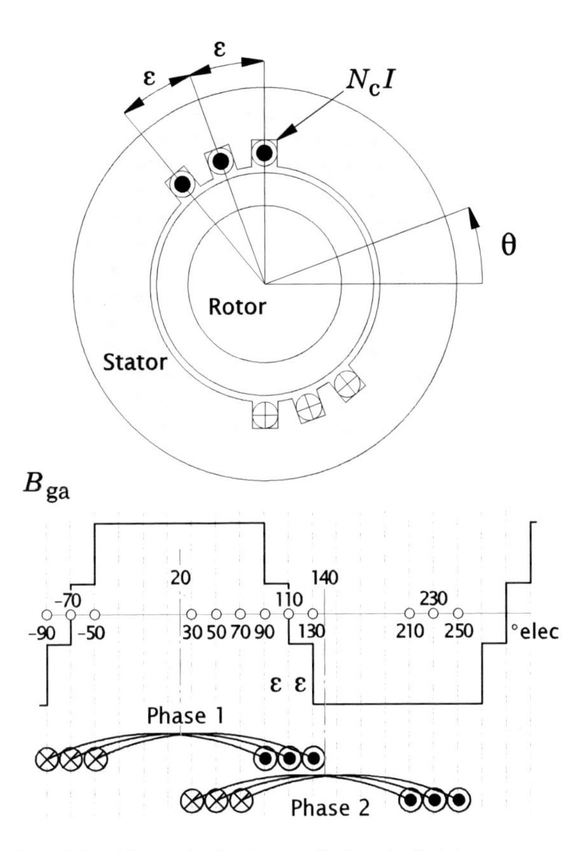

Fig. 5.3 Airgap inductance; 3 slots/pole/phase

When the mutual inductance is evaluated, using the same method as before, it is found that the distribution of the second winding cancels the effect of the step in the flux distribution, so that the actual value of the mutual inductance is the same as with one slot per pole per phase (provided the total turns are the same). The ratio between the self and mutual inductances is therefore

$$\frac{M_g}{L_g} = \frac{-1/3}{k_w} = -0{\cdot}4. \qquad (5.19)$$

Once L_g has been calculated, this equation can be used for M_g provided that the flux distribution is as shown in Fig. 5.2.

A further example is shown in Fig. 5.3 with 3 slots per pole per phase. The conductors of a second, unexcited phase are shown in their correct positions for calculating the mutual inductance between phases. Again by adding together the flux-linkages of the individual coils, the self inductance is found to be given by equation (5.17) where

$$k_w = 1 - \frac{16}{27q} \tag{5.20}$$

is the winding factor for $q = 3$, i.e. 0·802. The airgap self-inductance is thus only 80·2% of the value which would be obtained with the same number of turns concentrated in one slot per pole per phase.

It is again found that the distribution of the second winding cancels the effect of the steps in the flux distribution, so that the mutual inductance has the same value as with one slot per pole per phase (provided the total turns are the same). The ratio between L_g and M_g is given again by eqn. (5.19) , and its value is $-(1/3)/0{\cdot}802 = -0{\cdot}415$. Once L_g has been calculated, this equation can be used for M_g provided that the flux distribution is as shown in Fig. 5.3.

Example — Suppose we have a 12-slot, 4-pole motor with a mean airgap diameter D = 51 mm, stack length L_{stk} = 50 mm, airgap length g = 1 mm, Carter's coefficient k_c = 1·0086; and suppose the magnet length is L_m = 5·5 mm with recoil permeability μ_{rec} = 1·1. The winding has four full-pitch coils, all in series, each with 12 turns. Then a = 1 and T_{ph} = 4 × 12/1 = 48. The effective airgap is 1·0086 × 1·0 + 5·5/1·1 = 6·0086 mm. From eqn. (5.14),

$$L_g = \frac{\pi}{4} \times \frac{\mu_0 \times 48^2 \times 50 \times 10^{-3} \times 51 \times 10^{-3}}{2^2 \times 6{\cdot}0086 \times 10^{-3}} \ [\mathrm{H}]$$

$$= 0{\cdot}2413 \ [\mathrm{mH}].$$

The mutual inductance is given by eqn. (5.16) as −1/3 × 0·2413 = −0·0804 mH.

If the number of slots was increased to 24 and the same number of turns was split into q = 2 slots/pole/phase, the self-inductance would be reduced by the factor k_w in eqn. (5.18), that is, 1 − 1/(3 × 2) = 0·833, giving L_g = 0·2011 mH. The mutual inductance is obtained using eqn. (5.19) as −0·4 × L_g = −0·0804 mH, and it is unchanged as explained above.

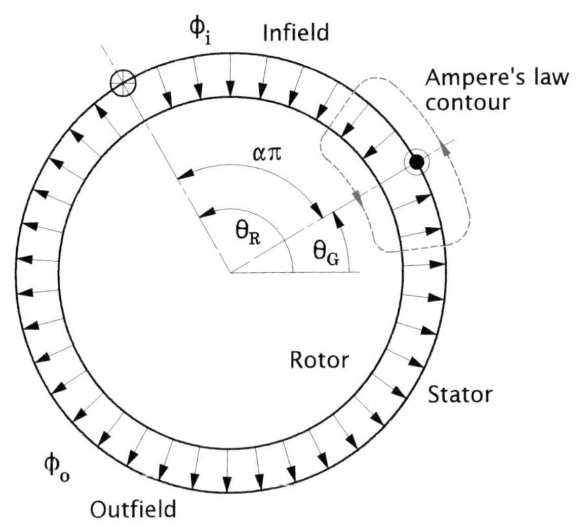

Fig. 5.4 Airgap flux of a single coil

5.4.4 General case of airgap inductance

The airgap inductance of any distribution of conductors can be computed following the principles described above. The calculation can include the mutual inductance between any two windings regardless of the distribution of their conductors, provided these are known. The accumulation of flux-linkage in the winding is done by exciting each coil in turn, and adding the flux-linkage of every coil including the excited coil. In this way the total inductance can be seen as being composed of a set of n self-inductances and $n(n-1)$ mutual inductances, where n is the number of coils in the winding. It is useful to employ a *coil table* to organize the calculation. For each coil the coil table contains its number, the number of its turns, and the slot-numbers of the "go" and "return" coilsides.

The basis of the method is shown in Fig. 5.4, which shows a single coil with the "go" conductor located at θ_G and the "return" conductor at θ_R. Applying Ampère's and Gauss' laws,

$$(H_i + H_o)g'' = N_c i \tag{5.22}$$

where N_c is the number of turns in the coil, and

$$\phi_i = \phi_o \tag{5.23}$$

where H_i is the magnetic field strength in the airgap "inside" the coil (i.e., between θ_G and θ_R) and H_o is the magnetic field strength in the airgap "outside" the coil. These sections of the magnetic field are labelled "infield" and "outfield" in Fig. 5.4. ϕ_i is the flux crossing the airgap in the infield, inside the coil, and ϕ_o is the flux crossing the airgap in the outfield, outside the coil. Now

$$\begin{aligned} \phi_i &= \mu_0 H_i L_{stk} r_1 (\theta_R - \theta_G) \quad \text{and} \\ \phi_o &= \mu_0 H_i L_{stk} r_1 [2\pi - (\theta_R - \theta_G)]. \end{aligned} \tag{5.24}$$

If we write $\alpha = (\theta_R - \theta_G)/\pi$ and use $B = \mu_0 H$, we get

$$B_i = \frac{\mu_0 N_c i}{g''}\left[1 - \frac{\alpha}{2}\right]; \quad B_o = -\frac{\mu_0 N_c i}{g''}\frac{\alpha}{2}, \tag{5.25}$$

where the negative sign added to B_o signifies that when B_i is radially inward, B_o is radially outward and *vice versa*. The flux-linkage is

$$\begin{aligned} \psi_{11} &= N_c \phi_i = N_c \times L_{stk} r_1 \theta_i B_i \\ &= N_c L_{stk} r_1 \times \alpha\pi \times \frac{\mu_0 N_c i}{g''}\left[1 - \frac{\alpha}{\pi}\right], \end{aligned} \tag{5.26}$$

so that

$$L_g = L_{max} \times 2\alpha \left[1 - \frac{\alpha}{2}\right] \tag{5.27}$$

where, if $D = 2r_1$,

$$L_{max} = \frac{\pi}{4}\frac{\mu_0 N_c^2 L_{stk} D}{g''}. \tag{5.28}$$

The inductance is zero if $\alpha = 0$ or $\alpha = 2$: in both these cases the coil-span is zero. The airgap inductance is maximum if $\alpha = 1$, which corresponds to the full-pitch coil, eqn. (5.14) and Fig. 5.1.

The airgap mutual inductance can be formulated in a similar manner except that different categories of overlap must be taken into account. Fig. 5.5 shows the basic geometry and Fig. 5.6 shows the idealised flux-distribution with partial overlap between coils 1 and 2, assuming coil 1 is the excited coil. If coil 1 has N_{c1} turns and coil 2 has N_{c2} turns, the flux linkage of coil 2 due to coil 1 is

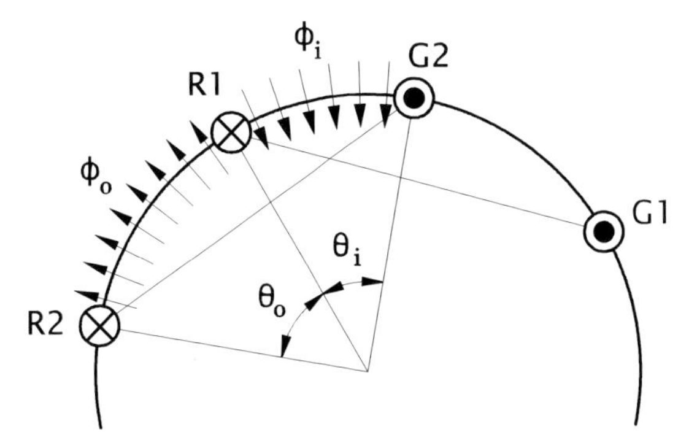

Fig. 5.5 Airgap mutual inductance between coils 1 and 2

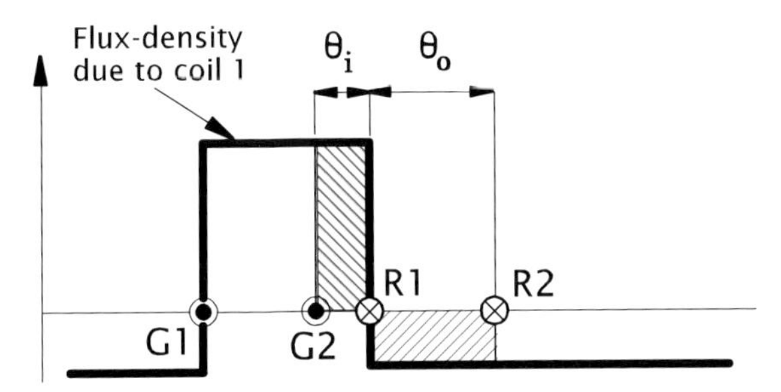

Fig. 5.6 Idealised flux distribution

$$\begin{aligned}
\psi_{21} &= N_{c2} L_{stk} r_1 \, [B_i \theta_i + B_o \theta_o] \\
&= N_{c2} L_{stk} r_1 \, [B_i(\theta_{R1} - \theta_{G2}) - B_o(\theta_{R2} - \theta_{R1})] \\
&= \frac{\mu_0 L_{stk} r_1 i_1 N_{c1} N_{c2}}{g''} \left[\left(1 - \frac{\alpha_1}{2}\right)(\theta_{R1} - \theta_{G2}) - \frac{\alpha_1}{2}(\theta_{R2} - \theta_{R1}) \right].
\end{aligned} \tag{5.29}$$

where θ_{G1} is the location of the "go" conductor of coil 1 and θ_{R1} is the location of its "return" conductor, and similarly for coil 2. The mutual airgap inductance between coil 2 and coil 1 is evaluated as ψ_{21}/i_1.

The signs of the flux-linkage terms in these summations are important, and in the general case a number of possibilities arise, depending on the locations of the coils. The full range of possibilities is given in Fig. 5.7, where the notation has been simplified so that G_1 and R_1 are written instead of θ_{G1} and θ_{R1} respectively.

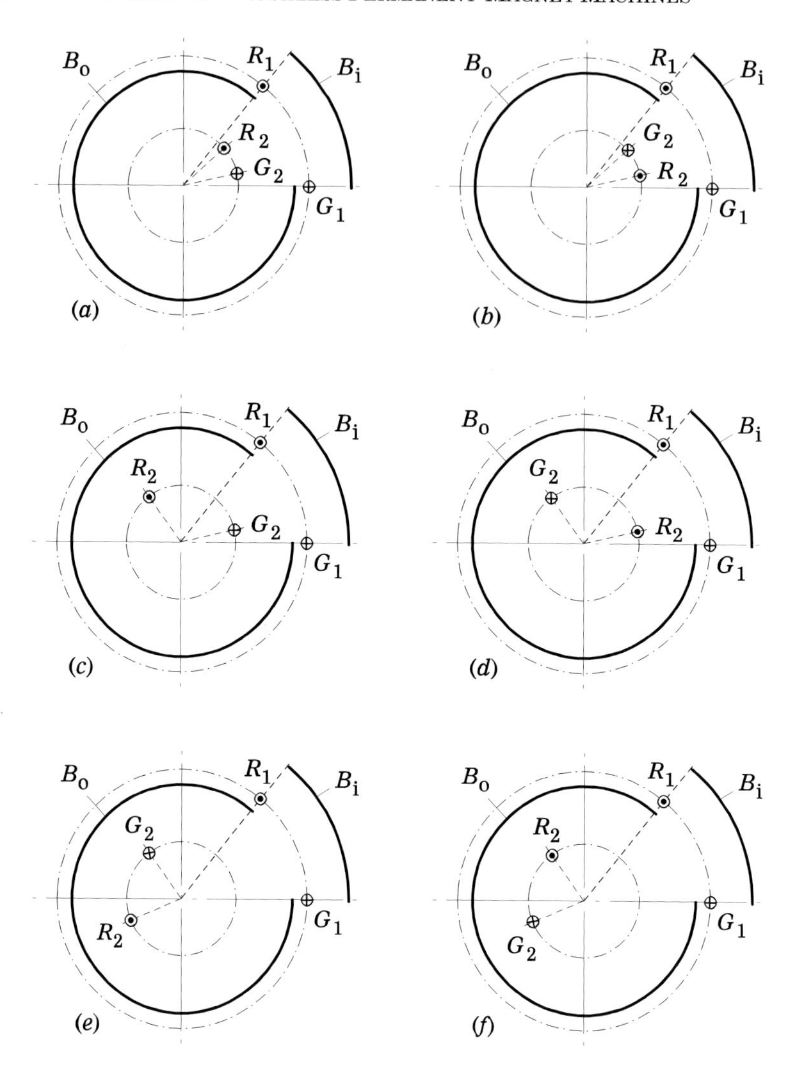

Fig. 5.7 Calculation of mutual airgap flux-linkages

In all cases the outer coil has a "go" coilside at G_1 and a return coilside at R_1, and the current in this coil produces a flux-density B_i "inside" the arc G_1R_1 and B_o outside it. If the azimuthal angles of the coilsides are G_1, R_1, etc., then by Gauss' law we have

$$B_i(R_1 - G_1) + B_o[2\pi - (R_1 - G_1)] = 0. \qquad (5.30)$$

As before, the flux-linkage of a second coil is obtained by integrating the flux-density between the limits G_2 and R_2. For example in (*a*) the flux-linkage of coil 2 due to current in coil 1 is

$$\psi_{21} = B_i(R_2 - G_2). \tag{5.31}$$

In (*b*) we get the negative of this value, because R_2 and G_2 have changed places. In case (*c*), we get

$$\psi_{21} = B_i(R_1 - G_2) + B_o(R_2 - R_1), \tag{5.32}$$

and case (*d*) gives

$$\psi_{21} = -[B_i(R_1 - R_2) + B_o(G_2 - R_1)]. \tag{5.33}$$

which proves to be the negative of case (*c*) when the values of the angles are substituted correctly.

The equations for ψ_{mn}, the flux-linkage of coil m due to current in coil n, are derived in the same way as in eqn. (5.29). Then the total airgap self flux-linkage of the phase winding is then

$$\psi_{ph} = \sum_{m=1}^{N_{coils}} \sum_{n=1}^{N_{coils}} \psi_{mn}. \tag{5.34}$$

where N_{coils} is the total number of coils in the phase winding. The mutual inductance between two phases is evaluated in the same way, except that the summation over m is taken for the coils of one phase while the summation over n is taken for the coils of the second phase.

If Hague's method [eqn. (4.45)] is used instead of eqn. (5.11), it will account for the attenuation of the space-harmonic components of flux-density away from the stator surface, which is ignored in eqn. (5.11). However, a large number of harmonics (e.g., 100) may be required to produce a satisfactory result. Hague's method uses a Fourier series expansion of the space-harmonics of the winding distribution, which can be written in terms of winding factors

$$k_d = \frac{1}{k_{w1}^2} \sum_{n>1} \frac{k_{wn}^2}{n^2} \tag{5.35}$$

This makes it possible to isolate the fundamental winding harmonic, which is the one that gives rise to the "magnetizing" or "airgap" component of the synchronous inductance. Then the sum of all higher harmonic terms is called the "differential leakage inductance" L_{diff}, and added to the overall leakage inductance. (See p. 247ff).

It will be clear that the airgap inductances L_g and M_g depend on the effective airgap length. In salient-pole machines such as the interior permanent-magnet machines (IPM) the effective airgap length is not uniform, but depends on the direction of the flux. This difficulty will be surmounted by defining separate effective airgap lengths for the d-axis and the q-axis, using the functions Γ_d and Γ_q in eqns. (5.89) on p. 252.

5.5 Slot-leakage inductance

Slot leakage flux is depicted in Fig. 5.8. The ampere-conductors in the slot drive flux not only across the airgap, but also across the slot itself. The inductance of a single coil is given by

$$L_{c\_slot} = \mu_0 L_{stk} N^2 (P_1 + P_2) \tag{5.36}$$

where N is the number of turns, L_{stk} is the stack length, and P_1 and P_2 are the **permeance coefficients** for the two slots in which the two coilsides are located. The permeance coefficient for each slot permits the inductance to be calculated as though all N conductors linked the same flux. In practice conductors near the bottom of the slot link more flux than those near the top. Therefore in calculating the permeance coefficient the distribution of flux within the slot must be taken into account.

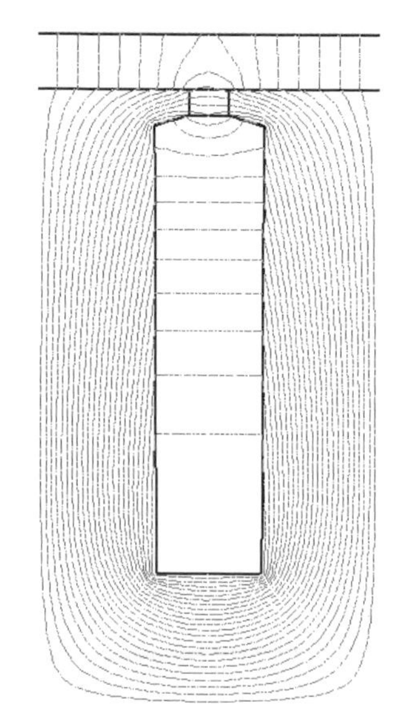

Fig. 5.8 Slot leakage

When the slot can be considered to be made up of sections, that are segments of circles or trapezoids, Fig. 5.9, analytical expressions for P can be derived if it is assumed that the flux crosses the slot in the x-direction (that is, $\mathbf{B} = (B_x,0,0)$. The contribution ΔP of any section depends on the variation $B_x(y)$ through the depth of the slot, and on the MMF of all sections lying below that section.

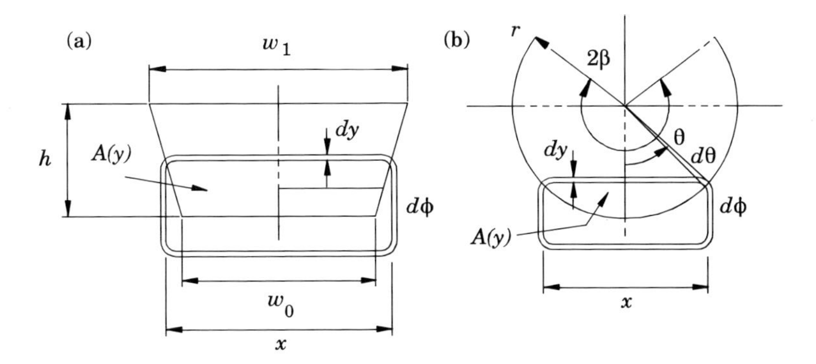

Fig. 5.9 Calculation of slot-leakage permeance coefficient

Consider an isolated section as in Fig. 5.9. (a) or (b) with an elementary flux tube $d\phi$. This flux element is driven by the MMF $JA(y)$, where J is the average current-density in the wound part of the slot: i.e., $J = NI/A_w$, where A_w is the total wound area. Then $d\phi = \mu_0 JA(y)L_{stk}\, dy/x = [\mu_0 L_{stk} NI/A_w]\, A(y)\, dy/x$. The flux $d\phi$ is linked by the fraction $A(y)/A_w$ of the total turns N, so the contribution $d\psi$ to the total flux-linkage is equal to $d\psi = d\phi.N\ A(y)/A_w = [\mu_0 L_{stk} N^2 I/A_w^{\ 2}]\ A^2(y)\, dy/x$. We can write this as $dP = (1/A_w^{\ 2})\, A^2(y) dy/x$, where dP is the contribution of the flux element to the slot permeance P.

The contribution ΔP of any complete section is obtained from the integral of dP over the height h of the section. If there is another current-carrying section of area U below the current section, then we must integrate $dP = (1/A_w^{\ 2})\ [U + A(y)]^2 dy/x$ over h to include the flux-linkage excited by the current in the lower section.

The feasibility of building up P in this way depends on the integrability of the expression for dP. Simple slots can be treated algebraically, using a few sections, but slots with more complicated shapes may need to be divided into a large number of layers, each of which is calculated with eqn. (5.39) below.

As a simple example, ΔP is calculated for a slot bottom that is a circular segment spanning an angle 2β, Fig. 5.9(b). Since the section is at the bottom, $U = 0$ and $dP = (1/A_w^{\ 2})\ [A(y)]^2\, dy/x$. It is convenient to integrate with respect to θ rather than y, writing $y = r(1 - \cos\theta)$; $dy = r\sin\theta\, d\theta$; and $x = 2r\sin\theta$.

$A(y)$ is the sector area $r^2(2\theta - \sin 2\theta)/2$, and A_w is also given by this formula with $\theta = \beta$. Making all these substitutions and performing the integration with respect to θ from 0 to β, we get

$$\Delta P = \frac{\beta[4\beta^2/3 + 1/2 + 2\cos 2\beta] - (5/4)\sin 2\beta}{2[2\beta - \sin 2\beta]^2}. \tag{5.37}$$

When $\beta = \pi/2$, the slot-bottom is semicircular and $\Delta P = 0{\cdot}1424$. With $\beta = \pi$ we get the "classical" value for the slot permeance coefficient of a round slot, 0·6231.

Now consider the trapezoidal section, Fig. 5.9 (a). The area $A(y)$ is written in terms of x as $k(x^2 - w_0^2)$ where $k = h/2(w_1 - w_0)$ and $x = w_0 + (w_1 - w_0)y/h$. When dP is integrated with respect to x from w_0 to w_1, we get the following expression (with $B = U - kw_0^2$):

$$\Delta P = \frac{2k}{A_w^2}\left[B^2 \ln\frac{w_1}{w_0} + \frac{h}{2}(w_1 + w_0)\left\{B + \frac{k}{4}(w_1^2 + w_0^2)\right\}\right] \tag{5.38}$$

When the trapezium has parallel sides, $w_1 = w_0 = w$, so $k \rightarrow \infty$ and if $a = hw$, ΔP simplifies to

$$\Delta P = \frac{1}{A_w^2}\left[U(U + a) + \frac{a^2}{3}\right]\frac{h}{w}. \tag{5.39}$$

For a rectangular section at the bottom of the slot, $U = 0$. If this is the only section there are no conductors above it, so $A_w = a$ and

$$\Delta P = \frac{1}{3}\frac{h}{w} \tag{5.40}$$

which is the well known formula for a rectangular slot. Another special case arises at the bottom of a slot if $w_0 = 0$; then the section is triangular and

$$\Delta P = \frac{1}{A_w^2}\frac{h^3 w_1}{16}. \tag{5.41}$$

Empty sections: For a section that is empty of conductor we must integrate $dP = (1/A_w^2)\, U^2 dy/x$ over h. For a trapezoidal section

$$\Delta P = \frac{h}{w_1 - w_0}\ln\frac{w_1}{w_0}, \tag{5.42}$$

and if w_1 and w_0 are nearly equal this becomes

$$\Delta P = \frac{2h}{w_0 + w_1} \tag{5.43}$$

which is commonly quoted in textbooks. Veinott in his VICA-31 program for slot constants uses a modified form

$$\Delta P = \frac{4h}{3w_1 + w_0}\ ; \quad w_1 < w_0 \tag{5.44}$$

in which w_1 is equal to the slot opening and w_0 is the width at the bottom of the slot wedge. By giving three times more weight to w_1 than to w_0, he increases the value of ΔP and makes an allowance for the fact that the slot flux does not cross the slot in the x-direction, especially under the tooth-overhangs, and this tends to increase the permeance coefficient. This is one of the reasons why the formulas developed here tend to underestimate the slot permeance coefficient by a few percent, although saturation tends to reduce it again.

Finally, the contribution of the slot opening region is given by eqn. (5.43) with $w_1 = w_0 = w$ equal to the slot opening, and h equal to the depth of the tooth-tip: i.e., $\Delta P = h/w$ if there is no conductor in the slot opening. If there is conductor in the slot-opening, eqn. (5.39) is used; it gives a slightly lower result.

Closed slots are rare in brushless permanent-magnet machines, although magnetic wedges may sometimes be used to minimize cogging torque. When the slot-closures are saturable there is no formula for ΔP that gives a definite result, and the same may well be true for semi-closed slot when there is significant saturation of the tooth tips. In such cases finite-element analysis may be helpful.

Examples — The slot permeance coefficient can be calculated for various distributions of the conductors, and Fig. 5.10 summarizes some interesting special cases for the rectangular open slot, calculated for self-inductance, and Fig. 5.11 for mutual inductance.

The lowest possible value (0) is obtained when all the conductors are concentrated at the top of the slot, case (q); and the highest possible value (1) when all the conductors are concentrated at the bottom of the slot, case (p).

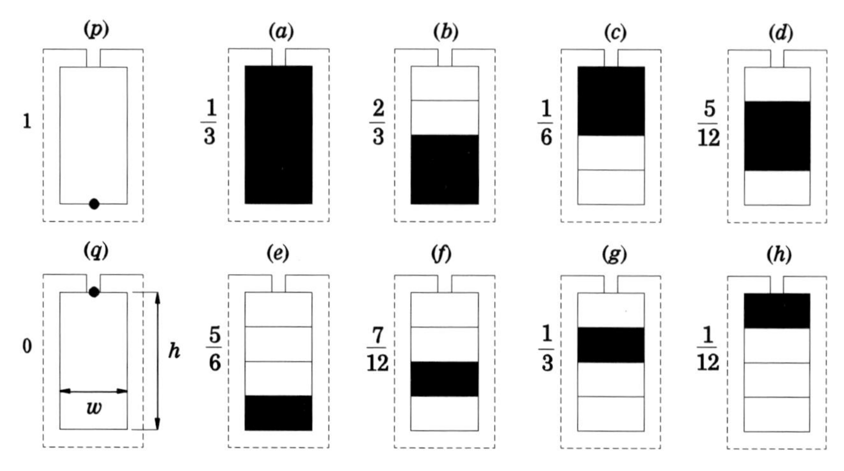

Fig. 5.10 Slot-permeance coefficients normalized to h/w : self-inductance

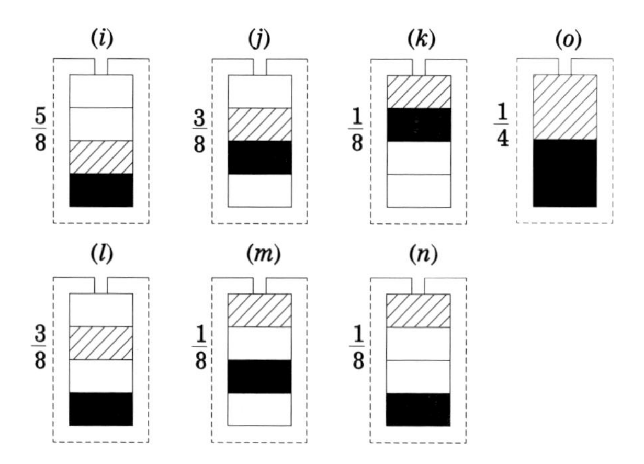

Fig. 5.11 Slot permeance coefficients : mutual inductance

When the conductors are evenly distributed over the slot, the coefficient falls to 1/3, case (*a*). In case (*b*), $2/3 \times h/w$ is 2/3 the maximum theoretical value of case (*p*), but twice the value obtained in case (*a*) with uniform distribution. In case (*c*), $1/6 \times h/w$ gives only half the slot-leakage inductance compared with the uniform conductor distribution, and only one-fourth the inductance of case (*b*). Cases (*b*) and (*c*) are both typical practical cases, and they show the significance of the position of the coilside in the slot, although the difference is muted when the slot-opening term is added.

When two conductors share the same slot, one in the top and one in the bottom, the mutual slot inductance is evaluated using $M_s = \mu_0 L_{stk} N^2 \times h/4w$, i.e. the slot permeance coefficient for mutual inductance is $h/4w$.

The rectangular open slot is a rarity in brushless permanent-magnet machines, partly because this type of slot is not ideal for automatic winding and partly because open slots increase the cogging torque. A more common slot type shown in Fig. 5.12 has "tangs" or "overhangs" that provide a small slot-opening without materially reducing the slot area. The rectangular slot-bottom, albeit with a fillet radius in each corner, is more common in brushless permanent-magnet machines than in mass-produced induction motors. Probably the reason is that the rectangular slot has a greater winding area, which is important to minimize the temperature rise, bearing in mind that (brushless motors are often totally enclosed. The round-bottom slot may prolong the life of the stamping die.

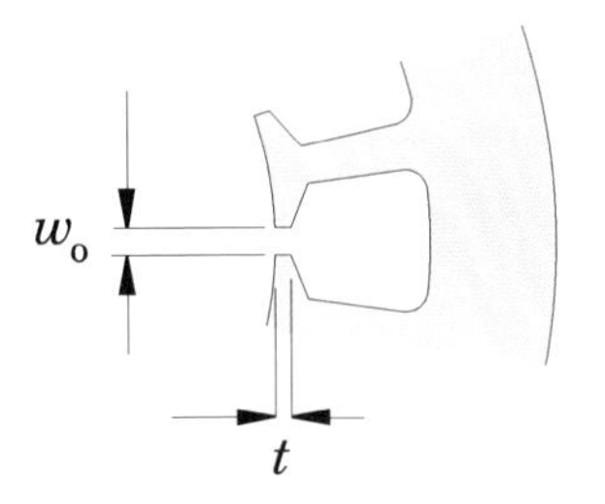

Fig. 5.12 Semi-closed slot

The tooth overhangs augment the slot permeance, making it necessary to add a separate component t/w_o to the simple P_{slot} values shown in Figs. 5.10 and 5.11. As already mentioned, this helps to "wash out" the uncertainty in calculating P_{slot} which arises from not knowing the precise location of the conductors within the slot. With one coilside per slot the slot permeance coefficient should be taken as

$$P_{slot} = P_0 + \frac{t}{w_o}, \tag{5.45}$$

where P_0 is the coefficient for the main part of the slot, calculated by the methods described earlier.

Many detailed formulas have been developed for slot permeance coefficients of various slot shapes, including allowances for gaps between coilsides sharing the slots. Alger in particular includes in the total stator leakage inductance the mutual inductance between coilsides of different phases sharing the same slot, so his formulas for slot permeance coefficient depend on the winding layout.

This helps in representing the induction motor by a per-phase equivalent circuit in which the mutual coupling between phases is implicit in the per-phase self-inductances. However, this model depends on having balanced three-phase sinewave currents and fluxes, which may not be the case in the brushless permanent-magnet machine. For computer simulation the analytical reduction of the equivalent circuit to its simplest form is not really necessary, and indeed for computer-aided design it is probably better to retain the simple formulation for self- and mutual inductance components and to accumulate them into the total phase self and mutual inductances by a suitable programming algorithm.

In the *PC-BDC* program the accumulation of self- and mutual inductance components is effected by means of a *coilside incidence vector*, **C**. This is a one-dimensional array in which the number of elements is equal to the number of slots. Each phase has its own coilside incidence vector. The element corresponding to the i'th slot is 1 if that slot contains a "go" conductor belonging to phase 1, −1 if it contains a "return" conductor, and 0 if it contains no conductor belonging to phase 1. The total slot-leakage component of the phase self-inductance is then given by

$$L_{\mathrm{slot}} = \frac{\mu_0 N_{\mathrm{c}}^2 L_{\mathrm{stk}}}{a^2} \sum_{k=1}^{N_{\mathrm{slots}}} P_{\mathrm{slot,self}}[k]\,\mathbf{C}[k] \quad [\mathrm{H}], \tag{5.46}$$

where a is the number of parallel paths and N_{c} is the number of turns per coil. It is assumed in equation (5.46) that the slot permeance coefficient is different for every slot, allowing for different coilside positions within the slot. In practice this refinement is rather impractical and a single permeance coefficient can be used outside the summation.

For the mutual slot inductance between two phases A and B, the corresponding formula is

$$M_{\mathrm{slot}} = \frac{\mu_0 N_{\mathrm{c}}^2 L_{\mathrm{stk}}}{a^2} \sum_{k=1}^{N_{\mathrm{slots}}} P_{\mathrm{slot,mutual}}[k]\,\mathbf{C}_{\mathbf{A}}[k]\,\mathbf{C}_{\mathbf{B}}[k] \quad [\mathrm{H}], \tag{5.47}$$

where $\mathbf{C}_{\mathrm{A}}$ and $\mathbf{C}_{\mathrm{B}}$ are the coilside incidence vectors for phases A and B respectively.

5.6 End-winding leakage inductance

End-winding inductance is difficult to calculate accurately, because the form of the end-windings is complex and is often not known precisely. Fortunately this inductance is generally quite small, and it suffices to have an approximate formula that includes the effects of the main dimensions. Refinements can be made according to the shape and packing density of the coils, and the presence of image currents in the stator core.

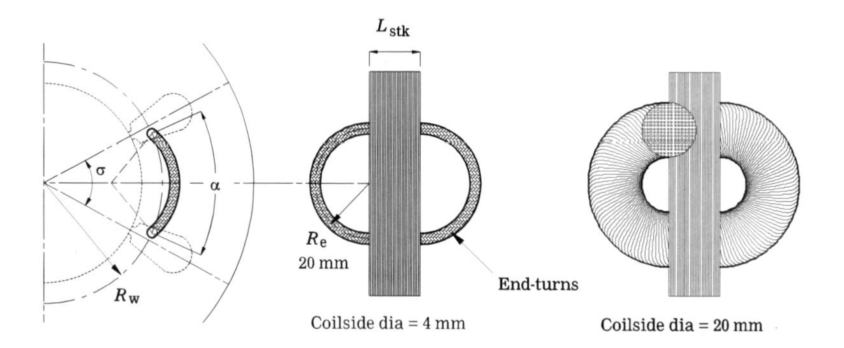

Fig. 5.13 Calculation of end-winding inductance

Fig. 5.13 shows the geometry assumed for the end-winding of a single coil. An arc length α is calculated along a circle of radius R_w, which is the radius of a cylinder on which the straight coilsides lie. If σ is the coil-span, α is rather less than $R_w\sigma$ because the coilsides do not lie exactly on the slot centre-lines, but tend to be closer to the slot wall. The end-turns curve around a surface that has additional curvature outside the radius R_w, but this is generally not known precisely at the design stage, and is neglected. The end-turns from both ends are flattened on to an imaginary circle of radius $R_e = \alpha/2$, and then the inductance of the circle is calculated as

$$L_{end} = \mu_0 R_e N_c^2 \left[\ln \frac{8R_e}{R} - 2 \right] \qquad (5.48)$$

where R is the geometric mean distance of the coilside from itself, and N_c is the number of turns per coil.

If the coilside is square, with area a, then R is given by

$$R = 0{\cdot}447 \sqrt{a} . \tag{5.49}$$

If the coilside is circular, with area a, $R = 0{\cdot}4394 \sqrt{a}$. Formulas for other shapes of coilside are given by Rosa and Grover.

Example — Suppose the arc length $\alpha = 40$ mm and that the coilside is circular with diameter 4 mm and $N_c = 100$ turns. Then $R_e = 20$ mm, $a = \pi/4 \times 4^2 = 12{\cdot}57$ mm^2, $R = 0{\cdot}4394 \times \sqrt{12{\cdot}57} = 1{\cdot}558$ mm, and

$$L_{end} = \mu_0 \times 20 \times 10^{-3} \times 100^2 \left[\ln \frac{8 \times 20}{1{\cdot}558} - 2 \right] = 0{\cdot}66 \quad [\text{mH}] . \tag{5.50}$$

The proportions of this coil are those of the "thin" coil in Fig. 5.13, i.e. $R_e/R = 12{\cdot}8$. On the right-hand side of Fig. 5.13 is shown a "fat" coil with the same R_e but 5 times the coilside diameter, so that $R = 7{\cdot}788$ mm and $R_e/R = 2{\cdot}568$, and now

$$L_{end} = \mu_0 \times 20 \times 10^{-3} \times 100^2 \left[\ln \frac{8 \times 20}{7{\cdot}788} - 2 \right] = 0{\cdot}257 \quad [\text{mH}], \tag{5.51}$$

which is only 39% of the inductance of the thin coil.

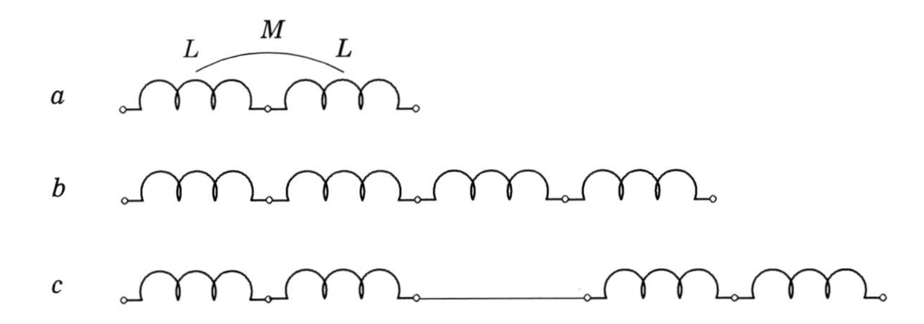

Fig. 5.14 Coupled inductances

So far the end-winding inductance has been calculated for only a single coil. The effect of mutual inductance between different coils of the same phase is much more difficult to calculate precisely. The following approach is one of estimation based on certain basic principles of coupled inductances in series.

Fig. 5.14(a) shows two inductors in series. Each has self-inductance L. The mutual inductance between them is $M = kL$, where k is the coupling coefficient. The inductance of the series combination is

$$L_t = L + L \pm 2M = 2L(1 \pm k). \tag{5.52}$$

The coupling coefficient can be positive or negative, and $|k| \leq 1$. Perfect coupling is achieved when $|k| = 1$. When $k > 0$, the flux linkages of the two separate inductors add; when $k < 0$, they subtract.

It is easy to extend eqn. (5.52) when more than two inductors are connected in series. Fig. 5.14(b) shows four inductors L_1, L_2, L_3, L_4 with mutual inductances $M_{12} = M_{21}$, $M_{13} = M_{31}$, $M_{14} = M_{41}$, $M_{23} = M_{32}$, $M_{24} = M_{42}$, and $M_{34} = M_{43}$. The series inductance is

$$\begin{aligned} L_t &= L_1 + L_2 + L_3 + L_4 \\ &+ 2M_{12} + 2M_{13} + 2M_{14} + 2M_{23} + 2M_{24} + 2M_{34}. \end{aligned} \tag{5.53}$$

If $L_1 = L_2 = L_3 = L_4 = L$ and $M_{12} = M_{13} = M_{14} = M_{23} = M_{24} = M_{34} = L$,

$$L_t = 16L = 4(L_1 + L_2 + L_3 + L_4). \tag{5.54}$$

In other words, if all the coils are perfectly coupled and all the flux-linkages are adding, the total inductance is equal to the sum of the self-inductances multiplied by the number of inductors. Moreover, the total inductance exceeds the value that would be obtained if the coils were uncoupled, by a factor that is simply the number of inductors:

$$L_t = n \sum_1^n L = n^2 L = n \times nL. \tag{5.55}$$

This is the maximum inductance that can possibly be obtained with the n inductors. It is of passing interest to construct this sum as the sum of n self-inductances L and $(n - 1)$ pairs of mutual inductances $M = L$, giving $nL + (n - 1)n/2 \times 2L = n^2 L$. If the mutuals are all equal to kL, the sum is

$$L_t = n\left[1 + (n - 1)k\right]L. \tag{5.56}$$

Suppose the n inductors are grouped as in Fig. 5.14(c) into m groups each containing $q = n/m$ inductors. The q inductors of each group are perfectly coupled ($M = L$), but there is no mutual coupling between groups. Then the total series inductance is $nL + (q - 1)q/2 \times m \times 2L = n^2L/m$. In Fig. 5.14($c$), $m = 2$ groups and $n = 4$, so $q = 2$ and $L_t = 8L$. This is twice the inductance that would be obtained if all the coils were uncoupled, but only half the inductance that would be obtained if they were all perfectly coupled. If the mutuals within the group are all equal to kL, the sum is

$$L_t = n\left[1 + (q - 1)k\right]L. \tag{5.57}$$

With $k = 0{\cdot}5$, the total inductance is only $6L$.

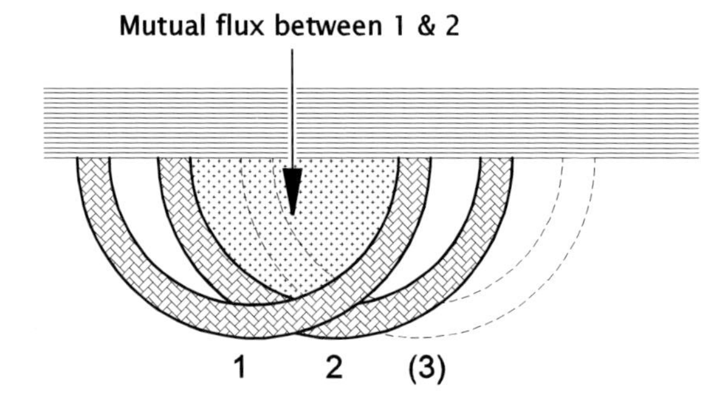

Fig. 5.15 End-windings of a group of 2 or 3 coils

In the phase winding of a brushless PM motor, in many cases the coils are identical and they all have the same end-turn self-inductance L. It is clearly not the case that they are all perfectly coupled. Fig. 5.15 shows an example where there might be $q = 2$ or 3 coils per group; but this machine might have $m = 4$ or even many more groups, depending on the number of slots and poles. Let us suppose that $m = 8$, with $q = 2$. Then $n = 16$, and even if both coils of one group were perfectly coupled, the total end-turn inductance would be no more than $16^2/8L = 32L$. If all the coils of one group were uncoupled, the total would be no more than $16L$. Inspection of Fig. 5.15 suggests that the mutual coupling between the two coils of each group is quite weak, with k perhaps of the order of $0{\cdot}5$. Eqn. (5.57) then gives $24L$.

The *PC-BDC* program computes $\sum L$ coil-by-coil, initially without regard to mutual coupling between coils. The end-turn inductance of each individual coil is calculated independently so that any differences in coil-span or number of turns is included in $\sum L$. The sum $\sum L$ must be multiplied by a correction factor k_m to account for the mutual coupling. If all the coils are identical this correction factor is obtained from eqn. (5.57) as

$$k_m = 1 + (q - 1)k. \tag{5.58}$$

giving

$$L_t = k_m \sum L. \tag{5.59}$$

The example just quoted with $q = 2$ and $m = 8$ and $k = 0{\cdot}5$ has $k_m = 1 + (2 - 1) \times 0{\cdot}5 = 1{\cdot}5$. The maximum possible value of k_m is n, when all the coils are perfectly coupled in one group ($q = n$ and $k = 1$). The minimum value is 1, when all the coils are uncoupled ($k = 0$). Low values of q are common in brushless motors ($q = 1$ or 2), and k will often be near zero, so k_m will often be close to 1.

If $m = 8$ with $q = 3$ (including the third dotted coil in Fig. 5.15), we have $n = 24$. The coupling coefficient between coils 1 & 2 might be 0·5, as before, and this value can be assumed also for coils 2 & 3. But between coils 1 & 3 it is clearly lower, maybe of the order of 0·25. Taking the weighted average for the coupling coefficient gives $k = (2 \times 0{\cdot}5 + 1 \times 0{\cdot}25)/3 = 0{\cdot}42$, so that eqn. (5.58) gives $k_m = 1{\cdot}833$. This can be compared with the case where all coils are perfectly coupled, which has $k_m = n = 24$; or with the case where the three coils in each group are perfectly coupled but the groups are uncoupled, giving $k_m = 1 + (3 - 1) \times 1 = 3$.

Returning for a moment to eqns. (5.48) and (5.49), if the coilsides in Fig. 5.13 were square (as assumed in *PC-BDC*), the end-turn inductance of the thin coil would be 0·657 mH and that of the thick coil would be 0·253 mH, hardly any different from the values obtained with circular coilsides.

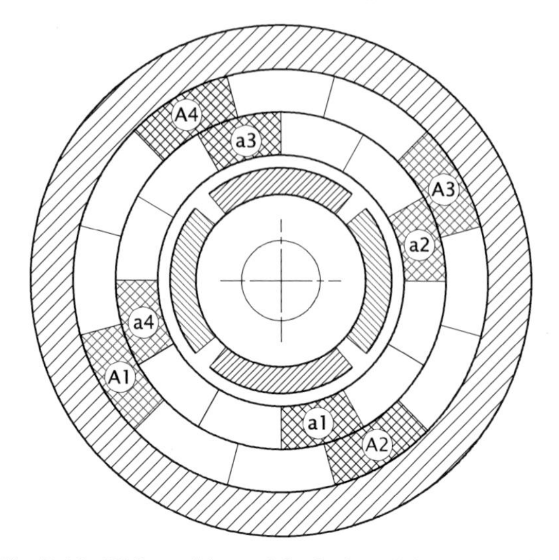

Fig. 5.16 PM machine with slotless (airgap) winding

5.7 Inductances of slotless (airgap) windings

Fig. 5.16 shows the general arrangement of a machine with a slotless winding, also known as an airgap winding. The stator core is a smooth-bore tube, and the magnets are set on a smooth cylindrical shaft. The annular space between these cylindrical components has a relative permeability of 1, apart from the magnets which have a relative permeability slightly higher than 1.

In this particular example there are 4 poles and 4 coils per phase, making a total of 12 stator coils. Each coil has a mean span of $5/6 \times 180 = 150°$elec, and there are 2 layers. The hatching shows the positions of the coilsides of one phase.

The mutual inductance M between two phases is calculated from the ratio of the flux-linkage ψ_{21} produced in phase 2 to the current in phase 1. It is necessary to begin by calculating the flux distribution produced by current I in phase 1. The coilsides of phase 1 are placed on two layers but it is more convenient to work with an equivalent set of coilsides taken in pairs, each pair being at the same radius. This prescription can be extended to individual filaments within the coilsides, but the theory will be developed first as though each coilside was represented by a filament at its centroid.

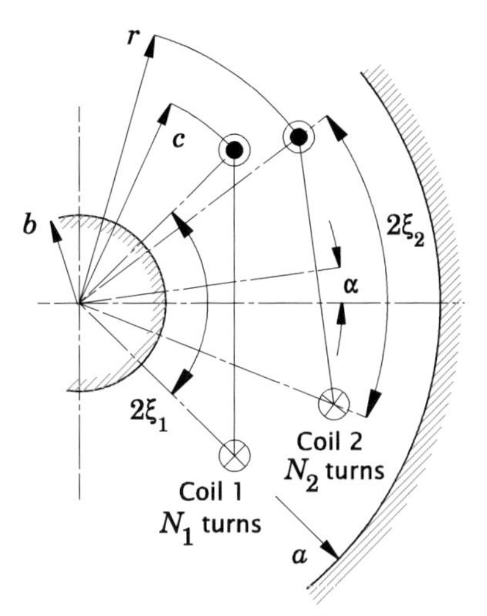

Fig. 5.17 Calculation of inductance

Thus instead of the actual coils A_1a_1, A_2a_2, A_3a_3 and A_4a_4, we consider the equivalent coil-pairs A_1A_2, A_3A_4 and a_1a_2, a_3a_4. The first two equivalent coils are on a larger radius, and have a larger span, than the first two; but the flux-distribution is exactly the same as that which is produced by the original actual coilsides, since the ampere-conductor distribution is the same.

We already have the solution for the field produced by a set of $2p$ uniformly-distributed filamentary coils from eqn. (4.45), and we can use this with the p coils of layer 1: thus

$$B_r = \frac{p\mu_0 I}{\pi r} \sum_n^{\infty} f_n(r) \cos n\theta \tag{5.60}$$

where $n = (2j-1)p, j = 1,3,5,...$[27]

$$\begin{aligned} f_n(r) &= \frac{a^n}{c^n} \cdot \frac{c^{2n}+b^{2n}}{a^{2n}-b^{2n}} \cdot \left[\frac{r^n}{a^n} + \frac{a^n}{r^n}\right] \cdot k_{\sigma n} \sin n\xi, \quad r \geq c; \\ f_n(r) &= \frac{b^n}{c^n} \cdot \frac{c^{2n}+a^{2n}}{a^{2n}-b^{2n}} \cdot \left[\frac{r^n}{b^n} + \frac{b^n}{r^n}\right] \cdot k_{\sigma n} \sin n\xi, \quad r < c. \end{aligned} \tag{5.61}$$

[27] See Hughes A. and Miller T.J.E., *Analysis of fields and inductances in air–cored and iron–cored synchronous machines*, Proceedings IEE, Vol. 124, No. 2, February 1977, pp. 121–131.

Referring to Fig. 5.17, the flux-linkage ψ_{21} of a set of p coils in layer 2 is given by[28]

$$\begin{aligned}\psi_{21} &= pN_2N_1L_{\text{stk}}\frac{\mu_0 I}{\pi r}\sum_n f_n\int_{\alpha-\xi_2}^{\alpha+\xi_2}\cos n\theta\, r d\theta \\ &= 2pN_2N_1\frac{\mu_0 I}{\pi}L_{\text{stk}}\sum_n\frac{f_n}{n}\cos n\alpha\,\sin n\xi_2.\end{aligned}\tag{5.62}$$

To obtain the mutual inductance ψ_{21} must be accumulated for both layers of the excited and unexcited coils.

The self-inductance L can be obtained as a special case of the mutual inductance by making the coils coincident, and if all coils are considered to lie on a single layer p will be replaced by $2p$. Then with $\xi_1 = \xi_2 = \xi$, $N_1 = N_2 = N$, and $\alpha = 0$ we get

$$\psi_{21} = 2(2p)^2N^2\frac{\mu_0 I}{\pi}\sum_n\frac{f_n}{n}k_{pn}{}^2k_{dn}{}^2k_{\sigma n}{}^2.\tag{5.63}$$

Considering the fundamental alone, the effective number of turns in series per phase is $T_{ph1} = k_{w1}N/a$ where $k_{w1} = k_{p1}k_{d1}k_{\sigma 1}$ and a is the number of parallel paths. If we let the airgap g diminish to a value much smaller than the radius b, we will find that f_1 tends to D/pg, where $D = 2 \times (a + b)/2$; and with $n = p$ we get a formula for the airgap component of the self-inductance of one phase,

$$L = \frac{2\mu_0 T_{ph1}{}^2 D L_{\text{stk}}}{\pi p^2 g}.\tag{5.64}$$

In a 3-phase machine the airgap component of the synchronous inductance follows as $3/2 \times L$, i.e.,

$$L = \frac{3\mu_0 T_{ph1}{}^2 D L_{\text{stk}}}{\pi p^2 g}.\tag{5.65}$$

This can be shown to be identical to Alger's formula for the magnetizing inductance per phase of a 3-phase motor.

---

[28] Note that f_n can be written in the form $g_n \sin n\xi = g_n k_{pn}$, where k_{pn} is interpreted as a harmonic pitch factor. If the coils are spread (distributed), the distribution factor appears. If they are skewed, the skew factor $k_{\sigma n}$ appears (as in eqn. (4.45). These factors can be found in Hague's original analysis [1929].

5.7.1 Helical windings

A helical winding was patented for use in an alternator with a superconducting field winding in 1971,[29] and at least one large prototype has been built and tested in Japan. Small permanent-magnet motors[30] using rhombic windings (related to helical windings but with cranked-back coils) are made for high-precision motion-control applications. Bumby gives a useful summary with key references.

The helical winding has no end-windings and short axial length. Once the winding is assembled and somehow encapsulated in a monolithic block, it forms a neat, compact mechanical component.

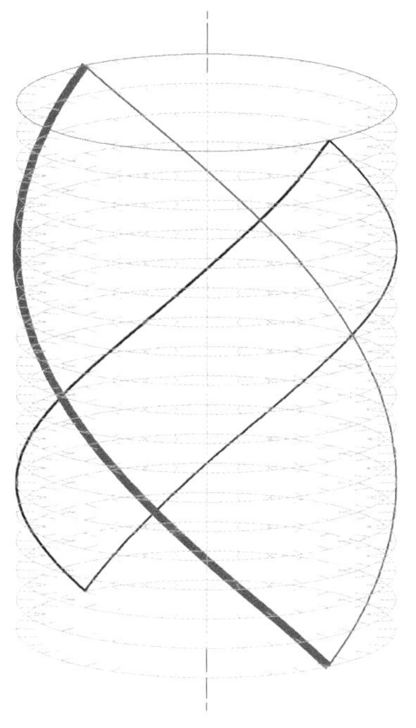

Fig. 5.18 2-pole helical winding

5.7.2 Lawrenson's method[31]

Lawrenson's method of calculating end-winding inductances is equally applicable to the calculation of the inductance of slotless windings, and it is mentioned briefly here. It relies on the principle that the vector potential of a short element of conductor can be obtained by formula. The flux-linkage of an entire coil can then be calculated by eqn. (5.117). The calculation of the entire winding inductance is obtained as a sum of elemental contributions.

---

[29] Ross J.S.H., Anderson A.F. and MacNab R.B., *Alternating Current Dynamo-Electric Machine Windings*, UK Patent No. 1,395,152, 1 February 1971. See also Anderson A.F., Bumby J.R. and Hassall B.I., *Analysis of helical armature windings with particular reference to superconducting a.c. generators*, IEE Proceedings, Vol. 127, Part C, No. 3, May 1980, pp. 129-144.

[30] Stemme O. and Wolf P., *Principles and Properties of Highly Dynamic DC Miniature Motors*, Interelectric AG, Switzerland, 1994.

[31] Lawrenson P.J., *Calculation of machine end-winding inductances with special reference to turbogenerators*, Proc. IEE, Vol. 117, No. 6, June 1970, pp. 1129-1134.

5.8 Equivalent sine-distributed windings

A sine-distributed winding cannot be realized in practice, but it is an important element in the theory of windings. It is also the basis of the related concept of the *space vector*.

We can think of a sine-distributed winding as the fundamental space-harmonic component of an actual winding. The conductor distribution can be written $C_1 \sin p\theta$ conductors per radian, so with 2 conductors per turn the number of turns/pole is

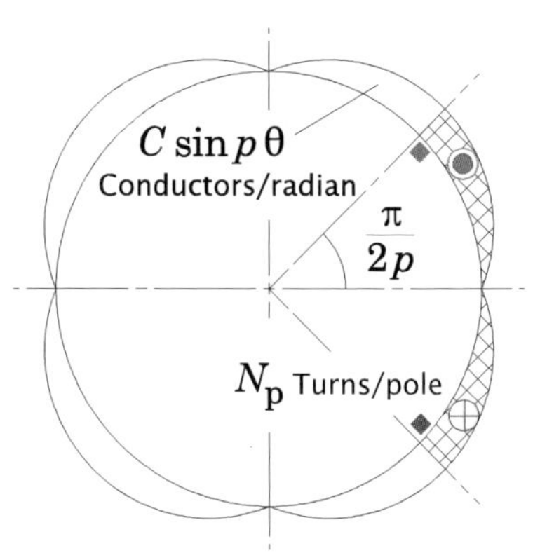

Fig. 5.19 Sine-distributed winding

$$N_p = \int_0^{\pi/2p} C_1 \sin p\theta \, d\theta = \frac{C_1}{p}. \tag{5.66}$$

The total number of sine-distributed turns in the winding is $N_s = 2p \times N_p = 2C_1$, so the distribution can be written $N_s/2 \sin p\theta$ conductors/radian.

Now if all the turns per pole of a winding with T_{ph} total turns were concentrated with 180° pitch, as shown by the diamonds in Fig. 5.19, with a current i and all turns in series, the winding would produce a fundamental space-harmonic component of airgap flux proportional to $4T_{ph}i/\pi$. This would become $4k_{w1}T_{ph}i/\pi$ for a real winding with a fundamental winding factor k_{w1}, establishing the equivalent number of sine-distributed turns as

$$N_s = \frac{4}{\pi} k_{w1} T_{ph}. \tag{5.67}$$

The winding factor k_{w1} isolates the fundamental space-harmonic and strips away the higher-order harmonics. If k_{w1} is replaced by the harmonic winding factor k_{wn} for the nth harmonic, we immediately obtain the conductor distribution $C_n \sin np\theta$ for that harmonic. By these principles the entire airgap field including all its harmonics can be analyzed in terms of a set of sine-distributed current sheets; (see Hughes and Miller, *op. cit.*; also see DBPMM94).

5.9 Synchronous inductance

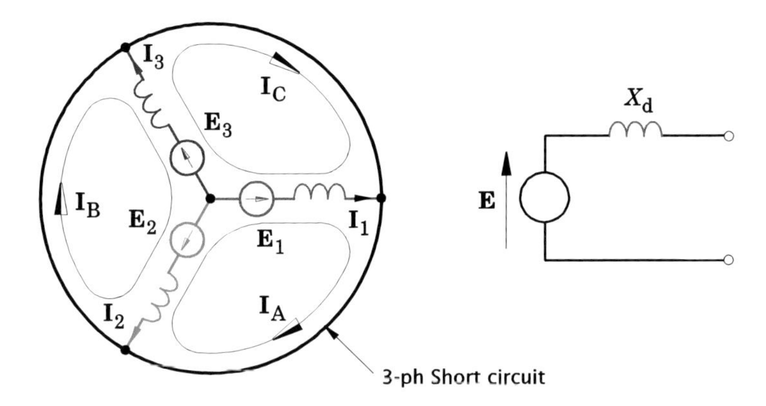

Fig. 5.20 3-phase short-circuit

Synchronous inductance L_d accounts for the inductive voltage drop in each phase of a synchronous machine with all three phases conducting balanced sinusoidal currents.[32] In phase 1, for example, it includes the mutual inductive voltage drops due to the currents in phase 2 and phase 3, in addition to the self-inductance voltage drop due to current in phase 1 itself. L_d thus eliminates the mutual inductances from AC circuit calculations under balanced conditions. In a balanced machine L_d replaces three self- and three mutual inductances by a single parameter.

This can be seen in Fig. 5.20, where each phase is represented by an EMF and a reactance, resistance being small enough to be neglected. If the machine is symmetrical and the operation is balanced, only one phase need be analyzed, and this is the principle on which the familiar single-phase equivalent circuit is based. In Chapter 4 we determined the EMF; we are now in a position to determine the reactance X_d, at least for nonsalient-pole machines.

The reactance X_d is given by

$$X_d = \omega L_d, \tag{5.68}$$

where $\omega = 2\pi f$ is the fundamental radian frequency.

[32] Synchronous inductance is not applicable with nonsinusoidal current.

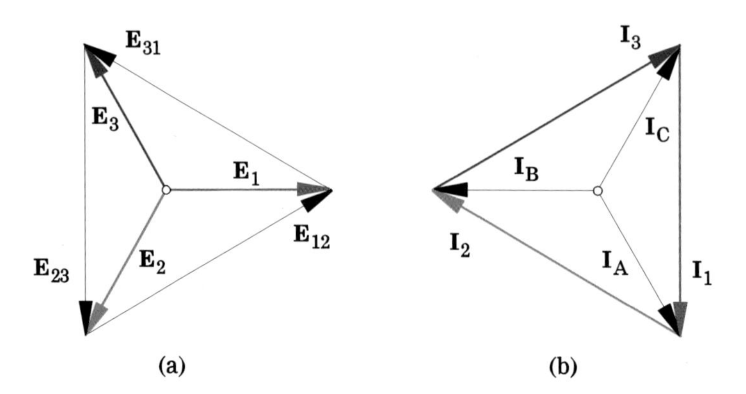

Fig. 5.21 Phasor diagrams of **E** and **I**; 3-phase short-circuit

A simple way to determine L_d is to run a synchronous machine with all three phases shorted together: i.e., with a balanced three-phase short circuit. The EMF generated in the three phases drives a current in each phase which is limited only by the resistance and inductances of the windings. Except at very low speed, the resistance can be neglected, and the following analysis shows that the short-circuit current is then limited by the single parameter L_d or X_d.

For the loop containing $\mathbf{E}_1$ and $\mathbf{E}_2$ we have the following mesh voltage equation, where L is the phase self-inductance and M is the mutual inductance between phases:

$$\begin{aligned} \mathbf{E}_1 - \mathbf{E}_2 &+ \mathrm{j}\omega L(\mathbf{I}_A - \mathbf{I}_C) - \mathrm{j}\omega L(\mathbf{I}_B - \mathbf{I}_A) \\ &+ \mathrm{j}\omega M(\mathbf{I}_B - \mathbf{I}_A) - \mathrm{j}\omega M(\mathbf{I}_A - \mathbf{I}_C) \\ &+ \mathrm{j}\omega M(\mathbf{I}_C - \mathbf{I}_B) - \mathrm{j}\omega M(\mathbf{I}_C - \mathbf{I}_B) = 0. \end{aligned} \tag{5.69}$$

But $\mathbf{I}_A - \mathbf{I}_C = \mathbf{I}_1$, $\mathbf{I}_B - \mathbf{I}_A = \mathbf{I}_2$, and $\mathbf{I}_C - \mathbf{I}_B = \mathbf{I}_3$; and with $\mathbf{E}_{12} = \mathbf{E}_1 - \mathbf{E}_2$ we get

$$\mathbf{E}_{12} + \mathrm{j}\omega(L - M)\mathbf{I}_1 - \mathrm{j}\omega(L - M)\mathbf{I}_2 = 0. \tag{5.70}$$

From Fig. 5.21(a) and (b), $\mathbf{E}_{12} = \sqrt{3}\,\mathbf{E}_1\,\mathrm{e}^{\mathrm{j}\pi/6}$ and $\mathbf{I}_2 = \mathbf{I}_1\,\mathrm{e}^{\mathrm{j}2\pi/3}$, so

$$\sqrt{3}\,\mathbf{E}_1\,\mathrm{e}^{\mathrm{j}\pi/6} + \mathrm{j}\omega(L - M)\mathbf{I}_1[1 - \mathrm{e}^{-\mathrm{j}2\pi/3}] = 0. \tag{5.71}$$

The apparent impedance per phase is the ratio $\mathbf{E}_1/\mathbf{I}_1$, which is

$$\frac{\mathbf{E}_1}{\mathbf{I}_1} = \frac{\mathrm{j}\omega(L-M)[1-\mathrm{e}^{-\mathrm{j}2\pi/3}]}{\sqrt{3}\mathrm{e}^{\mathrm{j}\pi/6}} = \mathrm{j}\omega(L-M) = \mathrm{j}\omega L_\mathrm{d} = \mathrm{j}X_\mathrm{d}. \quad (5.72)$$

If the phase resistance is negligible, this shows that the synchronous inductance L_d is equal to $(L - M)$. The 'j' also establishes that $\mathbf{I}_1$ lags $\mathbf{E}_1$ by 90°, as shown in Fig. 5.21(b).

In classical synchronous machine theory, the self-inductance of each phase of a nonsalient-pole machine comprises an airgap component $L_{\mathrm{g}0}$ associated with airgap flux, together with a leakage component L_σ which is associated with slot-leakage flux and end-winding flux. Likewise the mutual inductance comprises an airgap component M_g and a leakage component M_σ. For 3-phase sinewound nonsalient-pole machines with balanced windings, M_g is equal to $L_{\mathrm{g}0}$ multiplied by cos 120°, i.e., $-L_{\mathrm{g}0}/2$. Consequently

$$L_\mathrm{d} = L - M = \frac{3}{2}L_{\mathrm{g}0} + (L_\sigma - M_\sigma). \quad (5.73)$$

This explains why the synchronous inductance is often thought to be 3/2 times the phase self-inductance—though not exactly 3/2 times, because of the leakage components L_σ and M_σ.

So far we have considered only nonsalient-pole 3-phase machines, and then only sinewound machines operating with sinusoidal current and voltage, and negligible saturation. The commonest example of this is the surface-magnet permanent-magnet AC brushless motor operating with sinewave drive. The steady-state operation of this machine is described in Chapter 7 in terms of the phasor diagram.

It will be clear from the analysis in this section that the synchronous reactance determines the steady-state short-circuit current $I_{\mathrm{d(sc)}} = E/X_\mathrm{d}$, where E is the open-circuit EMF per phase. During sudden short-circuits, the current can exceed this level by a factor of 2 or more, as a result of DC offset and subtransient effects which are treated in Chapter 9.

First, however, the analysis of inductance is extended to salient-pole machines such as the interior PM motor, in §5.9. We shall see that two synchronous reactances are needed for these machines, L_d and L_q. The effect of saturation is taken into account later.

5.9.1 Static measurement of synchronous inductance

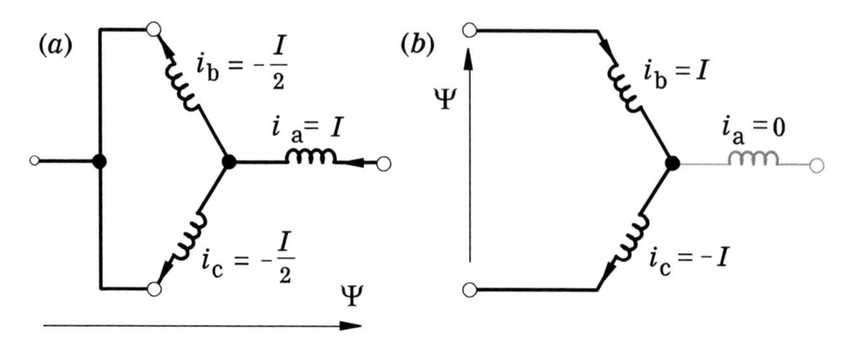

Fig. 5.22 Connections for DC measurement of synchronous inductance

It is very helpful to think about the measurement of L_d with the rotor stationary. We have seen in Chapter 4 that when the equations of the synchronous machine are transformed into synchronously rotating dq axes, the currents, flux-linkages, and voltages become constant in the steady state. If we imagine the frequency reduced to zero, the rotor comes to rest with its flux in a particular position, while the currents in the stator windings become "frozen" with DC values. Such a situation is depicted in Fig. 5.22(a), with $i_a = I$ and $i_b = i_c = -I/2$. This combination of currents normally occurs once per cycle in normal operation; but here we have frozen that instant.

The total flux-linkage of the circuit is given by

$$\Psi = Li_a - Li_b - Mi_a + Mi_b = \frac{3}{2}(L - M)I = \frac{3}{2}L_d I. \tag{5.74}$$

This shows that L_d can be measured as 2/3 the ratio of flux-linkage and current, using the connection in Fig. 5.22(a). It is shown in eqns. (5.114) and (5.115) that the line-line connection in Fig. 5.22(b) measures $2L_d$. The measurement is described in Chapter 13.

Now we can make a simple but profound statement. So far we have not defined the orientation of the rotor relative to the windings. When the d-axis (the magnet axis) is aligned with the axis of phase a, 5.22(a) measures the d-axis synchronous inductance L_d. When the q-axis (interpolar axis) is aligned with the axis of phase a, it measures the q-axis synchronous inductance L_q. In general, $L_d \neq L_q$.

5.10 Inductances of salient-pole machines

We have already seen in Chapter 4 that when a synchronous machine is operating in the steady-state, the magnetic field viewed from the rotor is constant. In a frame of reference attached to the rotor, all the currents, voltages and fluxes are constant, and we used this to calculate an equation for the electromagnetic torque, eqn. (4.114). The steady state was shown to be a special case of a more general analysis in which the operating equations are written in dq axes or coordinates; these equations included a torque equation (4.112) that is valid under transient as well as steady-state conditions, and voltage equations (4.108) that describe the electrical behaviour. Park's transform [eqn. (4.103) and its inverse eqn. (4.104)] was used to develop this model by mapping or projecting the ordinary phase variables on to the dq coordinate axes.

An essential component of the dq-axis model is the relationship between flux-linkage and current. In phase variables this is

$$\boldsymbol{\psi}_{\mathrm{abc}} = [L]_{\mathrm{abc}} \mathbf{i}_{\mathrm{abc}} \tag{5.75}$$

where ψ_{abc} is the column vector of flux-linkages $[\psi_a, \psi_b, \psi_c]$, $\mathbf{i}_{\mathrm{abc}}$ is the vector of phase currents $[i_a, i_b, i_c]$, and $[L]_{\mathrm{abc}}$ is a square inductance matrix. Using Park's transform,

$$\boldsymbol{\psi}_{\mathrm{dq0}} = \mathbf{T}\boldsymbol{\psi}_{\mathrm{abc}} = \mathbf{T}[L]_{\mathrm{abc}}\mathbf{i}_{\mathrm{abc}} = \mathbf{T}[L]_{\mathrm{abc}}\mathbf{T}^{-1}\mathbf{i}_{\mathrm{dq0}} = [L]_{\mathrm{dq0}}\mathbf{i}_{\mathrm{dq0}}. \tag{5.76}$$

When the elements of $[L]_{\mathrm{abc}}$ are of the form given by eqn. (4.95), the $dq0$ inductance matrix $[L]_{\mathrm{dq0}}$ turns out to be diagonal, and if the magnet flux-linkage is defined along the d-axis with symbol $\Psi_{1\mathrm{Md}}$ and included in ψ_d, we get the flux-linkage equations in dq axes,

$$\begin{aligned} \psi_d &= \Psi_{1\mathrm{Md}} + L_d i_d; \\ \psi_q &= L_q i_q. \end{aligned} \tag{5.77}$$

These equations are fundamental in understanding the steady-state behaviour of synchronous machines. L_d is the ***d*-axis synchronous inductance** and L_q is the ***q*-axis synchronous inductance**.

The zero-sequence equation $\psi_0 = L_0 i_0$ is set aside because $i_0 = 0$ when $i_a + i_b + i_c = 0$, as is normally the case with a 3-wire connection except during earth faults.

5.10.1 dq-axis inductances from Park's transform

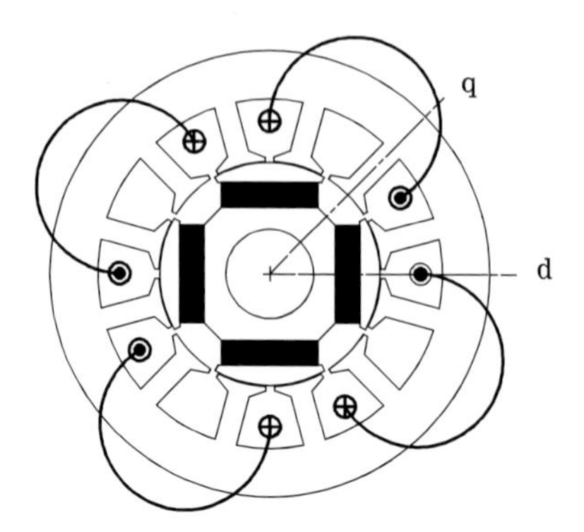

Fig. 5.23 4-pole IPM

In "embedded-magnet" machines, including "interior-magnet" and "inset-magnet" types, the winding inductances vary as the rotor rotates. This property is known as *saliency* and such machines are classified as *salient-pole* machines. Most salient-pole machines have a narrow airgap, which increases the likelihood of saturation and causes the inductance to vary with current as well as rotor position, as we shall see later. Even without saturation it is practically essential to use the *dq*-axis model for salient-pole machines: the circuit calculations are hopelessly complicated and lengthy when phase variables with time-varying inductances are used. Under saturated conditions the *dq*-axis model proves even more valuable, because the saturation can be taken into account by one or two saturation factors that are constant at one operating point. Moreover, the performance can be analyzed in terms of flux-linkage alone, without the complication of inductance; this is especially important when performing finite-element calculations.

In this section the *dq*-axis inductances $[L]_{dq}$ are derived from the phase inductances $[L]_{abc}$ using Park's transform. In many texts this is the *only* method of derivation, which is unfortunate in view of everything we have been saying about "inductance avoidance" and the direct measurement and physical meaning of L_d and L_q. Indeed the origins of *dq*-axis theory (Blondel's two-reaction principle and the salient-pole phasor diagram) are much older than Park's transform, but the transform delivers the unsaturated 2-axis model in a form that will satisfy the most ardent acolytes of inductance.

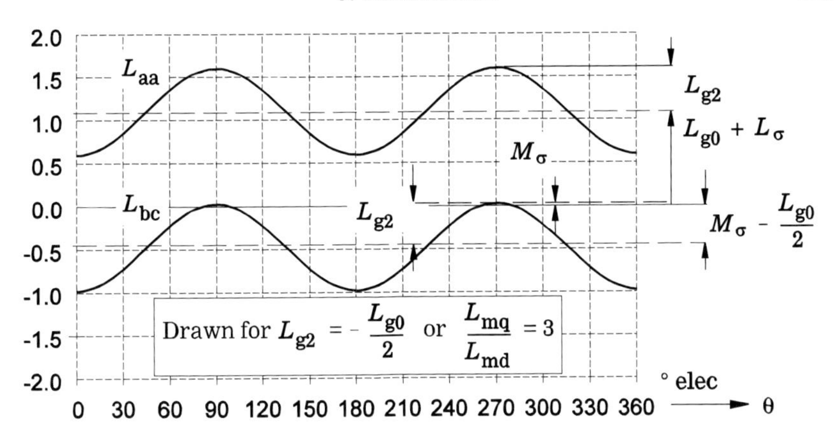

Fig. 5.24 Variation of L_{aa} and L_{bc} with rotor position θ

Fig. 5.24 shows the variation of self-inductance L_{aa} and mutual inductance L_{bc}, in arbitrary units, with rotor position θ defined in Fig. 4.22. In both L_{aa} and L_{bc} there is a "double-frequency" variation. In the IPM machine the maxima usually occur when the q-axis is aligned with the axis of phase a, and the minima occur when the d-axis is aligned with the axis of phase a, because the d-axis presents a lower permeance to armature-reaction MMF than the q-axis. This behaviour is opposite to the saliency of conventional wound-field machines, and is sometimes called inverse saliency. In every electrical revolution there are two d-axis alignments and two q-axis alignments. Inductances L_{bb} and L_{cc} are similar to L_{aa}, but displaced in phase by 120° and 240° respectively, while L_{ca} and L_{ab} are similar to L_{bc} but displaced in phase by corresponding angles.

The actual shape of the inductance variation is rich in harmonics. It also varies with current. To get the constant-parameter 2-axis model from Park's transform it is necessary to ignore all harmonics in $L(\theta)$ higher than the second,[33] and to ignore all variation caused by current; in other words, the transform is applicable only to magnetically linear, unsaturated machines. With these constraints the inductances can be expressed by eqn. (4.95). With inverse saliency, both L_2 and M_2 are negative.

[33] Attempts to include higher-order harmonics will be found in the literature, but they are algebraically complicated and since they do nothing to help with the greater issue of saturation, they are of marginal value.

Self-inductance — The constant term L_0 in the phase inductance comprises a leakage component L_σ and a component L_{g0} attributed to the average "airgap" component of the magnetic field produced by the fundamental space-harmonic component of the stator ampere-conductor distribution. With fixed current in one phase, the saliency of the rotor is considered to induce a double-frequency modulation in the fundamental airgap flux, so we write L_2 as L_{g2}.

The leakage component L_σ includes the slot-leakage, end-turn leakage, and "differential" leakage inductance associated with higher-order space harmonics of the winding distribution and the effects of any skew. These components are often considered to be constant.

The maxima and minima of the self-inductance are expressed as follows; the notation refers to the alignment of the d- and q-axes with the phase axis: thus, for phase a:

$$\begin{aligned} L_{aa[d]} &= (L_\sigma + L_{g0}) + L_{g2} \\ L_{aa[q]} &= (L_\sigma + L_{g0}) - L_{g2}. \end{aligned} \tag{5.78}$$

These inductances can be measured. If measured values are available, eqn. (5.78) can be solved to give

$$(L_\sigma + L_{g0}) = \frac{L_{aa[d]} + L_{aa[q]}}{2}; \quad L_{g2} = \frac{L_{aa[d]} - L_{aa[q]}}{2}. \tag{5.79}$$

Mutual inductance — The constant term M_0 in the mutual inductance comprises a leakage component M_σ together with a component $L_{g0}\cos(2\pi/3) = -L_{g0}/2$ which reflects the 120° spacing between the axes of adjacent phases. M_σ represents mutual coupling between phases in the slots and end-turns, together with any contributions from higher-order space-harmonics of the winding distribution. Saliency induces the same double-frequency modulation in the mutual as in the self-inductance (F&K-II), so we write $M_2 = L_{g2}$. With sufficient saliency it is possible for L_{bc} to reverse sign, as shown in Fig. 5.24; [see also eqns. (5.86) and (5.92)].

The phase-phase mutual inductance attains extreme values when the d- and q-axes are aligned mid-way between the respective phase axes. For example L_{bc} has the value $M_\sigma - L_{g0}/2 + L_{g2}$ when $\theta = 0$, 180°, ...; and the value $M_\sigma - L_{g0}/2 + L_{g2}$ when $\theta = 90°$, 270°, ...

With wye connection the inductance between lines b and c is

$$L_{LL} = L_{bb} + L_{cc} - 2L_{bc}, \tag{5.80}$$

the negative sign of $-2L_{bc}$ being due to the reverse connection of phase c in series with phase b in the line-line circuit. When eqns. (4.95) are substituted in eqn. (5.80), L_{LL} simplifies to

$$L_{LL} = L_{LL0} - 3L_{g2}\cos(2\theta) \quad \text{with} \quad L_{LL0} = 2(L_\sigma - M_\sigma) + 3L_{g0}. \tag{5.81}$$

Like the phase inductance, L_{LL} also has a constant term and a second-harmonic term. It attains an extreme value at $\theta = 0$, when the q-axis is aligned with the effective magnetic axis of the series connection of phases b and c; and another extreme value when $\theta = \pm\pi/2$, when the d-axis is aligned with this axis. Thus

$$\begin{aligned} L_{LL[d]} &= 2(L_\sigma - M_\sigma) + 3[L_{g0} + L_{g2}] = L_{LL0} + 3L_{g2} \text{ when } \theta = \pi/2; \\ L_{LL[q]} &= 2(L_\sigma - M_\sigma) + 3[L_{g0} - L_{g2}] = L_{LL0} - 3L_{g2} \text{ when } \theta = 0. \end{aligned} \tag{5.82}$$

With $L_{g2} < 0$, $L_{LL[d]} < L_{LL[q]}$. If the windings are connected in delta, the line-line inductance between lines b and c can be shown to be

$$L_{LL[\Delta]} = \frac{L_{LL0}}{3} - L_{g2}\cos(2\theta) \tag{5.83}$$

which is 1/3 the value obtained with wye connection in eqn. (5.81).

The extreme values of L_{LL} could be measured, and then eqns. (5.82) could be solved for L_{LL0} and L_{g2} :

$$L_{LL0} = \frac{L_{LL[d]} + L_{LL[q]}}{2} \; ; \; L_{g2} = \frac{L_{LL[d]} - L_{LL[q]}}{6} \tag{5.84}$$

Synchronous inductances — When eqns. (4.95) are substituted in the transform eqn. (5.76), the result is $[L]_{dq0} = diag[L_d, L_q, L_0]$, in which the synchronous inductances L_d, L_q are independent of θ: thus

$$L_d = L_\sigma - M_\sigma + L_{md}; \quad L_q = L_\sigma - M_\sigma + L_{mq}; \tag{5.85}$$

where

$$L_{md} = \frac{3}{2}(L_{g0} + L_{g2}); \quad L_{mq} = \frac{3}{2}(L_{g0} - L_{g2}). \tag{5.86}$$

With inverse saliency $L_{g2} < 0$, $L_{md} < L_{mq}$ and $L_d < L_q$. In contrast, wound-field salient-pole machines usually have $L_d > L_q$.

5.10.2 Synchronous inductance coefficients

Because L_{md} and L_{mq} are defined in a frame of reference that is synchronous with the rotating magnetic field, they can be calculated directly from the flux-linkage of a sine-distributed winding oriented along the d or q axis: thus

$$\begin{aligned} L_{md} &= \Gamma_d L_{m0}; \\ L_{mq} &= \Gamma_q L_{m0}, \end{aligned} \tag{5.87}$$

where L_{m0} is the airgap component of the synchronous inductance of a nonsalient-pole machine having an airgap length equal to $g' = k_c g$, where g is the actual airgap and k_c is the Carter coefficient. Thus

$$L_{m0} = \frac{3\mu_0 D L_{stk}}{\pi p^2 g'} (k_{w1} T_{ph})^2. \tag{5.88}$$

where k_{w1} is the fundamental winding factor, T_{ph} is the number of turns in series per phase, and $\omega = 2\pi f$. For 2-phase motors, 3 is replaced by 2 in this equation.

The **synchronous inductance coefficients** Γ_d, Γ_q are given by

$$\Gamma_d = \frac{g'}{g_d''}; \quad \Gamma_q = \frac{g'}{g_q''}. \tag{5.89}$$

Here g_d'' is the effective airgap in the d-axis *including the effects of the magnet and the saliency*; and g_q'' is the same in the q-axis. Formulas for g_d'' and g_q'' can be determined directly from a magnetic field solution in dq-axes, completely avoiding the need to precalculate L_{g0} and L_{g2}; (see p. 253). The synchronous *reactances* follow as

$$\begin{aligned} X_d &= 2\pi f L_d = X_{md} + X_\sigma \\ X_q &= 2\pi f L_q = X_{mq} + X_\sigma \end{aligned} \tag{5.90}$$

where

$$\begin{aligned} X_{md} &= 2\pi f L_{md} = \Gamma_d X_{m0} \\ X_{mq} &= 2\pi f L_{mq} = \Gamma_q X_{m0}. \end{aligned} \tag{5.91}$$

Once L_{md} and L_{mq} have been calculated from eqn. (5.87), L_{g0} and L_{g2} can be extracted by means of eqn. (5.86): thus

$$L_{g0} = \frac{1}{3}[L_{md} + L_{mq}]; \quad L_{g2} = \frac{1}{3}[L_{md} - L_{mq}]. \tag{5.92}$$

5.10.3 Direct calculation of synchronous inductance

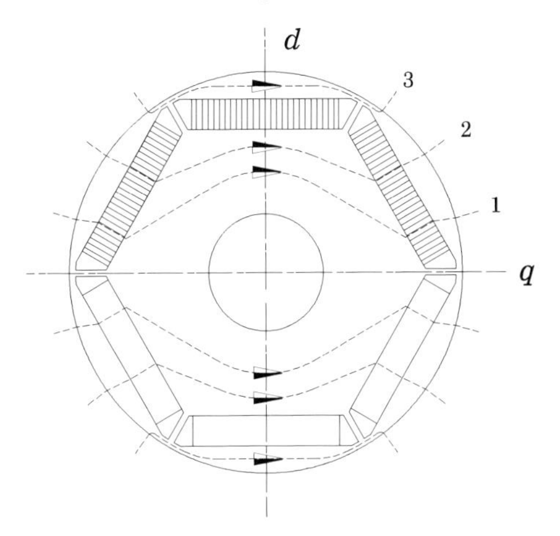

Fig. 5.25 Salient-pole rotor

The stator MMF distribution has the form

$$u(\theta) = \hat{u}_s \cos\theta \tag{5.93}$$

where θ is measured from the horizontal axis and

$$\hat{u}_s = \frac{4}{\pi}\frac{k_{w1}T_{ph}}{2p} \times \frac{3}{2} \times I\sqrt{2}. \tag{5.94}$$

Fig. 5.25 shows a 2-pole IPM rotor with $n = 3$ magnet blocks per pole, in a particular position with its d-axis vertical and its q-axis horizontal. The magnets in the upper half of the rotor are shaded to indicate that they have the same polarity. Three lines 1,2,3 of *stator* flux ("armature reaction") are shown passing across the poles.

Referring to Fig. 5.26, the magnetic potential of each pole-piece is considered to be floating with value u_1, so that the flux-density of armature-reaction across the face of the pole-cap is given by

$$B_{ga}(\theta) = \frac{\mu_0}{g'}\left[\hat{u}_s \cos p\theta - u_1\right], \qquad \theta_1 < \theta < \theta_2 \tag{5.95}$$

The flux of armature reaction passing into the pole-cap is obtained by integrating $B_g(\theta)$ between θ_1 and θ_2 : thus

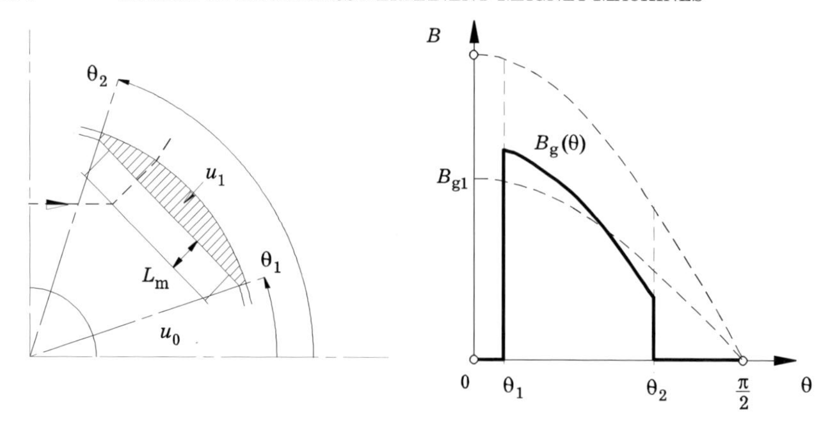

Fig. 5.26 Calculation of L_d and L_q

$$\begin{aligned}\Phi_{ga} &= \int_{\theta_1}^{\theta_2} B_g(\theta) r_1 L_{stk} d\theta \\ &= \frac{1}{R_g}\left[\frac{\hat{u}_s}{\alpha\pi}(\sin p\theta_2 - \sin p\theta_1) - u_1\right],\end{aligned} \tag{5.96}$$

where $r_1 = D/2$ is the radius at the airgap, $\alpha\pi/p = \theta_2 - \theta_1$, and

$$R_g = \frac{2pg'}{\mu_0 D L_{stk} \alpha \pi} \tag{5.97}$$

is the reluctance of the airgap between θ_1 and θ_2. In the particular case $\theta_2 = -\theta_1 = \alpha\pi/2p$, α is seen to be the "per-unit pole-arc", and

$$\Phi_{ga} = \frac{1}{R_g}[\hat{u}_s k_{\alpha d} - u_1], \tag{5.98}$$

where

$$k_{\alpha d} = \frac{\sin \alpha\pi/2}{\alpha\pi/2}. \tag{5.99}$$

By Gauss' law, the flux Φ_{ga} entering the pole-cap is equal to the flux leaving it. A fraction Φ_m passes through the magnet, while the remainder Φ_y passes from pole to pole through the bridges. Thus

$$\Phi_g = \Phi_y + P_m(u_1 - u_0) \tag{5.100}$$

where u_0 is the magnetic potential of the rotor hub or body, and P_m is the effective permeance of the magnet, eqn. (4.3).

Substituting these relationships into eqn. (5.96) with $u_0 = 0$, we obtain an expression for the undetermined magnetic potential u_1 :

$$u_1 = \frac{\hat{u}_s \left[\dfrac{\sin p\theta_2 - \sin p\theta_1}{\alpha\pi} \right] - R_g \Phi_y}{1 + P_m R_g}. \tag{5.101}$$

The field distribution is now completely determined. It has the form shown in the graph in Fig. 5.26, following the sinusoid of the ampere-conductor distribution but depressed by the effect of the "floating" magnetic potential u_1. Note that because of the constant bridge flux Φ_y, u_1 is not proportional to the current, so the synchronous reactance becomes a function of current even when the rest of the iron is considered infinitely permeable.

In the particular case $\theta_2 = -\theta_1 = \alpha\pi/2p$,

$$u_1 = \frac{\hat{u}_s k_{\alpha d} - R_g \Phi_y}{1 + P_m R_g}. \tag{5.102}$$

The synchronous reactance is associated with the fundamental component of armature-reaction flux, which can be computed from the fundamental component of $B_{ga}(\theta)$. By Fourier's theorem this is

$$\begin{aligned} B_{ga1} &= 2p \times \frac{2}{2\pi} \int_{\theta_1}^{\theta_2} B_{ga}(\theta) \cos\theta \, d\theta \\ &= \frac{2}{\pi} \frac{\mu_0}{g'} \left\{ \frac{\hat{u}_s}{2} \left[\alpha\pi + \sin\alpha\pi \cos p(\theta_1 + \theta_2) \right] - 2u_1 \sin\frac{\alpha\pi}{2} \cos\frac{p(\theta_1 + \theta_2)}{2} \right\}. \end{aligned} \tag{5.103}$$

In the particular case $\theta_2 = -\theta_1 = \alpha\pi/2p$,

$$B_{ga1} = \frac{\mu_0}{g'} \left\{ \hat{u}_s \left[\alpha + \frac{\sin\alpha\pi}{\pi} \right] - \frac{4}{\pi} u_1 \sin\frac{\alpha\pi}{2} \right\}. \tag{5.104}$$

and this can be written

$$B_{ga1} = \frac{\mu_0}{g'} \left[k_{1ad} \hat{u}_s - k_1 u_1 \right], \tag{5.105}$$

where

$$k_{1ad} = \alpha + \frac{\sin\alpha\pi}{\pi} \tag{5.106}$$

and

$$k_1 = \frac{4}{\pi} \sin \frac{\alpha \pi}{2}. \tag{5.107}$$

If we substitute eqn. (5.102) in eqn. (5.105), the result can be written

$$B_{\mathrm{ga1}} = \frac{\mu_0}{g_{\mathrm{d}}''} \hat{u}_{\mathrm{s}}, \tag{5.108}$$

where the bridge fluxes Φ_{y} have been ignored and

$$g_{\mathrm{d}}'' = \frac{g'}{k_{1\mathrm{ad}} - \dfrac{k_1 k_{\alpha\mathrm{d}}}{1 + P_{\mathrm{m}} R_{\mathrm{g}}}}. \tag{5.109}$$

This is precisely the effective airgap in the d-axis that is needed to calculate the d-axis synchronous inductance coefficient Γ_{d} in eqn. (5.89) on p. 252.

A similar process for the q-axis gives

$$g_{\mathrm{q}}'' = \frac{g'}{k_{1\mathrm{aq}}} \tag{5.110}$$

where

$$k_{1\mathrm{aq}} = \alpha - \frac{\sin \alpha \pi}{\pi}. \tag{5.111}$$

Returning to the general case of a single section of a pole with more than one section, Fig. 5.26, its contribution to the synchronous inductance in any axis is given (with suitable values of θ_1 and θ_2), by

$$\Gamma = \frac{B_{\mathrm{ga1}}}{\mu_0 \hat{u}_{\mathrm{s}} / g'}, \tag{5.112}$$

which can be obtained from eqn. (5.103), its contribution to the fundamental flux of armature reaction. Then the contributions of the n sections can be added. It will be found that symmetric rotors with $n > 1$ have little or no saliency with respect to the fundamental MMF distribution, although a strong magnet and the bridges may bias the field to induce a degree of saliency, especially if the steel saturates. In practical terms, the saliency (and reluctance torque) obtained with a 2-pole rotor such as that of Fig. 5.25 will be disappointing.

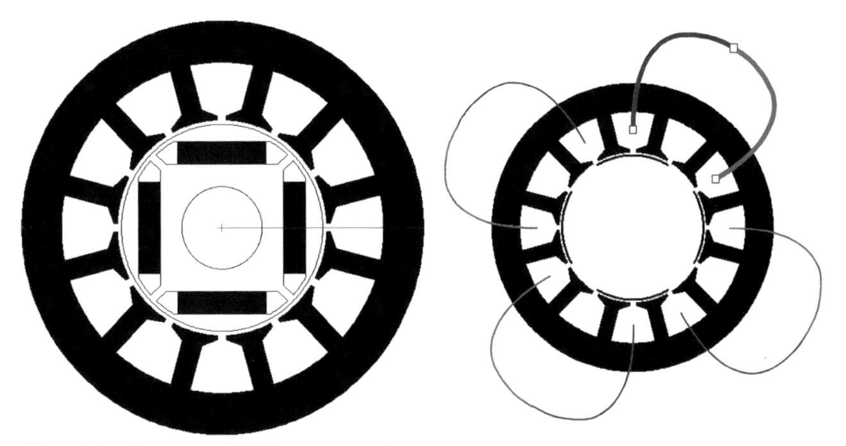

Fig. 5.27 Example IPM cross-section Fig. 5.28 Example IPM phase winding

Example — Consider the 4-pole machine in Fig. 5.27, which has a stator bore diameter D = 52 mm and stack length L_{stk} = 50 mm. The magnet width is 22 mm and the magnet length is L_m = 5·5 mm in the direction of magnetization. With a recoil permeability of 1·1, the magnet permeance is

$$P_m = \mu_0 \times 1 \cdot 1 \times \frac{22 \times 50}{5 \cdot 5} = 2 \cdot 765 \times 10^{-7} \quad \text{Wb/A}$$

and if we assume a rotor leakage permeance of p_{rl} = 0·1 we can increase this to $3 \cdot 04 \times 10^{-7}$ Wb/A.

The airgap length is 1·0 mm and Carter's coefficient for slotting is k_c = 1·0438, so g' = 1·0438 mm. The pole-arc is 120° elec so the per-unit pole-arc is α = 2/3, with $\alpha\pi$ = 2·0944 rad, and the airgap reluctance can be calculated from eqn. (5.97) at mid-gap as

$$R_g = \frac{2 \times 2 \times 1 \cdot 0438 \times 10^{-3}}{\mu_0 \times 51 \times 50 \times 10^{-6} \times 2 \cdot 0944} = 0 \cdot 622 \times 10^6 \quad \text{A/Wb}.$$

From eqn. (5.107) we get k_1 = 1·103; from eqn. (5.106) we get k_{1ad} = 2/3 + sin(120°)/π = 0·942, and from eqn. (5.99) we get $k_{\alpha d}$ = 0·827. Hence from eqn. (5.109) we get

$$g_d'' = \frac{1 \cdot 0438}{0 \cdot 942 - \dfrac{1 \cdot 103 \times 0 \cdot 827}{1 + 3 \cdot 04 \times 10^{-7} \times 0 \cdot 622 \times 10^6}} = 5 \cdot 97 \text{ mm}.$$

The number of turns per coil is 12, and all the coils are in series, so T_{ph} = 58. The fundamental winding factor is k_{w1} = 0·866, so from eqn. (5.88) we get

$$L_{m0} = \frac{3\mu_0 \times 51 \times 50}{\pi \times 2^2 \times 1{\cdot}0438} \times (0{\cdot}866 \times 48)^2 = 1{\cdot}266 \text{ mH}$$

Then with $\Gamma_d = g'/g_d'' = 1{\cdot}0438/6{\cdot}385$ we get, finally,

$$L_{md} = 1{\cdot}266 \times \frac{1{\cdot}0438}{5{\cdot}97} = 0{\cdot}221 \text{ mH}.$$

This is, of course, only the magnetizing component L_{md}. The leakage components must be added to get the total L_d.

From eqn. (5.111), $k_{1aq} = 2/3 - \sin(120°)/\pi = 0{\cdot}391$, and so from eqn. (5.110) we get

$$g_q'' = \frac{1{\cdot}0438}{0{\cdot}391} = 2{\cdot}67 \text{ mm},$$

and with $\Gamma_q = g'/g_q'' = 1{\cdot}0438/2{\cdot}67$ we get

$$L_{mq} = 1{\cdot}266 \times \frac{1{\cdot}0438}{2{\cdot}67} = 0{\cdot}495 \text{ mH}.$$

Effect of *q*-axis web — The motor in Fig. 5.27 has a web between the magnet apertures. The width of this web is 2 mm. It carries q-axis armature-reaction flux, and if it subtends an angle $\Omega\pi$ electrical radians from the airgap to the centreline, we can account for its contribution to L_{mq} using eqn. (5.106)) with Ω substituted for α, which is appropriate because there is no magnet in series with the flux in the web.

Thus we have $\Omega = [2 \times 2 \times \text{ArcSin}(1/(51/2))]/180 = 0{\cdot}05$ approximately. The formula for k_{1ad} gives $0{\cdot}05 + \sin(9°)/\pi = 0{\cdot}0998$, and we should add this to the value of k_{1aq}, giving $0{\cdot}391 + 0{\cdot}0998 = 0{\cdot}491$. The adjusted value of g_q'' is $1{\cdot}0438/0{\cdot}491 = 2{\cdot}126$ mm and the adjusted value of L_{mq} is $1{\cdot}266 \times 1{\cdot}0438/2{\cdot}126 = 0{\cdot}622$ mH.

The web thus increases L_{mq} by about 25%, but it will saturate very quickly as soon as stator current flows in the q-axis. This illustrates the uncertainty that attaches to the calculation of L_q particularly, as a result of its sensitivity to saturation in this type of machine.

5.10.4 Differential leakage inductance

This component of phase inductance is supposed to represent the effect of winding harmonics other than the fundamental. It thus represents the difference in inductance between the actual phase winding and an equivalent winding which has only the fundamental space-harmonic of MMF. The differential leakage appears in both the self and mutual inductances.

A sine-distributed three-phase winding has an airgap inductance of L_{g0} and a mutual inductance of $-L_{g0}/2$ between phases. Therefore if L_g and M_g are the actual airgap self- and mutual inductances (including winding harmonics), the respective components of differential leakage inductance can be estimated as

$$L_{diff} = L_g - L_{g0}; \qquad M_{diff} = M_g - (-L_{g0}/2). \tag{5.103}$$

L_{diff} and M_{diff} can be added to L_σ and M_σ to account for the harmonic terms above the second-harmonic in θ in eqn. (4.95).

The procedure used in the *PC-BDC* program begins by calculating the airgap inductance L_{gg} per phase, with the rotor replaced by a steel cylinder of infinite permeability and zero conductivity. The calculation of L_{gg} uses the actual winding distribution and it assumes that flux crosses the airgap in the radial direction. It accumulates the flux-linkage in every coil with 1A flowing in the winding, using B_{gap} distributions of the type shown in Fig. 5.1. Then L_g is scaled from L_{gg} according to the following equations. For surface-magnet machines,

$$L_g = L_{gg} \times \frac{g'}{g''} \tag{5.104}$$

where g' is the actual airgap modified by Carter's coefficient, and g'' is given by eqn. (5.9). For salient-pole machines,

$$L_g = L_{gg} \times \frac{\Gamma_d + \Gamma_q}{2}. \tag{5.105}$$

where Γ_d and Γ_q are the synchronous inductance coefficients given by eqns. (5.89). Since eqn. (5.105) takes the average of the d- and q-axis values, L_{diff} will be some kind of average between the d- and q-axes. Furthermore, Γ_d and Γ_q are strictly only valid for sine-distributed windings, so it is not strictly correct to use them for L_g. This means that L_{diff} will be, at best, only an indicative value.

Returning to eqn. (5.103), L_{g0} is computed from the fundamental of the MMF distribution by eqn. (5.92) which is written as

$$L_{g0} = \frac{\Gamma_d + \Gamma_q}{2} \times \frac{2}{3} L_{m0}, \tag{5.106}$$

where L_{m0} is the classical value of the magnetizing inductance per phase, when the rotor is a cylinder of infinite permeability and zero conductivity. The 2/3 factor comes from the particular choice of dq transformation for 3-phase motors, and is not necessary for 2-phase motors. L_{m0} is given by eqn. (5.88).

Substituting L_g from eqn. (5.105) and L_{g0} from eqn. (5.106) in eqn. (5.103) for L_{diff}, we get

$$L_{diff} = \frac{\Gamma_d + \Gamma_q}{2}\left[L_{gg} - \frac{2}{3}L_{m0}\right]. \tag{5.107}$$

5.10.5 Static measurement again

We can now return to the two particular connections in Fig. 5.22 to verify in terms of the transformed inductance components that they are indeed suitable for the measurement of L_d and L_q.

For the left-hand connection (a) the current I flows through phase a and divides equally between phases b and c, so that $i_a = I$, $i_b = i_c = -I/2$. The flux-linkages in phases a and b are

$$\psi_a = \left[L_{aa} - \frac{1}{2}(L_{ab} + L_{ca})\right]I; \quad \psi_b = \left[L_{ab} - \frac{1}{2}(L_{bb} + L_{bc})\right]I. \tag{5.108}$$

Substituting from eqns. (4.95) and rearranging, we get

$$\begin{aligned}\Psi &= \psi_a - \psi_b \\ &= \frac{3}{2}\left[L_\sigma - M_\sigma + \frac{3}{2}L_{g0} + L_{g2}\left\{\cos 2\theta - \frac{1}{\sqrt{3}}\sin\left(2\theta - \frac{2\pi}{3}\right)\right\}\right]I.\end{aligned} \tag{5.109}$$

When $\theta = 0$ this reduces to

$$\Psi = \frac{3}{2}\left[L_\sigma - M_\sigma + \frac{3}{2}(L_{g0} + L_{g2})\right]I = \frac{3}{2}L_d I, \tag{5.110}$$

after comparing with eqns. (5.85) and (5.86). By the same process it is shown that when $\theta = \pm\pi/2$,

$$\Psi = \frac{3}{2}\left[L_\sigma - M_\sigma + \frac{3}{2}(L_{g0} - L_{g2})\right]I = \frac{3}{2}L_q I. \tag{5.111}$$

The inductance Ψ/I of the connection Fig. 5.22(a) varies between $3/2L_d$ and $3/2L_q$ as the rotor rotates. At a general position θ it is given by eqn. (5.109). Note that with $i_a = I$, $i_b = i_c = -I/2$, $\psi_c = \psi_b$.

The right-hand connection Fig. 5.22(*b*) is the line-line connnection with $i_a = 0$, $i_b = I$, and $i_c = -I$. Then

$$\psi_b = (L_{bb} - L_{bc})I \quad \text{and} \quad \psi_c = (L_{bc} - L_{cc})I \tag{5.112}$$

and

$$\Psi = \psi_b - \psi_c = 2\left[L_\sigma - M_\sigma + \frac{3}{2}\left(L_{g0} - L_{g2}\cos 2\theta\right)\right]I. \tag{5.113}$$

When $\theta = 0$ this reduces to

$$\Psi = 2\left[L_\sigma - M_\sigma + \frac{3}{2}\left(L_{g0} - L_{g2}\right)\right]I = 2L_qI. \tag{5.114}$$

after comparing eqns. (5.85) and (5.86). By the same process it is shown that when $\theta = \pm\pi/2$,

$$\Psi = 2\left[L_\sigma - M_\sigma + \frac{3}{2}\left(L_{g0} + L_{g2}\right)\right]I = 2L_dI. \tag{5.115}$$

Therefore the inductance Ψ/I of the connection in Fig. 5.22(*b*) varies between $2L_q$ and $2L_d$ as the rotor rotates. At a general position θ it is given by eqn. (5.113). From eqns. (5.82), (5.81), (5.85) and (5.86),

$$L_{LL[q]} = 2L_q \quad \text{and} \quad L_{LL[d]} = 2L_d, \tag{5.116}$$

in agreement with eqns. (5.114) and (5.115).

Eqns. (5.81), (5.109) and (5.113) show that the terminal inductance presented to the drive varies with rotor position even when the machine is perfectly sinewound. This underlines the fact that the constant synchronous inductances L_d and L_q exist only in the synchronously rotating frame of reference. In general there will be slight differences between the values of L_d and L_q obtained with the two connections in Fig. 5.22, if the inductance harmonics are significant and the windings are not perfectly sine-distributed.

The direct measurement of L_d and L_q using eqns. (5.110), (5.111), (5.114) and (5.115) is described in Chapter 13.

5.11 Inductance from finite-element calculations

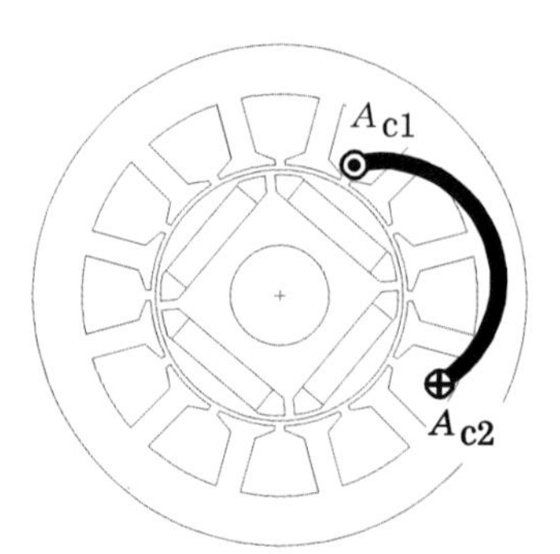

Fig. 5.29 Calculation of flux-linkage

Most finite-element programs claim to be able to calculate stored field energy W, (and coenergy), suggesting that inductance can be deduced from the formula $W = ½LI^2$, if the current I is known. However, if there is any saturation the meaning of L obtained from this formula becomes unclear, because it relies on the assumption that L does not vary with current. In the presence of permanent magnets the computation of W must distinguish between stored energy that is attributable to the magnetization of the magnets, and that which is attributable to the current. If there is any saturation, it is impossible to do this uniquely.

A more rigorous approach is to use the vector potential **A** directly, with the equation

$$\phi = \int \mathbf{A} \cdot \boldsymbol{dl} \tag{5.117}$$

in which ϕ is the flux linking the contour along which **A** is integrated. In 2-D problems, the flux ϕ linking a coil (per metre of axial length) is given by $\phi = A_{c1} - A_{c2}$, where A_{c1} and A_{c2} are the vector potential values at the coilside positions, Fig. 5.29. If there is a complete winding with coilsides in different locations, the method can be extended by adding the fluxes with appropriate polarities according to the direction of the conductors. If the coils are in series carrying current I, and all have N_c turns, the inductance is $L = N_c \Sigma\phi / I$. This inductance is the *total* inductance, not the incremental inductance. The method is simple to implement because it uses point values of vector potential.

Incremental inductance — For calculations relating to the power electronic circuit, it may be important to know the incremental inductance $d\psi/dI$ when the machine is fully fluxed with full current, because this is the inductance presented to the current regulator. Using the **A** method described above, the incremental inductance is given by $\Delta\psi/(I_1 - I_2)$, where $\Delta\psi$ is the difference in computed flux-linkage at two slightly different current levels I_1, I_2. Alternatively, the inductance can be calculated with the $W = \frac{1}{2}LI^2$ formula after freezing the permeabilities in the solution domain at the end of a nonlinear solution at the required load point.

Synchronous inductance — The vector-potential method of eqn. (5.117) calculates the *total* flux-linkage of a winding: it cannot be used to resolve the flux-linkage into separate "leakage" and "magnetizing" components, or into harmonic components. For a winding which is essentially sinewound, a practical procedure is to use a finite-element calculation with the connection of Fig. 5.22(*a*) together with eqn. (5.110) or (5.111); or that of Fig. 5.22(*b*) together with eqn. (5.114) or (5.115). End-winding inductances (not calculated in 2-D FE) must be added, but since these are generally small, approximate values will often suffice.

5.12 Magnetization curves — beyond inductance

Design and performance calculations often involve the solution of the terminal voltage equations by numerical integration. The simplest case is that of a single-phase machine which has only one terminal voltage equation,

$$v = Ri + \mathbf{p}\psi, \tag{5.118}$$

where v is the applied voltage at the terminals, R is the resistance, i is the current, ψ is the flux-linkage, and $\mathbf{p}$ is the operator d/dt so that $\mathbf{p}\psi$ is the rate of change of flux-linkage. By Faraday's law, the term $\mathbf{p}\psi$ is the total voltage induced by time-variation of the flux-linkage, including any EMF as well as the familiar $L\, di/dt$. Thus it includes both "transformer" and "rotation" voltages.

Eqn. (5.118) is an ordinary differential equation in v, i and ψ. Usually the voltage v is known at each instant during a simulation, from the states of the power electronic switches in the drive. This leaves two unknowns, i and ψ. For permanent-magnet machines it is common to write

$$\psi = \Psi_M(\theta) + Li \tag{5.119}$$

where $\Psi_M(\theta)$ is the flux-linkage produced by the magnet as a function of rotor position θ, and L is the inductance.

As the rotor rotates, the flux-*linkage* Ψ_M varies, often sinusoidally, even though the magnet *flux* is approximately constant. In that case

$$\mathbf{p}\psi = \frac{\partial \Psi_M}{\partial t} + \frac{\partial \Psi_M}{\partial \theta}\frac{d\theta}{dt} + L\frac{di}{dt} + i\frac{dL}{dt}. \tag{5.120}$$

The first term is zero if the variation of Ψ_M is solely due to rotation, and the fourth term is zero if the inductance is constant, giving

$$\mathbf{p}\psi = \omega\frac{\partial \Psi_M}{\partial \theta} + L\frac{di}{dt} + i\omega\frac{dL}{d\theta} = e + L\frac{di}{dt} + i\omega\frac{dL}{d\theta}, \tag{5.121}$$

where $\omega = \mathbf{p}\theta$ or $d\theta/dt$, the angular velocity, and e is the EMF,

$$e = \omega\frac{\partial \Psi_M}{\partial \theta} \tag{5.122}$$

which is a known function of θ. Substituting in eqn. (5.118), we get

$$v = Ri + e + L\frac{di}{dt} + i\omega\frac{dL}{d\theta}, \tag{5.123}$$

Eqn. (5.119) relies on the principle of superposition, so it and eqns. (5.120) – (5.123) are valid only when the magnetic circuit is linear. This is a reasonable assumption for many surface-magnet machines, but it is generally not adequate for IPM machines.

At constant speed the numerical integration of eqn. (5.118) by Euler's method can be written as a time-stepping process

$$\psi = \int (v - Ri)\,dt \approx (v - Ri)\,\Delta t + [\psi], \tag{5.124}$$

where ψ is the new value at each time-step, Δt is the time step, and $[\psi]$ means the value of ψ at the previous time-step.

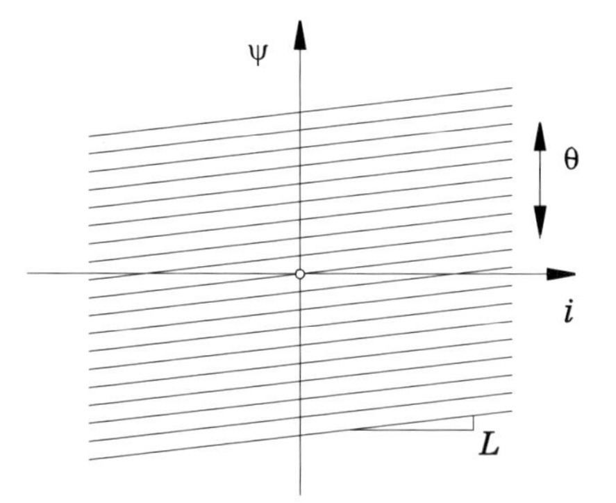

Fig. 5.30 Linear magnetization curves

After each time-step the current must be found from the new values of ψ and θ. If the machine is linear, eqn. (5.119) can be used to extract the new current i, and then the integration process can proceed to the next step. If it is nonlinear, the new current must be extracted by inverting or solving a relationship of the form

$$\psi = \psi(i,\theta), \tag{5.125}$$

which expresses the so-called *magnetization curves*.[34] Eqn. (5.119) is an example of linear magnetization curves, Fig. 5.30. The curves move up and down cyclically as the magnet rotates; they are not *static*, since they depend on the rotor position.

Eqn. (5.120) is often integrated with current as the state variable rather than flux-linkage. But current varies much more rapidly than flux-linkage, requiring a smaller time-step and ultimately resulting in a slower solution. With current as state variable, it is necessary to resort to "incremental inductance" and "frozen permeability" models to extract the separate terms in eqn. (5.120). This is another instance where the use of inductance makes matters needlessly complicated.

Eqns. (5.118-5.125) are valid for all linear single-phase machines including reluctance machines (in which $\Psi_M = 0$), and also for machines with saliency on the rotor or the stator or both. For motors having more than one phase, a voltage equation of the form of eqn. (5.123) is written for each phase, including mutual inductance terms. The electromagnetic torque is calculated using eqn. (4.94).

---

[34] In this process the flux-linkage is the state variable, not the current.

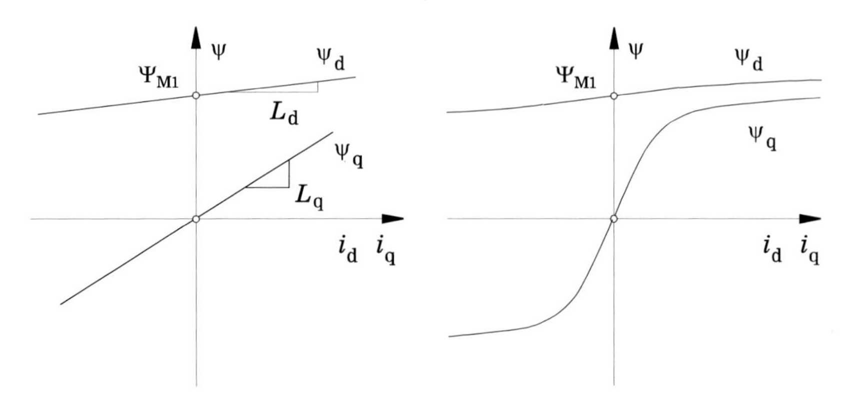

Fig. 5.31 Linear dq-axis mag. curves Fig. 5.32 Nonlinear dq-axis mag. curves

5.12.1 Magnetization curves in *dq*-axes

Step-by-step integration of the differential equations (4.108) is the same as for eqn. (5.118). For example, by Euler's method the d-axis voltage equation becomes

$$\begin{aligned} \psi_d &= \int (v_d - R i_d + \mathbf{p}\theta \cdot \psi_q)\, dt \\ &\approx (v_d - R i_d + \mathbf{p}\theta \cdot \psi_q)\, \Delta t + [\psi_d], \end{aligned} \tag{5.126}$$

At the end of each integration-step, the currents i_d and i_q must be updated from the new flux-linkages. In the classical case with sine-distributed windings and no saturation, we can use eqns. (5.77), which express the *static* magnetization curves shown in Fig. 5.31. These curves are uncoupled and independent of the rotor position θ, and the inversion of eqns. (5.77) is trivial.

Especially in IPM motors L_d and L_q are not constant, but vary greatly as a result of saturation. In the simplest case ψ_d is assumed to be a function only of i_d, and ψ_q only of i_q, with no "cross-saturation" and no variation with rotor position. The magnetization curves then have the form

$$\psi_d = \psi_d(i_d) \quad \text{and} \quad \psi_q = \psi_q(i_q), \tag{5.127}$$

as shown in Fig. 5.32. Although these are nonlinear, they can easily be inverted to get i_d from ψ_d and i_q from ψ_q.

Unfortunately there often is cross-coupling between the d and q axes. The q-axis flux path is normally highly permeable and may saturate easily at quite low values of i_q. In doing so it reduces the permeability of the d-axis flux-path and interferes with the values of both Ψ_{1Md} and L_d. In Fig. 5.32 this would appear as a distortion of the $\psi_q(i_q)$ curve that depends on the value of i_d. Conversely the $\psi_d(i_d)$ curve is distorted by i_q. In a sinewound machine these effects will remain independent of the rotor position; the magnetization curves will remain *static*, with the general form

$$\psi_d = \psi_d(i_d, i_q) \quad \text{and} \quad \psi_q = \psi_q(i_d, i_q). \tag{5.128}$$

A still more complex case is where the nonlinear cross-coupled magnetization curves vary with the rotor position θ in spite of the fact that they are in dq axes. The magnetization curves then have the general form

$$\psi_d = \psi_d(i_d, i_q, \theta) \quad \text{and} \quad \psi_q = \psi_q(i_d, i_q, \theta). \tag{5.129}$$

In other words, ψ_d is a function not only of i_d but also of i_q (cross-coupling) and θ, and likewise ψ_q is a function of i_d and θ as well as i_q. The additional dependence on θ makes matters very much more complicated and is liable to arise if the windings are not sinewound; in other words, if the harmonic winding factors are not all zero. Unfortunately this is often the case, to a greater or lesser degree, with all practical windings. The curves (5.129) require a vast number of finite-element calculations to define them, and an appropriate interpolating function that could be used to invert them.

5.13 Saturation in the *dq*-axis model

We need a practical method to determine saturated values of L_d, L_q and Ψ_{1Md}. For any set of values of i_d and i_q, the flux-linkages ψ_d and ψ_q can be computed by finite-element analysis, and then L_d and L_q can be deduced from eqns. (5.77) as

$$L_d = \frac{\psi_d - \Psi_{1Md}}{i_d}; \qquad \text{(d)}$$

$$L_q = \frac{\psi_q}{i_q}. \qquad \text{(q)} \tag{5.130}$$

A unique value of L_q can be deduced from eqn. (5.130q), for any value of i_q. But for L_d, eqn. (5.130d) needs a value for the "open-circuit" value Ψ_{1Md}. The obvious choice is to set Ψ_{1Md} equal to the value of ψ_d computed with $i_d = i_q = 0$: that is, point **Z** in Fig. 4.37. However, because of cross-saturation, the numerator $(\psi_d - \Psi_{1Md})$ can be nonzero when i_q is restored to the normal load-point value, even when $i_d = 0$. Eqn. (5.130d) would then produce an indefinite result for L_d if it was used at (or near) such a load-point where $i_d = 0$ and i_q was nonzero, which is quite a normal condition.

This problem is avoided if Ψ_{1Md} is calculated with $i_d = 0$ and the *load-point* value of i_q: that is, at point **Q** in Fig. 4.37. In this case Ψ_{1Md} is computed with the full effect of cross-saturation in the q-axis, which tends to decrease its value. Thereafter the additional term $L_d i_d$ can be interpreted as the flux-linkage of armature reaction in the d-axis, *in the presence of the cross-magnetizing current* i_q.

Although it still uses superposition, the process is systematic and reproducible. Although there is an infinite number of possible values of Ψ_{1Md} and L_d that will satisfy eqn. (5.130d), a unique result is obtained at each operating point. It makes sense in engineering terms because it accounts for cross-saturation without introducing any additional cross-saturation terms.

5.14 Demagnetization

The subject of demagnetization can be said to belong in a chapter on inductance, because the demagnetizing MMF of armature reaction exerts itself through the inductance to produce flux that may oppose the magnet flux. In bulk terms, the most direct demagnetizing influence is that of the d-axis armature reaction, which we have already seen in §5.8 in terms of the short-circuit current $I_{d(sc)}$.

Current in the d-axis produces a flux Φ_{ga} given by eqn. (5.98). If we substitute eqn. (5.102) in eqn. (5.98) the result is

$$\Phi_{ga} = \frac{\hat{u}_s k_{\alpha d} P_m + \Phi_y}{1 + P_m R_g} . \qquad (5.131)$$

The flux Φ_y flows through the saturable bridges, leaving most of the remainder to flow through the magnets. An example illustrates this.

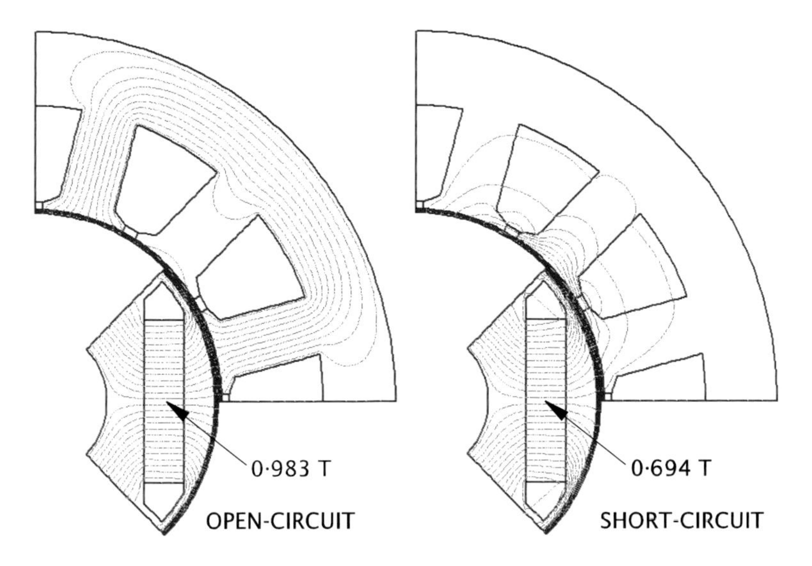

Fig. 5.33 Demagnetization calculation (open- and short-circuit)

Example — The motor of Fig. 5.27 has a phase EMF $E = 5{\cdot}32$ V at 1000 rpm with a frequency of 33·3 Hz. We have already calculated the synchronous inductance $L_{md} = 0{\cdot}221$ mH. Suppose that the leakage inductances (not calculated) add to L_{md} to give $L_d = 0{\cdot}45$ mH, so $X_d = 2\pi \times 33{\cdot}3 \times 0{\cdot}45 \times 10^{-3} =$ 0·0942 ohm, and the short-circuit current is then 5·32/0·0942 = 56·5 A RMS.

From eqn. (5.94),

$$\hat{u}_s = \frac{4}{\pi} \times \frac{0{\cdot}866 \times 58}{2 \times 2} \times \frac{3}{2} \times 56{\cdot}5\sqrt{2} = 1{,}916 \quad [\text{At}]. \tag{5.132}$$

From eqn. (5.131), ignoring Φ_y,

$$\Phi_{ga} = \frac{1{,}916 \times 0{\cdot}827 \times 2{\cdot}765 \times 10^{-7}}{1 + 2{\cdot}765 \times 10^{-7} \times 0{\cdot}622 \times 10^6} = 0{\cdot}374 \quad [\text{mWb}]. \tag{5.133}$$

Since the magnet pole-face area is 22 × 50 mm, the flux-density of armature reaction in the magnet is

$$B_{ma} = \frac{0{\cdot}374 \times 10^{-3}}{22 \times 50 \times 10^{-6}} = 0{\cdot}340 \quad [\text{T}] \tag{5.134}$$

This is the amount by which the open-circuit flux-density in the magnet is depressed by armature-reaction during a steady-state short-circuit.

The calculation is verified in Fig. 5.33 by two finite-element calculations which show the flux-densities on open-circuit and short-circuit.

The depression in the magnet flux-density predicted by the finite-element calculation is 0·289 T, slightly smaller than calculated, but this can be explained by the bridges and the fact that the winding is far from being sine-distributed. Provided that the knee of the demagnetization curve of the magnet is below about 0·6 T at this temperature, the magnet should be safe against demagnetization due to a steady-state 3-phase short-circuit.

A *transient* short-circuit can produce an instantaneous stator current at least twice the peak value of $I_{d(sc)}$. Assuming linearity, the flux-density in the magnet in this example could transiently be depressed by 2 × 0·340 T = 0·68 T. Using the finite-element value of open-circuit flux-density, 0·983 T, this means that the transient flux-density in the magnet could be as low as 0·983 − 0·68 = 0·303 T, which is considerably more severe. If this condition is to be met at high temperature, it will require a magnet with very good high-temperature coercivity, with a knee point below about 0·3 T. Further allowances might be appropriate to be sure that *local* demagnetization will not occur. This can only be investigated by detailed finite-element analysis.

This example shows the importance of accuracy in calculating L_d, which must also take into account the additional saturation that is likely to be present during a short-circuit. To some extent the saturation of the stator teeth may absorb armature reaction mmf and help to protect the magnet from demagnetization, but this again can only be investigated by detailed finite-element analysis.

Squarewave drive — Another example of the demagnetization calculation is developed for a motor with squarewave drive, in which full voltage is applied with the rotor stationary. Normally in the locked-rotor condition the current would be limited by the drive, but here we will make the pessimistic assumption that it is limited only by the stator resistance, so $I_{LR} = V_s/R_{LL}$. The stator ampere-turns F_a appear in the simple magnetic circuit in series with the airgap reluctance R_g, as in Fig. 5.34. The flux of armature reaction is

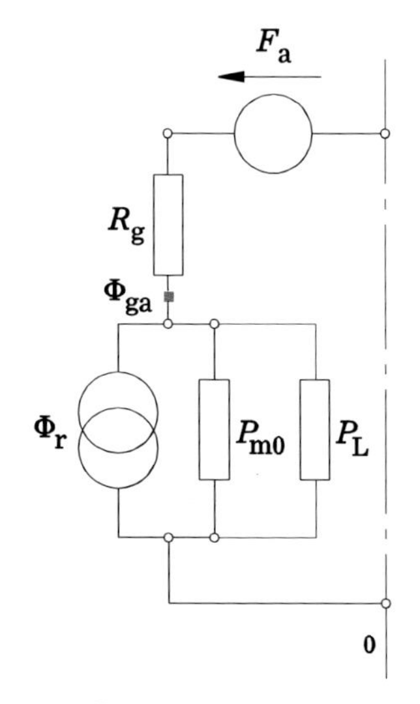

Fig. 5.34 Demag

$$\Phi_{ga} = \frac{F_a}{R_g + \dfrac{1}{P_{m0} + P_L}}. \tag{5.135}$$

P_{m0} is the magnet internal permeance and P_L is the rotor leakage permeance.

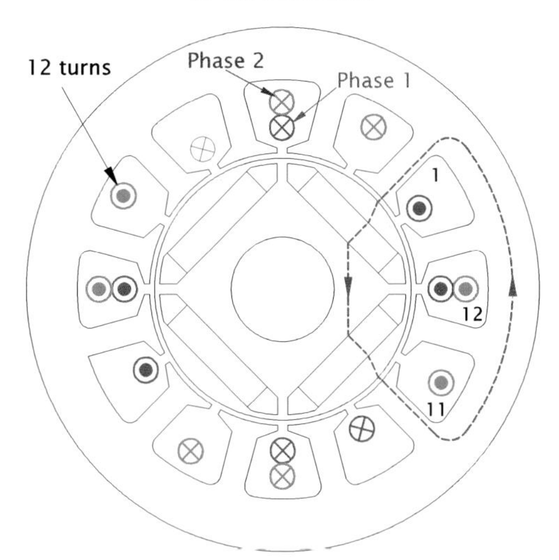

Fig. 5.35 Demag calculation

The fraction of Φ_{ga} that passes through the magnet is $P_{m0}/(P_{m0} + P_L)$, and if P_L is written as $p_{rl}P_{m0}$, we can calculate this fraction as

$$\Phi_{ma} = \frac{F_a P_{m0}}{1 + (1 + p_{rl}) P_{m0} R_g} . \qquad (5.136)$$

Then if A_m is the pole-face area of the magnet, the flux-density in the magnet will be depressed by Φ_{ma}/A_m if F_a is demagnetizing.

Example — The motor of Fig. 5.27 has R_{LL} = 0·106 ohm and operates from a DC source of 12 V. Neglecting volt-drops in transistors, I_{LR} = 12/0·106 = 113 A. The MMF F_a can be seen in Fig. 5.35: with 2 phases conducting, the total number of ampere-conductors per pole is $F_a = 4 \times 12 \times 113/2 = 2712$ A, so

$$\Phi_{ma} = \frac{2{,}712 \times 2{\cdot}765 \times 10^{-7}}{1 + 1{\cdot}1 \times 2{\cdot}765 \times 10^{-7} \times 0{\cdot}622 \times 10^{6}} = 0{\cdot}631 \quad [\text{mWb}].$$

Then the flux-density of armature reaction in the magnet is

$$B_{ma} = \frac{0{\cdot}631 \times 10^{-3}}{22 \times 50 \times 10^{-6}} = 0{\cdot}573 \quad [\text{T}].$$

An even simpler calculation is based on the MMF F_a expended across the gap g' (1·0438 mm) in series with a magnet of effective length L_m/μ_{rec}: thus

$$B_{ma} = \frac{\mu_0 F_a}{g' + L_m/\mu_{rec}} = \frac{\mu_0 \times 2{,}712}{(1{\cdot}0438 + 5{\cdot}5/1{\cdot}1) \times 10^{-3}} = 0{\cdot}564 \quad [\text{T}].$$

6 SQUAREWAVE DRIVE

Introduction

In this chapter we turn to the subject of squarewave control and current regulation.

In the *squarewave* system, the ampere-conductor distribution of the stator ideally remains constant and fixed in space for a predetermined **commutation interval** while the magnet rotates past it, producing a linear variation in phase flux-linkage and from it a flat-topped EMF waveform. With constant current, constant torque is produced. At the end of each commutation interval, the ampere-conductors are switched (*commutated*) to the next position, and the process repeats.

We have seen in Chapter 4 that the required flat-topped EMF waveform can be produced with windings in which the coilsides are concentrated rather than distributed, and with magnets that give a flat-topped distribution of flux in the airgap. Saliency is generally undesirable with squarewave drive, because it produces a reluctance torque that varies as the rotor rotates. For these reasons the most common squarewave motors have surface-mounted magnets.

The phasor diagram does not apply to squarewave drive, because it requires sinusoidal voltages and currents.[35] Analysis is therefore performed in terms of instantaneous quantities; that is to say, waveforms of voltage, EMF, current and torque.

---

[35] In practice, the distinctions between sinewave and squarewave motors and drives may not be so rigid. For example, salient-pole IPM motors are sometimes run from squarewave drives, while in other cases the EMF waveform may be a compromise between a good trapezoid and a good sinewave. The theory of space vectors relies on the assumption of sinusoidally distributed *windings*, so that the voltages and currents need not be sinusoidal. The theory of space vectors could be applied to the squarewave drive, but only if the motor had sine-distributed windings — in which case it would be a sinewave motor fed with squarewave currents, not a squarewave motor in the normal sense of the electronically commutated brushless DC motor. Again, dq-axis theory can be used with the squarewave machine without restriction, since it makes no assumption about the winding distribution or the voltage or current waveforms; but there would be no advantage, because the magnetic conditions in the rotating reference frame (i.e., in the rotor) are not constant even in the steady state.

6.1 Three-phase bipolar drives

We will start with three-phase drives. At power levels above a few watts, they are by far the most common. Single-phase and two-phase drives are treated in later sections of this chapter.

6.1.1 Waveforms and commutation sequences

Fig. 6.3 shows the ideal motoring waveforms for a three-phase wye-connected drive, Fig. 6.1. Similarly Fig. 6.4 shows the ideal motoring waveforms for a three-phase delta-connected drive, Fig. 6.2. In each case the table at the bottom of the waveform diagram shows the transistors that are conducting in each commutation interval. The line current waveforms are identical in both cases; so far as the drive is concerned, it is practically immaterial whether the machine is connected in wye or delta, provided that it is balanced and there is no neutral connection.[36] However, the way in which the current divides between the phases is different in the two cases.

The commutation table ("truth table") for the transistors is shown in Table 6.1. DC current is fed from the supply to the motor via two lines for an interval of 60°. During this interval the third line is idle and carries no current. At the end of each 60° interval the current commutates from one of the conducting lines into the idle line. There are normally 2 transistors conducting at any time: one upper and one lower transistor, Fig. 6.1 or 6.2. This is a "2Q" switch control strategy.[37] The switching is synchronized with the rotor position.

It appears from the ideal waveforms in Fig. 6.3 that there is really only one DC current which is switched or commutated among the phases. This suggests that the current could be measured with only one current sensor in the DC supply, and regulated by chopping only one transistor. However, the operation of the circuit is complicated by the action of the freewheel diodes, so that the three phase currents are not necessarily "observable" to a sensor in the DC supply.

---

[36] The 4-wire connection is sometimes used with a 4-leg inverter, which gives independent control of the three phase voltages and currents.

[37] The "dwell" or conduction interval of the transistors in a 2Q drive can be shortened below 120°. It can also be extended beyond 120°, in which case there are periods with 3 transistors conducting. If the dwell is extended to 180° the 2Q scheme becomes a 3Q scheme all the time.

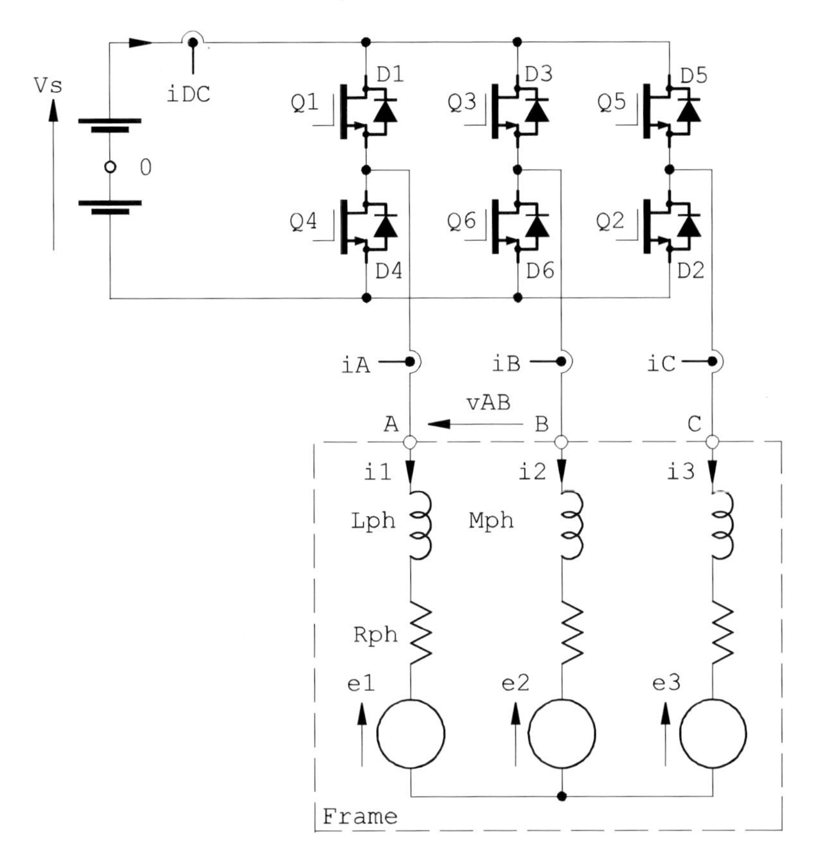

Fig. 6.1 Drive circuit : wye-connected machine

Rotor position [°elec]	Line			Phaseleg A		Phaseleg B		Phaseleg C	
	A	B	C	Q_1	Q_4	Q_3	Q_6	Q_5	Q_2
330-30	0	-1	+1	0	0	0	1	1	0
30-90	+1	-1	0	1	0	0	1	0	0
90-150	+1	0	-1	1	0	0	0	0	1
150-210	0	+1	-1	0	0	1	0	0	1
210-270	-1	+1	0	0	1	1	0	0	0
270-330	-1	0	+1	0	1	0	0	1	0

TABLE 6.1
COMMUTATION TABLE: 120° SQUAREWAVE LINE CURRENTS

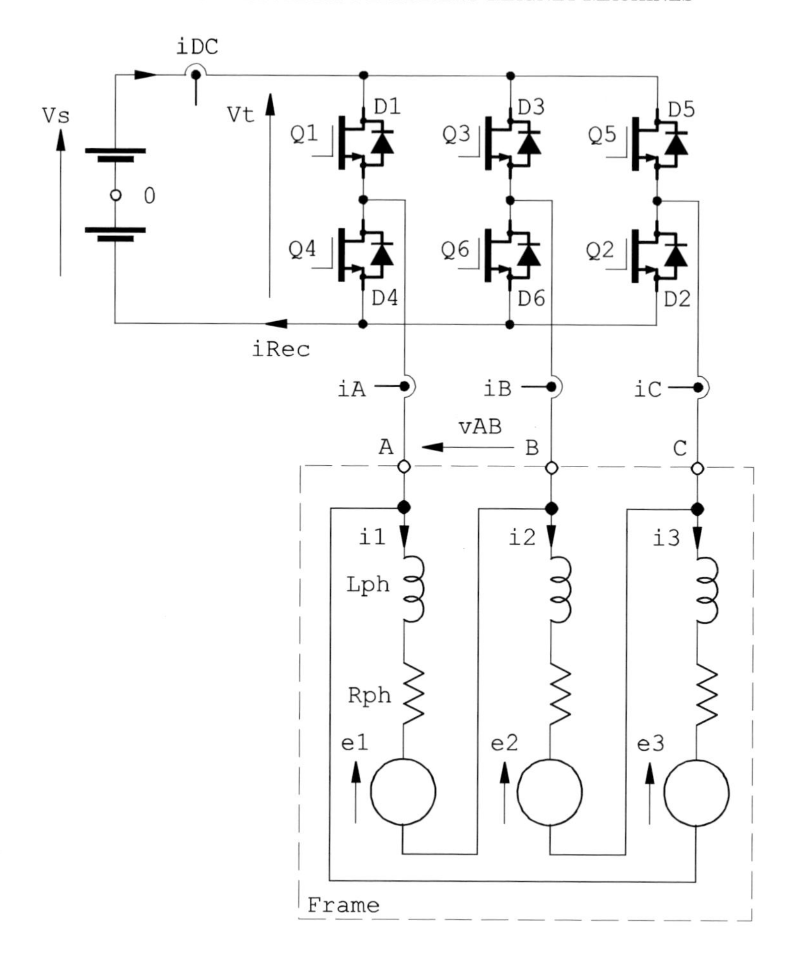

Fig. 6.2 Drive circuit : delta-connected machine

For full control of the current at all times, it is generally necessary to measure the line currents directly by means of isolated current sensors in the lines. With a 3-wire connection $i_A + i_B + i_C = 0$, so only two currents need be measured, the third being determined from the sum of the other two.

When the control strategy is *voltage PWM* in the sense described in connection with Fig. 2.13, or with the unipolar drives described later, a single current non-isolated sensor in the DC supply can be used for current regulation and protection.

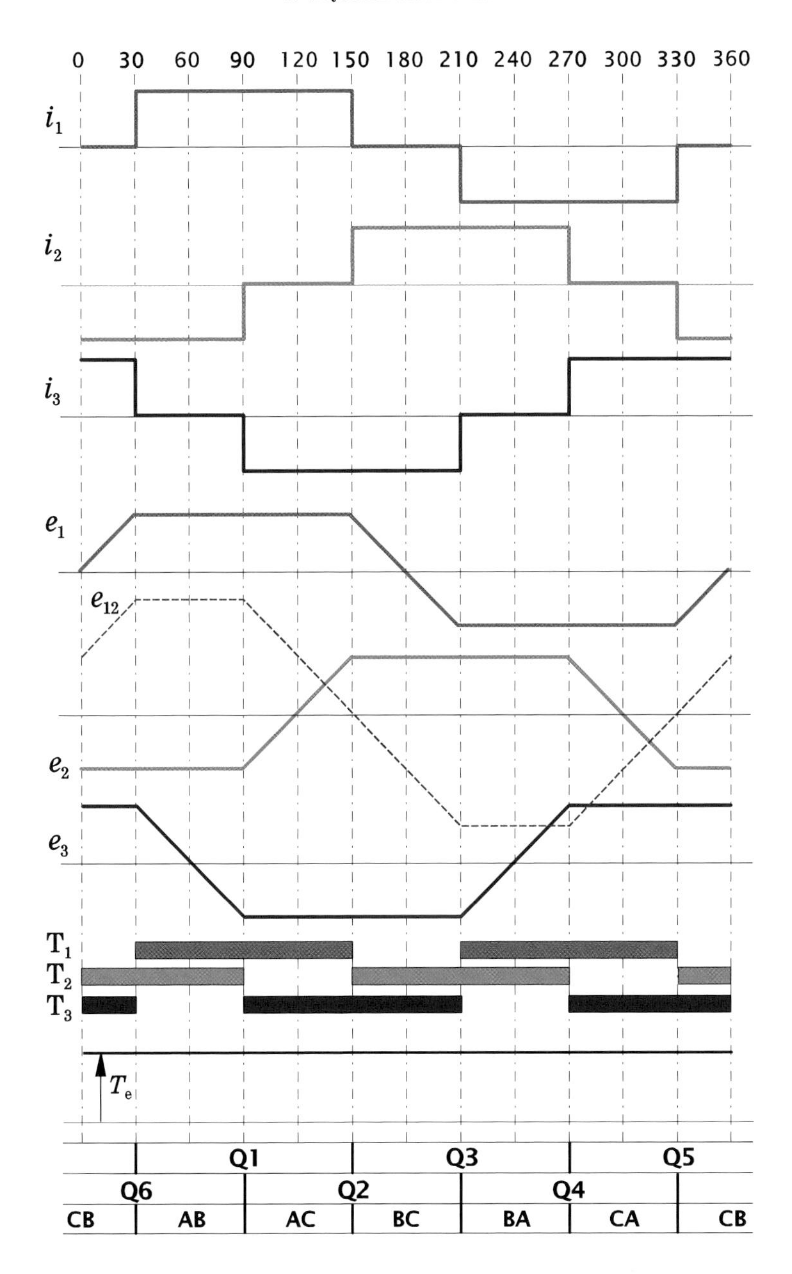

Fig. 6.3 Motoring waveforms; wye-connected machine

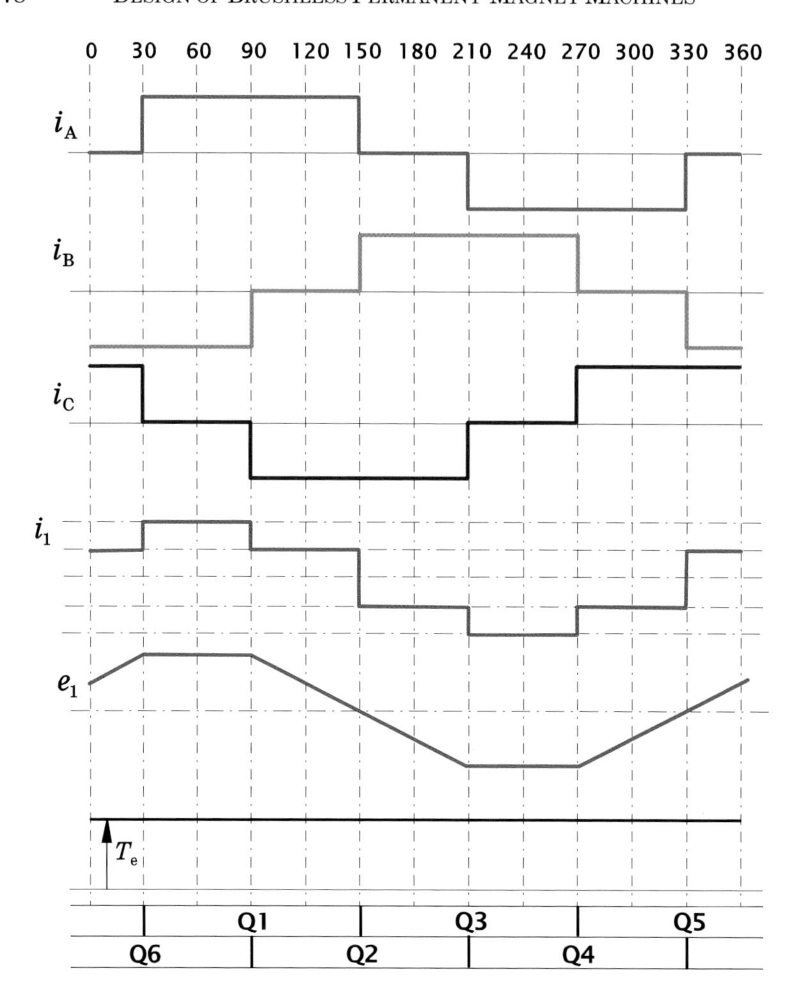

Fig. 6.4 Motoring waveforms; delta-connected machine

In Fig. 6.4 with delta connection, the line-line EMF has a 60° flat-top, the same as in Fig. 6.3 for the wye connection. In the delta connection the line-line EMF is the same as the phase EMF, but the 60° flat top is not an automatic consequence of connecting the winding in delta. The winding pitch and/or the pole-arc must be designed to achieve it. It is important to avoid triplen harmonics in the phase EMF waveforms, otherwise there will be a circulating current in the delta. (See §3.6).

6.1.2 Current regulation

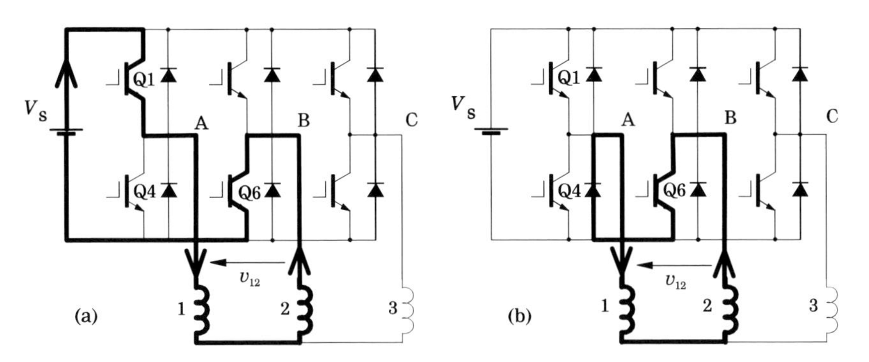

Fig. 6.5 3-phase drive : switching transistor Q_1

The current is *regulated* by chopping one or more power transistors in the drive.[38]

In Fig. 6.5(a) the normal path of the current is shown in two lines A and B, and in two phases 1 and 2 in series, during the interval from 30° to 90° in Fig. 6.3; transistors Q_1 and Q_6 are conducting. In Fig. 6.5(b), transistor Q_1 is switched off or "chopped", while Q_6 continues to conduct. The current in line A commutates from transistor Q_1 to diode D_4 and continues in lines A and B and transistor Q_6.

With both Q_1 and Q_6 conducting, the voltage across the series combination of phases 1 and 2 is $v_{12} = V_s$. When Q_1 switches off, $v_{12} = 0$, because the phases are short-circuited by Q_6 and D_4 as the current freewheels through diode D_4, as shown in Fig. 6.5(b).[39]

Instead of switching off Q_1, we can equally well switch off Q_6; again $v_{12} = 0$ and the current freewheels through D_3. If *both* Q_1 and Q_6 are turned off, the current freewheels through *both* diodes D_4 and D_3, but now $v_{12} = -V_s$. This is summarized in Table 6.2.

---

[38] "Chopping" means switching the power transistors on and off at a frequency much higher than the fundamental frequency, typically a few kHz.

[39] The voltage is not exactly zero because of the combined voltage-drop in the two devices, which can be considerable in low-voltage circuits. However, for the purposes of explaining the basic operation, it is convenient to treat the freewheeling circuits as "zero-volt loops"

Q_1	D_4	Q_6	D_3	v_{12}
1	0	1	0	V_s
0	1	1	0	0
1	0	0	1	0
0	1	0	1	$-V_s$

TABLE 6.2
TRUTH TABLE FOR SWITCHES IN FIG. 6.5

If the transistors are switched at sufficiently high frequency, the motor inductance keeps the current waveform smooth and the motor responds to the *average* applied voltage V_{12}. Suppose the circuit is switched between the states in Fig. 6.5(a) and 6.5(b) at high frequency, by chopping Q_1 with a *duty-cycle d*; d is the ratio t_{on}/t_s : see Fig. 6.6. The switching frequency is $f_s = 1/t_s$.

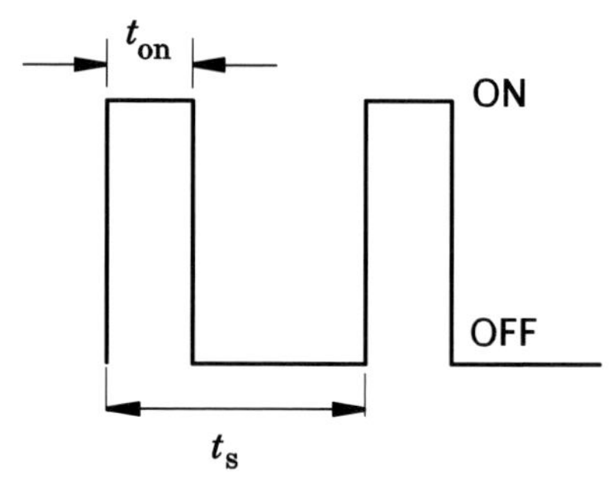

Fig. 6.6 Switching duty-cycle

The average voltage V_{12} is given by

$$V_{12} = \frac{V_s \times t_{on} + 0 \times (t_s - t_{on})}{t_s} = \frac{t_{on} V_s}{t_s} = d V_s. \quad (6.1)$$

The effect of the chopping on the current can be determined from the simplified circuit in Fig. 6.7, which represents phases 1 and 2 in series. We have

$$\begin{aligned} v_1 &= e_1 + R i_1 + L p_1 + M p_2 \\ v_2 &= e_2 + R i_2 + L p_2 + M p_1 \end{aligned} \quad (6.2)$$

where $p_1 = di_1/dt$ and $p_2 = di_2/dt$. R is the phase resistance, L is the phase self-inductance, and M is the mutual inductance between phases.

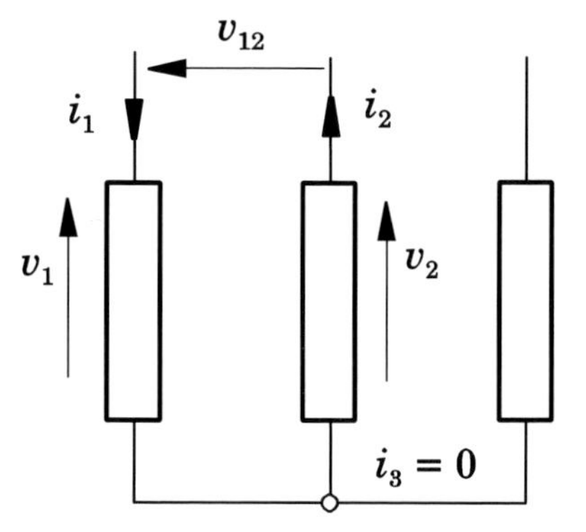

Fig. 6.7 Simplified circuit; chopping

Since $i_3 = 0$ during the $60°$ interval of interest, we have $i_2 = -i_1$ and therefore $p_2 = -p_1$. Then if we write $e_{12} = e_1 - e_2$,

$$v_{12} = v_1 - v_2 = e_{12} + 2Ri_1 + 2(L - M)p_1. \qquad (6.3)$$

Now if the circuit is switched at high frequency between Fig. 6.5(a) and Fig. 6.5(b), we can replace v_{12} by $V_{12,}$ and p_1 by the averaged value of p_1 in the sense depicted in Fig. 6.8: this is denoted $P_1 = \Delta i/\Delta t$.

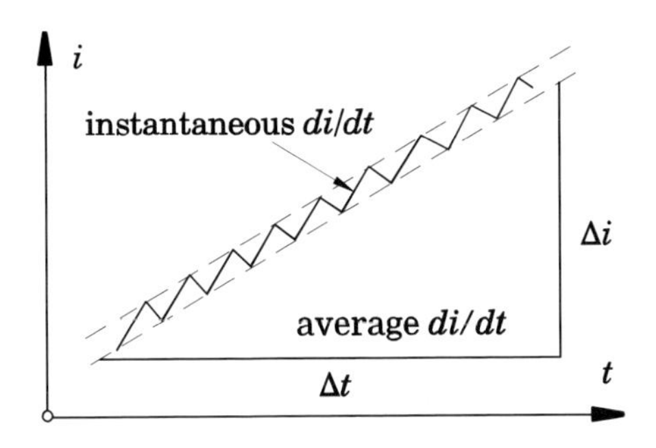

Fig. 6.8 Average di/dt

The most important practical case is where the chopping is arranged to maintain the current constant and equal to a set-point value I_{sp}, as shown in Fig. 6.9.

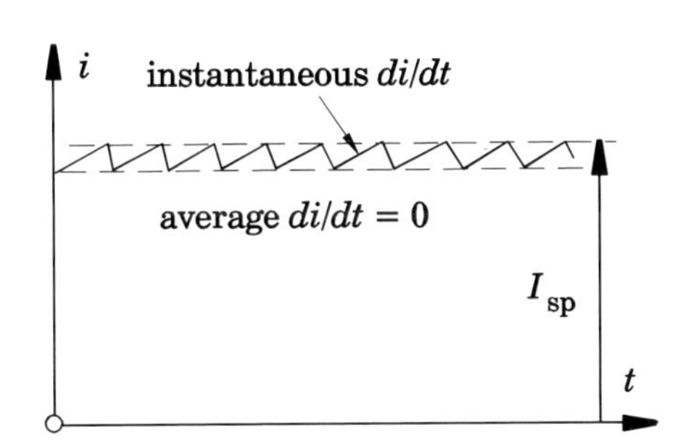

Fig. 6.9 Chopping with constant current

In this case $P_1 = 0$ and from eqns. (6.1) and (6.3), the required duty-cycle d is given by

$$d = \frac{e_{12} + 2RI_{sp}}{V_s}. \qquad (6.4)$$

The maximum value of d is 1. When $d = 1$, the chopping transistor (Q_1) is on throughout the 60° interval. Since e_{12} (the line–line voltage e_{LL}) is proportional to speed, this condition occurs at a particular speed, called the **base speed** ω_b. Evidently

$$\omega_b = \frac{V_s - 2RI_{sp}}{k_E}. \tag{6.5}$$

The base speed is the maximum speed at which the set-point current I_{sp} can be forced into the motor. If I_{sp} is equal to the rated current, ω_b is the maximum speed at which rated torque can be developed. At higher speeds, the rising EMF rapidly makes it impossible to force current into the motor, and the torque decreases quickly to zero as the speed rises. This is shown in Fig. 6.10, which also shows the hyperbola of constant power P_{max} passing through the base-speed point. Sometimes this is called the "corner point".

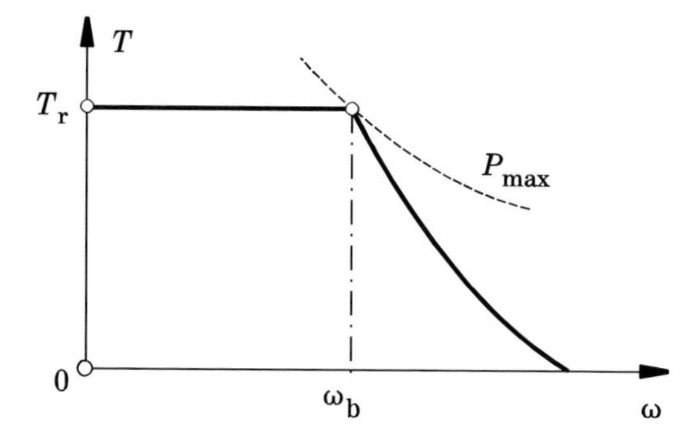

Fig. 6.10 Torque/speed curve

6.1.3 Commutation

At the end of each 60°interval the current must switch from one pair of lines to another pair. In the 60° interval from −30° to 30°the current was flowing in lines CB, and at the end of that interval it is "commutated" into lines AB.

Ideally, the current in line B remains constant while the current in line C switches to line A. In practice, however, i_C cannot fall to zero instantaneously, nor can i_A rise from zero to I_{sp} instantaneously. Rather, there is a brief period **A** when i_C is falling and i_A is rising, and there is current in all three lines at once, Figs. 6.11 and 6.12.

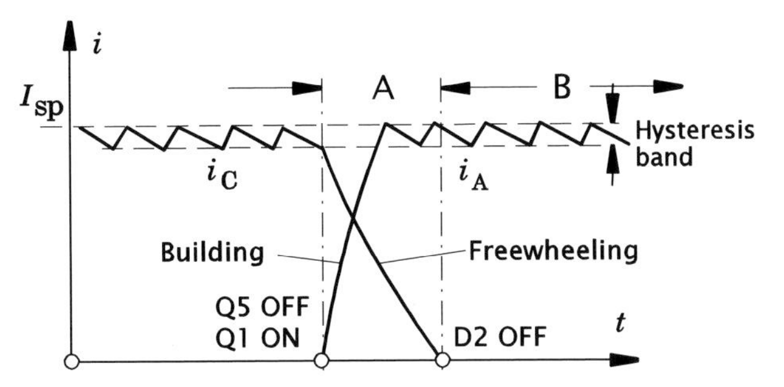

Fig. 6.11 Commutation of line current

The circuit can be analyzed during commutation by solving the voltage equations for two meshes: one in which the current is "building", and the other in which it is "freewheeling". We will apply this to the commutation from lines CB to lines AB, where transistor Q_5 has reached the end of its conduction interval and Q_1 is switched on. The current in line C freewheels through D_2, and when this current is extinguished the current in lines AB continues for the rest of the 60° interval. The chopping analysis in the preceding section applies to this condition, after the extinction of i_C.

The voltage V_{bld} controlling the build-up of current in phases 1 and 2 (lines A and B) is the line-line voltage across these two phases in series, which can be written

$$V_{bld} = v_{12} = v_1 - v_2 = v_{AB}. \tag{6.6}$$

Similarly the voltage V_{fwh} ("fwh" = "freewheel") controlling the decay of current in phases 3 and 2 (lines C and B) is the line-line voltage across these two phases in series, which can be written

$$V_{fwh} = v_{23} = v_2 - v_3 = v_{BC}. \tag{6.7}$$

V_{bld} is determined by the state of the chopping transistor Q_1, s_{Q1}:

$$V_{bld} = \left| \begin{array}{ll} V_s - 2V_q - 2R_q i_1 & (s_{Q1}=1) \\ -V_q - R_q i_1 - V_d & (s_{Q1}=0) \end{array} \right. \tag{6.8}$$

Each transistor is modelled by a voltage-drop V_q and resistance R_q; and each diode by a voltage-drop V_d. Combining these equations,

$$V_{bld} = s_{Q1}(V_s - 2V_q - 2R_q i_1) + (1 - s_{Q1})(-V_q - R_q i_1 - V_d). \tag{6.9}$$

The value of V_{fwh} is not affected by the state of Q_1:

$$V_{fwh} = V_d + V_q + R_q(-i_B). \qquad (6.10)$$

If Q_1 is chopped at a sufficiently high frequency then s_{Q1} can be set equal to the duty-cycle d, and V_{bld} can be interpreted as the average voltage across the terminals AB, or V_{12}. When we make s_{Q1} equal to d we are using the principle of "state-space averaging", to replace a binary value s_{Q1} by a real number d, as suggested by eqn. (6.1). d is the *effective* value of s_{Q1} under the stated conditions, when the chopping frequency is sufficiently high and the inductance is sufficient to keep the current waveform reasonably smooth.

Using the state-space average value d, an algebraic solution of eqns. (6.9) and (6.10) can be formulated. The same formulas for V_{bld} and V_{fwh} can be used in digital simulation, where s_{Q1} is the actual state of the chopping transistor, either 1 or 0 (on or off).

At the end of period **A** (Fig. 6.11) the line current $i_C = i_3$ reaches zero and the line current $i_A = i_1$ arrives close to I_{sp}, the set-point value of the current-regulator. i_A is then maintained constant by chopping Q_1. The current i_A is essentially a DC value during period **B** (Fig. 6.11). This is possible only if $d \leq 1$. Evidently

$$i_1 = \frac{V_{bld} - (e_1 - e_2)}{2R}. \qquad (6.11)$$

If we set $i_1 = I_{sp}$ then d can be calculated as

$$d = \frac{e_1 - e_2 + 2RI_{sp} + V_d + V_q + R_q I_{sp}}{V_s - V_q + V_d - R_q I_{sp}}. \qquad (6.12)$$

A simplified version of this arises if the voltage drops across the transistors and diodes are negligible compared with the supply voltage V_s and the line-line back-EMF of the motor, $e_1 - e_2 = e_{12}$. In this case, writing $V_d = V_q = R_q = 0$,

$$d = \frac{e_{12} + 2RI_{sp}}{V_s} \qquad (6.13)$$

which is the same as eqn. (6.4). In 12V systems this approximation is often not admissible because the volt-drops across the transistors and diodes can be an appreciable fraction of the supply voltage V_s.

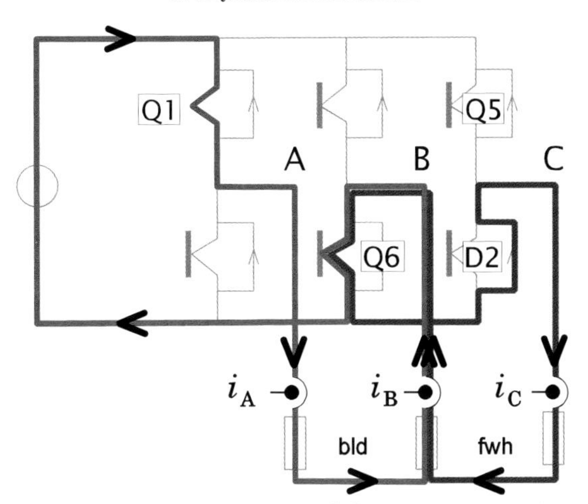

Fig. 6.12 Current control during commutation

The use of independent current sensors in the lines does not by itself guarantee the prevention of overcurrents in all branches of the circuit, since this depends on the association of the current-feedback signal with the gate control of the transistor that is chopping at the time. For example, Fig. 6.12 shows a circuit in which only the upper transistors are used for chopping. At the particular instant shown, the building and freewheeling currents are combining in line B: thus $i_B = i_A + i_C$, and this has a negative value relative to the normal direction of positive curent in line B. Although i_B is observed by the current sensor in line B, the controlling transistors (Q_5 at first, followed by Q_1) are controlled by i_A and i_C respectively, so there is nothing to prevent a temporary overcurrent in line B, as shown in Fig. 6.13.

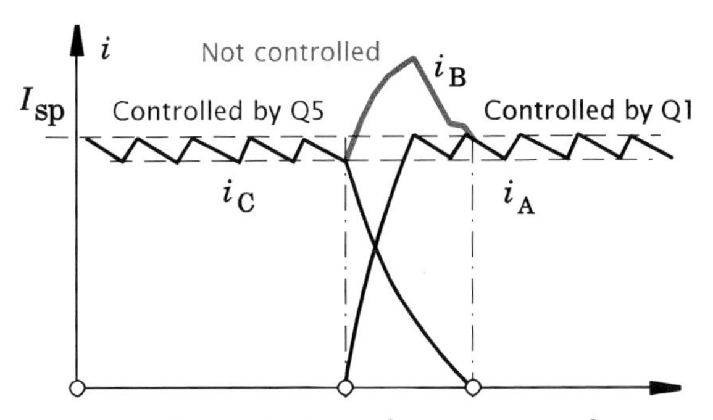

Fig. 6.13 Loss of current control

6.1.4 3-phase squarewave control strategies

Five different control strategies will be described. Three of these regulate the line currents. The other two regulate the line-line voltage. In all cases, however, the *commutation sequence* is the one given on p. 275. Only one transistor is used for chopping at any time. This may be an upper or a lower transistor.

The current waveforms are divided into 60° or 120° intervals, which are identical except for the commutation or re-distribution at the end of each one. Any interval can be constructed from one 60° or 120° interval chosen as the "base" interval, by "commutating" the currents according to the rotor position. The 60° base interval is chosen from 30–90° following the turn-off of Q_5. This is also the start of the 120° conduction period for Q_1, and it is the instant when i_A takes over the DC conduction from i_C. The 120° base interval is from 30–150°, covering the entire 120° conduction of Q_1.

C 60 Q6 — **C** means that *current* is regulated. Q_6 is the control transistor (chopping transistor). Q_6 is called the *outgoing* transistor, because the base interval is the second of its two 60° conduction intervals; Q_1 is the *incoming* transistor, since the base interval is the first of its two 60° conduction intervals, Fig. 6.14.

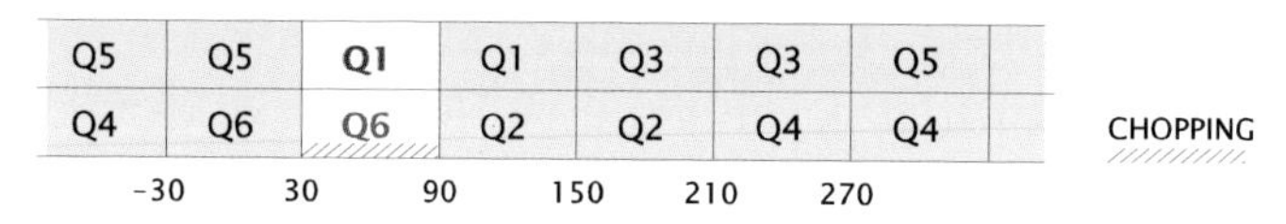

Fig. 6.14 Base interval — 60° switching strategy

Throughout the base interval Q_6 is paired with Q_1, which remains on throughout the whole 60°. All six transistors do identical duty. Each one conducts for a total of 120°, but it is chopping only for the second 60° of its conduction interval, when it is outgoing. This is shown again in Fig. 6.15. If Q_6 is wired to control i_B, the overcurrent in Fig. 6.13 will be suppressed.

V 60 Q6 — **V** means that the voltage is controlled by PWM, instead of regulating the current with a current-feedback loop. Otherwise this mode is the same as **C 60 Q6**.

C 60 Q1 — This is similar to **C 60 Q6**, with the same base interval as in Fig. 6.14, except that the *incoming* transistor is chopping.

0 30 60 90 120 150 180 210 240 270 300 330 360
i_A
Q1
D4
Q6
D3
Q1
Q3
Q5
Q6
Q2
Q4

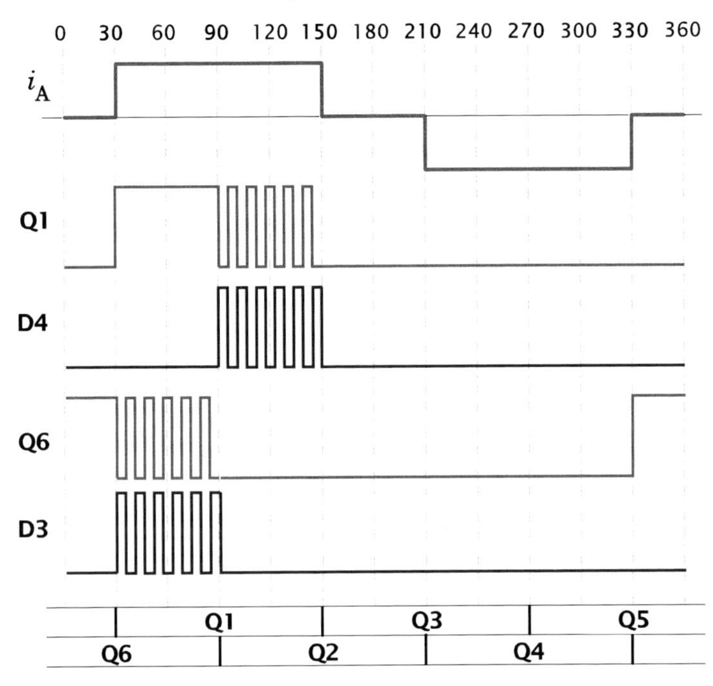

Fig. 6.15 Switching patterns for **C 60 Q6** and **V 60 Q6** modes.

C 120 Q1 — 120 means that Q_1 is chopping for the entirety of its 120° conduction interval; only the upper transistors are used for chopping. If Q_1 is wired to control i_A, the overcurrent in Fig. 6.13 will not be suppressed. The upper and lower transistors have different switching patterns, so their losses and temperature rises may differ.

V 120 Q1 — This is similar to **C 120 Q1**, except that the voltage is controlled by PWM, instead of regulating the current with a current-feedback loop. Only the upper transistors are used for PWM; the lower ones only switch at the commutation frequency.

Fig. 6.16 shows the **C 120 Q1** or **V 120 Q1** switching patterns. Note that they have a 120° base interval.

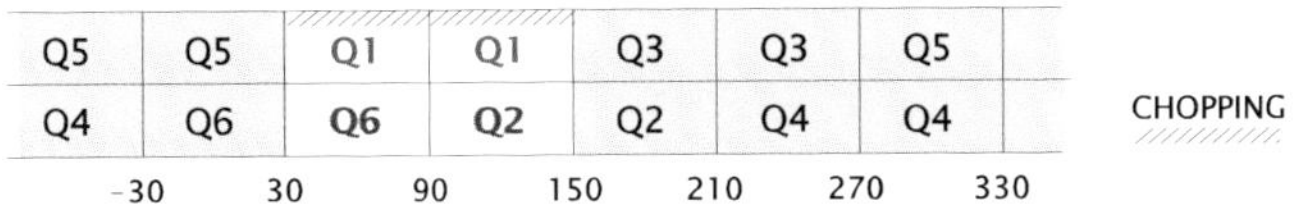

Q5 Q5 Q1 Q1 Q3 Q3 Q5
Q4 Q6 Q6 Q2 Q2 Q4 Q4
CHOPPING
-30 30 90 150 210 270 330

Fig. 6.16 Base interval — 120° switching strategy

6.1.5 Accumulations for mean and RMS currents

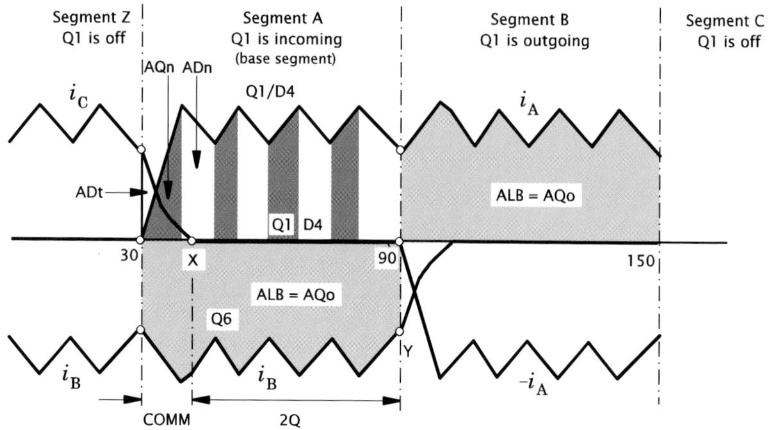

Fig. 6.17 Accumulation of current and (current)^2

Fig. 6.15 can be constructed for this or any of the strategies, and used to accumulate integrals of current and (current)^2 in each transistor and diode, for the purpose of calculating mean and RMS currents in the power semiconductor devices.

The accumulation is shown in detail in Fig. 6.17 for mean currents in the **C 60 Q1** switching mode. The diagram for RMS currents is similar, but i^2 is plotted instead of i in every branch of the circuit. During Segment A, Q_1 is chopping together with its complementary diode D_4. The accumulations are **AQn** for Q_1 and **ADn** for D_4. At the same time Q_6 is on, and i_B accumulates **AQo** in line B. During the COMM period, i_C freewheels in line C through D_2, extinguishing at **X** and accumulating **ADt**. In line A, i_A accumulates **ALA** = **AQn** + **ADn**, while **ALB** is the same as the accumulation for the outgoing transistor, **AQo**. Since $i_A + i_B + i_C = 0$, **ALA** and **ALB** must be equal.

The calculation is done for one 60° base interval, at the end of which the mean current in any transistor is calculated as (**AQn** + **AQo**)/6n, where n is the number of samples collected in the base interval. Similarly the mean current in any diode is (**ADn** + **ADt**)/6n. The mean current in any line is calculated as **ALB**/n or **ALA**/n.

Tables 6.3 and 6.4 give the peak, mean and RMS currents in the lines, phases, transistors and diodes for 120° and 60°controls.

(d = duty-cycle)	Peak	Mean	RMS
Line and Phase (wye)	1	2/3	$\sqrt{[2/3]}$
Phase (delta)	2/3	4/9	$\sqrt{[2]}/3$
Chopping transistor	1	$d/3$	$\sqrt{[d/3]}$
Chopping diode	1	$(1-d)/3$	$\sqrt{[(1-d)/3]}$
Commutating transistor	1	1/3	$\sqrt{[1/3]}$
Commutating diode	1	0	0

TABLE 6.3
PEAK, MEAN AND RMS CURRENTS IN SQUAREWAVE THREE-PHASE DRIVE
C 120 Q1, C 120 Q6, V 120 Q1, AND V 120 Q6 CONTROLS.

(d = duty-cycle)	Peak	Mean	RMS
Transistor	1	$(1+d)/6$	$\sqrt{[(1+d)/6]}$
Diode	1	$(1-d)/6$	$\sqrt{[(1-d)/6]}$

TABLE 6.4
PEAK, MEAN AND RMS CURRENTS IN SQUAREWAVE THREE-PHASE DRIVE
C 60 Q1 AND C 60 Q6 CONTROLS.
All transistors and all diodes do the same duty.

6.1.6 Selection of appropriate switching strategy

The **C** strategies are for hysteresis-control, and tend to be used with isolated line current sensors. The **V** strategies are for voltage-PWM, and they may be used with only a DC link sensor to save cost.

In the 60° strategies, all transistors do identical duty, so they will have the same losses and the same temperature rise. In the 120° strategies, only the upper transistors (or only the lowers) are used for chopping. Since the upper and lower transistors do not have the same duty, they need not be the same type of device, and in general they will not have the same losses or temperature rise. The 120° strategies may be susceptible to overcurrents during commutation, as in Figs. 6.12, 6.13, and 6.19.

In the 60° **Q1** strategies, the incoming transistor is chopping and controlling the current. In the 60° **Q6** strategies, it is the outgoing transistor. An example of **C 60 Q6** is shown in Fig. 6.18.

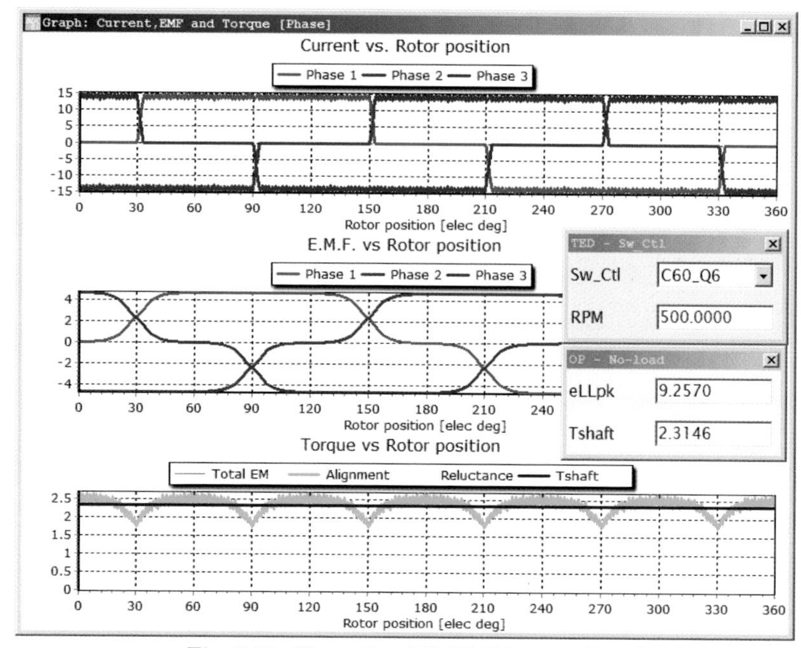

Fig. 6.18 Example of **C 60 Q6** control mode

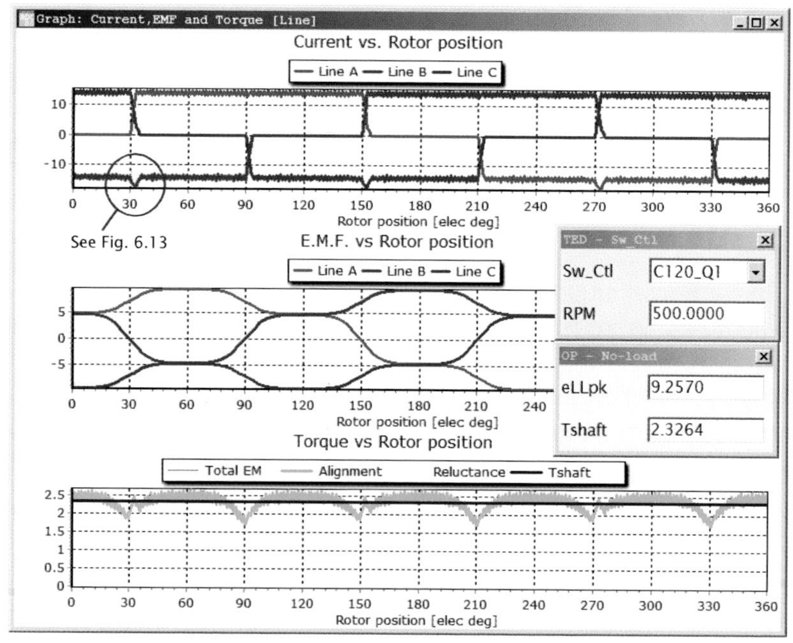

Fig. 6.19 Example of **C 120 Q1** control mode

6.2 Transient analysis of 3-phase drives

In §6.1 we used the principle of state-space averaging to estimate the effect of the switching duty-cycle on the current. We will now consider the transient analysis of a commutation interval, using the differential voltage equations of the circuit to calculate the current waveforms. The equations are presented in a form suitable for computer simulation, but they provide considerable insight into the operation of the brushless squarewave system.[40]

Computer simulation using these equations is essential for the detailed analysis of commutation, particularly when the analysis includes the details of voltage-drops in transistors, diodes, and connecting leads, and the effects of freewheeling currents.

The equations are presented here in ordinary phase variables, assuming a nonsalient pole machine. They can also be solved in *dq* axes, permitting the analysis to cover salient-pole machines.

The circuit diagram is shown in Fig. 6.1 for the wye-connected motor and Fig. 6.2 for the delta connection. The switching sequence is given at the bottom of Fig. 6.3. These waveforms are of course idealised, with trapezoidal EMF and 120° block-rectangular current.

We will assume that the EMF waveform is known as a function of rotor position, without any restriction as to its shape. Magnetic saturation is neglected, and the self- and mutual inductances are assumed to be independent of current and rotor position. Under these conditions, the instantaneous airgap torque is given by eqn. (4.74) on p. 186.

The commutation process was introduced in §6.1.3, where the voltages applied to the building and freewheeling loops were derived as eqns. (6.9) and (6.10) respectively. These voltages appear again in Fig. 6.20, which shows the main switching states of interest. They represent the driving functions for the calculation.

---

[40] They also represent a classical analysis of a simple power-electronic circuit simulation which also includes the linear equations of the motor. The equations are a simplified form of the ones used in the *PC-BDC* computer program. Note that the method is that of "variable circuit topology", in the sense that the circuit equations change every time a transistor or diode switches on or off. The computer simulation therefore requires a "state machine" as well as a differential equation solver.

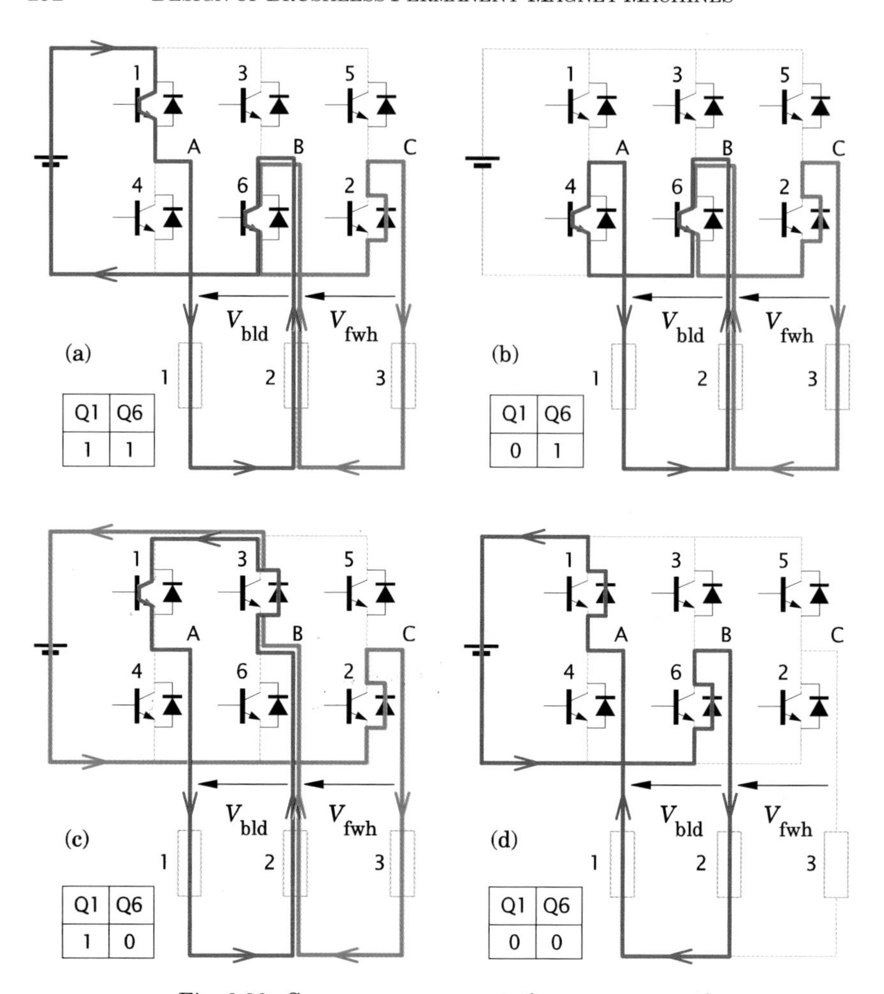

Fig. 6.20 Squarewave commutation; wye connection

When Q_1 is chopping , the state of the circuit switches between Fig. 6.20(a) and (b). The freewheeling current remains in a zero-volt loop and extinguishes at the end of the commutation interval. When Q_6 is the chopping transistor, the state of the circuit switches between (a) and (c). The freewheeling mesh is a zero-volt loop when Q_6 is on; but when Q_6 is off the reverse supply voltage $-V_s$ appears in this loop and accelerates the decay of the freewheeling current. For this reason the Q_6 control mode achieves faster commutation especially at low duty-cycles when Q_6 is off for most of the time.

The voltages v_1, v_2, v_3 across phases 1,2,3 are

$$\begin{aligned} v_1 &= e_1 + Ri_1 + Lp_1 + Mp_2 + Mp_3; \\ v_2 &= e_2 + Ri_2 + Mp_1 + Lp_2 + Mp_3; \\ v_3 &= e_3 + Ri_3 + Mp_1 + Mp_2 + Lp_3. \end{aligned} \tag{6.14}$$

where $p_1 = di_1/dt$, etc., and i_1, i_2, and i_3 are the phase currents. These equations are independent of the circuit connections, whether wye, delta, or any other configuration.

6.2.0.1 Wye connection

In the 3-wire wye connection

$$i_1 + i_2 + i_3 = 0 \tag{6.15}$$

and therefore

$$p_1 + p_2 + p_3 = 0. \tag{6.16}$$

If eqn. (6.16) is substituted into eqns. (6.14), we get

$$\begin{aligned} v_1 &= e_1 + Ri_1 + (L - M)p_1; \\ v_2 &= e_2 + Ri_2 + (L - M)p_2; \\ v_3 &= e_3 + Ri_3 + (L - M)p_3. \end{aligned} \tag{6.17}$$

These equations are solved for the derivatives p_1, p_2, and p_3: thus

$$p_1 = \frac{1}{L'}\left[\frac{2}{3}(V_{\text{bld}} - e_{12R}) + \frac{1}{3}(V_{\text{fwh}} - e_{12R})\right]; \tag{6.18}$$

$$p_3 = -\frac{p_1}{2} - \frac{1}{2L'}(V_{\text{fwh}} - e_{23R}); \tag{6.19}$$

$$p_2 = -p_1 - p_3. \tag{6.20}$$

where

$$e_{12R} = e_1 - e_2 + R(2i_1 + i_3); \tag{6.21}$$

$$e_{23R} = e_2 - e_3 - R(i_1 + 2i_3); \tag{6.22}$$

$$L' = L - M. \tag{6.23}$$

Eqns. (6.18–19) are in the form required for integration, e.g. by Euler's method or the method of Runge-Kutta. Eqn. (6.20) is not needed, because i_2 can be determined from i_1 and i_3 directly.

A special case arises if V_d, V_q, R_q, and R are all zero, while $e_1 + e_2 + e_3 = 0$. Then if Q_1 is the chopping transistor, p_1 and p_3 reduce to

$$p_1 = \frac{1}{L'}\left[\frac{2}{3}\, s_{Q1} V_s - e_1\right] \tag{6.24}$$

and

$$p_3 = -\frac{1}{L'}\left[\frac{1}{3}\, s_{Q1} V_s + e_3\right]. \tag{6.25}$$

We can see from Fig. 6.3 that from 30° to 60°, $e_3 > 0$, tending to make p_3 negative: in other words, the EMF of phase 3 acts to decrease the current i_3 towards zero. Eqn. (6.25) also shows that the negative value of p_3 is increased when $s_{Q1} = 1$, that is, when Q_1 is on; this is illustrated in Fig. 6.21, where Q_1 switches off three times during the commutation interval, decreasing the rate of fall of i_3 each time.

In period **B** after the freewheeling current i_3 has extinguished (Fig. 6.11), there is only one mesh with $i_1 = -i_2$, and $i_3 = 0$. Then

$$p_1 = \frac{1}{2L'}\,[V_{bld} - (e_1 - e_2) - 2Ri_1]. \tag{6.26}$$

Again if V_d, V_q, R_q, and R are all zero, if we write $e_{12} = e_1 - e_2$ then with Q_1 chopping

$$p_1 = \frac{1}{2L'}\,[s_{Q1} V_s - e_{12}]. \tag{6.27}$$

This value of p_1 is obviously less than eqn. (6.24), so it appears that with Q_1 on, p_1 decreases at the end of the commutation interval. An example is shown in Fig. 6.22, in which di_1/dt suddenly decreases when the freewheeling current i_3 reaches zero.

For completeness we might note the equations for V_{bld} and V_{fwh} when Q_6 is the chopping transistor instead of Q_1; the circuit then switches between states (a) and (c), instead of between (a) and (b) in Fig. 6.20. Thus

$$V_{bld} = s_{Q6}(V_s - 2V_q - 2R_q i_1) + (1 - s_{Q6})(-V_q - R_q i_1 - V_d); \tag{6.28}$$

$$V_{fwh} = s_{Q6}(V_q - R_q i_B + V_d) + (1 - s_{Q6})(V_s + 2V_d). \tag{6.29}$$

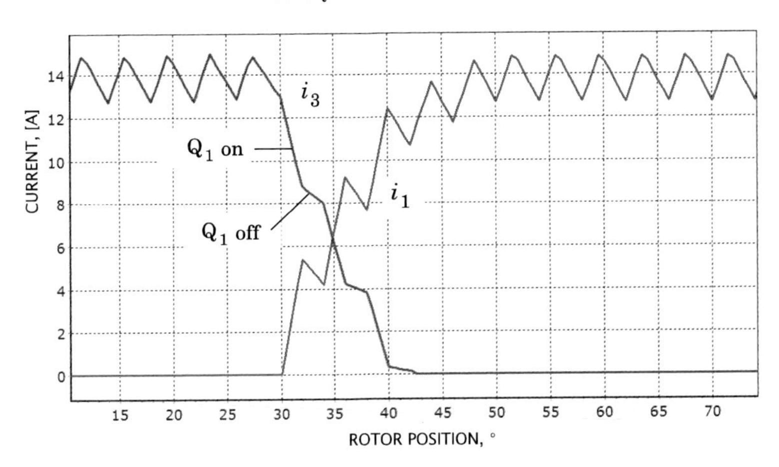

Fig. 6.21 Commutation with V 120 Q1 control

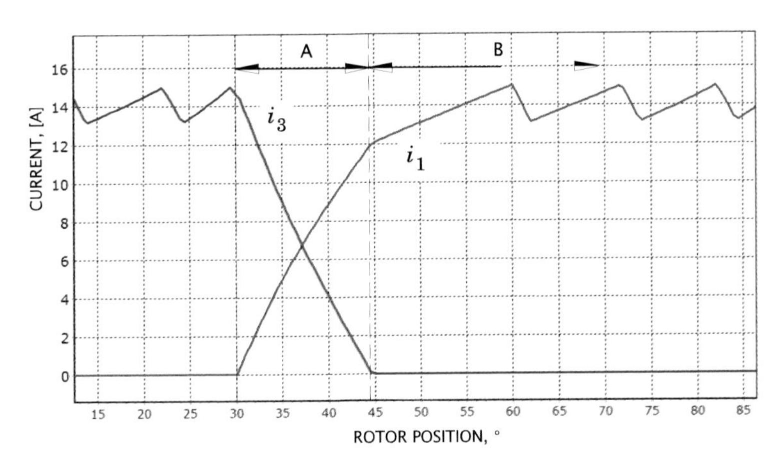

Fig. 6.22 Commutation with C 60 Q1 control

Initial conditions — The final conditions for the 60° base interval become the initial conditions for the next 60° interval. To find the final values i_{1F}, i_{2F}, and i_{3F}, assume that by the end of period **B** the line current $i_1 = i_A$ has arrived in the hysteresis-band of the current-regulator, and that this band is a small percentage of I_{sp}; see Fig. 6.11. This is possible only if the duty-cycle s_{Q1} is less than 1. From eqn. (6.26) with $p_1 = 0$, we get eqn. (6.11), in which the current i_1 is essentially a DC value. The required duty-cycle is given by eqn. (6.12), or approximately by eqn. (6.4), with $s_{Q1} = d$.

If $s_{Q1} < 1$, the initial conditions can be assigned according to the "commutated" sequence

$$i_{1S} = -i_{3F} = 0; \quad i_{2S} = -i_{1F} = -I_{sp}; \quad i_{3S} = -i_{2F} = +I_{sp}. \qquad (6.30)$$

where S denotes an initial or starting value.

If, on the other hand, s_{Q1} turns out greater than 1, it means that there is insufficient voltage to drive the current up to the set-point value of the regulator. This can mean one of two things. Either the set-point current is greater than the resistance-limited DC value of the current at the end of the 60° interval; or the current is never reaching a steady state within the 60° interval. In the first case the final steady-state DC value can be calculated as

$$i_{1F} = \frac{V_s - 2V_q - (e_1 - e_2)}{2(R + R_q)} \qquad (6.31)$$

with $s_{Q1} = 1$. The current-regulator will be saturated in this case and Q_1 will remain on for the entire 60° interval. The second case with $s_{Q1} > 1$ can arise at high speed. Unfortunately there is no way the final current can be calculated analytically. However, the integration can still be started with initial conditions calculated by eqns. (6.30) or (6.31), or with zeros.

Recursion is necessary in all cases to allow the inevitable DC offset transient to decay to a negligible level. The estimation of initial currents from an algebraic estimate of the final steady-state saves computing time and provides a means of checking the results. The recursion of the 60° base interval is repeated until the final values and starting values converge to within a predefined tolerance, and the resulting base interval is used to compose an entire cycle simply by commutating appropriate segments from one phase to another.

6.2.0.2 Delta connection

Fig. 6.23 shows the (a) and (b) states of the inverter with a delta-connected motor, similar to the (a) and (b) states of Fig. 6.20. (States (c) and (d) are also similar but not shown). The same "build" and "freewheel" voltages appear at the motor terminals as before. Again, s_{Q1} is either the state-space averaged duty-cycle of Q_1, or its binary state, and likewise for s_{Q6}.

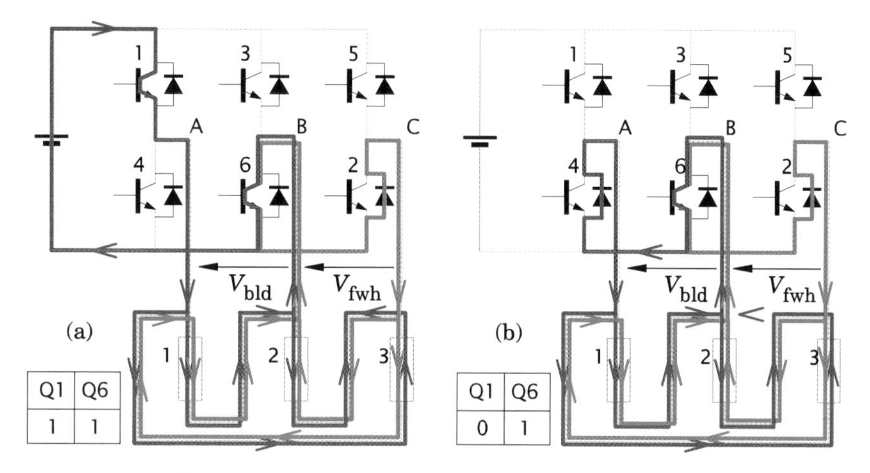

Fig. 6.23 Squarewave commutation; delta connection

The "build" and "freewheel" voltages are given by

$$\begin{aligned} V_{bld} &= v_1 = -(v_2 + v_3); \\ V_{fwh} &= v_2 = -(v_1 + v_3), \end{aligned} \tag{6.32}$$

where v_1, v_2, v_3 are the phase voltages expressed by eqns. (6.14).

When Q_1 is the chopping transistor, from Fig. 6.23(a) and (b)

$$\begin{aligned} V_{bld} &= s_{Q1}[V_s - 2V_q - R_q(2i_1 - i_2 - i_3)] \\ &\quad + (1 - s_{Q1})[-V_d - V_q - R_q(i_1 - i_2)]; \\ V_{fwh} &= V_q + V_d + R_q(i_1 - i_2). \end{aligned} \tag{6.33}$$

Eqns. (6.33) are similar to eqns. (6.9–10) for the wye connection.

When Q6 is the controlled transistor,

$$\begin{aligned} V_{bld} &= s_{Q6}[V_s - 2V_q - R_q(2i_1 - i_2 - i_3)] \\ &\quad + (1 - s_{Q6})[-V_d - V_q - R_q(i_1 - i_3)]; \\ V_{fwh} &= s_{Q6}[V_q + V_d + R_q(i_1 - i_2)] \\ &\quad + (1 - s_{Q6})[V_s + 2V_d]. \end{aligned} \tag{6.34}$$

Eqns. (6.34) are similar to eqns. (6.28–29) for the wye connection.

We can now solve for the phase-current derivatives p_1, p_2 and p_3 by substituting eqns. (6.32) in eqns. (6.14): after some rearranging,

$$\begin{aligned} p_1 &= \frac{1}{L''}\left[U + \frac{M'}{L'}(W + R_{32}) - R_{12}\right]; \\ p_3 &= -\frac{1}{L'}\left[W + M'p_1 + R_{32}\right]; \\ p_2 &= \frac{1}{L}\left[V_{\mathrm{fwh}} + R_{\mathrm{q}}(i_1 - i_2) - e_2 - Ri_2 - M(p_1 + p_3)\right], \end{aligned} \tag{6.35}$$

where

$$L'' = \left[L' - \frac{M'^2}{L'}\right]; \quad L' = L - \frac{M^2}{L} \quad M' = M - \frac{M^2}{L}; \tag{6.36}$$

$$R_{12} = Ri_1 - \frac{RM}{L}i_2; \quad R_{32} = Ri_3 - \frac{RM}{L}i_2; \tag{6.37}$$

$$W = V_{\mathrm{bld}} + (e_2 + e_3) + \frac{L + M}{L}(V_{\mathrm{fwh}} - e_2); \text{ and} \tag{6.38}$$

$$U = V_{\mathrm{bld}} - (e_1 - \frac{M}{L}e_2) - \frac{M}{L}V_{\mathrm{fwh}}. \tag{6.39}$$

In period **B** (Fig. 6.11) there is only one active mesh, but this divides into two parallel branches in the delta, Fig. 6.24. Accordingly there are two differential equations. With D_2 off,

$$i_2 = i_3; \tag{6.40}$$

$$V_{\mathrm{bld}} = v_1 = e_1 + Ri_1 + Lp_1 + 2Mp_2; \text{ and} \tag{6.41}$$

$$\begin{aligned} V_{\mathrm{bld}} &= -v_2 - v_3 \\ &= -(e_2 + e_3) - L(p_2 + p_3) - R(i_2 + i_3) - M(2p_1 + p_2 + p_3). \end{aligned} \tag{6.42}$$

Solving these equations for p_1 and p_2, we get

$$p_1 = \frac{\left[Y - Ri_1 + \dfrac{2RM}{L + M}i_2\right]}{\left[L - \dfrac{2M^2}{L + M}\right]} \tag{6.43}$$

where

$$Y = V_{bld} - e_1 + \frac{M}{L + M}[V_{bld} + e_2 + e_3]; \tag{6.44}$$

and

$$p_2 = \frac{\left[-(V_{bld} + e_2 + e_3) - 2Ri_2 - 2Mp_1\right]}{2(L + M)}. \tag{6.45}$$

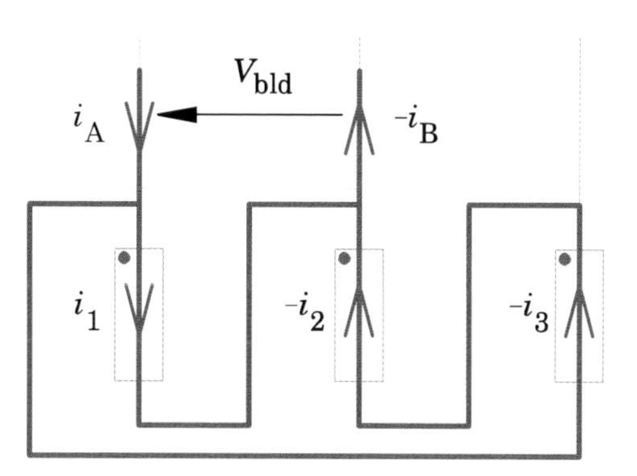

Fig. 6.24 Final DC in delta

Initial conditions — The initial conditions are determined in the same way as for the wye connection, p. 295. The circuit at the end of the commutation interval is regarded as a DC source feeding two parallel paths as in Fig. 6.24, so that

$$\begin{aligned} V_{bld} &= e_1 + R_1 i_1; \\ V_{bld} &= -(e_2 + e_3) - (R_2 + R_3) i_3. \end{aligned} \tag{6.46}$$

The line current i_A is given by

$$i_A = i_1 - i_3. \tag{6.47}$$

Solving these equations for i_{1F}, i_{2F} and i_{3F},

$$\begin{aligned} i_{1F} &= \frac{2}{3} i_A - \frac{e_1 + e_2 + e_3}{3R}; \\ i_{3F} &= i_{2F} = -\frac{1}{3} i_A - \frac{e_1 + e_2 + e_3}{3R}. \end{aligned} \tag{6.48}$$

In an ideal brushless motor designed for delta connection,

$$e_1 + e_2 + e_3 = 0 \tag{6.49}$$

and therefore

$$\begin{aligned} i_{1F} &= \frac{2}{3} i_A; \\ i_{3F} &= i_{2F} = -\frac{1}{3} i_A = -\frac{1}{2} i_{1F}. \end{aligned} \tag{6.50}$$

The current phase 1 is thus twice the current in the branch containing phases 2 and 3 in series. Since eqns. (6.48–50) do not contain V_{bld}, they are independent of s_{Q1} and are valid for any value of duty-cycle, including 1.

Eqn. (6.48) shows that if the loop EMF $e_1 + e_2 + e_3$ is not zero, the division of current between the phases of the delta is disturbed from the ideal 2/3:1/3 ratio. In a severe case this can prevent the motor reaching the desired torque, greatly increasing the losses.

Of course, the attainment of a steady DC line current at the end of period **B** is possible only if there is sufficient voltage, i.e., if $s_{Q1} \leq 1$. For a given value of i_A (e.g., I_{sp}), the duty-cycle s_{Q1} can be calculated from eqns. (6.33), (6.46) and (6.50) as

$$s_{Q1} = \frac{e_1 + (2R/3 + R_q)I_{sp} + V_d + V_q}{V_s - V_q + V_d - R_q I_{sp}}. \tag{6.51}$$

If $s_{Q1} < 1$, the initial conditions can be assigned from eqns. (6.30), with i_{1F}, i_{2F} and i_{3F} obtained from eqns. (6.50). But if $s_{Q1} > 1$, there is insufficient voltage to drive the current up to the set-point value I_{sp}. Either the set-point current is greater than the resistance-limited value at the end of the 60° base interval, or the current never reaches a steady state within the 60° interval. In the first case the final values can be obtained from the DC loop equations with $i_2 = i_3$:

$$\begin{aligned} V_s - 2V_q - 2R_q(i_1 - i_3) &= e_1 + Ri_1 \\ &= -(e_2 + e_3) - 2Ri_3 \end{aligned} \tag{6.52}$$

$$2Ri_3 + Ri_1 + (e_1 + e_2 + e_3) = 0 \tag{6.53}$$

The final DC currents are then obtained with $s_{Q1} = 1$ by

$$i_{1F} = \frac{1}{3R_q + R}\left[V_s - 2V_q - e_1 - \frac{R_q}{R}(e_1 + e_2 + e_3)\right]; \qquad (6.54)$$

$$i_{2F} = i_{3F} = -\frac{1}{2R}[e_1+e_2+e_3+Ri_1] \qquad (6.55)$$

The current-regulator will be saturated in this case and Q_1 will remain on for the entire $60°$ interval.

The second case (failure to reach a steady-state current) arises at higher speeds and, as in the case of wye connection, there is no way the final current can be calculated analytically. However, the integration can still be started with initial conditions calculated by eqns. (6.54–55), or from eqns. (6.50) with $i_A = I_{sp}$; or with zeros.

As in the case of the wye connection, recursion is necessary in all cases to allow the DC offset transient to decay to a negligible level, and the resulting base interval is used to compose an entire cycle by commutating appropriate segments from one phase to another.

When Q_6 is the chopping transistor, the equations are similar except that s_{Q1} is replaced by s_{Q6} in equation (6.51).

6.2.0.3 Regeneration (over-running); no-load speed

The regenerating condition tends to arise at speeds slightly above the no-load speed, when the load may be overhauling or over-running the motor. When the line-line EMF exceeds the supply voltage, the current may flow in the reverse direction back to the supply, as shown in Fig. 6.20(d) for the wye connection. The delta connection is similar. If uncontrolled or undetected, this can cause dangerous overvoltage on the DC bus.

When the EMF is high enough, the power transistors never conduct, and the freewheel diodes then form a classical uncontrolled bridge rectifier. Diodes then conduct together in pairs for $60°$ intervals, with commutation every $60°$. The conducting diodes (D_1 and D_6 in Fig. 6.20(d)) communicate the supply voltage to the series combination of phases 1 and 2 in opposition to the line-line EMF, just as the transistors do in the motoring condition. The polarities of the EMF and the supply voltage remain the same as in the motoring condition, while the current and the power both reverse direction.

The simplest example of over-running is the plain **generating** condition with rectifier load, in which there is a diode bridge but no transistor inverter. In this case the line current begins to flow as soon as the line-line EMF $e_{LL} > V_s + 2V_d$. Conduction through any pair of diodes continues until a natural point of commutation. In any commutation interval the conducting line-pair is essentially the one with the highest positive EMF, and the succession is **AB**, **AC**, **BC**, **BA**, **CA**, **CB**, **AB**, ... exactly as in the motoring mode in Fig. 6.3. Each individual diode conducts for 120°. The precise instants of commutation depend on the inductance and other factors. Generating is considered in more detail in Chapter 9.

In the example in Fig. 6.25, the speed is high enough so that the peak line-line EMF $e_{LLpk} = 37{\cdot}02$ V is well above the DC supply voltage $V_s = 24$ V. The current waveforms are reversed relative to those in Fig. 6.3, and phase-shifted as a result of inductance, as already noted. Each diode conducts continuously for 120°. The lower traces in Fig. 6.25 show the torque, which is negative.

Fig. 6.26 shows an example of a motor running at no-load with practically zero shaft torque T_{shaft}. At 30° Q_1 switches on and positive line current i_A starts to flow. The rising line-line EMF e_{LL} reaches the DC voltage $V_s = 24$ V at a rotor angle of about 38°, at which point (neglecting resistance and device volt-drops) there is no voltage across the motor inductance and di/dt becomes zero. As the line-line EMF continues to rise, the voltage across the inductance becomes negative, di/dt becomes negative, and the current begins to decrease. When it reaches zero it reverses direction, so transistor Q_1 ceases to conduct and the current commutates into diode D_1. At about 75° e_{LL} falls below 24V and di/dt becomes positive again.

The motor in Fig. 6.26 has $k_E = 0{\cdot}177$ Vs/rad (defined as e_{LLpk}/ω_m), so the no-load speed calculated by formula is

$$\frac{V_s}{k_E} = \frac{24}{0{\cdot}177} = 135{\cdot}6 \text{ rad/s} = 1{,}295 \text{ rpm}. \tag{6.56}$$

Fig. 6.26 shows that the true no-load speed is 1400 rpm, because the EMF must exceed V_s for a fraction of a cycle, to bring the mean current (and more particularly the mean torque) to zero. If the line EMF waveform was flatter, the two values would be closer.

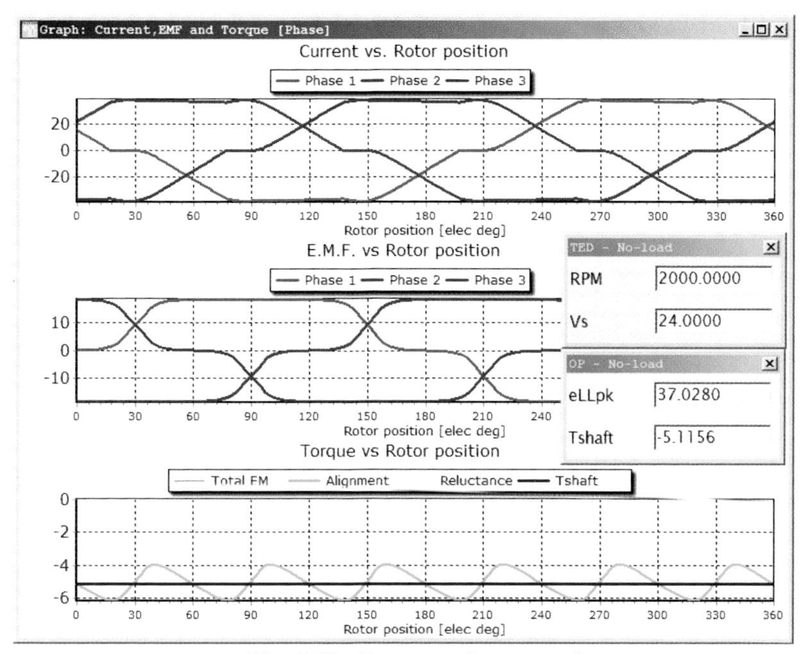

Fig. 6.25 Regeneration example

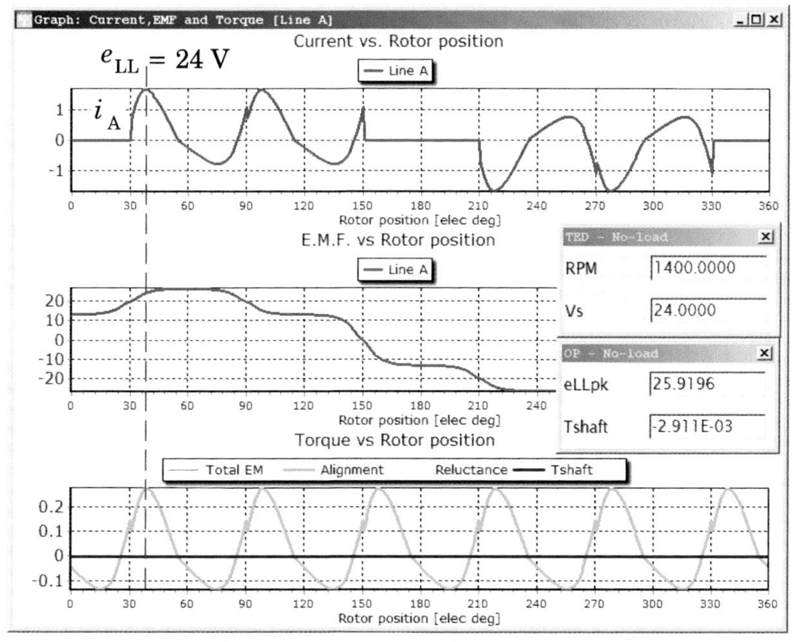

Fig. 6.26 No-load example; V_s = 24 V; V_d = 0·6 V

6.2.0.4 Phase advance

The voltage available to drive current into the motor windings is the difference voltage $\Delta V = V_s - e_{LL}$, if the voltage-drops in the transistors are neglected. At high speed the EMF e_{LL} approaches V_s and the drive voltage diminishes towards zero, while the time available to ramp the current from zero to the set-point value I_{sp} also decreases.

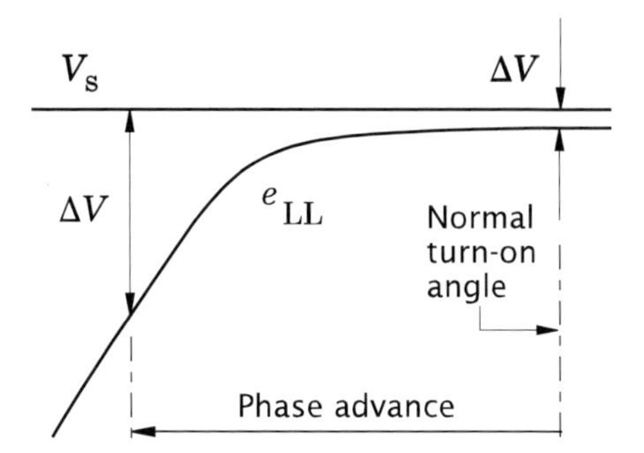

Fig. 6.27 Available drive voltage

Fig. 6.27 shows the principle of advancing the turn-on angle to an earlier point on the EMF waveform, where ΔV is greater. This has the effect of increasing di/dt at the start of the conduction interval. Over a certain speed range it restores the current waveform that would otherwise be collapsing as a result of the high EMF, and so it extends the speed range over which a given torque can be maintained.

If the conduction angle or commutation interval remains the same (120° for each transistor, or 60° for each transistor-pairing), the end of the commutation interval is advanced in phase as well as the start, so that the whole current waveform is advanced relative to the EMF waveform. This phase displacement tends to decrease the torque; (obviously a phase displacement of 90° would reduce it to zero). At any given level of speed and torque there is consequently an optimal phase-advance angle that maximizes the torque.

A hazardous condition can arise as a result of phase advance, if the drive to the transistors is suddenly lost when e_{LL} is substantially higher than V_s. In that case there will be uncontrolled rectification through the freewheel diodes. Phase advance in a squarewave motor drive is closely related to flux-weakening in sinewave drives.

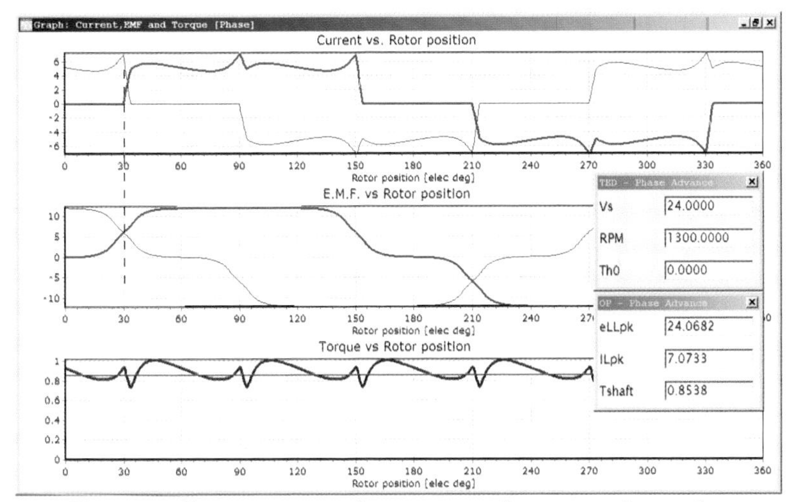

Fig. 6.28 Current, EMF and torque waveforms : no phase advance

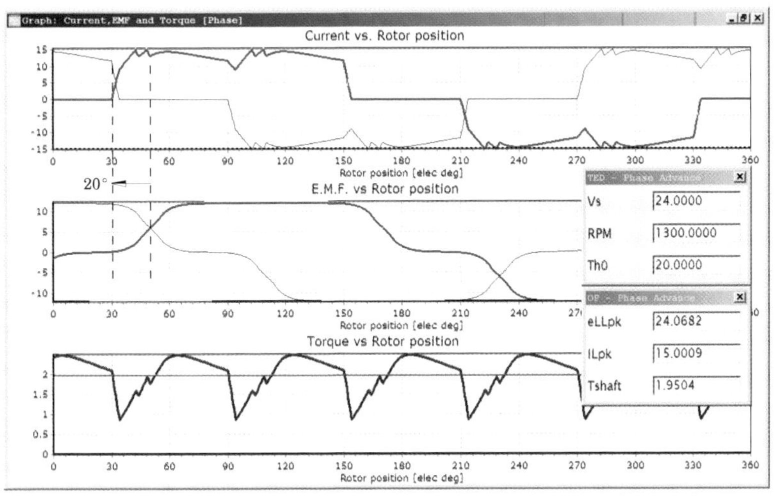

Fig. 6.29 Current, EMF and torque waveforms : 20° phase advance

An example of phase advance is shown in Figs. 6.28 and 6.29. The motor has a peak line-line EMF e_{LLpk} equal to the DC supply voltage V_s. In Fig. 6.28 there is no phase advance. The peak current is only about 7 A compared with the set-point value of 15A. With 20° phase advance in Fig. 6.29, the set-point current is achieved and the torque is increased from 0·85 to 1·95 Nm. (With the same peak current the torque would be about 2·25 Nm if unlimited voltage was available). Note the increase in torque ripple when phase advance is used.

6.2.0.5 Dwell control

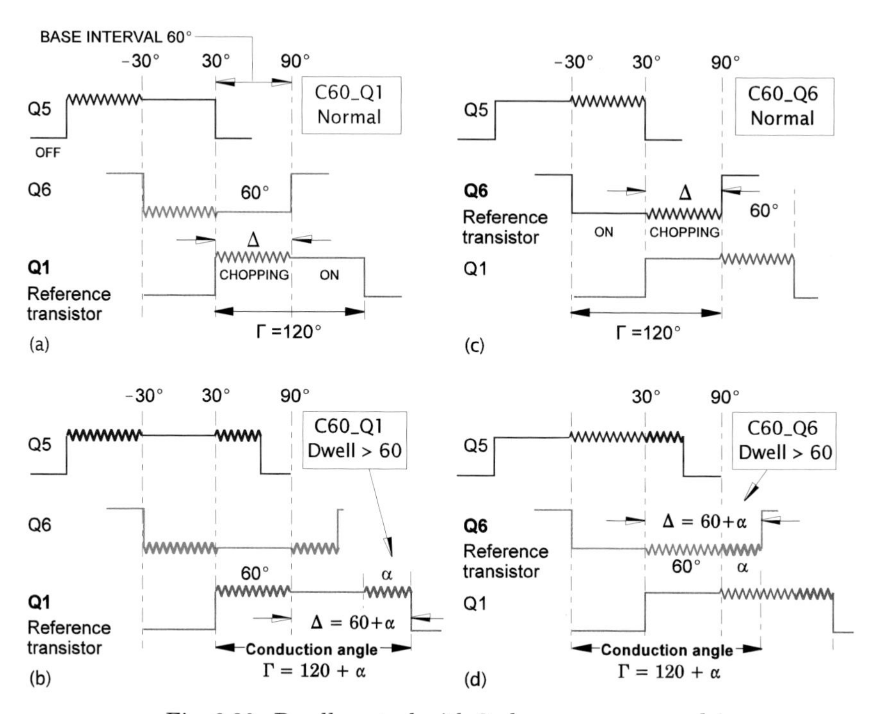

Fig. 6.30 Dwell control with 3-phase squarewave drive

"Dwell" Δ can be defined as the angle of rotation through which one transistor is chopping (i.e., regulating the current). The "conduction angle" Γ of a transistor is the total angle through which it conducts in each block of conduction. Up to now we have considered 3-phase drives with $\Gamma = 120°$, and control strategies with $\Delta = 60°$ (designated C60 or V60), or 120° (C120 or V120).

A conduction angle of 120° is consistent with "two-phase-on" (2Q) operation, which is normal for squarewave drive. If the conduction angle exceeds 120°, there will be intervals when three lines are conducting (3Q).[41] The maximum permissible conduction angle with the 6-transistor bridge is 180°: any greater value would destroy the symmetry of the positive and negative half-cycles.

[41] The brief periods of freewheeling during commutation are not considered as "three-phase-on" operation, but as an incidental detail of "two-phase-on" operation.

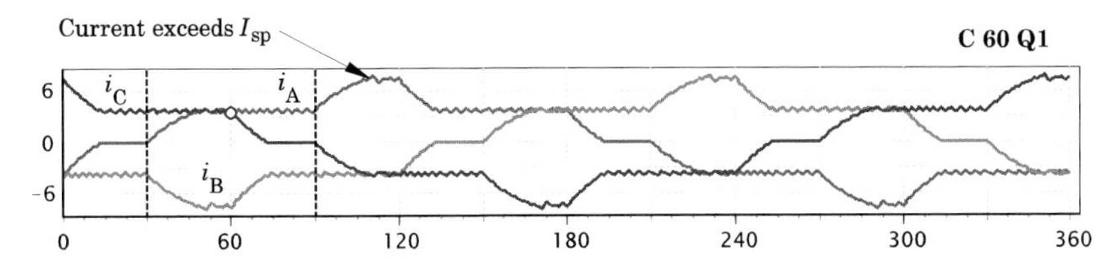

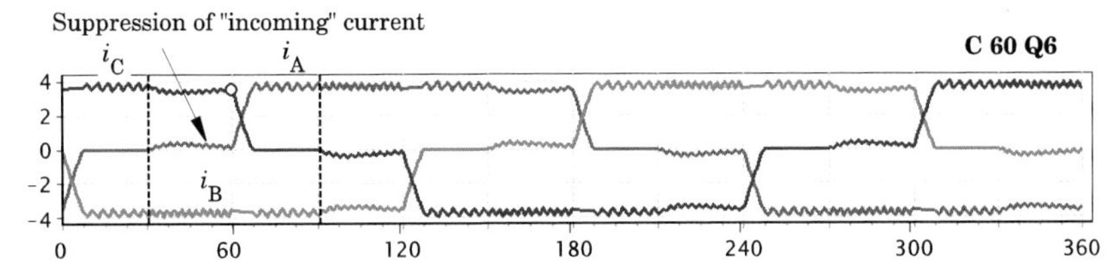

Fig. 6.31 Effect of increasing dwell from 60° to 90°; **C 60 Q1** and **C 60 Q6**

The dwell Δ can be used as an alternative means of control.[42] With a 3-wire connection, $i_A + i_B + i_C = 0$, so Δ influences all three current waveforms and the interaction between phases becomes more complicated when Δ departs from its normal 60°.

The upper diagrams in Fig. 6.30 show normal operation with Δ = 60°. Cases (a) and (b) are for **C 60 Q1**, in which transistor Q_1 chops during the *first* 60° of its 120° conduction angle. Figs. 6.30 (c) and (d) are for **C 60 Q6** or **V 60 Q6**, in which transistor Q_6 chops during the *second* 60° of its conduction angle. If Δ > 60°, the chopping angle is extended by $\alpha = \Delta - 60°$, and the conduction angle is

$$\Gamma = 60° + \Delta = 120° + \alpha. \tag{6.57}$$

The default value $\Delta = 60°$ gives $\Gamma = 120°$, with $\alpha = 0$. The maximum value $\Delta = 120°$ gives a conduction angle $\Gamma = 180°$, with $\alpha = 60°$. For a Q_6 control with $\Delta > 60°$, the chopping simply *continues* beyond 60°, as in Fig. 6.30(d); but for a Q_1 mode the transistor *resumes* chopping after the end of its ON interval, as in Fig. 6.30(b). In both cases the additional chopping angle α is added at the *end* of the normal conduction interval, not at the beginning.

Examples are given in Figs. 6.31 and 6.32, in which the base interval is marked by vertical dashed lines at 30° and 90°, and the commutation of Q_5 by the blue circle at 60° instead of its normal 30°.

---

[42] The **C 120** and **V 120** controls considered earlier represent variations from normal 60° dwell for either the upper or the lower transistors (but not for both).

For **C 60 Q1** (Figs. 6.30(a) and (d)), the main current i_A is regulated by Q_1 throughout the base interval. If $\Delta = 0$, Q_5 remains off throughout the base interval, having just commutated i_C which freewheels through D_2 during the first part of the base interval. Q_6 remains on and carries $i_A + i_C$, but it makes no attempt to regulate this "return line" current. When $\Delta > 60°$, the commutation of Q_5 is delayed by $\alpha°$, and Q_5 *resumes* chopping i_C. The extended conduction of Q_5 into the base interval is shown in heavy line in Fig. 6.30(b). Until Q_5 commutates, there are two chopping transistors: Q_1 regulating i_A, and Q_5 regulating i_C. However, there is no regulation of $-i_B$, since Q_6 remains on during the entire base interval. It is therefore possible for $|i_B|$ to exceed the set-point current I_{sp}, as can be seen in Fig. 6.31.

For **C 60 Q6** the return-line current $-i_B$ is regulated by Q_6 throughout the base interval. If $\Delta = 0$, Q_5 remains off throughout the base interval, having just commutated i_C, which freewheels through D_2 during the first part of the base interval. Q_1 remains on and carries i_A, leaving the regulation entirely to Q_6. When $\Delta > 60°$, the conduction of Q_5 is extended by $\alpha°$, and Q_5 *continues* chopping i_C. The extended conduction of Q_5 into the base interval is shown in heavy line in Fig. 6.30(d). Until Q_5 commutates, there are two chopping transistors: Q_6 regulating $-i_B$, and Q_5 regulating i_C. Since $-i_B = (i_A + i_C)$, the sum of i_A and i_C is limited to I_{sp}. Therefore if Q_5 maintains i_C close to I_{sp}, i_A will be suppressed during the extension of the conduction of Q_5, as can be seen in Fig. 6.31.

Fig. 6.32 shows an example for a voltage-PWM control, **V 60 Q1**. This is similar to **C 60 Q1**, except that the main current i_A is regulated by PWM control of Q_1 throughout the base interval, and $|i_B|$ can again exceed the set-point current I_{sp}. If Δ is increased to 120° the conduction angle Γ becomes 180° for each transistor, with continuous conduction in all three lines; this is similar to 6-step operation except that the voltage is modulated by the PWM.

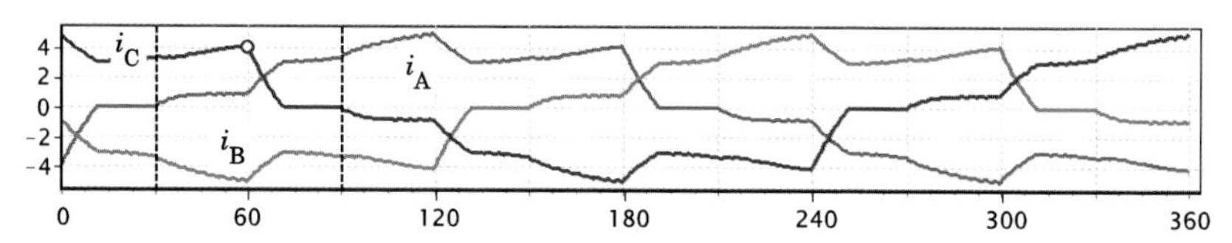

Fig. 6.32 Effect of increasing dwell from 60° to 90° : **V 60 Q1**

6.2.1 Salient-pole machines with squarewave drive

Sometimes the interior-magnet motor (IPM) is coupled to a squarewave drive. The IPM is a salient-pole machine, and with nonsinusoidal currents there will be a ripple torque component in both the alignment torque and the reluctance torque. Both these torques can be calculated using eqn. (4.94), but first the phase currents must be calculated. For *non*salient-pole machines we have so far assumed constant inductances in the voltage equations (6.14), but this is not valid for salient-pole machines. However, if we assume that the inductances vary with rotor position according to eqns. (4.95), we can use the *dq*-axis form of the voltage equations, (4.108) to solve for the currents. The currents can then be substituted back into eqn. (4.94) to calculate the electromagnetic torque.

The driving voltages v_d and v_q are needed in eqns. (4.108). In Chapter 4 they were defined by Park's transform in terms of the phase voltages, but with a 3-wire connection the phase voltages are unknown: it is the line-line voltages that are known, and we have established them earlier in the notation V_{bld} and V_{fwh} for the squarewave drive, using eqns. (6.9–10) for the wye connection when Q_1 is chopping and eqns. (6.28–29) when Q_6 is chopping; and eqns. (6.33) and (6.34) for the delta connection.

To express v_d and v_q in terms of the line-line voltages, the required relationships are as follows. Firstly for the wye connection we have $v_{AB} = v_{12} = v_1 - v_2 = V_{bld}$ and $v_{BC} = v_{23} = v_2 - v_3 = V_{fwh}$

$$
\begin{aligned}
v_d &= \frac{2}{3}\left[v_{AB} \cos \theta + v_{BC} \cos (\theta - \pi/3)\right]; \\
v_q &= -\frac{2}{3}\left[v_{AB} \sin \theta + v_{BC} \sin (\theta - \pi/3)\right].
\end{aligned}
\tag{6.58}
$$

Only v_{AB} and v_{BC} are required, if $v_{AB} + v_{BC} + v_{CA} = 0$. The inverse is

$$
\begin{aligned}
v_{AB} &= -\sqrt{3}\,[v_d \sin (\theta - \pi/3) + v_q \cos (\theta - \pi/3)] \\
v_{BC} &= +\sqrt{3}\,[v_d \sin \theta + v_q \cos \theta] \\
v_{CA} &= -\sqrt{3}\,[v_d \sin (\theta + \pi/3) + v_q \cos (\theta + \pi/3)].
\end{aligned}
\tag{6.59}
$$

As before, θ is the angle between the *d*-axis and the axis of phase 1, and positive rotation is from phase 1 to phase 2. [Cf. Fig. (4.21)].

Eqns. (4.108) are solved for i_d and i_q, with v_d and v_q as driving functions, and then the inverse transformation eqn. (4.102) is used to recover the phase currents. There is no distinction between phase currents and line currents in the wye connection.

For the delta connection the line currents are reconstructed from

$$i_A = i_1 - i_3; \quad i_B = i_2 - i_1; \quad i_C = i_3 - i_2, \tag{6.60}$$

in accordance with Fig. 6.2. The phase voltages are identical to the line-line voltages, so v_d and v_q can be obtained directly using eqns. (4.100) written for voltages, with

$$v_{AB} = v_1; \quad v_{BC} = v_2; \quad v_{CA} = v_3. \tag{6.61}$$

When the delta is closed, $v_1 + v_2 + v_3 = 0$, and if this is used to eliminate v_3 (i.e., v_{CA}), the result is

$$\begin{aligned} v_d &= \frac{2}{3}\sqrt{3}\left[v_{AB}\sin\left(\theta + \frac{\pi}{3}\right) + v_{BC}\sin\theta\right]; \\ v_q &= \frac{2}{3}\sqrt{3}\left[v_{AB}\cos\left(\theta + \frac{\pi}{3}\right) + v_{BC}\cos\theta\right]. \end{aligned} \tag{6.62}$$

The *dq* formulation can be used during period **A** (Fig. 6.11), because all three line-line voltages are known. During period **B**, however, one of the line terminals is floating, and in our chosen base segment this condition is defined by $i_C = 0$. As a result, only one line-line voltage is known (i.e., defined by the states of the transistors and diodes), and so the *dq* transform cannot be used.

For period **B**, therefore, the analysis must be reformulated and it is a relief to learn that we have already derived the necessary equations for V_{bld} — eqns. (6.72) and (6.71) on p. 314. The solution in period **B** uses ordinary phase variables and shares the same assumptions about the variation of inductance with rotor position as the *dq* transform itself, so there is no loss of rigour in this process.

An example of this type of analysis is shown in Fig. 6.34 for the motor in Fig. 6.33. This motor has a flat-topped EMF waveform suitable for squarewave drive, and it would produce ripple-free torque but for the reluctance torque, which appears as a ripple composed of 6 sinusoidal sections similar to a sawtooth waveform.

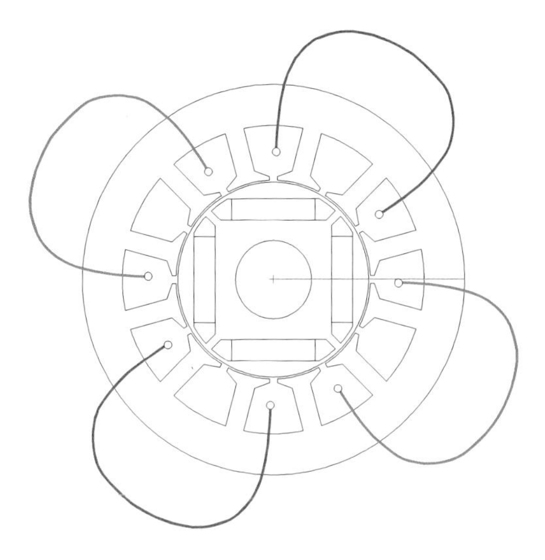

Fig. 6.33 IPM example showing one phase winding

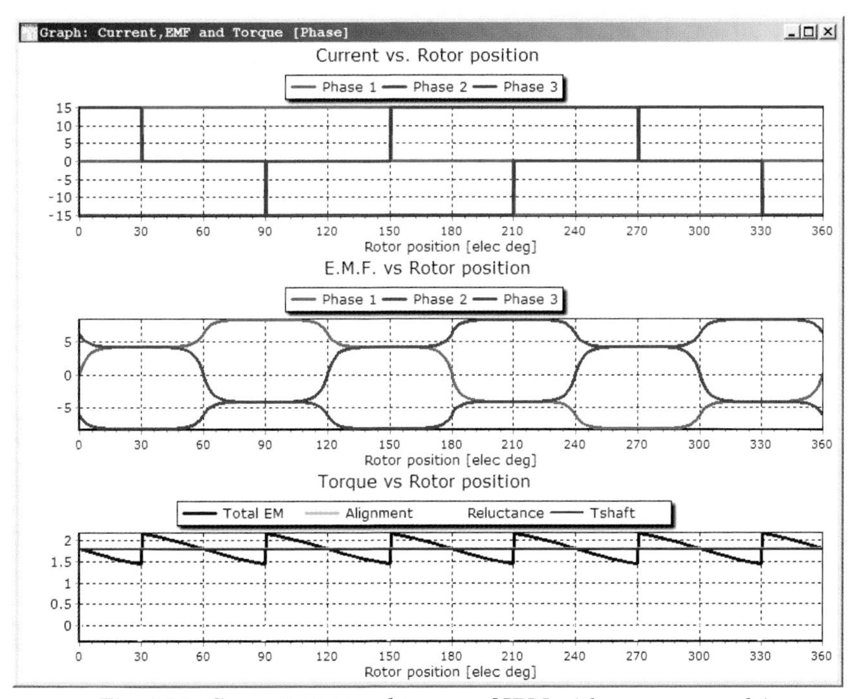

Fig. 6.34 Current, EMF and torque of IPM with squarewave drive

6.2.2 Back-EMF sensing

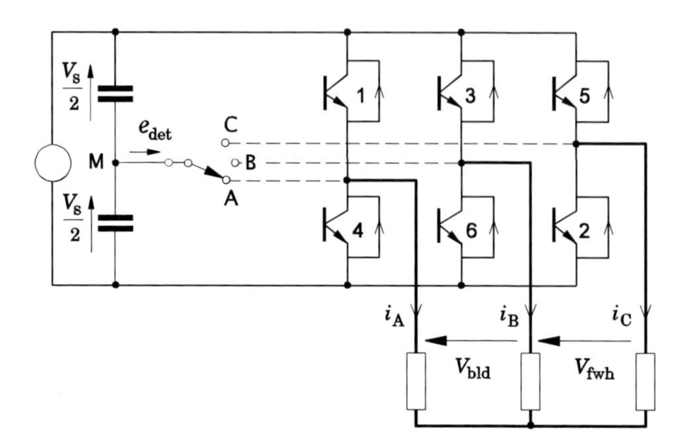

Fig. 6.35 Back-EMF sensing

Motors with 120° squarewave currents are often operated with "back-EMF sensing" to eliminate the need for a shaft position sensor. By switching the detection circuit to the idle line every 60°, the circuit in Fig. 6.35 produces a waveform of the detection voltage e_{det}, whose zero-crossings are used for commutation.

The detection EMF e_{det} is multiplexed from the voltages e_{AM}, e_{BM}, and e_{CM} according to the states of the power transistors. Because of the 60° periodicity, only the base interval need be analysed. At the beginning of this interval Q_5 has just switched off, and i_C continues to freewheel through D_2, forcing $e_{det} = e_{CM} = -V_s/2$. During the freewheeling period labelled COMM in Fig. 6.17, current flows in all three lines. Since $e_{det} = -V_s/2$, due to the clamping action of D_2, the detection voltage is useless during this period.

When D_2 switches off, the COMM period ends and the segment labelled 2Q in Fig. 6.17 continues to the end of the base interval, with only two lines conducting, A and B. There is only one mesh current, that is, the one flowing through phase 1 and negatively through phase 2. The detection voltage is given by

$$e_{det} = \frac{V_s}{2} - v_1 + e_3 \tag{6.63}$$

where

$$v_1 = e_1 + R_{ph} i_1 + \frac{d\psi_1}{dt}. \tag{6.64}$$

The flux-linkage ψ_1 includes a self- and a mutual term, and since $i_2 = -i_1$ this is

$$\psi_1 = (L_1 - L_{12}) i_1. \tag{6.65}$$

In a nonsalient pole motor, $L_1 = L_{ph}$ and $L_{12} = M_{ph}$, and both these inductances are constant, so that

$$v_1 = e_1 + R_{ph} i_1 + (L_{ph} - M_{ph}) \frac{di_1}{dt}. \tag{6.66}$$

In a salient–pole motor, if it is a *sinewound* motor then

$$\begin{aligned} L_1 &= L_\sigma + L_{g0} + L_{g2} \cos 2\theta \\ L_{12} &= M_\sigma - \frac{1}{2} L_{g0} + L_{g2} \cos (2\theta - 2\pi/3) \end{aligned} \tag{6.67}$$

with $L_{g2} < 0$ in most cases. Both i_1 and the inductances are functions of time, so that ψ_1 in eqn. (6.64) must be differentiated by the chain rule. If we write $L_{1B} = L_1 - L_{12}$ for the apparent inductance of phase 1 during the 2Q segment, then

$$\frac{d\psi_1}{dt} = L_{1B} \frac{di_1}{dt} + i_1 \frac{dL_{1B}}{dt} = L_{1B} \frac{di_1}{dt} + i_1 \omega_e \frac{dL_{1B}}{d\theta} \tag{6.68}$$

where

$$\begin{aligned} L_{1B} &= (L_\sigma - M_\sigma + \frac{3}{2} L_{g0}) + L_{g2} \sqrt{3} \cos (2\theta + \pi/6) \quad \text{and} \\ \frac{dL_{1B}}{d\theta} &= -L_{g2} 2\sqrt{3} \sin (2\theta + \pi/6). \end{aligned} \tag{6.69}$$

By substituting all these equations back into eqn. (6.63), we arrive at an equation for the detection voltage e_{det} during the 2Q interval. However, we still need the differential voltage equation for the whole circuit so that the current waveform i_1 can be calculated. This is simple enough if we combine all the inductances in the single conducting loop AB into one line-line inductance:

$$\begin{aligned} L_{LL} &= L_1 + L_2 - 2L_{12} \\ &= 2(L_\sigma - M_\sigma) + 3L_{g0} - 3L_{g2} \sin(2\theta - \pi/6). \end{aligned} \tag{6.70}$$

The derivative of L_{LL} with respect to θ is

$$\frac{dL_{LL}}{d\theta} = -6L_{g2} \cos(2\theta - \pi/6) \tag{6.71}$$

and the required voltage equation is

$$V_{bld} = e_1 - e_2 + 2R_{ph} i_1 + L_{LL} \frac{di_1}{dt} + \omega_e i_1 \frac{dL_{LL}}{d\theta}. \tag{6.72}$$

This can be rearranged for integration by Euler's method. The "build" voltage V_{bld} is the voltage applied to loop A–B or 1–2, to build up the current in phase 1. If both Q_1 and Q_6 are on, it is equal to the supply voltage V_s minus the voltage drops in the power transistors. Eqn. (6.63) is valid only for chopping strategies in which Q_1 remains on during the 2Q interval, which requires that any chopping must be performed by Q_6 during that interval. It is straightforward to program the solution for i_1 in the 2Q interval using direct phase variables, because there is only one conducting mesh or loop. However, the COMM period with all three phases conducting is slightly more complicated.

The zero-crossing angles are subject to variation caused by induced speed voltages associated with any second-harmonic variation in the self- and mutual inductances of the phases. Other sources of variation in the zero-crossings include even-harmonic distortion of the EMF, causing the waveform over one half-pole to differ from the waveform over the second half-pole. This would happen if the magnets were not centred, or if their magnetization varied over their width, or if the magnetization of magnets was not uniform under all the poles. These effects can readily be checked by running the motor on open-circuit and recording the line-neutral (phase) voltage waveforms.

Originally developed by Harms and Erdman at GE in the 1970s and 1980s, the back-EMF sensing scheme is a common feature of microchips for brushless DC motor controls.

6.3 1- and 2-phase unipolar drives

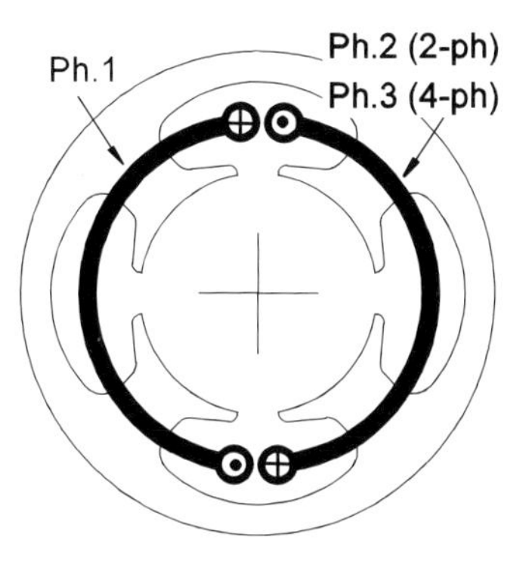

Fig. 6.36 Bifilar motor

Fig. 6.37 shows the basic waveforms of EMF, current and torque in motors with one or two phases. In any phase winding the EMF waveform e_1 has symmetrical positive and negative half-cycles, requiring a symmetrical current waveform such as the squarewave i_1 to produce a sequence of equal torque impulses.[43] The torque produced by the interaction of e_1 and i_1 is shown as T_1. The EMF and the current both require a finite time to change from positive to negative, and this results in a dip in the torque waveform every half-cycle, i.e., at twice the fundamental frequency.

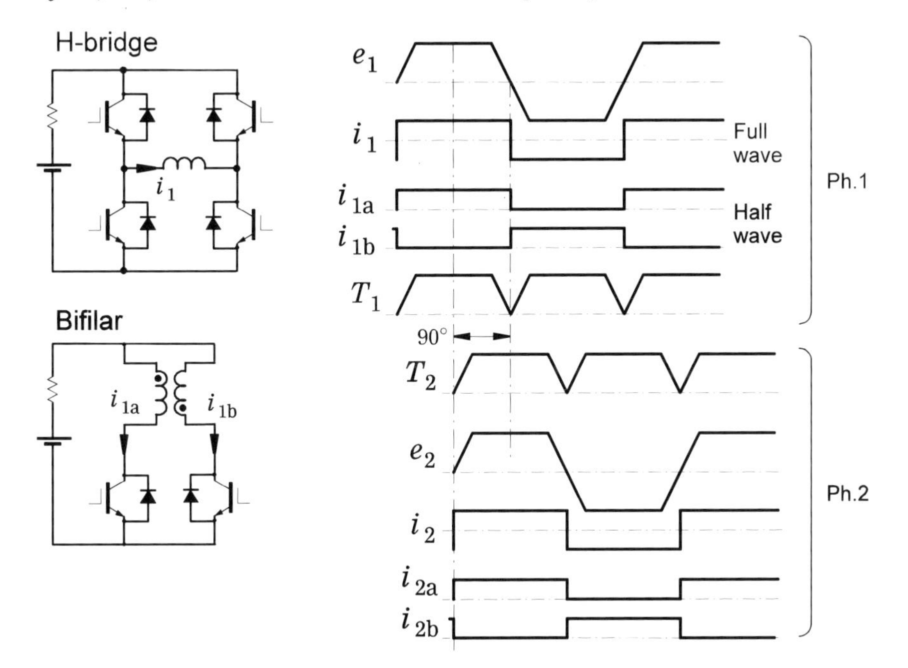

Fig. 6.37 Single-phase and 2-phase motor waveforms

[43] i.e., there are no even harmonics in the EMF waveform unless they are deliberately introduced by means of geometric or other imbalances or asymmetry in the magnetic circuit. Generally such imbalances are acceptable only in very small motors.

A bridge circuit such as the one labelled "H-bridge" in Fig. 6.37 is capable of driving a symmetrical alternating current waveform i_1. This circuit has four transistors, two of which are referenced to the negative supply rail and the other two to the positive rail. The upper transistors are called "high-side" transistors and the lower ones "low-side" transistors. The gating and protection circuits for low-side devices are simpler than for high-side ones, and for this reason the **bifilar circuit** is sometimes used. In this case the phase winding is split into two equal parallel paths which are connected within the motor with opposite polarity, as shown in Fig. 6.36. The half-wave or "unipolar" current i_{1a} flows in one path for half a cycle; then it is switched off and the current i_{1b} flows in the other path.

In Fig. 6.36 the paths are shown as separate phases 1 and 2, but this is a matter of convention; the bifilar motor in Fig. 6.36 is often termed "1-phase bifilar". Complementary switching is used with the transistors controlling the two paths or phases: normally each conducts for half a cycle in any full cycle. When one switches off, the current ideally transfers immediately to the other, but in practice the mutual coupling between the two paths is imperfect and the resulting leakage inductance retains a fraction of the inductive energy, which must be dissipated. There is also an overvoltage on the outgoing transistor, which may cause avalanching if a snubber is not used.

The torque dips in the T_1 waveform in Fig. 6.37 are not a problem in applications such as low-powered fans or blowers, provided that the motor can start satisfactorily. Sometimes a tapered airgap is used to "park" the rotor at a position away from the location of zero torque when the motor comes to rest. Alternatively the torque dips can be eliminated by adding a second phase, similar to the one in Fig. 6.36, but with windings displaced 90°elec from those of the first phase, and currents 90° out of phase with those of the first phase. The current, EMF and torque contribution of a second phase are shown in Fig. 6.37. The drive circuit requires a duplication of the first H-bridge (leading to a total of 8 transistors for 2 phases), or a duplication of the bifilar drive circuit (leading to a total of 4 transistors). The bifilar drive with two orthogonal sets of windings is often termed "2-phase bifilar" but it can equally well be regarded as a 4-phase motor in which the complementary phases (1&3 and 2&4) are tightly coupled.

The total torque $(T_1 + T_2)$ in the case shown in Fig. 6.37 will have no zeroes, but it may have considerable ripple because of the particular waveforms of the individual phase torques. This ripple can be reduced by reducing the conduction angle from 180° to 90° in each half-cycle in each phase, which is easily accomplished with the H-bridge full-wave circuit. But in the bifilar circuit, with less than 180° conduction the inductive energy in the winding is not transferred to the complementary winding. Unipolar circuits usually have no means of returning it to the supply, being designed for low component cost: therefore this energy must be dissipated, with inevitable loss of efficiency.

If the number of phases is increased to 3, the 3-wire connection can be used (with internal wye or delta connection), and the 6-transistor bridge can be used with no restriction on the current control, in the sense that positive and negative current *and* voltage can be applied to the motor terminals by appropriate switching controls. The 3-phase motor has better overlap to cover the natural torque dips, since each line needs to conduct for only 120° in each half-cycle, leaving 60° for the EMF waveform to change polarity. Also the 3-phase drive requires only 3 leads and 6 transistors. For these and other reasons it is by far the most popular choice except where extremely low component cost is required.

Analysis of unipolar circuits

Fig. 6.38 shows the simplest form of unipolar circuit,[44] in which the winding W is controlled by a single transistor Q. There is no separate freewheel diode; diode D is the body diode if Q is a FET. Positive current i flows from the DC supply V_s when Q is switched on. When Q switches off, a reverse voltage $v < 0$ must be developed across the winding in order to reduce the current to zero. The only source of the necessary reverse voltage is the avalanche voltage of the transistor or diode, V_z.

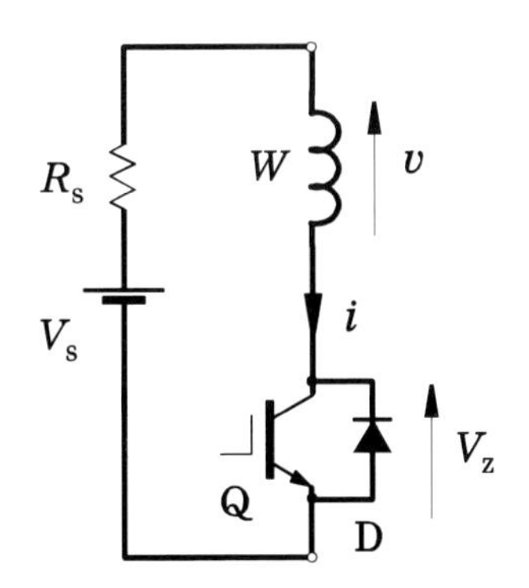

Fig. 6.38 Single-ended circuit

[44]Unipolar or "half-wave" circuits are sometimes called "single-ended".

It is possible to protect the transistor by means of a voltage-limiting circuit in parallel. Fig. 6.39 shows such a circuit with a Zener diode V_z and a damping resistor R_d. To ensure that $v < 0$ it is obviously necessary to have $V_z + R_d \times i > V_s - R_s \times i$ where R_s is the supply resistance. The peak forward voltage appearing across the transistor when it turns off is $V_z + R_d \times i$.

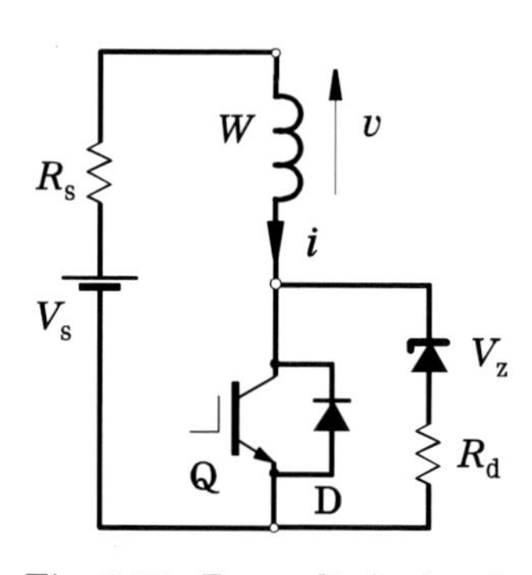

Fig. 6.39 Zener diode circuit

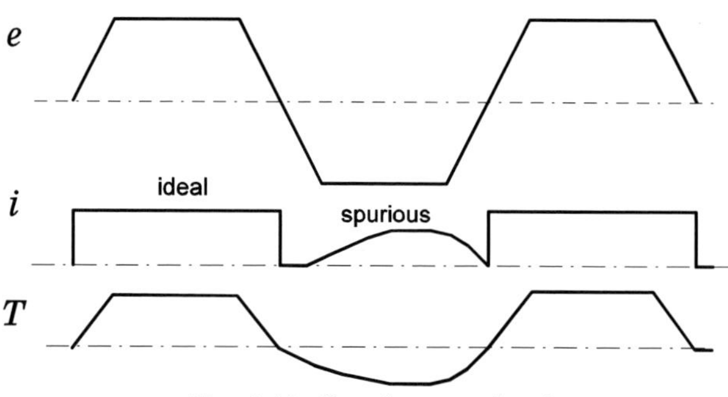

Fig. 6.40 Spurious conduction

For a single-ended circuit such as the one in Fig. 6.38, the EMF, current and torque waveforms are ideally of the form shown in Fig. 6.37. However, if the sum of V_s and the peak EMF e_{pk} exceeds the avalanche voltage V_z, there is a possibility of spurious conduction during the negative half-cycles of EMF, as shown in Fig. 6.40. This uncontrolled current produces a pulse of negative torque. As we shall see shortly, the prevention of the spurious conduction requires a zener diode with a certain minimum avalanche voltage V_z, which can be estimated using eqn. (6.76).

The equations for the circuit in Fig. 6.39 are:

$$\begin{aligned} \textbf{ON}: \quad v &= V_s - V_q - (R_s + R_q)\,i; \\ \textbf{OFF}: \quad v &= V_s - V_z - (R_s + R_d)\,i. \end{aligned} \qquad (6.73)$$

where V_q is the forward voltage drop in the transistor and R_q is its resistance. These equations can also be used with the circuit of Fig. 6.38 if $R_d = 0$.

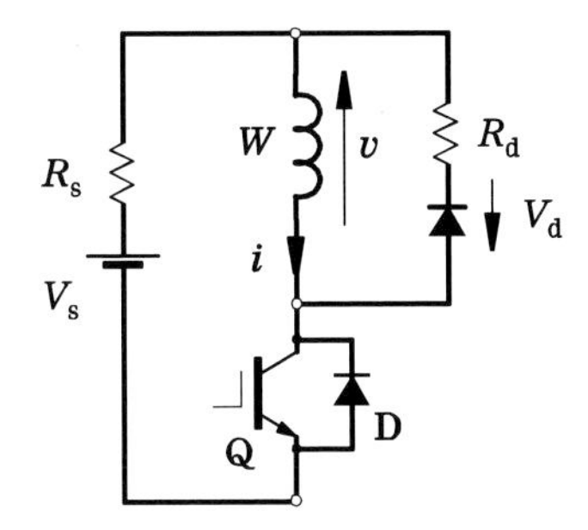

Fig. 6.41 Plain freewheel diode

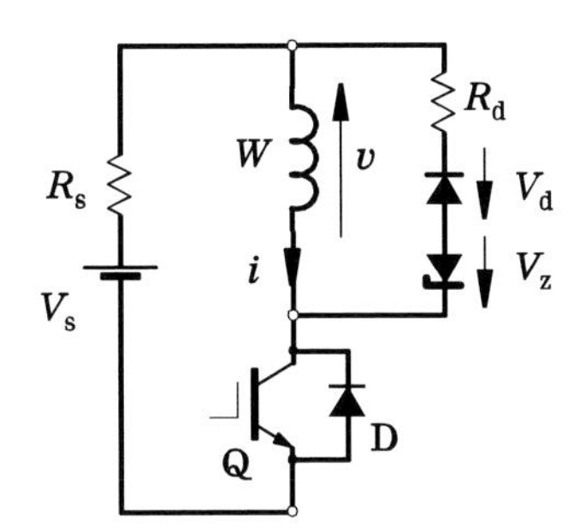

Fig. 6.42 Zener freewheel circuit

Fig. 6.41 shows an alternative single-ended circuit in which the suppression circuit is in parallel with the *winding*, so that the supply voltage does not appear in the freewheeling path. The suppression voltage is developed across the damping resistor R_d together with a small additional forward voltage drop across the freewheel diode. A disadvantage is that the suppression voltage $R_d \times i$ decays with i, so that the defluxing of the motor winding is slow.

Fig. 6.42 shows a modification with a Zener diode to sustain the suppression voltage at a higher level. As in the circuits of Figs. 6.38 and 6.39, spurious conduction is possible during negative half-cycles of EMF, unless V_z is high enough to exceed the peak EMF e_{pk}.

When the transistor is on, eqn. (6.73) also describes the operation of the circuits in Figs. 6.41 and 6.42. When it is off, the operation is described by the equation

$$\textbf{OFF}: \quad v = -V_d - V_z - R_d i. \tag{6.74}$$

The circuits in Fig. 6.41 and 6.42 can be used with any number of phases, with or without bifilar windings, and they can be used with tapered-gap motors or motors with a "parking" device. However, there is no point in using them with 2-phase motors which have phases displaced by 90°, or with 4-phase motors which have phases displaced by 45°, because they cannot deliver the alternating (full-wave) currents required in these cases.

It is important to account for mutual coupling between phases during the freewheeling period after each phase transistor turns off.

The circuit equations for the bifilar motor can be taken in pairs, since there is no coupling between the first pair (phases 1&3) and the second pair (phases 2&4) in a 4-phase motor. With no loss of generality we can consider the 2-phase motor, labelling the phases 1&2. (This is the circuit that is called "single-phase bifilar"). Thus

$$\begin{aligned} v_{t1} &= e_1 + R_{ph} i_1 + L_{ph} p_1 + M_{ph} p_2 \\ v_{t2} &= e_2 + R_{ph} i_2 + M_{ph} p_1 + L_{ph} p_2 \end{aligned} \qquad (6.75)$$

where $p = di/dt$ and v_{t1} and v_{t2} are the terminal voltages of the phase windings, which depend on the states of the transistors and diodes. These equations will normally be solved by computer simulation, according to the switching algorithm and the values of the currents. but for the Zener diode circuit of Fig. 6.39, which also represents the circuit of Fig. 6.38 when the transistor is avalanching, they can be solved algebraically for the turn-off period of the transistor. If EMF and resistance are neglected and $M_{ph}/L_{ph} = k$, the coupling coefficient, the solution for p_1 and p_2 is

$$p_1 = \frac{(1-k)V_s - V_z}{L(1-k^2)}; \qquad p_2 = \frac{(1-k)V_s + kV_z}{L(1-k^2)}. \qquad (6.76)$$

If k is nearly -1 and $V_z \le 2V_s$, then $p_1 = p_2 \ge 0$, implying that commutation requires $V_z > 2V_s$. For example if $V_z = 3V_s$, $p_1 = p_2 = -V_s/L\,(1-k^2)$, and since both of these are negative it is evident that when one transistor switches off, a negative current is induced in the complementary phase. This current appears as a spike, followed by the positive current pulse after a few degrees of rotation, Fig. 6.43.

If chopping is employed, the negative spike current recurs every time a transistor is switched off, dissipating the inductive energy in the leakage inductance. To avoid chopping, phase advance can be used to control the torque, (also at the expense of efficiency). High voltage stress on the transistor ($>V_z$) is inevitable with these unipolar circuits during turn-off.

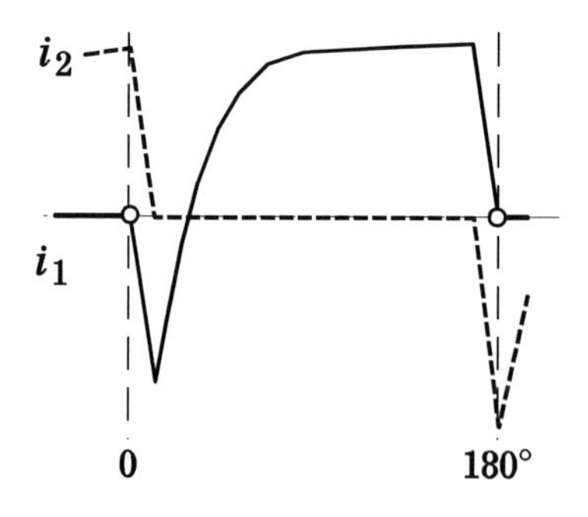

Fig. 6.43 Commutation spike

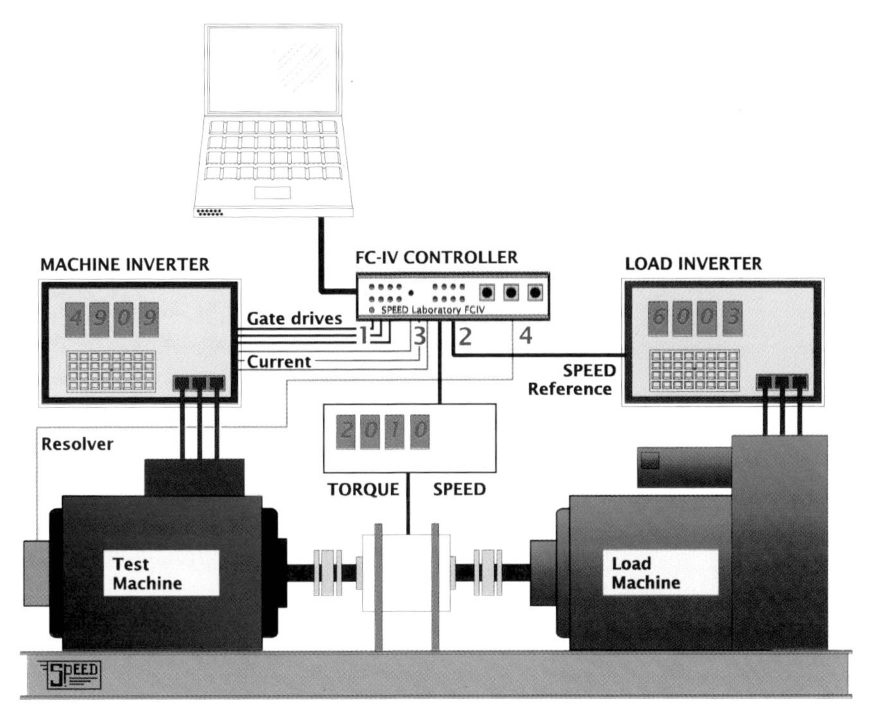

Fig. 6.44 FCIV Test stand. *Courtesy of Calum Cossar, SPEED Lab.*

6.4 Controller architecture

One can readily find manufacturers' datasheets and application notes for proprietary integrated-circuit controllers, and textbooks explaining various aspects of digital control systems.[45] However, what is needed for prototype development is a complete test environment where all the theories can be held to account, and all the simulations can be found meaningful or otherwise.

Such a system is illustrated in Figs. 6.44, 6.46 and 6.45. One of the most important developments in this field is the ability to "port" or "download" software from a simulation directly into a real-time controller. This not only saves development time but helps to validate the original simulation, which can then be extended to improve the control algorithms or to solve problems.

---

[45] See for example Dote Y., *Servo Motor and Motion Control Using Digital Signal Processors*, Texas Instruments/Prentice Hall, 1990.

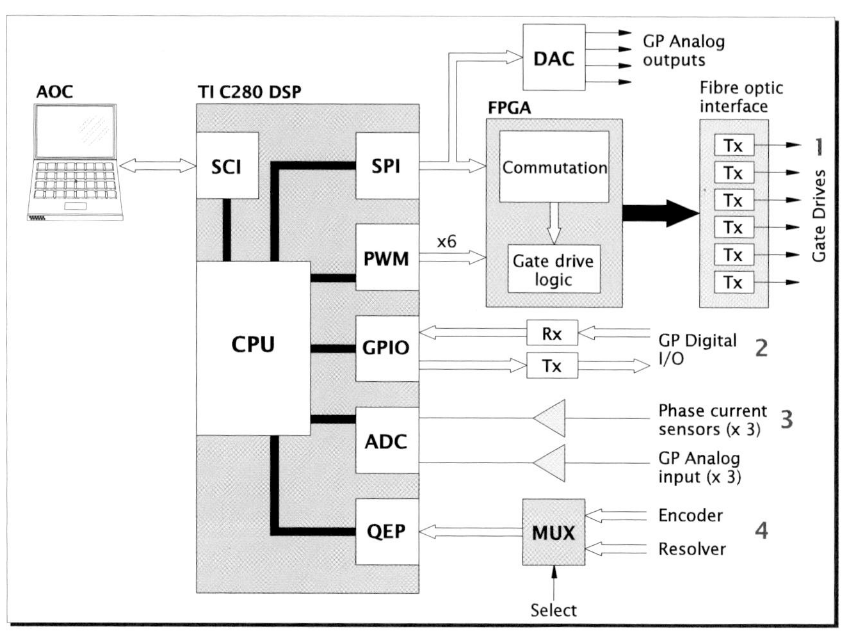

Fig. 6.45 FC-IV controller architecture. *Courtesy of Calum Cossar, SPEED Lab.*

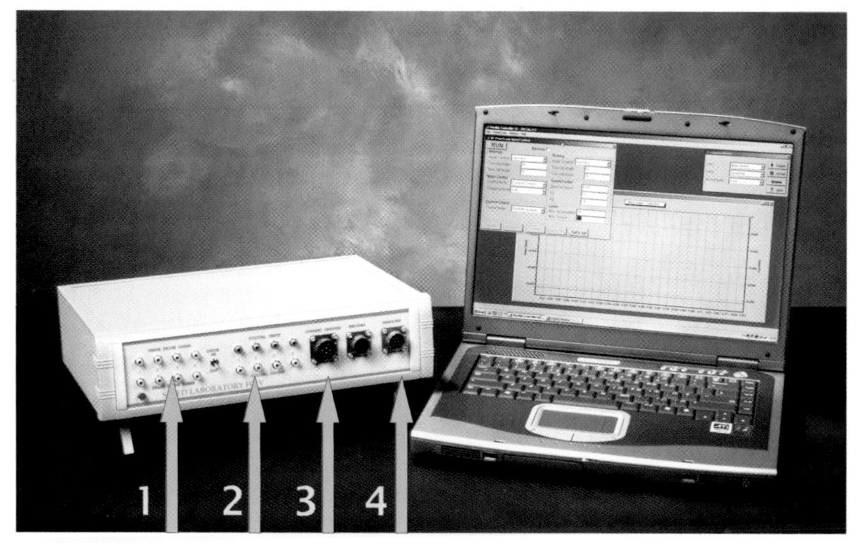

Fig. 6.46 FC-IV controller. *Courtesy of Calum Cossar, SPEED Lab.*

The ideal "platform" for such control development work is a digital signal processor (DSP), which is essentially a computer having specialized input/output (I/O) facilities adapted for coupling the kind of signals used in motor drives and in measurement transducers commonly used with them. The processing power and speed of the DSP is so great that it can execute all the control loops including the current-regulator and the speed loop, together with the processing of signals from a shaft position transducer (encoder or resolver or Hall sensor). For all practical purposes these tasks appear to be being performed simultaneously. The DSP communicates with a PC for user-control, and processes signals from transducers, sensors, and instruments. It can thus be used as the basis of the machine controller, the load controller, and a data logging system all at once.

So comprehensive is the power of the DSP system that the block diagram in Fig. 6.45 is relatively simple. The functional complexity resides in the software rather than the external wiring.

The FC-IV system in Figs. 6 44–6.45 uses a separate FPGA (field-programmable gate array) to execute the final binary logic in coupling the controller to the gate drives of individual power transistors. The gate drives are coupled using fibre-optics which provide immunity from noise and interference and can work at any voltage level. The duty-cycle or space-vector value can be set with a precision of 12 bits at 20kHz, or 10 bits at 80kHz switching frequency.

The central processor unit (CPU) is programmed in C. It executes an inner loop of the current regulator in typically 5μs. It has 32-bit precision and a clock speed of 150 MIPs (million instructions per sec).

Analog inputs such as phase currents, filtered line voltages, and torque-transducer signals are received *via* analog/digital converters (ADCs) at 12-bit resolution, sampled at up to 10^6/sec. Analog outputs with the same resolution are used to display any parameter, such as phase currents or computed flux-linkage. Another unusual use of these outputs is to control a linear power amplifier with specific current or voltage waveforms for special tests.

The PC interface displays parameters and graphs, and provides access for all control inputs. *Any* drive control can be programmed — squarewave or sinewave — for *any* motor or generator system.

7 SINEWAVE DRIVE

Introduction

This chapter is concerned with sinewave drive and current regulation.

In the ideal sinewave system, the ampere-conductor distribution of the stator rotates at the synchronous speed fixed by the frequency and the number of poles, as in eqn. (1.1). In the steady state the rotor and the flux also rotate at the same speed, in synchronism with the ampere-conductor distribution. To an observer on the rotor, the flux and the ampere-conductor distribution appear constant. In any one phase winding the flux-linkage, the current, EMF and terminal voltage all vary sinusoidally at the fundamental frequency.

In dealing with squarewave drives we used actual waveforms of these electrical quantities. These waveforms can be constructed manually for ideal cases, but under dynamic conditions they can be determined only by computer simulation. Both approaches work equally well with sinewave drives, but in the steady state we also have the option of using *phasor* quantities introduced in §1.4.1. Phasors have enormous advantages for steady-state analysis: the theory of performance and control can be developed using the algebra of complex numbers, while the phasor diagram and the voltage locus diagram give compact, powerful graphical methods of analysis and physical interpretation. By resolving them into dq-axes, we can apply them to salient-pole machines like the IPM, which were hardly considered in connection with squarewave drives.

These ideal properties require the machine to be **sinewound**.[46] This property is also a necessary condition for the current, EMF, flux-linkage and terminal voltage to be represented as **space-vectors**, complex numbers that completely represent their *instantaneous* states, including all three phases, in extremely compact form.

---

[46] *Sinewound* means a machine that has a sinusoidal EMF waveform and a sinusoidal variation of inductance with rotor position. A sufficient condition for a machine to be sinewound is that its windings are sinusoidally distributed. In practice this is not strictly achievable, but well-designed "sinewave" machines come very close.

Because of the instantaneous representation (rather than peak, mean or RMS values of steady-state sinewaves), space-vectors provide a natural means of including the motor and the power electronic drive in the same theoretical model. They can even be used to represent the states of the switches in the inverter, and they can be used for transient calculations on any time-scale, including the infinite time-scale of the steady state.[47]

The first part of this chapter develops the theory of the sinewave drive and the speed/torque characteristic using the phasor diagram, the **voltage-locus diagram**, and the **ellipse diagram**. We will see the effect of saliency and saturation (both important for the IPM), and the principles of **flux-weakening**.

The second part is concerned with the **PWM control algorithms** and current regulators that determine the switching of the power transistors, starting with simple controllers like six-step, sine/triangle modulation, and current hysteresis control, and developing the story to the synchronous regulator, the space-vector field-oriented control, and direct torque control (DTC).

We laid the foundations of phasor theory in Chapter 1, and in Chapter 4 we studied the EMF and the torque, introducing *dq*-axis theory *via* Park's transform. Readers may be glad to find in this chapter that the *dq*-axis phasor diagram used for nonsalient- and salient-pole machines is intuitive and requires little mathematics.[48]

Most importantly, what we have to do in this Chapter is to couple the elements of the circuit together — from the voltage source to the shaft — by solving the voltage equations of the system, just as we did for squarewave drives in Chapter 6.

---

[47] The space-vector is a *deus ex machina* for the control engineer, because it enables him or her to formulate control strategies without bothering with the nasty things that go on in the machine — harmonics, saturation, vibration, torque ripple, noise, heat, insulation failure,.... At the same time it is handy for the motor engineer who wants to understand a bit about control technology. Neat idea.
Much fuss has been made about the origin of space vectors and even about the terminology: *space phasors* and *instantaneous symmetrical components* are two alternatives. Of equal or greater importance is what has been done with them. (§7.2)

[48] We can thank Blondel for that. His "two-reaction theory" pre-dates Park by more than 30 years (and this book by more than 110 years).

7.1 The phasor diagram — motor operation

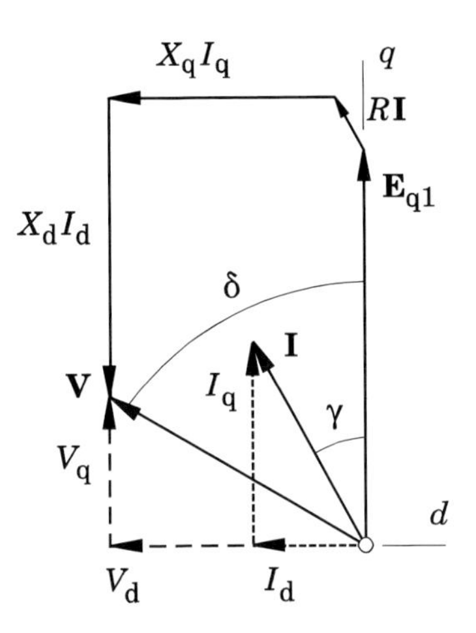

Fig. 7.1 Phasor diagram in dq axes

The phasor diagram represents the voltage equation of one phase in the steady state. In terms of dq-axis components, we have

$$V_d = RI_d - X_q I_q; \tag{7.1}$$

$$V_q = E_{q1} + RI_q + X_d I_d. \tag{7.2}$$

In these equations, voltages and currents are in RMS units; and we need to be careful with the sign of I_d, which is negative in Fig. 7.1. The phase voltage is

$$\mathbf{V}_{ph1} = V_d + jV_q \tag{7.3}$$

and the phase current is

$$\mathbf{I} = I_d + jI_q. \tag{7.4}$$

All these equations are derived from the steady-state expressions for current and flux-linkage on p. 204, substituted into the dq voltage equations (4.108) with $\mathbf{p} = 0$.

The inductive part of $\mathbf{V}_{ph1}$ is the voltage $\mathbf{U} = \mathbf{V}_{ph1} - R\mathbf{I}$, and

$$\mathbf{U} = U_d + jU_q = j\omega\Psi = j\omega(\Psi_d + j\Psi_q) = -\omega\Psi_q + j\omega\Psi_d. \tag{7.5}$$

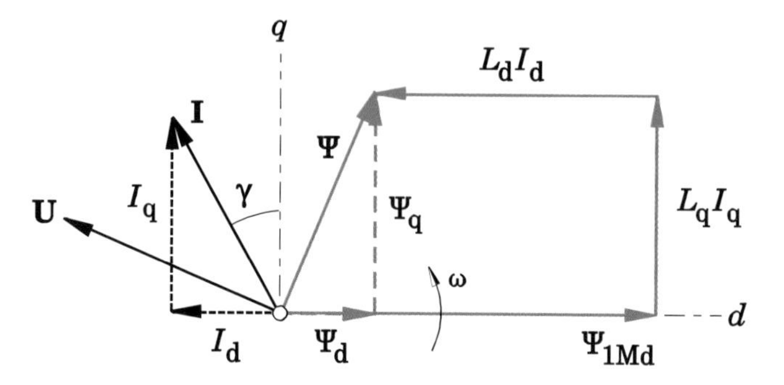

Fig. 7.2 Phasor diagram of flux-linkages

The flux-linkage components Ψ_d and Ψ_q are given by eqn. (5.77), and in terms of RMS quantities

$$\Psi_d = \Psi_{1Md} + L_d I_d; \tag{7.6}$$

$$\Psi_q = L_q I_q. \tag{7.7}$$

The total phase flux-linkage **Ψ** is shown in Fig. 7.2 together with its components and the voltage **U** which leads it by 90°. In a genuine physical sense this diagram represents components of the rotating flux, but scaled to the units of flux-linkage.

For the purposes of calculating torque, eqn. (4.114) can be used without decomposing Ψ_d into separate components associated with the magnet and the stator current; this may be important under saturated conditions, as discussed in §5.13. For the remainder of this chapter we will assume that the values of L_d, L_q and Ψ_{1Md} are known and appropriate to the operating point being considered.

The flux-linkage component L_dI_d in Fig. 7.2 is *demagnetizing* because it is opposing the magnet flux-linkage Ψ_{1Md}, consistent with the fact that $I_d < 0$ in Figs. 7.1 and 7.2. With the proportions shown in these figures, I_d is very strongly demagnetizing. The result is that the terminal voltage V is less than the EMF E_{q1}, and we would say that Figs. 7.1 and 7.2 show a somewhat extreme case of **flux-weakening**. Suppression of the magnet flux-linkage to such a degree is possible only when there is sufficient inductance, and even then it might require a large current. Whether this current is *available* from the inverter is one of the questions to be addressed below.

Torque — The time-averaged power associated with **U** and **I** is

$$P_e = m \operatorname{Re}\{\mathbf{U}\mathbf{I}^*\} = m(U_d I_d + U_q I_q), \tag{7.8}$$

where m is the number of phases. Using **U** instead of $\mathbf{V}_{ph1}$ removes the $R\mathbf{I}$ term, which represents only losses. As before, we can deduce the mean electromagnetic torque T_e as P_e/ω_m or $P_e/(\omega/p)$. Substituting from eqn. (7.5) in eqn. (7.8), we get

$$T_e = mp(\Psi_d I_q - \Psi_q I_d). \tag{7.9}$$

which is the same as eqn. (4.114). Now if we substitute Ψ_d from eqn. (7.6) and Ψ_q from eqn. (7.7) we get the time-averaged torque

$$\begin{aligned} T_e &= mp[\Psi_{1Md} I_q + I_d I_q (L_d - L_q)] \\ &= \frac{mp}{\omega}[E_{q1} I_q + I_d I_q (X_d - X_q)] = T_A + T_R . \end{aligned} \tag{7.10}$$

The two components are the PM **alignment** torque $T_A = mp\Psi_{1Md}I_q$ or $mpE_{q1}I_q/\omega$; and the **reluctance torque** $T_R = mpI_dI_q(L_d - L_q)$ or $mp(X_d - X_q)/\omega$. In a nonsalient-pole machine, $L_d = L_q$ and the reluctance torque T_R is zero. If the EMF is constant, the torque is then proportional to I_q, and the torque constant $k_T = T_e/I$ is constant provided that $\mathbf{I} = jI_q$. This is called "quadrature control".

Quadrant	I_d	I_q	T_A	T_R
Q1	+	+	+	–
Q2	–	+	+	+
Q3	–	–	–	–
Q4	+	–	–	+

TABLE 7.1
SIGNS OF ALIGNMENT AND RELUCTANCE TORQUES

In the IPM, usually $L_q > L_d$, so I_d must be negative if the reluctance torque T_R is to be positive. Negative I_d is in the demagnetizing direction. Table 7.1 shows the signs of T_A and T_R for currents in all four quadrants of the phasor diagram. Evidently T_A and T_R are in the same direction only when $I_d < 0$, suggesting that for normal motoring the current phasor **I** should be in the second quadrant Q2, while for normal generating **I** should be in Q3.

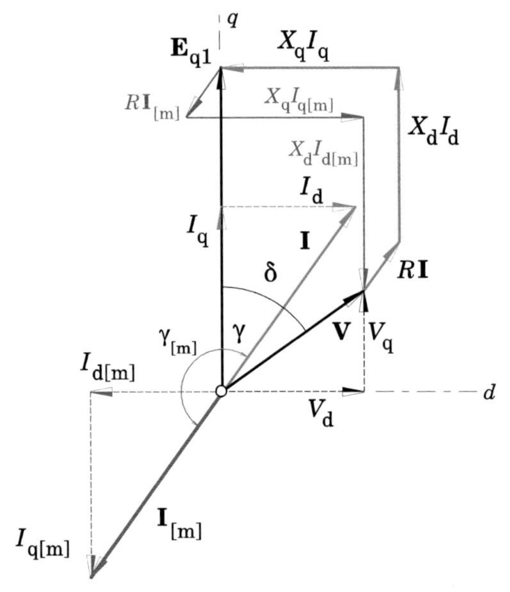

Fig. 7.3 Phasor diagram for generating

Table 7.1 prompts the question of how to draw the phasor diagram for generating. According to the convention we have used up to now with motor current positive, $\mathbf{I}_{[m]}$ in Fig. 7.3 represents generating operation, with negative torque and negative I_d (demagnetizing). If we adopt a generator sign convention by reversing the sign of the current, we have $\mathbf{I} = -\mathbf{I}_{[m]}$, and the phasor $\mathbf{I}$ is displaced 180° from $\mathbf{I}_{[m]}$. Likewise its components I_d and I_q are also reversed relative to the respective "motoring" components $I_{d[m]}$ and $I_{q[m]}$.

The EMF $\mathbf{E}_{q1}$ is unchanged, but eqns. (7.1) and (7.2) become

$$V_d = -RI_d + X_q I_q; \qquad (7.11)$$

$$V_q = E_{q1} - RI_q - X_d I_d. \qquad (7.12)$$

The reversal of the sign of the current means that positive I_d is demagnetizing. This is the case in Fig. 7.3, where the voltage-drop $X_d I_d$ in the d-axis synchronous reactance tends to make the terminal voltage smaller than the open-circuit voltage; this is characteristic of a so-called **overexcited** generator. It is also noted that the power-factor is lagging. The red and green volt-drop phasors at top right show that the voltage is the same whichever convention is used.

The signs of the voltage-drop phasors $X_d I_d$, $X_q I_q$, RI_d and RI_q are not intuitively obvious from eqns. (7.1) and (7.2), and it is easy to make a mistake. It is really safest to use the complex form of these equations :

$$\text{MOTORING:} \quad \begin{aligned} \mathbf{V} &= \mathbf{E}_{q1} + R\mathbf{I} + jX_q(jI_q) + jX_d I_d \\ &= jE_{q1} + R\mathbf{I} - X_q I_q + jX_d I_d. \end{aligned} \tag{7.13}$$

$$\text{GENERATING:} \quad \begin{aligned} \mathbf{V} &= \mathbf{E}_{q1} - R\mathbf{I} - jX_q(jI_q) - jX_d I_d \\ &= jE_{q1} - R\mathbf{I} + X_q I_q - jX_d I_d. \end{aligned} \tag{7.14}$$

The separate treatment of I_d and I_q in these equations represents exactly the two-reaction theory of Blondel, I_d being multiplied by X_d and I_q by X_q. When $X_d = X_q$ there is no saliency and the equations simplify to

$$\text{MOTORING:} \quad \begin{aligned} \mathbf{V} &= \mathbf{E}_{q1} + R\mathbf{I} + jX_d(I_d + jI_q) \\ &= jE_{q1} + (R + jX_d)\mathbf{I}. \end{aligned} \tag{7.15}$$

$$\text{GENERATING:} \quad \begin{aligned} \mathbf{V} &= \mathbf{E}_{q1} - R\mathbf{I} - jX_d(I_d + jI_q) \\ &= jE_{q1} - (R + jX_d)\mathbf{I}. \end{aligned} \tag{7.16}$$

The scalar forms tumble out from eqns. (7.13–16) when the components are separated using eqns. (7.3) and (7.4). As a final helper, it is noted that in the *motoring* phasor diagram, the voltage-drop phasors $X_d I_d$ and $X_q I_q$ reflect the direction of the armature-reaction fluxes, just as $L_d I_d$ and $L_q I_q$ do in Fig. 7.2.

In Fig. 7.4 the operation of an **underexcited PM generator** is shown on the right-hand side, in which the open-circuit voltage E_{q1} is less than the terminal voltage V_G; the power-factor is leading, and the *d*-axis current I_d is *magnetizing*, as it must be to create enough airgap flux to generate the rather high terminal voltage. Since the angle ϕ_g is about 71°, the power-factor in this example is cos 71° = 0·326 leading — a very low value.

If we reverse the direction of the current, the machine turns to motoring, and if we also change the sign convention from "positive generating" to "positive motoring", the current phasor remains unchanged, while the voltage-drop phasors are added to $\mathbf{E}_{q1}$ instead of being added to $\mathbf{V}$. The power factor cos ϕ is now 0·97 lagging.

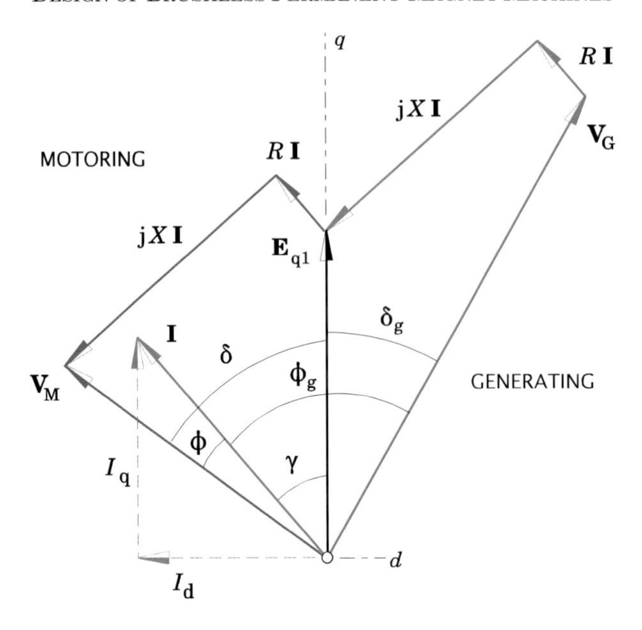

Fig. 7.4 Underexcited PM generator, nonsalient-pole, with equivalent motor

7.1.1 Torque/angle curves

In this section we will continue to investigate the operation at a fixed speed. Having understood most of the important properties of the phasor diagram, we can now consider the control of torque.

In a salient-pole motor where L_d and L_q are unequal, the mix of permanent-magnet alignment torque and reluctance torque can be adjusted by changing the phase angle γ of the current as well as its magnitude, provided that the inverter has the required current capability *and* sufficient voltage to force the required current. These two constraints will be considered in turn.

Current-limited maximum torque — Noting that γ is measured from the q-axis in the positive (anticlockwise) direction in the phasor diagram, we can write

$$I_d = -I \sin \gamma ; \quad I_q = I \cos \gamma , \tag{7.17}$$

and if we substitute eqns. (7.17) in eqn. (7.10) we get

$$T_e = mp[\Psi_{1Md} I \cos \gamma - I^2 \sin \gamma \cos \gamma \, (L_d - L_q)]. \tag{7.18}$$

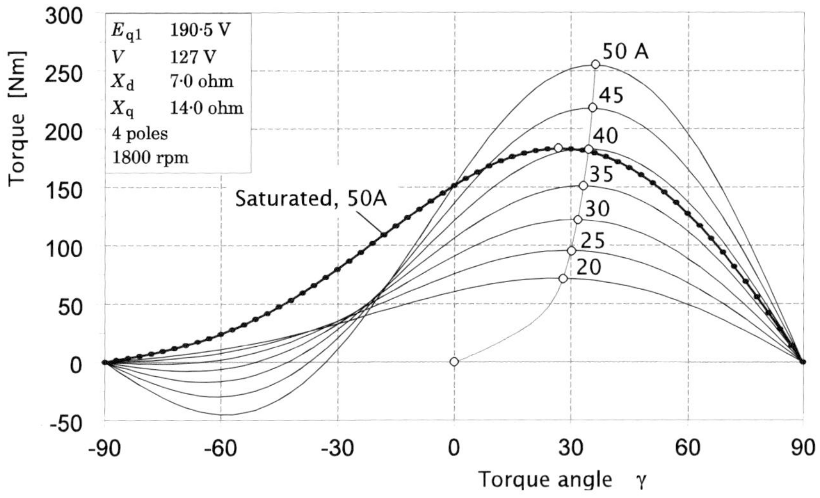

Fig. 7.5 Torque vs. torque angle γ

This torque equation can be written in terms of E_{q1}, X_d and X_q :

$$T_e = \frac{mp}{\omega}\left[E_{q1} I \cos\gamma - \frac{1}{2} I^2 (X_d - X_q) \sin 2\gamma\right]. \tag{7.19}$$

All quantities in eqns. (7.18) and (7.19) are RMS. At any given current level I, we can differentiate this expression with respect to γ to find the value of γ which gives maximum torque. The result is

$$\gamma_{\mathrm{Tmax}} = \sin^{-1} \frac{1}{4}\left[\frac{E_{q1}}{\Delta V} + \sqrt{\left(\frac{E_{q1}}{\Delta V}\right)^2 + 8}\,\right] \tag{7.20}$$

where $\Delta V = (X_d - X_q)I$. Unfortunately γ_{Tmax} is not fixed, but depends on the current. Torque is not proportional to current, so k_T is not constant. Moreover, saturation causes X_d and X_q (and even E_{q1}) to vary, complicating the problem of finding the optimum value of γ.

If there is no saliency $\Delta V = 0$; then from eqn. (7.18) the phase angle that maximizes the torque is $\gamma = 0$: i.e., the current must be oriented in the q-axis in phase with the EMF E. As we have already seen, phase advance ($\gamma > 0$) in a nonsalient-pole motor reduces the torque constant k_T, by the factor $\cos\gamma$.

A typical set of torque/angle curves is shown in Fig. 7.5, with parameters as noted in the chart. For most of the range of currents the torque-maximizing angle γ_{Tmax} is in the range 30–35°. The curves in Fig. 7.5 were calculated with fixed reactances X_d and X_q, but at high current saturation reduces the saliency. To show the effect, the "saturated" curve at 50 A was recalculated with X_q reduced from 14 to 10 ohm, a typical result of saturation in an IPM. The peak torque decreases from 255 to 184 Nm, a reduction of 28%, while γ_{Tmax} decreases from 35·7° to 27·2°.

Voltage-limited maximum torque — With constant voltage V_m but variable phase angle δ between V_m and E, the torque can be calculated by solving eqns. (7.1) and (7.2) for I_d and I_q, and then substituting these currents in eqn. (7.18). Neglecting resistance,

$$I_d = \frac{V_q - E_{q1}}{X_d} = \frac{V\cos\delta - E_{q1}}{X_d}; \quad \text{and}$$
$$I_q = \frac{-V_d}{X_q} = \frac{V\sin\delta}{X_q}, \tag{7.21}$$

where δ is the phase angle between the voltage $\mathbf{V}$ and the EMF $\mathbf{E}_{q1}$. The result is

$$T_e = \frac{mp}{\omega}\left[\frac{E_{q1}V_m}{X_d}\sin\delta + \frac{V_m^{\,2}}{2}\left(\frac{1}{X_q} - \frac{1}{X_d}\right)\sin 2\delta\right]. \tag{7.22}$$

We can differentiate eqn. (7.22) to find the phase angle δ_{Tmax} which maximises the torque. After some simplification the result is

$$\delta_{Tmax} = \cos^{-1}\left[\frac{\zeta \mp \sqrt{\zeta^2 + 8}}{4}\right] \tag{7.23}$$

where

$$\zeta = \frac{E/V_m}{1 - X_d/X_q}. \tag{7.24}$$

If there is no saliency, $\delta_{Tmax} = 90°$. Eqn. (7.23) can be used as the basis of a torque-maximizing control strategy when the current is limited by the available inverter voltage, as explained on p. 349. The disadvantage is that the magnitude and phase of the current will vary in a more complex manner as δ varies.

Ratio of reluctance torque to alignment torque — From eqn. (7.19) we can derive the ratio of reluctance torque to alignment torque T_R/T_A, and from that the proportion of the total torque that is reluctance torque. Thus if $\xi = X_q/X_d$ is the *saliency ratio* and $I_{sc} = E_{q1}/X_d$ is the short-circuit current, we get

$$\frac{T_R}{T_A} = \frac{I(X_q - X_d)}{E_{q1}} \sin\gamma = \frac{I}{I_{sc}}(\xi - 1)\sin\gamma . \qquad (7.25)$$

In a highly saturated machine we would be lucky to get $\xi = 2$, and if γ_{Tmax} is about 30° this means that even with $I = I_{sc}$ the maximum reluctance torque is about 0·5 T_A — no more than 1/3 of the total.

In the general case of a saturated machine we have seen in §5.13 that X_d and E_{q1} are not unique, while X_q may experience a large reduction of 60–70%. Consequently T_R/T_A is not unique even though the total ($T_A + T_R$) is unique. Unique values of X_d and E_{q1} can be determined using the finite-element method with the constraint applied in §5.13, but this itself is arbitrary. The very concept of reluctance torque relies on superposition, which is strictly invalid under saturated conditions. Moreover, the types of machine which are intended to exploit reluctance torque are precisely the ones that are most likely to saturate, the IPM being an obvious example.

Example — In Fig. 7.5, with I = 50 A, X_d = 7 ohm, X_q = 14 ohm, and E_{q1} = 190·5 V, if we take $\gamma = \gamma_{Tmax}$ = 35·7° we get

$$\frac{T_R}{T_A} = \frac{50 \times (14{\cdot}0 - 7{\cdot}0)}{190{\cdot}5} \sin 35{\cdot}7° = 1{\cdot}07 . \qquad (7.26)$$

Thus the reluctance torque is 1·07/(1 + 1·07) = 51·7% of the total.

When the machine is saturated the saliency is reduced. Continuing with the example in Fig. 7.5, if X_q decreases to 10 ohm and γ_{Tmax} to 27·2°, we get

$$\frac{T_R}{T_A} = \frac{50 \times (10{\cdot}0 - 7{\cdot}0)}{190{\cdot}5} \sin 27{\cdot}2° = 0{\cdot}36 . \qquad (7.27)$$

The reluctance torque is 0·36/(1 + 0·36) = 26·5% of the total. However, we saw that the total torque was reduced from 255 Nm to 184 Nm, so the saturated reluctance torque is only 0·265 × 184 = 48·8 Nm compared with 0·517 × 255 = 132 Nm unsaturated, a fall of about 63%. At the same time the alignment torque T_A *increased* — from (1 – 0·517) × 255 = 123·2 Nm to (1 – 0·265) × 184 = 135·2 Nm; this increase being entirely due to the smaller value of γ.

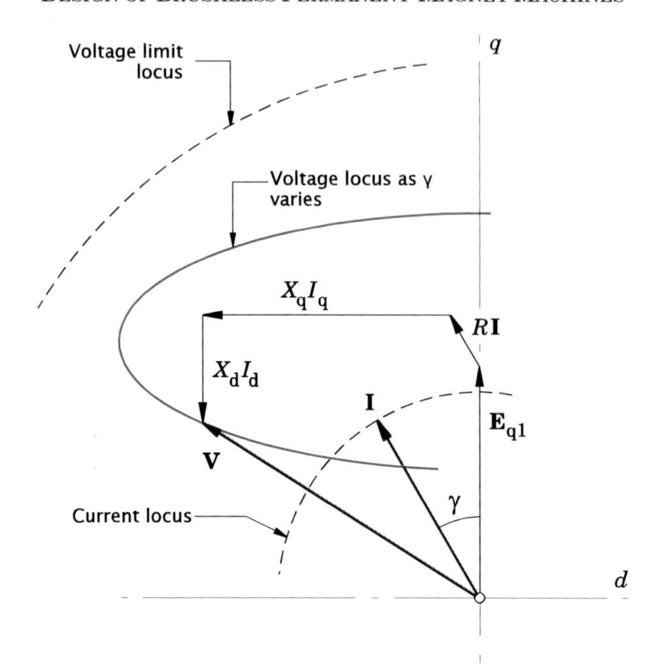

Fig. 7.6 Voltage locus as γ varies

7.1.2 The voltage locus diagram

A more general appreciation of the effect of limited drive voltage can be obtained from the voltage locus diagram, which is an important guide to the operating capability over a range of speed.

The voltage phasor **V** for motoring is given by eqn. (7.13), and by eqn. (7.14) for generating. Substituting for I_d and I_q from eqn. (7.17) in eqn. (7.13), we get

$$\begin{aligned} V_d &= (-R \sin \gamma - X_q \cos \gamma) I; \\ V_q &= (R \cos \gamma - X_d \sin \gamma) I + E_{q1}. \end{aligned} \tag{7.28}$$

Eqn. (7.28) describes the *locus* of the voltage phasor required to force the current $I_d + jI_q$ into the machine. Fig. 7.6 shows an example in which the current I remains constant while the phase angle γ varies. The tip of the *current* phasor traces a *circular* locus, but the corresponding *voltage* locus [eqn. (7.28)] is *elliptical*. It shows several interesting properties of the voltage required from the inverter.

For example, when the current has a demagnetizing component $I_d < 0$, the required voltage is reduced; this is known as *flux-weakening*. When $\gamma > 90°$, $I_q < 0$ and the torque reverses, so the machine is generating and in this case **V** lags behind **E**; the tip of the voltage phasor then lies on that part of the ellipse to the right of the q-axis. It is possible to plot constant-torque and constant-power loci on Fig. 7.6, as we shall see.

However, the most important feature of the voltage locus is that it defines the operating capability of the motor within the voltage-limit of the inverter, V_m. This voltage is expressed by the circular **voltage-limit locus**,

$$V_m{}^2 = V_{dm}{}^2 + V_{qm}{}^2 . \qquad (7.29)$$

V_m is the maximum fundamental voltage available from the inverter, and it depends on the particular PWM control algorithm together with the DC bus voltage V_s. This is analyzed in more detail later, but it can be noted here that the maximum possible value of V_m is obtained with the 180° six-step inverter, and is equal to $\sqrt{(6)}/\pi\, V_s$ (RMS line-line).

Example — An inverter has a DC bus voltage of 300 V. It drives a motor that requires a maximum line-line voltage of 200 V RMS. Will 300 V DC be sufficient?

The maximum fundamental voltage available at the motor terminals is obtained with 180° six-step drive. Ignoring voltage drops in the transistors, we have $V_m = \sqrt{(6)}/\pi \times 300 = 0{\cdot}780 \times 300 = 234$ V line-line RMS. Therefore with six-step drive, the inverter voltage is sufficient. Note that the *peak* of the six-step *fundamental* voltage is 331 V, higher than the DC bus voltage. However, if the inverter is limited to the linear range of sine/triangle PWM (§7.2), the available fundamental voltage is only $0{\cdot}612 \times 300 = 184$ V, which is not sufficient.

The voltage locus diagram is a useful basis for dialogue between the motor engineer **M** and the control engineer **C**. Together with the maximum current I_m, it presents itself as a natural currency in which they can negotiate the matching of the motor to the drive, absolving each from the need to encroach on the territory of the other.

C "Give me a motor that produces 184 Nm at 1800 rpm. You can have 50 A max. RMS line current. I know you can do it: I've seen your Fig. 7.5."

M "Done. I need 220 V (line-line RMS). From Table 7.3 I reckon you'll need a DC bus voltage between 280 V (six-step) and 360 V (max linear range of sine/triangle PWM). The closer you can get to the six-step voltage with your PWM, the lower the DC voltage we can use."

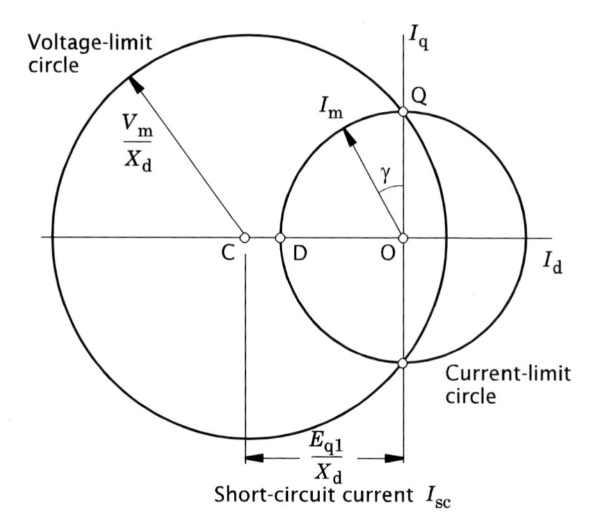

Fig. 7.7 Current-limit and voltage-limit circles

7.1.3 The circle and ellipse diagrams

The **current-limit circle** is a circular boundary $\mathbf{I} = I_m \, e^{j(\gamma + 90°)}$ with $0 \leq \gamma \leq 2\pi$, that encloses all current phasors whose RMS value does not exceed I_m, Fig. 7.7. I_m can represent either the maximum current available from the inverter, or the maximum current of the motor. A current-regulated drive normally has complete control of the current waveform, and it can place the current phasor anywhere inside the circle, provided it has sufficient voltage available to overcome the EMF and the impedance of the machine.

The **voltage-limit ellipse** is a *current* locus defining all possible currents that can be obtained when the inverter *voltage* is limited, rather than its current. Let V_m be the maximum available supply voltage per phase. If we substitute eqns. (7.21) in eqn. (7.29) we get

$$(X_q I_q)^2 + (E_{q1} + X_d I_d)^2 = V_m^2 . \qquad (7.30)$$

This is an ellipse in the plane of (I_d, I_q); see Fig. 7.11 on p. 348. If $X_d = X_q$, the voltage-limit ellipse becomes a circle, centre $(-E_{q1}/X_d, 0)$, as in Figs. 7.7 and 7.9. Note that E_{q1}/X_d is the **short-circuit current** I_{sc}, which may well exceed the maximum inverter current. In that case point **C** will lie outside the current-limit circle.

Variable speed — In eqn. (7.30), V_m is fixed; but the EMF $E_{q1} = \omega\Psi_{1Md}$ and the reactances $X_d = \omega L_d$ and $X_q = \omega L_q$ all increase in proportion to speed, while the short-circuit current E_{q1}/X_d remains constant. Consequently as the speed increases, the voltage-limit circle or ellipse shrinks, while it remains centred on point **C** in Fig. 7.7. At certain values of γ the drive may not have sufficient voltage to maintain the current I_m, so the current becomes *voltage-limited.*

"Corner" speed — For nonsalient-pole motors with $X_d = X_q$ there is a clearly defined maximum speed at which rated current I_m can be driven with $\gamma = 0$, producing rated torque. It is given by point **Q** in Fig. 7.7, where the voltage-limit circle is just large enough to intersect the current-limit circle with $I_q = I_m$ and $I_d = 0$.

The phasor diagram at **Q** is shown in Fig. 7.8, and

$$\left[\frac{V_m}{X_d}\right]^2 = \left[\frac{E_{q1}}{X_d}\right]^2 + I_m^2. \quad (7.31)$$

In this equation X_d and E_{q1} are both proportional to speed or frequency ω, but I_m and V_m are fixed. If we substitute $X_d = \omega L_d$ and $E_{q1} = \omega\Psi_{1Md}$, we can arrange it to give the "corner frequency":

$$\omega_Q = \frac{V_m}{\sqrt{\Psi_{1Md}^2 + (L_d I_m)^2}}. \quad (7.32)$$

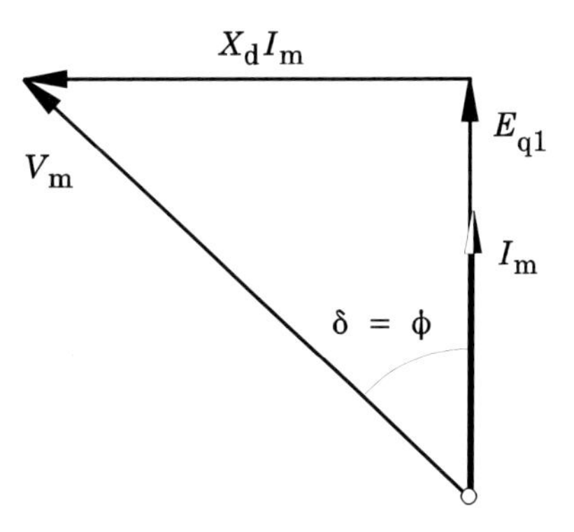

Fig. 7.8 Phasor diagram at **Q**

The corresponding speed in rpm is $N_Q = \omega_Q / p \times 30/\pi$. This speed is called the **corner speed**. It is the point on the torque/speed characteristic at which the torque begins to fall.

The torque is proportional to I_q, so constant-torque loci in Figs. 7.7 and 7.9 are horizontal lines. Also, for any point **B** along **CQ**,

$$I_q = \frac{V_m}{X_d} \cdot \frac{I_m}{I_{sc}} \quad (7.33)$$

Since V_m, I_m and I_{sc} are constant while $X_d \propto \omega$, we find that $I_q \propto 1/\omega$ and therefore the power is constant along **CQ**.

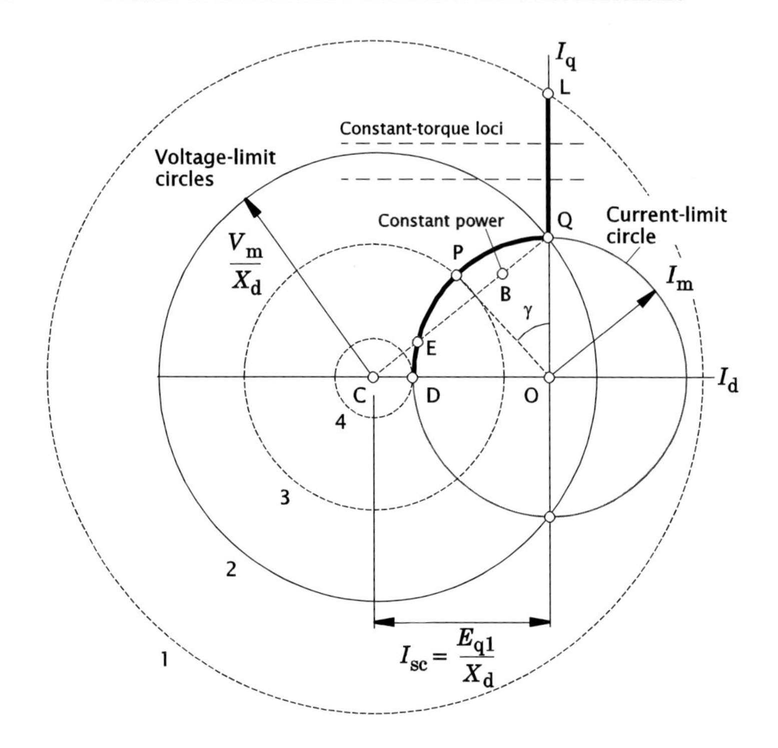

Fig. 7.9 Circle diagram for nonsalient-pole motor

At speeds higher than N_Q it is still possible to drive rated current I_m into the motor, but not at the maximum-torque angle $\gamma = 0$. We can therefore begin to formulate a control strategy for achieving maximum torque at any speed, as follows.

As the speed and frequency increase, the voltage-limit circle shrinks and the intersection with the rated-current circle moves along the arc **QD.** To illustrate this, Fig. 7.9 shows the conditions at four different speeds, $N_1 < N_2 < N_3 < N_4$. At **Q**, $N_Q = N_2$. The maximum torque at any speed is obtained at the intersection point.

At low speed (circle 1) the voltage-limit circle completely encloses the current-limit circle, which means that the current I_m can be driven into the machine with any phase angle. The current could even be increased up to the value **OL**, approximately twice I_m, under the control of the current regulator; this would be an example of short-term overload at low speed.

With increasing speed the voltage-limit circle shrinks, until at the corner speed N_Q we see the maximum permissible current I_m being driven with $\gamma = 0$, circle 2. Circle 3 shows operation at a higher speed **P**, still with $I = I_m$, but only by using phase advance γ as shown. The torque is reduced by the factor $\cos \gamma$, but the power is greater than it was at the corner speed, since **P** is above the constant-power line **CQ**.

Eventually a speed is reached at which the current I_m can be driven only along the negative d-axis, circle 4. All the current is now used for flux suppression or flux weakening, and none of it is available to produce torque. The maximum speed is at point **D**, with zero torque. To achieve this point the current regulator must operate with a phase advance of $\gamma = 90°$ and maximum current.

Maximum achievable speed in motoring — The speed N_D at which point **D** is reached is related to the corner speed N_Q by

$$\frac{N_Q}{N_D} = \frac{\mathrm{CD}}{\mathrm{CQ}} = \frac{\mathrm{OC} - \mathrm{OQ}}{\mathrm{CQ}} = \frac{\mathrm{OC}}{\mathrm{CQ}} - \sqrt{1 - \left[\frac{\mathrm{OC}}{\mathrm{CQ}}\right]^2}. \tag{7.34}$$

But $\mathrm{OC/CQ} = (E_Q/X_d)/(V_m/X_d) = E_Q/V_m = \omega_Q \Psi_{1Md}/V_m = u$, where E_Q is the value of E_{q1} at the corner speed. We can call u the **per-unit EMF**. Taking the inverse ratio N_D/N_Q, we get

$$\frac{N_D}{N_Q} = \frac{1}{u - \sqrt{1 - u^2}}. \tag{7.35}$$

For a solution to exist at a positive speed, we must have

$$\frac{1}{\sqrt{2}} < u < 1. \tag{7.36}$$

If $u = 1$, $N_D = N_Q$, and CD = CQ. This cannot be attained in practice because it would require **C** to be infinitely far to the left in Fig. 7.9, indicating a motor with such low inductance that I_{sc} is infinitely greater than I_m. While it is not a practical condition, it begins to suggest that low inductance is somehow associated with a limited speed range above the corner speed.

If $u = 1/\sqrt{2}$ the maximum speed N_D is infinite. This corresponds to Fig. 7.8 with $\phi = 45°$, in which the motor has so much inductance that its power-factor at the corner speed is only $\cos \phi = 0{\cdot}707$.

Example — The motor EMF is 90% of the maximum fundamental inverter voltage at 4000 rpm. Estimate the maximum attainable speed, neglecting losses.

We have $u = E_Q/V_m = 0{\cdot}9$, so from eqn. (7.35), $N_D = N_Q/[0{\cdot}9 - \surd(1 - 0{\cdot}9^2)] = 2{\cdot}155\,N_Q = 2{\cdot}155 \times 4{,}000 = 8{,}620$ rpm.

Example — A nonsalient-pole sinewave motor is required to maintain maximum torque at speeds up to a corner speed of 3,000 rpm, and to be capable of just reaching 9,000 rpm with no torque.

(a) Estimate the ratio of EMF to maximum fundamental inverter voltage at the corner speed.

(b) Draw the phasor diagram at the corner speed, and determine the power factor at this point.

(c) Draw the phasor diagram at the maximum speed.

(a) We have $N_D/N_Q = 3$, so according to eqn. (7.35),

$$3 = \frac{1}{u - \sqrt{1 - u^2}} \tag{7.37}$$

This is a quadratic equation with solution $u = 0{\cdot}85385$, so E_Q/V_m must be no higher than $0{\cdot}85385$.

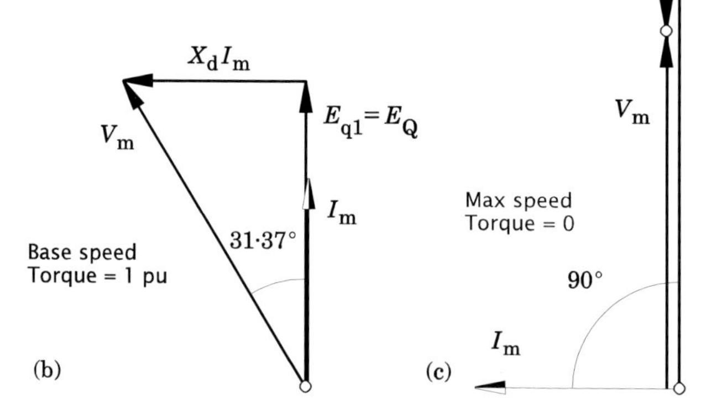

(b) Power factor $\cos\phi = E_Q/V_m = u = 0{\cdot}85385$. Angle $\phi = 31{\cdot}367°$. Hence $V_m = E_Q/u = E_Q/0{\cdot}85385 = 1{\cdot}17116\,E_Q$.

Also $X_d I_m = E_Q \tan\phi = V_m \sin\phi = 0{\cdot}60961 E_Q$.

(c) $E_{q1} = 3E_Q$. The current phase-advance is $\gamma = 90°$ and the current remains the same, I_m. V_m also remains the same, but $X_d I_d$ is increased to $3 \times 0{\cdot}60961 E_Q = 1{\cdot}82884 E_Q$. Check that $1{\cdot}82884 E_Q + 1{\cdot}17116 E_Q = 3E_Q$. The phasor diagrams for (b) and (c) are as shown (to scale).

The ratio of the speeds N_D and N_Q can also be expressed in terms of the reactance or inductance of the motor. From Fig. 7.9,

$$\frac{N_D}{N_Q} = \frac{CQ}{CD} = \frac{CQ}{OC - OD} = \frac{\sqrt{OC^2 + OQ^2}}{OC - OQ}. \tag{7.38}$$

But OQ = I_m and OC = I_{sc}, the short-circuit current. We can define the **per-unit short-circuit current**, normalized to I_m, as

$$s = \frac{I_{sc}}{I_m} = \frac{E_{q1}}{X_d I_m} = \frac{\Psi_{1Md}}{L_d I_m} = \frac{u}{x}. \tag{7.39}$$

In this we have included the definition of the **per-unit *d*-axis synchronous reactance** as $x = X_d/(V_m/I_m)$ — in other words, using V_m/I_m from the inverter to define the base impedance. Substituting these definitions in eqn. (7.31) we get

$$u^2 + x^2 = 1, \tag{7.40}$$

which expresses the phasor diagram of Fig. 7.8 in per-unit terms. And if we substitute eqns. (7.39) and (7.40) in eqn. (7.38) we get

$$\frac{N_D}{N_Q} = \frac{\sqrt{s^2 + 1}}{s - 1} = \frac{\sqrt{u^2 + x^2}}{u - x} = \frac{1}{\sqrt{1 - x^2} - x}, \tag{7.41}$$

as well as confirmation of eqn. (7.35). When $s = 1$, $u = x = 1/\sqrt{2}$: these are the same conditions we saw in Fig. 7.8, and again the maximum speed is infinite. From eqn. (7.41) it is clear that if $x = 0$ there is no speed range above the corner speed, since $N_D/N_Q = 1$.

It appears from eqns. (7.39) and (7.40) that s, x and u are not independent, and this leads to the conclusion that the torque/speed characteristic of the lossless nonsalient-pole motor depends on a single parameter, at least as far as its shape and per-unit properties are concerned. This makes it possible to derive an analytical expression for the **speed range over which constant power can be maintained**, as follows. Referring to Fig. 7.9, constant power can be maintained from **Q** to **E**, and ω_E/ω_Q = CQ/CE. Working in per-unit, we have $CE^2 = 1 + s^2$, while the equation of the line **CQ** is

$$i_q = \frac{i_d}{s} + 1. \tag{7.42}$$

On the current-limit circle $i_d^2 + i_q^2 = 1$, and if we solve this together with eqn. (7.42) we can find the per-unit value i_d at **E**:

$$i_d = \frac{-2s}{1 + s^2}. \tag{7.43}$$

Using this it is straightforward to calculate CQ/CE, obtaining

$$\omega_E = \frac{1 + s^2}{s^2 - 1}\omega_Q \tag{7.44}$$

In a typical surface-magnet PM brushless motor/drive we might have $u = 0{\cdot}9$, which gives $x = 0{\cdot}436$ and $s = 2{\cdot}065$. Eqn. (7.44) gives the speed range over which constant power can be maintained as $\omega_E/\omega_Q = 1{\cdot}613$, and eqn. (7.41) the maximum speed $\omega_D = 2{\cdot}15\,\omega_Q$.

It is emphasized that u, x and s are defined in relation to the *combination* of the motor and the drive, since the normalization involves I_m and V_m which are *inverter* parameters.

We have seen that inductance is necessary for flux-weakening. A motor with no inductance cannot run faster than its corner speed. The need for inductance is obvious in that flux-weakening is an inductive magnetostatic effect. With inductance comes a reduction in power factor, as we saw in Fig. 7.8 and on p. 341. Inductance makes the system more responsive to phase advance, but only at the expense of additional flux-linkage that is in phase with the current and unable to contribute directly to the torque.

External inductance in series with the machine is subject to the same reading. It is effective in countering the EMF only to the extent that the current is advanced in phase to $\gamma = 90°$, but since this reduces the torque to zero, it would seem to be self-defeating unless the objective is to get high speed with very low torque.

The use of phase advance to overcome the rising EMF can also be explained in terms of Fig. 6.27, but with a sinusoidal EMF waveform. The action of the inductance in sustaining the current flow after the instantaneous EMF has risen above the driving voltage is exactly the same as in the squarewave drive; however, as already mentioned, the squarewave drive cannot benefit from the powerful analysis based on the phasor diagram and the voltage-limit circle.

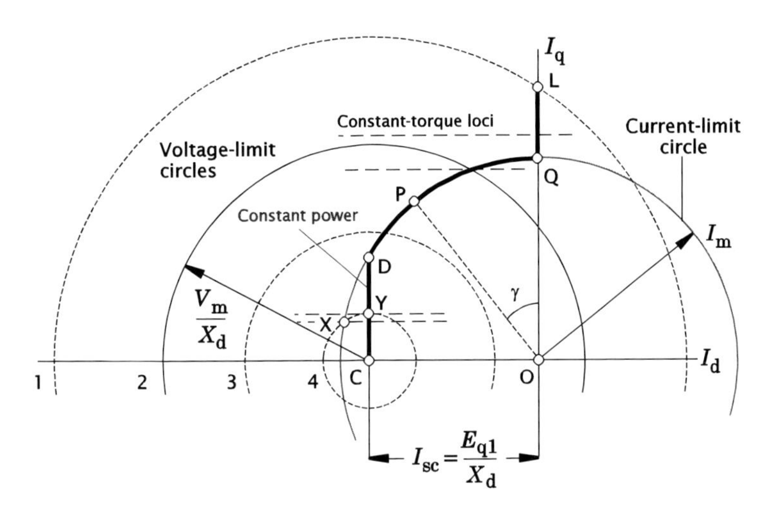

Fig. 7.10 Circle diagram with oversized inverter

Oversized inverter — Up to now we have tacitly assumed that **C** is outside the current-limit circle: that is, $I_{sc} > I_m$, meaning that the maximum current available from the inverter is less than the short-circuit current of the motor. Fig. 7.10 is drawn for the same motor as in Fig. 7.9, but with I_m increased by 50% so that now $I_m > I_{sc}$. The maximum voltage V_m is unchanged. The inverter rating is increased by 50% and we can say that it is **oversized** relative to I_{sc}.

Consider operation at a high speed such that the voltage-limit locus is circle 4. There is still an intersection **X** with the maximum-current circle; but the torque is higher, and the current lower, at **Y**. Once I_d has increased to I_{sc}, the *d*-axis flux of the magnet is completely suppressed and there is no point in driving it negative. This observation gives rise to the operating mode **CD**, in which I_d is held constant while the torque is controlled by I_q. It is self-evident that the power along **CD** is constant. Moreover, there is no limit to the speed, since the torque does not reach zero until the voltage-limit circles have collapsed to point **C** at infinite speed. This mode of operation could not be contemplated with $I_{sc} > I_m$ because the torque was always maximized at the intersection of the voltage-limit circle and the current-limit circle. On a practical point, it might be pointed out that this flux-suppression mode is inherently sensitive to errors in the phase angle γ and to changes in operating temperature.

In Fig. 7.9, constant-power operation was possible only from **Q** to **E**, and the maximum speed was limited to N_D, but oversizing the inverter extends the constant-power operating range to infinite speed, remembering of course that the theory is for a lossless machine. The optimum rating I_m and the amount of any oversizing must be determined by detailed calculations that try to match the torque/speed characteristic with the requirements of the load, and this level of calculation can only be done with the use of specialist simulation programs that take losses and saturation into account.

This is an important point because the sheer size and cost of an inverter capable of serious flux-weakening can easily be lost in academic theories about infinite maximum speeds — especially when the ratings are in per-unit, normalized to the short-circuit current which is typically a very large current.

When the inverter is "oversized", the speed is no longer limited by the maximum current available from the inverter. This is just another way of saying that if the inverter is big enough, it can supply whatever current is necessary to suppress the EMF. Anyone familiar with field-weakening in DC drives could be forgiven for questioning the cost-effectiveness of over-sizing an expensive *inverter* for this purpose, particularly as it is being used to suppress the immutable flux of expensive magnets.

Discussion example — How can the motor produce any torque, if its flux is completely suppressed by flux-weakening?

This is a deep question, but one way to look at it is like this. Consider that the magnet flux Φ_M is exactly countered by the armature-reaction flux of the stator, Φ_A, and consider that these two fluxes exist separately. The magnet flux Φ_M produces torque by interacting with the q-axis current I_q in the normal way. But the armature-reaction flux Φ_A does not produce any torque : it is like the flux in a fixed inductor, in which there is no question of torque production. In fact some of the armature-reaction flux can be said to be in the leakage inductances, which are, in effect, fixed inductors. It is even immaterial whether the fixed inductors of armature-reaction are inside the machine or outside: what matters is that the resulting voltage-drop is in phase opposition to the EMF produced by the magnet.

For this argument to hold up, the machine must be magnetically linear (that is, no saturation), so that the principle of superposition can be used to justify considering the two fluxes as separate. *Also*, the machine must have no saliency, because the MMF of armature reaction most definitely *does* produce torque — reluctance torque — in a salient-pole machine.

Operation of salient-pole motor/generator (IPM) — Fig. 7.11 shows the operation of an IPM with two inverter ratings I_{m1} and I_{m2}, with $I_{m2} > I_{sc} > I_{m1}$. With a salient-pole rotor (such as that of the IPM), we have reluctance torque as well as alignment torque, and if there is sufficient voltage the maximum torque is obtained with the phase advance γ_{Tmax} which was calculated earlier by eqn. (7.20) on p. 333, the torque being given by eqn. (7.19). Label **Q** is used in both cases in Fig. 7.11 for low-speed operation at γ_{Tmax}, in keeping with Figs. 7.9 and 7.10, even though the current is no longer entirely in the q-axis. Note that γ_{Tmax} is slightly larger when operating with the larger inverter at I_{m2}.

Because of the reluctance torque, the loci of constant torque are no longer horizontal straight lines, but rectangular hyperbolae derived by writing the torque equation

$$T = \frac{mp}{\omega} I_d' I_q \Delta X \tag{7.45}$$

where

$$\Delta X = X_d - X_q \quad \text{and} \quad I_d' = I_d + \frac{E_{q1}}{\Delta X}. \tag{7.46}$$

The asymptotes are the negative d-axis and a false q-axis which is shifted to the right of the true q-axis by $E_{q1}/\Delta X$. (Also see Eqns. (7.73) and (7.74) on p. 356). The constant-torque loci are marked **T** in Fig. 7.11. The voltage-limit loci **V** form a series of ellipses, as before [eqn (7.30)]. For each ellipse the ratio between the major axis and the minor axis is the saliency ratio $\xi = X_q/X_d$. The generating and motoring modes are symmetrical if the machine is lossless and if it has the same saturated EMF and inductance in both modes.

With the smaller inverter $I_{m1} < I_{sc}$, and the operating modes are much the same as for the nonsalient-pole (surface-magnet) machine. At a certain speed the collapsing voltage-limit ellipse becomes too small for operation at **Q** with I_{m1} and γ_{Tmax}, and the maximum available torque at any speed is then found at the intersection between the voltage-limit ellipse for that speed and the current-limit circle at I_{m1}. This applies at all speeds from point **Q** down to point **D**. As with the nonsalient-pole machine, constant power can be sustained over only the lower-speed parts of the arc **QD**, and the maximum speed at **D** is finite.

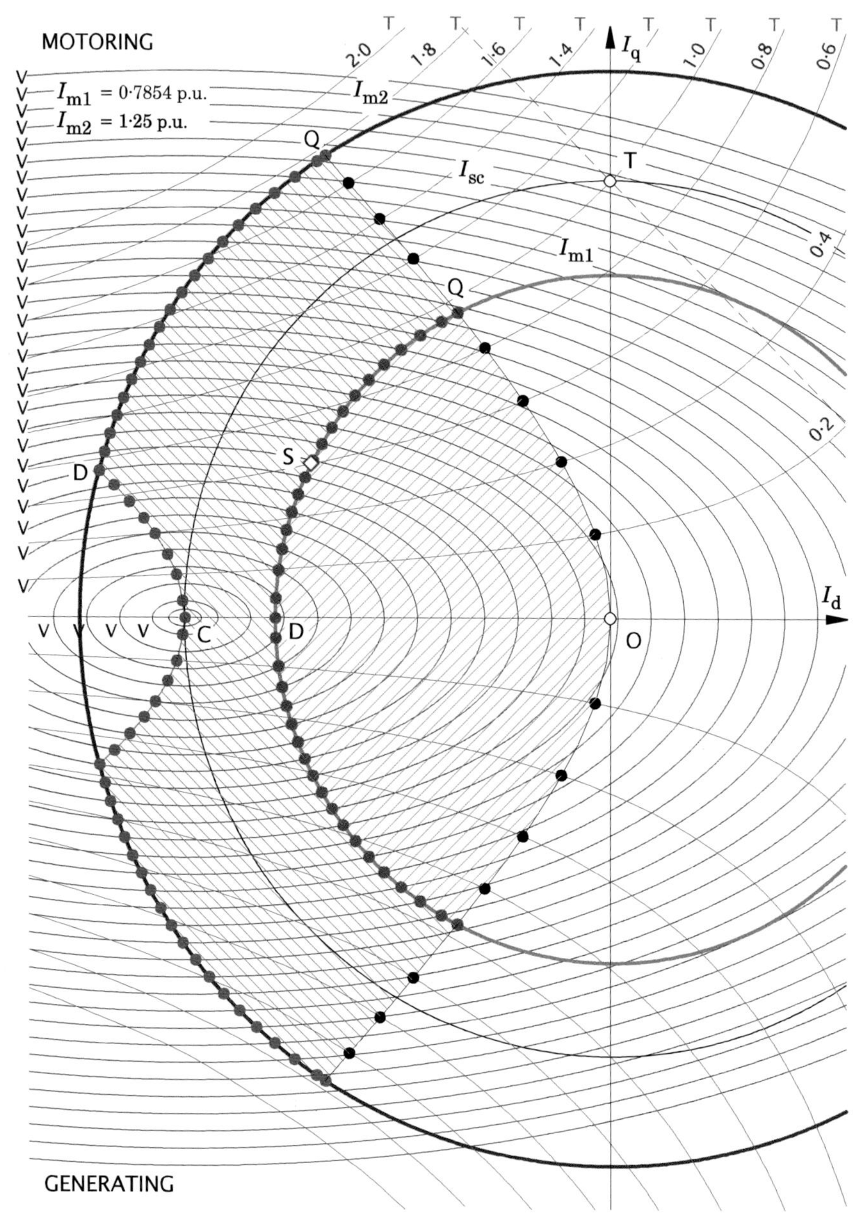

Fig. 7.11 Mode diagram for control of IPM motor or generator with $\xi = 2$

The hatched regions show the normal range of the current phasor for the appropriate inverter.

With the larger inverter $I_{m2} > I_{sc}$, and the lossless machine is capable of attaining infinite speed. As with the vertical segment **DC** in the operating locus in Fig. 7.10, above a certain speed at **D** the maximum torque becomes the *voltage*-limited maximum torque obtained using eqns. (7.22–24) with $I < I_{m2}$, less than the maximum available current. This condition is maintained along **DC** up to infinite speed. Even though I_{m2} could still be achieved at the lower end of this speed range, there would be no advantage.

Earlier comments about the sensitivity of the control apply to the IPM control as well: at high speed the flux-weakening in Fig. 7.11 is extreme, and any error in γ, or a change of magnet temperature, could cause significant error in the current. In the lower-speed part of the high-speed region **DC**, the inverter may have more capacity to force d-axis current than what is actually required, and there is theoretically an increased risk of demagnetization in this range.

7.1.4 Calculation of the torque/speed characteristic

The torque/speed characteristic is best calculated in per-unit form to reduce the number of independent variables while treating the motor and drive as one. In §7.1.3 (p. 343) for the nonsalient-pole machine we used a per-unit system based on the *inverter* parameters V_m and I_m, but here the base quantities will be chosen from the *machine*, because this makes it easier to manage the greater complexity of the salient-pole machine. The inverter parameters V_m and I_m are just as easily incorporated in this per-unit system.[49]

With the saliency ratio defined as $\xi = X_q/X_d$ (normally > 1), neglecting resistance and losses, we have

$$\begin{aligned} V_d &= -\xi X_d I_q; \\ V_q &= \omega \Psi_{1md} + X_d I_d = E_{q1} + X_d I_d. \end{aligned} \tag{7.47}$$

The base current is chosen as the short-circuit current

$$I_{sc} = \frac{E_{q1}}{X_d}. \tag{7.48}$$

---

[49] The per-unit equations are more powerful than might appear from their simple form. The per-unit system used in §7.1.4 works with V/E rather than the earlier E/V, and with a different current base. Please be careful!

The base voltage for normalization is chosen to be the open-circuit EMF at the base speed ω_0 elec rad/s, that is, $E_0 = \omega_0 \Psi_{1Md}$, where ω_0 is arbitrary. Normalizing eqns. (7.47) to these base quantities, with $\Omega = \omega/\omega_0$ the per-unit speed and p.u. quantities in lower-case, we get

$$\begin{aligned} v_d &= -\xi \Omega i_q ; \\ v_q &= \Omega (1 + i_d). \end{aligned} \tag{7.49}$$

It is implicit in the choice of base current and base voltage that the per-unit synchronous reactance in the d-axis is 1·0 p.u. at 1 p.u. speed and frequency, while in the q-axis it is ξ. In general,

$$x_d = \Omega \text{ p.u.} ; \qquad x_q = \xi \Omega \text{ p.u.} \tag{7.50}$$

Also the per-unit EMF is $e = 1$ at 1 p.u. speed and frequency. In general it is given by

$$e = \Omega. \tag{7.51}$$

In ordinary units the torque is given as a function of I_d and I_q by eqn. (7.10). With m phases the base power is $P_0 = m E_0 I_0$, so the base torque is $T_0 = P_0/(\omega_0/p)$, where (ω_0/p) is the base mechanical speed. Eqn. (7.10) is normalized by dividing both sides by the appropriate base values, giving the per-unit "current-limited" torque equation

$$\tau = i_q [1 - (\xi - 1) i_d]. \tag{7.52}$$

Substituting $i_d = -i \sin \gamma$ and $i_q = i \cos \gamma$, where i is the per-unit phase current, we get this equation in terms of i and γ :

$$\tau = i \cos \gamma \, [1 + (\xi - 1) i \sin \gamma]. \tag{7.53}$$

Again we can see that the reluctance torque is zero if $\xi = 1$ (no saliency). In salient-pole PM brushless machines usually $\xi > 1$, so i_d must be negative (demagnetizing) to get positive reluctance torque.

If we substitute eqns. (7.49) in eqn. (7.52), we get the per-unit form of the "voltage-limited" torque equation

$$\tau = -\frac{v_d}{\Omega} \left[1 - \frac{v_q}{\Omega} \left(1 - \frac{1}{\xi} \right) \right]. \tag{7.54}$$

Substituting $v_d = -v \sin \delta$ and $v_q = v \cos \delta$, where v is the per-unit phase voltage, we get

$$\tau = \frac{v \sin \delta}{\Omega}\left[1 - \frac{v \cos \delta}{\Omega}\left(\frac{\xi - 1}{\xi}\right)\right]. \tag{7.55}$$

The second term in eqn. (7.55) is not the same as the reluctance torque in eqn. (7.52). (This is clear when deriving eqn. (7.54) from eqn. (7.52)). The "reluctance" term in eqn. (7.54) or (7.55) is positive only if $v_q < 0$ which means that the flux in the d-axis has been *reversed*. The maximum torque thus occurs at a value of δ where the current is extremely high and demagnetizing, as we can see in Fig. 7.11 along **DC** with the large inverter. To avoid demagnetization at this point, the magnet should have a straight recoil line extending into the 3rd quadrant, even at its maximum operating temperature.[50]

From zero speed to the corner point — Along **OQ**, up to the corner speed, there is enough voltage to work at γ_{Tmax}, which is obtained by differentiating eqn. (7.53) with respect to γ:

$$\sin \gamma_{Tmax} = \frac{-1 \pm \sqrt{1 + 8 i^2 (\xi - 1)^2}}{4 i (\xi - 1)} \tag{7.56}$$

This is the per-unit form of eqn. (7.20), and the corner speed is the maximum speed at which rated current can be fed to the motor at the optimum phase angle γ_{Tmax}. We now obtain the current components $i_{dTmax} = -i \sin \gamma_{Tmax}$ and $i_{qTmax} = i \cos \gamma_{Tmax}$. If we substitute $i = i_m$ ($= I_m/I_{sc}$), we have the currents and the torque at the corner point **Q**. For example, the smaller inverter in Fig. 7.11 has $i_{m1} = 0{\cdot}7854$ and $\xi = 2$, and eqn. (7.56) gives $\gamma_{Tmax} = 27{\cdot}2°$, so **Q** is drawn with $i = 0{\cdot}7854\, e^{j(90+27\cdot2)°} = -0{\cdot}359 + j0{\cdot}699$ p.u. (See Fig. 7.12).

Point **Q** defines the corner speed precisely as the maximum speed at which rated current can be forced into the machine at the maximum-torque angle.[51] To find the *value* of this speed, we could use eqn. (7.32) on p. 339, or more generally from the intersection of the current-limit circle and the voltage-limit ellipse through **Q**.

---

[50] This point is experienced transiently in line-start motors during the final stages of start-up, when there is precious little screening from the rotor cage.

[51] The term *corner speed* is used in this chapter to avoid confusion with the base speed used in the normalization or per-unit system. The corner-point is always associated with label **Q** (not to be confused with "q" *qua* quadrature-axis).

If $i_m = I_m/I_{sc}$ is the maximum per-unit current available from the drive, we can express the current-limit circle as

$$i_d^2 + i_q^2 = i_m^2. \tag{7.57}$$

The voltage-limit ellipse eqn. (7.30) is expressed in terms of i_d and i_q in per-unit as

$$\xi^2 i_q^2 + (1 + i_d)^2 = \frac{v_m^2}{\Omega^2} = w_m^2 \tag{7.58}$$

where $w_m = v_m/\Omega$ and $v_m = V_m/E_0$ is the maximum per-unit voltage available from the drive. The centre of the voltage-limit ellipse **C** is at the short-circuit point $i_d = -1$, $i_q = 0$; see Fig. 7.11.

If we write

$$q_d = 1 + i_d \tag{7.59}$$

then the voltage-limit eqn. (7.58) becomes [52]

$$\xi^2 i_q^2 + q_d^2 = \frac{v_m^2}{\Omega^2} = w_m^2. \tag{7.60}$$

We can calculate Ω for any operating condition if we rearrange eqn. (7.60) to give Ω directly:

$$\Omega = \frac{v_m}{\sqrt{\xi^2 i_q^2 + (1 + i_d)^2}}. \tag{7.61}$$

For example at the corner point

$$\Omega_Q = \frac{v_m}{\sqrt{2^2 \times 0{\cdot}699^2 + (1 - 0{\cdot}359)^2}} = 0{\cdot}6506\, v_m. \tag{7.62}$$

Thus if the available voltage is, say, 1·0 p.u., the corner speed ω_Q at **Q** for the smaller inverter is 0·6506 p.u.

---

[52] It is easy to locate points of interest on the voltage-limit ellipse, Fig. 7.11. When $i_d = -1$, $q_d = 0$ and $i_q = \pm v_m/\Omega\xi = \pm w_m/\xi$, which locates the maximum positive and negative values of i_q that can possibly be supplied within the voltage limitation of the drive at the per-unit speed Ω. When $i_q = 0$, $q_d = \pm w_m = \pm v_m/\Omega$, which locates the maximum positive and negative *d*-axis currents that can possibly be supplied, in both the magnetizing and demagnetizing directions.

Conversely, to operate at **Q** with a speed of 1·0 p.u. requires a voltage of 1/0·6506 = 1·537 p.u. Note also that w_m = 1·537 at this point. Eqn. (7.61) shows that the higher the saliency ratio, the lower the corner speed ω_Q.

Example — We will continue the example in Fig. 7.11 by defining base speed as 2400 rpm.[53] Then if the corner-point speed is 1·0 p.u., the voltage required to operate at γ_{Tmax} with a current of i_{m1} is v_m = 1·537 p.u. In ordinary units 1·0 p.u. voltage is the value of the EMF at the base speed, and this is given by $E_0 = \omega_0 \Psi_{1Md}$, where $\omega_0 = \pi/30 \times 2400 \times p$. In terms of the EMF constant k_E, defined as line-line peak volts per 1000 rpm on open-circuit, we would have

$$E_0 = k_E \times \frac{2400}{1000} \times \frac{1}{\sqrt{3}} \times \frac{1}{\sqrt{2}} \text{ V LN RMS} \tag{7.63}$$

for a wye-connected motor. Now assume k_E = 48 V/krpm, so E_0 = 47·0 V. The inverter voltage required at base speed is 1·537 × 47·0 = 72·3 V LN RMS, or 72·3 × √2 × √3 = 177 V LL peak.

For a nonsalient-pole machine with quadrature control, $i_d = 0$ and $i_q = i_m$, and with $\xi = 1$ eqn. (7.61) becomes

$$\Omega_Q = \frac{v_m}{\sqrt{1 + i_m^2}}. \tag{7.64}$$

This shows that the drive voltage must exceed the EMF at the corner speed, and if $i_m = 1$ and $\Omega_Q = 1$ we get $v_m = \sqrt{2}$, as in Fig. 7.8.

At speeds above the corner speed the torque can still be maximized by working at the intersection of the voltage-limit ellipse and the current-limit circle, as we see in qualitative terms in Fig. 7.11. But it is no longer possible to sustain i_m at γ_{Tmax}, and additional flux-weakening by phase advance becomes necessary. The intersection is obtained by solving equations (7.57) and (7.58). If we substitute $i_q^2 = i_m^2 - i_d^2$ from eqn. (7.57) into eqn. (7.58), we have

$$(1 - \xi^2) i_d^2 + 2 i_d + (1 + \xi^2 i_m^2 - w_m^2) = 0, \tag{7.65}$$

which is a quadratic equation that can be solved for i_d. There can be intersections at one or at most two values of i_d, with two values of i_q at each one, and the solution is given by

---

[53] This figure is normally decided in relation to the load requirements.

$$i_d = \frac{1 \mp \sqrt{1 + (\xi^2 - 1)(1 + \xi^2 i_m{}^2 - w_m{}^2)}}{\xi^2 - 1}. \qquad (7.66)$$

A necessary (but not sufficient) condition for intersection is that

$$w_m{}^2 \leq 1 + \xi^2 i_m{}^2 + \frac{1}{\xi^2 - 1}. \qquad (7.67)$$

If w_m exceeds this value, the ellipse encloses the current-limit circle and the voltage does not limit the current or its phase angle.

Example — Suppose the speed in the previous example is increased from 1·0 to 2·0 p.u.: then $\Omega = 2{\cdot}0$. If the voltage v_m remains the same, we have $w_m = 1{\cdot}537/2{\cdot}0 = 0{\cdot}7685$. With $i_m = 0{\cdot}7854$ p.u., eqn. (7.67) gives $3{\cdot}8 > w_m{}^2$, so we expect intersections between the voltage-limit ellipse and the current-limit circle at two values of i_d. From eqn. (7.66),

$$\begin{aligned} i_d &= \frac{1 \mp \sqrt{(1 + (2^2 - 1)(1 + 2^2 \times 0{\cdot}7854^2 - 0{\cdot}7685^2))}}{2^2 - 1} \\ &= \frac{1 \mp 3{\cdot}103}{3} = 1{\cdot}367 \; or \; -0{\cdot}701. \end{aligned} \qquad (7.68)$$

The first solution exceeds the rated current ($i_{m1} = 0{\cdot}7854$ p.u.), but the second is valid with $i_q = \surd(0{\cdot}7854^2 - 0{\cdot}701^2) = 0{\cdot}354$ p.u., or $I = (-0{\cdot}701 + j\,0{\cdot}354)I_{sc}$. This point is marked in Fig. 7.11 with a small diamond at **S** on the arc **QD.**

The RMS current is the same as it was at the corner speed, which was made equal to 1 p.u. speed in the per-unit system by choosing an inverter with voltage $v_m = 1{\cdot}537$ p.u. However, the flux-weakening component i_d has increased from $-0{\cdot}359$ p.u. to $-0{\cdot}701$ p.u., while i_q has decreased from 0·699 p.u. to 0·354 p.u.

From eqn. (7.52) the torque at the corner speed at **Q** is given by

$$\tau_Q = 0{\cdot}699 \times [1 - (2 - 1) \times (-0{\cdot}359)] = 0{\cdot}949 \quad \text{p.u.} \qquad (7.69)$$

and at $\Omega = 2{\cdot}0$ times corner speed by

$$\tau_S = 0{\cdot}354 \times [1 - (2 - 1) \times (-0{\cdot}701)] = 0{\cdot}602 \quad \text{p.u.} \qquad (7.70)$$

which is only 63·4% of the value at corner speed. However, the *power* is 0·602 × 2·0 = 1·204 p.u., which is 26.8% greater than the power at corner speed. Along **QD** the power is not constant but rises and falls back to the corner-speed value.

The component voltages are $v_d = -\Omega\xi\, i_q = -2{\cdot}0 \times 2 \times 0{\cdot}354 = -1{\cdot}416$ p.u. and $v_q = \Omega\,(1 + i_d) = 2{\cdot}0 \times (1 - 0{\cdot}701) = 0{\cdot}598$ p.u.; that is, $\mathbf{v} = 1{\cdot}537e^{j157^\circ}$. The per-unit magnitudes of the reactive voltage drops are $\Omega x_d i_d = 2{\cdot}0 \times 1{\cdot}0 \times 0{\cdot}701 = 1{\cdot}402$ p.u. and $\Omega x_q i_q = 2{\cdot}0 \times 2 \times 0{\cdot}354 = 1{\cdot}416$ p.u. Of course the EMF is increased to 2·0 p.u. The phasor diagram is drawn to scale in Fig. 7.12.

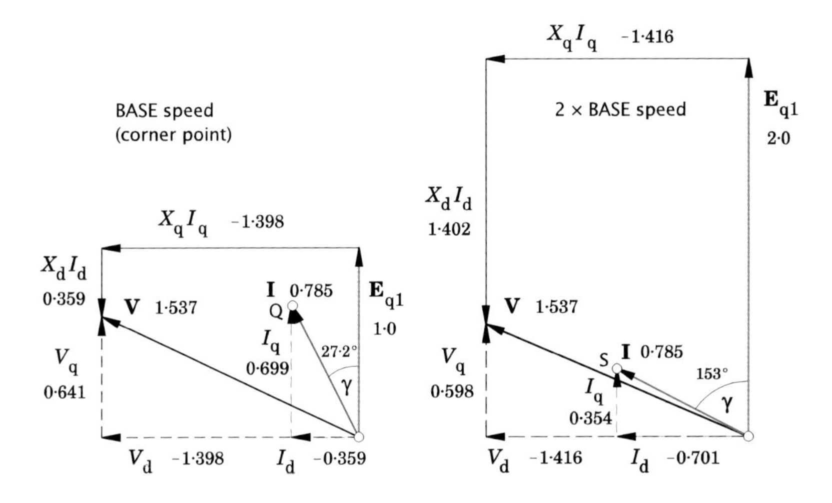

Fig. 7.12 Phasor diagram for numerical example

Again, with a lossless motor the maximum speed that is theoretically attainable is when the current is at its rated value and entirely in the negative d-axis, giving the maximum possible flux-weakening effect. The torque is zero with $i_q = 0$. From eqn. (7.60), with $i_d = - i_m$ and $\gamma = 90°$,

$$\Omega = \frac{v_m}{1 + i_d} = \frac{v_m}{1 - i_m}. \tag{7.71}$$

Example — Continuing the earlier example we have $v_m = 1{\cdot}537$ and $i_{m1} = 0{\cdot}7854$ for the smaller inverter in Fig. 7.11, indicating that the maximum speed will be $1{\cdot}537/(1 - 0{\cdot}7854) = 7{\cdot}16$ times the corner speed.

The larger drive in Fig. 7.11 has $i_{m2} = 1{\cdot}25$ p.u. and therefore has the capacity to supply 1·25 times the short-circuit current of the machine, so it can increase the speed without limit. Along **DC** for this larger drive, the maximum torque is found from eqn. (7.55), with δ_{Tmax} having been found by means of eqn. (7.23) with

$$\zeta = \frac{1}{w\beta}, \tag{7.72}$$

where $w = v/\Omega$ and $\beta = (\xi - 1)/\xi$ in eqn. (7.55).

So far we have woven a numerical example into the theoretical story. We defined the base voltage as the EMF at the base speed of 2400 rpm: $E_0 = 47$ V LN RMS in eqn. (7.63) on p. 353. To complete the example in ordinary units we must define the base current I_0, which has not been mentioned except to define it as the short-circuit current I_{sc}. We have seen nothing to define this current in *amps*, and in fact the entire account up to this point is completely general, meaning that it applies to *any* machine with $E_0 = 47$ V at a base speed of 2400 rpm and a saliency ratio $\xi = 2$. For the sake of completeness, suppose the example machine has a short-circuit current of 130 A. The currents in amperes can now be added.

Example — Find the currents in amperes for the example used in this section.

First note that the base current $I_0 = I_{sc}$ is defined as RMS line current, assuming wye connection. The ratings of the smaller inverter is therefore $I_{m1} = i_{m1} \times I_{sc} = 0{\cdot}7854 \times 130 = 102$ A; and of the larger one, $I_{m2} = i_{m2} \times I_{sc} = 1{\cdot}25 \times 130 = 162{\cdot}5$ A.

From p. 350, base power is $P_0 = mE_0I_0 = 3 \times 47 \times 130 = 18{\cdot}33$ kW, and if the base speed is 2400 rpm or 251·3 rad/s, the base torque must be 18,330/251·3 = 72·9 Nm. This is the torque whose locus is marked 1·0 on the I_{m1} circle in Fig. 7.11. Note that is passes through the I_q axis at $I_q = I_{sc}$, that is, $i_q = 1$. This is consistent with the torque equations (7.52) and (7.53) and reflects the fact that the base torque is defined with a phase-advance angle $\gamma = 0$.

Referring back to the example on p. 354, the torque values in ordinary units are $T_Q = \tau_Q \times T_0 = 0{\cdot}949 \times 72{\cdot}9 = 69{\cdot}2$ Nm, and at double speed $T_S = \tau_S \times T_0 = 0{\cdot}602 \times 72{\cdot}9 = 43{\cdot}9$ Nm. The corresponding powers are $0{\cdot}949 \times 18{\cdot}33 = 17{\cdot}4$ kW at **Q**, and $0{\cdot}602 \times 2 \times 18{\cdot}33 = 22{\cdot}1$ kW at **S**.

With the calculated values of torque in [Nm] we can revisit the constant-torque loci in eqns. (7.45) and (7.46) on p. 347. Eqn. (7.52) on p. 350 is the per-unit torque equation, and it can be written

$$\tau = i_q j_d \tag{7.73}$$

if we define the offset current

$$j_d = 1 - (\xi - 1) i_d . \tag{7.74}$$

When $i_d = 0$, $j_d = 1$ and $\tau = i_q$. Consequently with $i_q = 1$ (or $I_q = I_{sc}$) point **T** in Fig. 7.11 defines the base torque. Eqns. (7.73) and (7.74) also show that the constant-torque loci are symmetric about the false q-axis at $j_d = 0$ or $i_d = 1/(\xi - 1)$. In the example, this is at $i_d = 1$.

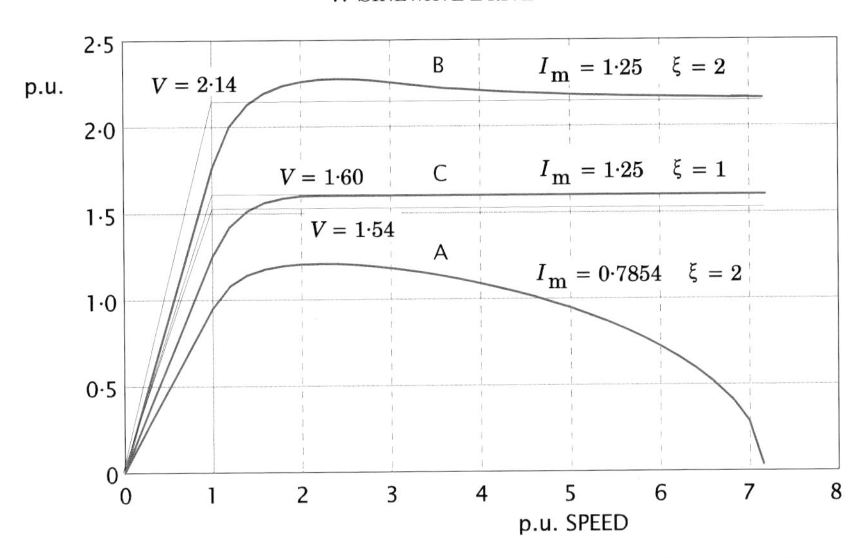

Fig. 7.13 Power/speed and voltage/speed comparison of three motor/drives

Calculated characteristic curves — The power/speed curves of three motor/drives are compared in Fig. 7.13, together with the **voltage curves** which have not been discussed in detail up to now:

A The motor/drive of Fig. 7.11 with saliency ratio $\xi = 2$, with the smaller inverter $I_{m1} = 0.7854$ p.u., having a voltage rating of 1·54 p.u. and a kVA rating of $0{\cdot}7854 \times 1{\cdot}54 = 1{\cdot}21$ p.u.

B The same motor as in **A**, with the larger inverter $I_{m2} = 1{\cdot}25$ p.u., having a voltage rating of 2·14 p.u. and a kVA rating of $1{\cdot}25 \times 2{\cdot}14 = 2{\cdot}675$ p.u.

C A nonsalient-pole motor with the same EMF as motor **A**, with the same X_d and the same I_{sc}, but no saliency. The inverter current rating is increased to 1·25, and the voltage rating to 1·60 p.u., giving a kVA rating of $1{\cdot}25 \times 1{\cdot}60 = 2{\cdot}00$ p.u.

All three motors have the same EMF and short-circuit current, so the comparison mainly shows the effect of the inverter size. As expected, the larger inverter not only increases the power at a given speed, but it also increases the speed range over which constant power can be maintained. Because of the increased voltage required with the higher current, the larger inverter in Fig. 7.11 has a kVA rating that is $2{\cdot}675/1{\cdot}20 = 2{\cdot}23$ times the rating of the smaller one.

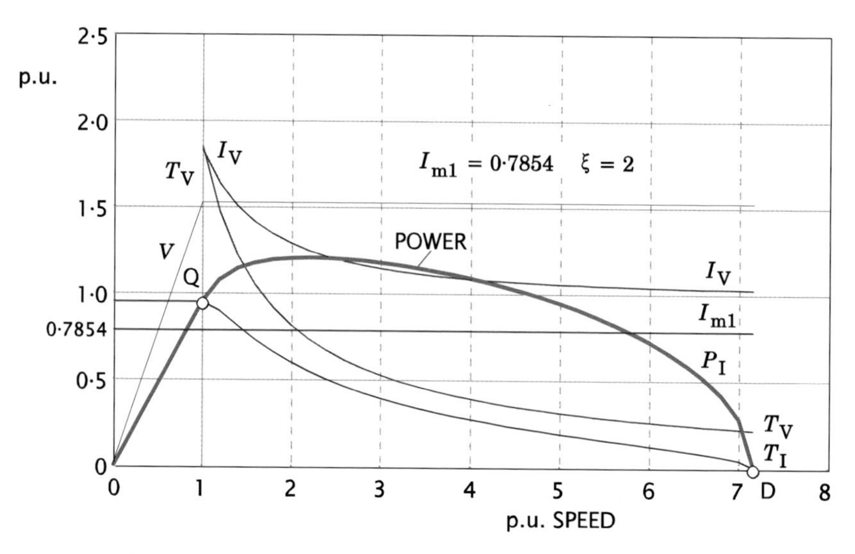

Fig. 7.14 Drive **A** of Fig. 7.11 with the smaller inverter I_{m1}

We are now in a position to study the detailed characteristics of the three individual motor/drives. In all cases the "optimal" control strategy is used: that is, the current and phase advance are selected for maximum torque at any attainable speed.

The characteristics of drive **A** are plotted in Fig. 7.14 with the smaller inverter I_{m1}, (kVA rating 1·21 p.u.). The current is equal to the maximum inverter current I_{m1} at all speeds above the corner point **Q**. The torque labelled T_I reaches zero at 7·16 p.u. speed or 17,184 rpm, calculated on p. 355.

The maximum power P_I exceeds the corner-point value (0·949 p.u. or 17·4 kW) at speeds up to about 4·8 p.u., rising to a peak of about 1·21 p.u. at 2·2 p.u. speed. This shows that the definition of "speed range at constant power" is open to interpretation, since the maximum power is not constant.

The power factor falls off at an increasing rate at speeds above about 5 p.u., because the power is decreasing while the voltage and current remain constant. The flux-weakening takes up a reactive kVA that increases as a proportion of the kVA of the inverter.

Fig. 7.14 also shows the voltage-limited torque and current T_V and I_V; they are not used, since $I_V > I_{m2}$.

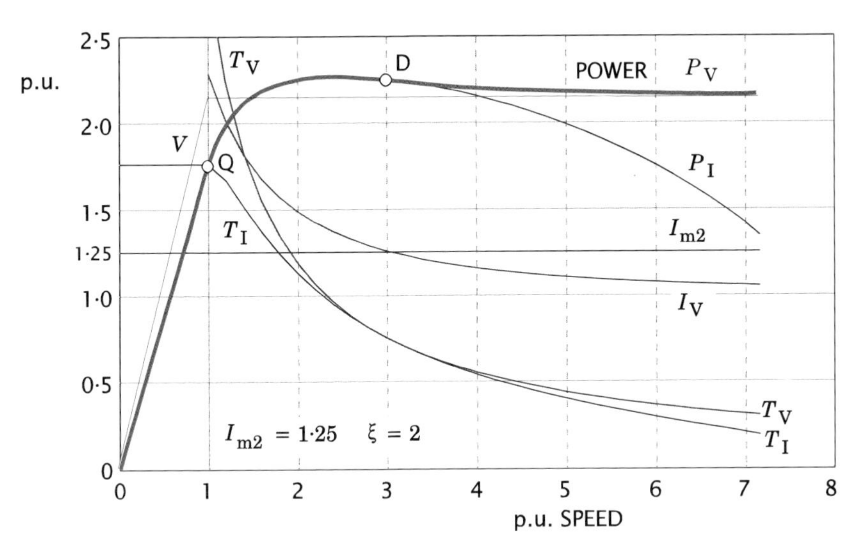

Fig. 7.15 Drive **B** of Fig. 7.11 with the larger inverter I_{m2}

The characteristics of drive **B** are plotted in Fig. 7.15 with the larger inverter I_{m2}, (kVA rating 2·675 p.u.).

Again it is evident that increasing the size of the inverter greatly increases not only the available power at a given speed, but also the speed range over which constant power can be maintained. The maximum power is maintained above 2·1 p.u. (38·5 kW) over the entire speed range, with effectively infinite speed range. It peaks at about 2·28 p.u. (42·7 kW) at about 2·4 p.u. speed (5,760 rpm).

At **D** there is a changeover to operation with δ_{Tmax} from the "voltage-limited" torque equation. This mode corresponds to the segment **DC** in Fig. 7.11. The changeover speed at **D** is 3 p.u. The current is still controlled, but its value is smaller than I_{m2}, and indeed this mode is used only if the required current is less than I_{m2}. This control mode also sustains and even increases the power-factor as the speed increases, since the power and voltage are both constant while the current is falling.

As in the case of drive **A**, extreme flux-weakening is required to operate at the higher speeds above **D**. Although the speed range above **D** appears quite wide, the current phasor is confined to a relatively small region in the phasor diagram, Fig. 7.11.

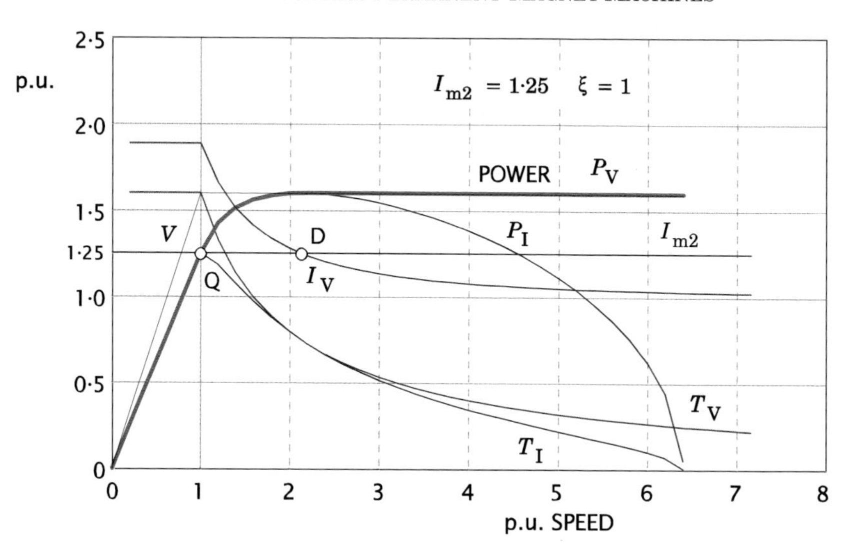

Fig. 7.16 Torque/speed characteristic of the motor/drive of Fig. 7.11

Finally Fig. 7.16 shows the characteristics of the nonsalient-pole (surface-magnet) machine **C** with the inverter whose current rating is I_{m2}. The only difference between this machine and the others is that X_q is reduced to the same value as X_d. The voltage requirement is therefore lower, and the kVA rating of the inverter is only 2·0 p.u.

Again we see that increasing the size of the inverter increases not only the available power at a given speed, but also the speed range over which constant power can be maintained. In this case we have a true constant-power characteristic at 1·6 p.u. (29·3 kW) with effectively infinite speed range.

Again there is a changeover to operation with δ_{Tmax} from the "voltage-limited" torque equation, corresponding to the segment **DC** in Fig. 7.10. The changeover speed at **D** is 2·14 p.u. The d-axis current remains constant at $i_d = -1$ p.u., indicating 100% flux-weakening, so that there is no d-axis flux-linkage and no induced voltage in the q-axis; the EMF is completely suppressed. The q-axis current i_q decreases with increasing speed, and the torque decreases proportionally. (See the discussion example on p. 346). As in cases **A** and **B**, extreme flux-weakening is required to operate at the higher speeds above **D**.

7.1.5 The synchronous reluctance motor

The synchronous reluctance motor (Chapter 2) can be treated as a salient-pole PM motor with no EMF. Continuing with the idealized lossless machine, eqns. (7.47) on p. 349 become

$$\begin{aligned} V_\mathrm{d} &= -\xi X_\mathrm{d} I_\mathrm{q}; \\ V_\mathrm{q} &= X_\mathrm{d} I_\mathrm{d}. \end{aligned} \tag{7.75}$$

With no EMF, there is no short-circuit current. Therefore we do not have the same base quantities for normalization that we used for the IPM in the previous section. Let the maximum inverter current I_m be chosen as the base current, I_0,[54] and let the base voltage V_0 be chosen as $X_\mathrm{d} I_\mathrm{m}$, where X_d is the d-axis synchronous reactance at the base frequency ω_0. The reactance at any other frequency ω is equal to ΩX_d, where $\Omega = \omega/\omega_0$, and likewise with X_q. With the base quantities consistently defined we can now normalize eqns. (7.75):

$$\begin{aligned} v_\mathrm{d} &= -\xi \Omega i_\mathrm{q}; \\ v_\mathrm{q} &= \Omega i_\mathrm{d}. \end{aligned} \tag{7.76}$$

The per-unit reactances are again found to be

$$x_\mathrm{d} = \Omega; \quad x_\mathrm{q} = \xi\Omega. \tag{7.77}$$

The per-unit torque is obtained from eqn. (7.52):

$$\tau = -(\xi - 1) i_\mathrm{q} i_\mathrm{d}. \tag{7.78}$$

Substituting $i_\mathrm{d} = -i \sin\gamma$ and $i_\mathrm{q} = i\cos\gamma$, where i is the per-unit phase current, we get this equation in terms of i and γ :

$$\tau = (\xi - 1)\frac{i^2}{2} \sin 2\gamma. \tag{7.79}$$

Again the reluctance torque is zero if $\xi = 1$ (no saliency). If we define the q-axis to be the most inductive axis, then $\xi > 1$, and i_d must again be negative to get positive reluctance torque. A negative i_d is neither magnetizing nor demagnetizing, since there are no magnets. The negative sign is purely a consequence of choosing d,q reference axes to be consistent with the earlier treatment of the IPM.

---

[54] As before, I_m is the RMS value of the line current, assuming wye connection.

For current-limited operation the maximum torque occurs at the phase advance angle $\gamma_{Tmax} = \pi/4$ or 45°.

If we substitute eqns. (7.76) in eqn. (7.78), we get the per-unit form of the "voltage-limited" torque equation

$$\tau = \frac{\xi - 1}{\xi} \frac{v_d}{\Omega} \frac{v_q}{\Omega}. \tag{7.80}$$

Substituting $v_d = -v \sin \delta$ and $v_q = v \cos \delta$, where v is the per-unit phase voltage and δ is the angle between the voltage and the q-axis,

$$\tau = -\frac{\xi - 1}{\xi} \frac{v^2}{2\Omega^2} \sin 2\delta. \tag{7.81}$$

Maximum torque thus occurs when $\delta = 3\pi/4$ or 135°.

We thus have two operating modes: the current-limited mode of eqns. (7.78) and (7.79), and the voltage-limited mode of eqns. (7.80) and (7.81). As before, the current-limited mode can be used without restriction at low speed, but before we can examine higher speeds we need to define the corner-point. (See Fig. 7.17).

The current-limit circle is still described by eqn. (7.57) on p. 352, but the voltage-limit ellipse becomes centred on the origin with

$$\xi^2 i_q^2 + i_d^2 = \frac{v_m^2}{\Omega^2}. \tag{7.82}$$

We can calculate Ω for any operating condition if we rearrange eqn. (7.82) to give Ω directly:

$$\Omega = \frac{v_m}{\sqrt{\xi^2 i_q^2 + i_d^2}}. \tag{7.83}$$

The corner point is defined as the highest speed at which the current i_m (1 p.u.) can be driven at the phase angle $\gamma_{Tmax} = 45^\circ$, that is, with $-i_d = i_q = i_m/\sqrt{2}$, and in this case eqn. (7.83) gives

$$\Omega = \frac{v_m \sqrt{2}}{i_m \sqrt{\xi^2 + 1}}. \tag{7.84}$$

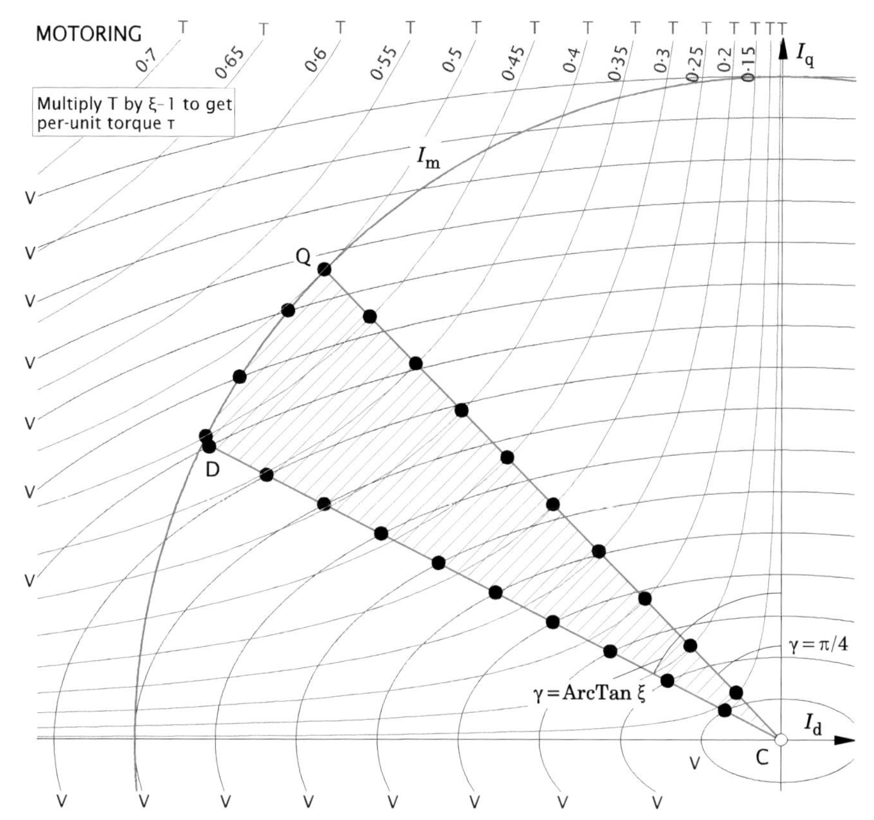

Fig. 7.17 Mode diagram for synchronous reluctance motor with ξ = 2.

As on p. 352, it appears that we have the choice of defining the corner point to be at 1 p.u. speed or 1 p.u. voltage. If we define it as 1 p.u. speed with $\Omega = 1$ and $i_m = 1$, the required voltage is $\sqrt{[(\xi^2 + 1)/2]}$ p.u. For example if $\xi = 5$, $v_m = \sqrt{13} = 3{\cdot}6$ p.u. Conversely, if we define it as the speed at which the required voltage is $v_m = 1$ p.u. with $i_m = 1$, then the speed is $\sqrt{[2/(\xi^2 + 1)]}$ p.u. With $\xi = 5$, this is 0·277 p.u.

The intersection is found by solving eqns. (7.57) with eqn. (7.82):

$$i_d = -\sqrt{\frac{\xi^2 i_m{}^2 - (v_m/\Omega)^2}{\xi^2 - 1}}; \quad i_q = \sqrt{i_m{}^2 - i_d{}^2}. \tag{7.85}$$

If $v_m/\Omega < i_m$, the ellipse is too small to interest the circle. Points along the arc **QD** in Fig. 7.17 are calculated using these equations.

Fig. 7.17 shows that above a certain speed, the intersection between the voltage-limit ellipse and the current-limit circle does not give the maximum possible torque: more torque is available by working on the voltage-limit ellipse, at the voltage phase angle δ_{Tmax} = 135°. This condition applies at speeds above point **D**, as in the voltage-limited operation of the nonsalient-pole motor along **DC** in Fig. 7.10 on p. 345, and the IPM in Fig. 7.11 on p. 348.

Along the voltage-limited maximum-torque locus **DC**, the voltage is given by

$$v_d = -v \sin \delta = -\frac{v}{\sqrt{2}}; \qquad v_q = v \cos \delta = -\frac{v}{\sqrt{2}} = v_d. \tag{7.86}$$

The current is obtained by substituting eqns. (7.76) in eqns. (7.86):

$$i_d = \frac{v_q}{\Omega} = -\frac{v}{\Omega\sqrt{2}}; \quad i_q = -\frac{v_d}{\Omega\xi} = \frac{v}{\Omega\xi\sqrt{2}}. \tag{7.87}$$

The ratio $-i_d/i_q$ gives the value of tan γ :

$$\tan \gamma = \frac{-i_d}{i_q} = \xi. \tag{7.88}$$

With the voltage-limit ellipse centred on the origin, the maximum speed of the lossless motor is theoretically infinite, regardless of the size of the inverter. Of course in practice losses render the torque small, useless, or zero long before the speed becomes infinite.

If ξ is very large, the torque is apparently maximized by making γ approach 90°, that is, with $i_q = 0$ and $i = -i_d$, and therefore $v_q = -v$ and $v_d = 0$. The machine is then operating with a lagging power factor of 0, and is indistinguishable from a reactor. Its torque, though maximized, is zero. All the current is in the *least* inductive axis (in our case the d-axis), and all the voltage is dropped across the d-axis synchronous reactance ΩX_d. The obvious invention is to add a weak magnet — one that does not generate enough EMF to take up too much of the voltage, but will provide some torque and improve the power factor. We then have, perhaps, what could be termed a **PM-assisted synchronous reluctance motor**, although generically it is no different from an IPM with a low per-unit EMF.

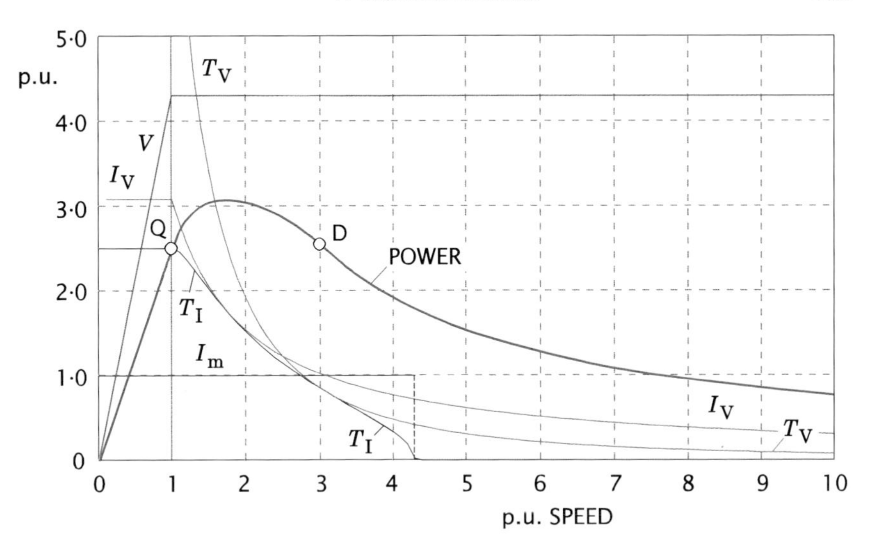

Fig. 7.18 Torque/speed characteristic of the motor/drive of Fig. 7.17

Fig. 7.18 shows the characteristics of a synchronous reluctance motor with a saliency ratio of $\xi = 6$, which is more or less typical of the values obtainable in practice with 4- or 6-pole machines. The corner-point speed is defined to be 1·0 p.u., so the voltage required at the corner point is $v_m = \sqrt{[(\xi^2 + 1)/2]} = 4{\cdot}3$ p.u., from eqn. (7.84).

The torque at the corner point is given by eqn. (7.78) with $i_d = -1/\sqrt{2}$ and $i_q = 1/\sqrt{2}$ p.u., so $\tau = -(6-1) \times (-1/\sqrt{2}) \times 1/\sqrt{2} = 2{\cdot}5$ p.u., and hence the power at the corner-point (with $\Omega = 1$) is 2·5 p.u. The power factor can be deduced as $2{\cdot}5/v_m i_m = 2{\cdot}5/4{\cdot}3 = 0{\cdot}58$ (lagging).

Maximum power of 3·07 p.u. occurs at about 1·75 p.u. speed, with maximum voltage 4·3 p.u. and maximum current $i_m = 1$ p.u., so the power factor is $3{\cdot}07/4{\cdot}3 = 0{\cdot}714$. The corner-point power can be maintained up to 3·0 p.u. speed at **D**. Above this speed the operating point moves on to the voltage-limited segment **DC** in Fig. 7.17, whence it makes a beeline for the origin with falling current and torque. The torque is maximized with a current that is less than I_m. (Note that I_m can be maintained up to a speed of about 4·3 p.u.)

In theory a true constant-power characteristic can be achieved only with an infinite saliency ratio, but with 4- and 6-pole machines the highest feasible value is only about 10.

Example — A synchronous reluctance motor has a d-axis synchronous reactance of 3·615 ohm at the frequency corresponding to a speed of 2400 rpm, and a saliency ratio of 6. It is fed by an inverter with a maximum line current of 10 A RMS. Calculate the maximum power and the required inverter voltage.

From Fig. 7.18 the maximum power is 3·07 p.u. and the required voltage is 4·3 p.u. Base voltage is $V_0 = X_d I_m = 3{\cdot}615 \times 10 = 36{\cdot}15$ V, so the required voltage in ordinary units is $V_m = 4{\cdot}3 \times 36{\cdot}15 = 155{\cdot}4$ V. This is the phase voltage or line-neutral voltage. The line-line voltage will be $\sqrt{3} \times 155{\cdot}4 = 269$ V RMS, assuming wye connection. Base power is $P_0 = 3V_0 I_0 = 3V_0 I_m = 3 \times 36{\cdot}15 \times 10 = 1084{\cdot}5$ W, so the maximum power is $3{\cdot}07 \times 1084{\cdot}5 = 3{\cdot}33$ kW. The current at the maximum power point is $I_m = 10$ A RMS.

Other controller strategies — Because this book is written by motor engineers, it is understandably preoccupied with the ultimate capability of the motor and its drive. But it is not always the objective to run the machine at maximum power. For example the synchronous reluctance motor can be operated at maximum power factor by using the phase angle[55]

$$\gamma = \mathrm{ArcTan}\,\sqrt{\xi}. \tag{7.89}$$

The maximum power-factor obtained with this control angle is

$$\cos\phi = \frac{\xi - 1}{\xi + 1}. \tag{7.90}$$

For example with a saliency ratio of 6, the maximum power factor is $(6 - 1)/(6 + 1) = 0{\cdot}714$, which we saw in Fig. 7.18 at the maximum-power point. Many other control strategies are possible, for example $\gamma = \mathrm{ArcTan}\ \xi$ which maximizes the potential rate of change of torque.[56]

Similar comments apply to the control of the surface-magnet and interior-magnet PM machines, where the objective may not be to maximize the power but to maintain high efficiency or to achieve rapid dynamic response.

---

[55] See Staton DA, Miller TJE and Wood SE [1993] *Maximising the saliency ratio of the synchronous reluctance motor*, IEE Proceedings-B, Vol.140, No.4, July 1993, pp. 249-259.

[56] See Chiba A and Fukao T [1992] *A closed-loop operation of super high-speed reluctance motor for quick torque response*, IEEE Trans. Ind. Appl., Vol. 28, May/June 1992, pp. 600-606.

7.1.6 Summary — calculated characteristics

We have used three different per-unit systems to simplify the *mathematics* of the SPM, the IPM, and the synchronous reluctance motor in turn, but the complexity of the operation and control of these machines remains far from trivial. We have also presented detailed examples in ordinary units, and explained how to convert between per-unit and ordinary units. The per-unit values can mask some important properties. For example, while the current is clear enough from a chart such as Fig. 7.11, the *voltage* requirement is not quite so explicit in this chart. For a full undertanding of the voltage limitations in ordinary units we have to go back to the voltage locus diagram, Fig. 7.6. Even then we must remember to multiply the voltage and the current, in volts and amps, to find the kVA rating of the inverter, which is what determines its size and cost.

Again, when we "normalized" the current of the IPM to I_{sc}, we were normalizing to the base of a very large current — sometimes (inappropriately) called the "characteristic current". There is nothing "normal" or "characteristic" about running a machine with 100% suppression of its flux. Of course it is done, especially in electric and hybrid vehicles, but it is an inelegant and brutal way to emulate the field-weakening performance of the separately-excited commutator machine. It can even be said to be an unnatural way to use "permanent" magnets — using an expensive inverter and a huge short-circuit current to annul the flux.

In the development of this subject we have seen the IPM developed to a high level, and the use of saliency has been an important theme. The underlying fact is that constant-power operation requires an inverter whose rating is commensurate with that of the motor. No amount of fiddling with characteristic currents and saliency ratios can get round the law of conservation of energy. This being so, what is important in the motor—even the lossless motor—is its *power factor*: how effectively it uses the volts and amps. The effect of saliency on power-factor is difficult to determine, mainly because saturation undermines the concept of reluctance torque (see p. 335) and makes the parameters vary. It may be desirable to forget about the distinction between alignment torque and reluctance torque, and concentrate on flux, current, total torque and power-factor.

7.2 Electronic control

Up to now we have assumed that the current is sinusoidal, that it is under the control of the drive inverter, and that it can provide the required fundamental voltage to the motor. None of this comes free.

This second part of our study of sinewave drives is intended as a motor engineer's view of the current regulator. It explains the principles of several important types of current-regulator, paying particular attention to the factors that affect the current waveform and the ability to provide the necessary voltage. The factors include the inductance and the EMF of the motor, and the current ripple and switching frequency of the inverter.

The treatment is at more or less the same level as in §7.1. Simple controllers are introduced with a description of their operation in real time, but the more sophisticated ones such as the space-vector controller and direct torque control (DTC) require the use of space vectors, for which the necessary theory is included. As a means of maintaining an overview of the subject, the voltage-locus diagram of Fig. 7.6 on p.336 should be helpful, and indeed the whole of §7.2 can be understood thoroughly with no more understanding of the requirements of the motor than what is in that diagram. Also the voltage capability of different controllers is summarized in Table 7.3 on p. 404 (§7.2.13).

The treatment of the current regulator includes enough theory to form the basis of simulations that include the motor and the drive.[57] Such simulations are important because the two elements must usually be considered together. The simplified theory based on lossless machines in the later parts of §7.1 does not take account of losses or saturation; nor does it take account of real-life limitations of the inverter other than the available fundamental voltage and current. In practice losses limit the speed and the torque to lower values than the ideal theory suggests. The same is true of effects in the inverter such as the thermal rating and the constraints on voltage, current, and switching frequency. The currents (and even more particularly, the voltages) produced by switchmode power electronics are rich in harmonics that must be taken into account.

---

[57] The *PC-BDC* program is an example.

7.2.1 The need for current regulation

Fig. 7.19(b) shows the most basic model of the motor. As the torque is essentially determined by the current, this model is enough to explain why current control is important.

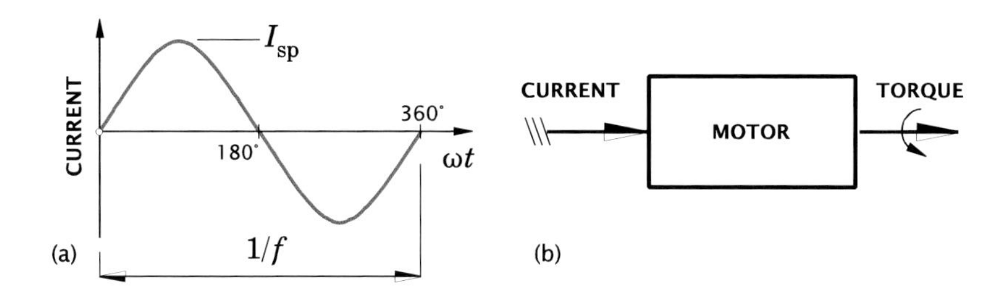

Fig. 7.19 Simple motor model

The current waveform controls the torque waveform, and motors are usually designed to produce smooth torque when the current waveform conforms to a particular shape. In "sinewave" motors this waveshape is sinusoidal, as in Fig. 7.19(a); ideally the EMF waveform is also nearly sinusoidal.

"Sinewave" motors are usually associated with high performance, which means smooth torque, rapid response, and a linear relationship between torque and current.[58] The sinewave current is defined by its peak value or amplitude I_{sp}, together with its fundamental frequency f and its phase angle γ relative to the EMF. If $\gamma > 0$, the phase of the current is advanced relative to the EMF.

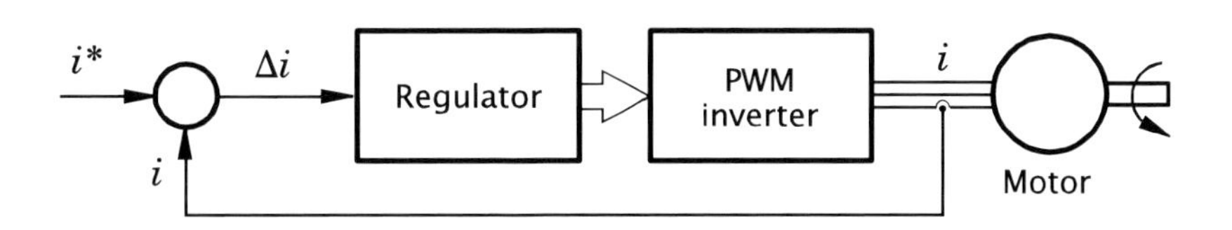

Fig. 7.20 Control block diagram

[58] The IPM or "interior permanent-magnet" motor is also usually a sinewave motor, but the torque/current relationship is non-linear because of saliency and saturation. Nevertheless, because of the advantages of this motor, (particularly its flux-weakening capability), it is sometimes used in spite of the nonlinearities. Modern control technology is capable of overcoming most of their negative effects.

The control of the phase angle usually requires a shaft position measurement, either by means of a resolver or encoder, or by means of a "sensorless" electronic equivalent which determines the rotor angle from measurements at the motor terminals while it is running.

Modern inverters operate in switched mode, in which the transistors are rapidly switched on and off. Control is implemented through the *timing* of the switching pulses, and this gives rise to the name *pulse-width modulation* or PWM. The inverter actually applies a *voltage* waveform to the motor, under the control of a closed-loop current-regulator, Fig. 7.20.

Current sensors feed the motor current i back to a comparator which generates the current error Δi, which is the difference between the reference (commanded) current i^* and the actual current i. The regulator and PWM generator together act as a high-gain amplifier which forces Δi to zero. The reference current is given by

$$i^* = I_{sp} \sin \omega t . \tag{7.91}$$

Closed-loop current-regulated PWM inverters can supply current waveforms close to the ideal sinusoidal waveform, provided that the voltage is sufficient to overcome the EMF and impedance of the motor. Close tracking of the reference signal requires high gain in the feedback loop, including integral as well as proportional gain. Advanced controllers often operate in dq axes, or in a coordinate system that rotates with the flux. This has the advantage that in the steady state the reference signal i^* is a DC signal, which can be tracked with zero steady-state error.

As we have seen, the required voltage increases with speed and current. When the required voltage approaches the maximum available inverter voltage, the current regulator begins to lose control, and the current waveform becomes distorted. We often speak of "saturation" of the current-regulator, or "overmodulation". In 3-phase inverters in the fully-saturated condition, the required voltage is so large that all PWM control is lost, and the inverter degenerates into "six-step" mode. Although this mode produces the maximum possible fundamental voltage, control is limited to the *phase* of this voltage with respect to the rotor position.

7.2.2 Historical development

The permanent-magnet synchronous machine was certainly known in the early 1950's. Although most permanent-magnet machines at that time were generators, motors were also manufactured, and the two-axis theory was used to analyze them. The motors were "line-start" motors supplied directly from the AC mains, without electronics.

In the 1970's the discovery of high-energy Samarium-Cobalt magnets gave new impetus to the development of permanent-magnet AC motors. Lower-energy ferrite magnets were already used in DC brush-type motors,[59] and improvements in these magnets also encouraged new work in AC line-start machines, notably by Brown Boveri (Isosyn motor, 1978) and Reliance Electric (1979). Some of these motors were used with inverters, but they were still "line-start" motors without shaft position sensing: their design drew heavily on the induction motor and the line-start synchronous reluctance motor, and they were not self-synchronous in the sense that modern servomotors and brushless DC motors are.

While brushless DC and line-start AC motors were emerging through the 1970's, many engineers envisaged the possibility of removing the rotor cage from the line-start AC motor and of feeding it with sinewave currents phase-shifted to maximize the torque per ampere. An account of such an investigation was reported by Lajoie-Mazenc, including a salient-pole IPM motor, self-synchronization by means of shaft encoder feedback, variable phase shift to optimize the torque production, and the use of a digital encoder signal to index a sinewave reference for the current waveform.

---

[59] The so-called "brushless DC" motor emerged at this time (mid-1970's), notably from Papst. This system is equivalent to a DC machine with electronic commutation, and it has been treated in chapter 6 and elsewhere in this book. Although the machine is physically similar to the AC brushless permanent-magnet machine, and in many cases identical, the method of driving it is fundamentally different. The brushless DC or "electronically commutated" motor, sometimes also known as the "squarewave" or "trapezoidal" motor, does not have a rotating ampere-conductor distribution. Since it does not have sine-distributed windings, phasor analysis and dq-axis theory are not applicable to it. Squarewave drive is usually applied with surface-magnet motors which have no "saliency" (i.e. $L_d = L_q$) and no reluctance torque. If squarewave drive is used with a salient-pole motor such as the IPM, the torque ripple will generally be substantial; see §6.4 .

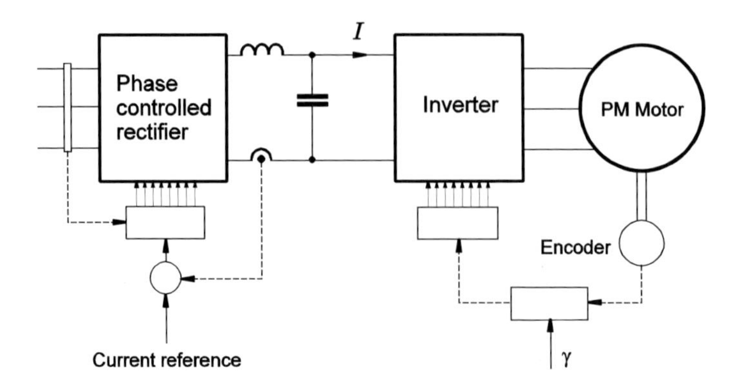

Fig. 7.21 Lajoie-Mazenc's I-γ controller (1983)

The architecture of Lajoie-Mazenc's controller is reproduced in Fig. 7.21. Although he used dq-axis theory in deriving equations for the optimum phase-shift angle, he did not describe what would now be termed a field-oriented dq controller. Nevertheless, it is an "I-γ controller" in the fullest sense in that it provides for the adjustment or control of the magnitude and phase of the current in the steady state, as discussed in the previous section. Since the current magnitude is determined in the rectifier upstream of the inverter, it is not possible for this controller to exercise direct independent control of I_d and I_q.

A field-oriented dq controller is one in which the d- and q-axis components of the current are controlled independently. Typically one of them is oriented to control the flux while the other is oriented to control the torque. In general this gives rise to a control block diagram in which the separate d- and q-axis components are identifiable, as well as the means of controlling them. An example is shown in Fig. 7.22. The block labelled **C** represents all the theory of operation described in §7.1, in that it takes a torque demand signal T^* and produces current demand signals i_d^* and i_q^* in dq-axes, representing the currents that are required in order to generate the demanded torque. The block labelled **2/3** converts these signals into line-current reference signals i_a^*, i_b^*, i_c^* for the current-regulator.

Whereas block **C** was the concern of §7.1, block **2/3** and the current regulator are the subject of §7.2.

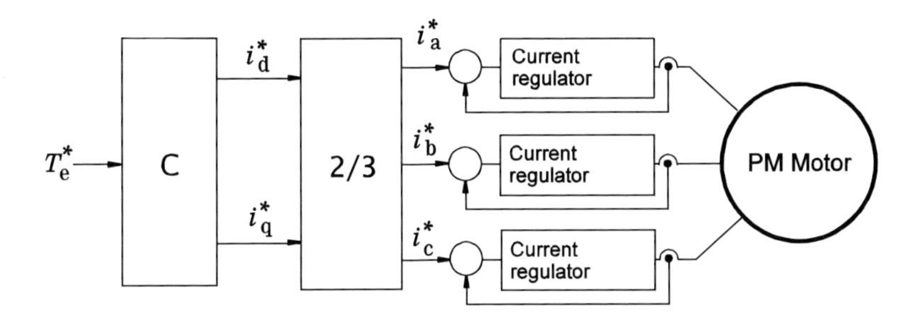

Fig. 7.22 Generic field-oriented dq controller (Jahns [1987])

7.2.3 Overview of controllers

The following controllers are considered in the remaining sections of this chapter.

1. Six-step, with no PWM or chopping.
2. Hysteresis-band current regulator.
3. dq_VV_CR, a primitive regulator based on a simple voltage-vector selection algorithm.[60]
4. The ramp-comparison regulator.
5. Sine-triangle voltage-PWM.
6. The synchronous regulator in dq axes.
7. The space-vector modulator with predictive control and overmodulation.
8. Direct torque control.

The first three controllers have the advantage of simplicity. They operate with very few control parameters and there is no need to consider proportional or integral gains. With the hysteresis and dq_VV_CR methods it is difficult to control the switching frequency precisely, and there is no orderly transition to six-step in the overmodulation range.

[60] "dq_VV_CR" is not a standard term. It has been used as one of the control options in the *PC-BDC* program for many years and is included here for its study value. It is not used in any products although it has been proven in the laboratory.

The remaining methods are derived from classic works published in the last 20 years. They require a progressively deeper theoretical understanding. Controllers 1–5 are **stationary regulators**, operating on the actual line currents in the stationary reference frame. By contrast, the **synchronous regulators** 6, 7 and 8 work in a frame of reference that is synchronous with the rotor or the total flux. The space-vector controller 7 of Prof. Holtz shows how space vectors link the digital switching in the controller to the complex-plane analytical models of the machine. The final controller DTC has the potential for fast response and avoids the problems of inductance and non-uniqueness discussed in §5.13 and on p. 335.

7.2.4 Switching representation by voltage vectors

Switching voltage vectors are extremely useful in analyzing and understanding the operation of three-phase current regulators. As well as providing visualization, their mathematical expression is the theoretical basis of some of the most advanced controllers. They also fit perfectly together with the motor theory in terms of phasors developed in §7.1.

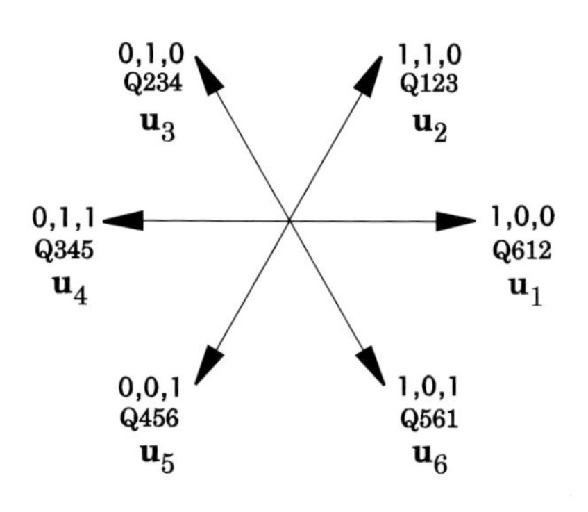

Fig. 7.23 Switching voltage vectors

The six voltage vectors in Fig. 7.23 correspond to the connection diagrams in Fig. 7.24, which show the polarities of the motor line terminals A,B,C corresponding to the states of the six transistors Q_1–Q_6 in the inverter bridge circuit, Fig. 6.1.

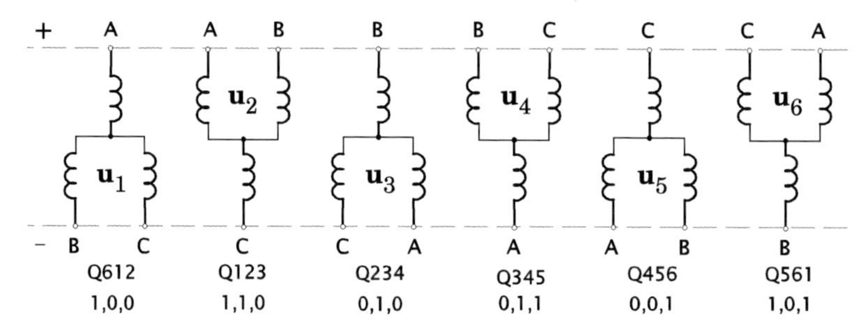

Fig. 7.24 Connections associated with the main non-zero voltage vectors

The transistors in Fig. 7.24 are numbered in the order of their conduction intervals in six-step mode. In sinewave drives it is normal to have three transistors conducting at any time, so the polarity of each motor line terminal is defined at all times by the state of the phaseleg to which it is connected.

Each of the six vectors in Fig. 7.23 corresponds to one of the connections in Fig. 7.24. For example, Q612 means that transistors 6,1 and 2 are on, so line A is connected to the positive terminal and lines B and C to the negative terminal.

We will see later that the voltage vectors are also represented by **space vectors** labelled $\mathbf{u}_1$, $\mathbf{u}_2$, ..., $\mathbf{u}_6$, corresponding exactly to their appearance in Fig. 7.23. These are complex numbers to be defined later. There are two additional voltage vectors (not shown in Figs. 7.23 and 7.24) which represent three-phase short-circuits or zero-voltage states. One of these is $\mathbf{u}_0$ = Q246, with all the lower transistors switched on. The other one is $\mathbf{u}_7$ = Q135, with all the upper transistors switched on. The total number of states is eight.

7.2.5 Six-step

In a simple "six-step" controller, each of the connections in Fig. 7.24 is held for 60°, and then it is followed by the next in sequence. In each 60° interval, the orientation of the stator ampere-conductor distribution (MMF vector) in the motor advances 60°, but not instantaneously because the inductance prevents abrupt changes of current and tends to make the current waveform more sinusoidal than the applied voltage waveform.

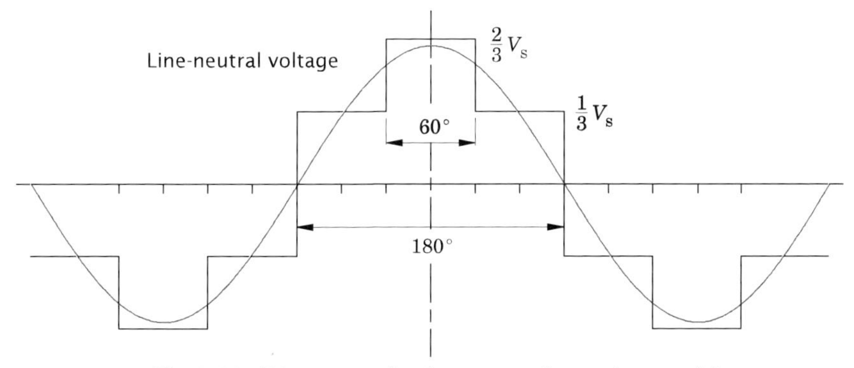

Fig. 7.25 Line-neutral voltage waveform; six-step drive

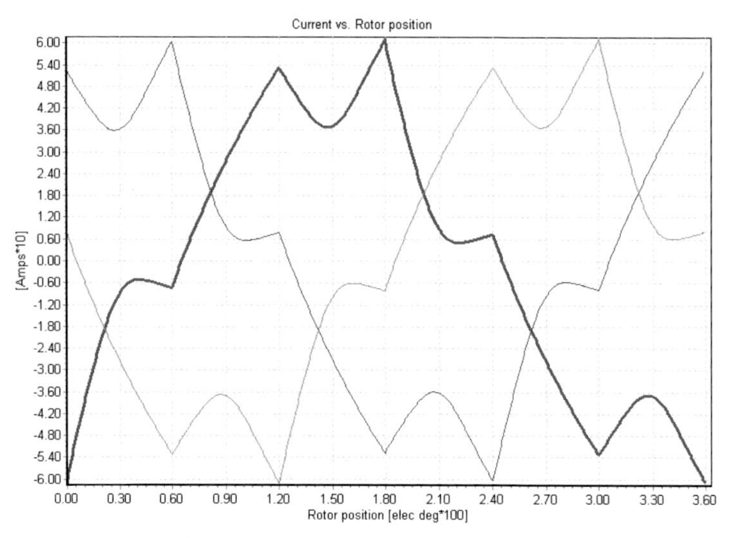

Fig. 7.26 Six-step current waveforms

Six-step switching results in the *line-neutral* voltage waveform shown in Fig. 7.25, and typical current waveforms are shown in Fig. 7.26. The fundamental of the line-neutral voltage has a peak value

$$V_{AN1} = \frac{2}{\pi} V_s, \tag{7.92}$$

and this is also shown in Fig. 7.25. In §7.2 we will work with the RMS value of the line-line voltage, and this is

$$V_{LL1} = V_{AN1} \times \frac{\sqrt{3}}{\sqrt{2}} = \frac{\sqrt{6}}{\pi} V_s = 0{\cdot}780\, V_s. \tag{7.93}$$

Six-step gives the **highest fundamental line-line voltage** possible with a 3-phase, 3-wire connection. It is used as a benchmark against which all other schemes are measured; see Table 7.3 on p. 404.

Six-step is the electronic equivalent of *full throttle*: it does not control the current or the voltage waveform, and the only means of regulation is the phase of the voltage relative to the rotor position. Some PWM controllers are capable of orderly migration towards six-step operation to maximize the speed range of the motor. In other cases this migration is impossible, or disorderly, as we shall see.

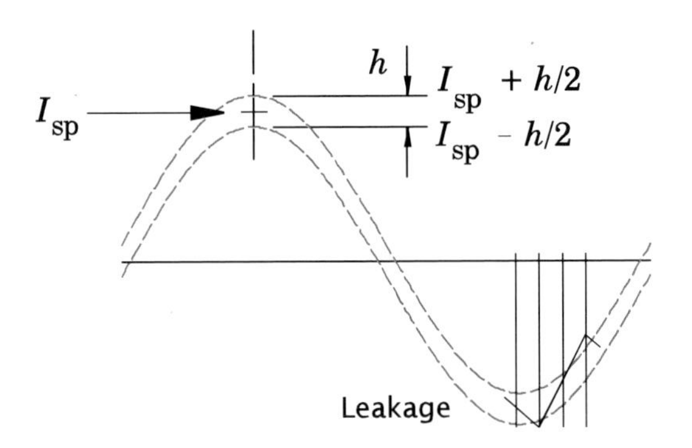

Fig. 7.27 Hysteresis-band current regulator

7.2.6 Hysteresis-band current regulator

The hysteresis-band is a pair of sinewaves, one higher and one lower than the reference sinewave of eqn. (7.91), Fig. 7.27. When the line current $i > I_{sp} + h/2$, the upper transistor in the appropriate phaseleg is switched off and the lower one is switched on. Conversely when $i < I_{sp} - h/2$ the upper transistor is switched on and the lower one switched off. h is called the *hysteresis band*. An example is shown in Fig. 7.29.

Obviously there is no control of the rate at which the transistors switch on and off, so the switching frequency is said to be *wild* or uncontrolled. It depends mainly on the voltage, the EMF, the inductance of the motor, and the sampling rate f_0.

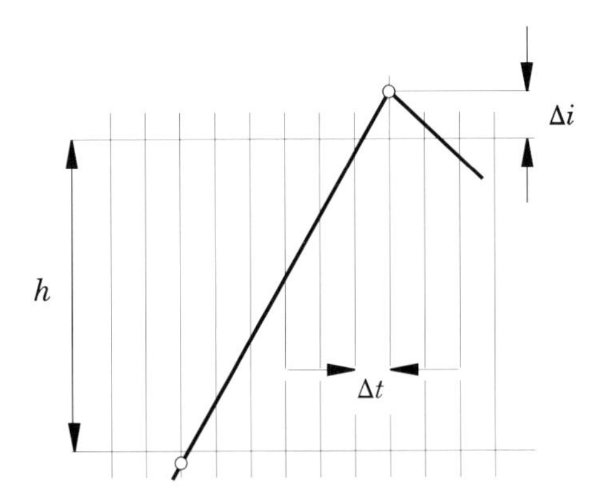

Fig. 7.28 Leakage outside the hysteresis band

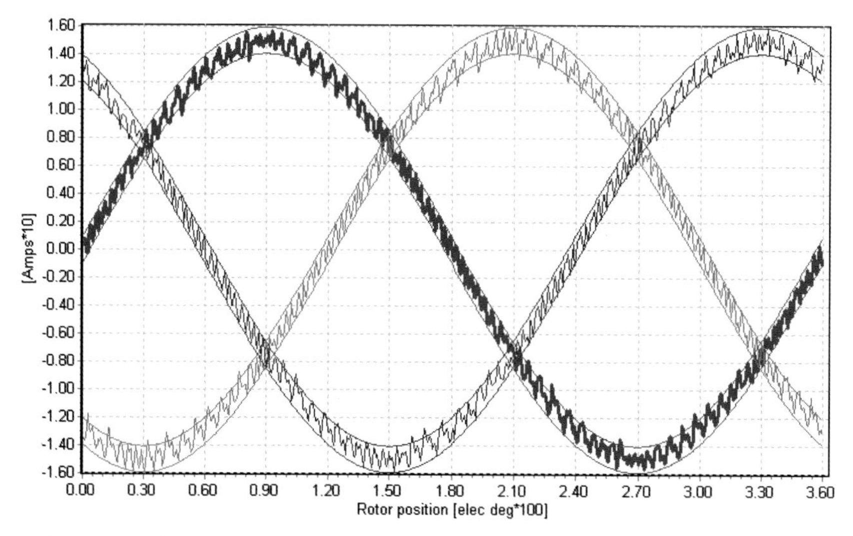

Fig. 7.29 Calculated current waveforms of hysteresis-band controller

The current can "leak" outside the hysteresis-band, as a result of the fixed sampling rate. A simple analysis of leakage is shown in Fig. 7.28. The sampling interval is $\Delta t = 1/f_0$, and switching events can occur only at discrete instants shown by the vertical lines. Suppose the current is changing at a rate $di/dt = m$. At the top of the diagram it just misses a possible switching opportunity, and has to wait Δt for the next one. The maximum leakage error is $\Delta i = m\Delta t$. In the worst case the same error can occur at the lower end of the hysteresis band, so the total error is $2\Delta i = 2m/f_0$. The relative error is $2m/f_0 h$, scaled to the size of the hysteresis band in amperes (h).

Now the time between switchings is of the order of h/m. The switching frequency is defined as $f_s = m/2h$, taking one *switching cycle* to be one "on" and one "off" for each transistor. From this we can express the relative leakage error as

$$\lambda = \frac{2\Delta i}{h} = \frac{2m/f_0 h}{m/h} = 4\frac{f_s}{f_0}. \tag{7.94}$$

This gives an idea of the sampling rate f_0 required to achieve a certain hysteresis-band within the constraint of a limited switching frequency f_s.

For example, if f_s is limited to 8 kHz and we want a leakage error within 10% of the hysteresis-band, $\lambda/h < 0{\cdot}1$ and we must sample at a rate f_0 no less than $4 \times 8/0{\cdot}1 = 320$ kHz — a surprisingly high value.

Because of the sinusoidal shape of the EMF and reference current waveforms, the switching cycle is susceptible to large variations, as shown in Fig. 7.30. This diagram shows three switching cycles, each of which is drawn on the assumption that the DC voltage v is three times the motor EMF e. If L is the incremental motor inductance, the positive slope of the rising current is approximately $(v - e)/L$ when the line terminal is positive, and approximately $-e/L$ when it is negative, so the slopes are in the ratio 2:1. The duration of cycle *abc* is t_1 and that of *def* is t_2, and t_1 and t_2 are not very different. But the duration t_3 of cycle *ghi* is much longer because the negative di/dt just happens to be similar to the negative slope of the reference current waveform. While this is not a rigorous analysis, it shows how the switching frequency can vary throughout one cycle, with lengthy intervals when there is no switching at all. This problem cannot be eliminated by making the hysteresis band h very small, even if it is made zero. (Operation with $h = 0$ is simetimes called *delta modulation*).

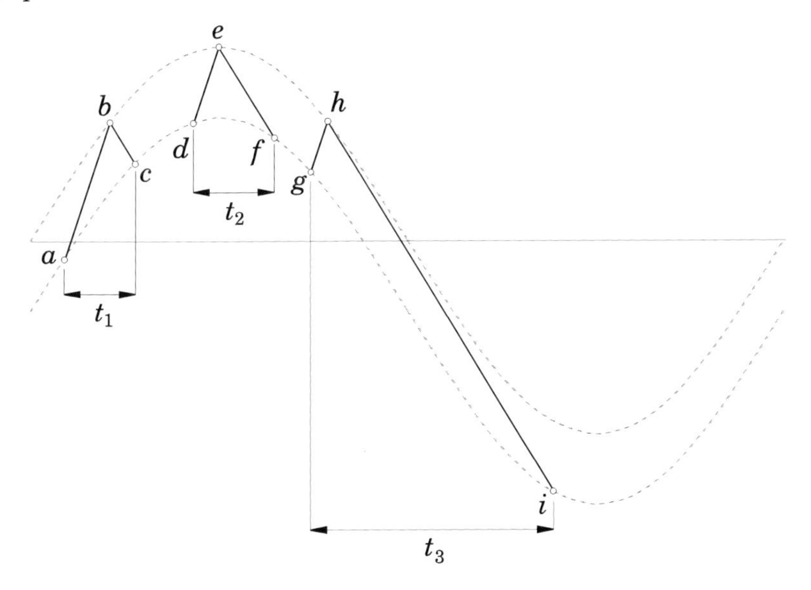

Fig. 7.30 Variation of switching frequency

Phaseleg switches must be protected against *shoot-through*, the short-circuiting of the DC supply voltage that can occur when both the upper and lower transistors are switched on simultaneously. There is a minimum interval between switching one transistor off and switching the complementary transistor on. This interval is called the *lockout time* or *dead time*, and it limits the switching frequency at which the regulator can work. The "authority" of the lockout protection is absolute, and when it acts to limit the switching frequency it can spoil the action of the regulator, resulting in a deviation of the current waveform from the reference sinewave through part of the cycle. The effect is not dissimiliar to what is seen in Fig. 7.30.

Yet another shortcoming of the hysteresis-band arises when all three line currents are regulated separately. With a 3-wire connection $i_A + i_B + i_C = 0$, so only two of the line currents can be independent and the third cannot be controlled independently. It is not obvious which of the three currents will be independent and which will be the "odd man out"; indeed it is not at all obvious what arbitrates this selection. But the end result is further distortion of the current waveform, and even different switching frequencies in the three phaselegs. The effect can be seen in Fig. 7.29.

It should be pointed out that Fig. 7.29 displays only every 32nd sample of the calculated waveforms, so there is an appreciable loss of information similar to that which occurs through aliasing in instruments of limited bandwidth. Consequently that display (and others like it) are only indicative of the actual behaviour.

A solution to the problem of variable switching frequency is to switch the phaseleg, say, from the 0 state to the 1 state at a predetermined frequency (such as the 8 kHz instanced earlier), and to calculate the "off" time according to the value of the current error. This principle, or a variant of it, lies behind most of the controllers that operate with a fixed or controllable switching frequency, and in a most elegant form in the space-vector modulator of Prof. Holtz, which is described later.

Above a certain speed the voltage is insufficient to drive the required current, and control of the waveform will tend to be lost in an unpredictable way. There is no orderly transition to six-step.

7.2.7 dq_VV_CR

The name "dq_VV_CR" means "*dq*-axis voltage-vector current-regulator". It works in the *dq* frame of reference and is a practical attempt to apply a little intelligence to the switching decision at each cycle of the sampling frequency f_0. In these respects it presages the more formal space-vector modulator and especially the DTC scheme described later. Although there is no connection between these schemes, the mechanics of dq_VV_CR require no mathematics and are simple to understand, and it can be used as an introduction to some of the objectives of the more highly-developed methods.

At each sampling instant, the current is sampled in all three lines and the kth samples are denoted i_{k1}, i_{k2} and i_{k3}. Then depending on whether the currents are above or below their respective sinusoidal reference current waveforms i_1^*,i_2^*,i_3^*, a voltage vector (p.374) is selected according to the following logic:

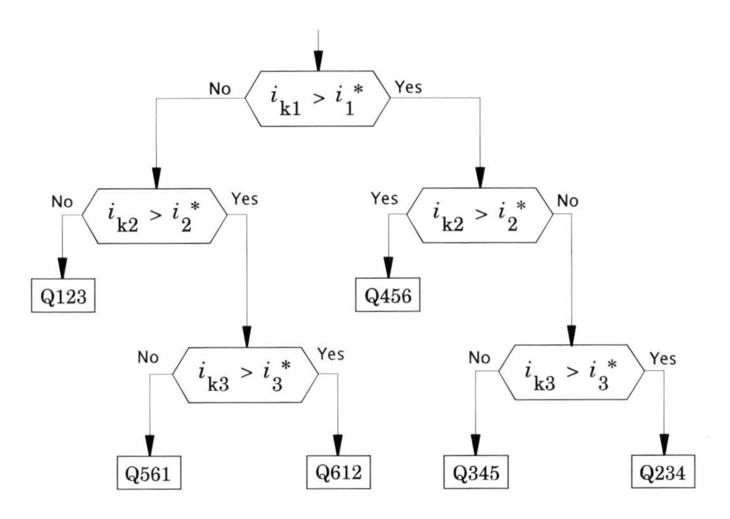

Fig. 7.31 dq_VV_CR logic

The reference current waveforms are

$$
\begin{aligned}
i_1^* &= I_{sp} \sin(\omega t + \gamma); \\
i_2^* &= I_{sp} \sin(\omega t + \gamma - 2\pi/3); \\
i_3^* &= I_{sp} \sin(\omega t + \gamma + 2\pi/3).
\end{aligned}
\tag{7.95}
$$

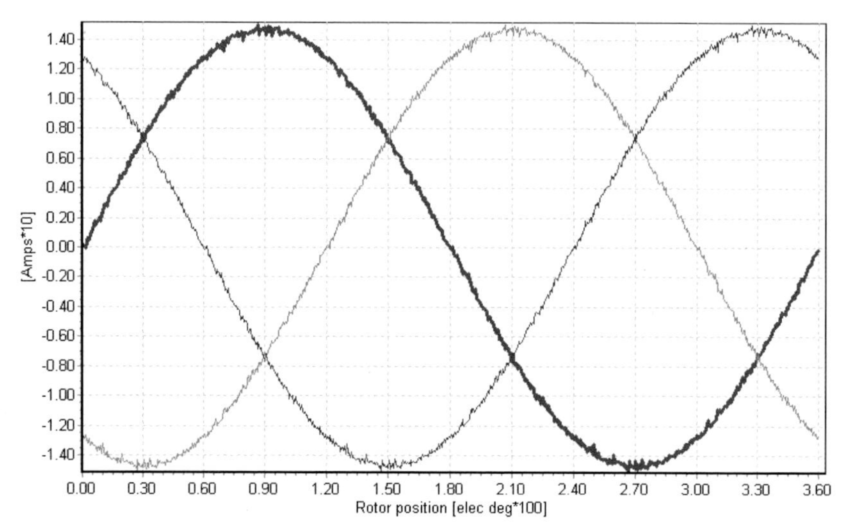

Fig. 7.32 dq_VV_CR controller waveforms

Example — Suppose that $\omega t = 47°$ and $I_{sp} = 15$ A with $\gamma = 0$. Then

$$i_1^* = 10{\cdot}97 \text{ A}; \qquad i_2^* = -14{\cdot}345 \text{ A}; \qquad i_3^* = 3{\cdot}374 \text{ A}.$$

Also suppose that

$$i_{k1} = 9{\cdot}1 \text{ A}; \qquad i_{k2} = -13{\cdot}5 \text{ A}; \qquad i_{k3} = 4{\cdot}4 \text{ A}.$$

Thus

$$i_{k1} < i_1^*; \qquad i_{k2} > i_2^*; \qquad i_{k3} > i_3^*.$$

According to Fig. 7.31 the dq_VV_CR algorithm selects voltage vector Q612. This tends to increase i_{k1} because transistor Q_1 holds line A positive. Likewise Q_6 holds line B negative, tending to decrease i_{k2} (i.e., to increase it in the negative direction). Finally Q_2 holds line C negative, tending to decrease i_{k3}.

Current waveforms are shown in Fig. 7.32. Each voltage vector can change state only once per sampling period, so the maximum possible switching frequency is $f_0/2$. The performance is similar to that of delta modulation: the phase and magnitude errors are very small when the speed is low enough for full control to be exercised, for these regulators operate with almost infinite gain. However, there is no control over the switching frequency and no orderly transition to six-step at high speed. Because the zero-voltage states are not used, there is no freewheeling state, and this tends to increase the switching frequency.

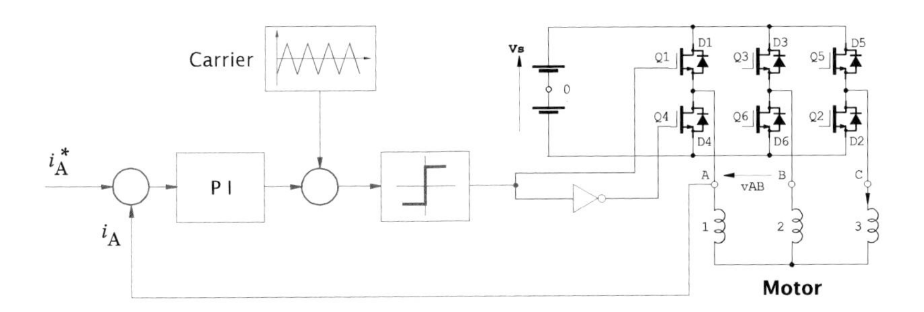

Fig. 7.33 Ramp comparison current regulator schematic

7.2.8 Sine/triangle ramp comparison

This is a modified hysteresis current regulator, in which the current error in each line is compared with a triangular "carrier" waveform . The schematic is shown in Fig. 7.33, and an example of successful sinewave regulation is shown in Fig. 7.34, with a carrier frequency f_0 = 24 kHz at 1000 rpm.

The ratio of the current-error signal to the carrier voltage is called the modulation index, m. m controls the ratio of "on" to "off" times in each phaseleg to raise or lower the current. As m is derived from the current error, the operation is sensitive to the values of proportional and integral gain in the PI control. Moreover, m has no innate relationship to the motor or inverter voltages, and there is a reduction in the effective gain of the modulator when m is high, as tends to be the case at high speeds. Unfortunately there is no magic formula to pre-determine the required gains. The phase and magnitude errors with the ramp-comparison method constitute a well-documented limitation of this type of regulator. The current error is an AC quantity and it has been pointed out in the literature that zero steady-state error is virtually impossible to attain.

Fig 7.35 shows an example of the ramp-comparison controller in saturation. The speed has been increased to 2400 rpm, and "pulse dropping" has reduced the switching frequency to 17·2 kHz.

The current waveform can be restored at higher speeds by means of phase advance gamma (flux-weakening), but only at the expense of torque, and this is possible only over a limited range of speed.

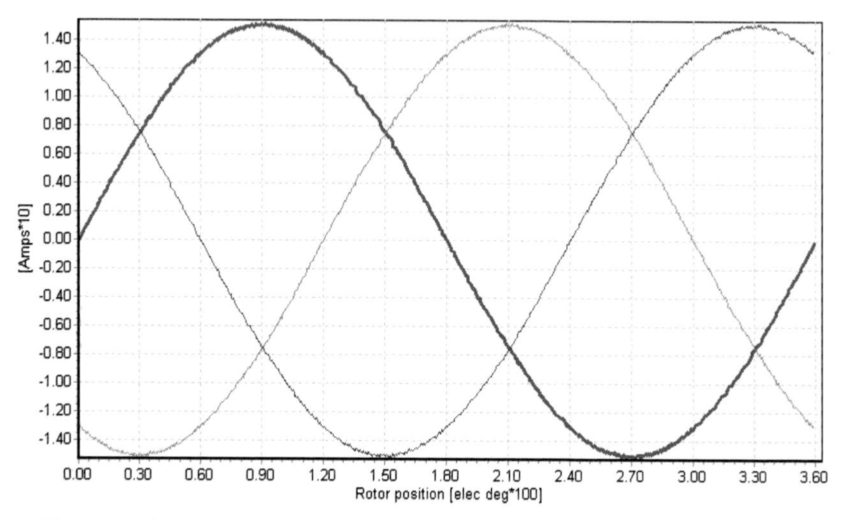

Fig. 7.34 Sinewave current regulation with ramp comparison controller

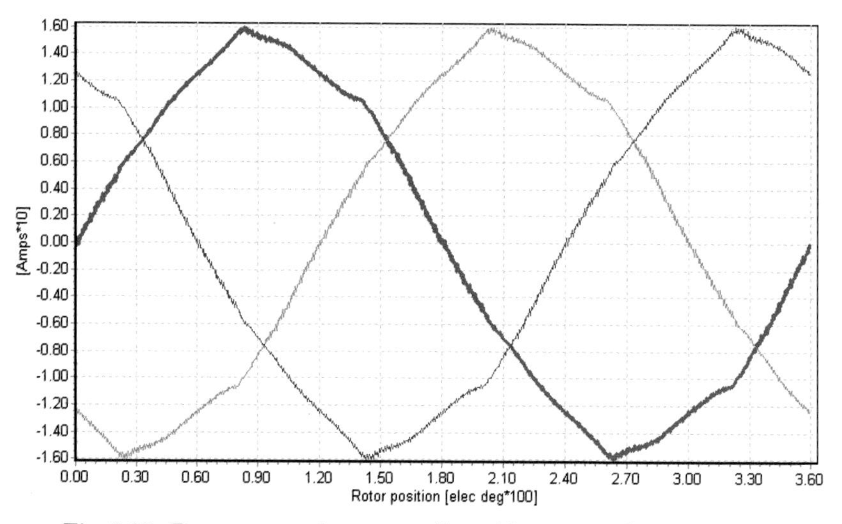

Fig. 7.35 Ramp comparison controller with saturated current loop

According to Rowan and Kerkman, the ramp-comparison controller snaps into six-step prematurely at only 90% of the maximum available fundamental voltage. They also say that the degradation in the steady-state current regulation (at higher speeds) is an inherent characteristic of the stationary regulator, not directly attributable to gain reduction or to the rising EMF.

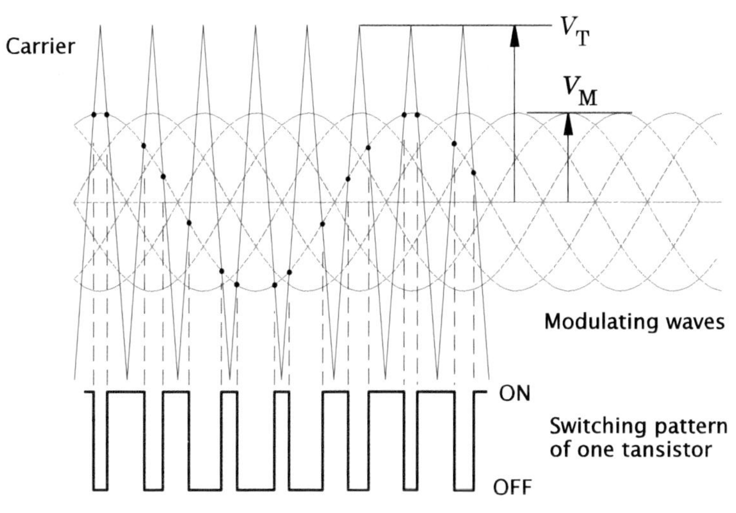

Fig. 7.36 Sine/triangle pulse-width modulation

7.2.9 Voltage PWM (sine/triangle)

This voltage PWM algorithm is not a current regulator *per se*, but a means of producing a controlled fundamental voltage by means of pulse-width-modulated switching of the inverter. Although it has long been surpassed in usage and performance, it is historically important and serves as a stepping-stone towards the study of more advanced controller.

The principle is shown in Fig. 7.36. A triangular "carrier" wave is established with an amplitude of V_T and frequency f_0, usually several kHz. The sinusoidal modulating waves V_M form a balanced 3-phase set, representing the required amplitude and frequency of the fundamental of the output voltage. The modulating waves are at the actual frequency required at the inverter output, while the amplitude V_M is scaled as shown below. The ratio V_M/V_T is called the modulation index m.

The transistors in the inverter phaselegs are switched in complementary mode, which means that when one transistor in a phase-leg is on, the other is off, and one of the two transistors is on at any instant. The phase-legs are switched at the intersections of the modulating waves and the carrier wave, as shown in Fig. 7.36.

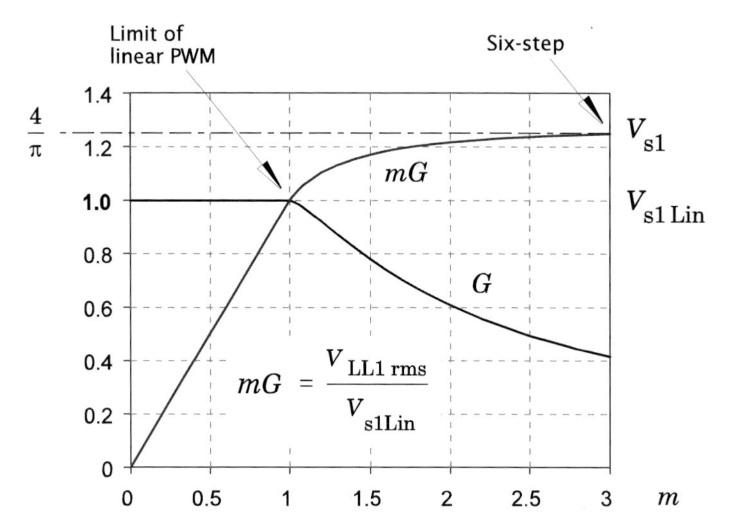

Fig. 7.37 Describing function of Rowan and Kerkman

If $m < 1$ the fundamental voltage at the output of the inverter is proportional to m, and in this range the modulator is said to be linear. If $m > 1$, pulses are "dropped" and the relationship between the inverter fundamental output voltage and m is nonlinear. The controller is then said to be "overmodulated".

Ultimately when m is very large, there is only one voltage pulse per phase per cycle of the fundamental frequency, and the inverter is then in six-step mode. Transition through the overmodulation range, in which more and more pulses are dropped as m increases, is not a controlled process. Consequently the harmonic content of the line voltage at the output of the inverter changes in a complex manner. However, the fundamental can be predicted by the describing function of Rowan and Kerkman, eqn. (7.97). When $m \leq 1$, we get

$$V_{LL1} = m \frac{\sqrt{3}}{\sqrt{2}} \frac{V_s}{2} = 0{\cdot}612\, m\, V_s = m \times V_{s1\,Lin} \quad \text{V RMS.} \tag{7.96}$$

When $m > 1$, we get

$$\begin{aligned} V_{LL1} &= \frac{\sqrt{3}}{\sqrt{2}} \frac{V_s}{2}\, m \frac{\left[\sin^{-1}(\nu) + \nu\sqrt{1 - \nu^2}\right]}{\pi/2} \\ &= V_{s1\,Lin} \times m\, G(\nu) \quad \text{V RMS,} \end{aligned} \tag{7.97}$$

where $\nu = 1/m$. The functions $G(\nu)$ and $mG(\nu)$ are plotted in Fig. 7.37. When m is large, we get six-step operation with

$$V_{LL1} = \frac{\sqrt{6}}{\pi} V_s = 0{\cdot}780\, V_s = V_{s1} \quad \text{V RMS}. \tag{7.98}$$

The product mG is the ratio of $V_{LL1\ rms}$ and the voltage V_{s1Lin} which defines the limit of linear modulation or proportionality between m and the fundamental output voltage. G is a component of this function, expressed as a feedforward gain in theory of the closed-loop form of the sine-triangle as a current regulator, and also in the synchronous regulator below.

An example of the operation of the sine/triangle modulator is shown in Fig. 7.38 with a fixed modulation index at low speed with a motor having a sinusoidal EMF waveform. Fig. 7.39 shows the same operating condition as Fig. 7.38, but with a trapezoidal EMF waveshape. The current waveform is distorted by all the low-order harmonics in the EMF waveform. With fixed modulation index and no current feedback, there is nothing the controller can do about it.

In overmodulation the controller behaves in an orderly if uncontrolled fashion, with the fundamental inverter voltage increasing with m according to Fig. 7.37.

The actual switching frequency is normally equal to the sampling frequency, f_0.

Third-harmonic injection — It is known that if a third-harmonic of magnitude 1/6 is added to the fundamental modulating wave V_M in each phase, the *fundamental* modulation index can be increased to $2/\sqrt{3}$ or 1·1547 without overmodulation and without distorting the resulting line-line voltage. This permits a useful 15% increase in the line-neutral voltage which is otherwise limited to $V_s/2$. It is interesting to compare this with the "hexagon tracking" principle in space-vector modulation (below). See also Table 7.3 on p. 404.

Example — A sinewave motor requires a fundamental line-line voltage of 198 V rms. If the DC supply voltage is 270 V, determine the required modulation index m and the describing-function gain G.

With $V_s = 270$ V, $V_{s1Lin} = 0{\cdot}612 \times 270 = 165{\cdot}2$ V, so $mG = 198/165{\cdot}2 = 1{\cdot}2$. From Fig. 7.37, $m = 1{\cdot}75$ and $G = 0{\cdot}68$.

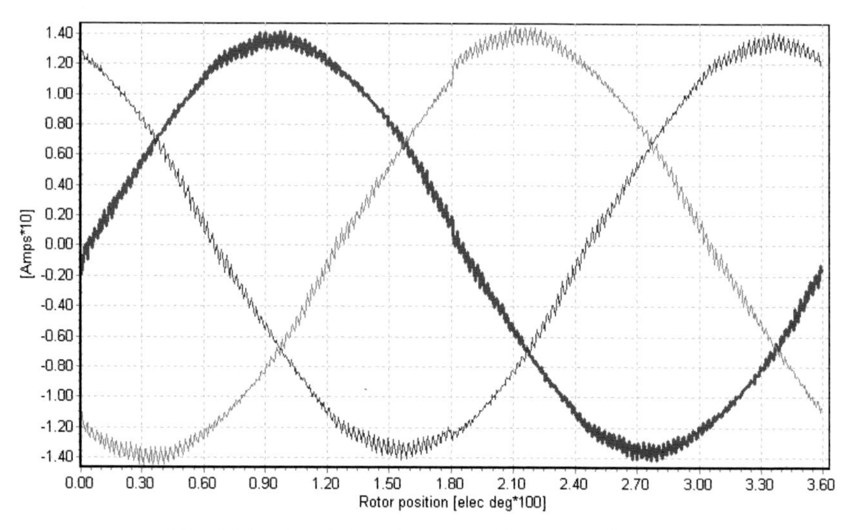

Fig. 7.38 Sine/triangle PWM with sinusoidal EMF

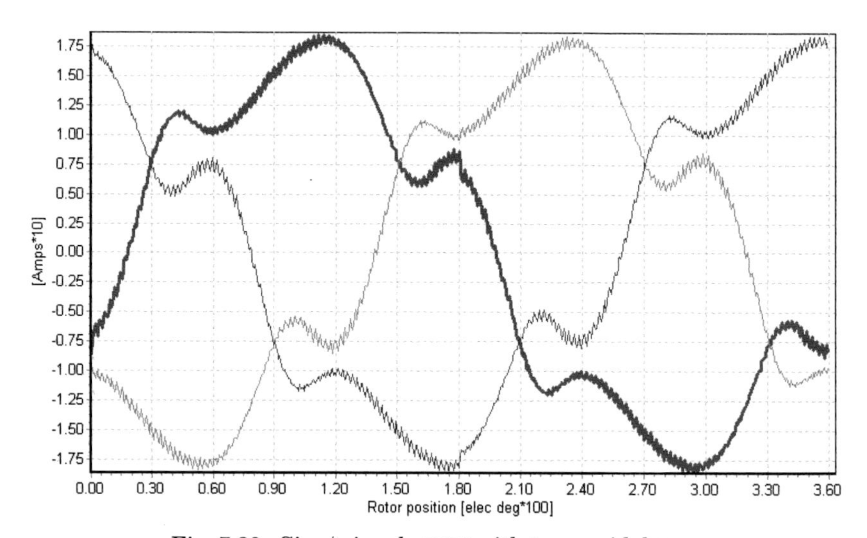

Fig. 7.39 Sine/triangle PWM with trapezoidal EMF

The sine-triangle voltage-source inverter is a founder member of the family of PWM inverters and it has spawned such terms as *modulation index* and *overmodulation* which are now part of the vocabulary of the subject. It is also the basis of the more complex synchronous regulator in the next section, and it can be used as a diagnostic tool to get inside the control loop of Fig. 7.20.

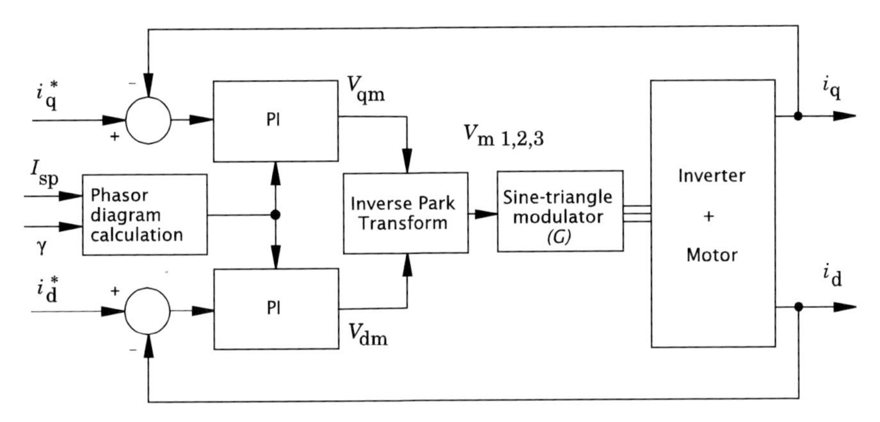

Fig. 7.40 Synchronous regulator of Rowan and Kerkman

7.2.10 The synchronous regulator

Fig. 7.40 shows the structure of the synchronous regulator. The dq-axis currents i_d and i_q are controlled by separate feedback loops in each axis. These are DC quantities in the steady-state, so the steady-state error can theoretically be zero.

The sine/triangle modulator is the same as in the previous section, and it has has the feedforward transfer function developed in eqn. (7.97) for the fundamental component. The normalized phase voltages V_{m1}, V_{m2}, V_{m3} applied to the sine-triangle modulator are predicted from

$$\begin{aligned} V_{m1} &= [V_{dm}\cos\theta - V_{qm}\sin\theta]/V_{ph\,pk\,max\,Lin};\\ V_{m2} &= [V_{dm}\cos(\theta-2\pi/3) - V_{qm}\sin(\theta-2\pi/3)]/V_{ph\,pk\,max\,Lin};\\ V_{m3} &= [V_{dm}\cos(\theta+2\pi/3) - V_{qm}\sin(\theta+2\pi/3)]/V_{ph\,pk\,max\,Lin}, \end{aligned} \quad (7.99)$$

where

$$V_{ph\,pk\,max\,Lin} = \frac{\sqrt{2}}{\sqrt{3}} V_{s1Lin} = \frac{\sqrt{2}}{\sqrt{3}} \times \frac{\sqrt{3}}{2\sqrt{2}} V_s = \frac{V_s}{2}. \quad (7.100)$$

This is the peak value of the maximum fundamental phase voltage available from the inverter in the linear range of sine-triangle modulation. The RMS line-line value of this voltage has been given as V_{s1Lin} in eqn. (7.96) on p. 386. The amplitude of the sine-triangle carrier waveform is 1, so no further scaling is necessary.

The commanded voltages V_{dm}, V_{qm} in eqn. (7.99) are estimated from the calculated phasor diagram of the motor operating with the given I_{sp} and γ. They include the EMF and the voltage drops in the synchronous reactances X_d and X_q, and are expressed as follows:

$$\begin{aligned} V_{dm} &= -X_q I_{qm} + R_{ph} I_{dm} + G_d \,\Delta I_d + G_{dq}\,\Delta I_q ; \\ V_{qm} &= E_{q1} + X_d I_{dm} + R_{ph} I_{qm} + G_q \,\Delta I_q + G_q \,\Delta I_d . \end{aligned} \tag{7.101}$$

G_d, G_q, G_{dq} and G_{qd} are adjustment parameters for the dq-axis error currents ΔI_d and ΔI_q which are obtained as follows from eqn. (7.102) ("Acc" means "accumulated") :

$$\begin{aligned} \Delta I_d &= G_P (I_{dm} - i_d) + G_I \,\mathrm{Acc}(\Delta I_d); \\ \Delta I_q &= G_P (I_{qm} - i_q) + G_I \,\mathrm{Acc}(\Delta I_q). \end{aligned} \tag{7.102}$$

Eqn. (7.102) shows that the gains operate on the current *error*. At low speed with sinusoidal EMF this regulator can theoretically operate with $G_P = G_I = 0$, since the feedforward signals derived from E_{q1} and the impedance voltage drops provide the necessary drive.

As an example of operation with a saturated regulator *and* a nonsinusoidal EMF waveform, Fig. 7.41 shows the orderly behaviour of the synchronous regulator even in the overmodulation range . At a lower speed, even with a low gain G_P = 5 and no integral gain, the current waveform is nearly sinusoidal.

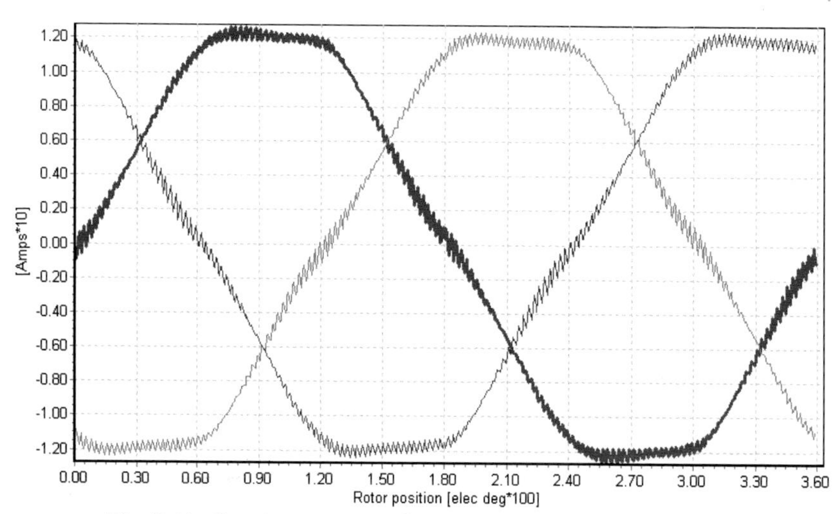

Fig. 7.41 Synchronous regulator in saturation at 2500 rpm

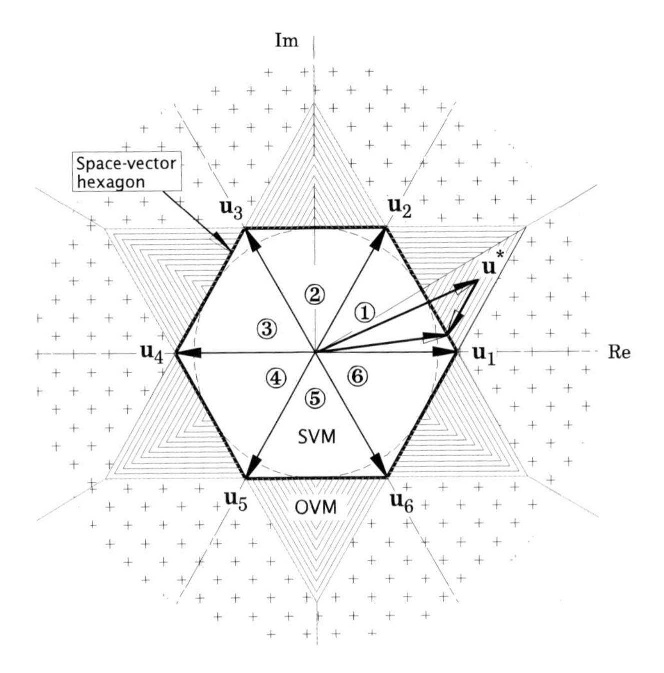

Fig. 7.42 Space-vector hexagon (Krah and Holtz)

7.2.11 Space-vector controller

Space vectors were defined graphically on p. 374 and used in the dq_VV_CR regulator on p. 381. As with the synchronous regulator in the previous section, the idea is to predict the required space vectors from the calculated voltage required to operate the motor at a given current I_{sp} and phase advance angle γ. The space vectors are calculated and set at the sampling rate f_0. Fig. 7.42 shows the entire range or domain of the space-vector controller in the complex plane.[61]

The controller uses the same "commanded voltages" V_{dm}, V_{qm} as the synchronous regulator, calculated using eqn. (7.101) on p. 390. These voltages are transformed into a space vector

$$\mathbf{u}^* = u_\alpha + \mathrm{j}\, u_\beta \tag{7.103}$$

[61] Fig. 7.42 is derived from J.-O. Krah and J. Holtz, IEEE Trans. Ind. Appl., Vol. IA-35, Sept/Oct. 1999, pp. 1039-1049.

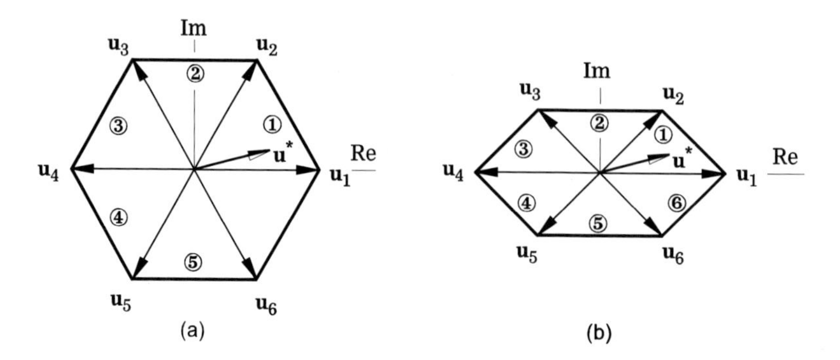

Fig. 7.43 Space vector hexagon with transformed imaginary axis (Holtz)

where

$$u_\alpha = \frac{(V_{dm}\cos\theta - V_{qm}\sin\theta)}{2/3 \times V_s}; \; u_\beta = \frac{1}{\sqrt{3}} \frac{(V_{dm}\sin\theta + V_{qm}\cos\theta)}{2/3 \times V_s}. \quad (7.104)$$

Both components are normalized to $(2/3\ V_s)$, which is the "length" of each of the space-vectors $\mathbf{u}_1$, $\mathbf{u}_2$, ..., $\mathbf{u}_6$. The additional scaling of the imaginary component $\mathbf{u}_\beta$ by the factor $1/\sqrt{3}$ has the effect of "flattening" the hexagon of space-vectors as shown in Fig. 7.43. This ingenious artefact simplifies the arithmetic in the control processor: see Krah and Holtz, *op. cit*.

We now have the commanded or desired voltage in terms of a space vector $\mathbf{u}^*$ in the "flattened" hexagon diagram of Fig. 7.43(b). The next step is to determine a PWM switching sequence that will produce an inverter output voltage whose time-average over a short interval is equal to $\mathbf{u}^*$.[62] The method is explained assuming that $\mathbf{u}^*$ is in sector ① of Fig. 7.42 or 7.43. Since the inverter can produce only discrete space vectors of voltage we use the ones nearest to $\mathbf{u}^*$, namely, $\mathbf{u}_1$, $\mathbf{u}_2$ and $\mathbf{u}_0$, and we try to find a set of times or durations (t_1, t_2, t_0) for these three space-vectors such that

$$t_1\mathbf{u}_1 + t_2\mathbf{u}_2 + t_0\mathbf{u}_0 = \frac{T}{2}\mathbf{u}^*, \quad (7.105)$$

i.e., the weighted sum of volt-second impulses is equal to the required volt-second impulse $\mathbf{u}^*T/2$ in the half-period $T/2$ or $1/2f_0$.

[62]This technique recalls the method of state-space averaging in Chapter 6.

We can solve for t_1, t_2 and t_0, given that $\mathbf{u}_0 = \mathbf{0}$ and that

$$t_1 + t_2 + t_0 = \frac{T}{2}. \tag{7.106}$$

The solution is given below in tabular form for all six sectors, with

$$t_a = \frac{t_1}{T/2}; \quad t_b = \frac{t_2}{T/2}; \quad \text{and} \quad t_0 = \frac{T}{2} - (t_1 + t_2). \tag{7.107}$$

Location of $\mathbf{u}^* = u_\alpha + ju_\beta$	Sector	t_a	t_b
$(u_\beta \geq 0)$ and $(u_\alpha \geq u_\beta)$	1	$u_\alpha - u_\beta$	$2\,u_\beta$
$(u_\alpha \geq -u_\beta)$ and $(u_\alpha < u_\beta)$	2	$u_\alpha + u_\beta$	$-u_\alpha + u_\beta$
$(u_\beta \geq 0)$ and $(u_\alpha < -u_\beta)$	3	$2\,u_\beta$	$-u_\alpha - u_\beta$
$(u_\beta < 0)$ and $(u_\alpha < u_\beta)$	4	$-u_\alpha + u_\beta$	$-2\,u_\beta$
$(u_\alpha < -u_\beta)$ and $(u_\alpha \geq u_\beta)$	5	$-u_\alpha - u_\beta$	$u_\alpha - u_\beta$
$(u_\beta < 0)$ and $(u_\alpha \geq -u_\beta)$	6	$-2\,u_\beta$	$u_\alpha + u_\beta$

The modulation strategy is thus reduced to a simple set of comparisons and arithmetic equations.

It remains to determine the sequence of the space vectors, or the order of switching transistors. As explained by Krah and Holtz, if the commanded voltage $\mathbf{u}^*$ is within the inner "SVM" hexagon in Fig. 7.42, the preferred sequence in one whole cycle at f_0 is

SVM : odd-numbered sectors in Fig. 7.42							
$\mathbf{u}_0$	$\mathbf{u}_1$	$\mathbf{u}_2$	$\mathbf{u}_7$	$\mathbf{u}_7$	$\mathbf{u}_2$	$\mathbf{u}_1$	$\mathbf{u}_0$
$t_0/2$	t_1	t_2	$t_0/2$	$t_0/2$	t_2	t_1	$t_0/2$

The sequence is divided into two symmetrical intervals; this explains why $T/2$ appears in eqn. (7.106). To ensure that commutation takes place in only one phaseleg at a time, the space-vector sequence is modified in each even-numbered sector by transposing $\mathbf{u}_1$ and $\mathbf{u}_2$:

SVM : even-numbered sectors in Fig. 7.42							
$\mathbf{u}_0$	$\mathbf{u}_2$	$\mathbf{u}_1$	$\mathbf{u}_7$	$\mathbf{u}_7$	$\mathbf{u}_1$	$\mathbf{u}_2$	$\mathbf{u}_0$
$t_0/2$	t_2	t_1	$t_0/2$	$t_0/2$	t_1	t_2	$t_0/2$

Circle tracking and Hexagon tracking — The SVM mode can operate with $\mathbf{u}^*$ all the way out to the outer hexagon in Fig. 7.42, but the dotted circle shows the limit of operation with a *constant magnitude* of the fundamental inverter voltage. The radius of the circle is $2/3 \times V_s \times \cos 30° = V_s/\sqrt{3}$, corresponding to the peak value of the fundamental line-neutral voltage. The line-line value is

$$V_{LL1rms} = \frac{2}{3} V_s \cos 30° \times \frac{\sqrt{3}}{\sqrt{2}} = \frac{2}{3} V_s \times \frac{\sqrt{3}}{2} \times \frac{\sqrt{3}}{\sqrt{2}} = \frac{V_s}{\sqrt{2}}. \quad (7.108)$$

This is larger than V_{s1Lin}, the linear limit of the sine-triangle modulator, in the ratio 0·707/0·612 = 1·155, a 15·5% increase in the linear modulation range.

Prof. Holtz also points out that operation along the hexagonal locus in Fig. 7.42 increases the fundamental voltage by the further ratio $6\sqrt{3}/\pi^2 = 1{\cdot}053$, which is 21·6% higher than V_{s1Lin}, although operation between the circle and the outer hexagon begins to introduce low-order harmonics into the inverter output voltage.

Overmodulation — When the demanded voltage $\mathbf{u}^*$ is outside the hexagon, Holtz proposed a strategy in which $\mathbf{u}^*$ is reduced by shifting its tip to the nearest side of the hexagon, along a line parallel to the nearest neighbouring side. The direction of this migration depends on the 30° sub-sector in which $\mathbf{u}^*$ lies. The implementation of Prof. Holtz is a decision tree with simple modifications to the timings t_1 and t_2. On the outer hexagon,

$$t_1 + t_2 = \frac{T}{2} \quad \text{or} \quad t_a + t_b = 1, \quad \text{with} \quad t_0 = 0. \quad (7.109)$$

The "shifting" algorithm permits smooth, controlled transition between the linear control range inside the hexagon, throughout the hatched escribed triangles in Fig. 7.42. Ultimately when $\mathbf{u}^*$ falls outside these triangles, the controller "degenerates" to a bang-bang mode in which the nearest space vector of the set $\mathbf{u}_1$, $\mathbf{u}_2$, ..., $\mathbf{u}_6$ is selected. In the steady-state, this corresponds to six-step operation.

Fig. 7.44 shows calculated examples of the operation of the space-vector modulator with a surface-magnet motor, through a speed range that ends up with six-step operation.

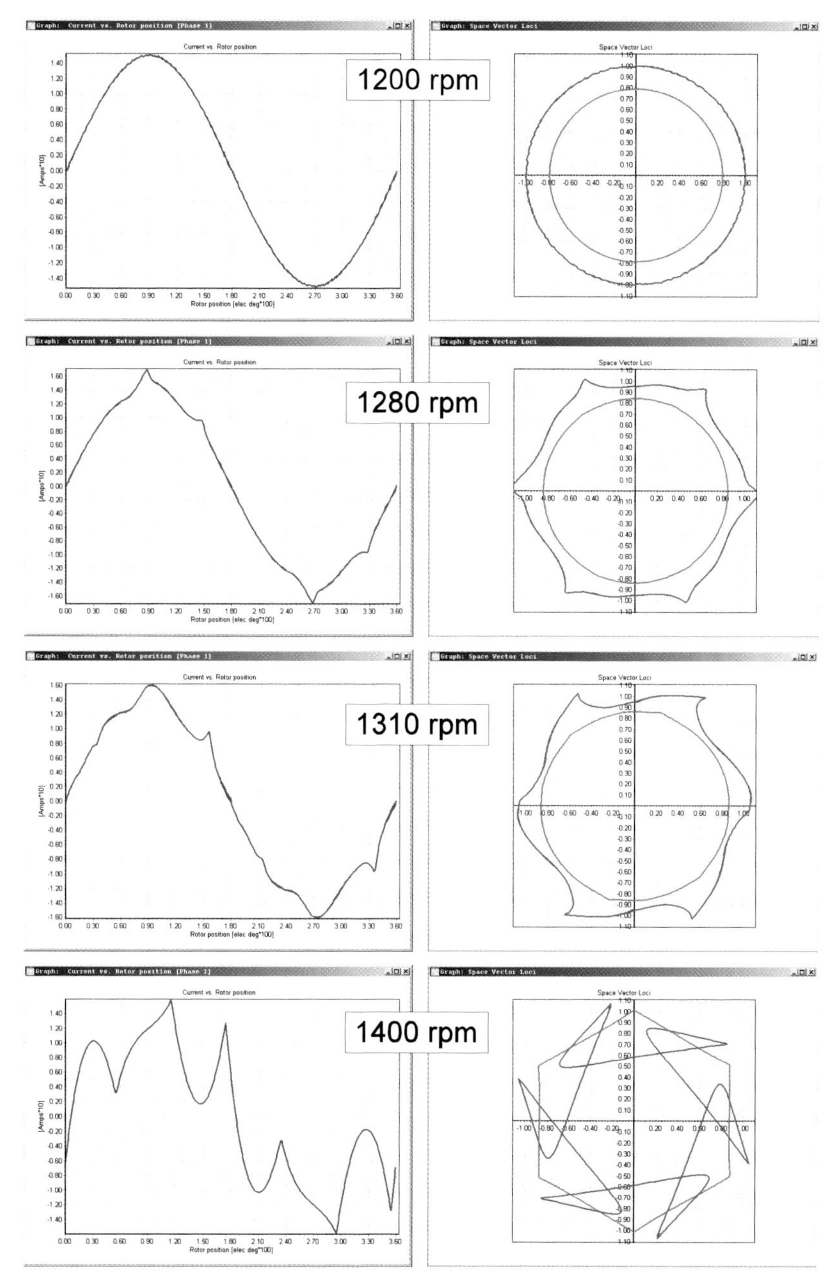

Fig. 7.44 Space-vector modulator : transition through the high-speed range

The orderly transition through the overmodulation range is clear.

7.2.12 Direct torque control (DTC)

Direct torque control is a departure from the development of current regulators considered up to this point. Instead of controlling torque *via* the regulation of current, DTC attempts to integrate the control of flux and torque in a single switching algorithm, taking advantage of the fact that the *voltage* can be changed extremely quickly when the inverter transistors change state.

It is worth taking stock of the classical field-oriented control principles before presenting the DTC principle. Classical field-oriented control is based on machine equations written in a frame of reference that is fixed to the rotor, so that the magnet axis defines the d-axis and the q-axis is 90° ahead of the d-axis.

The starting point is the general equation for the instantaneous electromagnetic torque of a rotating-flux AC machine, eqn. (4.112):

$$T = \frac{mp}{2}(\psi_d i_q - \psi_q i_d) \qquad (7.110)$$

where m is the number of phases and p is the number of pole-pairs. The flux-linkages ψ_d and ψ_q are given by eqn. (5.77):

$$\psi_d = \Psi_{1Md} + L_d i_d; \quad \psi_q = L_q i_q, \qquad (7.111)$$

where Ψ_{1Md} is the fundamental flux-linkage due to the magnet; L_d and L_q are the d- and q-axis synchronous inductances; and i_d and i_q are the d- and q-axis components of the phase current. Substituting eqns. (7.111) into eqn. (7.110) gives eqn. (7.10):

$$T = \frac{mp}{2}[\Psi_{1Md} i_q + (L_d - L_q) i_d i_q]. \qquad (7.112)$$

For surface-magnet motors $L_d = L_q$, and

$$T = \frac{mp}{2}\Psi_{1Md} i_q. \qquad (7.113)$$

If the magnet flux-linkage is fixed, the torque is proportional to the current i_q, so the torque is regulated by controlling i_q.

Controlling i_q means controlling both the magnitude and phase of the current. The phase is defined relative to the rotor position (which also defines the phase of Ψ_{1Md} and the EMF).

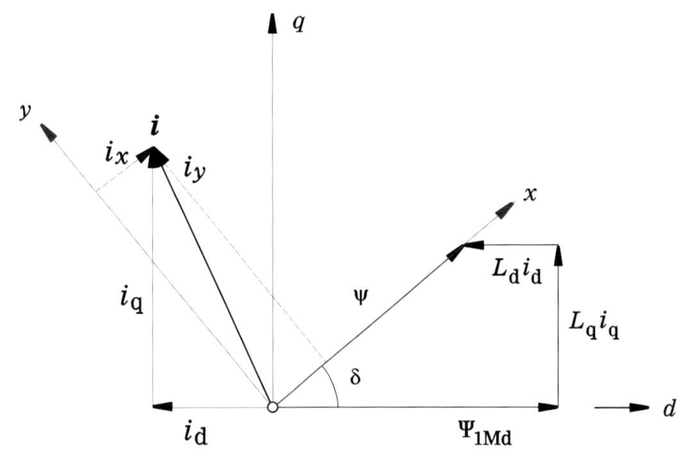

Fig. 7.45 Phasor diagram showing dq and xy axes

A field-oriented current regulator therefore typically has the following components in addition to the power transistor bridge:

a rotor position signal (generally from a resolver);
at least two current sensors to measure the phase currents;
a coordinate transformation of the phase currents into i_d and i_q;
a PI regulator;
a PWM modulator;
a means of calculating the required values of i_d and i_q; and
a means of determining the torque demand.

Direct torque control is based on machine equations written in a frame of reference that is fixed to the airgap flux, which includes not only the magnet flux in the d-axis but also the armature reaction fluxes $L_d i_d$ and $L_q i_q$ in the d- and q-axes. Whereas the classical theory often uses separate scalar equations for the d- and q-axis components, as in eqn. (7.111), DTC is almost always expressed in terms of space vectors, which represent physical quantities that are rotating in space, rather than simply advancing in time-phase.

To establish the required space vectors, we take the components ψ_d and ψ_q from eqn. (7.111) and write

$$\psi = \psi_d + j\,\psi_q . \qquad (7.114)$$

This is a complex number that is constant in the steady-state, and remains in the fixed position in Fig. 7.45. If we attach the operator $e^{j\omega t}$ we have a "vector" rotating at the angular velocity ω, and this is what we call a space vector. The $e^{j\omega t}$ is normally omitted since it is common to all variables; what is important is the phase of the space vectors relative to each other, not their absolute phase.

Now instead of defining ψ in dq axes, let us define it as

$$\psi = \psi_x + j\,\psi_y \tag{7.115}$$

where the x,y axes are oriented at an angle δ relative to the d-axis. If δ is chosen such that the x-axis lies along the space-vector ψ, then

$$\psi = \psi_x \quad \text{and} \quad \psi_y = 0. \tag{7.116}$$

From the phasor diagram, Fig. 7.45, we can see that

$$\delta = \text{Arc tan}\left[\frac{L_q i_q}{\Psi_{1\text{Md}} + L_d i_d}\right]. \tag{7.117}$$

The components ψ_x and ψ_y can be obtained from ψ_d and ψ_q by the transformation

$$\begin{bmatrix}\psi_x \\ \psi_y\end{bmatrix} = \begin{bmatrix}\cos\delta & \sin\delta \\ -\sin\delta & \cos\delta\end{bmatrix} \cdot \begin{bmatrix}\psi_d \\ \psi_q\end{bmatrix} \tag{7.118}$$

with inverse

$$\begin{bmatrix}\psi_d \\ \psi_q\end{bmatrix} = \begin{bmatrix}\cos\delta & -\sin\delta \\ \sin\delta & \cos\delta\end{bmatrix} \cdot \begin{bmatrix}\psi_x \\ \psi_y\end{bmatrix}. \tag{7.119}$$

The same transformation applies to the current $\mathbf{i} = i_x + j i_y = i_d + j i_q$, and if these substitutions are made in the torque eqn. (7.112), we get

$$T = \frac{mp}{2}(\psi_x i_y - \psi_y i_x) = \frac{mp}{2}\psi i_y \tag{7.120}$$

where ψ is just the amplitude $|\psi| = \psi_x$. This equation is identical in form to eqn. (7.113), except that ψ is no longer the fixed magnet flux-linkage but the *total* flux-linkage, which is controllable. This opens up the possibility of controlling the torque by regulating either ψ or i_y, or both of them.

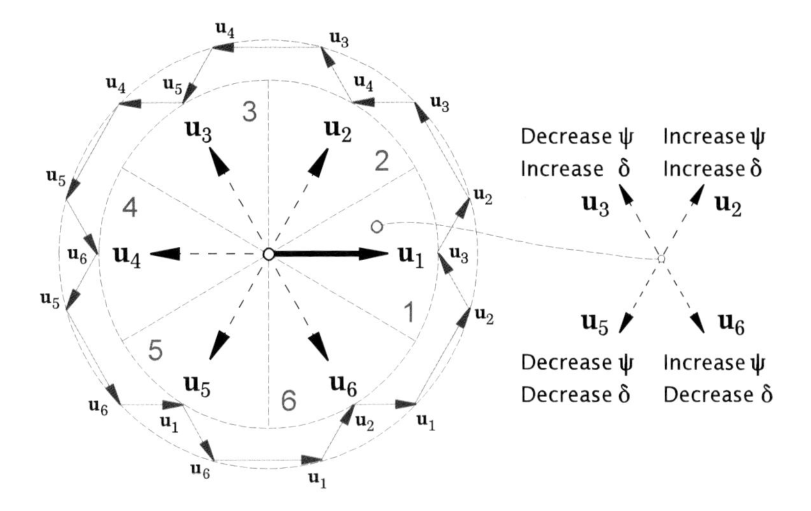

Fig. 7.46 DTC switching algorithm

We can use the inverse transformation eqn. (7.119)to solve for i_y:

$$i_y = \frac{1}{L_d} \sin \delta \left[\Psi_{1Md} - \psi (L_q - L_d) \cos \delta \right]. \tag{7.121}$$

In a surface-magnet motor with $L_d = L_q$ this simplifies to

$$i_y = \frac{\Psi_{1Md}}{L_d} \sin \delta . \tag{7.122}$$

Substituting in eqn. (7.120), we get the electromagnetic torque

$$T = \frac{mp}{2} \frac{\Psi_{1Md}}{L_d} \psi \sin \delta . \tag{7.123}$$

The torque is now expressed entirely in terms of the magnitude and phase of the total flux-linkage ψ, and it is at this point that the bold inventions of the DTC concept come into view. In simple terms, DTC observes that the torque can be increased or decreased by increasing or decreasing δ — that is, by advancing or retarding the phase of the total flux-linkage. The principle comes from the voltage equation

$$\mathbf{u} = R\mathbf{i} + \frac{d\psi}{dt} \tag{7.124}$$

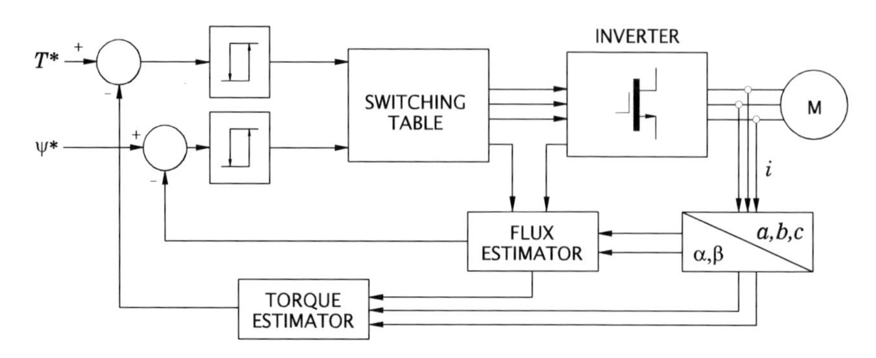

Fig. 7.47 DTC block diagram

Neglecting resistance R (which is generally small), the rate of change of flux-linkage ψ is equal to the terminal voltage $\mathbf{u}$. This means that the tip of the flux-linkage space-vector will move in a direction parallel to the voltage space-vector.

We can use this principle to explain the control action of a 6-transistor bridge inverter. The inverter has eight switching states $\mathbf{u}_0$, $\mathbf{u}_2$,...$\mathbf{u}_7$ including two zero-voltage states $\mathbf{u}_0$ and $\mathbf{u}_7$ previously defined; (p. 375). The flux-linkage space-vector ψ can be constrained to follow a more-or-less circular trajectory by rapid switching of the voltage states of the inverter, Fig. 7.46. At any instant such as the one shown, there is typically a choice of four voltage-space-vectors, two of which increase the flux-linkage ψ while the other two decrease it; and two of which advance δ while the other two retard it. Clearly there exists the possibility to control the phase and magnitude of ψ at will. Fig. 7.46 shows an example of an 18-sided polygon as a coarse approximation to a circular flux-linkage locus.

In the example in Fig. 7.46, the magnitude of the flux-linkage $|\psi|$ is maintained within limits represented by the two concentric circles. What is not shown in Fig. 7.46 is that the ψ space-vector is simultaneously "hustled" around the loop by the torque error signal in Fig. 7.47. In the classical DTC scheme, the torque error signal and the flux-linkage error signal are used to select the voltage space-vector at any instant, and the key element in this process is a truth table defining the required voltage vectors to achieve the required movement of the flux-linkage space-vector in any of the six sectors.

ψ, τ, θ		1	2	3	4	5	6
$\psi = 1$	$\tau = 1$	$\mathbf{u}_2$	$\mathbf{u}_3$	$\mathbf{u}_4$	$\mathbf{u}_5$	$\mathbf{u}_6$	$\mathbf{u}_1$
	$\tau = 0$	$\mathbf{u}_0$	$\mathbf{u}_0$	$\mathbf{u}_0$	$\mathbf{u}_0$	$\mathbf{u}_0$	$\mathbf{u}_0$
	$\tau = -1$	$\mathbf{u}_6$	$\mathbf{u}_1$	$\mathbf{u}_2$	$\mathbf{u}_3$	$\mathbf{u}_4$	$\mathbf{u}_5$
$\psi = 0$	$\tau = 1$	$\mathbf{u}_3$	$\mathbf{u}_4$	$\mathbf{u}_5$	$\mathbf{u}_6$	$\mathbf{u}_1$	$\mathbf{u}_2$
	$\tau = 0$	$\mathbf{u}_0$	$\mathbf{u}_0$	$\mathbf{u}_0$	$\mathbf{u}_0$	$\mathbf{u}_0$	$\mathbf{u}_0$
	$\tau = -1$	$\mathbf{u}_5$	$\mathbf{u}_6$	$\mathbf{u}_1$	$\mathbf{u}_2$	$\mathbf{u}_3$	$\mathbf{u}_4$

TABLE 7.2

OPTIMAL SWITCHING TABLE OF TAKAHASHI AND NOGUCHI

The truth table given by Takahashi is reproduced in Table 7.2.[63]

This simple task can be performed almost instantaneously, and it is the key to the inherently rapid response of DTC. It is necessary for the controller to "know" which sector the flux-linkage is in, and this requires knowledge of the rotor position to within 60°, although once the drive is running this information can be self-generated and does not require a position sensor.

Table 7.2 is often called the *optimal switching table*. The torque error signal is mapped into the table either by a 3-level comparator (which permits the use of the zero space-vectors); or by a 2-level comparator. Whether or not to use the zero vectors depends on the available switching speed of the power transistors and the required torque response rate. The flux-linkage error is mapped into the table by a 2-level comparator.

We can now see from eqn. (7.120) that if the torque and flux-linkage are both controlled, the current is uniquely determined. This suggests that *current-regulators are not necessary*. The control is reduced to the simple on/off control of the voltage vectors by the truth table at the sampling or clock frequency.

DTC thus eliminates two basic elements of the field-oriented controller, the PWM modulator and the current regulator; and it improves the response by eliminating time-delays in these elements.

[63] Again it recalls the decision logic in Fig. 7.31 on p. 381, which might be helpful in understanding the purpose, if not the mathematics, of the DTC scheme.

Although current-*regulators* are not required in DTC, current-*sensors* are required. In a practical system the flux-linkage is estimated by integrating ($\mathbf{u} - R\mathbf{i}$) with respect to time, and for an accurate result both the current $\mathbf{i}$ and the resistance R must be known precisely, especially at low speed. Errors in the flux-linkage integral can arise from several causes, including drift in the integration, and an alternative method is sometimes provided for estimating the flux-linkage from the current and the known inductances of the machine. DTC drives often include parameter estimation algorithms and auto-tuning processes to improve this process. Most importantly, the current is also required in the torque calculator, Fig. 7.47. For all these reasons, current-sensors are indispensable.

The DTC scheme described here uses hysteresis-comparators which produce a variable and unpredictable switching frequency, but methods exist to stabilize the switching frequency, following principles similar to those used with stationary and synchronous current-regulators.

DTC also requires a control strategy relating the correct flux-linkage to the torque demand, while keeping the inverter within its current and voltage limits. The strategy relies on a mathematical motor model, part of which is already expressed in the above equations, and which is calculated at a very high rate of repetition. The motor model is also necessary as part of the process of observing the actual flux-linkage by estimation, using the measured phase currents and the DC link voltage together with a knowledge of the motor parameters. With salient-pole machines additional constraints apply to the flux-linkage level to ensure a monotonic relationship between the torque and the phase angle δ.

In summary, a DTC controller has the following components: (1) a high-speed DSP (digital signal processor) capable of calculating the motor model, and often including adaptive algorithms to "measure" the motor parameters during setup; (2) a switching table; (3) at least two current sensors to measure the phase currents; (4) a means of calculating the required values of ψ and δ to meet the torque demand; and (5) a means of determining the torque demand in response to a speed demand.

Rate of response — In per-unit terms the rate of change of torque is practically equal to the rate of change of current. It is limited by the available drive voltage and the orientation of the voltage space vector. There is no fundamental reason why DTC should be able to change the torque any faster than a current-regulated field-oriented controller, except to the extent that delays arise in the current-regulators themselves. As the DTC controller operates directly on the torque, it does not need to calculate a suitable current space vector as part of its switching-control algorithm. These points are frequently cited as the basis for the fast torque reponse of the DTC system.

For example, to reverse the torque corresponding to Fig. 7.45, all that is necessary is to apply a voltage in the negative q-axis so that the flux-linkage component $L_q i_q$ decreases to zero, then changes sign, then increases to the original value (but with opposite sign). All the controllable flux-linkage components in Fig. 7.45 are voltage-time integrals, which suggests that the quickest way to change or reverse the torque is by changing the phase angle δ rather than by changing the magnitude of the total flux ψ, because the voltage-time integral required to change the sign of δ is much less than the voltage-time integral required to reverse the flux-linkage space-vector ψ.

Similarity with constant-voltage supply — For operation at constant speed, if we write $V = \omega\psi/\sqrt{2}$ and $E = \omega\psi_{1Md}/\sqrt{2}$ in eqn. (7.123), V is recognizable as the RMS "airgap" voltage per phase, and E is as the open-circuit EMF per phase. Substituting in eqn. (7.123), and setting $\omega_m = \omega/p$, we get the electromagnetic torque

$$T = \frac{m}{\omega_m} \frac{EV}{X_d} \sin \delta . \qquad (7.125)$$

This equation is familiar from the classical theory of synchronous machines, often expressed in terms of the power $P = \omega_m T$. It is normally used where the torque is constant or varying only slowly, especially as E and V are time-averaged RMS values. However, it reinforces the fact that DTC is based on the control of the voltage and its phase angle δ, and not the magnitude and phase of the current.

The DTC concept is generally attributed separately to Takahashi & Noguchi [1986]; and Depenbrock [1988]. (See also Luukko [2000] for a modern account; and the simpler dq_VV_CR method, Fig. 7.31).

7.2.13 Summary of voltage capabilities

Voltage	$V_{LL\,1\,rms}/V_s$	Relative to SixStep
SixStep 180°[64] V_{s1}	$\dfrac{\sqrt{6}}{\pi} = 0{\cdot}780$	1
Hexagon tracking : piecewise linear	$\dfrac{3\sqrt{6}}{\pi^2} = 0{\cdot}7446$	0·9545
Circle tracking	$\dfrac{1}{\sqrt{2}} = 0{\cdot}707$	0·9069
SixStep 120°[65]	$\dfrac{3}{\sqrt{2}\,\pi} = 0{\cdot}675$	0·8660
Maximum linear range of sine/triangle $V_{s1\,Lin}$	$\dfrac{\sqrt{3}}{2\sqrt{2}} = 0{\cdot}612$	0·7854
Sine/triangle with 3rd harmonic injection	$\dfrac{1}{\sqrt{2}} = 0{\cdot}707$	0·9069

TABLE 7.3
SUMMARY OF VOLTAGES PRODUCED BY DIFFERENT PWM ALGORITHMS

Table 7.3 summarizes the voltages produced by the PWM algorithms described in this chapter, in terms of the RMS line-line value of the fundamental. These are theoretical values; whether or not they can be achieved in practice depends on the design of the individual controller. Harmonics are not included; for them it is necessary to consult the original works and their derivatives.

---

[64] Conventional 6-step with 3 transistors conducting at any time. Transistors conduct for 120°; also called "3-phase-on".

[65] Transistors conduct for 120° : 2 transistors conducting at any time; also called "2-phase-on". The load is assumed to be resistive.

8 kT AND kE, AND FIGURES-OF-MERIT

8.1 Introduction

The torque constant k_T and the back-EMF constant k_E introduced in Chapter 1 represent the essential relationships between current and torque, and between EMF and speed. They are widely used to match the motor to the drive in the design of motion control systems that are driven by electric motors, especially when the motor and controller are obtained from different sources. They are also sometimes combined with other motor parameters (notably the resistance and the inertia) to define figures-of-merit that are used to compare motors and drives from different manufacturers.

Unfortunately there is scope for confusion in the way these constants are used. To begin with, there is no standard definition of k_E or k_T. Subtle differences can be found in the conventions used by different manufacturers and systems engineers, and there is a risk of incorrect results arising from imprecise definition.

Laxity in the definition of "motor constants" crept up unnoticed as the industry moved away from the DC commutator motor to the brushless DC motor and finally to the brushless AC motor, with added complications of the type of drive and the use of hybrid combinations of motor and drive. With the DC commutator motor there was little scope for misinterpretation, but it is too easy to assume that the definitions formulated for the DC motor automatically apply to brushless motor drives. The definitions *can* be applied consistently to brushless motor drives, but only if the terms and parameters are precisely defined, as we shall see.

"Precise definition" means that we must distinguish between *peak*, *mean* and *RMS* currents and EMFs; and that we must specify *where* in the circuit these quantities are measured or calculated. To say, for example, that k_T is the "torque per ampere" is so vague as to be almost meaningless, except in a very general sense. An example of a more precise definition is "the ratio of the mean electromagnetic torque to the RMS line current in the motor"; but even this is not complete without stating the temperature (of the magnets).

In simple treatments, k_T and k_E are often presented as identical. We have seen (p. 11) that this equality appears only in "consistent units", but even in consistent units the measured values are generally unequal, as discussed briefly in Chapter 1 and again in Chapter 13. Here we will treat them as *given*, but we will not assume them to be *equal*, and we will keep them distinct from one another except where stated. It is virtually essential to develop the theory in S.I. units, and to apply any unit conversions only at the very end.

The definitions of k_T and k_E are developed with respect to a lossless energy-conversion process, in common with all other works on the subject, but consistent with the usual methods of measurement; (see Chapter 13). **Speed is treated as constant** throughout this chapter. Losses are generally treated as parasitic effects added later, although resistance, inductance, inertia, and even gear ratio appear in some of the figures-of-merit introduced in §8.3.

Instead of issuing "definitions by decree", we will evolve k_T and k_E for different combinations of motor and drive, starting in §8.2 with the DC commutator motor which is the original basis on which the constants were defined and used. k_T and k_E are related by the power balance equation, and it is shown that they are unique, unambiguous, *and equal* when defined with reference to the DC supply. However, this is not how they are defined or used in practice: the industry prefers to define them directly in terms of *motor* EMF and current. Differences then arise that are almost entirely due to differences in EMF and current waveforms between different motors and drives.

For a brushless DC motor with flat-topped or trapezoidal EMF, fed with a current waveform that is flat-topped or essentially formed of rectangular blocks, k_T and k_E can be defined to be exactly equivalent to their counterparts in the DC commutator motor. In this book, such systems are termed **squarewave motor** with **squarewave drive**.

Uncertainties first appear in the case of brushless AC motors with sinusoidal EMF, even when the current waveform is sinusoidal. These motors are sometimes coupled to squarewave drives to form a **hybrid** system, and we need to know the effect on the definition and meaning of k_T and k_E. Conversely, squarewave motors may be coupled to sinewave drives, forming a hybrid of the opposite kind. Again the consequences in terms of k_T and k_E are to be ascertained.

8.2 kT & kE of squarewave and sinewave motor/drives

8.2.1 DC commutator motor and drive

The DC commutator motor is the most basic of all electrical machines in terms of its control characteristics. It is described by three or four simple equations as follows,[66] and these are introduced in the same order in which we will use them to develop the theory of k_E and k_T for brushless motors.

First and foremost, the EMF E_d is proportional to the speed

$$E_d = \mathbf{k}\,\omega_m \qquad [\mathrm{V}] \tag{8.1}$$

where ω_m is the angular velocity in mechanical radians/sec. The constant of proportionality is the EMF constant, $\mathbf{k}$ [Vs/rad], written in **boldface** with no subscript for the **ideal DC motor** because of its generic importance, as we will see. The italic form k_E is used in general, with subscripts added later where we need extra precision.

k_E is often quoted in "volts per thousand rpm", and we can write

$$K_E\ [\mathrm{V/krpm}] = k_E\ [\mathrm{Vs/rad}] \times \frac{1000}{30/\pi} = k_E \times 104{\cdot}72. \tag{8.2}$$

The proportionality of EMF and speed is found in all permanent-magnet motors, even though there are considerable differences in their EMF waveforms. K_E is almost always measured in the factory, and quoted in catalogue data, and we shall see that the waveform is important in its interpretation and use.

In the DC commutator motor E_d is actually the **mean rectified** EMF of a set of armature coils, in each of which the EMF is AC with a triangular waveform. This is important, because the rectifier action of the commutator and brushes presages the theory that we will use to deal with the various EMF waveforms of brushless machines.

The central concept is that of an ideal power conversion process expressed by

$$T\omega_m = E_d I_d. \tag{8.3}$$

[66] Saturation and losses are neglected throughout this chapter.

T is the electromagnetic torque and I_d is the DC current. If we substitute eqn. (8.1) in eqn. (8.3), we get

$$T = \mathbf{k} I_d \quad \text{[Nm]}. \tag{8.4}$$

In the ideal DC motor, the torque is proportional to the current. This principle is important and extremely widely used. The constant of proportionality is the *torque constant* and we usually write

$$T = k_T I_d \quad \text{[Nm]} \tag{8.5}$$

with

$$k_T = \mathbf{k}. \tag{8.6}$$

The equality of k_E and k_T is an inherent property of the ideal DC motor. It follows from eqns. (8.1)–(8.3). It is emphasized that *numerical* equality requires the use of consistent units (such as [Nm/A] and [Vs/rad]). If k_T is in [Nm/A] and K_E is in [V/1000 rpm], the relationship, quite generally, is

$$k_T = \frac{K_E \text{ [V/1000]}}{\dfrac{2\pi}{60} \times 1000} = \frac{K_E \text{ [V/1000]}}{104{\cdot}72} \quad \text{[Nm/A]}. \tag{8.7}$$

Example — A DC motor has K_E = 16 V/1000 rpm. Calculate k_T. From eqn. (8.7), k_T = 16/104·72 = 0·1528 Nm/A. Also from eqn. (8.6) k_E = 0·1528 Vs/rad.

Note that no mention has been made of the power supply, the drive. This is an important point, because when we apply these principles to the brushless motor we have to be careful to differentiate the inherent properties of the motor from its performance when connected to a particular drive.

The role of the drive is clearly exemplified by the DC system. The drive must supply a *total* DC voltage V_s sufficient to force the current through the whole equivalent circuit including the loss-producing elements as well as the ideal DC motor. In the steady state, with no inductive volt-drop,

$$V_s = E_d + RI_d + V_b \tag{8.8}$$

where R is the armature resistance and V_b is the brush volt drop.

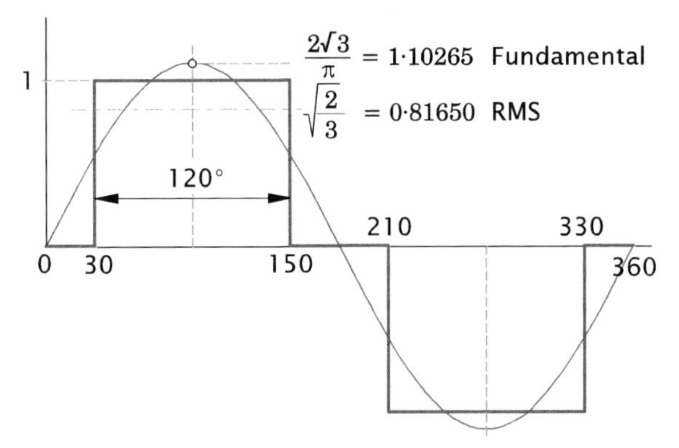

Fig. 8.1 120° block squarewave current waveform

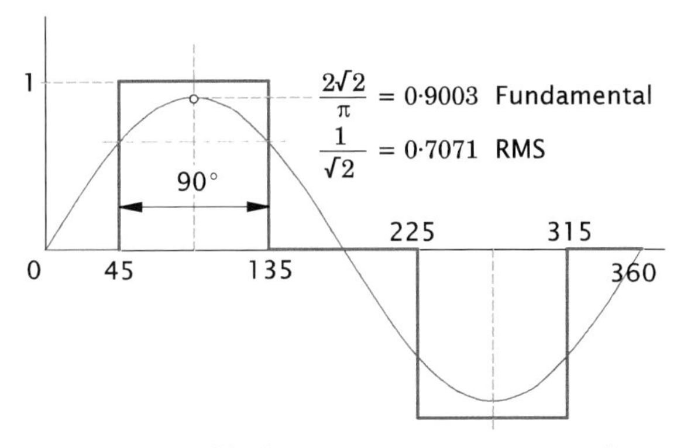

Fig. 8.2 90° block squarewave current waveform

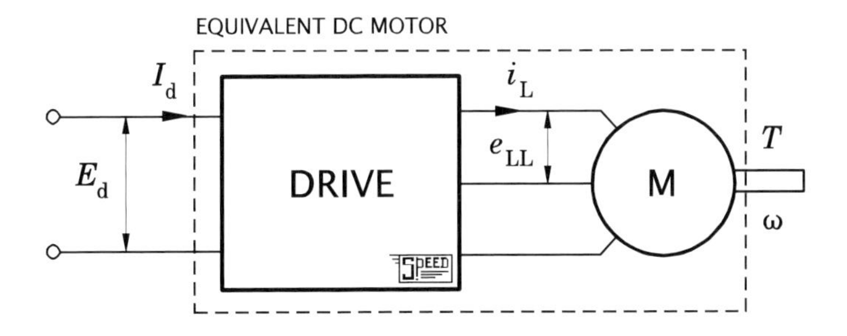

Fig. 8.3 Circuit configuration including DC filter capacitor

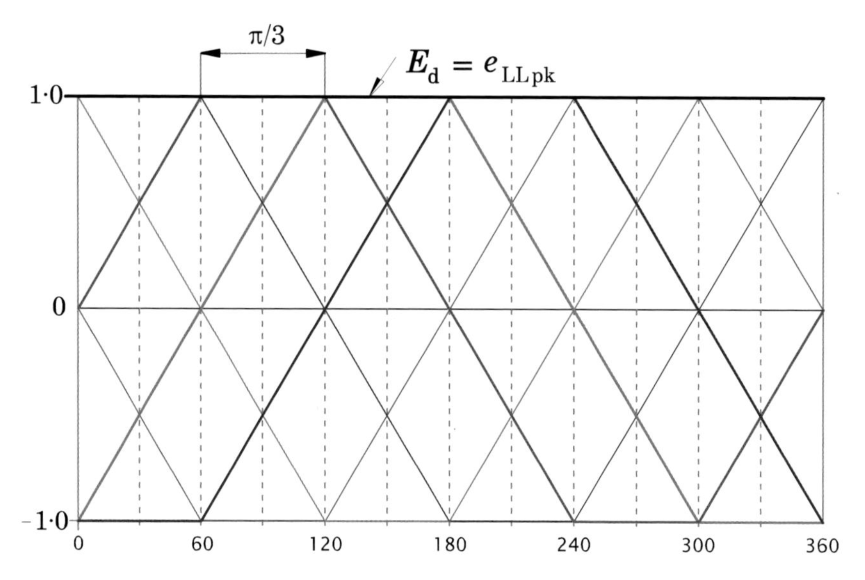

Fig. 8.4 Full-bridge rectifier waveforms; trapezoidal EMF

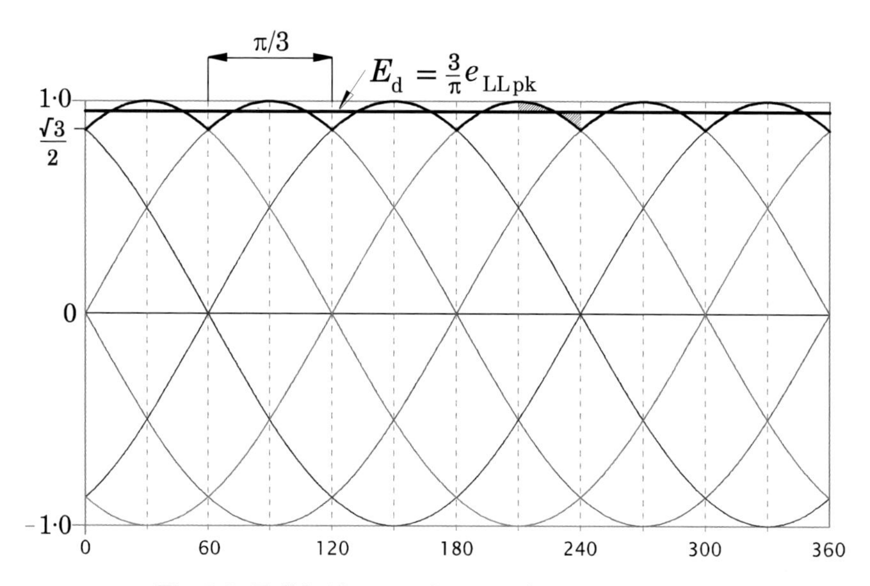

Fig. 8.5 Full-bridge rectifier waveforms : sinewave EMF

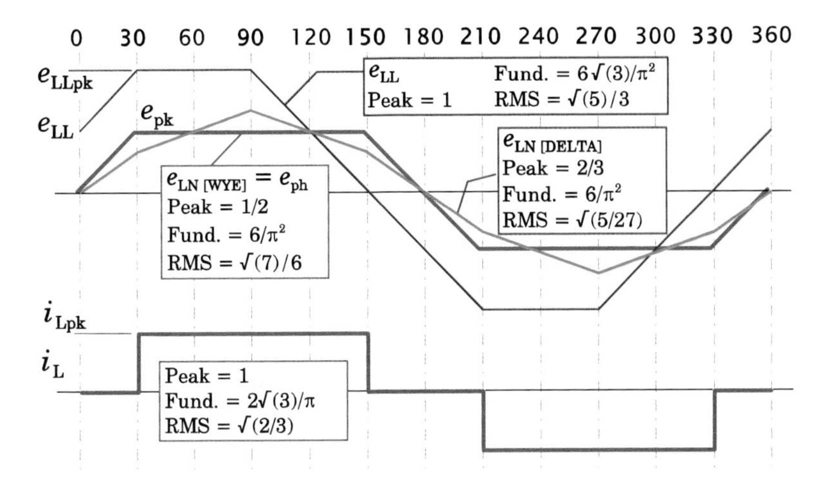

Fig. 8.6 Trapezoidal EMF waveforms and squarewave current (3-phase)

8.2.2 3-phase squarewave motor and drive

A 3-phase squarewave motor has a trapezoidal EMF, Fig. 8.6. In a wye-connected motor the phase EMF e_{ph} has a flat-top width of 120° and a peak value e_{pk}, while the line-line EMF e_{LL} has a flat-top width of 60° and a peak value e_{LLpk}. The line current is a 120° block squarewave of peak value i_{Lpk}, Figs. 8.1 and 8.6. It is commutated between pairs of lines every 60°. In any 60° interval, $i_{Lpk} = I_d$, the DC supply current. The ideal power conversion equation is

$$T\omega_m = e_{LLpk} i_{Lpk} = e_{LLpk} I_d. \tag{8.9}$$

This equation applies in every 60° interval as well as continuously, even though I_d flows in a different pair of lines in each interval.

Following the method outlined for the DC commutator motor, the next step is to identify the EMF E_d of the equivalent ideal DC motor as the mean rectified line-line EMF, which we can see from Fig. 8.4 is

$$E_d = e_{LLpk}. \tag{8.10}$$

E_d represents the DC voltage associated with energy conversion in the motor. It is independent of any voltage drops in the resistance or the power semiconductors.

The primary EMF constant is defined as the ratio

$$\mathbf{k} = \frac{E_d}{\omega_m} \tag{8.11}$$

where the boldface notation signifies equivalence with the ideal DC motor. Since $E_d = e_{LLpk}$ for this particular motor, we get

$$k_{E\,[LLpk]} = \mathbf{k} = \frac{E_d}{\omega_m} = \frac{e_{LLpk}}{\omega_m}, \tag{8.12}$$

where $k_{E[LLpk]}$ could be said to be the practical value, as obtained by direct measurement. The notation $k_{E[LLpk]}$ is used here to emphasize the definition of k_E using e_{LLpk}; in practice we would just use k_E.

If we now invoke the power conversion equation of the ideal DC motor, in the form of eqn. (8.3) or (8.4), we can obtain the current I_d required to produce a given torque T : thus

$$I_d = \frac{T}{\mathbf{k}}. \tag{8.13}$$

We are now in a position to determine the practical form of k_T. Suppose we define $k_{T[pk]}$ as the ratio T/i_{Lpk}. Since $i_{Lpk} = I_d$, we get

$$k_{T\,[pk]} = \frac{T}{i_{Lpk}} = \frac{T}{I_d} = \mathbf{k} = k_{E\,[LLpk]}. \tag{8.14}$$

T/i_{Lpk} is a practical definition of k_T, conveniently equal to k_E defined as e_{LLpk}/ω_m. However, it is not the only way to define k_T. We could choose to define k_T as $T/I_{L\,rms}$, where I_{Lrms} is the RMS line current. In that case, being careful to denote the RMS-based torque constant with its own symbol, we would have

$$k_{T\,[rms]} = k_T \times \frac{i_{Lpk}}{I_{Lrms}} \tag{8.15}$$

The ratio i_{Lpk}/I_{Lrms} depends on the current waveform. Referring to Fig. 8.1 or Fig. 8.6, we can calculate the RMS current as

$$I_{Lrms} = \sqrt{\frac{2}{3}}\, i_{Lpk}. \tag{8.16}$$

It follows that

$$k_{\mathrm{T[rms]}} = k_{\mathrm{T[pk]}} \times \sqrt{\frac{3}{2}} = k_{\mathrm{T[pk]}} \times 1{\cdot}22475, \qquad (8.17)$$

where the symbol $k_{\mathrm{T[pk]}}$ denotes k_{T} defined with respect to i_{Lpk}.

Example — A 3-phase brushless squarewave motor has $k_{\mathrm{Trms}} = 0{\cdot}19$ Nm/A RMS of motor line current with squarewave drive. Deduce k_{E}. From eqn. (8.17) with eqn. (8.14), $k_{\mathrm{E[LLpk]}} = 0{\cdot}19 \times \surd(2/3) = 0{\cdot}155$ Vs/rad $= 16{\cdot}25$ V/1000 rpm.

Use of phase quantities — The 3-phase wye-connected motor is normally supplied with three terminals and the star point is not accessible, but even so it is instructive to consider the definition of k_{E} in terms of the phase EMF (line-neutral EMF), because it prepares the ground for studying the 2-phase motor later. The phase EMF has a peak value e_{pk} and a 120° flat top, and from Fig. 8.6 we have

$$e_{\mathrm{LLpk}} = 2\, e_{\mathrm{pk}}. \qquad (8.18)$$

It follows that if $k_{\mathrm{E[LNpk]}}$ is defined as $e_{\mathrm{pk}}/\omega_{\mathrm{m}}$, we have

$$k_{\mathrm{E[LNpk]}} = \frac{1}{2}\, k_{\mathrm{E[LLpk]}}. \qquad (8.19)$$

There is no advantage in defining k_{E} using the phase EMF e_{pk}, since e_{pk} is not directly measurable and $k_{\mathrm{E[LNpk]}}$ is not equal to $k_{\mathrm{T[pk]}}$.

In the delta-connected motor the phase EMF is the same as the line-line EMF, but we can also define a false neutral point (provided that there are no zero-sequence components in the phase EMFs). The fictitious line-neutral EMF $e_{\mathrm{LN[DELTA]}}$ is shown in Fig. 8.6, corresponding to the 60° flat-top line-line EMF. This EMF cannot be measured and is calculated only for the sake of completeness.

It *is* preferable to use the mean rectified EMF to define k_{E}, because it is closest to the canonical norm of the ideal DC motor. This cannot be said of the RMS EMF, and even the peak value is sensitive to harmonics that contribute nothing to the torque. The following sections underline the importance of the mean rectified EMF in the process of defining k_{E}, and they develop conversion coefficients for the peak line-line or phase EMFs. The use of RMS *current* in the definition of k_{T} is a somewhat safer practice, provided that the current waveform is precisely defined.

Summary — For the 3-phase brushless DC squarewave motor with squarewave drive, if we define k_E using the peak line-line EMF or the mean rectified EMF (it does not matter which), and if we define k_T using the peak line current, we get $k_T = k_E$ and both are equal to **k** of the ideal DC motor.

The same step-by-step process is to be used again for motors of different EMF waveforms, supplied by different current waveforms from different drives, and we will find that the simple relationships of the 3-phase squarewave motor are not repeated.

Indeed eqn. (8.17) is an example of the kind of complication or inconvenience that can arise with brushless motors — but not with the DC motor, in which peak, mean and RMS quantities are the same.

The step-by-step method also reflects industrial practice. It is common for manufacturers to measure k_E and quote it in their catalogues. Not so with k_T. Practical measurement of k_T requires a drive and a dynamometer, which is not only expensive and time-consuming, but also particularizes k_T to that drive, which might not even be capable of supplying the ideal current waveform. Moreover, k_T is affected by friction and saturation (see Fig. 13.6), so that if measured values of k_T were to be quoted in catalogue data they would need to be very carefully qualified, and they would *never* be equal to k_E, no matter how they were defined or what units were used.

Very sensibly, therefore, the industry follows the convention of quoting k_E (usually verified in the factory by measurement), and presenting k_T as *derived* from k_E. From this data, users can determine with sufficient accuracy the current they will need — and therefore the size of amplifier or drive — to obtain a certain torque.

Perhaps because of the evolution of the squarewave brushless DC system from the DC commutator system, the complexities and subtleties — in other words, the *pitfalls* — of defining k_E and k_T which arise in the following sections were not widely anticipated, although much careful analysis was published in the early days.[67]

---

[67] See, for example, Fratta A. and Vagati A. *Synchronous vs. DC brushless Servomotor: the Machine Behaviour*, Symposium on Electric Drives, Cagliari, September 1987, pp. 53-60; Boenig J.H., *Optimization of Magnetic Materials Utilization in Semiconductor-Commutated Electric Machines*, PhD thesis, University of Wisconsin, 1971.

8.2.3 3-phase sinewave motor and drive

A three-phase sinewave motor has a sinusoidal EMF, with peak line-line value e_{LLpk}, Fig. 8.5. The sinusoidal line currents have a peak value i_{Lpk} and an RMS value $I_{Lrms} = i_{Lpk}/\sqrt{2} = 0{\cdot}70711 i_{Lpk}$, while the peak fundamental current I_1 is equal to i_{Lpk}. If all losses and reactive effects are neglected, the power balance gives

$$T\omega_m = \sqrt{3}\, E_{LLRMS} I_{LRMS} = \sqrt{3}\, \frac{e_{LLpk}}{\sqrt{2}} \frac{i_{Lpk}}{\sqrt{2}} = \frac{\sqrt{3}}{2}\, e_{LLpk} i_{Lpk}. \tag{8.20}$$

Following the method outlined for the DC commutator motor, the next step is to identify the EMF E_d of the equivalent ideal DC motor as the mean rectified line-line EMF, which we can see from Fig. 8.5 is

$$E_d = \frac{3}{\pi}\, e_{LLpk} = 0{\cdot}95493\, e_{LLpk}. \tag{8.21}$$

Again this value of E_d represents the DC voltage associated with energy conversion in the motor, and again it is independent of any voltage drops in the resistance or the power semiconductors. For the same peak value of e_{LLpk}, E_d is about 4·5% less than the DC voltage obtained for the 3-phase squarewave drive.

The primary EMF constant **k** is defined by eqn. (8.11) as the ratio E_d/ω_m, where the boldface notation again signifies exact equivalence with the ideal DC motor. Since $E_d = 3/\pi \times e_{LLpk}$ for the sinewave motor, we get

$$k_{E[LLpk]} = \frac{e_{LLpk}}{\omega_m} = \frac{\pi}{3} \frac{E_d}{\omega_m} = \frac{\pi}{3}\mathbf{k} = 1{\cdot}04720\,\mathbf{k}, \tag{8.22}$$

where $k_{E[LLpk]}$ could be said to be the practical value, as obtained by direct measurement. If we now substitute the power conversion equation (8.3) of the ideal DC motor in eqn. (8.20), we get

$$T\omega_m = E_d I_d = \frac{3}{\pi}\, e_{LLpk} I_d = \frac{\sqrt{3}}{2}\, e_{LLpk} i_{Lpk}, \tag{8.23}$$

from which it follows that

$$I_d = \frac{\pi}{2\sqrt{3}}\, i_{Lpk} = 0{\cdot}90690\, i_{Lpk}. \tag{8.24}$$

The current I_d required to produce a given torque T is again given by eqn. (8.13), and we are now in a position to determine the practical form of k_T. Suppose we define $k_{T[pk]}$ as the ratio T/i_{Lpk}. Then

$$k_{T[pk]} = \frac{T}{i_{Lpk}} = \frac{T}{I_d} \times \frac{I_d}{i_{Lpk}} = \mathbf{k} \times \frac{\pi}{2\sqrt{3}}. \quad (8.25)$$

Substituting for **k** from eqn. (8.22), we get

$$k_{T[pk]} = \frac{\sqrt{3}}{2} k_{E[LLpk]}. \quad (8.26)$$

The "practical" definitions of k_E and k_T based on peak quantities e_{LLpk} and i_{Lpk} no longer preserve the equality $k_T = k_E$, as they did with the 3-phase squarewave motor. This represents a significant difference between the sinewave and squarewave systems.

We can explore several alternatives. The RMS definition of k_T is

$$k_{T[rms]} = \frac{T}{I_{Lrms}} = \frac{T}{i_{Lpk}/\sqrt{2}} = k_{T[pk]}\sqrt{2} = \sqrt{\frac{3}{2}} k_{E[LLpk]}. \quad (8.27)$$

With sinusoidal EMF, in theory we could define $k_{E[rms]}$ as

$$k_{E[LLrms]} = \frac{E_{LLrms}}{\omega_m} = \frac{e_{LLpk}}{\omega_m\sqrt{2}} = \frac{k_{E[LLpk]}}{\sqrt{2}}. \quad (8.28)$$

Substituting $k_{T[rms]}$ and $k_{E[LLrms]}$ into eqn. (8.26) results in

$$k_{T[rms]} = \sqrt{3}\, k_{E[LLrms]}. \quad (8.29)$$

We could also define $k_{E[LNrms]}$ in terms of the line-neutral EMF, which is $E_{LL\,rms}/\sqrt{3}$. We would then find that

$$k_{T[rms]} = 3\, k_{E[LNrms]}. \quad (8.30)$$

As already mentioned, there are good reasons not to use peak or RMS values of EMF, and if we use instead the **mean rectified** EMF E_d from eqn. (8.21) we will get

$$k_{T[pk]} = \frac{\sqrt{3}}{2} \times \frac{\pi}{3}\mathbf{k} = \frac{\pi}{2\sqrt{3}}\mathbf{k} = 0{\cdot}90690\,\mathbf{k} \quad (8.31)$$

and

$$k_{T[rms]} = \sqrt{2} \times k_{T[pk]} = \frac{\pi}{\sqrt{6}} \mathbf{k} = 1{\cdot}28255\,\mathbf{k}. \qquad (8.32)$$

Example — A 3-phase brushless sinewave motor has K_E = 16 V/1000 rpm measured using the mean rectified line-line EMF. Calculate the RMS value of sinusoidal line current required to obtain 3 Nm of torque.

$k_E = \mathbf{k}$ = 16/(1000 × π/30)) = 0·15279 Vs/rad. From eqn. (8.32), $k_{T[rms]}$ = π/√6 × 0·15279 = 0·19596 Nm/A. Hence I_{Lrms} = 3/0·19596 = 15·31 A RMS.

It appears that the equality $k_T = k_E$ cannot be obtained for the pure 3-phase sinewave system for any definitions of k_E and k_E that use plain peak or RMS values of motor current and EMF — a most inconvenient conclusion. It might be worth noting that for both squarewave and sinewave systems

$$k_{T[rms]} = \sqrt{\frac{3}{2}}\, k_{E[LLpk]}, \qquad (8.33)$$

but whether this holds for the other systems described later remains to be seen.

8.2.4 3-phase sinewave motor with squarewave drive

Up to now we have matched sinewave motors with sinewave drives, and squarewave motors with squarewave drives. It is also of interest to mix them, that is, to couple a sinewave motor with a squarewave drive and *vice versa*. The first of these is quite common.

When a motor having a sinewave EMF is fed with squarewave current, only the fundamental component of current contributes to the torque. The peak fundamental component of the squarewave current in Fig. 8.1 is $I_1 = I_d \times 2\sqrt{3}/\pi$, with $I_d = i_{Lpk}$. The peak fundamental line-line EMF is $E_{LL1} = e_{LLpk}$, and the ideal power conversion equation (8.20) becomes

$$T\omega_m = \frac{\sqrt{3}}{2} E_{LL1} I_1 = \frac{\sqrt{3}}{2} e_{LLpk} \times \frac{2\sqrt{3}}{\pi} i_{Lpk} = \frac{3}{\pi} e_{LLpk} I_d = E_d I_d. \qquad (8.34)$$

Note that eqn. (8.21) has been used again to determine the mean rectified EMF E_d.

The primary EMF constant **k** is again defined by eqn. (8.11) as the ratio E_d/ω_m, and eqn. (8.22) again defines $k_{E[LLpk]}$, as expected since the EMF waveform is still sinusoidal.

The current I_d required to produce a given torque T is again given by eqn. (8.13), and we are now in a position to determine the practical form of k_T. Suppose we define $k'_{T[pk]}$ as the ratio T/i_{Lpk}; (the prime signifies that we have a hybrid system, a motor with sinewave EMF and a squarewave drive). Then

$$k'_{T[pk]} = \frac{T}{i_{Lpk}} = \frac{T}{I_d} \times \frac{I_d}{i_{Lpk}} = \mathbf{k}, \tag{8.35}$$

since $I_d = i_{Lpk}$. This is an important result for cases where a motor with sinusoidal EMF is coupled to a squarewave drive: provided that consistent units are used, the torque constant $k'_{T[pk]}$ defined as T/i_{Lpk} is numerically equal to the EMF constant defined using the mean rectified EMF.

It follows from eqn. (8.22) that

$$k'_{T[pk]} = \frac{3}{\pi} k_{E[LLpk]}. \tag{8.36}$$

Comparing this with eqn. (8.26), it appears that the torque constant $k'_{T[pk]} = T/i_{Lpk}$ is greater than its sinewave-drive value by the ratio $(3/\pi)/(\sqrt{(3)}/2) = 2\sqrt{3}/\pi$ or 1·10266. This is exactly the increase in the fundamental line current when the sinewave of peak value i_{Lpk} is replaced by a 120° squarewave of the same peak value.

The RMS value of the squarewave motor current is equal to $I_d\sqrt{(2/3)} = i_{Lpk}\sqrt{(2/3)} = 0{\cdot}8165\, I_d$. Hence

$$k'_{T[rms]} = \frac{T}{I_{Lrms}} = \frac{T}{i_{Lpk}} \times \frac{i_{Lpk}}{I_{Lrms}} = k'_{T[pk]} \sqrt{\frac{3}{2}}. \tag{8.37}$$

Combining this with eqn. (8.36),

$$k'_{T[rms]} = \frac{3}{\pi} \sqrt{\frac{3}{2}}\, k_{E[LLpk]}. \tag{8.38}$$

Since $k_{E[LLpk]}$ has remained the same throughout, we can compare this with the earlier $k_{T[rms]}$ for sinewave drive, given by eqn. (8.33).

Taking the ratio of these equations,

$$k'_{\mathrm{T[rms]}} = \frac{3}{\pi} k_{\mathrm{T[rms]}} = 0{\cdot}9549\, k_{\mathrm{T[rms]}}. \tag{8.39}$$

This means that the torque per RMS ampere of motor line current decreases by about 4·5% when a sinewave motor is coupled to a squarewave drive.

When the sinewave-EMF motor operates with squarewave current at the same speed and torque as it did with sinewave current, the DC current I_d must be the same. The RMS motor line current is $I_d\sqrt{(2/3)}$ for the squarewave, while for the sinewave drive it is $i_{Lpk}/\sqrt{2}$ which must be deduced from eqn. (8.24) as $\sqrt{6}/\pi \times I_d$. The RMS currents in the two cases are in the ratio

$$\frac{\text{Squarewave Drive}}{\text{Sinewave Drive}} : \frac{I_d\sqrt{2/3}}{I_d\sqrt{6}/\pi} = \frac{\pi}{3} = 1{\cdot}0472, \tag{8.40}$$

which is the inverse of eqn. (8.39). The I^2R losses will be in the square of this ratio, about 1·09662. The additional losses are caused by the harmonics in the squarewave current, which contribute nothing to the torque.

8.2.5 3-phase squarewave motor with sinewave drive

This combination is almost the dual of the previous one, but it is less common in practice.

When the current is sinusoidal, only the fundamental component of the EMF contributes to the torque, and the power balance equation can be written

$$T\omega_m = \frac{\sqrt{3}}{2} E_{LL1} I_1 = E_d I_d. \tag{8.41}$$

The peak fundamental line current I_1 is equal to the peak line current i_{Lpk}, or $\sqrt{2}$ times the RMS line current I_{Lrms}, these relationships being familiar for sinewaves.

To determine E_{LL1} precisely it is necessary to define an idealized trapezoidal EMF waveform such as the one in Fig. 8.6, which is reproduced in Fig. 8.7.

Fig. 8.7 shows an idealized line-neutral trapezoidal EMF of one phase e_{ph} together with the corresponding trapezoidal line-line EMF e_{LL}. The peak of e_{ph} is $0{\cdot}5e_{LLpk}$ and the peak of e_{LL} is e_{LLpk}. By Fourier analysis it can be shown that the fundamental component of e_{ph} is $6/\pi^2 e_{LLpk}$, while the fundamental of e_{LL} is

$$E_{LL1} = \sqrt{3} \times \frac{6}{\pi^2} e_{LLpk} = 1{\cdot}05296\, e_{LLpk}. \tag{8.42}$$

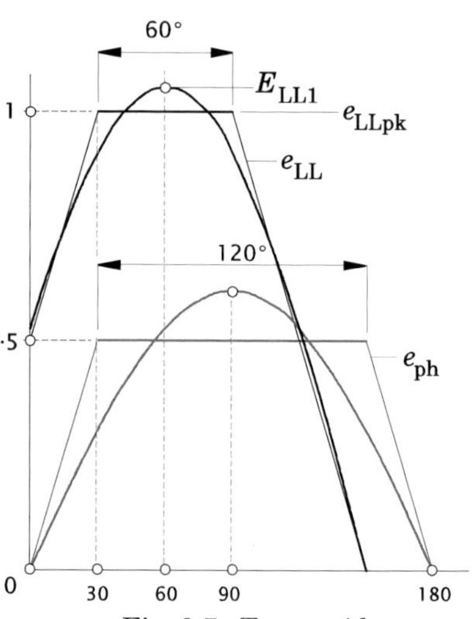

Fig. 8.7 Trapezoids

Substituting E_{LL1} and I_1 in eqn. (8.41), we get

$$T\omega_m = \frac{\sqrt{3}}{2} \times \sqrt{3} \times \frac{6}{\pi^2} e_{LLpk} i_{Lpk} = \frac{9}{\pi^2} e_{LLpk} i_{Lpk} = E_d I_d. \tag{8.43}$$

The mean rectified EMF E_d is equal to e_{LLpk}, as it was for the 3-phase squarewave motor, so the EMF constant is defined in eqns. (8.11) and (8.12). Substituting $E_d = e_{LLpk}$ in eqn. (8.43), we get

$$I_d = \frac{9}{\pi^2} i_{Lpk}. \tag{8.44}$$

The current I_d required to produce a given torque T is again given by eqn. (8.13), so we can define the torque constant k''_T as

$$k''_{T[pk]} = \frac{T}{i_{Lpk}} = \frac{T}{I_d} \times \frac{I_d}{i_{Lpk}} = \frac{9}{\pi^2} \mathbf{k}, \tag{8.45}$$

where the double prime indicates the hybrid system (squarewave motor with sinewave drive). Finally with eqn. (8.12) we get

$$k''_{T[pk]} = \frac{9}{\pi^2} k_{E[LLpk]} = 0{\cdot}91189\, k_{E[LLpk]}. \tag{8.46}$$

By a process similar to the one in the previous section, we can also derive $k''_{T[rms]}$ with reference to the RMS line current: thus

$$k''_{T[rms]} = \frac{T}{I_{Lrms}} = \frac{T}{i_{Lpk}} \times \frac{i_{Lpk}}{I_{Lrms}} = k_{T[pk]}\sqrt{2} = \frac{9\sqrt{2}}{\pi^2} k_{E[LLpk]}. \quad (8.47)$$

Since $k_{E[LLpk]}$ has remained the same throughout, we can compare this with the earlier $k_{T[rms]}$ for squarewave drive, which is given by eqn. (8.33). Taking the ratio of these equations, we find that

$$k''_{T[rms]} = \frac{6\sqrt{3}}{\pi^2} k_{T[rms]} = 1{\cdot}05296\, k_{T[rms]} \quad (8.48)$$

This means that the torque per RMS ampere of motor line current increases by a factor of $6\sqrt{(3)}/\pi^2$ or 1·05296 if a squarewave-EMF motor is coupled to a sinewave drive.

When the squarewave-EMF motor operates with sinewave current at the same speed and torque as it did with squarewave current, the DC voltage E_d and current I_d must be the same. With squarewave drive the RMS motor line current is $I_d\sqrt{(2/3)}$, while for the sinewave drive it is $i_{Lpk}/\sqrt{2}$ which is deduced from eqn. (8.44) as $\pi^2/9\sqrt{2} \times I_d$. The RMS currents in the two cases are in the ratio

$$\frac{\text{Sinewave Drive}}{\text{Squarewave Drive}} : \frac{I_d \pi^2/9\sqrt{2}}{I_d\sqrt{2/3}} = \frac{\pi^2}{6\sqrt{3}} = 0{\cdot}94970, \quad (8.49)$$

which is the inverse of eqn. (8.48). The I^2R losses will be in the square of this ratio, about 0·90194. Thus it emerges that by switching from squarewave drive to sinewave drive while keeping the same torque, the losses caused by the harmonics in the squarewave current decrease by more than their contribution to the torque.

We thus have the interesting conclusion from eqn. (8.39) that a motor with sinewave EMF works more efficiently with sinewave current, since $k_{T[rms]}$ is about 4·5% greater than when it is operated with squarewave drive. From eqn. (8.48), a motor with squarewave EMF *also* works more efficiently with sinewave current, since $k_{T[rms]}$ is about 5·3% greater when it is operated with sinewave drive.

However, this is not enough to establish which of the two motors has the higher $k_{T[rms]}$. This question is addressed in the next section.

8.2.6 3-phase squarewave and sinewave systems compared

Tables 8.1 and 8.2 compare all the motor/drive combinations so far considered, with fixed values of torque, speed, DC voltage E_d and DC current I_d. In all cases the power conversion $T\omega_m$ is equal to the product of the DC voltage E_d and the DC current I_d.

Motor/Drive (EMF/current)	Peak line-line EMF	Peak line current	RMS line current
	e_{LLpk}/E_d	i_{Lpk}/I_d	I_{Lrms}/I_d
DC	1	1	1
Square/Square	1	1	$\sqrt{(2/3)} = 0{\cdot}81650$
Sine/Sine	$\pi/3 = 1{\cdot}0472$	$2\sqrt{3}/\pi = 1{\cdot}10266$	$\sqrt{6}/\pi = 0{\cdot}77970$
Sine/Square	$\pi/3 = 1{\cdot}0472$	1	$\sqrt{(2/3)} = 0{\cdot}81650$
Square/Sine	1	$\pi^2/9 = 1{\cdot}09662$	$\pi^2/9\sqrt{2} = 0{\cdot}77543$

TABLE 8.1
3-PHASE MOTOR/DRIVE SYSTEMS; EMF AND CURRENT (SAME TORQUE AND SPEED)

Motor/Drive (EMF/current)	$k_{E[LLpk]}$	$k_{T[pk]}$	$k_{T[rms]}$
	e_{LLpk}/ω_m; E_d fixed	T/i_{Lpk}; I_d fixed	T/I_{Lrms}; I_d fixed
DC	1	1	1
Square/Square	1	1	$\sqrt{(3/2)} = 1{\cdot}22474$
Sine/Sine	$\pi/3 = 1{\cdot}0472$	$\pi/2\sqrt{3} = 0{\cdot}90690$	$\pi/\sqrt{6} = 1{\cdot}28255$
Sine/Square	$\pi/3 = 1{\cdot}0472$	1	$\sqrt{(3/2)} = 1{\cdot}22474$
Square/Sine	1	$9/\pi^2 = 0{\cdot}91189$	$9\sqrt{2}/\pi^2 = 1{\cdot}28961$

Table 8.2
3-PHASE MOTOR/DRIVE SYSTEMS; K_T AND K_E (SAME TORQUE AND SPEED)

Table 8.1 confirms, for example, that a sinewave-EMF motor with sinewave drive requires 0·7797/0·8165 = 0·9549 times the RMS current to produce the same torque, compared with squarewave drive, eqn. (8.39). Table 8.2 gives corresponding k_E and k_T values relative to **k** of the ideal DC motor.

The RMS current is important for efficiency and the rating of power transistors (particularly MOSFETS). Sinewave drive requires the least RMS current in all cases. The squarewave-EMF motor with sinewave drive has the lowest figure, but it has additional torque ripple that will likely offset the very small saving in current.

Sinewave-EMF motors also produce the highest peak EMF, though the fundamental EMF of the squarewave motor is higher; [eqn. (8.42)]. Beyond this it is difficult to develop the comparison between squarewave and sinewave motors much further from the tables. They are silent on the question of winding resistance, so it is not possible to compare I^2R losses between different motors. The motor constant K_m addresses this point (see below).

Internal design factors — It is clear from the EMF and torque calculations in Chapter 4 that k_T and k_E depend on the turns, as well as on the distribution of conductors and the strength and distribution of the magnet flux. The performance of a motor/drive system over a wide speed range is strongly affected by inductance, while interior-magnet machines have reluctance torque which breaks the link between k_T and k_E, and makes k_T dependent on the current, even before saturation is considered. All these factors show that the selection of a machine should not be based purely on k_T and k_E.

In both squarewave and sinewave motors the peak EMF is proportional to the peak airgap flux-density. If the sinewave motor is designed with a sinusoidal flux distribution of peak value B in the airgap, the flux/pole is BDL/p, where D is the airgap diameter, L is the stack length, and p is the number of pole-pairs. In the squarewave motor a rectangular flux distribution of peak value B has a flux/pole of $B \times \pi D/2p \times L$, which is greater than that of the sinewave motor in the ratio $\pi/2$. Yet k_T and k_E can be made the same in both motors, simply by adjusting the turns.

Pursuing this a little further, the two motors cannot both be optimally designed, since one will have a greater flux in the yokes than the other, leading to a higher saturation level and higher iron losses. If the rotor diameters and lengths are freely chosen to optimize the designs for squarewave or sinewave operation, we may well end up with motors of widely different inertia, weight, inductance, and even efficiency, even though k_T and k_E may be the same. Obviously these factors should be included in any comparison.

The entry for the DC motor in Table 8.1 emphasizes these points still further. According to the numbers it has the highest RMS line current, implying the lowest k_{Trms}; but what the table does not show is that this current is flowing in only two leads, not three.

8.2.7 Example calculations (3-phase)

Example — A 3-phase brushless DC motor has a trapezoidal EMF of peak value 23·2 V (line-line) at 988 rpm. Calculate

(i) k_E in V/1000 rpm and Vs/rad;

(ii) k_T in Nm/A[pk] with squarewave drive;

(iii) k_T in oz-in per RMS ampere of line current (squarewave).

This motor is now coupled to a *sine*wave drive and fed with 3 A RMS of sinusoidal current. Calculate

(iv) the torque;

(v) the no-load speed in rpm.

Solution —

(i)

$$k_E = 23{\cdot}2 \times \frac{1000}{988} = 23{\cdot}48 \text{ V/1000rpm}$$

$$k_E = \frac{23{\cdot}48}{1000} \times \frac{60}{2\pi} = 0{\cdot}2242 \text{ Vs/rad.}$$

(ii) For the squarewave motor with squarewave drive,

$$k_T = k_E = 0{\cdot}2242 \text{ Nm/A[pk].}$$

(iii) By plain conversion of units, 1 oz-in = 1/141·6 Nm, so

$$k_T = 0{\cdot}2242 \times 141{\cdot}6 = 31{\cdot}75 \text{ oz–in/A[pk].}$$

With squarewave drive the RMS current is equal to the peak current multiplied by $\sqrt{(2/3)}$, so

$$k_T = \frac{31{\cdot}75}{\sqrt{(2/3)}} = 38{\cdot}9 \text{ oz–in/A[rms].}$$

(iv) From eqn. (8.47),

$$T = \frac{9\sqrt{2}}{\pi^2} k_{E[pk]} I_{rms} = 1{\cdot}2896 \times 0{\cdot}2242 \times 3{\cdot}0 = 0{\cdot}867 \text{ Nm.}$$

(v) The no-load speed cannot be determined because we do not know the drive voltage waveform at no-load (or indeed at any load).

Example — a 3-phase brushless DC motor has a sinusoidal EMF of peak value 23·2 V at 988 rpm. Calculate

(i) k_E in V/1000 rpm and Vs/rad;

(ii) k_T in Nm/A[rms] (sinewave drive);

(iii) k_T in lb-in per RMS ampere of line current (sinewave).

The motor is coupled to a sinewave drive operating from a 40 V DC bus and fed with 3 A RMS of sinusoidal current. Calculate

(iv) the torque;

(v) the no-load speed in rpm, if the drive inverter operates in 6-step mode (Chapter 7).

Solution —

(i)
$$k_E = 23{\cdot}2 \times \frac{1000}{988} = 23{\cdot}48 \text{ V/1000rpm}$$

$$k_E = \frac{23{\cdot}48}{1000} \times \frac{60}{2\pi} = 0{\cdot}2242 \text{ Vs/rad.}$$

(ii) From eqn. (8.33),

$$k_{T[rms]} = \sqrt{\frac{3}{2}}\, k_E = \sqrt{\frac{3}{2}} \times 0{\cdot}2242 = 0{\cdot}2746 \text{ Nm/A[rms].}$$

(iii) By plain conversion of units, 1 lb-in = 1/8·85 Nm,

$$k_T = 0{\cdot}2746 \times 8{\cdot}85 = 2{\cdot}43 \text{ lb–in/A[rms].}$$

(iv) The torque is simply

$$T = k_T I_{rms} = 2{\cdot}43 \times 3{\cdot}0 = 7{\cdot}29 \text{ lb–in.}$$

(v) A 6-step drive can produce a line-line RMS fundamental voltage of $(\sqrt{6}/\pi)E_d$ = 0·779 × 40 = 31·19 V RMS or 44·11 V peak. The no-load speed is therefore

$$\frac{44{\cdot}11}{23{\cdot}48} \times 1000 = 1{,}878{\cdot}5 \text{ rpm.}$$

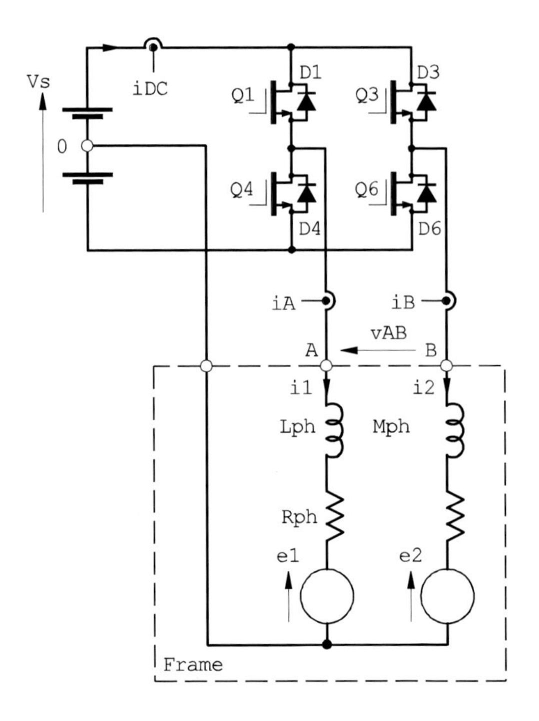

Fig. 8.8 Electric circuit of 2-phase motor and drive

8.2.8 2-phase squarewave motor and drive

Fig. 8.8 shows the circuit of a 2-phase motor and drive.[68] The EMF waveform is ideally trapezoidal with a 90° flat top in each phase, so the line-line EMF $e_{LL} = e_1 - e_2$ is triangular (Fig. 8.9), with peak value

$$e_{LLpk} = 2\, e_{pk}, \tag{8.62}$$

where e_{pk} is the peak phase EMF. The mean rectified line-line EMF is

$$E_d = \frac{1}{2} e_{LLpk} = e_{pk}. \tag{8.63}$$

The current waveform in each phase is a 90° block squarewave of peak value i_{pk}, also shown in Fig. 8.2. The DC current I_d is commutated from phase to phase every 90°, and in any 90° interval, only one phase is conducting, with $i_{Lpk} = I_d$.

---

[68] See the *Electro-Craft Engineering Handbook*, 5th edition.

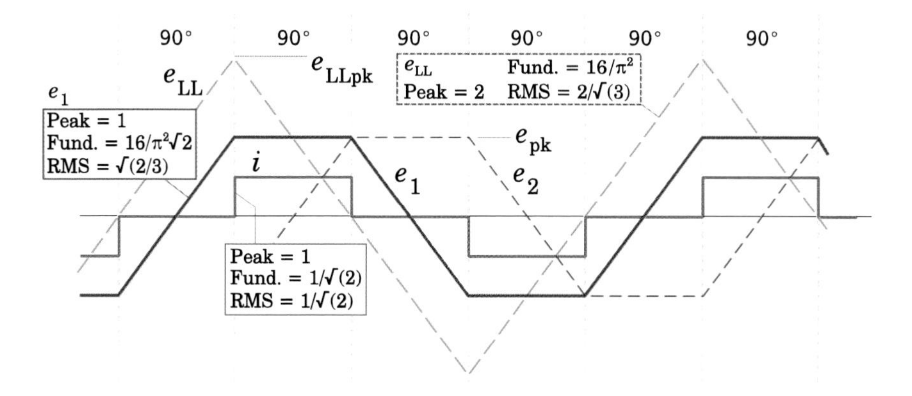

Fig. 8.9 Waveforms of 2-phase squarewave motor with squarewave drive

With losses neglected, the ideal power conversion equation is

$$T\omega_m = e_{pk} i_{pk} = e_{pk} I_d = E_d I_d. \tag{8.64}$$

The primary EMF constant **k** is again defined as the ratio E_d/ω_m in eqn. (8.11), where the boldface notation signifies equivalence with the ideal DC motor. Since $E_d = e_{pk}$ for this particular motor, it is natural to define k_E with reference to the phase EMF rather than to the line-line EMF, and we get

$$k_{E\,[pk]} = \mathbf{k} = \frac{E_d}{\omega_m} = \frac{e_{pk}}{\omega_m}. \tag{8.65}$$

The current I_d required to produce a given torque T is again given by eqn. (8.13), and we can define $k_{T[pk]}$ as T/i_{Lpk}. Since $i_{Lpk} = I_d$, we get

$$k_{T\,[pk]} = \frac{T}{i_{Lpk}} = \frac{T}{I_d} = \mathbf{k} = k_{E\,[pk]}, \tag{8.66}$$

which does not apply in the case of the squarewave 3-phase motor. In each line the RMS current is $I_{L\,rms} = I_d/\sqrt{2} = 0{\cdot}70711\, I_d$, so

$$k_{T\,[rms]} = k_T \times \frac{i_{Lpk}}{I_{Lrms}} = k_{T\,[pk]}\sqrt{2}. \tag{8.67}$$

As in the 3-phase systems there are alternatives. If we define k_E as $k_{E[LLpk]}$ using the peak line-line EMF, while keeping $k_{T[pk]}$ defined as T/i_{Lpk}, we would find that

$$k_{T[pk]} = \frac{1}{2} k_{E[LLpk]}. \tag{8.68}$$

Finally if we defined E_d as the mean rectified value of the *phase* EMF, the value of which is $3/4 \times e_{pk}$, we would have

$$k_{E[pk]} = \frac{e_{pk}}{\omega_m} = \frac{4}{3}\frac{E_d}{\omega_m} = \frac{4}{3}\mathbf{k}. \tag{8.69}$$

The ideal power conversion equation is

$$T\omega_m = e_{pk} i_{Lpk} = E_d I_d = \frac{3}{4} e_{pk} I_d, \tag{8.70}$$

whence $i_{Lpk} = 3/4 \times I_d$. The DC current required to produce a given torque is again equal to $T/\mathbf{k}$, so if we define $k_{T[pk]}$ as T/i_{Lpk}, we get

$$k_{T[pk]} = \frac{T}{i_{Lpk}} = \frac{T}{I_d} \times \frac{I_d}{i_{Lpk}} = \frac{4}{3}\mathbf{k} = k_{E[pk]}. \tag{8.71}$$

8.2.9 2-phase sinewave motor and drive

The circuit is the same as in Fig. 8.8. The EMF of each phase is sinusoidal with a peak value e_{pk}, and the phase-shift between them is 90°, so the line-line EMF is also sinusoidal with a peak value $e_{LLpk} = \sqrt{2} \times e_{pk}$. The mean rectified EMF is given by

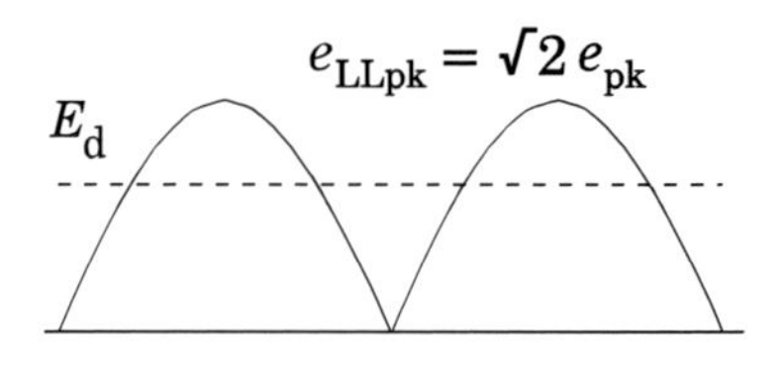

Fig. 8.10 Mean rectified line-line EMF

$$E_d = \frac{2}{\pi} e_{LLpk} = \frac{2\sqrt{2}}{\pi} e_{pk}, \tag{8.72}$$

as shown in Fig. 8.10. There is only one line-line EMF.

The line currents are the same as the phase currents and each is a sinewave of peak value i_{Lpk}. The RMS line current is $I_{Lrms} = i_{Lpk}/\sqrt{2} = 0{\cdot}7071\, i_{Lpk}$, while the fundamental current is equal to i_{Lpk}. Both phases are conducting at all times except at the current-zeroes. If all losses and reactive effects are neglected, the ideal power conversion equation is

$$T\omega_m = 2\, E_{rms} I_{rms} = 2\, \frac{e_{pk}}{\sqrt{2}} \frac{i_{Lpk}}{\sqrt{2}} = e_{pk} i_{Lpk}, \tag{8.73}$$

where E_{rms} is the RMS value of the EMF in each phase. This happens to be the same equation as for the 2-phase squarewave system, in spite of the differences in the waveforms.

Substituting eqns. (8.3) and (8.72) in eqn. (8.73), we get

$$T\omega_m = E_d I_d = \frac{2\sqrt{2}}{\pi} e_{pk} I_d = e_{pk} i_{Lpk}, \tag{8.74}$$

whence

$$I_d = \frac{\pi}{2\sqrt{2}} i_{Lpk} = \frac{\pi}{2\sqrt{2}} I_1. \tag{8.75}$$

The primary EMF constant is again defined by eqn. (8.11) on p. 412. Using the previous notation we find

$$k_{E[pk]} = \frac{e_{pk}}{\omega_m} = \frac{E_d}{\omega_m} \times \frac{e_{pk}}{E_d} = \frac{\pi}{2\sqrt{2}} \mathbf{k} \tag{8.76}$$

and

$$k_{E[LLpk]} = \frac{e_{LLpk}}{\omega_m} = \frac{E_d}{\omega_m} \times \frac{e_{LLpk}}{E_d} = \frac{\pi}{2} \mathbf{k}. \tag{8.77}$$

The current I_d required to produce a given torque T is again given by eqn. (8.13). If we define $k_{T[pk]}$ as T/i_{Lpk}, we get

$$k_{T[pk]} = \frac{T}{i_{Lpk}} = \frac{T}{I_d} \times \frac{I_d}{i_{Lpk}} = \frac{\pi}{2\sqrt{2}} \mathbf{k} = k_{E[pk]}. \tag{8.78}$$

Also

$$k_{T[rms]} = k_{T[pk]} \times \frac{i_{Lpk}}{I_{Lrms}} = k_{T[pk]} \sqrt{2} = \frac{\pi}{2} \mathbf{k} = k_{E[LLpk]}. \tag{8.79}$$

A final alternative is to define E_d as the mean rectified phase EMF instead of the mean rectified line-line EMF; that is, $E_d = 2/\pi \times e_{pk}$. Then

$$k_{E[pk]} = \frac{e_{pk}}{\omega_m} = \frac{E_d}{\omega_m} \times \frac{e_{pk}}{E_d} = \frac{\pi}{2}\,\mathbf{k}. \tag{8.80}$$

and $k_{E[LLpk]} = k_{E[pk]}\sqrt{2} = \pi\sqrt{2}/2 \times \mathbf{k}$. The power conversion equation becomes

$$T\omega_m = E_d I_d = e_{pk} i_{Lpk} = \frac{2}{\pi} e_{pk} I_d, \tag{8.81}$$

whence $I_d = \pi/2 \times i_{Lpk}$, and it follows, again, that

$$k_{T[pk]} = \frac{T}{i_{Lpk}} = \frac{T}{I_d} \times \frac{I_d}{i_{Lpk}} = \frac{\pi}{2}\,\mathbf{k} = k_{E[pk]}. \tag{8.82}$$

In this system there are no fewer than three ways to define k_E and k_T in such a way as to make them numerically equal (in consistent units) : we can use T/I_d with E_d/ω_m; $k_{T[pk]} = T/i_{Lpk}$ with $k_{E[pk]} = e_{pk}/\omega_m$; or $k_{T[rms]} = T/I_{rms}$ with $k_{E[LLpk]} = e_{LLpk}/\omega_m$.

We are now in a position to begin to summarize the differences between the squarewave and sinewave systems; see Tables 8.3 and 8.4 on p. 435. For example, at the same torque and speed, E_d and I_d are the same in both systems, but the sinewave system will have a higher peak phase EMF in the ratio $\pi/2\sqrt{2} : 1$, that is, 1·11:1; a lower peak line current in the ratio $2\sqrt{2}/\pi : 1$, that is, 0·900 : 1; and a lower RMS line current in the ratio $(2/\pi) : (1/\sqrt{2})$, that is, 0·900 : 1.

The comments about internal design factors on p. 423 also apply to the 2-phase motor/drive.

8.2.10 2-phase sinewave motor with squarewave drive

As in the case of 3-phase systems, it is also of interest to couple a sinewave motor with a squarewave drive and *vice versa*.

When a motor having a sinewave EMF is fed with squarewave current, only the fundamental component of current contributes to the torque. The fundamental component of the squarewave current in Fig. 8.2 is $I_1 = i_{Lpk} \times 2\sqrt{2}/\pi$.

The fundamental line-line EMF is $E_{LL1} = e_{LLpk} = e_{pk}\sqrt{2}$, and the mean rectified line-line EMF is $E_d = 2/\pi \times e_{LLpk} = 2\sqrt{2}/\pi \times e_{pk}$, as in Fig. 8.10. The ideal power conversion is

$$T\omega_m = E_d I_d = 2\,E_{rms}\frac{I_1}{\sqrt{2}} = 2\,\frac{e_{pk}}{\sqrt{2}}\frac{I_1}{\sqrt{2}} = e_{pk}I_1 \tag{8.83}$$

and if we substitute E_d we get

$$I_d = \frac{\pi}{2\sqrt{2}} I_1 = i_{Lpk}. \tag{8.84}$$

The primary EMF constant is again defined by eqn. (8.11) on p. 412, and as this is the same sinewave motor as in the previous section we have, again,

$$k_{E[pk]} = \frac{e_{pk}}{\omega_m} = \frac{E_d}{\omega_m} \times \frac{e_{pk}}{E_d} = \frac{\pi}{2\sqrt{2}}\,\mathbf{k} \tag{8.85}$$

and

$$k_{E[LLpk]} = \frac{e_{LLpk}}{\omega_m} = \frac{E_d}{\omega_m} \times \frac{e_{LLpk}}{E_d} = \frac{\pi}{2}\,\mathbf{k}. \tag{8.86}$$

The current I_d required to produce a given torque T is again given by eqn. (8.13). If we define $k_{T[pk]}$ as T/i_{Lpk}, we get

$$k_{T[pk]} = \frac{T}{i_{Lpk}} = \frac{T}{I_d} \times \frac{I_d}{i_{Lpk}} = \mathbf{k} = \frac{2\sqrt{2}}{\pi} k_{E[pk]} = \frac{2}{\pi} k_{E[LLpk]}. \tag{8.87}$$

Also with $I_{Lrms} = i_{Lpk}/\sqrt{2}$ we have

$$\begin{aligned} k_{T[rms]} &= k_{T[pk]} \times \frac{i_{Lpk}}{I_{Lrms}} = k_{T[pk]}\sqrt{2} \\ &= \mathbf{k}\sqrt{2} = \frac{4}{\pi} k_{E[pk]} = \frac{2\sqrt{2}}{\pi} k_{E[LLpk]}. \end{aligned} \tag{8.88}$$

A final alternative is to define E_d as the mean rectified phase EMF instead of the mean rectified line-line EMF; that is, $E_d = 2/\pi \times e_{pk}$. Then

$$k_{E[pk]} = \frac{e_{pk}}{\omega_m} = \frac{E_d}{\omega_m} \times \frac{e_{pk}}{E_d} = \frac{\pi}{2}\,\mathbf{k}. \tag{8.89}$$

and $k_{E[LLpk]} = k_{E[pk]}\surd 2$. The power conversion equation becomes

$$T\omega_m = E_d I_d = e_{pk} I_1 = e_{pk} \times \frac{2\sqrt{2}}{\pi} i_{Lpk} \tag{8.90}$$

and if we substitute E_d we get

$$I_d = \frac{\pi}{2} I_1 = i_{Lpk}\sqrt{2}. \tag{8.91}$$

The current I_d required to produce a given torque T is again given by eqn. (8.13). If we define $k_{T[pk]}$ as T/i_{Lpk}, we get

$$k_{T[pk]} = \frac{T}{I_d} \times \frac{I_d}{i_{Lpk}} = \mathbf{k}\sqrt{2} = \frac{2\sqrt{2}}{\pi} k_{E[pk]} = \frac{2}{\pi} k_{E[LLpk]}. \tag{8.92}$$

Also with $I_{rms} = i_{Lpk}/\surd 2$ we have

$$k_{T[rms]} = k_{T[pk]}\sqrt{2} = 2\mathbf{k} = \frac{4}{\pi} k_{E[pk]} = \frac{2\sqrt{2}}{\pi} k_{E[LLpk]}. \tag{8.93}$$

These results are similar to those in eqns. (8.87) and (8.88), the difference being the definition of **k** itself.

8.2.11 2-phase squarewave motor with sinewave drive

This combination is almost the dual of the previous one. When the current is sinusoidal, only the fundamental component of the EMF contributes to the torque. Referring to Fig. 8.9, the fundamental line-line EMF has a peak value E_{LL1} given by

$$E_{LL1} = \frac{8}{\pi^2} e_{LLpk} = \frac{16}{\pi^2} e_{pk}, \tag{8.94}$$

while the fundamental phase EMF has a peak value E_1 given by

$$E_1 = \frac{8}{\pi^2\sqrt{2}} e_{LLpk} = \frac{16}{\pi^2\sqrt{2}} e_{pk}. \tag{8.95}$$

As before, the mean rectified line-line EMF is

$$E_d = \frac{1}{2} e_{LLpk} = e_{pk}. \tag{8.96}$$

The primary EMF constant is again defined by eqn. (8.11) on p. 412, and as this is the same squarewave motor as in §8.2.8 we have, again,

$$k_{E[pk]} = \frac{e_{pk}}{\omega_m} = \frac{E_d}{\omega_m} \times \frac{e_{pk}}{E_d} = \mathbf{k} \qquad (8.97)$$

and

$$k_{E[LLpk]} = \frac{e_{LLpk}}{\omega_m} = \frac{E_d}{\omega_m} \times \frac{e_{LLpk}}{E_d} = 2\,\mathbf{k}. \qquad (8.98)$$

The ideal power conversion equation is

$$T\omega_m = E_d I_d = 2\frac{E_1}{\sqrt{2}}\frac{I_1}{\sqrt{2}} = E_1 i_{Lpk} = \frac{16}{\pi^2\sqrt{2}} e_{pk} i_{Lpk}. \qquad (8.99)$$

and if we substitute E_d from eqn. (8.96) we get

$$I_d = \frac{16}{\pi^2\sqrt{2}} i_{Lpk}. \qquad (8.100)$$

The current I_d required to produce a given torque T is again given by eqn. (8.13) on p. 412, and if we define $k''_{T[pk]}$ as T/i_{Lpk} we get

$$\begin{aligned} k''_{T[pk]} &= \frac{T}{I_d} \times \frac{I_d}{i_{Lpk}} \\ &= \frac{16}{\pi^2\sqrt{2}}\mathbf{k} = \frac{16}{\pi^2\sqrt{2}} k_{E[pk]} = \frac{8}{\pi^2\sqrt{2}} k_{E[LLpk]}. \end{aligned} \qquad (8.101)$$

where the double prime indicates the hybrid system (sinewave motor with squarewave drive). Also with $I_{rms} = i_{Lpk}/\sqrt{2}$, we have

$$\begin{aligned} k''_{T[rms]} &= k''_{T[pk]} \times \frac{i_{Lpk}}{I_{rms}} \\ &= k''_{T[pk]}\sqrt{2} = \frac{16}{\pi^2}\mathbf{k} = \frac{16}{\pi^2} k_{E[pk]} = \frac{8}{\pi^2} k_{E[LLpk]}. \end{aligned} \qquad (8.102)$$

A final alternative is to define E_d as the mean rectified phase EMF instead of the mean rectified line-line EMF; that is, $E_d = 3/4 \times e_{pk}$.

Then $k_{E[pk]}$ is defined by eqn. (8.69) on p. 428, that is,

$$k_{E[pk]} = \frac{e_{pk}}{\omega_m} = \frac{4}{3}\frac{E_d}{\omega_m} = \frac{4}{3}\mathbf{k}_E. \tag{8.103}$$

and $k_{E[LLpk]} = 2\ k_{E[pk]} = 8/3 \times \mathbf{k}_E$. The power conversion equation becomes

$$T\omega_m = E_d I_d = \frac{3}{4} e_{pk} I_d = E_1 I_1 = \frac{16}{\pi^2\sqrt{2}} e_{pk} i_{Lpk} \tag{8.104}$$

whence

$$I_d = \frac{4}{3} \times \frac{16}{\pi^2\sqrt{2}} i_{Lpk} = 1{\cdot}5284 \times i_{Lpk}. \tag{8.105}$$

The current I_d required to produce a given torque T is again given by eqn. (8.13). If we define $k''_{T[pk]}$ as T/i_{Lpk}, we get

$$\begin{aligned} k''_{T[pk]} &= \frac{T}{I_d} \times \frac{I_d}{i_{Lpk}} \\ &= \frac{4}{3} \times \frac{16}{\pi^2\sqrt{2}}\mathbf{k}_E = \frac{16}{\pi^2\sqrt{2}} k_{E[pk]} = \frac{16}{\pi^2\sqrt{2}} k_{E[LLpk]}. \end{aligned} \tag{8.106}$$

Also with $I_{rms} = i_{Lpk}/\surd 2$ we have

$$k''_{T[rms]} = \frac{4}{3} \times \frac{16}{\pi^2}\mathbf{k}_E = \frac{16}{\pi^2} k_{E[pk]} = \frac{16}{\pi^2} k_{E[LLpk]}. \tag{8.107}$$

These results are similar to those in eqns. (8.101) and (8.102), the difference being the definition of $\mathbf{k}_E$ itself.

It has to be said that 2-phase drives are very rare, so all these relationships are relatively academic: they do not have the practical importance of the equivalent relationships for 3-phase drives, where a mistake can lead to an error in the predicted torque of the order of as much as 20–30%. Even so, the 2-phase drive is interesting as a theoretical entity. Two is the minimum number of phases required to achieve completely controllable rotation in both directions, and 2-phase systems (such as in the *dq*-axis theory) are of immense analytical value.

8.2.12 2-phase squarewave and sinewave systems compared

Tables 8.3 and 8.4 provide the same summary for 2-phase motors as Tables 8.1 and 8.2 for 3-phase motors.

Motor/Drive (EMF/current)	Peak phase EMF	Peak line-line EMF	Peak line current	RMS line current
	e_{pk}/E_d	e_{LLpk}/E_d	i_{Lpk}/I_d	I_{Lrms}/I_d
DC	1	1	1	1
Square/Square	1	2	1	$1/\sqrt{2}$
Sine/Sine	$\pi/2\sqrt{2}$	$\pi/2$	$2\sqrt{2}/\pi$	$2/\pi$
Sine/Square	$\pi/2\sqrt{2}$	$\pi/2$	1	$1/\sqrt{2}$
Square/Sine	1	2	$\pi^2\sqrt{2}/16$	$\pi^2/16$

TABLE 8.3
2-PHASE MOTOR/DRIVE SYSTEMS; EMF AND CURRENT (SAME TORQUE AND SPEED)

Motor/Drive (EMF/current)	$k_{E[pk]}$	$k_{E[LLpk]}$	$k_{T[pk]}$	$k_{T[rms]}$
	e_{pk}/ω_m	e_{LLpk}/ω_m	T/i_{Lpk}	T/I_{Lrms}
DC	1	1	1	1
Square/Square	1	2	1	$\sqrt{2}$
Sine/Sine	$\pi/2\sqrt{2}$	$\pi/2$	$\pi/2\sqrt{2}$	$\pi/2$
Sine/Square	$\pi/2\sqrt{2}$	$\pi/2$	1	$\sqrt{2}$
Square/Sine	1	2	$16/\pi^2\sqrt{2}$	$16/\pi^2$

Table 8.4
2-PHASE MOTOR/DRIVE SYSTEMS; K_T AND K_E (SAME TORQUE AND SPEED)

As in the case of 3-phase drives, k_E and k_T are not in general equal. Even under ideal conditions of magnetic linearity, no losses, and ideal waveforms of EMF and current, the relationship between k_E and k_T depends on these waveforms and on the method of definition. The choice of peak or RMS quantities in the definitions does not magically make $k_T = k_E$. Defining k_E using the mean rectified EMF also does not make $k_T = k_E$, except in the case of 3-phase or 2-phase motors with sinusoidal EMF operating with squarewave drive, provided that k_T is defined as T/i_{Lpk}; these again are special cases, not general ones. However, the mean rectified EMF is important in the theoretical derivation, since it provides the link with the ideal DC machine.

8.3 Figures of merit

A figure of merit is an attempt to place a numerical value on something that is really too complex to describe with a single number. Figures of merit are often found in sales data especially in connection with motion-control products. We have to reckon with them.

Figures of merit are often used to compare one motor against another. Although they may have an intuitive appeal, it is often unclear how to use them for practical calculations in an application. The literature is often obscure on this point, and engineers can be forgiven for the idea that figures of merit are nothing more than semi-technical parameters used to promote sales. They are certainly vulnerable to specmanship. When used to compare motors from different manufacturers, they should be taken together with many other factors: there is simply no way to reduce the performance profile of a motor to a single parameter.

8.3.1 kT and kE

The torque per ampere k_T and the EMF constant k_E are the most common figures of merit or "characteristic parameters" used with brushless permanent magnet motors. They provide a simple and essential link between the motor designer and the control engineer. We have already met them and developed formulas for them, and we have noted differences between squarewave and sinewave systems. (See §4.2.1 for details of k_E and §4.3.1 for details of k_T).

The relationship between k_T and k_E will be discussed further in Chapter 10 when we consider methods of measuring them. All that remains here is to emphasize the importance of precise definition when quoting values of these constants, and to remember that they are temperature-dependent.

8.3.2 Efficiency and power factor

Efficiency is obviously important in overall terms, but it is often of secondary importance during the design of control systems: unlike the other figures of merit, it has little to do with system dynamics. It is also zero in the stall condition, which is a perfectly normal operating point for servo-motors, and it varies widely with speed and torque. Similar comments can be made in respect of power factor.

8.3.3 Torque/Inertia ratio

The torque/inertia ratio is a simple figure of merit. It gives an idea of the acceleration capability of the motor, but it is important to make clear *which* of many possible torque values is used to define it, and of course the load inertia must not be forgotten. Torque/inertia ratio contains no information about the efficiency or temperature rise, unless T is defined as continuous rated torque; if T is defined as the peak instantaneous torque, there is no indication as to how long it may be sustained, or how often it can be used. As with all figures of merit, these considerations show that the T/J ratio is not only vulnerable to specmanship, but also conveys an oversimplified view of motion-control applications.

8.3.4 Power rate

Power rate (PR) is a composite figure-of-merit that combines torque T and the torque/inertia ratio T/J: thus PR $= T \times T/J = T^2/J$. There is no obvious logic or intuitive meaning in this combination, so we have to dig a little deeper to understand its origins. Arnold[69] introduces PR through the idea of the rate of change of mechanical power, dP_m/dt: thus if ω_m is the angular velocity,

$$\frac{dP_m}{dt} = \frac{d}{dt}(T\omega_m) = T\frac{d\omega_m}{dt} = T \times \frac{T}{J} = \frac{T^2}{J}. \qquad (8.108)$$

This equation presupposes that the load is a pure inertia driven by a constant torque T. If we consider the kinetic energy U of the rotating mass, its rate of change is

$$\frac{dU}{dt} = \frac{d}{dt}\left[\frac{1}{2}J\omega_m^2\right] = \frac{J}{2} \times 2\omega_m\frac{d\omega_m}{dt} = \frac{J}{2} \times 2\omega_m \times \frac{T}{J} \qquad (8.109)$$
$$= T\omega_m = P_m.$$

Therefore PR $= d^2U/dt^2$, the second derivative of kinetic energy. It expresses the speed at which the motor can build up the rate of increase of kinetic energy.

---

[69]Arnold F. and Floresta J.G., *Power Rate — A Most Important Figure-of-Merit for the Incremental Motion Designer*, Incremental Motion Control Systems Society, Proceedings of the 13th Annual Symposium, Champaign, Illinois; Prof. B.C. Kuo, Editor, May 1984, pp. 11–18.

Power rate has another aspect derived by considering the minimum time required to move an inertial load over a certain angle. The "move" in Fig. 8.11 is accomplished in minimum time by accelerating at the maximum possible rate from 0–t_1 along OA, reaching maximum permissible speed at A and continuing at that speed along AB, then finally decelerating at the maximum possible rate along BC. Setting aside any consideration of the maximum velocity, consider what is needed to minimize the acceleration time t_1 along OA. This time is given by

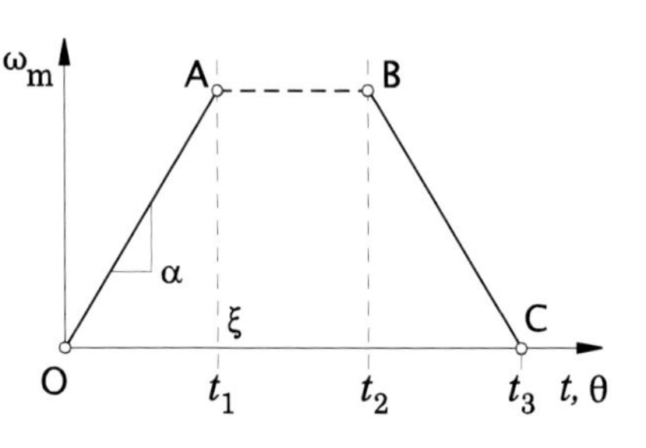

Fig. 8.11 Power rate

$$\xi = \frac{1}{2}\alpha t_1^2 \tag{8.110}$$

From eqns. (14.20) and (14.21) with ideal gear ratio n, we get

$$\alpha = \frac{T}{n\left[J_m + \dfrac{J_L}{n^2}\right]} = \frac{T}{\sqrt{\dfrac{J_L}{J_m}} \times \left[J_m + J_m\right]} = \frac{T}{2\sqrt{J_L J_m}}. \tag{8.111}$$

Combining eqns. (8.110) and (8.111), we get

$$t_1 = \frac{2\sqrt{2\xi\sqrt{J_L}}}{\sqrt{T/\sqrt{J_m}}} = \frac{2\sqrt{2\xi\sqrt{J_L}}}{\sqrt[4]{T^2/J_m}} = \frac{2\sqrt{2\xi\sqrt{J_L}}}{\sqrt[4]{\mathrm{PR}}} \tag{8.112}$$

which says that t_1 is minimized if T^2/J_m is maximized. In words, the move time t_1 is inversely proportional to the fourth root of the power rate PR. Eqn. (8.112) says that to reduce t_1 by a factor of 2, the PR must increase by a factor of 2^4 or 16 times. This can be achieved by increasing T by a factor of 4, or by decreasing J_m by a factor of 16. The effect of reducing J_m is weaker because the system is "carrying" a fixed load inertia J_L, and although the gear ratio n is optimized to make the referred load inertia equal to the motor inertia, this does not change the amount of kinetic energy that must be imparted to the load.

Power rate is susceptible to specmanship because it depends on which value of torque is used to calculate it — the rated continuous torque, the stall torque, the torque at the demagnetization point, or the short-circuit torque — any of these could be used (in increasing order of magnitude and decreasing order of credibility). Therefore when *Power Rate* is quoted, it should be stated what value of torque is being used. Moreover, as we have just seen, the value of *Power Rate* inflates much faster than the improvement in move-time t_1.

8.3.5 Speed rate and mechanical time-constant

Speed rate is defined as

$$\mathrm{SR} = \frac{k_E k_T}{JR} = \frac{1}{\tau_m}. \tag{8.113}$$

This is the reciprocal of the traditional **mechanical time-constant** $\tau_m = JR/k_E k_T$. A higher value indicates a better motor, in common with all the other figures-of-merit, and this is advanced as an argument why speed rate is preferable to τ_m as a figure-of-merit.

If we multiply numerator and denominator of eqn. (8.113) by $I^2 R$, assuming $k_T = k_E$, we get

$$\mathrm{SR} = \frac{T^2/J}{I^2 R} = \frac{\mathrm{PR}}{I^2 R} \tag{8.114}$$

which says that the speed rate is the ratio of the power rate to the $I^2 R$ loss. The speed rate thus incorporates all the other figures-of-merit in a single parameter — the electromagnetic torque-producing capability k_T, the inertia J, and the resistive dissipation *via* the resistance R. At the same time it remains a motor "constant" not dependent on the level of current or torque.

The original mechanical time-constant τ_m derives from the classical analysis of variable-speed DC motors in which the speed was controlled by the armature *voltage*. It is the time-constant of the exponential response of motor speed, following a step-change of supply voltage. Speed rate can therefore be interpreted as the initial gradient of this response, in "per unit speed per second". However, its value as a figure-of-merit is quite general; it applies to all kinds of motor and is not contingent on the method of control.

8.3.6 Motor constant

Motor Constant K_m is the ratio of torque to the *square-root* of the I^2R loss. If torque T is expressed as $k_T I$, where k_T is the torque constant, and R is the motor resistance (line-line), then

$$K_m = \frac{k_T}{\sqrt{R}}. \tag{8.115}$$

The underlying objective is to express the torque capability of the motor in relation to its loss dissipation, but the obvious ratio of the "torque per I^2R loss" would result in $k_T I/I^2R = k_T/IR$, which is inversely proportional to current and therefore not a "constant".[70]

K_m is primarily an indicator of stall performance. Unlike the power rate, K_m is independent of inertia, so it gives no indication of acceleration capability, although Hanselman has argued that in practice a high K_m is often *correlated* with a high torque/inertia ratio.

The origin of K_m is not as arbitrary as might seem from the above definition. If we go back to Chapter 1 we can see from eqns. (1.13) and (1.14) that the ratio of stall torque and no-load speed is

$$\frac{T_{LR}}{\omega_{NL}} = \frac{k_T k_E}{R}. \tag{8.116}$$

If $k_T = k_E$, this ratio is the same as K_m^2. It defines the gradient of the torque/speed characteristic that is constrained by constant voltage. Evidently a high value of K_m indicates a high stall torque.

Example[71] — Stall torque comparison using Motor Constant K_m

The stall torques of three motors will be compared using K_m, in such a way as to emphasize the importance of temperature rise and thermal resistance.

Neglecting all losses except copper losses, the temperature rise at stall is

$$\Delta T = W_{Cu}\theta = I^2 R\theta \tag{8.117}$$

so the stall current is limited to

$$I = \sqrt{\frac{\Delta T}{R\theta}} \tag{8.118}$$

[70] By this argument, T/J and T^2/J are also not motor "constants".

[71] This example was prepared by Mel Amato of Maxim Electronic Sales, and is reproduced with permission.

The maximum allowable stall torque is then

$$T_s = k_T I = k_T \sqrt{\frac{\Delta T}{R\theta}} = K_m \sqrt{\frac{\Delta T}{\theta}} \tag{8.119}$$

Comparing two motors 1 and 2,

$$\frac{T_{s2}}{T_{s1}} = \frac{K_{m2}}{K_{m1}} \sqrt{\frac{\theta_1}{\theta_2} \cdot \frac{\Delta T_2}{\Delta T_1}} \tag{8.120}$$

If the motors have the same temperature rise, $\Delta T_1 = \Delta T_2$ and

$$\frac{T_{s2}}{T_{s1}} = \frac{K_{m2}}{K_{m1}} \sqrt{\frac{\theta_1}{\theta_2}} \tag{8.121}$$

If the motors *also* have the same thermal resistance, $\theta_1 = \theta_2$ and

$$\frac{T_{s2}}{T_{s1}} = \frac{K_{m2}}{K_{m1}}. \tag{8.122}$$

The effect of temperature on k_T and R can be calculated using

$$k_T = k_{T0}(1 + \alpha_K \Delta T) \tag{8.123}$$

and

$$R = R_0(1 + \alpha_R \Delta T) \tag{8.124}$$

where α_K is effectively the temperature coefficient of remanence of the magnet, and α_R is the temperature coefficient of resistivity (0·00393/°C for copper). If the motors both have copper windings, use the same magnetic material, and have the same temperature rise, then the temperature factors cancel out from the ratio K_{m2}/K_{m1} so the (cold) values can be used. If the motors have different temperature coefficients in eqns. (8.120) or (8.121), or different temperature rises, then K_m must be adjusted using eqns. (8.123) and (8.124) in eqn. (8.119).

All stall torques are calculated for the same temperature rise (ΔT = 100°C), using eqn. (8.121), since the motors have different thermal resistances.

Motor	K_m [oz-in/A/√ohm]	θ [°C/W]	T_s [oz-in]
1	10·8	2·79	51
2	25·7	1·26	181 (*121*)
3	183·7	0·52	2009 (*867*)

TABLE 8.3
COMPARISON OF STALL TORQUES CALCULATED WITH MOTOR CONSTANT

For motor 2,

$$T_{s2} = T_{s1}\frac{K_{m2}}{K_{m1}}\sqrt{\frac{\theta_1}{\theta_2}} = 51 \times \frac{25{\cdot}7}{10{\cdot}8}\sqrt{\frac{2{\cdot}79}{1{\cdot}26}} = 181 \text{ oz–in.} \tag{8.125}$$

For Motor 3,

$$T_{s3} = T_{s1}\frac{K_{m3}}{K_{m1}}\sqrt{\frac{\theta_1}{\theta_3}} = 51 \times \frac{183{\cdot}7}{10{\cdot}8}\sqrt{\frac{2{\cdot}79}{0{\cdot}52}} = 2009 \text{ oz–in.} \tag{8.126}$$

If the thermal resistances were not taken into account, the results would be $T_{s2} = 121$ oz-in and $T_{s3} = 867$ oz-in. These figures are shown in italics alongside the correct ones in Table 8.3.

8.4 The brushless PM motor in control systems

The principles of feedback control (closed-loop control) were developed long ago for DC commutator motors. The classical theory starts with the relationship between speed and voltage, because the simplest concept of speed control is *via* the control of armature voltage. Although we have studied the relationship between speed and voltage in previous chapters, we have done so only for steady-state operation at constant speed. The presumption of constant speed removes all questions of control from the machine designer.

The control engineer is concerned with *dynamic* variation of speed, and the design of control systems for variable-speed drives is by now a very complex subject far beyond the scope of this book.[72] In the remaining sections of this chapter we will take a few steps into the territory of the control engineer. This excursion will perhaps be helpful to motor engineers who need a general idea of what control systems do. It might also be helpful to control engineers to get a better understanding of the role of the motor constants in the design of the control system.

We will confine our attention to the brushless DC drive, because of its simplicity. The so-called outer loops (the speed loop and any position loop, for example) are in any case fundamentally the same for squarewave and sinewave drives.

---

[72] Not only the speed is variable. The torque, current, and often position and acceleration are also controlled.

8.4.1 Classical transfer function between voltage and speed

We have seen that the brushless DC motor with squarewave drive can be represented by the same model as that of a DC commutator motor, in which V represents the supply voltage, I is the armature current, R is the armature resistance, k_E is the EMF constant, k_T is the torque constant, T is the motor torque, J is the rotor inertia, and ω_m is the angular velocity. Armature inductance is at first assumed to be zero, and any mechanical shaft resonance is ignored.

The voltage determines the *no-load* speed according to eqn. (1.13). Under load, the actual speed deviates from the no-load speed because of the voltage-drop in the resistance (and the transistors) when current is drawn:

$$V = RI + k_E \omega_m . \tag{8.127}$$

This *steady-state* equation gives no indication as to how the speed varies dynamically if the supply voltage V is changed, as it might be by the action of the electronic controller. A changing speed requires an acceleration torque, and in the absence of other load torques

$$T = J \frac{d\omega_m}{dt} . \tag{8.128}$$

The Laplace transform is applied to this equation, giving[73]

$$T(s) = J s \omega_m (s) . \tag{8.129}$$

If we write the torque equation as $T(s) = k_T I(s)$ and substitute it in the transform of eqn. (8.127), we can combine that with eqn. (8.129) to determine the **transfer function** between speed and voltage, which is expressed as the ratio

[73] We speak of replacing the differential operator d/dt by the algebraic operation of multiplying by s, so that all subsequent differential equations become algebraic equations. After any necessary manipulation to get the required output variable as a function of s and the other parameters, the inverse Laplace transform is used to recover it as a function of time. This extremely convenient process is underpinned by rigorous mathematics, which we owe to Heaviside, Bromwich, Laplace himself and others. The variable s is interpreted as a complex frequency; it has the units of frequency. To pay our dues to the mathematicians (and to avoid chaos in the calculations), all *variables* are written in the functional form (s) in the domain of the transform. We generally don't bother to write them with the functional form (t) in the time domain, however.

$$\frac{\omega_m(s)}{V(s)} = \frac{1/k_E}{1 + s\tau_m}. \qquad (8.130)$$

τ_m is the mechanical time-constant defined on p. 439. Suppose a voltage step V_0 is applied at $t = 0$; its Laplace transform is

$$V(s) = \frac{V_0}{s}, \qquad (8.131)$$

so that

$$\omega_m(s) = \frac{V_0/k_E}{s(1 + s\tau_m)}. \qquad (8.132)$$

The inverse Laplace transform of this expression can be obtained from standard tables as

$$\omega_m(t) = \frac{V_0}{k_E}\left[1 - e^{-t/\tau_m}\right]. \qquad (8.133)$$

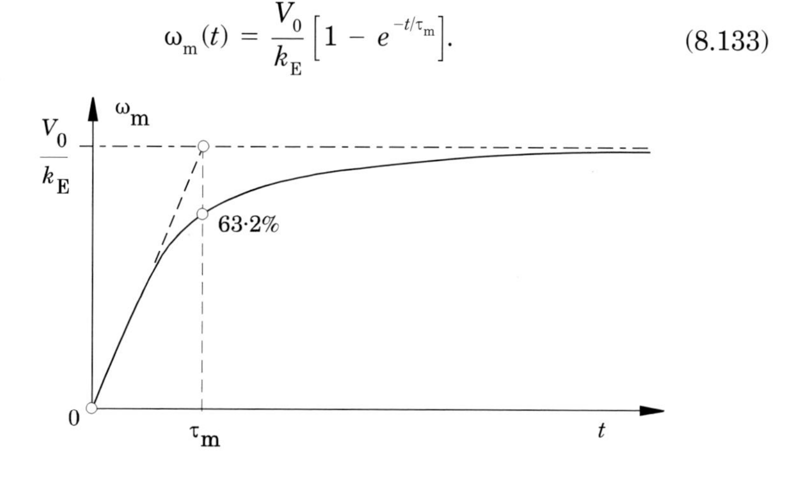

Fig. 8.12 Step-response of first-order system

The step-response is shown in Fig. 8.12. It is one of the most common classical examples of a "control system response" and also one of the simplest. Its main value here is to show the importance and physical significance of the mechanical time contant, even though practical control systems do much more than apply step voltages when they want to change the speed.

The denominator of the transfer function in eqn. (8.130) has only one root, so the system is described as being a **first-order system**.

This means that the characteristic response of the system to almost any disturbance is a simple exponential function; the larger the time-constant τ_m, the more sluggish the response and the longer it takes to settle. The final value of ω_m can be determined by setting $s = 0$ (ignoring the $1/s$ term in the exciting funtion); the result is V_0/k_E as expected, and in control-engineering parlance $1/k_E$ is called the **gain**.

8.4.2 Brushless DC motor model including inductance

The simple dynamic model of the brushless DC motor can be extended to include the effects of inductance as follows. Assuming two-phase-on operation, we have the frequency-domain equation

$$V(s) = (R + Ls)I(s) + k_E \omega_s(s). \tag{8.134}$$

In the mechanical equation we can introduce a little additional detail by adding a torque proportional to velocity, $D\omega_m$. Then

$$T(s) = (Js + D)\omega_m(s). \tag{8.135}$$

With manipulations similar to those of the previous section, the transfer function emerges as

$$\frac{\omega_m(s)}{V(s)} = \frac{1/k_E}{(Ls + R)[Js + D] + k_E k_T}. \tag{8.136}$$

The denominator is now a second-order function of s with two roots, and the transfer function can be written in the standard form

$$\frac{\omega_m(s)}{V(s)} = \frac{1/k_E}{(1 + s\tau_e)(1 + s\tau_m)}. \tag{8.137}$$

If τ_e and τ_m are sufficiently distinct, it will be found that τ_m is the same mechanical time-constant as before, while τ_e is the so-called electrical time-constant L/R. In general, however, the simple formulas for τ_m and τ_e are not exact.

The quadratic denominator introduces the possibility of an overshoot or even an oscillation in the response. Before investigating that further, it is well to consider the addition of **feedback**, making the control system **closed-loop**, because this tends to increase the order of the system (i.e. the order of the denominator polynomial in s), and can thus increase the risk of an oscillatory response.

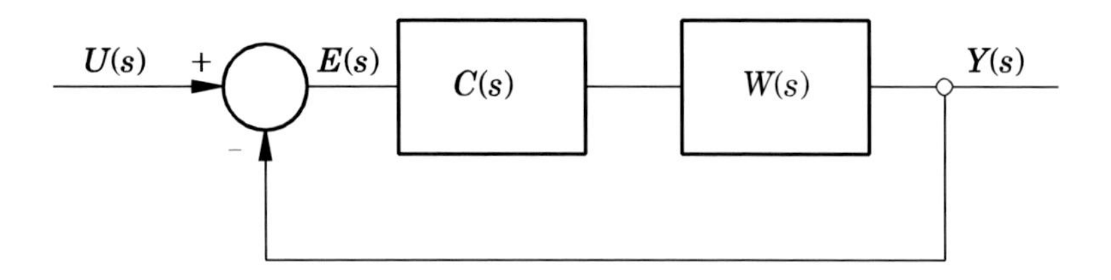

Fig. 8.13 Closed-loop feedback system

8.4.3 Closed-loop feedback system

Fig. 8.13 shows a closed-loop feedback control system in the most general terms. The output signal $Y(s)$ is typically the speed $\omega_m(s)$, while $U(s)$ is the reference value, which would be written $\omega_m^*(s)$ if speed were the controlled variable. $W(s)$ is the open-loop transfer function of the motor and its drive; eqn. (8.137) is a simple example in which the drive is simply a voltage source, but in a current-regulated controller there are additional "dynamics" which increase the order of both the numerator and denominator of $W(s)$ written as polynomials in s. $C(s)$ is a *compensator*, which is the generic term for any means of modifying the control signal to improve the response. Typically $C(s)$ includes a proportional gain together with integral and even derivative terms in so-called PI or PID controllers. The **error** term $E(s)$ is equal to $U(s) - Y(s)$ and it is the signal on which the controller operates.

The so-called **closed-loop transfer function** is evident from Fig. 8.13 as

$$\frac{Y(s)}{U(s)} = \frac{C(s)\,W(s)}{1 + C(s)\,W(s)}. \tag{8.138}$$

The final-value theorem states that

$$\lim_{t \to \infty} f(t) = \lim_{s \to 0} \left[sF(s) \right]. \tag{8.139}$$

It can be used to calculate the steady-state value of a system whose transfer function is $F(s)$. Referring to Fig. 8.13, suppose $C(s) = 1$ for the sake of simplicity, and let $W(s) = G/(1 + s\tau_m)$. This is the first-order open-loop transfer function of the motor that we saw earlier.

The closed-loop transfer function $Y(s)/U(s)$ is

$$Y(s) = \frac{W(s)}{1 + W(s)} U(s) = \frac{G}{(1 + G) + s\tau_m} U(s) \tag{8.140}$$

while the transfer function between the error signal and the input is

$$E(s) = \frac{1}{1 + W(s)} U(s) = \frac{1 + s\tau_m}{(1 + G) + s\tau_m}. \tag{8.141}$$

We can use the final-value theorem to determine the steady-state response $y(t \to \infty)$ reached an infinite time after the application of a step-change of unit magnitude in the reference signal $u(t)$. This is the limit as $s \to 0$ of $[s \times 1/s \times Y(s)]$. From equation (8.140) this is

$$y(t \to \infty) = \frac{G}{1 + G}. \tag{8.142}$$

Similarly for the error $e(t)$, the limit as $s \to 0$ of $[s \times 1/s \times E(s)]$ is

$$e(t \to \infty) = \frac{1}{1 + G}. \tag{8.143}$$

This important result shows the final (steady-state) value of the error with respect to the reference input. The **steady-state error** decreases as the forward gain G of the system is increased. It appears that zero steady-state error can only be attained with infinite gain. However, in practice, increasing the gain generally produces instability sooner than it reduces the steady-state error to an acceptable value.

Integral gain compensation — If the error amplifier has a transfer function $C(s) = 1/s$, it is an integrator rather than a plain amplifier, and the combined open-loop transfer function becomes

$$C(s)W(s) = \frac{G}{s(1 + s\tau_m)}. \tag{8.144}$$

The effect on the steady-state output signal is that

$$y(t \to \infty) = \lim_{s \to 0} \left[\frac{G}{s(1 + s\tau_m) + G} \right] = 1. \tag{8.145}$$

Similarly

$$e(t \to \infty) = \lim_{s \to 0} \left[\frac{s(1 + s\tau_m)}{s(1 + s\tau_m) + G} \right] = 0. \tag{8.146}$$

This means that the integrator eliminates the steady-state error.

8.4.4 Response of generic second-order system

We have already observed that when the denominator of the transfer function is quadratic, the step-response can be oscillatory. The denominator can be written as

$$\tau_e \tau_m (s^2 + 2\zeta\omega_n s + \omega_n^2) \tag{8.147}$$

where

$$\omega_n = \frac{1}{\sqrt{\tau_e \tau_m}} \quad \text{and} \quad \zeta = \frac{\omega_n(\tau_e + \tau_m)}{2}. \tag{8.148}$$

The roots (also known as the *poles* of the system) are given by

$$s = [-\zeta \pm j\sqrt{1 - \zeta^2}]\omega_n. \tag{8.149}$$

The parameter ζ is called the **damping ratio** and ω_n is the **undamped natural frequency** of the system. If $\zeta < 1$ the response is oscillatory, and if $\zeta > 1$, it is not. For $\zeta > 1$ the two roots are both real. The case $\zeta = 1$ is called *critical damping*. A critically damped system has no overshoot, whereas an underdamped system ($\zeta < 1$) has an overshoot and at least one cycle of oscillation before settling. If the steady-state value of the response is unity, the maximum value of the response during the first overshoot is

$$y_{max} = 1 + e^{-\pi\zeta/\sqrt{1 - \zeta^2}} \tag{8.150}$$

and this occurs at time $t = \pi/\omega_n\sqrt{(1 - \zeta^2)}$. The settling time is estimated as $4/\zeta\omega_n$ seconds, or four "effective time constants".

Examples of damped response are shown in Fig. 8.14 with various values of ζ and $\omega_n = 40$ rad/s. The *y*-axis is normalized. The response with $\zeta = 0{\cdot}7$ is a typical design objective; although it has a slight overshoot the response is faster than when critically-damped.

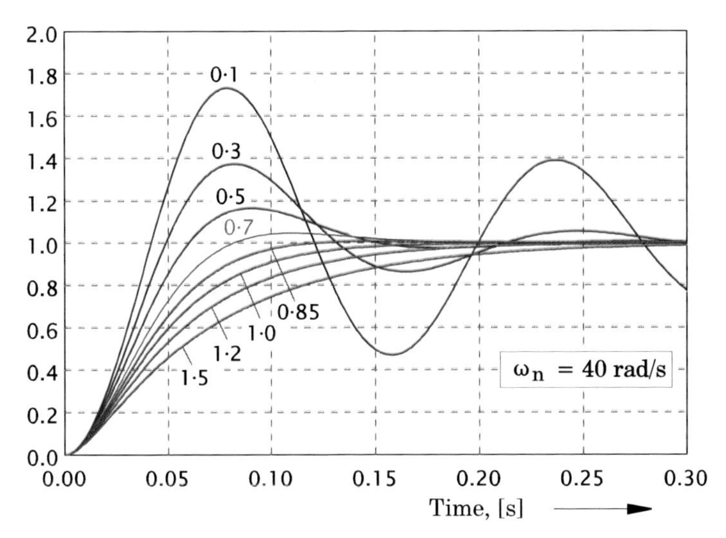

Fig. 8.14 Damping curves

If the damping ratio is $1/\surd 2 = 0{\cdot}707$, $y_{max} = 1{\cdot}043$. This value of ζ causes the poles to lie at 45° from the negative real axis. At 60° from the negative real axis the damping ratio is $\zeta = 0{\cdot}5$ and the maximum value is $y_{max} = 1.163$, i.e., a maximum overshoot of 16·3%. In the interests of rapid response, some degree of overshoot may sometimes be tolerated and this helps to explain why control systems are often designed with the objective of locating the poles somewhere between 45° and 60° from the negative real axis.

For further reading in the field of motion control, there are many good books (for example, Dote; Dote and Kinoshita) and a rich literature in all the major conferences dealing with motor drives.

8.4.5 Dynamic braking

The brushless permanent-magnet motor can be used as a brake by short-circuiting its terminals together. The kinetic energy of the machine and its load are dissipated in the winding resistance. A complete analysis requires a computer simulation, but it can be said that the mechanical time-constant has a significant influence especially when the speed is low enough for the current to be limited by the resistance rather than the inductance.

9 GENERATING

9.1 Introduction

Permanent-magnet generators are manufactured in a wide range of sizes, and for a wide range of speeds up to at least 100 krpm. They have a wide range of applications including many in demanding environments, such as auxiliary generators mounted on engines in automobiles, motorcycles, and aircraft. In recent times they have begun to be developed for windpower and other renewable-energy generating systems. They are also found in starter/generator systems in mobile equipment or vehicles, and as an integral component of the traction system in hybrid vehicles, either as a single machine integrated with the main traction motor, or as a separate machine.

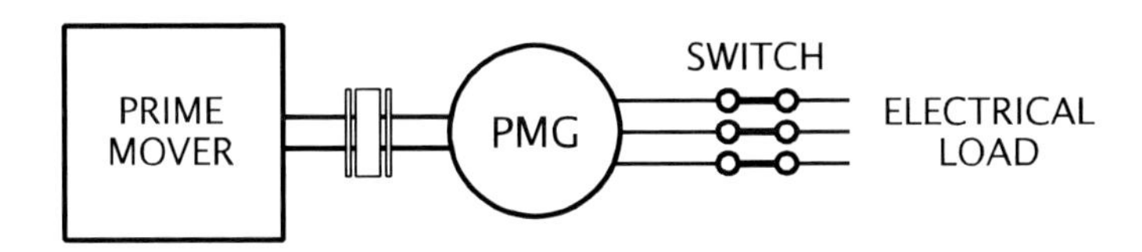

Fig. 9.1 General configuration of a generating system

The permanent-magnet generator is brushless, and this is its primary advantage over the wound-field generator. Its history is as old as electrical engineering, but with due respect to the pioneers we need trace it back no further than the 1950s, when generators up to at least 75 kW were known, and Hanrahan and Toffolo wrote

> "Only the recent development of the Alnicos has made the permanent-magnet generator practical in sizes larger than a tachometer-generator"

The permanent-magnet generator established itself quickly and benefited immediately from the development of high-energy rare-earth magnets from the late 1960s, followed by NdFeB magnets in the 1980s. Unlike the brushless permanent-magnet motor, it did not have to wait for the development of power electronics or digital control. Of course, when these technologies arrived, they expanded the scope of the permanent-magnet generator considerably.

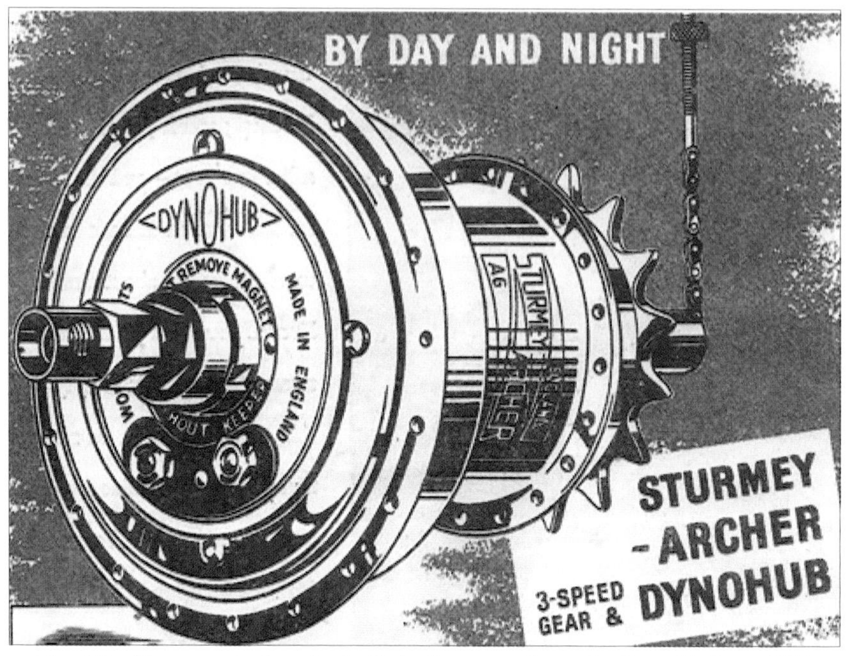

Fig. 9.2 Sturmey-Archer Cycle Hub Dynamo, from *Cycling*, 11 June 1953

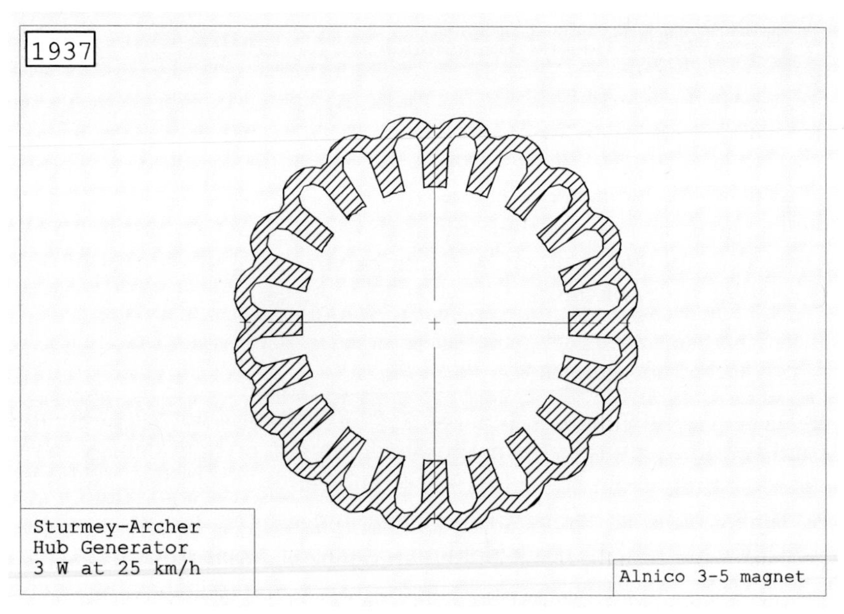

Fig. 9.3 Sturmey-Archer Dynohub magnet

A very famous example of a permanent-magnet generator is the Sturmey-Archer *Dynohub*™ invented in the late 1930s, Fig. 9.2. This early AC generator used an Alnico magnet in the form of a single casting (Fig. 9.3) with 20 poles, fitted inside the hub, which rotated around a stationary armature with a single coil inside a claw-pole assembly of magnetically soft steel.[74] The generator had sufficient reactance to limit the current at high speed, while providing useful light from about 3 m.p.h., so it was justifiably claimed to be self-regulating even though it had no external means of control.[75]

In a book that is mainly about motors, it might be argued that permanent-magnet generators are out of place. However, it is now commonplace for permanent-magnet generators to be controlled by power-electronic inverters acting as active rectifiers, and in such systems they are practically indistinguishable from motors that happen to be working in the 3rd or 4th quadrant of the torque/speed diagram (Chapter 1).

This being so, it is tempting to think of the permanent-magnet generator as a motor with the direction of power flow reversed. This is a valid idea with polyphase inverter-controlled machines, particulary those that operate in both modes: for example, starter/generators. But not all generators are suitable for use as motors: the *Dynohub*™, for example, is a single-phase machine with no practical potential whatsoever as a motor, in spite of its long and illustrious service as a generator.

Moreover, the equations and phasor diagrams of generators have positive current flowing out of the machine instead of into it, and generator engineers deserve to see these drawn according to their particular conventions.

---

[74] In a student project to "upgrade" the magnet from Alnico to high-energy NDFEB on the author's bicycle, the self-regulating property was lost because of the reduction in per-unit reactance with the more powerful magnet. A transistor chopper had to be added to regulate the voltage, with consequent loss of efficiency. Moreover, severe cogging torque was experienced with the high-energy magnet. This tale is told by way of reverence for the designers of the "original and best" version; (see http://www.sturmey-archerheritage.com). Electric bicycles now have hub motors not too much bigger than the *Dynohub*™ that are capable of *driving* the entire bicycle.

[75] To provide light while the bicycle was stationary, later de-luxe versions were offered with a battery with a "filter" to separate the DC from the AC of the generator.

9.2 Configurations and loads

Fig. 9.1 shows the general configuration of a permanent-magnet generator system. Our main concern is with the machine itself and the load, which may require a "power-conditioning" stage such as a rectifier. The prime mover provides the motive power: it can be anything from a bicycle wheel to a diesel engine to a power take-off on a gas turbine to a mighty windmill: but from our point of view as electrical engineers it can be represented with only two parameters, torque and speed.[76]

The machine itself can be of the surface-magnet or interior-magnet type, and examples can be seen in Chapter 2. It is practically indistinguishable from a permanent-magnet motor in almost all its physical aspects, including the stator laminations, the design of the rotor, and the winding. For this reason we can proceed immediately to the main subject of this chapter, which is the behaviour of the machine with different loads.

The loads are considered in order of complexity. They are

1. No load (i.e., open-circuit)
2. Short-circuit (...a zero-power load, but important for testing)
3. Passive impedance loads (plain resistive/inductive loads)
4. Infinite bus (i.e., direct connection to a large AC system)
5. Diode rectifier
6. Phase-controlled rectifier
7. Active rectifier (transistor inverter acting as a rectifier)

Although the active rectifier is the most complex "load", many of its details have already been covered in Chapter 7, while the diode rectifier load is fairly close to squarewave operation (Chapter 6).

EMF, flux, and torque have been covered in Chapter 4; windings in Chapter 3; and inductance in Chapter 5. Consequently we can focus on the volts and amps, the waveforms, and the control.

---

[76] Inertia might also be a factor, especially when considering stability or faults, although fault calculations usually assume that the speed remains constant.

9.2.1 No-load (open-circuit)

The no-load (open-circuit) test is equally applicable to motors and generators. It is the most convenient way to check that the magnets have been properly magnetized. After the machine has been running, it is also the most convenient way to check that is has not *lost* any magnetization. Since the remanence is temperature-dependent, the test is only as good as the knowledge of the rotor temperature.

Fortunately the rotor is normally not susceptible to very much heating during the no-load test, except that stator iron losses are of course being generated, and some of the heat will be transferred across the airgap. Further, the slot-modulation of the airgap field can excite eddy-current losses on the rotor, as explained in Chapter 12. For very precise measurement it is practically essential to have some means of measuring the rotor temperature, or at least of ensuring that the rotor temperature is stable and known.

Especially in cases where there is any doubt about the level of magnetization or the stability of the magnetization, the no-load test should be conducted on a new motor before any load testing is done. With prototype machines the EMF waveform should be measured at the same time, on all three phases.

Generators with Alnico magnets must generally be *stabilized*: i.e., exposed to the largest demagnetizing field that they are expected to meet in practice. Because of the relatively low coercivity of Alnico magnets, the permeance coefficient of the "out-of-stator" load-line can be low enough to cause partial demagnetization, and the magnet must be "keepered" as it is removed from the stator.[77]

---

[77] A warning stamped on the steel faceplate of the *Dynohub*™ says: "Do not remove magnet without keeper". The assembly is designed so that the magnet and armature can be removed from the hub without separating them from one another. Then the rotor is pushed out of the armature into the keeper so that the poles are always magnetically short-circuited. The workshop manual correctly warns that a spanner held across the magnet will not protect it against demagnetization.
If this advice is not heeded, the loss of remanence will be of the order of 30% and the generator will be useless.

Fig. 9.4 Keeper

The open-circuit test is also used to measure the EMF constant k_E. There is no difference in the meaning of k_E between motoring and generating. As explained in Chapter 8, there are good reasons to measure the mean rectified EMF rather than the peak line-line EMF.[78]

Finally, the open-circuit condition can be a fault condition. For example, if an open-circuit arises unexpectedly anywhere in the circuit for any reason when the machine is running faster than normal, the voltage must not be so high as to risk an insulation failure or the breakdown of a semiconductor device.

9.2.2 Steady-state short-circuit

Whereas the open-circuit condition is one of zero current, the short-circuit condition is one of zero voltage at the terminals. There is an important distinction between a *steady-state* short circuit and a *sudden* short-circuit. A steady-state short-circuit is used for testing to measure X_d. With all three phases shorted together, the phase current is given (for a sinewound machine) by

$$I_{ph} = I_{sc} = \frac{E_{q1}}{\sqrt{R_{ph}^2 + X_d^2}}. \tag{9.1}$$

If the speed (and therefore the frequency) is high enough, R_{ph} is insignificant compared to X_d and $I_{sc} = E_{q1}/X_d$.

The **short-circuit ratio** (sometimes abbreviated SCR) is often used to describe wound-field generators. Kimbark defines the SCR as the ratio of field current required to produce rated voltage on open-circuit to the field current required to produce rated current on short-circuit. If there is no saturation, the SCR is the reciprocal of the per-unit synchronous reactance $1/x_d$. Although PM generators have no field excitation, the SCR can still be defined as $1/x_d$. A machine with a high SCR has a low x_d, and low regulation, and this implies a design with a large airgap requiring high excitation in the form of the magnet length L_m and strength B_r. This increases the cost and size of the machine; so, as with wound-field machines, a high short-circuit ratio is correlated with higher cost.

---

[78] The peak EMF is sensitive to ripple caused by permeance harmonics. A precision rectifier should be used : that is, one that has no error due to diode voltage drops.

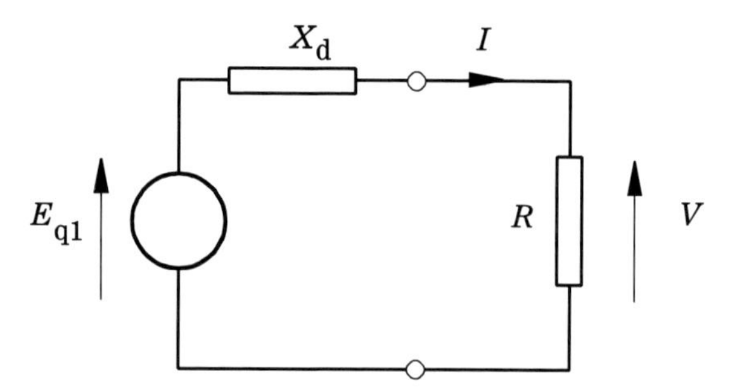

Fig. 9.4 Passive load; maximum power transfer

9.2.3 Passive impedance load

Fig. 9.4 shows the single-phase (line-neutral) equivalent circuit with a passive resistive load R. The permanent-magnet generator is represented by its EMF E_{q1} and its synchronous reactance X_d, assuming a nonsalient-pole machine. The internal resistance R_{ph} is neglected. This is the simplest possible model of a loaded generator.

Before we calculate the current and the power, it is useful to consider how this system is controlled. The speed is set by a governor on the prime-mover, and this determines E_{q1} and the frequency.

The only means of control on the electrical side is the value of the load resistance R, which determines the current:

$$I = \frac{E_{q1}}{\sqrt{R^2 + X_d^2}}. \tag{9.2}$$

By the maximum power-transfer theorem, the maximum power that can be transferred to the load is when $R = X_d$; then

$$P_{max} = 3\,\frac{E_{q1}^2}{2R} \tag{9.3}$$

for a 3-phase machine. At maximum power,

$$I = \frac{E_{q1}}{\sqrt{2}R} \quad \text{and} \quad V = \frac{E_{q1}}{\sqrt{2}}. \tag{9.4}$$

Example — Suppose E_{q1} = 298·5 V and X_d = 6·92 ohm, so

$$\therefore\ P_{max} = 3 \times \frac{E_{q1}^{\ 2}}{2R} = 3 \times \frac{298{\cdot}5^2}{2 \times 6{\cdot}92} \times \frac{1}{10^3} = 19{\cdot}3\ \text{kW}. \qquad (9.5)$$

The current at the maximum-power condition with $R = X_d$ is

$$I_{P\,max} = \frac{E_{q1}}{\sqrt{2}R} = \frac{298{\cdot}5}{\sqrt{2} \times 6{\cdot}92} = 30{\cdot}5\ \text{A}. \qquad (9.6)$$

The terminal voltage is

$$V_{P\,max} = RI_{P\,max} = 6{\cdot}92 \times 30{\cdot}5 = 211\ \text{V}. \qquad (9.7)$$

This example provides a convenient opportunity to define the **regulation**, which is the percentage drop in terminal voltage between no-load and a specified load (usually rated load). Thus

$$\text{Regulation} = \frac{|V - E_{q1}|}{E_{q1}} = \frac{298{\cdot}5 - 211}{298{\cdot}5} = 0{\cdot}293 \text{ or } 29{\cdot}3\%. \qquad (9.8)$$

The term "regulation" is an old and perhaps rather strange name. Remembering that wound-field generators have a voltage regulator that controls the field current, it suggests the increase in field current that is necessary to compensate for the voltage drop in the internal impedance of the generator. Although permanent-magnet generators do not have a controllable field current, the regulation defined by eqn. (9.8) is still meaningful as a measure of the "stiffness" of the generator as a voltage source. An infinitely-stiff voltage source has no voltage drop under load, and therefore it must have no internal impedance. Such a voltage source would have infinite short-circuit current. A generator with low regulation also has a high short-circuit ratio, as we have seen.

Particularly with generators loaded with rectifiers or active rectifiers, the short-circuit ratio and the regulation are essentially redundant concepts, since all necessary design calculations can be done using the open-circuit EMF and the synchronous reactance X_d (together with X_q when the machine has saliency, and R_{ph} when more precise calculations are required). The *values* of X_d, X_q, and even of E_{q1} may be variable as a result of saturation, just as they are in the PM motor and in wound-field machines; (see §5.13).

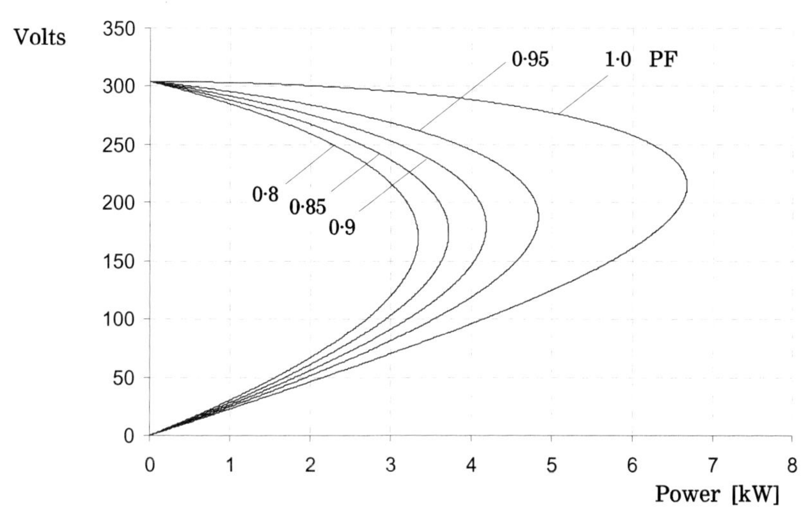

Fig. 9.5 Voltage regulation curves (lagging power-factor)

9.2.4 Voltage regulation curves

An important characteristic of any generator is the voltage variation at the terminals as the load varies. Fig. 9.5 shows the terminal voltage of a generator with $E_{q1} = 304$ V and $X = 6{\cdot}92$ ohm, as a function of the power per phase at five different power-factors. These curves are sometimes called *regulation* curves.[79]

The complex power of the *load* per phase is

$$P + \mathrm{j}Q = \mathbf{VI}^*. \tag{9.9}$$

where P is the real power in watts or kW and Q is the reactive power in reactive volt-amperes or kVAr. The volt-amperes VI is sometimes called the apparent power. If the terminal voltage $\mathbf{V}$ is the reference phasor $Ve^{\mathrm{j}0}$ we have $\mathbf{V}^* = \mathbf{V} = V$ and

$$\mathbf{I} = \frac{P - \mathrm{j}Q}{V}. \tag{9.10}$$

When Q is *positive*, the reactive (imaginary) component of the current is negative, so the *load* current is *lagging* the voltage.

[79] See Miller T.J.E. [Ed], *Reactive Power Control in Electric Systems*, John Wiley & Sons, New York, 1982, ISBN 0 47 186933-3

If we continue to use the simple generator model in Fig. 9.4 with only an EMF E_{q1} and a synchronous reactance X_d, we can write the following equation for the EMF as a function of the terminal voltage and the real and reactive powers:

$$\begin{aligned} \mathbf{E}_{q1} &= \mathbf{V} + jX_d\mathbf{I} = V + jX_d\left[\frac{P - jQ}{V}\right] \\ &= \left[V + \frac{X_d Q}{V}\right] + j\frac{X_d P}{V}. \end{aligned} \tag{9.11}$$

This equation indicates that the real power tends to produce a phase shift between $\mathbf{E}_{q1}$ and $\mathbf{V}$, while the reactive power tends to produce a difference in amplitude between $\mathbf{E}_{q1}$ and $\mathbf{V}$: in other words the regulation depends more on the reactive power than it does on the real power. Very roughly, if we ignore the phase-shift term (i.e., the imaginary term) altogether, we can write eqn. (9.11) as

$$V \approx E_{q1} - \frac{X_d Q}{V}. \tag{9.12}$$

Although V appears on the right-hand-side of this essentially quadratic equation, it shows that a positive value of Q decreases the voltage, as shown in Fig. 9.5. Positive Q means an inductive load. As the load becomes more inductive, the power-factor decreases and the voltage falls even more. Conversely, a negative Q means a capacitive load. Capacitive loads tend to *raise* the voltage V.

This explains the use of variable reactive shunt elements to control the terminal voltage as a function of load. Power-factor correction capacitors are the most common example of this. By improving the power-factor at the generator terminals when the load is inductive (lagging), they also support the voltage. Conversely, when the load is light, shunt reactors can be connected to bring the voltage down.

The use of shunt reactive elements is common in industrial power systems and in high-voltage power systems. They can be used effectively with PM generators to help control the terminal voltage. They have the advantage of requiring very little power themselves (only sufficient to supply the losses). Power-electronic compensators can provide *continuous* reactive power control.

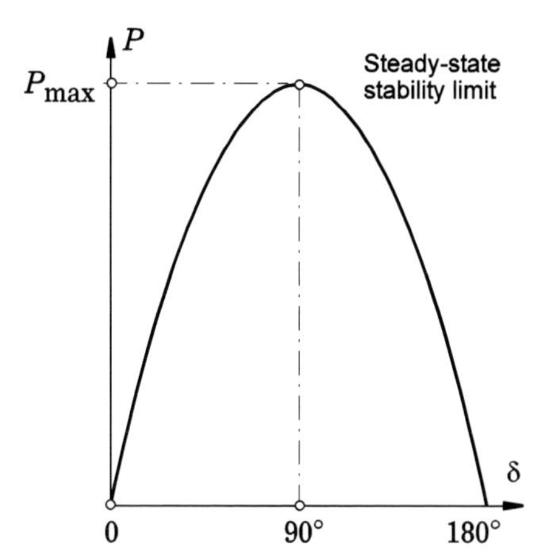

Fig. 9.6 Power vs. load-angle

The important power/load-angle curve shown in Fig. 9.6 can be deduced from a little further consideration of the phase-shift δ between $\mathbf{E}_{q1}$ and $\mathbf{V}$. This angle is called the **load angle** or power angle. Let $\mathbf{E}_{q1} = E_{q1}e^{j\delta}$ so that

$$\mathbf{E}_{q1} = E_{q1} \cos \delta + j E_{q1} \sin \delta. \tag{9.13}$$

If ϕ is the power-factor angle we also have

$$Q = P \tan \phi. \tag{9.14}$$

Solving eqns. (9.11), (9.13) and (9.14) for V, we get

$$V = E_{q1} (\cos \delta - \sin \delta \tan\phi) \tag{9.15}$$

and

$$P = \frac{E_{q1} V}{X_d} \sin \delta = P_{max} \sin \delta. \tag{9.16}$$

Eqn. (9.16) shows that the power transferred from the source to the load is proportional to the sine of the load-angle δ. There is a limit $P_{max} = E_{q1}V/X_d$ that can be delivered, and this is called the **steady-state stability limit**. It corresponds to the pull-out torque.

The power-angle curve is more useful when E_{q1} and V are both constant, as in the next section. With a passive load, the voltage V varies, and it is better to use Fig. 9.5. There is still a maximum transferable power P_{max} that clearly depends on the power factor.

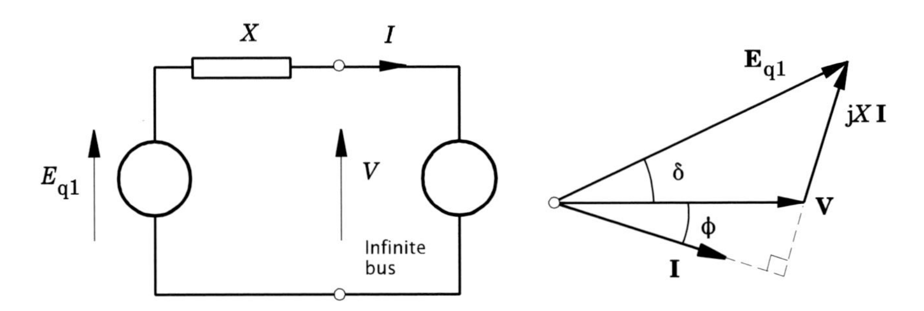

Fig. 9.7 PM Generator connected to infinite bus of voltage V

9.2.5 Connection to an infinite bus

Fig. 9.7 shows a PM generator supplying an AC load which is modelled as another synchronous machine with a fixed voltage V. When V is fixed, this load is called an "infinite bus".[80]

The power per phase can be calculated from the phasor diagram, in which ϕ is the power-factor angle and δ is the *load angle* — the phase angle by which $\mathbf{E}_{q1}$ leads the terminal voltage phasor $\mathbf{V}$. Evidently

$$P = VI \cos \phi . \tag{9.17}$$

By the sine rule for the voltage triangle,

$$\frac{XI}{\sin\delta} = \frac{E_{q1}}{\sin(\pi/2 + \phi)} = \frac{E_{q1}}{\cos \phi} . \tag{9.18}$$

Substituting for $I \cos \phi$ from eqn. (9.18) in eqn (9.17) , we get

$$P = \frac{E_{q1} V}{X} \sin \delta . \tag{9.19}$$

Like eqn. (9.16), this equation is familiar to power-system engineers.

[80] What is infinite about it is its short-circuit current or *fault level*. Although such a load is not exactly realisable in practice, it is one of the most important theoretical models in power systems engineering because it illuminates several important properties and concepts. The nearest practical approach is when the generator is connected to a large network such as the national grid at a point where the fault level is high. This situation is unlikely to be met by PM generators, but that does not diminish the theoretical importance of the model.

It shows that maximum power is transferred when $\delta = 90°$: then

$$P_{max} = \frac{E_{q1} V}{X}. \tag{9.20}$$

As in the case of the passive impedance load, maximum power corresponds to the pullout torque and it is called the steady-state stability limit. Operation at this point with $\delta = 90°$ is not feasible with a PMG because of *stability*. A small increase in load would increase δ slightly, causing a reduction in power, in turn causing δ to increase more. This *fall from synchronism* is to be avoided at all costs. For stable operation with a margin of stability, a good rule is to take $\delta = 30°$ so that the maximum *useable* power is $E_{q1}V/2X$, half the maximum. It is natural to design the generator for maximum efficiency when operating at such a load-angle.

Suppose the generator is to operate with a power-factor of 0·9 lagging, i.e. $\phi = 25{\cdot}84°$; and suppose the load angle is $\delta = 30°$. Then if $E_{q1} = 298{\cdot}5$ V, from eqn. (9.18) we have

$$I = \frac{E_{q1} \sin \delta}{X \cos \phi} = \frac{298{\cdot}5 \times \sin 30°}{6{\cdot}92 \times 0{\cdot}9} = 24 \text{ A}. \tag{9.21}$$

Also

$$\begin{aligned} V \cos \phi &= E_{q1} \cos (\delta + \phi), \\ \text{so} \quad V &= \frac{298{\cdot}5 \times \cos (30° + 25{\cdot}84°)}{0{\cdot}9} = 186 \text{ V}. \end{aligned} \tag{9.22}$$

This gives a power of $3 \times 186 \times 24 \times 0{\cdot}9 = 12$ kW, and a regulation of $(298{\cdot}5 - 186)/298{\cdot}5 = 37{\cdot}6\%$.

Example — It is interesting to see the effect of a leading power-factor. For example with $\phi = -25{\cdot}84°$ the power-factor is 0·9 leading, and if V and δ remain the same, we get $E_{q1} = 186 \times 0{\cdot}9/\cos(30° - 25{\cdot}84°) = 167{\cdot}8$ V. To operate with $\delta = 30°$ the current must be $I = 167{\cdot}8 \sin 30°/(6{\cdot}92 \times 0{\cdot}9) = 13{\cdot}47$ A, and the power is only 3·9 kW. Although we may have saved magnet material in designing for a lower E_{q1}, the power has fallen more than proportionally. The generator is *underexcited* with $E_{q1} < V$, while the regulation is negative, $(167{\cdot}8 - 186)/167{\cdot}8 = -10{\cdot}8\%$. The capacitive load supplies reactive power to the generator (with $Q < 0$), and in contrast with the passive load with fixed E_{q1}, it appears to offer no advantage on the infinite bus if the load-angle is kept the same.

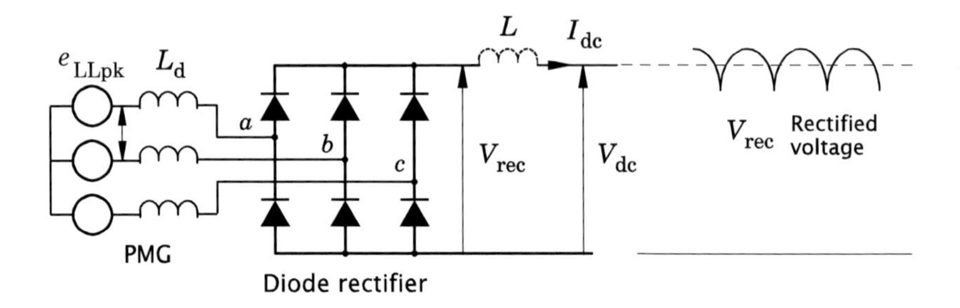

Fig. 9.8 Permanent-magnet enerator with Ideal diode rectifier

9.2.6 Diode rectifier load

Fig. 9.8 shows the circuit of a 3-phase PM generator connected to a plain diode rectifier. The simplest form of this circuit that gives useful formulas and guidance is obtained when the DC load is assumed to have enough inductance L so that the DC current I_{dc} is constant and ripple-free. The voltage V_{rec} contains all the ripple produced by the rectifier, while the load voltage V_{dc} is assumed to be constant. Therefore the DC circuit inductance L absorbs the ripple component. These relationships are shown in Fig. 8.5 for the open-circuit condition, $I_{dc} = 0$. When the rectifier is loaded with current I_{dc}, the terminal voltage V_{dc} is given by

$$V_{dc} = \frac{3}{\pi} e_{LLpk} \cos \alpha - \frac{3}{\pi} \omega L_d I_{dc} \tag{9.23}$$

where e_{LLpk} is the line-line *peak* EMF of the generator, ω is the fundamental AC radian frequency $2\pi f$, and L_d is the synchronous inductance of the generator. The angle α is the phase-control angle which applies when SCRs (thyristors) are used instead of diodes, permitting phase-control to adjust the dc voltage. $\alpha = 0$ in a diode rectifier. In rectifier theory, the inductance L_d is the **commutating inductance**. Evidently it is responsible for a voltage-drop which appears as a DC voltage drop in the DC circuit. The Thévenin equivalent circuit on the DC side has an open-circuit voltage equal to $(3/\pi)e_{LLpk}$ and an internal resistance equal to $(3/\pi)X_d$. The "regulation" on the DC side is very similar to that on the AC side.

With the ideal DC load having a very large inductance, the line current waveforms are 120° squarewaves, similar to those in Figs. 1.4, 6.3, or 8.6, but *inverted*, and with no ripple. The peak line current is I_{dc} and the RMS line current is

$$I_{Lrms} = \sqrt{\frac{2}{3}}\, I_{dc} = 0{\cdot}81650\, I_{dc}. \tag{9.24}$$

The fundamental line current is

$$I_{L1} = \frac{4}{\pi} \sin \frac{\pi}{3}\, I_{dc} = \frac{2\sqrt{3}}{\pi}\, I_{dc} = 1{\cdot}10266\, I_{dc}. \tag{9.25}$$

The foregoing equations are sufficient for preliminary design calculations of a permanent-magnet generator when the load is specified in terms of the mean DC voltage V_{dc} and mean current I_{dc}, the DC power being simply $V_{dc}I_{dc}$. Indeed such calculations are very similar to those that are used when designing a motor assuming ideal squarewave currents.

Often the DC circuit does not have such high inductance, but instead has a filter capacitor and additional elements. Moreover the EMF waveform of the generator may not be sinusoidal. More complex cases such as these are best dealt with by computer simulation if accurate prediction of the behaviour is required, and an example is shown in Figs. 9.10 and 9.11, in which the circuit is of the form shown in Fig. 9.9, with a large electrolytic capacitor C_{dc}.

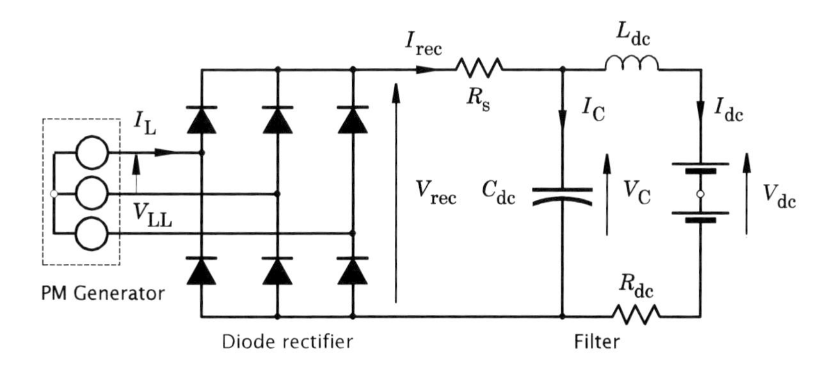

Fig. 9.9 3-phase diode rectifier with filter circuit

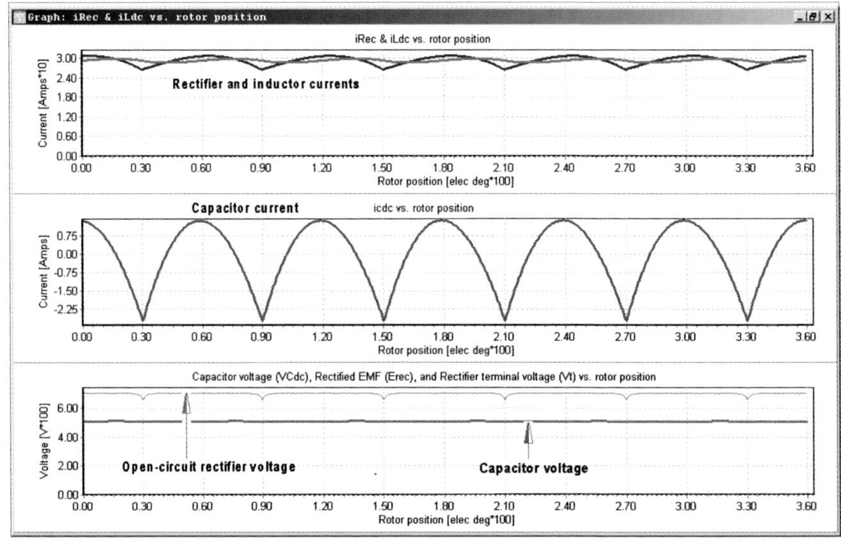

Fig. 9.10 Rectifier load : DC circuit waveforms

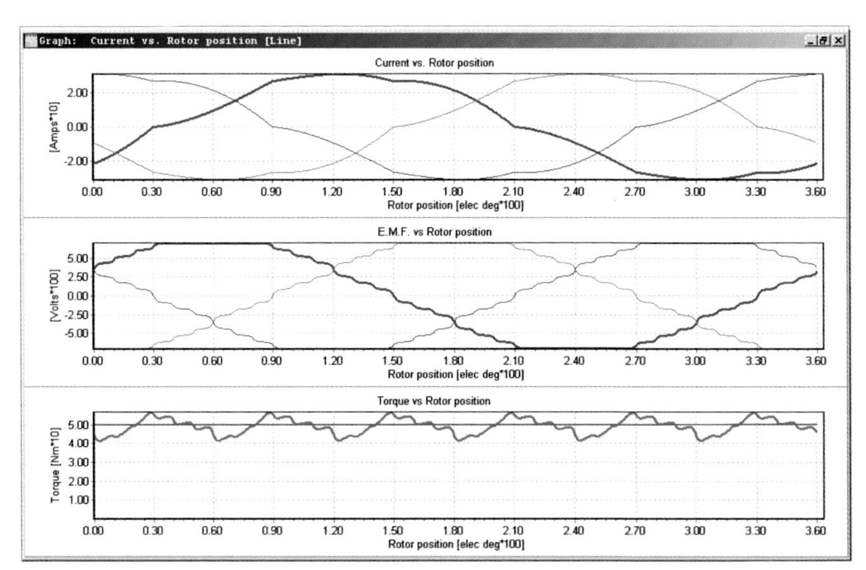

Fig. 9.11 Rectifier load : generator waveforms (current, EMF and torque)

In Fig. 9.9 the DC load is represented by a voltage source V_{dc} (which could represent a battery) together with a resistor R_{dc}. Through the action of the filter circuit, both the DC voltage V_{dc} and the DC current I_{dc} are held smooth — the voltage by the capacitor C_{dc} and the current by the inductor L_{dc}.

In the example in Fig. 9.11, the EMF waveform is flat-topped, and this leads to a relatively smooth open-circuit rectifier voltage V_{rec} in the lower trace in Fig. 9.10. The capacitor voltage V_C is very smooth, and slightly lower because of the volt-drop in the series resistance R_s. The capacitor voltage is considerably less than the *open-circuit* rectifier voltage because of the voltage drop in the machine reactance, as we have seen in eqn. (9.23).

The capacitor current is a series of pulses (6 per cycle) coinciding with the excursions of the line-line EMF above the mean capacitor voltage.

The line current in the generator is distinctly different from the 120° squarewaves obtained with the ideal inductive DC load. It is characterized by continuous conduction. The harmonics in the current waveform will combine with space-harmonics in the winding distribution, tending to produce additional rotor losses as described in Chapter 12.

9.2.7 Active rectification

The most advanced type of generator/rectifier is a fully-controlled system in which the transistor PWM inverter in Fig. 6.1 delivers a controlled DC current to the load while forcing sinusoidal currents to flow in the generator. In effect this is the same as a motor drive system with reverse power flow. All the control parameters are the same as they would be for a motor drive; in particular the set-point current I_{sp} (Fig. 7.19) and its phase angle γ (relative to the EMF) will be controlled in such a way as to reverse the normal power flow, leading to the phasor diagram shown in Fig. 7.3. This type of operation is suitable for motor drive systems requiring regeneration of kinetic energy, as in electric vehicle drives. The torque/speed characteristics of actively controlled generating systems are similar to those of motor drives developed in Chapter 7, and they are similarly constrained by the available voltage and current.

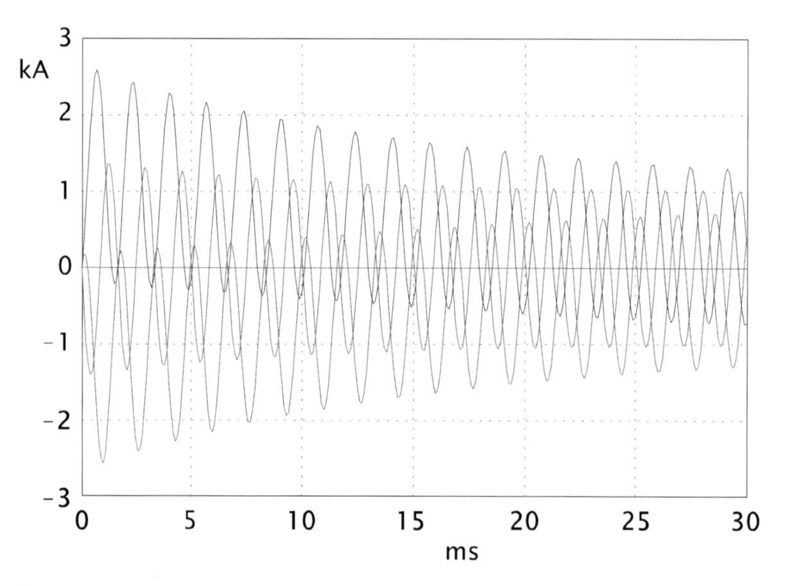

Fig. 9.12 Three-phase sudden short-circuit; current waveforms

9.3 Short-circuit faults

9.3.1 Classical analysis

The symmetrical 3-phase sudden short-circuit of an alternator is analyzed in many classic texts. Adkins gives the following formula for the phase current:

$$i_a = E\left[\underset{\text{SS}}{\frac{1}{X_d}} + \underset{\text{TRANSIENT}}{\left(\frac{1}{X_d'} - \frac{1}{X_d}\right)e^{-t/T_d'}} + \underset{\text{SUBTRANSIENT}}{\left(\frac{1}{X_d''} - \frac{1}{X_d'}\right)e^{-t/T_d''}}\right]\underset{AC}{\cos(\omega t + \lambda)} \tag{9.26}$$

$$- E\,e^{-t/T_a}\left[\underset{DC}{\frac{\cos\lambda}{x_m}} + \underset{2F}{\frac{\cos(2\omega t + \lambda)}{x_n}}\right].$$

where $E = \sqrt{2}E_{q1}$ is the peak phase EMF and

$$x_m = \frac{2X_d''X_q''}{X_d'' + X_q''}; \qquad x_n = \frac{2X_d''X_q''}{X_d'' - X_q''}. \tag{9.27}$$

The current is plotted for all three phases in Fig. 9.12. It contains an AC component cos $(\omega t + \lambda)$, a DC offset component cos λ shown for phase a, and a double-frequency component $2F$ which is present only in salient-pole machines. λ is the angle between the d-axis and the axis of phase a at time $t = 0$. The worst-case DC offset in phase a occurs when $\lambda = 0$. Its decay time-constant T_a is the so-called **armature time-constant**.

The AC component has a "steady-state" part controlled by the synchronous reactance $X_d = \omega L_d$; a "transient" part controlled by $(1/X_d' - 1/X_d)$; and a "subtransient" part controlled by $(1/X_d'' - 1/X_d')$. The permanent-magnet machine has no field winding, so the transient part simply does not appear. This can be represented in eqn. (9.26) by setting $X_d' = X_d$, which has the effect of eliminating the transient term and leaving the correct subtransient term. After the decay of the subtransient the current is limited solely by X_d. The transient time-constants T_d' and T_{d0}' are meaningless in the PM machine, but there is no harm in setting them equal to T_d'' and T_{d0}'', on the grounds that once the subtransient has subsided the period in which the current is limited by X_d establishes itself immediately.

The subtransient part decays with a time-constant T_d'', called the **subtransient time-constant**, or sometimes the "short-circuit" subtransient time-constant. Both X_d'' and T_d'' depend on the conductive components on the rotor, including the magnets, the shaft, and any retaining can. In conventional wound-field machines the subtransient decays rapidly within a few cycles, but the transient persists much longer because of the large inductance of the field winding.

At time $t = 0$, $i_a = 0$. Consider a nonsalient-pole machine, with $\lambda = 0$. After half a cycle, $\omega t = \pi$, and if we assume that the exponential decay terms are still substantially equal to 1, we get

$$i_a \approx -\sqrt{2}\frac{E_{q1}}{X_d''} - \sqrt{2}\frac{E_{q1}}{X_d''} = -2\sqrt{2}\frac{E_{q1}}{X_d''}. \qquad (9.28)$$

Thus the DC offset is at most equal to the AC subtransient term, and doubles the peak current at the beginning of the transient, as is well known, in accordance with simple AC circuit theory.

Now consider the case of a rapidly-decaying subtransient term with a persistent DC term. This will happen if $T_d'' << T_a$. In the PM generator this is theoretically possible, because T_d'' depends on the effective resistance of the magnets, while T_a depends on the resistance of the armature, which is usually small. To show the effect, put $T_d'' = 0$ in eqn. (9.26), and $T_a = \infty$. Then

$$i_a = \underbrace{\sqrt{2}\,\frac{E_{q1}}{X_d}\cos(\omega t + \lambda)}_{AC} - \underbrace{\sqrt{2}\,\frac{E_{q1}}{X_d''}\cos\lambda}_{DC}. \tag{9.29}$$

This suggests that a persistent DC term can exceed the AC term once the subtransient AC current has vanished. It is thus theoretically possible for the DC term to offset the current to such an extent that the entire AC waveform is displaced to one side of the t-axis, so that it is (for a time) all positive or all negative with no reversals. Provided that T_a is sufficiently longer than T_d'', this will happen if $X_d'' < X_d$, which is normally the case. This "total offset" condition arises because the persistence of the DC term depends on T_a and not on T_d'', even though its *magnitude* depends on X_d''.

In short-circuit oscillograms of conventional AC machines, it is uncommon to see this "total offset" effect because it is masked by the transient component, whose time-constant is intermediate between the subtransient time-constant and the armature time-constant. It spite of the theoretical possibility, it is also appears to be uncommon in PM generators, probably because the subtransient effects are weak and vanish quickly. However, the DC offset term is unavoidable and is the main cause of high peak currents.

The DC offset is an example of asymmetry in the fault current. It is also important to calculate asymmetrical faults such as the line-to-line short-circuit. The classic works (Concordia, Kimbark, Ku etc.) all attend to this topic with vigour, although not without simplifying assumptions. Today, calculations of such complexity are performed exclusively by computer simulation.

The subtransient reactance and time-constant of a PM machine can be calculated by the method described in §12.4.5, while the synchronous reactances have been treated in Chapter 5.

Armature time-constant — The final parameter required for the symmetrical short-circuit analysis is the armature time-constant T_a. For salient-pole machines this is given by

$$T_a = \frac{2L_d''L_q''}{R_{ph}(L_d'' + L_q'')}, \tag{9.30}$$

where R_{ph} is the resistance per phase. For nonsalient-pole machines $L_d'' = L_q''$ and

$$T_a = \frac{L_d''}{R_{ph}}. \tag{9.31}$$

T_a is not really a fixed property of the machine but is one of several "decrement" factors that depend on the type of fault. One of the complexities arising in the analysis of asymmetrical faults is that the armature decrement factors (time-constants) are less simple than eqns. (9.30) or (9.31), which apply only to the symmetrical fault.[81]

The important subject of demagnetization has been addressed in Chapter 5, and it is worth pointing out that the analysis of faults by circuit simulation should also be extended to the analysis of demagnetization, preferably by means of the finite-element method if local effects within the magnet are to be considered. To some extent the circuit-simulation and finite-element analysis can be combined, although it is a slow process.

The question sometimes arises as to whether the magnets are protected from demagnetization during the short-circuit by the reactive eddy-currents within them; or by eddy-currents in the retaining can (if fitted). The colloquial answer is *don't bank on it.* The formal answer is that we have seen the persistence of high peak currents due to the DC offset, while the subtransient time-constant associated with the induced currents in the magnet is very short, implying that any such protection will be worthless. This being so, the risk of demagnetization can be studied by means of a magnetostatic finite-element analysis (in 2D for economy), with currents derived from a circuit simulation.

---

[81] See Concordia C, *Synchronous Machines, Theory and Performance*, John Wiley and Sons, New York, 1951.

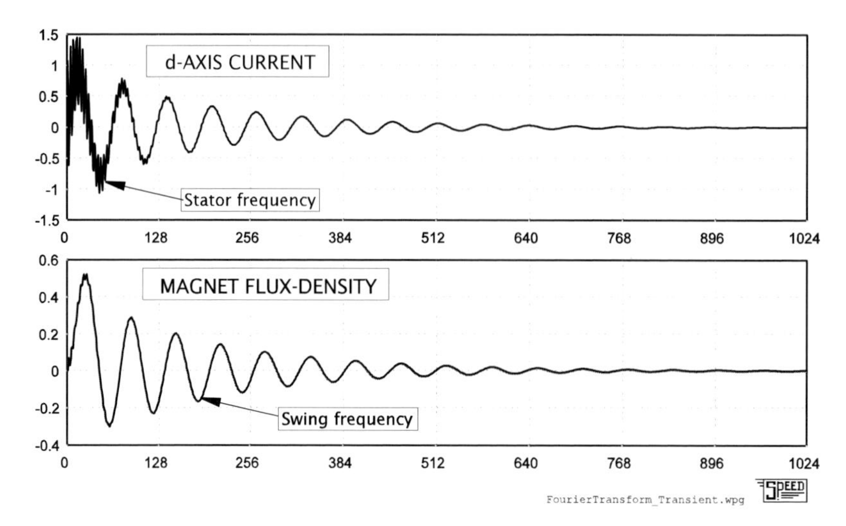

Fig. 9.13 Transient calculated by Fourier transform

9.3.2 Transient Magnetic Field by Fourier Transform

The short-circuit fault on p. 468 was calculated assuming constant speed, as is normally the case in such calculations; but this is not necessarily the worst-case transient for the magnet. Fig. 9.13 shows a fault condition in which the speed does not remain constant, but suffers a perturbation resulting in oscillations about synchronous speed at the so-called "swing frequency", which is typically of the order of 1–2 Hz. The swing-frequency oscillation is apparent in the *d*- and *q*-axis currents. If the speed was constant, the swing-frequency would be absent from Fig. 9.13. i_d and i_q also contain a line-frequency component due to the DC offset in the stator current, which decays to zero with the armature time-constant.

Fig. 9.13 is calculated for a PM machine with a conductive shield which attenuates the line-frequency component effectively, but has almost no shielding effect at the swing frequency. To calculate this type of transient by the finite-element method, it would be necessary to include mechanical equations permitting the speed to vary. A more efficient method is to calculate the *d*- and *q*-axis currents by a circuit-based simulation process in which the speed is allowed to vary, and then to apply the Fourier transform as described below.

This application of the Fourier transform method was originally developed for analyzing the transient fields in superconducting alternators, in which the transient field in the rotor is also of concern because of the fact that superconductors must be protected against rapid rates of change of field — a situation very similar to the one facing the designer of large PM machines.[82]

Let $B(t)$ represent the transient flux-density at a certain point in the magnet; then considering the effect of d-axis stator current we can obtain $B(t)$ from the inverse Fourier transform,

$$B(t) = F^{-1}\{S_d(j\omega)I_d(j\omega)\}. \tag{9.32}$$

where $I_d(j\omega)$ is the Fourier transform of the transient d-axis current and $S_d(j\omega)$ is a *screening function*, that is, the complex ratio of the flux-density at the point of interest and the d-axis current, both being expressed as phasors over a frequency range determined according to the Nyquist sampling frequency. An equivalent relationship exists for the q-axis, and the d- and q-axis components are added.

The current transform $I_d(j\omega)$ is the Fourier transform of the transient d-axis current $i_d(t)$ which is computed from the circuit model. Starting from the phase currents in Fig. 9.12 on p. 468, $i_d(t)$ and $i_q(t)$ can be determined by Park's transformation; or they may arise directly from a simulation in dq axes. Any DC offset in the phase current is automatically included in $I_d(j\omega)$ and $I_q(j\omega)$. Also note that $i_d(t)$ and $i_q(t)$ are "one-shot transients," not periodic functions.[83]

The screening function $S(j\omega)$ is obtained from the solution of the complex diffusion equation, for any component of flux-density B_r or B_θ at any point in the magnet. A frequency scan is necessary, which in principle must extend from $\omega = 0$ to $\omega = \infty$. The response $B(t)$ in eqn. (32) is then evaluated by the Fast Fourier Transform (F.F.T.) of Cooley and Tukey.

---

[82] See Miller T.J.E. and Lawrenson P.J., *Penetration of transient magnetic fields through conducting cylindrical structures, with particular reference to superconducting A.C. machines*, Proc. IEE, Vol. 123, No. 5, May 1976, pp. 437-443. Also Miller T.J.E., *Transient magnetic fields in the superconducting alternator*. Archiv für Elektrotechnik **62**, pp. 131-140, 1980.

[83] It is for this reason that the Fourier *transform* is required, rather than the Fourier *series*.

10 MULTIPLE-PHASE MACHINES

Introduction

This chapter is concerned with machines that have more than the usual 3 phases, and particularly with so-called **multiplex** machines in which the number of phases is an integer multiple of 2 or 3. Such machines are of interest in large sizes as motors or generators, one reason being that the electronic power conversion can be split into smaller units.

10.1 Polyphase machines

We can start by revisiting the properties of "polyphase" machines before developing the multiplex concept.

The traditional polyphase machine has three phases and is *balanced*, meaning that the phase voltages and currents are equal in magnitude and separated in phase by $\theta_3 = 120°$, Fig. 10.1(a). For a two-phase machine, balanced operation usually implies a phase displacement of $\theta_2 = 90°$, Fig. 10.1(b).

It would be convenient if the phase displacement θ in polyphase machines with m phases was always

$$\theta = \frac{360°}{m}. \tag{10.1}$$

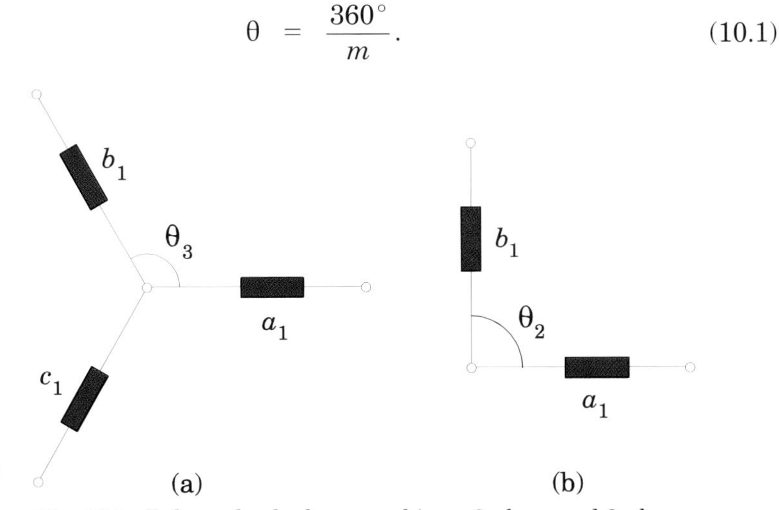

Fig. 10.1 Balanced polyphase machines: 3-phase and 2-phase

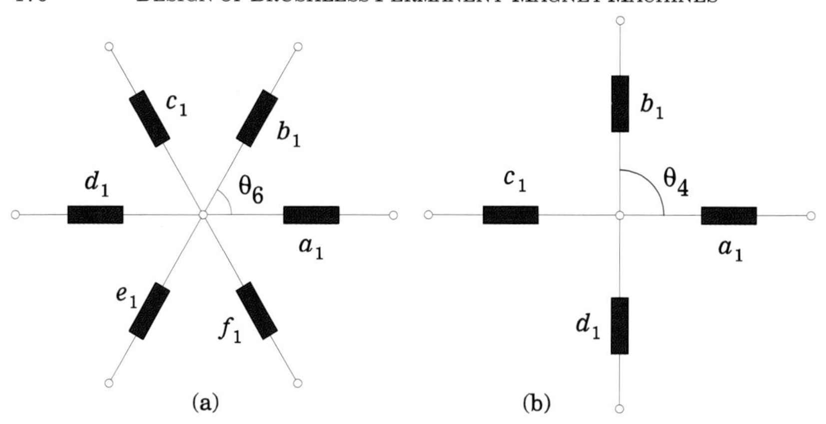

Fig. 10.2 Balanced polyphase machines : 6-phase and 4-phase

This works with $m = 3$, but with $m = 2$ we would get $\theta = 180°$. A 2-phase machine with a phase displacement of $180°$ cannot produce a rotating ampere-conductor distribution; in effect it is a single-phase machine with two anti-parallel windings. If one phase is reverse-connected, the windings will be in parallel rather than anti-parallel, with a phase displacement of 0, and it is still impossible to produce a rotating ampere-conductor distribution.

Eqn. (10.1) works with $m = 4$, in the sense that the resulting 4-phase machine in Fig. 10.2(b) can produce a rotating ampere-conductor distribution. Even so, phases a_1 and c_1 are anti-parallel, and so are phases b_1 and d_1, so this machine can be reduced to the 2-phase machine of Fig. 10.1(b).

With $m = 6$ and $\theta = 60°$, again we have a machine that can produce a rotating ampere-conductor distribution, but again pairs of phases (a_1 & d_1; b_1 & e_1; and c_1 & f_1) are anti-parallel, so this machine can be reduced to the 3-phase machine of Fig. 10.1(a).

We could define a balanced 6-phase machine as shown in Fig. 10.3(a), with

$$\theta = \frac{180°}{m}. \tag{10.2}$$

In that case $\theta = 180°/6 = 30°$ which is the same as $360°/12$, showing that the machine in Fig. 10.3 is the "irreducible" derivative of a 12-phase machine formed using eqn. (10.1).

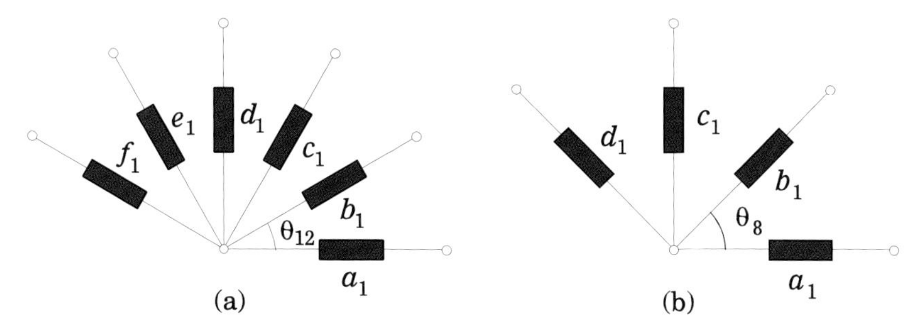

Fig. 10.3 Balanced polyphase machines : 6 and 4 phases

Similarly we could define a balanced 4-phase machine as shown in Fig. 10.3(b), which follows eqn. (10.2): $\theta = 180/4 = 45°$. Again this is the irreducible derivative of an 8-phase machine formed using eqn. (10.1).

Clearly the machines in Figs. 10.3(a) and (b) occupy only half the stator periphery, so we would expect to have another "set" of phases to occupy the other half. As we have already observed, every phase in the second set would be in phase or in anti-phase with one of the phases of the first set. Therefore the number of phases in the *supply* remains equal to 6 in Fig. 10.3(a), or 4 in Fig. 10.3(b).

More importantly, the same principle applies to the machine of Fig. 10.2(a). It appears to have 6 phases, evenly distributed around the stator periphery; but because they are in anti-parallel opposite pairs, only three phases are needed in the supply.

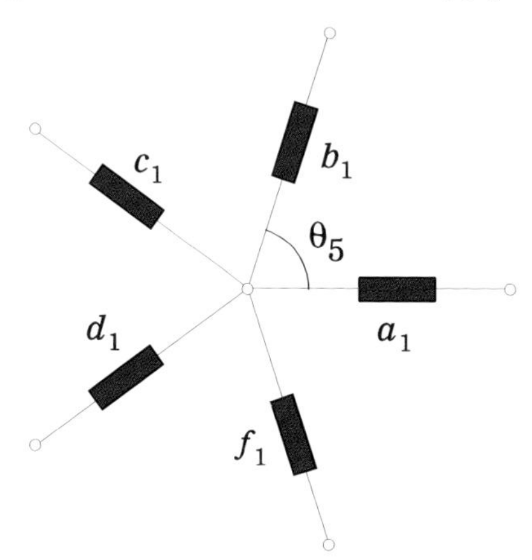

Fig. 10.4 Balanced polyphase machine : 5 phases

Next consider the 5-phase machine in Fig. 10.4. The phases are evenly distributed around the stator periphery, but no two phases are opposite. Therefore this is irreducibly a 5-phase machine requiring five *supply* phases. It obeys eqn. (10.1) for the number of phases in *both* the machine and the supply.

From this we can deduce that if m is odd, eqn. (10.1) can be used in general for the number of "machine phases" and the number of "supply phases". On the other hand, if m is even, eqn. (10.1) can still be used for the number of machine phases, but the number of supply phases could be reduced to $m/2$ — in effect, by using eqn. (10.2) for the number of supply phases.

10.2 Multiplex windings

Any of the polyphase sets in Figs. 10.1–10.4 can be *duplicated* or *triplicated* or — to coin a phrase, "multiplicated" to form a *duplex*, *triplex* or *multiplex* arrangement. For example, Fig. 10.5(a) shows a duplex 3-phase machine and Fig. 10.5(b) a duplex 2-phase machine. In each case there are two sets of polyphase windings. In practice the displacement α between the sets must be chosen so that the fluxes in common sections of the magnetic circuit make sensible utilization of the available cross-section, and to make the slot-fill factors even. We shall see later that the mutual coupling between sets imposes further constraints on α.

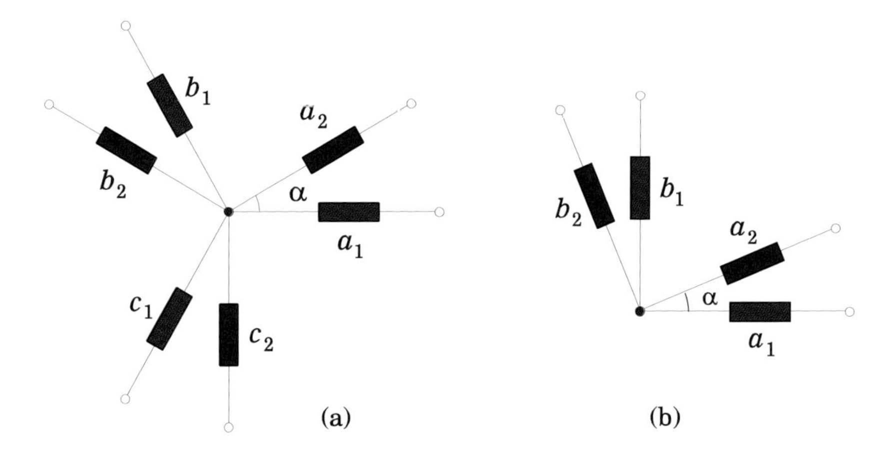

Fig. 10.5 Duplex 3-phase and 2-phase machines

The term *multiplex* has almost the same meaning here as it does in DC machines, although in DC machines the "phases" are not connected separately but form a continuous winding with multiple tappings to the commutator bars.

The term *plex* or "multiplicity" is used, with symbol x. Thus a duplex 3-phase system has $x = 2$ and six phases; a triplex 3-phase system has $x = 3$ and nine phases. A simplex winding has $x = 1$.

10.2.1 Reasons for using multiplex windings

- With very large machines, it may be more practical or more economical to use, say, x inverters of $1/x^{\mathrm{th}}$ the rating, rather than one huge inverter of 100% rating.
- With x inverters instead of 1, there is a chance of being able to operate even when one of the inverters is malfunctioning or switched off.
- It becomes possible to operate as many as x independent channels, by connecting the sets of windings to different buses. This can be done with pure AC systems, as in Fig. 10.6, or with a DC/inverter system, as in Fig. 10.7.
- For a given number of slots/pole, the winding factor of a duplex winding is higher than that of a simplex winding, because the "phase spread" is half the value.

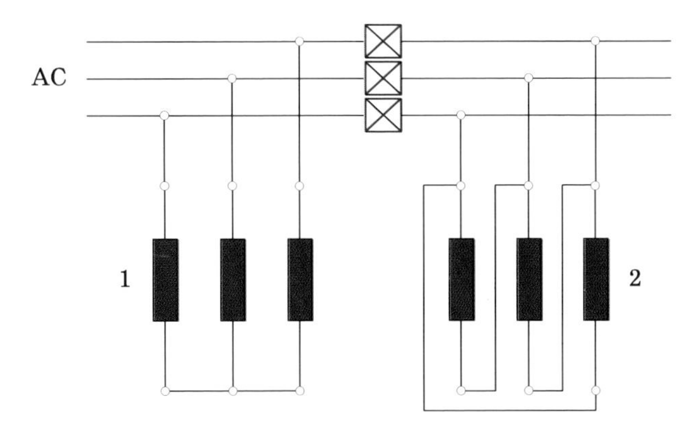

Fig. 10.6 Duplex wye/delta system, AC-fed; 6 phases

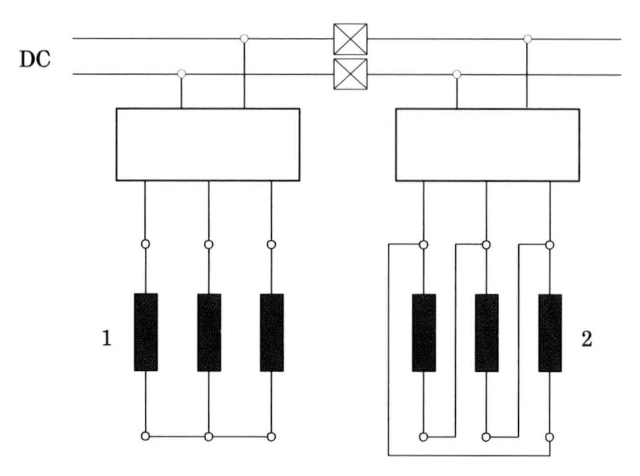

Fig. 10.7 Duplex wye/delta system, DC-fed; 6 phases

10.2.2 Fault-tolerant machines

The "multi-phase" concept suggests the idea of *independent channels* and *fault-tolerance*, whereby the machine can continue to operate even when one or more phases is faulty. Fig. 10.8 shows the idea of a 4-phase machine intended to have independent channels. Magnetic coupling between the four phases is nearly zero, while the reactance is made high to limit the fault current. However, this is a *simplex* machine that does not employ the multiplex concept. In multiplex machines, the x sets or channels of windings *are* coupled magnetically, and this must be taken into account in their analysis.

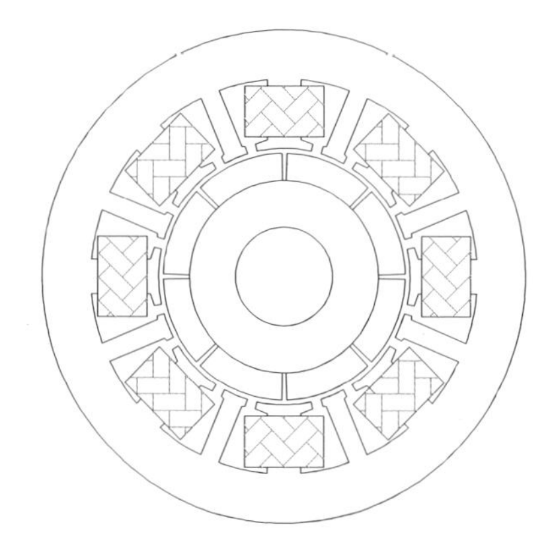

Fig. 10.8 "Fault tolerant" machine proposed by Jack and Mecrow

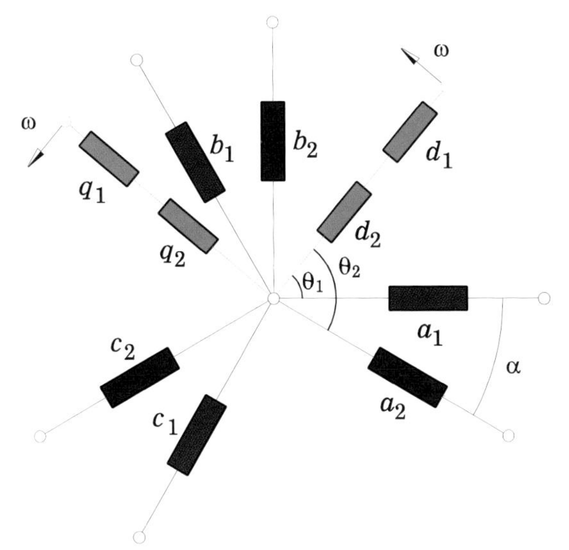

Fig. 10.9 Axes of multiplex windings

10.3 Analysis of multiplex windings

Fig. 10.9 shows the winding axes of a 6-phase machine which has two 3-phase windings $a_1b_1c_1$ and $a_2b_2c_2$ — in other words, a duplex three-phase winding. Each three-phase winding is wye-connected and is balanced in itself. In general all six phases are mutually coupled. If the rotor rotates anticlockwise, then the voltages and currents in $a_2b_2c_2$ lead those in $a_1b_1c_1$ by the phase angle α, which is the angular displacement between the two 3-phase windings.

The rotor d-axis is positioned at the angle θ_1 relative to the axis of phase a_1, and at the angle θ_2 relative to the axis of phase a_2, and

$$\alpha = \theta_2 - \theta_1. \tag{10.3}$$

The q-axis leads the d-axis by $\pi/2$ electrical radians.

The dq transformation applied to $a_1b_1c_1$ gives

$$\begin{aligned} v_{d1} &= R_1 i_{d1} + p\psi_{d1} - \omega\psi_{q1}; \\ v_{q1} &= R_1 i_{q1} + p\psi_{q1} + \omega\psi_{d1}. \end{aligned} \tag{10.4}$$

Normally with only 3 phases, there is just one d-coil and one q-coil and the flux-linkages are given by

$$\begin{aligned} \psi_{d1} &= \Psi_{Md1} + L_{d1} i_{d1}; \\ \psi_{q1} &= L_{q1} i_{q1}, \end{aligned} \qquad (10.5)$$

where Ψ_{Md1} is the flux-linkage produced by the magnet. We are going to transform the second winding $a_2b_2c_2$ into a second pair of coils d_2q_2 on the same direct and quadrature axes as the d_1q_1 coils, and these will be *coupled* to the d_1q_1 coils, so we can write

$$\begin{aligned} \psi_{d1} &= \Psi_{Md1} + L_{d1} i_{d1} + M_{d1d2} i_{d2}; \\ \psi_{q1} &= L_{q1} i_{q1} + M_{q1q2} i_{q2}. \end{aligned} \qquad (10.6)$$

The model can now be completed by adding the equations for the $a_2b_2c_2$ winding corresponding to eqns. (10.4) and (10.6):

$$\begin{aligned} v_{d2} &= R_2 i_{d2} + p\psi_{d2} - \omega\psi_{q2}; \\ v_{q2} &= R_2 i_{q2} + p\psi_{q2} + \omega\psi_{d2}, \end{aligned} \qquad (10.7)$$

and

$$\begin{aligned} \psi_{d2} &= \Psi_{Md2} + L_{d2} i_{d2} + M_{d2d1} i_{d1}; \\ \psi_{q2} &= L_{q2} i_{q2} + M_{q2q1} i_{q1}. \end{aligned} \qquad (10.8)$$

The mutual inductance M_{d1d2} or M_{d2d1} between the d_1 and d_2 coils is important, and we must consider whether it depends on the displacement angle α between the two 3-phase windings. Later we will also consider the possibility of cross-coupling between the d and q-axes, which is absent from eqns. (10.6) and (10.8).

If $\alpha = 0$, and if all phases have the same effective number of turns, then phases a_1 and a_2 will be aligned with the d-axis at the same time, as shown by the connection shown in Fig. 10.10. In this case we expect M_{d1d2} to be equal to L_{md}, the magnetizing component of L_d, plus another term $m_{\sigma 12d}$ arising from mutual coupling in the slots and in the end-windings: thus

$$M_{d1d2} = L_{md} + m_{\sigma 12d}(\alpha). \qquad (10.9)$$

The mutual inductance term $m_{\sigma 12d}$ may include a component due to differential or harmonic leakage, while L_{md} is related to the conventional leakage inductances L_σ and M_σ by eqn. (5.85), and is associated with the fundamental ampere-conductor distribution as noted in Fig. 10.10.

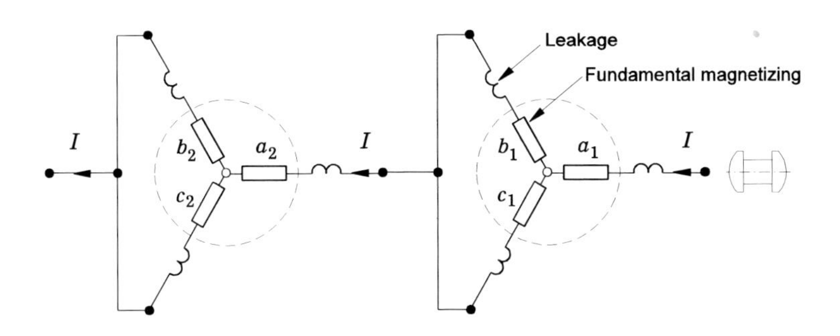

Fig. 10.10 Connection with $a_1b_1c_1$ and $a_2b_2c_2$ both aligned with the d-axis

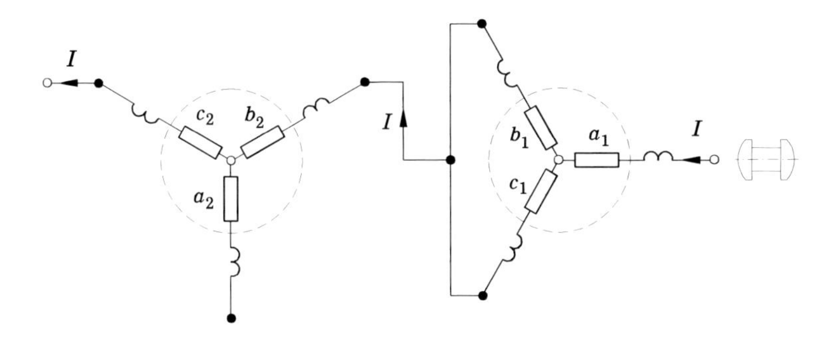

Fig. 10.11 Connection with $a_1b_1c_1$ and $a_2b_2c_2$ in quadrature

Any relationship between L_σ, M_σ and $m_{\sigma 12d}$ is not immediately obvious, but $m_{\sigma 12d}$ can be calculated formally by applying the dq-axis transformation to the entire inductance matrix as shown below.

If $\alpha = \pi/2$, phase a_2 will be aligned with a q-axis of the rotor when phase a_1 is aligned with a d-axis. Such is the case in the connection in Fig. 10.11. If the d-axis inductance L_d and its components L_{md}, L_σ and M_σ are independent of the orientation of the d-axis relative to the phase winding axes, eqn. (10.9) remains valid, but the *value* of $m_{\sigma 12d}$ will be different from what it was in Fig. 10.10.

As a simple verification of the main principle—that M_{d1d2} is independent of the rotor position or the orientation of the windings—

consider the flux-linkage produced in phase a_1 by the current I in Fig. 10.10. In per-unit terms it is

$$\psi_1 = 1 + \left(-\frac{1}{2}\right) \times \left(-\frac{1}{2}\right) + \left(-\frac{1}{2}\right) \times \left(-\frac{1}{2}\right) = \frac{3}{2} \quad (10.10)$$

In Fig. 10.11 the same flux-linkage is given by

$$\psi_1 = \frac{\sqrt{3}}{2} \times \frac{\sqrt{3}}{2} + \frac{\sqrt{3}}{2} \times \frac{\sqrt{3}}{2} = \frac{3}{2}, \quad (10.11)$$

since cos (30°) = −cos (150°) and the currents in phases b_2 and c_2 are $I\sqrt{3}/2$ and $-I\sqrt{3}/2$ respectively. At the instant shown, there is no flux in the q-axis. This example serves to show that in terms of normal phasor quantities, when $\alpha = \pi/2$ the currents in phases $a_2b_2c_2$ are 90° out of phase with the currents in phases $a_1b_1c_1$. In general, the currents (and voltages) must be phase-shifted by α.

By similar reasoning for the q-axis coils,

$$M_{q1q2} = L_{mq} + m_{\sigma 12q}(\alpha). \quad (10.12)$$

10.3.1 Balance

It seems possible to draw two important inferences from eqns. (10.9) and (10.12). In a duplex wye-connected 6-phase machine, there are only 2 coils on the d-axis and 2 coils on the q-axis. If there is no cross-coupling between the d- and q-axes, and if the phases are fed with equal voltages phase-shifted by α in the second set, the currents in the two sets will be equal in magnitude and phase-shifted by α : in other words, the two sets will be balanced, both within themselves and with respect to each other.

However, consider the extension to a 9-phase machine which will have 3 coils on the d-axis and 3 on the q-axis. We will have

$$\begin{aligned} M_{d1d2} &= L_{md} + m_{\sigma 12d}(\alpha); \\ M_{d2d3} &= L_{md} + m_{\sigma 23d}(\alpha); \\ M_{d3d1} &= L_{md} + m_{\sigma 31d}(\alpha). \end{aligned} \quad (10.13)$$

If $m_{\sigma 12d}$, $m_{\sigma 23d}$ and $m_{\sigma 31d}$ are not all equal, it will be impossible to achieve balance between the three sets of windings. For if they are all supplied with the same currents (correctly phase-shifted by 0, α and 2α respectively), the voltages will be unequal because of the differences in the mutual inductances. This imbalance will show itself in the actual phase voltages (if the currents are forced); or in the currents (if the voltages are forced).

To represent this inference as a general rule, if x is the *plex* of the windings and m is the number of phases, we can say that

- a duplex winding ($x = 2$; $m = 4$ or 6) can always be balanced regardless of α;
- a triplex 9-phase winding, or a winding of higher multiplicity ($x \neq 3$), cannot be balanced unless all the d-axis mutual inductances are equal to one another; and all the q-axis mutual inductances are separately equal to one another.

It can also be seen that the accuracy of performance calculations will depend on the accuracy of the values of the mutual inductances M_{d1d2}, M_{q1q2} etc. To pursue this further, it is necessary to resort to a matrix analysis of the inductances.

10.4 Matrix analysis of the inductances

The conventional dq-axis transformation for plain 3-phase machines is given in §4.4 and §5.9. In terms of flux-linkages $[\psi]$ and currents $[i]$, it is summarized as follows :

$$[\psi_{abc}] = [L_{abc}][i_{abc}]; \tag{10.14}$$

$$[i_{dq0}] = [T][i_{abc}]; \qquad [i_{abc}] = [T]^{-1}[i_{dq0}]. \tag{10.15}$$

$$[\psi_{dq0}] = [T][\psi_{abc}] = [T][L_{abc}][T]^{-1}[i_{dq0}] = [L_{dq0}][i_{dq0} \tag{10.16}$$

The matrix $[L_{abc}]$ is defined by eqns. (4.95), and the result is

$$[L_{dq0}] = \begin{bmatrix} L_d & & \\ & L_q & \\ & & L_0 \end{bmatrix} \tag{10.17}$$

where L_d and L_q are given in §5.9, and $[T]$ is given in §4.4.2.

To consider the duplex 6-phase machine we start with the *abc* inductance matrix:

	a_1	b_1	c_1	a_2	b_2	c_2
a_1	L_{a1}	M_{a1b1}	M_{a1c1}	M_{a1a2}	M_{a1b2}	M_{a1c2}
b_1	M_{b1a1}	L_{b1}	M_{b1c1}	M_{b1a2}	M_{b1b2}	M_{b1c2}
c_1	M_{c1a1}	M_{c1b1}	L_{c1}	M_{c1a2}	M_{c1b2}	M_{c1c2}
a_2	M_{a1a2}	M_{b1a2}	M_{c1a2}	L_{a2}	M_{a2b2}	M_{a2c2}
b_2	M_{a1b2}	M_{b1b2}	M_{c1b2}	M_{b2a2}	L_{b2}	M_{b2c2}
c_2	M_{a1c2}	M_{b1c2}	M_{c1c2}	M_{c2a2}	M_{c2b2}	L_{c2}

It is useful to partition this matrix into

	$a_1b_1c_1$	$a_2b_2c_2$
$a_1b_1c_1$	$[A_1]$	$[B]$
$a_2b_2c_2$	$[B']$	$[A_2]$

(10. 19)

If $[B] = 0$, there is no mutual coupling between the $a_1b_1c_1$ windings and the $a_2b_2c_2$ windings. In that case the $dq0$ transformation $[T_1] = [T(\theta_1)]$ can be applied to $[A_1]$, and $[T_2] = [T(\theta_2)]$ to $[A_2]$,[84] and the result is two completely independent, uncoupled $dq0$ systems

	$d_1q_10_1$	$d_2q_20_2$
$d_1q_10_1$	$[T_1][A_1][T_1]^{-1}$	
$d_2q_20_2$		$[T_2][A_2][T_2]^{-1}$

(10.20)

In practice the $d_1q_10_1$ system is mutually coupled to the $d_2q_20_2$ system, and we have already postulated the form of the mutual inductances in eqns. (10.9), (10.12) and (10.13). The situation so far can be summarized by writing the duplex $dq0$ inductance matrix as follows. (Extension to the triplex winding is obvious).

[84] The notation $[T(\theta)]$ means that the elements of $[T]$ are trigonometric functions of θ.

	d_1	q_1	0_1	d_2	q_2	0_2
d_1	L_{d1}			$L_{md}+m_{\sigma 12d}$		
q_1		L_{q1}			$L_{mq}+m_{\sigma 12q}$	
0_1			L_{01}			
d_2	$L_{md}+m_{\sigma 12d}$			L_{d2}		
q_2		$L_{mq}+m_{\sigma 12q}$			L_{q2}	
0_2						L_{02}

The terms in L_{md} and L_{mq} are easy but the terms in $m_{\sigma 12d}$ and $m_{\sigma 12q}$ require more analysis. First, the formal means of generating the duplex $dq0$ matrix is to apply the transformation

	$d_1q_10_1$	$d_2q_20_2$
$d_1q_10_1$	$[T_1]$	
$d_2q_20_2$		$[T_2]$

(10.22)

to the complete 6-way matrix $a_1b_1c_1a_2b_2c_2$. In terms of the partitions already considered, this gives

	$d_1q_10_1$	$d_2q_20_2$
$d_1q_10_1$	$[T_1][A_1][T_1]^{-1}$	$[T_1][B][T_2]^{-1}$
$d_2q_20_2$	$[T_2][B'][T_1]^{-1}$	$[T_2][A_2][T_2]^{-1}$

(10.23)

We already have the upper-left and lower-right partitions, and we also have the L_{md} and L_{mq} terms in the upper-right and lower-left partitions. The remaining mutual inductance terms are treated independently, by transforming the matrix of mutual inductances between pairs of phases of different channels, *excluding* the airgap fluxes which give rise to L_{md} and L_{mq}. To do this, define λ as the mutual inductance between a_1 and a_2; μ between a_1 and b_2; and ν between a_1 and c_2. λ, μ and ν are confined to slot-leakage flux, end-winding flux, and harmonic leakage, and we can consider them to be independent of rotor position. The matrix to be transformed is

	a_1	b_1	c_1	a_2	b_2	c_2
a_1				λ	μ	ν
b_1				ν	λ	μ
c_1				μ	ν	λ
a_2	λ	ν	μ			
b_2	μ	λ	ν			
c_2	ν	μ	λ			

Thus for the upper-right partition,

$$[T_1][B][T_2]^{-1} = [T_1] \cdot \begin{bmatrix} \lambda & \mu & \nu \\ \nu & \lambda & \mu \\ \mu & \nu & \lambda \end{bmatrix} \cdot [T_2]^{-1} \tag{10.24}$$

Without writing out the entire solution, it is instructive to work out and examine just the $(1,1)^{\text{th}}$ element, which represents $m_{\sigma 12d}$:

$$[T_1][B][T_2]^{-1}(1,1) = m_{\sigma 12d} = \lambda \cos(\theta_2 - \theta_1) + \\ + \mu \cos(\theta_2 - \theta_1 - 120°) + \nu \cos(\theta_2 - \theta_1 + 120°). \tag{10.24}$$

Since $\theta_2 - \theta_1 = \alpha$, we can write this as

$$m_{\sigma 12d} = \lambda \cos \alpha + \mu \cos(\alpha - 120°) + \nu \cos(\alpha + 120°). \tag{10.25}$$

By the same process we find that

$$[T_1][B][T_2]^{-1}(2,2) = m_{\sigma 12q} = \lambda \cos \alpha + \\ + \mu \cos(\alpha - 120°) + \nu \cos(\alpha + 120°) = m_{\sigma 12d}. \tag{10.26}$$

This shows the feature we might have hoped to avoid: that although $m_{\sigma 12d} = m_{\sigma 12q}$, these mutual inductances appear to depend on α, and further analysis is necessary to find out the constraints that apply to the choice of α for duplex, triplex, and higher multiplex windings.

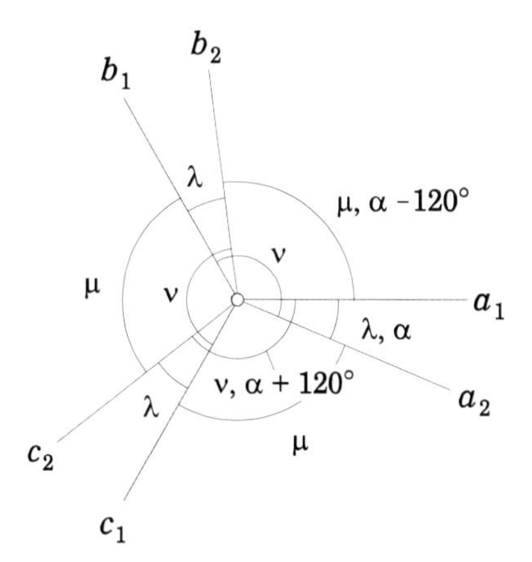

Fig. 10.12 Angles for contemplating λ,μ and ν

For the duplex winding we have already observed that it does not matter if $m_{\sigma 12d}$ and $m_{\sigma 12q}$ depend on α, because there is only one mutual inductance on the *d*-axis and one on the *q-axis*.

For triplex windings we can expect $m_{\sigma 12d}$ and $m_{\sigma 23d}$ both to be given by eqn. (10.25) directly, because the displacement angle between sets 1 and 2 is the same as the displacement angle between sets 2 and 3, both being equal to α. But the displacement angle between sets 1 and 3 is 2α, so we expect $m_{\sigma 31d}$ to be given by eqn. (10.25) with 2α substituted in place of α. Now we know that it is necessary to have

$$m_{\sigma 12d} = m_{\sigma 23d} = m_{\sigma 31d} \qquad (10.27)$$

to operate a triplex winding balanced. So what we really need, at this stage, is to understand whether, and under what conditions, eqn. (10.25) gives the same value for 2α as it does for α.

Now consider the mutual inductances λ, μ, ν in terms of the winding harmonics. From Fig. 10.12 we can see that λ is a function of the angle α, that is, λ = λ(α). Similarly μ is a function of the angle (α – 120°), and if we assume the same functional dependence, we can write μ = μ(α – 120°). Finally ν = ν(α + 120°). For each harmonic component of the inductance, let

$$\begin{aligned} \lambda &= \Lambda_n \cos n\alpha; \\ \mu &= \Lambda_n \cos n(\alpha - 120^\circ); \\ \nu &= \Lambda_n \cos n(\alpha + 120^\circ). \end{aligned} \tag{10.28}$$

This is, in effect, one term of a Fourier series expansion of the inductances λ, μ and ν. If we substitute this in eqn. (10.25) we get the total n^{th} harmonic inductance

$$\begin{aligned} m_n(\alpha) = \Lambda_n [&\cos n\alpha \cos \alpha \\ &+ \cos n(\alpha - 120^\circ)\cos(\alpha - 120^\circ) \\ &+ \cos n(\alpha + 120^\circ)\cos(\alpha + 120^\circ)]. \end{aligned} \tag{10.29}$$

It can be shown that $m_n(2\alpha) = m_n(\alpha)$ for $\alpha = 20^\circ, 40^\circ, 60^\circ, 80^\circ, 100^\circ$, 120° etc., but not for $\alpha = 15^\circ$ or 30°. This implies that $\alpha = 20^\circ$, 40° or even 80° is acceptable for triplex (9-phase) windings, but not 15° or 30°. On the other hand 15° and 30° are acceptable for duplex (6-phase) windings. In general it appears that $\alpha = 180k/mx^\circ$ gives the required result expressed by eqn. (10.27), at least for duplex and triplex cases.

It is of interest to give some thought to the conditions that would make $\lambda = \mu = \nu = 0$. If this could be achieved, then *any* value of the displacement angle α would be acceptable with any value of *plex*. If all the mutual coupling between phases of different sets were *via* the slot-leakage flux, this condition could be satisfied by ensuring that the windings of $a_1b_1c_1$ have no shared slots with $a_2b_2c_2$ or $a_3b_3c_3$. The differential leakage is more troublesome, since it is a function of several space-harmonics of MMF having different pole-pitches. For example, if $\alpha = 30^\circ$ there should be no third-harmonic linkage between a_1 and a_2, since $3 \times 30 = 90^\circ$, rendering a_1 and a_2 orthogonal and therefore uncoupled for this harmonic. But the same cannot be said of the non-triplen harmonics 5th, 7th, etc. One might hope that the differential leakage is small; but the very nature of multiplex windings is to reduce the number of slots per pole per phase, potentially increasing the winding factors of some of the harmonics we would like to eliminate. The inference is that it is safest to select α from the preferred values indicated earlier, when designing triplex or higher-multiplex windings.

Finally let us test the symmetry of the combined $dq0$ matrix by evaluating the $[1,1]^{\text{th}}$ term of $[T_2][B'][T_1]^{-1}$, the lower-left partition.

The evaluation is similar to that of the upper-right partition $[T_1][B][T_2]^{-1}$, with θ_1 and θ_2 interchanged. The result is

$$m_{\sigma 21d} = \lambda \cos \alpha + \mu \cos (\alpha - 120°) + \nu \cos (\alpha + 120°). \quad (10.30)$$

Thus

$$m_{\sigma 21d} = m_{\sigma 12d} \quad (10.31)$$

and the mutual (off-diagonal) inductances in the $dq0$ matrix are indeed reciprocal, as would be expected.

Simplified calculations — In order to proceed with manageable calculations, the simplest expedient is to drop $m_{\sigma 12d}$ from eqn. (10.9) and $m_{\sigma 12q}$ from its q-axis counterpart, leaving

$$M_{d1d2} = L_{md} \quad (10.32)$$

and

$$M_{q1q2} = L_{mq}. \quad (10.33)$$

Alternatively, $m_{\sigma 12d}$ and $m_{\sigma 12q}$ can be retained in the equations but treated as a user-defined "perturbation" parameter. This permits an experimental numerical approach to determine how large these parasitic mutual inductances must be to cause significant errors in the calculation (and/or to cause significant imbalance between winding sets in cases of multiplicity 3 or higher). This approach is followed in the remaining sections.

10.5 Torque

The electromagnetic torque is the result of interaction between the currents and the rotational voltages in eqns. (10.4) and (10.7). For the first set of windings,

$$T_1 = mp(\psi_{d1} i_{q1} - \psi_{q1} i_{d1}), \quad (10.34)$$

where m is the number of phases (3) in the set, and p is the number of pole-pairs. Substituting for the flux-linkages from eqns. (10.5),

$$\begin{aligned} T_1 = mp[\Psi_{Md1} i_{q1} &+ (L_{d1} - L_{q1}) i_{d1} i_{q1} \\ &+ M_{d1d2} i_{d2} i_{q1} - M_{q1q2} i_{d1} i_{q2}]. \end{aligned} \quad (10.35)$$

For the second set of windings the process is the same:

$$T_2 = mp(\psi_{d2}i_{q2} - \psi_{q2}i_{d2}), \tag{10.36}$$

so that

$$\begin{aligned} T_2 = mp[&\Psi_{Md2}i_{q2} + (L_{d2} - L_{q2})i_{d2}i_{q2} \\ &+ M_{d2d1}i_{d1}i_{q2} - M_{q2q1}i_{d2}i_{q1}]. \end{aligned} \tag{10.37}$$

In each of eqns. (10.35) and (10.37), the first term is the familiar permanent-magnet alignment torque, while the second term is the familiar reluctance torque. The third and fourth terms arise from interaction between the two sets of windings: d-axis flux produced by one set interacts with the orthogonal q-axis current of the other set. Consequently four additional terms appear for a duplex winding; eight for a triplex winding, and $4(x - 1)$ for an x-plex winding.

The torque equations (10.35) and (10.37) can be used for transient or steady-state torque. In the steady-state they can be written in terms of phasors (RMS AC quantities):

$$\begin{aligned} T_1 &= \frac{mp}{\omega}[E_{q1}I_{q1} + (X_{d1} - X_{q1})I_{d1}I_{q1} \\ &\qquad + X_{d1d2}I_{d2}I_{q1} - X_{q1q2}I_{d1}I_{q2}]; \\ T_2 &= \frac{mp}{\omega}[E_{q2}I_{q2} + (X_{d2} - X_{q2})I_{d2}I_{q2} \\ &\qquad + X_{d2d1}I_{d1}I_{q2} - X_{q2q1}I_{d2}I_{q1}]. \end{aligned} \tag{10.38}$$

where $\omega = 2\pi f$ and $X = \omega L$. Regrouping the terms of this equation, we can separate the alignment torques and the reluctance torques as

$$\begin{aligned} T_{ei} &= \frac{mp}{\omega}\left[E_{q1}I_{q1} + E_{q2}I_{q2}\right]; \\ T_{relA} &= \frac{mp}{\omega}\left[(X_{d1} - X_{q1})I_{d1}I_{q1} + (X_{d2} - X_{q2})I_{d2}I_{q2}\right]; \\ T_{relB} &= \frac{mp}{\omega}\left[(X_{d2d1} - X_{q1q2})I_{d1}I_{q2} + (X_{d1d2} - X_{q2q1})I_{d2}I_{q1}\right]; \end{aligned} \tag{10.39}$$

where T_{ei} is the total alignment torque, $T_{rel\,A}$ is the "self" reluctance torque, and $T_{rel\,B}$ is a "mutual" reluctance torque.

With a triplex winding the result is

$$
\begin{aligned}
T_{ei} &= \frac{mp}{\omega}\left[E_{q1}I_{q1} + E_{q2}I_{q2} + E_{q3}I_{q3}\right]; \\
T_{relA} &= \frac{mp}{\omega}\left[(X_{d1} - X_{q1})I_{d1}I_{q1} + (X_{d2} - X_{q2})I_{d2}I_{q2} + \right. \\
&\quad \left. + (X_{d3} - X_{q3})I_{d3}I_{q3} \right]; \\
T_{relB} &= \frac{mp}{\omega}\left[(X_{d1d2}-X_{q1q2})(I_{d1}I_{q2} + I_{d2}I_{q1}) + \right. \\
&\quad + (X_{d2d3}-X_{q2q3})(I_{d2}I_{q3} + I_{d3}I_{q2}) + \\
&\quad \left. + (X_{d3d1}-X_{q3q1})(I_{d3}I_{q1} + I_{d1}I_{q3}) \right] .
\end{aligned}
\tag{10.40}
$$

10.6 Steady-state operation : phasor diagram

Under AC steady-state conditions the RMS values of the d- and q-axis flux-linkages ψ_d and ψ_q in eqn. (10.5) can be combined into a phasor

$$\mathbf{\Psi}_1 = \Psi_{d1} + j\Psi_{q1}, \tag{10.41}$$

and likewise the current can be expressed as a phasor

$$\mathbf{I}_1 = I_{d1} + jI_{q1}. \tag{10.42}$$

The voltage phasor is then given by

$$\mathbf{V}_1 = V_{d1} + jV_{q1} = R_1\mathbf{I}_1 + j\omega\mathbf{\Psi}_1, \tag{10.43}$$

in which

$$
\begin{aligned}
V_{d1} &= R_1I_{d1} - X_{q1}I_{q1} - X_{q1q2}I_{q2}; \\
V_{q1} &= E_{q1} + R_1I_{q1} + X_{d1}I_{d1} + X_{d1d2}I_{d2}.
\end{aligned}
\tag{10.44}
$$

This can be expressed graphically in the phasor diagram, Fig. 10.13. The terms R_1I_{d1}, $-X_{q1}I_{q1}$, E_{q1}, R_1I_{q1}, and $X_{d1}I_{d1}$ are familiar from the simplex winding; but the cross-coupling terms $-X_{q1q2}I_{q2}$ and $X_{d1d2}I_{d2}$ are peculiar to the duplex winding. Without the cross-coupling terms the terminal voltage would be $\mathbf{U}_1$ (Fig. 10.13); but with them the terminal voltage is $\mathbf{V}_1$. A similar phasor diagram is obtained for the second set of windings, for which the corresponding voltage equations are eqns. (10.45).

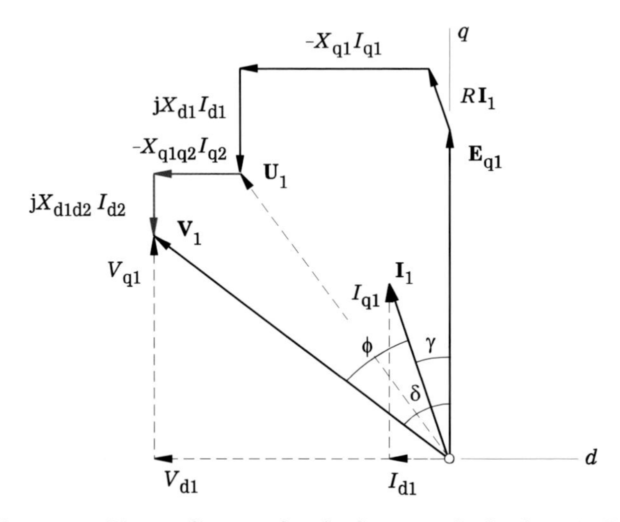

Fig. 10.13 Phasor diagram for the first set of a duplex winding

$$\begin{aligned} V_{d2} &= R_2 I_{d2} - X_{q2} I_{q2} - X_{q2q1} I_{q1}; \\ V_{q2} &= E_{q2} + R_2 I_{q2} + X_{d2} I_{d2} + X_{d2d1} I_{d1}. \end{aligned} \tag{10.45}$$

The cross-coupling terms appear in the phasor diagram as additional voltage-drops which tend to limit the current. If $\alpha = 0$, we have tightly coupled inductances between the two sets, as already observed; and if these sets are fed from a common voltage source the current in each set will be approximately half the current that would flow in one set if the other were open-circuited. This is an important practical point because it implies that in a duplex winding, if one set is open-circuited the current in the other set could increase by a factor approaching 200%, if it were not regulated. Likewise if one set is short-circuited, the impedance of the second set will be reduced and its current could also increase to a high value if it is not regulated.

The behaviour of the duplex sets is analogous to that of parallel inductances, Fig. 10.14, with an equivalent inductance

$$L_{eq} = \frac{L_1 L_2 - M^2}{L_1 + L_2 - 2M}. \tag{10.46}$$

If $L_1 = L_2 = L$, this simplifies to $(L + M)/2$, and the equivalent circuit is two parallel *uncoupled* inductances, each of value $L + M$.

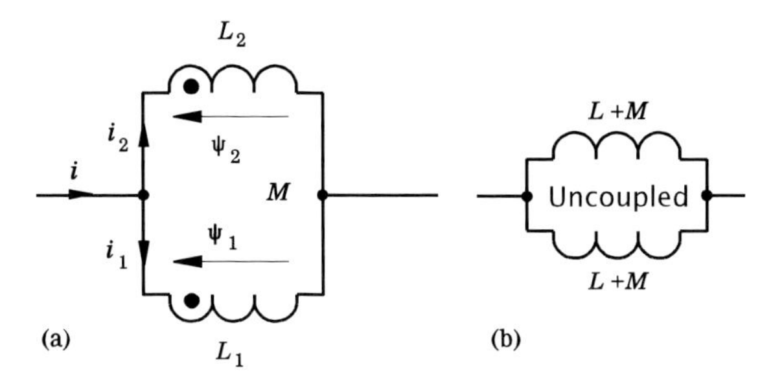

Fig. 10.14 Parallel inductances (aiding)

When $\alpha = 0$, M becomes close to L and the overall inductance is approximately $(L + M)/2 = L$. The total current is that which is limited by L, and half the current flows in each set. But if one set is open-circuited, the same total current will tend to flow in one set. The implication is that regulation of the current is essential.

We are now in a position to solve the system with any given voltages or currents applied to the terminals of the two sets of windings. In the steady state this is a question of solving eqns. (10.44) and (10.45) when either the voltages $\mathbf{V}_1$ and $\mathbf{V}_2$ are given, or the currents $\mathbf{I}_1$ and $\mathbf{I}_2$ are given.

10.7 Solution method — transient

When the machine is inverter-fed, the applied voltages are PWM waveforms determined by a current regulator. Where we normally solve only eqn. (10.4) for ψ_d and ψ_q in a 3-phase machine, we must now integrate eqns. (10.4) and (10.7) to produce updated values of ψ_{d1}, ψ_{q1}, ψ_{d2} and ψ_{q2} at each time-step, also inverting eqns. (10.6) and (10.8) for i_{d1}, i_{q1}, i_{d2} and i_{q2} and updating the torque.

The extension to triplex and multiplex windings is a straightforward matter of adding additional voltage equations of the form of eqn. (10.4), and additional mutual terms in the corresponding flux-linkage equations of the form of eqn. (10.6). Everything else follows as described above.

10.8 Finite-element analysis

The torque can be calculated from the i-ψ loop areas as described in §4.5, using instantaneous phase currents which represent steady-state operation over one electrical cycle with sinusoidal current waveforms. The calculation must use the total MMF of both sets of windings. Treating $a_1b_1c_1$ as the reference winding, we have

$$\begin{aligned} i_{a1} &= -\sqrt{2}\, I_1 \sin\, (\omega t + \gamma) \\ i_{b1} &= -\sqrt{2}\, I_1 \sin\, (\omega t + \gamma - 120°) \\ i_{c1} &= -\sqrt{2}\, I_1 \sin\, (\omega t + \gamma + 120°) \end{aligned} \qquad (10.47)$$

where I_1 is the RMS current in windings $a_1b_1c_1$. Similarly

$$\begin{aligned} i_{a2} &= -\sqrt{2}\, I_2 \sin\, (\omega t + \gamma + \alpha) \\ i_{b2} &= -\sqrt{2}\, I_2 \sin\, (\omega t + \gamma + \alpha - 120°) \\ i_{c2} &= -\sqrt{2}\, I_2 \sin\, (\omega t + \gamma + \alpha + 120°) \end{aligned} \qquad (10.48)$$

where I_2 is the RMS current in windings $a_2b_2c_2$, and the currents in $a_2b_2c_2$ are leading the corresponding currents in $a_1b_1c_1$ by α. This can readily be extended to the triplex winding, $x = 3$. The average electromagnetic torque can be computed from the sum of the areas of the mx i-ψ loops as described in §4.5.

By means of particular points on the i-ψ loop, the finite-element method can be used to determine saturation factors for the synchronous inductances, as described in §5.13. It is self-evident that L_{md} and M_{d1d2} will share the same d-axis saturation factor, while L_{mq} and M_{q1q2} will share the same q-axis saturation factor. These saturation factors can be determined in the usual way from the flux-linkages ψ_{a1}, ψ_{b1} and ψ_{c1} of the $a_1b_1c_1$ winding set, or their dq equivalents ψ_{d1}, ψ_{q1}.

11 LINE-START MOTORS

11.1 Introduction

The line-start permanent-magnet motor is capable of starting "across the line" by switching it on to an AC voltage source. Once started, it runs at synchronous speed. The torque is entirely determined by the load. In the steady state there is a maximum torque, the pullout torque, which must not be exceeded; otherwise the motor will "slip poles" and fall from synchronism.

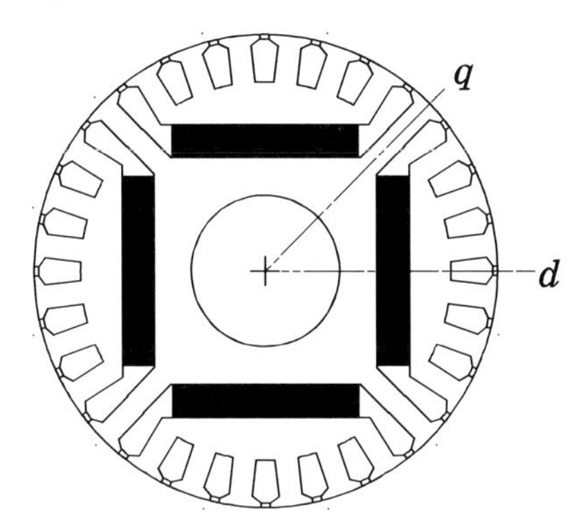

Fig. 11.1 Line-start motor rotor; Steen / Reliance [1979]

There are two main reasons to be interested in the line-start PM motor. The first is the ability of the polyphase line-start motor to start like an induction motor but to run at synchronous speed without slip losses. Since the slip losses or "rotor conduction losses" in induction motors are typically 30% of the total loss, the line-start motor appears to offer the prospect of a higher efficiency. A 30% loss reduction improves an efficiency of 85% to 89% for the same output power. Moreover, if the ratio of EMF to supply voltage is carefully chosen, the power factor can be improved. This leads to a further reduction in stator copper losses, and although there may be an increase in iron losses the part-load efficiency will still be better than that of the induction motor. As with any synchronous machine, it is even possible to operate with a leading power-factor if sufficient excitation is available in the form of "strong magnets".

Fig. 11.2 Stator and cut-away rotor of a 2-pole 2·5hp line-start PM motor. Photograph courtesy of A. O. Smith Corporation

Fig. 11.3 Computer sketch of 4-pole line-start PM motor

While the first advantage — higher efficiency — is of interest for general-purpose motors (especially those that operate more or less continuously), the second reason for being interested in the line-start motor is the fact that it runs precisely at synchronous speed. In some applications this can be used to avoid the need for a feedback control system using a dedicated current-regulated inverter. In some cases a single inverter drives many motors by providing an AC bus whose frequency determines the synchronous speed, ensuring precise synchronism between all the motors without using electronic feedback or mechanical linkages.

The price paid for these advantages obviously includes the cost of magnets and the means of fabricating the cage rotor without harm to the magnets. With high-energy magnets it is preferable to magnetize before assembly. In operation there is a risk of demagnetization if the rotor is overheated or if too much current is drawn, especially during synchronization. The application engineer must take into account the fact that the synchronizing or "pull in" capability is limited to loads of lower inertia than can be started with induction motors. Torque transients during across-the-line starting can exert severe repetitive stress on couplings and other components (including the load), and start-up tends to be noisy. Unlike the induction motor, the PM motor has live terminals when rotating, even when isolated from the supply; it also has persistent flux that sustains short-circuit currents indefinitely, whereas in the induction motor the flux decays to zero within a few cycles.

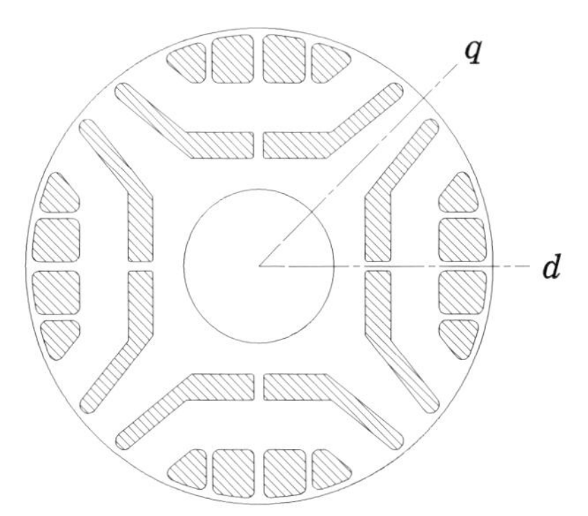

Fig. 11.4 4-pole *Synduction Motor*®; Honsinger [1964]; not to scale

11.2 History

By the early 1950s, PM generators had already been in service for several years, but examples of PM line-start motors from that era are hard to find.[85] One of the first appears to have been the 4-pole *Permasyn* motor described in 1955 by F.W. Merrill. Fig. 11.5 shows a 2-pole line-start motor rotor similar in construction to the *Permasyn* motor, described and analyzed by Cahill and Adkins in 1962. Both of these motors used Alnico magnets and standard induction-motor stators. By the early 1960s, Volkrodt (Siemens) was extolling the virtues of ferrite magnets in this type of motor.

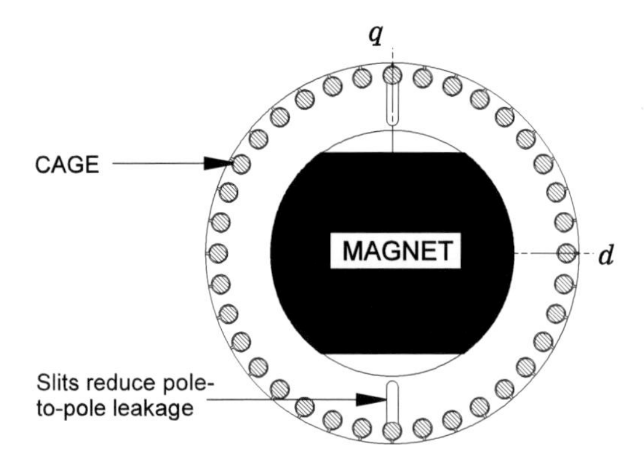

Fig. 11.5 2-pole PM line-start rotor [Adkins, 1962]

The development of PM line-start motors seems to have lain almost dormant during the 1960s and into the 1970s, while line-start synchronous reluctance motors were developed intensively by Siemens in Germany, by Lawrenson, Fong and others in the UK, and by Honsinger in the USA: an example attibutable to Honsinger is shown in Fig. 11.4. These motors were specially advocated for their synchronous operation, and were often used with variable-frequency inverters, with several motors operating in synchronism from a common inverter. The rotor cage makes it possible to start the motor "across the line", and provides damping to prevent speed oscillations; such oscillations were problematic and much analysis was published on them in the 1960s and 1970s especially by Lawrenson.

[85] Small timing motors and clock motors are not included in this discussion, which focusses on power levels above 100W or so.

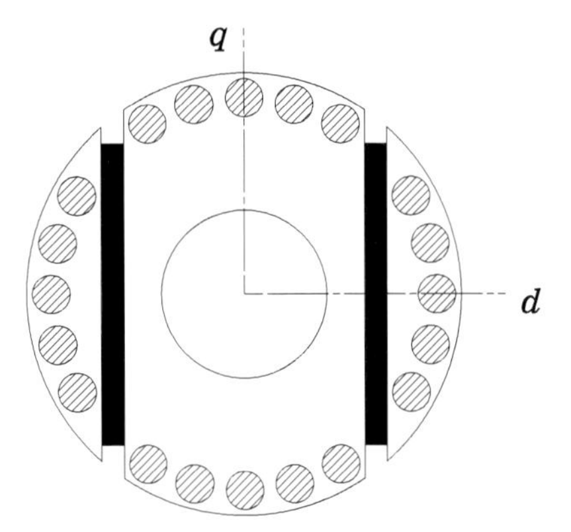

Fig. 11.6 Isosyn® motor described by Laronze [1978] (not to scale)

In retrospect the apparent preference at that time for the synchronous reluctance motor over the PM motor might seem strange. It becomes perfectly reasonable if we remember that before the mid-1970s the only available magnet materials suitable for PM motors were Alnico and ferrite. Alnico has a high remanent flux-density; but its low coercivity and high cost make it completely unsuitable for line-start motors. And although ferrite has much lower cost and is classed as a high-coercivity material, the coercivity is high only in relation to the remanent flux-density, which is low. Therefore ferrite line-start motors would have a low power-density and a susceptibility to demagnetization, making them uncompetitive with good induction motors. The saliency ratio achievable with PM motors (typically 2–4) is generally lower than that which is achievable in synchronous reluctance motors (up to 10), so there is very little reluctance torque to compensate for the weak alignment torque that would be achieved with ferrite magnets (or with Alnico magnets in a motor designed to be inherently safe from demagnetization). This historical analysis is often revisited in modern times as a result of concerns about the cost and availability of magnet materials.

In about 1977, interest in the PM line-start motor re-awakened, probably as a result of the development (in the late 1960s) of high-energy Samarium-Cobalt magnets. Although commercially available magnets were expensive at $100/lb (1980 prices), pressure on energy-saving was growing at that time, so the development of cost-effective energy-saving PM line-start motors started to gain momentum.

Fig. 11.6 on p. 501 shows a two-pole rotor based on the published description of the Isosyn® motor produced by CEM, a division of Brown Boveri (now ABB), in a range of sizes from 0·37kW to 18·5kW. Fig. 11.1 (p. 497) shows the much admired 4-pole Reliance motor described by C.R. Steen [1979]; and Fig. 11.7 a 2-pole motor similar to the one reported in 1980 by Miyashita of Hitachi. The d- and q-axes in these drawings are shown with the d-axis aligned with the magnet; in all cases illustrated so far, the q-axis is more inductive than the d-axis because of the low permeability of the magnet and its thickness relative to the radial length of the airgap.

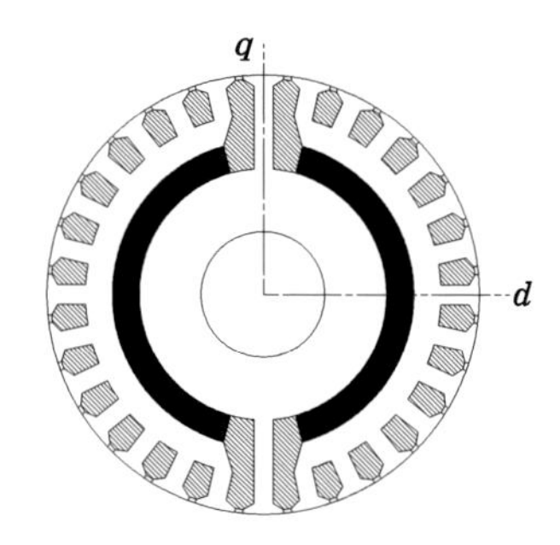

Fig. 11.7 Miyashita / Hitachi [1980]

During this period of experimentation with the new high-energy magnets, a wide range of rotor configurations was investigated. Typical of this period are the rotors shown in Fig. 11.8 described by Binns. Rotor (a) is quite similar to the Synduction® motor of Fig. 11.4, with magnets inserted in the low-inductance axis, [31]. In rotor (b), circumferentially-magnetized magnets add narrow "pulses" to the airgap flux near the edges of the main soft-iron pole-pieces. Rotors (b) and (c) both embody the idea that the magnet flux should be in parallel with the "reluctance" flux produced by the stator current. In (c), the d and q axes are not fixed, but depend on the load. The inventive variety is remarkable. In some cases the evolution is close to the synchronous reluctance motor, but in others not.

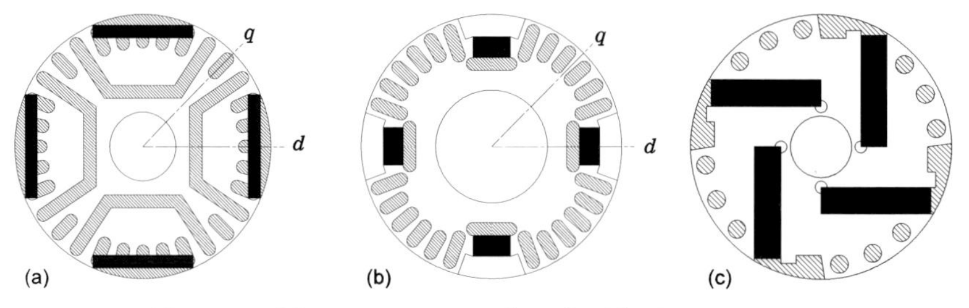

Fig. 11.8 Line-start motors described by Binns [1978]

Finally Fig. 11.9 shows a 2-pole rotor of a type suitable for single-phase applications at the highest efficiency levels such as hermetic compressors used in refrigerators. "Bracing" bridges can be used between the magnet segments to strengthen the lamination; (see §4.1.1.3). 2-pole rotors can have a fairly high saliency ratio and a useful component of reluctance torque.

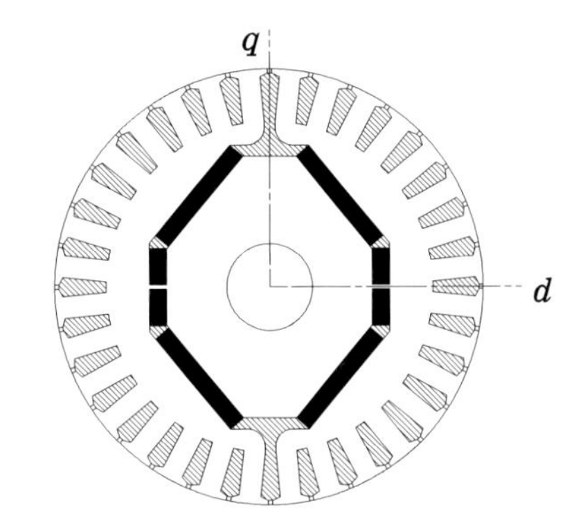

Fig. 11.9 2-pole line-start motor

11.3 Analysis of polyphase line-start motors

11.3.1 Steady state

Under balanced conditions, the steady-state performance of the polyphase line-start motor is described by the equations in §7.1, including the torque equation (7.22) which is reproduced here:

$$T_e = \frac{mp}{\omega}\left[\frac{E_{q1}V}{X_d}\sin\delta + \frac{V^2}{2}\left(\frac{1}{X_q} - \frac{1}{X_d}\right)\sin 2\delta\right]. \qquad (11.1)$$

The angle δ is the phase angle between the terminal voltage **V** and the open-circuit EMF **E**, and is called the **load angle** or **torque angle**. The phasor diagram is similar to Fig. 7.1, except that $V > E$ normally, resulting in a lagging power factor. A higher value of E increases the power-factor and can even make it leading.

Eqn. (11.1) can be written

$$T_e = T_1 \sin\delta + T_2 \sin 2\delta. \qquad (11.2)$$

An example is shown in Fig. 11.10 with the following parameter values: $E = 155\ \mathrm{V_{LL\,rms}}$; $V = 220\ \mathrm{V_{LL\,rms}}$; $X_d = 7$ ohm; $X_q = 10$ ohm; $\omega = 377$ rad/s; $m = 3$ phases; and $p = 2$ pole-pairs. With $X_q > X_d$, $T_2 < 0$, and the second term is positive only when $\delta > 90°$. However, the true reluctance torque is not the T_2 term but the sin 2γ term in eqn. (7.19). For comparison, the true alignment and reluctance torque components T_A and T_R are plotted in Fig. 11.11, for the same range of δ as Fig. 11.10. T_R is positive at most working values of δ.

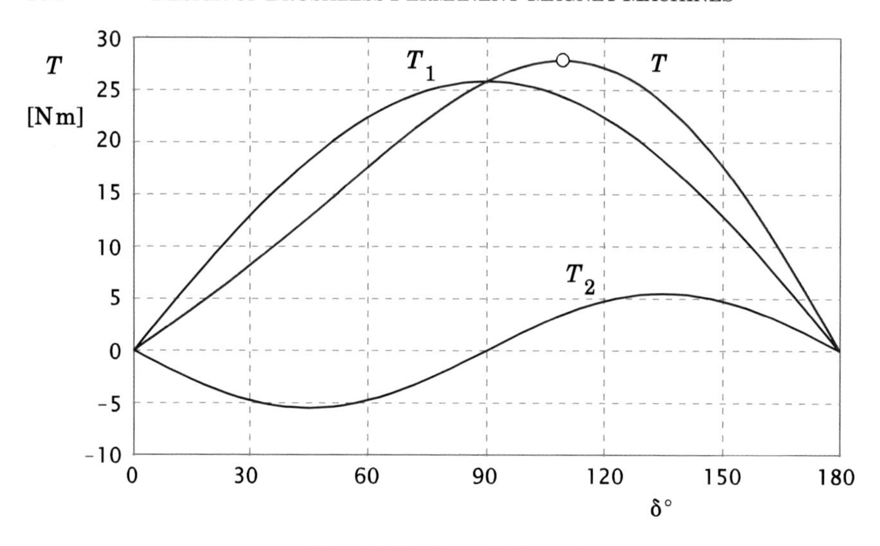

Fig. 11.10 T_1 and T_2 vs. δ

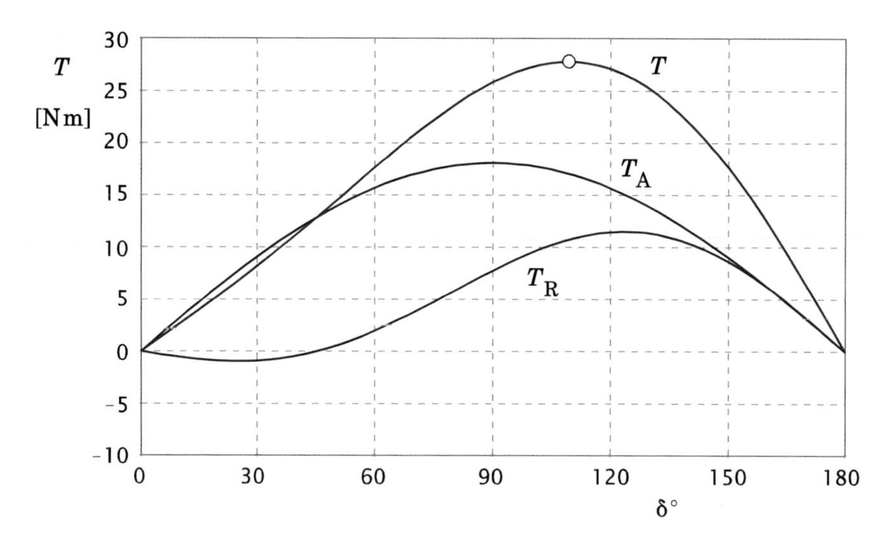

Fig. 11.11 Alignment and reluctance torque components vs. δ

Normal operation with δ in the range 60–70° is perfectly acceptable, since it gives a **steady-state stability margin** comparable with that of an induction motor, the pull-out torque then being of the order of twice the rated load torque. Fig. 11.12 shows this range in graphical form.

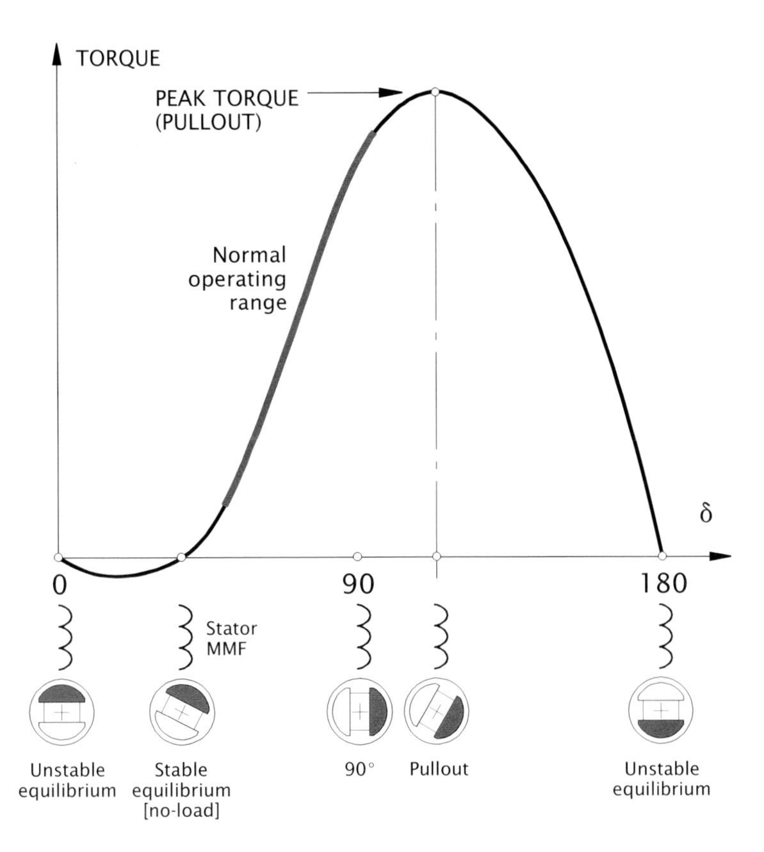

Fig. 11.12 Torque/angle curve for line-start motor

The **inverse saliency** of the PM motor ($X_q > X_d$) is in marked contrast to the conventional wound-field synchronous machine, in which T_2 has the opposite sign, and the torque/angle curve is the mirror-image of Fig. 11.12 about 90°. Conventional synchronous machines operate with δ in the neighbourhood of 30°, again at roughly half the pull-out torque.

Operation with $\delta = 0$ is unstable and the operating point at no-load will shift to an angle of the order of 10–30° depending on the voltage and the saliency ratio. The torque/angle curve can be quite shallow at low values of δ, but it steepens considerably as δ increases towards the pull-out value.

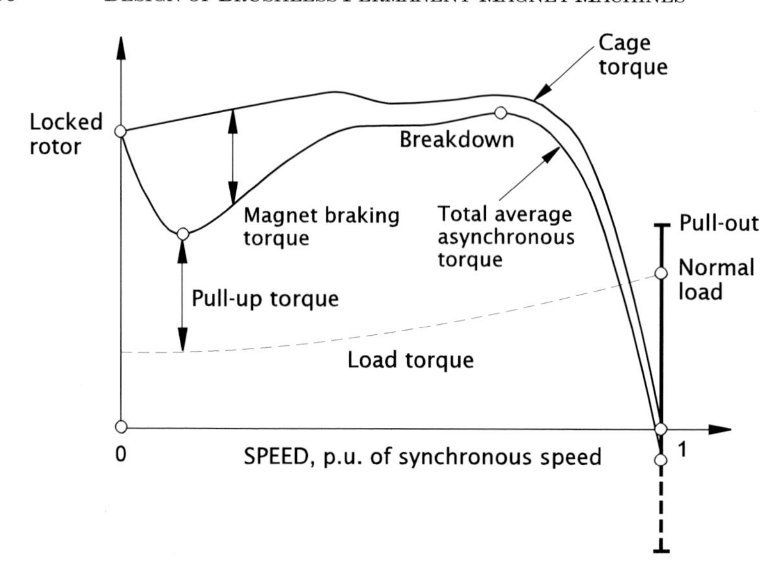

Fig. 11.13 Asynchronous torque/speed curve of PM line-start motor

11.3.2 Asynchronous operation and starting

The starting process can be considered in two separate phases: *asynchronous run-up* and *synchronization*. The rotor cage provides the asynchronous run-up torque, starting at zero speed. As the speed approaches the synchronous speed, the slip approaches zero and the motor enters the synchronization phase.

A typical average **asynchronous torque/speed curve** is shown in Fig. 11.13. *Average* means that the torque is averaged over each electrical cycle, using a method described on p. 526ff. for single-phase machines; this averaging method "removes" the transient torque components which can be seen in Fig. 11.14. They contribute nothing to the acceleration but create much noise and vibration.

Also shown in Fig. 11.13 is the synchronous torque, represented by a vertical line at synchronous speed. Different points on this line correspond to different load-angles according to eqn. (11.1). During the synchronization phase, the operating point must transfer from the asynchronous curve to the vertical line representing steady-state synchronous operation. The process is dynamic, as can be seen in the simulations in Figs. 11.14–11.16.

There is also a **magnet braking torque** produced by the rotation of the magnet. Current is induced in the stator circuit closed through the supply, and the associated power loss in the resistance of this circuit manifests itself as a braking torque: [86]

$$T_{mb} = -\frac{mp}{\omega}(1-s)E^2 \frac{R_{ph}\left[R_{ph}^2 + (1-s)^2 X_q^2\right]}{\left[R_{ph}^2 + (1-s)^2 X_d X_q\right]^2} \tag{11.3}$$

where s is the slip and m is the number of phases. The magnet braking torque reduces the so-called **pull-up torque** which is the minimum torque available for acceleration at any asynchronous speed. In severe cases it can even cause "lock-up" at a speed far below synchronous speed. This will not pass unnoticed: the noise and heat will be tremendous.

The E^2 term in eqn. (11.3) shows that the magnet braking torque is strongly dependent on the magnet and its EMF. At synchronous speed $s = 0$, and if $R_{ph} << X_d$ the magnet braking torque becomes approximately proportional to $(E/X_d^2) \times R_{ph}$, and it is not zero at synchronous speed. (Note that E/X_d is approximately the short-circuit current, as in chapter 7). At low speed, T_{mb} becomes inversely proportional to R_{ph}. At an intermediate speed there is a maximum magnet braking torque. In smaller motors where R_{ph} is relatively large, this occurs at a higher speed and the magnet braking torque is flatter; in larger machines where R_{ph} is relatively small, the curve is peaky and the peak occurs at a lower speed.

There is an additional drag torque due to the interaction of the saliency and the stator circuit, similar to the negative-sequence torque of the single-phase motor analyzed later. At speeds below synchronous speed this component is "buried" in the cage torque; but at synchronous speed it remains, while the induced currents in the cage are zero. An expression for this "saliency braking torque" can be derived from eqns. (11.63) and (11.65) with $s = 0$, and is

$$T_{sb} = -\frac{m}{2}\frac{V^2 p R_{ph}}{\omega}\frac{(X_d - X_q)^2}{\left[R_{ph}^2 + X_d X_q.\right]^2} \tag{11.4}$$

[86] Honsinger V.B., IEEE Trans., **PAS**-99, No. 4, Jul./Aug. 1980, pp. 1503-1509

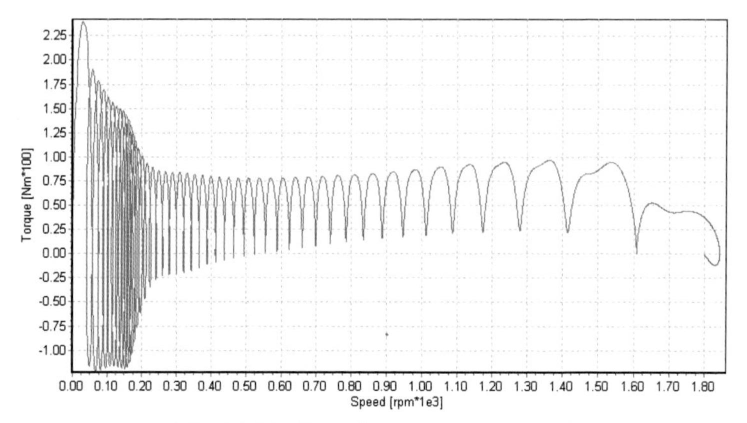

Fig. 11.14 Transient torque-vs-speed

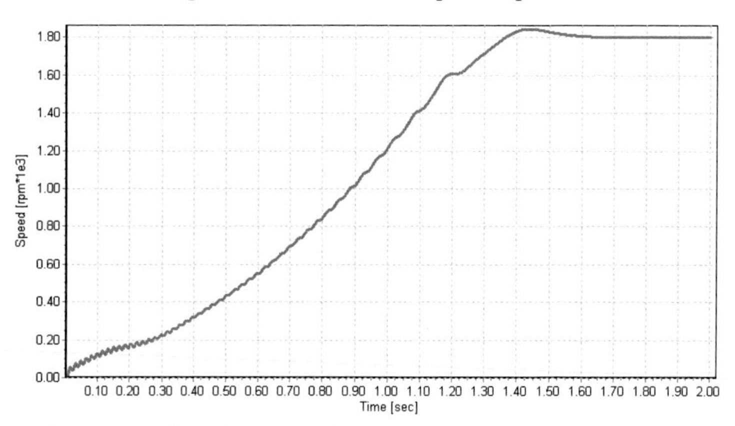

Fig. 11.15 Speed vs. time; load inertia = 10 × motor inertia

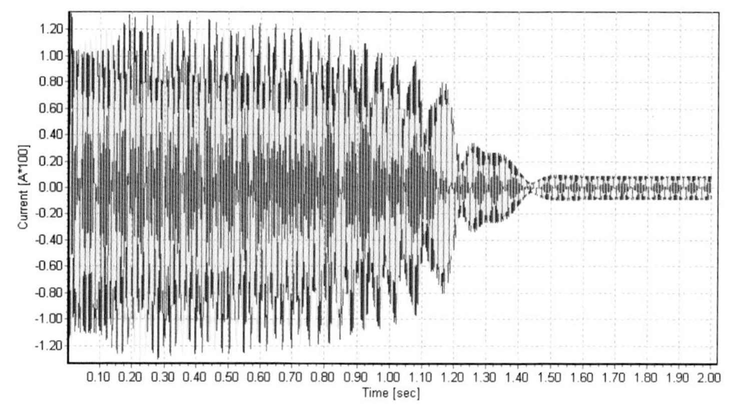

Fig. 11.16 Current vs. time

It is characteristic of the PM line-start motor that the starting current remains high throughout the run-up. The transient torque contains a strong oscillatory component due to the pole-slipping, and a very severe case of this can be seen in Fig. 11.14, which shows many reversals of the torque at low speed. Torque reversals impose severe duty on the shaft couplings and on the rotor itself, and on the load.

Similar torque reversals can occur in induction-motor starting, due to the DC offset component in the transient current, which gives rise to a "trapped flux" condition in the rotor.[87] The DC offset decays quickly in an induction motor, so the possibility of torque reversals is confined to the first few cycles; but in the PM motor the magnet provides a persistent trapped flux that sustains the torque reversals for many more cycles. Saliency contributes further to the torque fluctuations, as in the synchronous reluctance motor.

The effects of scale are important in the starting behaviour. The motor in Figs. 11.14–11.16 has a stator diameter of 100 mm and a stack length of 60 mm, and its rated power is of the order of 0·5kW. To obtain a rated power of 25 kW the linear dimensions would have to be increased by approximately 4·5 times. Because of the scaling laws, the per-unit resistance decreases, the cage torque becomes relatively smaller at low speed, the magnet braking torque peaks at a lower speed, and the inertia increases by more than the torque. Consequently the larger motor may have more difficulty starting.

On the other hand, in the smaller motor the rotor resistance is proportionally larger, and the torque/speed curve becomes less steep at small slip. This tends to make it more difficult for the small motor to jump into synchronism, but on the other hand its inertia is much smaller. These ideas corroborate the range of sizes introduced for the Isosyn® motor mentioned on p. 502, and suggest that there is a natural range of applicability for line-start PM motors, relative to their starting capability. Very roughly we can say that that range is about 0·3–30 kW. Of course, starting capability is only one aspect of the applicability of the line-start motor; the economics of energy-saving, the manufacturing cost, and many other application-engineering factors are also important.

---

[87] See Wood W.S. et al, *Transient torques in induction motors, due to switching of the supply*, Proc. IEE, Vol. 112, No. 7, July 1965, pp. 1348-1354

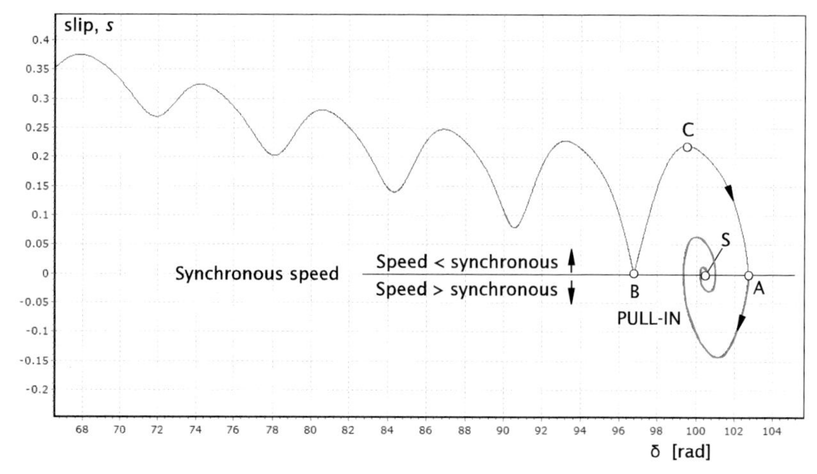

Fig. 11.17 s–δ trajectory

11.3.3 Analysis of synchronization

During the asynchronous run-up, the slip s is decreasing; but the load angle δ is continually increasing, because the voltage phasor **V** advances at synchronous speed while the EMF phasor **E** lags behind it at a lower speed. As the rotor slips past the poles of the stator ampere-conductor distribution, it passes through successive zones of positive and negative "synchronizing torque" corresponding to eqn. (11.1). The synchronizing torque has no average value, since the positive and negative impulses cancel each other. It therefore does not contribute to the overall acceleration below the synchronous speed. However, the alternating impulses impose a cyclic variation on the slip, which grows as the slip decreases, as in Fig. 11.17.

At **B** in Fig. 11.17 the slip nears zero for the first time, and synchronization almost occurs at that point. Instead, it just fails to synchronize, and the final complete *double* pole-slip **BCA** ensues, spanning a further increase in δ of approximately 2π radians. In a successful synchronization, the impulse imparted to the rotor during the final double pole-slip is sufficient to bring it to synchronous speed with sufficient synchronizing torque to complete the final **pull-in** from the "capture point" **A** to the synchronous steady state **S**.

The final double pole-slip is considered the critical phase of the synchronization process, and is analyzed a little later.

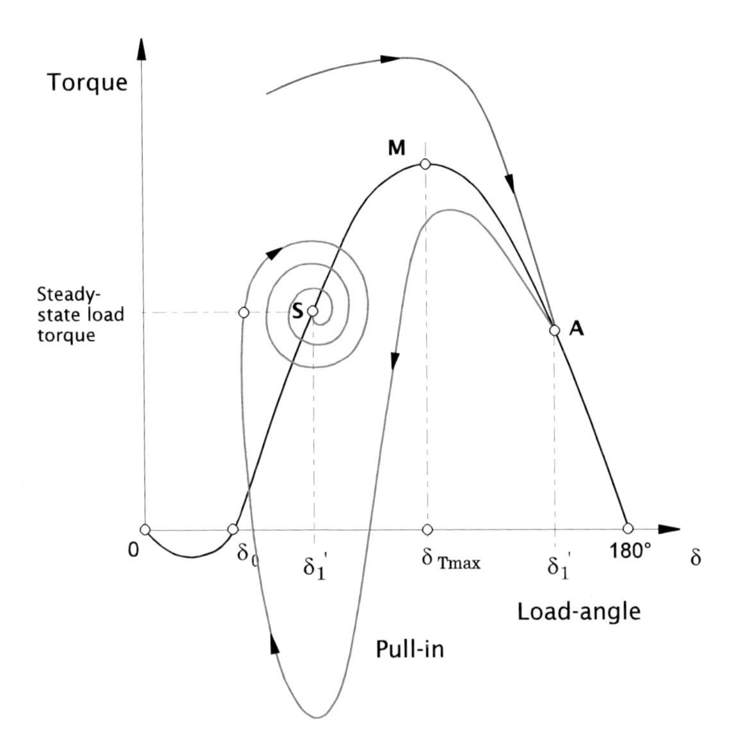

Fig. 11.18 Synchronization of PM line-start motor

The pull-in process is shown in Fig. 11.18 as a dynamic locus superimposed on the T–δ curve of Fig. 11.12 and eqn. (11.2). Synchronous speed is first reached at **A**. The cage torque is zero at **A**. The other two components of asynchronous torque given by eqns. (11.3) and (11.4) are not zero, but as long as they are less than the synchronizing torque the rotor will begin to accelerate above synchronous speed. The cage torque becomes negative, tending to decelerate the rotor back towards synchronous speed; but as long as the speed remains above synchronous speed δ will continue to decrease towards the stable side of the T–δ curve that lies to the left of the pull-out point **M**. The impulse of synchronizing torque ends in a damped oscillation which finally settles at synchronous speed at **S**.

If the synchronizing torque at **A** is *less* than the sum of the load torque and the asynchronous torques of eqns. (11.3) and (11.4), another double pole-slip will follow: that is, failure to synchronize.

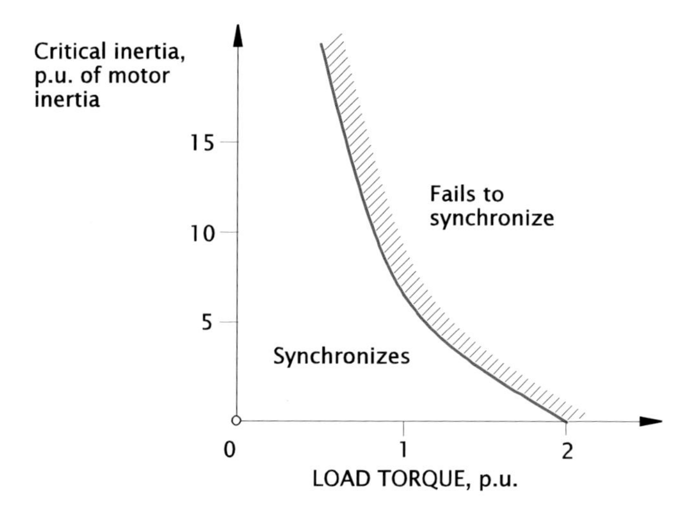

Fig. 11.19 Synchronizing capability

Synchronization failure is characterized by repeated pole-slips which settle into a dangerous limit-cycle. The motor must be protected against this eventuality by disconnecting it; otherwise it will overheat, and the magnets could easily be demagnetized.

The subsynchronous impulse imparted to the rotor during the final double pole-slip is limited by the characteristics of both the synchronizing torque and the asynchronous torques, so there is a limit to the inertia that can be synchronized with a given load torque. Fig. 11.19 shows the synchronizing capability as a chart of load torque vs. total inertia, normalized to the motor inertia. Only loads below this boundary can be synchronized. Thus loads with higher inertia can be synchronized only if the load torque is lower. The inertia scale in Fig. 11.19 is typical of small motors (< 2 kW).

Fig. 11.19 is a key application characteristic of line-start motors. The starting capability of induction motors could be characterized by a similar chart using the axes of load torque and inertia; but the induction motor is not required to synchronize and the limits are determined only by the heat dissipated in the rotor during run-up. Rotor heating is present also in the line-start motor during run-up, and this limits the number of repeated starts (or attempts to start) in any given period.

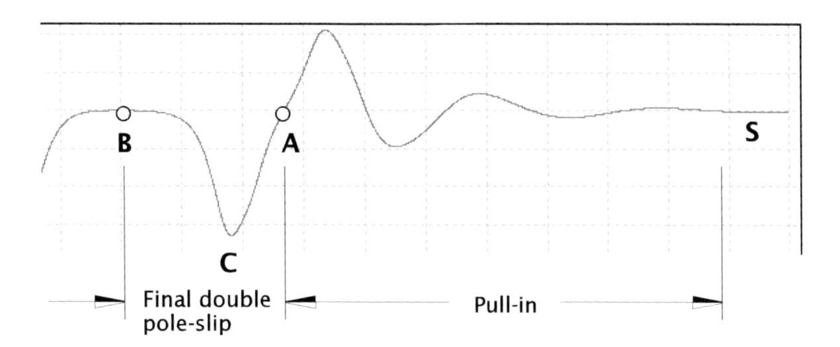

Fig. 11.20 Speed vs. time : last pole-slip before synchronization

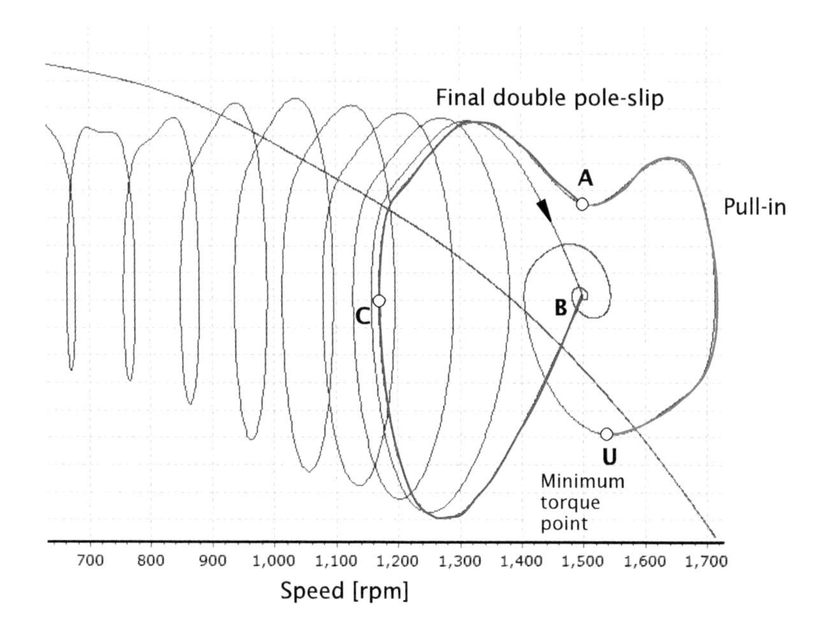

Fig. 11.21 Torque vs. speed in final stages of run-up

Details of the final stages of run-up are shown in Figs. 11.20 and 11.21, including the final double pole-slip and the pull-in. The points **A**, **B**, **C** etc are marked to show the correspondence between the graphs, including Figs. 11.17, 11.18 and 11.22 which are used for analysis.

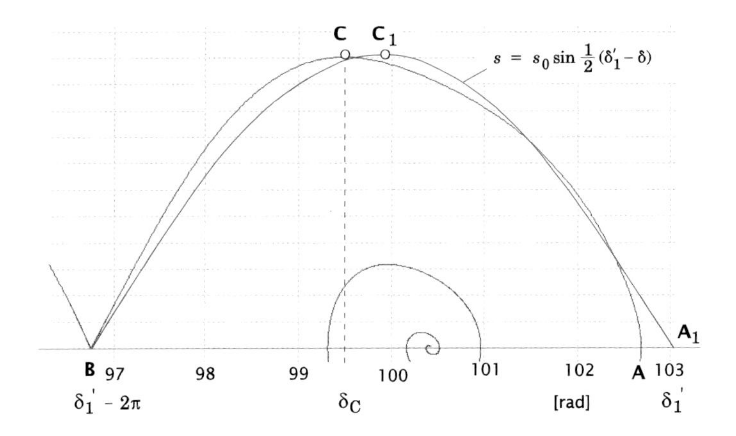

Fig. 11.22 Final critical synchronization trajectory in the δ-s plane

We can now return to the analysis of the synchronization process in the δ–s phase plane, Fig. 11.17.[88] The final double pole-slip trajectory is shown enlarged in Fig. 11.22. The marked points **B**, **C**, **A** are the same as those used in earlier figures. The equation of motion in the δ–s plane is

$$T_s(\delta) + T_a(s) - T_L(s) = -\frac{1}{p} J\omega^2 s \frac{ds}{d\delta} \qquad (11.5)$$

where J is the combined inertia of motor and load; ω is the radian frequency of the supply; $2p$ is the number of poles; $T_s(\delta)$ is the synchronizing torque including magnet alignment torque and reluctance torque; $T_a(s)$ is the sum of all the average asynchronous torques; and $T_L(s)$ is the sum of the load and friction torques.

At point **C**, $ds/d\delta = 0$; the net (accelerating) torque in eqn. (11.5) is zero, and so the acceleration rate is momentarily zero. The slip at **C** has a maximum value of s_0, but δ continues to increase. At point **A** the trajectory reaches an unstable equilibrium at synchronous speed with $s = 0$, and the acceleration is again zero. If the left-hand side of eqn. (11.5) is integrated with respect to δ between **C** and **A**,

[88] See Lawrenson P.J. and Mathur R.M., *Pull-in criterion for Reluctance Motors*, Proc. IEE, Vol. 120, No. 9, September 1973, pp. 982–986. Also Miller T.J.E., *Synchronization of Line-Start Permanent-Magnet AC Motors,* Trans. IEEE, **PAS**-103, 1984, 1822-1828.

the result is $\frac{1}{2} J\omega^2 s_0^2 = \frac{1}{2} J\Delta\omega^2$, where $\Delta\omega$ is the speed deficit at **C** relative to the synchronous speed. This represents the apparent kinetic energy of the inertia J at the instant corresponding to **C**, observed in the synchronous reference frame. Working against the load torque T_L, the torques T_s and T_a must together reduce this apparent kinetic energy to zero between **C** and **A**. The work done is evaluated in the synchronous reference frame by integrating the right-hand-side of eqn. (11.5) with respect to δ between **C** and **A**.

In general this integration cannot be done in closed form because T_a and T_L are both functions of the slip s, which is not a simple function of δ. But by means of the rough approximation

$$s = s_0 \sin \frac{1}{2}(\delta_1' - \delta) \tag{11.6}$$

which is shown in Fig. 11.22, the integral can be evaluated from $\mathbf{C}_1$ to $\mathbf{A}_1$, giving

$$\frac{1}{2} J \Delta\omega^2 = \int_{\delta_1' - \pi}^{\delta_1'} \left[T_s(\delta) + (T_a - T_L) s_0 \sin \frac{1}{2}(\delta_1' - \delta)\right] d\delta. \tag{11.7}$$

The evaluation of this integral throws considerable light on the nature of the synchronization process. The first term in T_s, can be integrated using eqn. (11.2) to give

$$\int_{\delta_1' - \pi}^{\delta_1'} \left[T_1 \sin \delta - T_2 \sin 2\delta\right] d\delta = -2T_1 \cos \delta_1'. \tag{11.8}$$

This expression shows that the available synchronizing energy increases in proportion to T_1 and is therefore proportional to E, which represents the strength of the magnets. The absence of T_2 from the expression is a consequence of the approximation of eqn. (11.6), which leads to the conclusion that during half the transition from $\mathbf{C}_1$ to $\mathbf{A}_1$ the reluctance torque is negative, and during the other half it is positive, so its net effect is zero.

For greater accuracy the integral should be evaluated from **C** to **A**, and this will show that with $\delta_C < \delta_1' - \pi$ the reluctance torque *does* contribute a useful increase of synchronizing energy, typically of the order of 25% of the total.

To integrate the second term in eqn. (11.7) we need $(T_a - T_L)$ as an integrable function of s. Such an approximating function is

$$T_a - T_L = a_1 s^2 + a_2 s + a_3. \tag{11.9}$$

The coefficients a_1, a_2 and a_3 can be evaluated from the asynchronous torque/speed curve (Fig. 11.13) together with the load characteristic. The result of integration is

$$\frac{\pi}{2} a_1 s_0^2 + 2a_2 s_0 + a_3 \pi. \tag{11.10}$$

In general it can be expected that a_1 has a negative value much larger than a_2 or a_3. This means that a large value of s_0, the slip at **C**, will reduce the synchronizing capability. We can see this in Fig. 11.19, in that a small increase in load torque produces a large decrease in the critical load inertia. It follows that the average asynchronous torque/speed curve (Fig. 11.19) should have the steepest possible gradient near synchronous speed. This requires, among other things, a low cage resistance, which conflicts with the requirement for a high torque at standstill and at low speeds. The conflict is made worse by the need to overcome the magnet braking torque, especially if it peaks at low speed, and also by the limited radial space available for the cage. The conflict is also more acute in larger motors than in small ones, because of scaling effects, and a double cage may be contemplated as a means of relieving it.

The magnet braking torque reduces the asynchronous motoring torque at all speeds. If the magnet strength (E) is increased there will be two opposing effects on the synchronizing capability. On the one hand the available synchronizing energy will increase according to eqn. (11.8). On the other hand, the critical slip s_0 will also increase because of the increase in magnet braking torque, eqn. (11.10). In large machines the stator resistance is relatively smaller, so the magnet braking torque peaks at a lower speed and is negligible near synchronous speed. An increase in E then leads to an increase in synchronizing capability because the effect in eqn. (11.8) prevails. In a smaller motor when E is increased the synchronizing capability decreases, because the decrease in the net asynchronous torque more than offsets the increase in available synchronizing energy. For a given size of motor it appears that there is an optimum value of E.

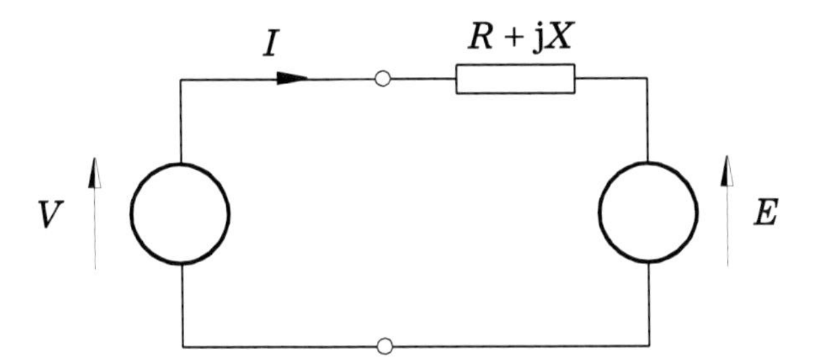

Fig. 11.23 Equivalent circuit for 1-phase operation

11.4 Analysis of single-phase line-start motors

11.4.1 Steady state; no rotor cage

The simplest representation of a single-phase synchronous motor is shown in Fig. 11.23. In this equivalent circuit the motor is represented by its EMF E and impedance R + jX. The model is sufficient if the motor has no saliency and no rotor cage. It also applies to one phase of a polyphase motor in balanced steady-state operation. The current is given by

$$\mathbf{I} = \frac{\mathbf{V} - \mathbf{E}}{R + \mathrm{j}X}. \tag{11.11}$$

As long as V and E are both sinusoidal, and R and X are constant, the current will be sinusoidal. The torque is given by eqn. (4.82), and the power and torque both have a double-frequency pulsation, as described on p. 188.

A single-phase motor with no rotor cage is impractical: it is not self-starting, and even if some means were provided to start and synchronize it, it would tend to oscillate about synchronous speed: in other words, it would not be stable. A rotor cage is necessary for both starting and stability.

It is best to design the cage with a more-or-less uniform ring of bars around the magnets, as in Fig. 11.9. The starting and running performance are strongly influenced by the rotor geometry. With saliency and/or a rotor cage, eqn. (11.11) is inadequate, and a detailed analysis is developed in the following pages. (See also p. 534).

The analysis of the single-phase motor is based on the principle of **forward and backward rotating fields**, which can be approached in two different ways. Consider a stator MMF distribution that is sinusoidally distributed around the airgap, but pulsating in proportion to the current $\sqrt{I} \cos \omega t$. (See also §3.2.1.3). It can be written

$$\begin{aligned} F &= F_{max} \cos p\theta \cos \omega t \\ &= \underbrace{\frac{1}{2} F_{max} \cos (p\theta - \omega t)}_{\text{FORWARD}} + \underbrace{\frac{1}{2} F_{max} \cos (p\theta + \omega t)}_{\text{BACKWARD}} \end{aligned} \qquad (11.12)$$

This states that a stationary pulsating MMF can be resolved into equal but oppositely-rotating components of half amplitude, the so-called forward and backward rotating components. These components can be represented in an extended equivalent circuit with separate forward and backward impedances and induced voltages.[89]

The second method is the more formal procedure of *symmetrical components*, and it is the basis of the method that will be used here. The symmetrical component method obtains the forward and backward components in phasor form by a mathematical transformation. They are called *positive* and *negative sequence* components. Since there are *two* distinct components, we have to start from a 2-phase circuit. This is not inconvenient, because the method is to be used later for capacitor motors which really do have two phases, even though they may be unbalanced. The pure single-phase motor will therefore be analysed as a 2-phase motor with zero current in one of the phases. The method provides useful physical interpretation of the operation of the pure single-phase motor.

Note that if there is no rotor cage, the circuit can be solved using eqn. (5.123) on p. 264, and the torque can then be obtained using eqn. (4.93) on p. 190, even if there is saliency. However, eqn. (5.123) is a differential equation whose solution is less convenient than the phasor solution. The phasor solution requires only algebraic calculations, albeit using complex numbers, and it is considerably easier to interpret.

---

[89] See Morrill, W.J., *The revolving-field theory of the capacitor motor*, Trans AIEE, April 1929, pp. 614–632.

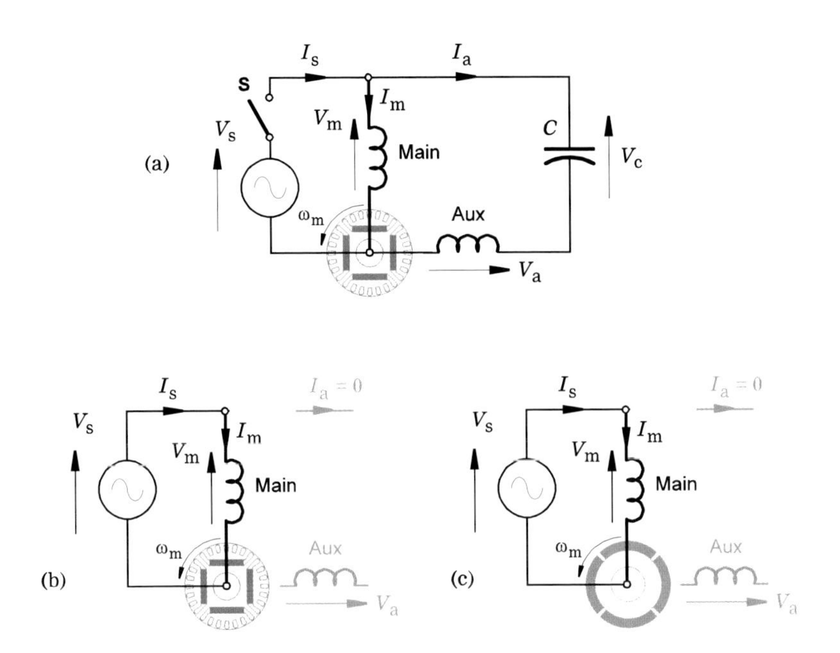

Fig. 11.24 Circuits for analysis of single-phase machines

11.4.2 Symmetrical components

Fig. 11.24 shows the electrical circuits to be used for machines connected to a single-phase AC source V_s. The most general case is Fig. 11.24(a), which has

a split-phase winding;
a salient-pole rotor with interior magnets;
a conducting cage on the rotor, and
an auxiliary capacitor to advance the phase of $\mathbf{I}_a$.

The term "split-phase" expresses the fact that the single-phase current from the supply is divided between two phases, the main and the auxiliary. The motor in Fig. 11.24(a) is really a two-phase motor, and it is generally unbalanced, which means that the main and auxiliary windings have different numbers of turns, different wire sizes, different distributions of coils, and different external circuits.

The displacement angle ζ between the auxiliary winding axis and the main winding axis is usually 90°, but other angles are sometimes used. The axis of the auxiliary winding is oriented so that with forward-rotating flux, the **voltage induced in the auxiliary winding leads the voltage induced in the main winding** by ζ°.

For self-starting "across the line" from standstill by means of a contactor **S**, the machine must have a rotor cage *and* a split-phase winding with a capacitor, as in Fig. 11.24(a). Without the cage, the machine cannot produce any average torque unless it is running exactly at synchronous speed.[90]

If the auxiliary winding is absent or open-circuited, as in Fig. 11.24(b) and (c), the machine can still operate as a motor provided that some external means is provided to start it and bring it to synchronous speed. When connecting to the AC line, a synchronizing procedure will be needed to control the transient currents when the switch **S** is closed. It can also operate as a generator.

Reference-frame transformations are used to derive a set of *balanced* windings which represent the forward-rotating field components that produce the useable average torque. Fig. 11.25 shows the successive application of transformations, starting with the most general case of non-orthogonal windings a (auxiliary) and m (main).

We will begin the analysis with $\zeta = 90^\circ$, i.e., with orthogonal windings. This means that the $[a,m]$ windings are identical to the $[a,b]$ windings. Non-orthogonal windings are considered later.

The main winding has N_m turns and the auxiliary winding has N_a turns. For the moment we can assume that both windings are sine-distributed, so that we do not have to carry the winding factors through all the equations.

[90] The capacitor can sometimes be omitted if the two phases have sufficiently different resistance/reactance ratios. The term "split-phase" is sometimes used (especially in the U.S.) to refer to such motors without capacitors. Further, the capacitor may be switched between two values, one for starting and one for running; or there may be a start capacitor and no run capacitor. All these variants are used with single-phase induction motors, but here the focus is on the analysis of PM motors and so we restrict attention to a small number of cases, sufficiently general so that other variants can be treated as special cases.

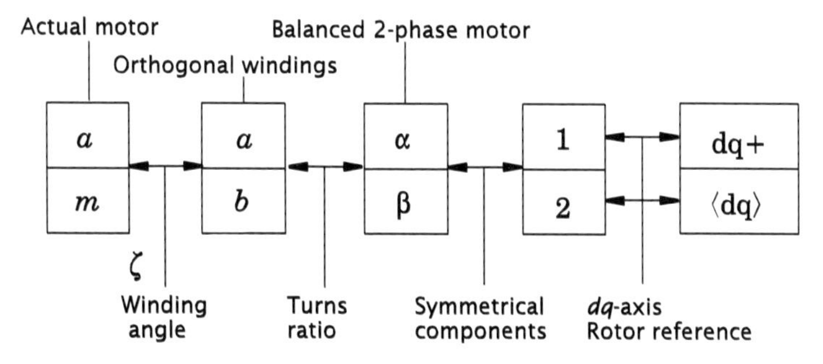

Fig. 11.25 Reference-frame transformations

Although the winding axes are orthogonal, the currents $\mathbf{I}_m$, $\mathbf{I}_a$ and the voltages $\mathbf{V}_m$, $\mathbf{V}_a$ are in general unbalanced, so that both forward and backward-rotating fields exist. The rotor rotates in the positive (CCW) direction so that the forward components of the voltages and currents in the auxiliary winding lead those in the main winding.

First the actual windings [a,m] are replaced by an imaginary set of balanced windings [α,β], in which both windings have N_a turns. Writing $\beta = N_m/N_a$, the currents are related by

$$\begin{bmatrix} \mathbf{I}_\alpha \\ \mathbf{I}_\beta \end{bmatrix} = \begin{bmatrix} 1 & 0 \\ 0 & \beta \end{bmatrix} \cdot \begin{bmatrix} \mathbf{I}_a \\ \mathbf{I}_m \end{bmatrix}; \quad \text{i.e.,} \quad [\mathbf{I}_{\alpha,\beta}] = [C][\mathbf{I}_{a,m}], \tag{11.13}$$

with inverse

$$\begin{bmatrix} \mathbf{I}_a \\ \mathbf{I}_m \end{bmatrix} = \begin{bmatrix} 1 & 0 \\ 0 & 1/\beta \end{bmatrix} \cdot \begin{bmatrix} \mathbf{I}_\alpha \\ \mathbf{I}_\beta \end{bmatrix}; \quad \text{i.e.,} \quad [\mathbf{I}_{a,m}] = [C]^{-1}[\mathbf{I}_{\alpha,\beta}]. \tag{11.14}$$

The transformation matrix [C] is real and symmetric, since $[C_t] = [C]$; but it is not orthogonal, because $[C_t] \neq [C]^{-1}$. To maintain power invariance we must transform the voltages using $[C_t]^{-1}$, giving

$$\begin{bmatrix} \mathbf{V}_\alpha \\ \mathbf{V}_\beta \end{bmatrix} = \begin{bmatrix} 1 & 0 \\ 0 & 1/\beta \end{bmatrix} \cdot \begin{bmatrix} \mathbf{V}_a \\ \mathbf{V}_m \end{bmatrix}; \quad \text{i.e.,} \quad [\mathbf{V}_{\alpha,\beta}] = [C_t]^{-1}[\mathbf{V}_{a,m}], \tag{11.15}$$

with inverse

$$\begin{bmatrix} \mathbf{V}_a \\ \mathbf{V}_m \end{bmatrix} = \begin{bmatrix} 1 & 0 \\ 0 & \beta \end{bmatrix} \cdot \begin{bmatrix} \mathbf{V}_\alpha \\ \mathbf{V}_\beta \end{bmatrix}; \quad \text{i.e.,} \quad [\mathbf{V}_{a,m}] = [C_t][\mathbf{V}_{\alpha,\beta}]. \tag{11.16}$$

The **symmetrical components** $\mathbf{V}_1$, $\mathbf{V}_2$ and $\mathbf{I}_1$, $\mathbf{I}_2$ are introduced by the following mapping from the balanced [α,β] machine:

$$\begin{bmatrix} \mathbf{V}_1 \\ \mathbf{V}_2 \end{bmatrix} = \frac{1}{\sqrt{2}} \begin{bmatrix} 1 & j \\ 1 & -j \end{bmatrix} \begin{bmatrix} \mathbf{V}_\alpha \\ \mathbf{V}_\beta \end{bmatrix}; \quad \text{i.e.,} \quad [\mathbf{V}]_{12} = [S][\mathbf{V}]_{\alpha\beta}, \tag{11.17}$$

with inverse

$$\begin{bmatrix} \mathbf{V}_\alpha \\ \mathbf{V}_\beta \end{bmatrix} = \frac{1}{\sqrt{2}} \begin{bmatrix} 1 & 1 \\ -j & j \end{bmatrix} \begin{bmatrix} \mathbf{V}_1 \\ \mathbf{V}_2 \end{bmatrix}; \quad \text{i.e.,} \quad [\mathbf{V}_{\alpha,\beta}] = [S]^{-1}[\mathbf{V}_{1,2}]. \tag{11.18}$$

The transformation matrix $[S]$ is complex and unitary, i.e. $[S_t^*] = [S]^{-1}$, and power invariance will be maintained if the same transformations are applied to the currents in both directions: i.e.,

$$\begin{bmatrix} \mathbf{I}_1 \\ \mathbf{I}_2 \end{bmatrix} = \frac{1}{\sqrt{2}} \begin{bmatrix} 1 & j \\ 1 & -j \end{bmatrix} \begin{bmatrix} \mathbf{I}_\alpha \\ \mathbf{I}_\beta \end{bmatrix}; \quad \text{i.e.,} \quad [\mathbf{I}]_{12} = [S][\mathbf{I}]_{\alpha\beta}. \tag{11.19}$$

with inverse

$$\begin{bmatrix} \mathbf{I}_\alpha \\ \mathbf{I}_\beta \end{bmatrix} = \frac{1}{\sqrt{2}} \begin{bmatrix} 1 & 1 \\ -j & j \end{bmatrix} \begin{bmatrix} \mathbf{I}_1 \\ \mathbf{I}_2 \end{bmatrix}; \quad \text{i.e.,} \quad [\mathbf{I}_{\alpha,\beta}] = [S]^{-1}[\mathbf{I}_{1,2}]. \tag{11.20}$$

Pure single-phase motor — The auxiliary phase is open-circuited, while the main phase β is connected to the supply voltage $\mathbf{V}_s$: thus

$$\mathbf{I}_\alpha = 0 \quad \text{and} \quad \mathbf{V}_\beta = \mathbf{V}_s. \tag{11.21}$$

If we substitute eqn. (11.21) into eqn. (11.19) we get

$$\mathbf{I}_1 = j\frac{\mathbf{I}_\beta}{\sqrt{2}} = -\mathbf{I}_2. \tag{11.22}$$

Now suppose that at a particular operating point, we can write[91]

$$\begin{aligned} \mathbf{V}_1 &= \mathbf{Z}_1 \mathbf{I}_1; \\ \mathbf{V}_2 &= \mathbf{Z}_2 \mathbf{I}_2. \end{aligned} \tag{11.23}$$

[91] When the impedance matrix $[\mathbf{Z}]_{12}$ is obtained formally from the transformation as $[S][\mathbf{Z}]_{\alpha\beta}[S]^{-1}$, off-diagonal impedances appear. They are omitted from eqns.(11.23) because they cancel in eqns. (11.24) and (11.25).

Note that $\mathbf{Z}_1$ is an *apparent* impedance since the term $\mathbf{Z}_1\mathbf{I}_1$ incorporates the EMF $\mathbf{E}_1$. If we substitute eqns. (11.23) into eqns. (11.18), we get for $\mathbf{V}_\alpha$ and $\mathbf{V}_\beta$:

$$\mathbf{V}_\alpha = \frac{1}{\sqrt{2}}(\mathbf{Z}_1\mathbf{I}_1 + \mathbf{Z}_2\mathbf{I}_2) = \mathrm{j}(\mathbf{Z}_1 - \mathbf{Z}_2)\frac{\mathbf{I}_\beta}{2}; \tag{11.24}$$

$$\mathbf{V}_\beta = \frac{1}{\sqrt{2}}(-\mathrm{j}\,\mathbf{Z}_1\mathbf{I}_1 + \mathrm{j}\,\mathbf{Z}_2\mathbf{I}_2) = (\mathbf{Z}_1 + \mathbf{Z}_2)\frac{\mathbf{I}_\beta}{2}. \tag{11.25}$$

If we now substitute eqns. (11.21), (11.24) and (11.25) in eqn. (11.17), we get expressions for $\mathbf{V}_1$ and $\mathbf{V}_2$:

$$\begin{aligned}\mathbf{V}_1 &= \frac{1}{\sqrt{2}}(\mathbf{V}_\alpha + \mathrm{j}\mathbf{V}_\beta) \\ &= \frac{\mathrm{j}\mathbf{V}_\mathrm{s}}{\sqrt{2}}\left[\frac{\mathbf{Z}_1 - \mathbf{Z}_2}{\mathbf{Z}_1 + \mathbf{Z}_2} + 1\right] = \mathrm{j}\sqrt{2}\mathbf{V}_\mathrm{s}\frac{\mathbf{Z}_1}{\mathbf{Z}_1 + \mathbf{Z}_2};\end{aligned} \tag{11.26}$$

$$\mathbf{V}_2 = \frac{1}{\sqrt{2}}(\mathbf{V}_\alpha - \mathrm{j}\mathbf{V}_\beta) = -\mathrm{j}\sqrt{2}\mathbf{V}_\mathrm{s}\frac{\mathbf{Z}_2}{\mathbf{Z}_1 + \mathbf{Z}_2}. \tag{11.27}$$

The circuit constraints on $\mathbf{I}_\alpha$ and $\mathbf{V}_\beta$ expressed by eqn. (11.21) have thus been translated into equivalent constraints on $\mathbf{V}_1$ and $\mathbf{V}_2$. When $\mathbf{Z}_1$ and $\mathbf{Z}_2$ are known, eqn. (11.26) gives $\mathbf{V}_1$ directly. Then $\mathbf{I}_1$ follows from eqn. (11.23), and $\mathbf{I}_2$ and $\mathbf{I}_\beta$ follow from eqns. (11.22).

Now $\mathbf{Z}_1$ is not fixed, but depends on the EMF and the operating point. If $\mathbf{Z}_2$ is assumed known, the following iterative method can be used for a pre-set value of δ, the the load angle in the positive-sequence diagram (i.e., the angle by which $\mathbf{V}_1$ leads $\mathbf{E}_1$)

Initialize $\mathbf{V}_1$ (for example, set $\mathbf{V}_1 = \mathbf{V}_\mathrm{s}$)
Repeat
    Using R, X_d and X_q, solve the positive-sequence phasor diagram for $\mathbf{I}_1$
    Calculate $\mathbf{Z}_1$ from eqn. (11.23)
    Update $\mathbf{V}_1$ from eqn. (11.26)
until $\mathbf{V}_1$ converges to a steady value.
Calculate $\mathbf{I}_\beta$ [eqn. (11.22)]; $\mathbf{I}_2$ [eqn. (11.22)]; and $\mathbf{V}_2$ [eqn. (11.23)].

The solution of the positive-sequence system requires the positive-sequence EMF $\mathbf{E}_1$, which is obtained as follows. Suppose the rotating magnet generates an EMF $\mathbf{E}_\alpha$ in phase α and $\mathbf{E}_\beta$ in phase β. If the two windings have equal effective numbers of turns we can write

$$\mathbf{E}_\beta = \mathbf{E} \; ; \qquad \mathbf{E}_\alpha = \mathrm{j}\,\mathbf{E}. \tag{11.28}$$

Eqn. (11.17) can now be used with $\mathbf{E}_\alpha$ and $\mathbf{E}_\beta$ to determine the positive- and negative-sequence EMFs

$$\mathbf{E}_1 = \mathrm{j}\sqrt{2}\,\mathbf{E} \; ; \qquad \mathbf{E}_2 = 0. \tag{11.29}$$

Backward flux suppression — From eqns. (11.26) and (11.27),

$$\mathbf{V}_2 = -\,\mathbf{V}_1 \times \frac{\mathbf{Z}_2}{\mathbf{Z}_1} \tag{11.30}$$

which is consistent with eqns. (11.22) and (11.23). The negative-sequence voltage $\mathbf{V}_2$ is associated with a backward-revolving flux, and in order to minimize it we need $\mathbf{Z}_2 << \mathbf{Z}_1$. The cage does this, exactly as in the single-phase induction motor. As described so elegantly by Veinott, the negative-sequence current in the cage suppresses the backward flux, so the negative-sequence flux and voltage become small, while the negative-sequence current is equal and opposite in phase to the positive-sequence current [eqn. (11.22)]. To achieve a low value of $\mathbf{Z}_2$ the cage should have the smallest possible resistance, although this tends to reduce the starting torque.

By combining eqns. (11.26) and (11.30) it can also be shown that

$$\mathbf{V}_2 = \mathbf{V}_1 - \mathrm{j}\sqrt{2}\,\mathbf{V}_\mathrm{s}. \tag{11.31}$$

Capacitor motor — The circuit is constrained by the equation

$$\mathbf{V}_\mathrm{s} = \mathbf{V}_\mathrm{m} = \mathbf{V}_\mathrm{a} - \mathrm{j}X_\mathrm{c}\mathbf{I}_\mathrm{a}. \tag{11.32}$$

In terms of the [α,β] voltages and currents, substituting from eqns. (11.14) and (11.16) in (11.32), we get

$$\mathbf{V}_\mathrm{s} = \beta\,\mathbf{V}_\beta = \mathbf{V}_\alpha - \mathrm{j}X_\mathrm{c}\mathbf{I}_\alpha. \tag{11.33}$$

Further substituting from eqns. (11.18) and (11.20) in (11.33), we get

$$\sqrt{2}\,\beta\,\mathbf{V}_\beta = \mathbf{a}_1\mathbf{V}_1 + \mathbf{a}_2\mathbf{V}_2 \tag{11.34}$$

where

$$\mathbf{a}_1 = 1 - \frac{jX_c}{\mathbf{Z}_1}; \qquad \mathbf{a}_2 = 1 - \frac{jX_c}{\mathbf{Z}_2}; \tag{11.35}$$

and again,

$$\mathbf{V}_1 = \mathbf{Z}_1 \mathbf{I}_1; \qquad \mathbf{V}_2 = \mathbf{Z}_2 \mathbf{I}_2. \tag{11.36}$$

Combining eqn. (11.34) with eqn. (11.18), we get the circuit constraints in terms of $\mathbf{V}_1$ and $\mathbf{V}_2$, just as we did earlier in eqns. (11.26) and (11.27) for the pure single-phase motor. The result is

$$\mathbf{V}_1 = \frac{\sqrt{2}}{\beta} \frac{\beta + j\mathbf{a}_2}{\mathbf{a}_1 + \mathbf{a}_2} \mathbf{V}_s \tag{11.37}$$

and

$$\mathbf{V}_2 = \mathbf{V}_1 - j\sqrt{2}\frac{\mathbf{V}_s}{\beta}. \tag{11.38}$$

As would be expected, these equations reduce to eqns. (11.26) and (11.27) if X_c is infinite.

Once $\mathbf{I}_1$ and $\mathbf{I}_2$ are known (from the solution described below), the actual winding currents follow:

$$\mathbf{I}_m = \frac{1}{\beta}\mathbf{I}_\beta = \frac{-j}{\sqrt{2}\,\beta}[\mathbf{I}_1 - \mathbf{I}_2] \tag{11.39}$$

and

$$\mathbf{I}_a = \mathbf{I}_\alpha = \frac{1}{\sqrt{2}}[\mathbf{I}_1 + \mathbf{I}_2]. \tag{11.40}$$

Solution of the positive-sequence system — The positive-sequence system must be solved to obtain $\mathbf{Z}_1$. If $\mathbf{V}_1$ is assumed known, the phasor diagram can be used to find $\mathbf{I}_1$, and since the positive-sequence system involves a forward-rotating ampere-conductor distribution synchronized with the rotor, it is convenient to solve the phasor diagram in *dq* axes as shown in Fig. 7.1. As for the pure single-phase motor, it is assumed that δ and $\mathbf{V}_1$ are known, and the phasor diagram is solved for $\mathbf{I}_1$. The torque is given by eqn. (7.10) with $m = 1$, (—really 2/2, because the positive-sequence quantities are effectively peak quantities as discussed next).

The scaling of the positive-sequence EMF E_1 needs care. When the magnet rotates on open-circuit it generates the EMF $\mathbf{E}_m = j\omega N_m \Phi$ in the main winding and $\mathbf{E}_a = -\omega N_a \Phi$ in the auxiliary winding, where Φ is the fundamental magnet flux/pole. Thus $\mathbf{E}_a = +j\mathbf{E}_m/\beta$. From eqn. (11.18) we get $\mathbf{E}_\alpha = \mathbf{E}_a = +j\mathbf{E}_m/\beta$ and $\mathbf{E}_\beta = \mathbf{E}_m/\beta$. Then from eqn. (11.17)

$$\mathbf{E}_1 = \frac{1}{\sqrt{2}}[\mathbf{E}_\alpha + j\mathbf{E}_\beta] = j\sqrt{2}\frac{\mathbf{E}_m}{\beta}. \tag{11.41}$$

Thus if E_1 is normally calculated as E_{q1} for the main winding (N_m turns), it must be scaled by $\sqrt{2}/\beta$ to get the positive-sequence value. Note that the dq axes in the phasor diagram can be interpreted as a further reference-frame transformation from [1,2] components into [d,q] components.

Solution of the negative-sequence system — The negative-sequence system must be solved to obtain $\mathbf{Z}_2$. For this purpose the motor equations are written in dq axes fixed to the rotor, and solved for a slip $s = 2$. The negative-sequence solution for variable s will also be useful for calculating the asynchronous torque/speed characteristic, as mentioned on p. 506.

For the stator we use the transformed voltage equations (4.108). Evidently all the impedances in this system, including $\mathbf{Z}_2$ itself, are referred to a winding with a particular number of turns. It is usual to calculate impedances referred to the main winding with N_m turns. If we take R_m for instance, the resistance of the main winding, and if we assume that the auxiliary winding has the same total copper cross-section, we can write $R_a = R_m/\beta^2$. The resistance matrix of the [a,m] machine is then

$$[R_{a,m}] = \begin{bmatrix} R_a & 0 \\ 0 & R_m \end{bmatrix} = \begin{bmatrix} R_m/\beta^2 & 0 \\ 0 & R_m \end{bmatrix}. \tag{11.42}$$

Using the transformations (11.13) and (11.15), if we first write

$$[V_{a,m}] = [R_{a,m}][I_{a,m}] \tag{11.43}$$

we get

$$\begin{aligned}[V_{\alpha,\beta}] &= [C_t]^{-1}[V_{a,m}] \\ &= [C_t]^{-1}[R_{a,m}]\,[I_{a,m}] \\ &= [C_t]^{-1}[R_{a,m}]\,[C]^{-1}\,[I_{\alpha,\beta}]\end{aligned} \tag{11.44}$$

from which

$$[R_{\alpha,\beta}] = [C_t]^{-1}[R_{a,m}]\,[C]^{-1}. \tag{11.45}$$

If we multiply this out we get the balanced resistance matrix

$$[R_{\alpha,\beta}] = \begin{bmatrix} R_m/\beta^2 & 0 \\ 0 & R_m/\beta^2 \end{bmatrix}. \tag{11.46}$$

The same process is applied to obtain $[R_{1,2}]$ from $[R_{\alpha,\beta}]$ using the transformations $[S]$ and $[S]^{-1}$ in eqns. (11.17) and (11.20): thus

$$[R_{1,2}] = [S]\,[R_{\alpha,\beta}]\,[S]^{-1} = [R_{\alpha,\beta}]. \tag{11.47}$$

From this it appears that in the solution of the negative-sequence system all resistances and inductances should be referred to the *auxiliary* winding: thus if they were initially calculated for the main winding turns N_m, they should be scaled by $1/\beta^2$.

The voltage and current must also be scaled correctly. The negative sequence voltage is not known *a priori*, but suppose the value is $\mathbf{V}_2$. Considering the negative-sequence system in isolation, we can set $\mathbf{V}_1 = 0$. Then from eqn. (11.18),

$$\mathbf{V}_\alpha = \frac{1}{\sqrt{2}}\mathbf{V}_2 \quad \text{and} \quad \mathbf{V}_\beta = \frac{j}{\sqrt{2}}\mathbf{V}_2. \tag{11.48}$$

Then from eqn. (11.16),

$$\mathbf{V}_a = \mathbf{V}_\alpha = \frac{1}{\sqrt{2}}\mathbf{V}_2 \quad \text{and} \quad \mathbf{V}_m = \beta\mathbf{V}_\beta = \frac{j\beta}{\sqrt{2}}\mathbf{V}_2. \tag{11.49}$$

From eqn. (11.49) it appears that if the voltages to be used in the negative-sequence system are to be referred to the auxiliary winding, they must be scaled from $\mathbf{V}_2$ by $1/\sqrt{2}$.

It is now possible to proceed with the solution of eqns. (4.108) under asynchronous conditions with a slip of $s = 2$. Relative to a balanced 2-phase [α,β] machine with N_a turns in both windings, the dq voltages can be written

$$\begin{bmatrix} v_d \\ v_q \end{bmatrix} = \begin{bmatrix} \cos\theta & \sin\theta \\ -\sin\theta & \cos\theta \end{bmatrix} \cdot \begin{bmatrix} v_\alpha \\ v_\beta \end{bmatrix}. \tag{11.50}$$

Now let the [α,β] machine be supplied with positive-sequence voltages

$$\begin{aligned} v_\alpha &= V_{pk} \cos \omega t, \\ v_\beta &= V_{pk} \sin \omega t, \end{aligned} \tag{11.51}$$

in which v_α leads v_β. The negative-sequence behaviour will be imposed by rotating the rotor backwards relative to the rotating ampere-conductor distribution established by these voltages. If we have

$$\theta = (1 - s)\,\omega t \tag{11.52}$$

and substitute eqns. (11.51) and (11.52) in eqn. (11.50), we get

$$v_d = V_{pk} \cos s\omega t \quad \text{and} \quad v_q = V_{pk} \sin s\omega t, \tag{11.53}$$

which shows that with positive slip, v_d leads v_q. The rotor is slipping backwards relative to the stator ampere-conductor distribution, which is rotating forwards at synchronous speed. For the purpose of analysis with eqns. (4.108) we can represent v_d and v_q as phasor values at the slip frequency $s\omega$:

$$\mathbf{V}_d = V_{pk} \quad \text{and} \quad \mathbf{V}_q = -\mathrm{j}\, V_{pk}. \tag{11.54}$$

Eqns. (4.108) are now expressed in phasor terms:

$$\begin{aligned} \mathbf{V}_d &= R_d \mathbf{I}_d + \mathrm{j}s\omega\, \mathbf{\Psi}_d - (1 - s)\omega \mathbf{\Psi}_q, \\ \mathbf{V}_q &= R_q \mathbf{I}_q + \mathrm{j}s\omega\, \mathbf{\Psi}_q + (1 - s)\omega \mathbf{\Psi}_d, \end{aligned} \tag{11.55}$$

in which

$$\begin{aligned} \mathbf{\Psi}_d &= L_d(\mathrm{j}s\omega)\,\mathbf{I}_d, \\ \mathbf{\Psi}_q &= L_q(\mathrm{j}s\omega)\,\mathbf{I}_q. \end{aligned} \tag{11.56}$$

The synchronous inductances $L_d(jsω)$ and $L_q(jsω)$ are functions of frequency because of the coupled rotor circuits in each axis. We can derive expressions for $L_d(jsω)$ and $L_q(jsω)$ as follows. First the stator and rotor flux-linkages are written in the d and q axes as

$$\begin{aligned} \mathbf{\Psi}_d &= L_d \mathbf{I}_d + M_d \mathbf{I}_{dr}, \\ \mathbf{\Psi}_{dr} &= M_d \mathbf{I}_d + L_{dr} \mathbf{I}_{dr}. \end{aligned} \tag{11.57}$$

where L_{dr} is the rotor self-inductance in the d-axis referred to the same circuit as L_d for the stator, and similarly for L_{qr} and L_q. The mutual inductance between these circuits is written as

$$M_d = k_d \sqrt{L_d L_{dr}} \tag{11.58}$$

where k_d is the d-axis coupling coefficient; $k_d < 1$. Similar equations can be written for M_q.

The rotor circuits are short-circuited, so that in the d-axis for example

$$\begin{aligned} 0 &= R_{dr} \mathbf{I}_{dr} + js\omega \mathbf{\Psi}_{dr} \\ &= R_{dr} \mathbf{I}_{dr} + js\omega (M_d \mathbf{I}_d + L_{dr} \mathbf{I}_{dr}). \end{aligned} \tag{11.59}$$

This equation can be used to eliminate $\mathbf{I}_{dr}$ from eqn. (11.57). First

$$\mathbf{I}_{dr} = \frac{-js\omega M_d}{R_{dr} + js\omega L_{dr}} \mathbf{I}_d, \tag{11.60}$$

then after some manipulation

$$L_d(js\omega) = L_d \left[1 - \frac{js\omega k_d^2 T_d}{1 + js\omega T_d} \right], \tag{11.61}$$

with

$$T_d = \frac{L_{dr}}{R_{dr}}, \tag{11.62}$$

the so-called "open-circuit" rotor time-constant. Equations similar to (11.61) and (11.62) can be written for the q-axis.

At any particular slip frequency $L_d(js\omega)$ and $L_q(js\omega)$ are calculated, and when the rotor current is eliminated using eqn. (11.60), eqns. (11.55), (11.56) become

$$\begin{aligned}(R_d + js\omega L_d)\mathbf{I}_d - (1 - s)\omega L_q\mathbf{I}_q - \mathbf{V}_d &= 0,\\ (1 - s)\omega L_d\mathbf{I}_d + (R_q + js\omega L_q)\mathbf{I}_q - \mathbf{V}_q &= 0.\end{aligned} \quad (11.63)$$

The voltages $\mathbf{V}_d$ and $\mathbf{V}_q$ are given by eqn. (11.54). These can be solved for $\mathbf{I}_d$ and $\mathbf{I}_q$, whence Ψ_d and Ψ_q follow from eqns. (11.56), and

$$\mathbf{Z}_2 = \frac{\mathbf{V}_d + j\mathbf{V}_q}{\mathbf{I}_d + j\mathbf{I}_q}. \quad (11.64)$$

Finally the average negative-sequence torque is computed as

$$T_{ns} = p\ \mathrm{Re}\,[\Psi_d{}^*\mathbf{I}_q - \Psi_q{}^*\mathbf{I}_d]. \quad (11.65)$$

Again, as in the positive-sequence case, the number of "phases" does not appear in eqn. (11.65) because, m is taken as 2/2 for the reason explained on p. 525.

Combined solution — So far we have treated the positive- and negative-sequence systems separately. In actual operation the link between them is provided by eqn. (11.37), which "ties" the positive-sequence voltage $\mathbf{V}_1$ to the supply voltage $\mathbf{V}_s$, and eqn. (11.38), which does the same for the negative-sequence voltage $\mathbf{V}_2$. Only a single control parameter is needed to set the "level of operation", and the one chosen is the positive-sequence load angle δ (see Fig. 11.26). The algorithm is expressed on p. 523.

"Natural" symmetrical components — Unfortunately the symmetrical component transformations on p. 522 give rise to a set of phasors for the positive and negative-sequence components that are hard to interpret. This problem can be remedied by a further transformation into a second set of symmetrical components $\mathbf{U}_1$ and $\mathbf{U}_2$ for voltages, and $\mathbf{Y}_1$ and $\mathbf{Y}_2$ for currents, as follows:

$$\begin{bmatrix}\mathbf{U}_1\\ \mathbf{U}_2\end{bmatrix} = \frac{1}{2}\begin{bmatrix}-j & 1\\ j & 1\end{bmatrix}\begin{bmatrix}\mathbf{V}_\alpha\\ \mathbf{V}_\beta\end{bmatrix}; \quad \text{i.e.,} \quad [\mathbf{U}]_{12} = [N][\mathbf{V}]_{\alpha\beta} \quad (11.66)$$

with inverse

$$\begin{bmatrix} \mathbf{V}_\alpha \\ \mathbf{V}_\beta \end{bmatrix} = \begin{bmatrix} j & -j \\ 1 & 1 \end{bmatrix} \begin{bmatrix} \mathbf{U}_1 \\ \mathbf{U}_2 \end{bmatrix}; \qquad \text{i.e.,} \qquad [\mathbf{V}]_{\alpha\beta} = [N]^{-1}[\mathbf{U}]_{12} \quad (11.67)$$

and similarly

$$\begin{bmatrix} \mathbf{Y}_1 \\ \mathbf{Y}_2 \end{bmatrix} = \frac{1}{2} \begin{bmatrix} -j & 1 \\ j & 1 \end{bmatrix} \begin{bmatrix} \mathbf{I}_\alpha \\ \mathbf{I}_\beta \end{bmatrix}; \qquad \text{i.e.,} \qquad [\mathbf{Y}]_{12} = [N][\mathbf{I}]_{\alpha\beta} \quad (11.68)$$

with inverse

$$\begin{bmatrix} \mathbf{I}_\alpha \\ \mathbf{I}_\beta \end{bmatrix} = \begin{bmatrix} j & -j \\ 1 & 1 \end{bmatrix} \begin{bmatrix} \mathbf{Y}_1 \\ \mathbf{Y}_2 \end{bmatrix}; \qquad \text{i.e.,} \qquad [\mathbf{I}]_{\alpha\beta} = [N]^{-1}[\mathbf{Y}]_{12}. \quad (11.69)$$

By substituting eqn. (11.18) in eqn (11.66) it is easy to show that

$$\begin{bmatrix} \mathbf{U}_1 \\ \mathbf{U}_2 \end{bmatrix} = \frac{-j}{\sqrt{2}} \begin{bmatrix} 1 & 0 \\ 0 & -1 \end{bmatrix} \begin{bmatrix} \mathbf{V}_1 \\ \mathbf{V}_2 \end{bmatrix}; \quad (11.70)$$

that is,

$$[\mathbf{U}]_{12} = [N]\,[S]^{-1}[\mathbf{V}]_{12}, \quad (11.71)$$

or

$$\mathbf{U}_1 = \frac{-j}{\sqrt{2}}\mathbf{V}_1 \quad \text{and} \quad \mathbf{U}_2 = \frac{j}{\sqrt{2}}\mathbf{V}_2. \quad (11.72)$$

Eqn. (11.67) is written

$$\begin{aligned} \text{Main} \quad \mathbf{V}_\beta &= \mathbf{U}_1 + \mathbf{U}_2; \\ \text{Aux} \quad \mathbf{V}_\alpha &= j\,\mathbf{U}_1 - j\,\mathbf{U}_2. \end{aligned} \quad (11.73)$$

Especially the first of these equations makes it easier to interpret the phasor diagram, since the voltage across the main winding β is simply the vector sum of the positive- and negative-sequence components $\mathbf{U}_1$ and $\mathbf{U}_2$. In contrast, it is hard work to interpret eqns. (11.18) in terms of the components $\mathbf{V}_1$ and $\mathbf{V}_2$.

If the EMFs are given by eqn. (11.28) on p. 524, the new transformation gives

$$\mathbf{E}_1 = \frac{1}{2}\left[-j(j\mathbf{E}_\beta) + \mathbf{E}_\beta\right] = \mathbf{E}_\beta = jE_{q1}\,; \qquad \mathbf{E}_\alpha = 0. \quad (11.74)$$

Also, since $\mathbf{I}_\beta = \mathbf{Y}_1 + \mathbf{Y}_2$, we can write the following equations for interesting special cases:

$$\begin{aligned} &(a)\ \text{If}\ \mathbf{I}_\alpha = 0\ \text{then}\ \mathbf{Y}_1 = \mathbf{Y}_2 = \frac{\mathbf{I}_\beta}{2}\,; \\ &(b)\ \text{If}\ \mathbf{Y}_2 = 0\ \text{then}\ \mathbf{I}_\beta = \mathbf{Y}_1\ \text{and}\ \mathbf{I}_\alpha = j\mathbf{Y}_1. \end{aligned} \quad (11.75)$$

Case (*a*) is the pure single-phase motor, while case (*b*) is a perfectly balanced motor. These equations are easy to check in the phasor diagram. Finally, it may be desirable to rotate the entire phasor diagram so that $\mathbf{E}_1$ appears on the q-axis, rather than having $\mathbf{V}_\beta$ on the real axis.

Interpretation of the phasor diagram — Fig. 11.26 shows the phasor diagram of a split-phase PM capacitor motor, including the "natural" symmetrical components and the αβ components. The orientation of the whole diagram is such that the positive-sequence EMF $\mathbf{E}_1$ is on the q-axis together with the EMF $\mathbf{E}_{q1}$ in the main phase.

The main and auxiliary phase voltages $\mathbf{V}_m$ and $\mathbf{V}_a$ are held almost at right-angles by the capacitor voltage $\mathbf{V}_c$, indicating relatively good balance. This is also evident from the small value of $\mathbf{V}_2$ (about 6 V), relative to the positive-sequence voltage $\mathbf{V}_1$ (308 V). The backward-rotating flux is much smaller than the forward-rotating flux.

The αβ voltages are also shown. We can see that $\mathbf{V}_\beta = \mathbf{V}_1 + \mathbf{V}_2$, in accordance with eqn. (11.73).[92] Note that $\mathbf{V}_\alpha = \mathbf{V}_a$, but $\mathbf{V}_\beta = \mathbf{V}_m/\beta$ in accordance with eqn. (11.15) on p. 521.

The angle between the main and auxiliary currents is less than 90°, and $\mathbf{I}_2$ is quite noticeable compared to $\mathbf{I}_1$, indicating that the currents are not as well balanced as the voltages.

---

[92] The symbols **V** and **I** are restored in Fig. 11.26. Symbols **U** and **Y** were used to differentiate the natural symmetrical components from the original ones, but there is no need to retain them once the point has been made.

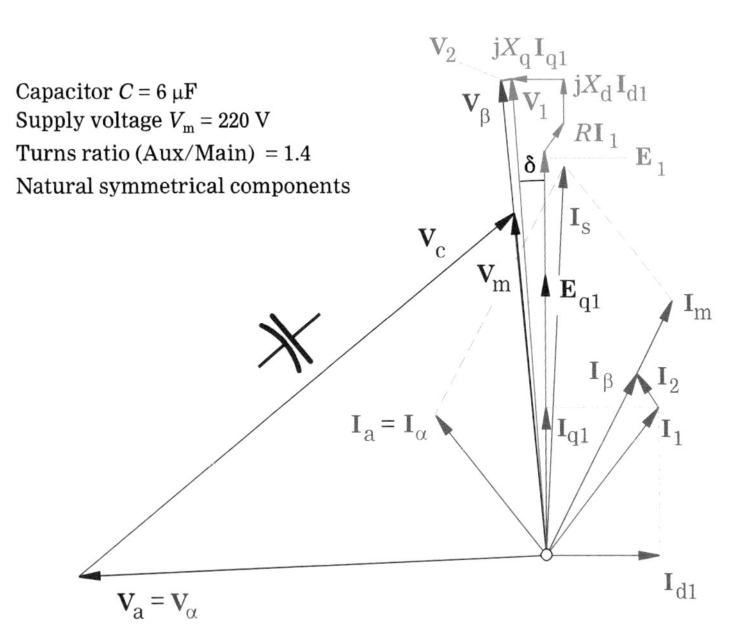

Fig. 11.26 Phasor diagram of split-phase PM capacitor motor

We can see that $\mathbf{I}_\beta = \mathbf{I}_1 + \mathbf{I}_2$, in accordance with eqn. (11.69). Similarly, $\mathbf{I}_\alpha = \mathbf{I}_a$, but $\mathbf{I}_\beta = \beta\mathbf{I}_m$, in accordance with the current eqn. (11.13) on p. 521. Also note that the auxiliary current leads the capacitor voltage $\mathbf{V}_c$ by exactly 90°.

Fig. 11.26 includes the entire positive-sequence phasor diagram $\mathbf{E}_1, R\mathbf{I}_1, jX_d\mathbf{I}_{d1}, jX_q\mathbf{I}_{q1}, \mathbf{V}_1$ together with $\mathbf{I}_1$ and its components $\mathbf{I}_{d1}$ and $\mathbf{I}_{q1}$. All these phasors are scaled to the number of effective turns on the auxiliary winding, by virtue of the choice of transformations (11.13) and (11.15) on p. 521. They are therefore scaled by 1/β (for voltages) or by β (for currents) relative to the effective number of turns on the main winding. Thus, for example, $E_1 = E_{q1}/\beta$, where E_{q1} is the fundamental EMF generated by the magnet flux in the main winding. In the induction motor, the components $jX_d\mathbf{I}_{d1}$ and $jX_q\mathbf{I}_{q1}$ would be replaced by a single phasor representing the voltage drop across the stator leakage reactance, but otherwise the diagram for a capacitor induction motor is similar.

The supply current $\mathbf{I}_s$ is the sum of $\mathbf{I}_m$ and $\mathbf{I}_a$. In Fig. 11.26 it lags behind the supply voltage $\mathbf{V}_m$ by about 8°, giving an overall power factor close to 1. The main and auxiliary phases are working at a lower power factor, with angles of about 33° between $\mathbf{V}_m$ and $\mathbf{I}_m$, and about 53·7° between $\mathbf{V}_a$ and $\mathbf{I}_a$. Both windings are absorbing reactive power. The sum of the reactive powers $\mathrm{Im}(\mathbf{V}_m\mathbf{I}_m^*) + \mathrm{Im}(\mathbf{V}_a\mathbf{I}_a^*)$ is equal to the sum of the reactive powers $\mathrm{Im}(\mathbf{V}_m\mathbf{I}_s^*) + \mathrm{Im}(\mathbf{V}_c\mathbf{I}_a^*)$ obtained from the supply and the capacitor respectively. Thus the capacitor is acting as a power-factor correction capacitor.

Finally the symmetrical components of the simple single-phase circuit on p. 517 can be found as follows. The current is given by eqn. (11.11), and the positive and negative sequence currents by eqn. (11.22). The positive-sequence EMF is given by

$$\mathbf{E}_1 = \mathrm{j}\sqrt{2}\,\mathbf{E} = \mathrm{j}\sqrt{2}\,\mathrm{j}E_{q1} = -\sqrt{2}\,E_{q1}. \qquad (11.76)$$

The positive-sequence voltage is given by

$$\begin{aligned}\mathbf{V}_1 &= \frac{1}{\sqrt{2}}(\mathbf{V}_\alpha + \mathrm{j}\,\mathbf{V}_\beta) = \frac{1}{\sqrt{2}}[-E_{q1} + \mathrm{j}\,(\mathrm{j}\,E_{q1} + (R + \mathrm{j}X)\mathbf{I}_\beta)] \\ &= \mathbf{E}_1 + (R + \mathrm{j}X)\mathbf{I}_1.\end{aligned} \qquad (11.77)$$

The load-angle δ for the positive-sequence system is equal to $\arg(\mathbf{V}_1) - \arg(\mathbf{E}_1)$. Similarly the negative-sequence voltage can be shown to be $\mathbf{V}_2 = (R + \mathrm{j}X)\mathbf{I}_2 = -\mathrm{j}/\sqrt{2}\,(R + \mathrm{j}X)\mathbf{I}_\beta$ with $\mathbf{E}_2 = 0$.

Torques — The positive-sequence system gives rise to a forward torque T_f that has a magnet-alignment component and a reluctance component :[93]

$$T_f = \frac{p}{\omega}\left[E_1 I_{q1} + (X_d - X_q) I_{d1} I_{q1}\right]. \qquad (11.78)$$

where I_{d1} and I_{q1} are the d- and q-axis components of the positive-sequence current $\mathbf{I}_1$.

---

[93] Note again that the number of phases does not appear in eqn. (11.78), as was noted on p. 525. The RMS values of the positive-sequence EMF E_1 and the d- and q-axis currents I_{d1} and I_{q1} already contain a $\sqrt{2}$ factor arising from the transformation from phase variables to symmetrical components in eqn. (11.19). When they appear in eqn. (11.78) they appear in pairs, so the $\sqrt{2}$ factors combine to give a factor of 2, equal to the number of phases.

The negative-sequence system gives rise to a backward torque T_b. This is exactly analogous to the asynchronous torque of an induction motor when the slip is $s = 2$, in which half the rotor loss ($W_{2R}/2$) is supplied across the airgap and half is supplied from the shaft. Since the speed of the rotor relative to the backward-rotating field is $2\omega/p$, with $\omega = 2\pi f$, the slip is $s = 2$ and the I^2R loss in the rotor cage is

$$W_{2R} = \frac{2\,\omega}{p} T_b. \qquad (11.79)$$

The total electromagnetic torque applied to the rotor is

$$T_e = T_f - T_b. \qquad (11.80)$$

This "electromagnetic" torque is available at the shaft after subtracting friction and windage losses. It is associated with the electromechanical power P_e which is given by

$$P_e = \frac{\omega}{p} T_e = \frac{\omega}{p}(T_f - T_b) = \frac{\omega}{p} T_f - \frac{W_{2R}}{2}. \qquad (11.81)$$

P_e is by definition the "synchronous watts" of induction-motor theory, as it gives the actual electromagnetic torque T_e when divided by ω/p. The power crossing the airgap is

$$\begin{aligned} P_g &= P_e + W_{2R} = \frac{\omega}{p} T_f + \frac{W_{2R}}{2} \\ &= \frac{\omega}{p}(T_f + T_b) = \frac{\omega}{p} T_f - \frac{-\omega}{p} T_b. \end{aligned} \qquad (11.82)$$

Eqns. (11.81) and (11.82) show that half the I^2R loss in the rotor cage is provided "electrically" across the gap as a component of P_g, while the other half appears as a deduction from the electromechanical power P_e. As in the induction motor, $P_g = P_e + W_{2R}$.

The term $(T_f + T_b)$ represents the combined action of forward and backward fields in transmitting power across the airgap. It does not represent a physical torque because T_f and T_b act in opposite directions and are associated with fields that are moving in opposite directions. The actual reaction torque on the stator is $T_e = T_f - T_b$, equal but opposite to the electromagnetic torque on the rotor.

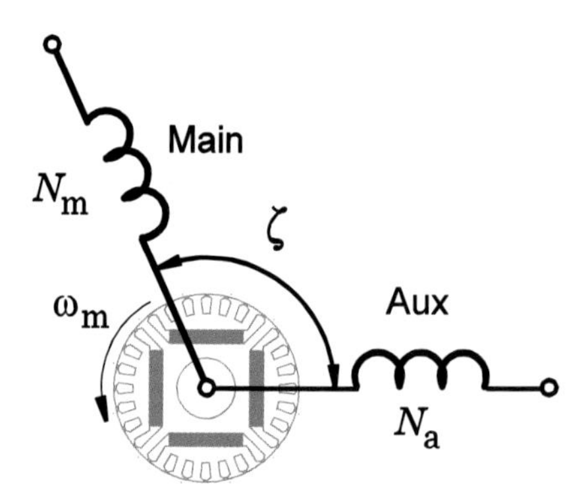

Fig. 11.27 Non-orthogonal windings

Non-orthogonal windings — Non-orthogonal windings may be used to give some design flexibility in the value of capacitor required for balanced operation. For non-orthogonal windings the reference transformations (11.13) and (11.14) must be modified to include the angle ζ, Fig. 11.27. The transformation for current is developed on the basis of equal MMF on two orthogonal axes. Again referring all windings to the auxiliary turns N_a,

$$\begin{aligned} N_a i_a + N_m i_m \cos\zeta &= N_a i_\alpha \\ N_m i_m \sin\zeta &= N_a i_\beta \end{aligned} \quad \text{or} \quad \begin{bmatrix} i_\alpha \\ i_\beta \end{bmatrix} = \begin{bmatrix} 1 & \beta\cos\zeta \\ 0 & \beta\sin\zeta \end{bmatrix} \cdot \begin{bmatrix} i_a \\ i_m \end{bmatrix}; \quad (11.83)$$

that is

$$[i_{\alpha,\beta}] = [N][i_{a,m}]. \quad (11.84)$$

The inverse is

$$\begin{bmatrix} i_a \\ i_m \end{bmatrix} = \begin{bmatrix} 1 & -\operatorname{ctg}\zeta \\ 0 & \dfrac{1}{\beta}\csc\zeta \end{bmatrix} \cdot \begin{bmatrix} i_\alpha \\ i_\beta \end{bmatrix} \quad \text{or} \quad [i_{a,m}] = [N]^{-1}[i_{\alpha,\beta}]. \quad (11.85)$$

Evidently $[N]$ is not orthogonal. The voltage transformation must therefore be

$$[v_{\alpha,\beta}] = [N_t]^{-1}[v_{a,m}]; \quad (11.86)$$

that is,

$$\begin{bmatrix} v_\alpha \\ v_\beta \end{bmatrix} = \begin{bmatrix} 1 & 0 \\ -\operatorname{ctg} \zeta & \dfrac{1}{\beta} \csc \zeta \end{bmatrix} \cdot \begin{bmatrix} v_a \\ v_m \end{bmatrix}. \tag{11.87}$$

The inverse is

$$[v_{a,m}] = [N_t][v_{\alpha,\beta}]; \tag{11.88}$$

that is,

$$\begin{bmatrix} v_a \\ v_m \end{bmatrix} = \begin{bmatrix} 1 & 0 \\ \beta \cos \zeta & \beta \sin \zeta \end{bmatrix} \cdot \begin{bmatrix} v_\alpha \\ v_\beta \end{bmatrix}. \tag{11.89}$$

These transformations replace eqns. (11.13-11.16). The subsequent theory follows the same lines as already described.

11.4.3 Asynchronous and starting performance

The asynchronous operation can be calculated exactly as for the negative-sequence components on the preceding pages, with the average asynchronous torque given by eqn. (11.65) on p. 530. The slip s is varied to cover the speed range of interest. The positive-sequence components are ignored, on the basis that there is no average positive-sequence torque at non-synchronous speeds.

The starting performance can be analyzed as for the polyphase motor discussed earlier, with suitable circuit constraints on the terminal voltages. The calculation requires the simultaneous solution of the differential voltage equations for each circuit in the machine, and this calculation is performed in dq axes. For the stator, the voltage equations are eqns. (4.108).

Additional circuit equations must be written for the rotor cage. Although it is possible to write a separate voltage equation for each pair of bars, or even for each bar, the simplest approach uses only two circuits — one for the d-axis and one for the q-axis. The properties of the d- and q-axis circuits are generally different, but in most other aspects they are similar to the rotor circuit parameters used in the theory of induction motors.

In *dq* axes the rotor circuit equations are

$$\begin{aligned} v_D &= 0 = R_D i_D + \mathbf{p}\psi_D; \\ v_Q &= 0 = R_Q i_Q + \mathbf{p}\psi_Q. \end{aligned} \tag{11.90}$$

where **p** means *d*/*dt*. Note that $v_D = v_Q = 0$, because the cage is short-circuited by its end-rings. We now need relationships linking all the flux-linkages with all the currents. In the *d*-axis the flux-linkages are ψ_d for the stator and ψ_D for the rotor, and likewise ψ_q and ψ_Q in the *q*-axis. Then we have

$$\begin{aligned} d\text{–axis} \quad \psi_d &= L_d i_d + L_{aD} i_D \quad \text{stator} \\ \psi_D &= L_{aD} i_d + L_D i_D \quad \text{rotor} \\ q\text{–axis} \quad \psi_q &= L_q i_q + L_{aQ} i_Q \quad \text{stator} \\ \psi_Q &= L_{aQ} i_q + L_Q i_Q \quad \text{rotor.} \end{aligned} \tag{11.91}$$

The procedure is to integrate eqns. (4.108) and (11.90) together with eqns. (11.91) on a step-by-step basis, using Euler's method or an equivalent such as the Runge-Kutta method.[94] At the end of each step, the currents are obtained from eqns. (11.91), which can be inverted algebraically as they are two independent pairs of simultaneous equations. The torque is calculated from eqn. (4.112) but without the 3/2 coefficient.

If the speed is free to vary, two mechanical differential equations must be added :

$$\mathbf{p}\,\omega_m = \frac{T}{J} \tag{11.92}$$

and

$$\mathbf{p}\theta = \omega_m, \tag{11.93}$$

where θ is the rotor position, ω_m is the angular velocity, J is the total inertia of the motor plus load, and T is the net torque, equal to the electromagnetic torque minus all the mechanical loss torque components (friction, windage, etc.).

Typical results of this type of simulation are similar to Figs. 11.14–16 on p. 508.

[94]With flux-linkages as state variables, Euler's method is usually adequate.

dq transformations for split-phase machines — In the solution of transients for 2-phase and single-phase machines, including split-phase capacitor motors, we need to be able to relate the *dq*-axis quantities to the phase quantities without using symmetrical components. The symmetrical components were useful in the steady-state for developing the phasor diagram, but the transient analysis is a simulation using real variables, not complex variables. So we need transformations between *dq*-axes and the αβ axes which were used to analyse the capacitor motor in the steady-state. In terms of Fig. 11.25 on p. 521, what we're talking about is "going from [αβ] to [*dq*+] directly without passing through [12]".

The αβ axes are identical to those of the symmetrical 2-phase motor, in which phase 1 corresponds to the α phase and phase 2 to the β phase. The phase sequence is 1-2 or α-β. In the split-phase capacitor motor, the α phase is the auxiliary and the β phase is the main; again, the phase sequence is α-β. The transformations are

$$\begin{aligned} i_d &= i_\alpha \cos\theta + i_\beta \sin\theta ; \\ i_q &= -i_\alpha \sin\theta + i_\beta \cos\theta . \end{aligned} \tag{11.94}$$

with inverse

$$\begin{aligned} i_\alpha &= i_d \cos\theta - i_q \sin\theta ; \\ i_\beta &= i_d \sin\theta + i_q \cos\theta . \end{aligned} \tag{11.95}$$

The same transformations are used for flux-linkages and voltages. The transformation actually represents a projection of MMFs, as in Fig. 11.28, with α written instead of *a*, β instead of *m*, and $\zeta = 90^\circ$.

In passing, and for no particular reason except that there is no other convenient place to mention it, it is perhaps of interest to add the transformations between 3-phase *abc* and 2-phase stationary αβ components.[95] These are already implicit in the 2-phase and 3-phase *dq* transformations and can easily be obtained by substitution:

$$i_\alpha = i_a ; \qquad i_\beta = \frac{1}{\sqrt{3}}(i_b - i_c) . \tag{11.96}$$

---

[95] For a feast of reference-frame transformations applied to power-engineering problems, see Y.H. Ku, *Electric Energy Conversion*, Ronald Press, N.Y. 1959.

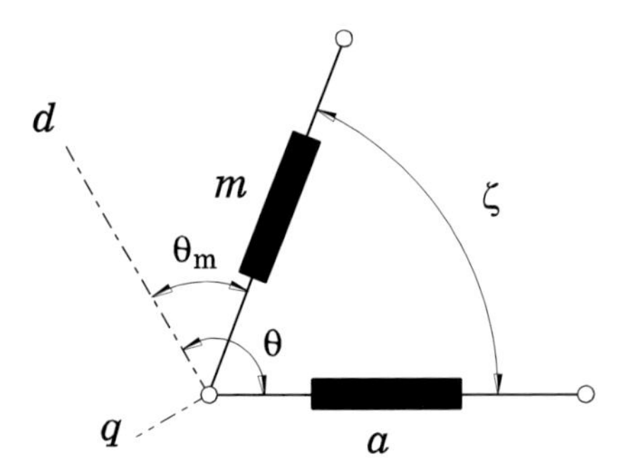

Fig. 11.28 Split-phase reference axes

with inverse

$$i_a = i_\alpha\,; \qquad i_b = -\frac{1}{2}i_\alpha + \frac{\sqrt{3}}{2}i_\beta\,; \qquad i_c = -\frac{1}{2}i_\alpha - \frac{\sqrt{3}}{2}i_\beta\,. \tag{11.97}$$

In general the transformation of three variables into only two variables is not complete, but 3-phase machines are usually assumed to have a 3-wire connection which enforces the condition

$$i_a + i_b + i_c = 0 \tag{11.98}$$

so that only two currents are independent. The same constraint applies to the voltages and flux-linkages.

Synchronous operation — For synchronous operation the rotor position θ advances in synchronism with ωt, but its phase must be coordinated with the phasor diagram.

Fig. 11.28 shows the reference axes for the split-phase motor. The rotor rotates in the anticlockwise (positive) direction, so that voltages and currents in the auxiliary (a) normally lead the corresponding voltages and currents in the main (m).

The position of a rotor d-axis is defined relative to the axis of the *auxiliary* winding by

$$\theta = \omega t + \theta_0 \qquad \text{elec rad.} \tag{11.99}$$

The position of the same d-axis relative to the *main* winding is

$$\theta_m = \theta - \zeta = \omega t + \theta_0 - \zeta\,. \tag{11.100}$$

When $\theta_m = 0$, the d-axis is aligned with the main winding, and the magnet flux-linkage in the main winding is at its maximum value Ψ_{1Md}. At other rotor positions the magnet flux-linkage in the main winding is

$$\psi_m = \Psi_{1Md} \cos \theta_m = \Psi_{1Md} \cos (\omega t + \theta_0 - \zeta). \tag{11.101}$$

The EMF in the main winding is $e_{q1} = d\psi_m/dt$

$$\begin{aligned} e_{q1} &= \frac{d\psi_m}{dt} = -\omega \Psi_{1Md} \sin (\omega t + \theta_0 - \zeta) \\ &= -\omega\sqrt{2}E_{q1} \sin (\omega t + \theta_0 - \zeta). \end{aligned} \tag{11.102}$$

The terminal voltage of the main winding has a peak value $v_{pk} = \surd 2V_s$, and its phase is defined by the load-angle δ_m, which can be seen in the phasor diagram as the angle between the phasors $\mathbf{V}_m$ and $\mathbf{E}_{q1}$. Keeping the same reference frame as above, it follows that

$$v_m = -v_{pk} \sin (\omega t + \theta_0 - \zeta + \delta_m). \tag{11.103}$$

For symmetrical 3-phase and 2-phase motors, the distinction between θ and θ_m disappears, because e_{q1} is defined for phase 1, which is the same as phase a in the above. Instead of (eqn. 11.103) we have

$$v_1 = -v_{pk} \sin (\omega t + \theta_0 + \delta_m). \tag{11.104}$$

For starting calculations, or other calculations at speeds other than synchronous speed, there is no *a priori* connection between θ and ωt. In this case we can use

$$v_1 = v_{pk} \sin \omega t. \tag{11.105}$$

and the same equation for v_m in the split-phase motor, while the rotor position is the result of the integration

$$\theta = \int \omega_m dt + \theta_0. \tag{11.106}$$

In all cases, θ_0 is the rotor position at $t = 0$.

11.5 Advanced topics

11.5.1 Winding harmonics

From experience with single-phase induction motors it is known that winding harmonics can significantly affect the torque/speed characteristic, Fig. 11.13. Dips appear in the torque at speeds related to the order of the space-harmonics. For example the 3rd winding harmonic produces a backward-rotating MMF at 1/3 speed.

The analysis of the effect of winding harmonics is a classical subject in induction-motor theory. For the line-start PM motor, however, it is significantly more complex because of the saliency. A thorough analysis was published by Popescu in collaboration with Kalluf and others.[96]

Popescu extended the model of Fig. 11.25 to include winding harmonics of arbitrary order. The harmonic components appear in all the reference frames in Fig. 11.25, and the relevant harmonic impedances are obtained mainly by scaling from the fundamental-frequency values. The main difference is that the harmonic components are not stationary in the dq+ reference frame, so the averaging principle described on pp. 526ff. is used to determine the torque at any value of slip. The value of slip is peculiar to each harmonic, since each harmonic has its own synchronous speed.

Even in a balanced polyphase machine the saliency causes an irregularity in the torque/speed curve at half speed. A mild form of this irregularity can be seen in Fig. 11.13 on p. 506. It is sometimes called the Görges effect, (Görges [1896]; see also Jones [1967], or Vas [1992]). A verbal explanation is instructive. With frequencies expressed in per-unit relative to the fundamental supply frequency, the rotor MMF pulsates at the slip frequency s, and it is equivalent to two contra-rotating MMFs rotating at the frequencies $+s$ and $-s$ relative to the rotor. Since the rotor itself is rotating at the frequency $1 - s$, the two components are rotating relative to the stator at the frequencies $1 - s \pm s$, i.e., 1 and $1 - 2s$.

---

[96] Popescu M., Miller T.J.E., McGilp M.I., Kalluf F.J.H., da Silva C.A., and von Dokonal L., *Effect of winding harmonics on the asynchronous torque of a single-phase line-start permanent-magnet motor*, IEEE Transactions on Industry Applications, Vol. 42, No. 4, July/August 2006, pp. 1014-1024.

The first of these is a forward component that is stationary relative to the rotor. The second is nominally a backward component that rotates forwards if $s < 1/2$, or backwards if $s > 1/2$. If $s = 1/2$ it is stationary (relative to the stator).

The forward component generates a loss in the stator circuit resistance, which produces a retarding torque on the rotor that is similar to the magnet braking torque. Likewise the backward component generates a loss in the stator circuit, but the associated reaction torque on the rotor changes direction at half speed, being an accelerating torque below half speed and a retarding or braking torque at speeds above half speed. This gives rise to the irregularity seen near half-speed in Fig. 11.13.

Similar effects arise for the harmonic components at the appropriate speeds depending on the harmonic order.[97,98]

11.5.2 Bar-pair-by-bar-pair model of the rotor cage

So far the rotor cage has been represented by a single circuit in each of the d and q axes. There are no definite formulas for the inductances and resistances of these cage circuits (p. 538), and the best that can be done is to adapt formulas from induction-motor theory; but this is less than satisfactory because of the difficulty in accounting for the saliency and the magnets. It is possible to measure the necessary parameters by means of locked-rotor frequency-response tests, and this provides a means of checking (and if necessary adjusting) approximate values obtained by calculation.

An alternative method is to formulate the calculation of the resistances and inductances (both self and mutual) for individual pairs of bars. These can be entered in an impedance matrix that can be reduced to a single circuit with frequency-dependent parameters.

---

[97] See Popescu M., Miller T.J.E., McGilp M.I., Strappazzon G., Trivillin N., and Santarossa R. , *Line Start Permanent Magnet Motor: Single Phase Starting Performance Analysis*, IEEE Transactions on Industry Applications, Vol.39, No.4, July/August 2003, pp. 1021-1030.

[98] See Popescu M., Miller T.J.E., McGilp M.I., Strappazzon G., Trivillin N., and Santarossa R., *Asynchronous Performance Analysis of a Single-Phase Capacitor-Start, Capacitor-Run Permanent Magnet Motor* IEEE Transactions on Energy Conversion, Vol.20, No.1, March 2005 pp.142-150.

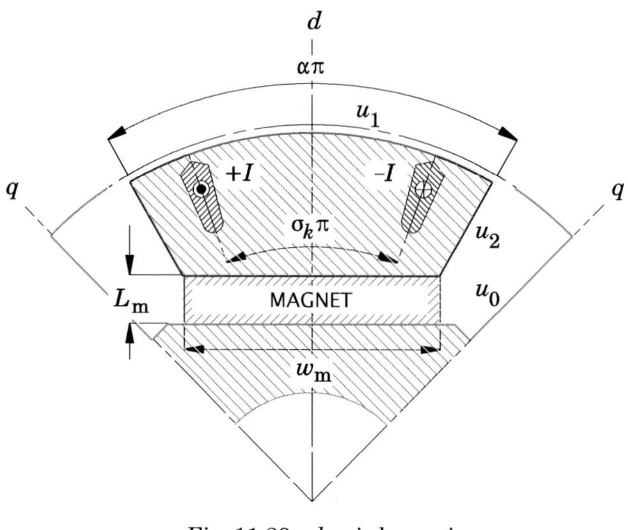

Fig. 11.29 d-axis bar-pair

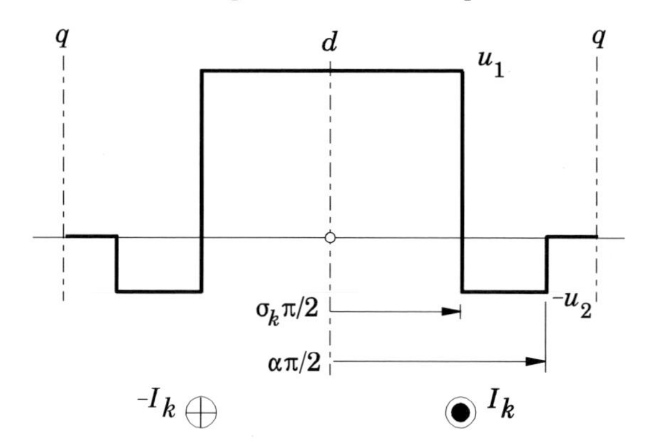

Fig. 11.30 Magnetic potential distribution; d-axis bar-pair

Bar inductances (d-axis) — Fig. 11.29 shows a single bar-pair centred on the d-axis, and Fig. 11.30 shows the distribution of magnetic potential in the airgap produced by current I going in one bar and returning in the other. If this is the kth pair of bars in a nested group, the current is denoted I_k. The span of the bar-pair circuit is $\sigma_k\pi$ radians. Equipotential surfaces u_0, u_1 and u_2 are defined as in the calculation of synchronous reactance (§5.10.3); these potentials are to be determined by the application of Ampère's and Gauss' laws. Thin saturable bridges are neglected.

By symmetry, with no other excitation than the kth bar-pair in each rotor pole, the magnetic potential of the stator iron and the magnetic potential of the rotor body are both zero: $u_0 = 0$. Also the q-axes are lines of zero magnetic potential, being parallel to the flux-lines that are excited by the current in the group of kth bar-pairs. With θ measured from the d-axis, the airgap flux density is given by

$$\begin{aligned} B_1 &= \frac{\mu_0 u_1}{g'}, \quad |\theta| \le \frac{1}{2}\sigma_k \pi; \\ B_2 &= \frac{\mu_0 u_2}{g'}, \quad \frac{1}{2}\sigma_k \pi \le |\theta| \le \frac{\pi}{2}. \end{aligned} \tag{11.107}$$

As before, g' is the effective airgap including Carter's coefficient (but not including the magnet length L_{m}).

The flux passing from the iron pole-piece to the rotor body is equal to $P_{\text{m0}}(1 + p_{\text{rl}})(u_2 - u_0) = P_{\text{m}} u_2$, the symbols being the same as in eqn. (4.3). The flux crossing the airgap within the span $\sigma_k \pi$ is equal to $\mu_0 u_1/g' \times \sigma_k \pi R L_{\text{stk}}/p$, where R is the radius of the stator bore, and if we write $R_{\text{g}} = g'p/\mu_0 \alpha \pi R L_{\text{stk}}$ as the airgap reluctance per pole, this flux is simply $u_1/R_{\text{g}} \times \sigma_k/\alpha$. Lastly the flux crossing the airgap between $\sigma_k \pi/2$ and $\alpha\pi/2$ is $u_2/R_{\text{g}} \times (1 - \sigma_k/\alpha)$. By Gauss' law the net flux leaving the pole-piece is zero, so if we write $\xi_k = \sigma_k/\alpha$ we have

$$u_1 \xi_k = u_2 [(1 - \xi_k) + P_{\text{m}} R_{\text{g}}]. \tag{11.108}$$

Also $u_1 - (-u_2) = u_1 + u_2 = I_k$. So we have two simultaneous equations that can be solved for u_1 and u_2 : the result is

$$u_1 = \frac{(1 - \xi_k) + P_{\text{m}} R_{\text{g}}}{1 + P_{\text{m}} R_{\text{g}}} I_k; \quad u_2 = \frac{\xi_k}{1 + P_{\text{m}} R_{\text{g}}} I_k. \tag{11.109}$$

The flux linkage with a second bar-pair of span $\sigma_j < \sigma_k$ is

$$\psi_{jk} = \frac{u_1 \xi_j}{R_{\text{g}}}, \tag{11.110}$$

where $\xi_j = \sigma_j/\alpha < \xi_k$. Treating all the bar-pairs as being in series, the flux-linkage per phase for the jth set of bar-pairs is $\psi_{jk\text{d}} = 2p\psi_{jk}$. The mutual inductance between the two sets of bar-pairs is $\psi_{jk\text{d}}/I_k$. The self-inductance of one set is obtained with $j = k$, $\sigma_j = \sigma_k$, etc.

Since the cage need be modelled only in dq-axes it remains only to determine the mutual inductance between the bar-pair and a single coil of $k_{w1}T_{ph}$ turns representing the stator winding and aligned with the d-axis. For this we use Fourier analysis of Fig. 11.30 to obtain the fundamental flux/pole produced by the kth set of bar-pairs: thus

$$\Phi_{k1} = \frac{8RL_{stk}}{\pi p}\left[B_1 \sin\frac{\sigma_k \pi}{2} - B_2\left[\sin\frac{\alpha\pi}{2} - \sin\frac{\sigma_k \pi}{2}\right]\right]. \quad (11.111)$$

The fundamental mutual flux-linkage with the stator winding is then $\psi_{k1d} = k_{w1}T_{ph}\Phi_{k1}$, and the mutual inductance is ψ_{k1d}/I_k. This completes the inductances required for the d-axis partition of the inductance matrix or L-matrix, which is given on p. 548.

Bar inductances (q-axis) — Fig. 11.31 shows a single bar-pair centred on the q-axis, and Fig. 11.32 shows the distribution of magnetic potential in the airgap produced by current I going in one bar and returning in the other. If this is the jth pair of bars in a nested group, the current is denoted I_j. The span of the bar-pair circuit is $(1 - \sigma_j\pi)$ radians. Equipotential surfaces u_0, and u_1 are defined as before, and again these potentials are to be determined by the application of Ampère's and Gauss' laws. Thin bridges and webs are neglected, though they can be added in a more detailed treatment.

The airgap flux-density due to current I_j in the jth bar-pair is

$$B_g = \mu_0 \frac{u_1}{g'}, \qquad (1-\alpha)\frac{\pi}{2} \le |\theta| \le (1-\sigma_k)\frac{\pi}{2}. \quad (11.112)$$

The flux produced by I_j does not pass through the magnet, so the potential of the rotor body is not involved, and we can set $u_0 = 0$.

Consider a second bar-pair having a span $(1 - \sigma_k) \le (1 - \sigma_j)$, i.e., with $\sigma_k \ge \sigma_j$. The flux linking bar-pair k due to current I_j in bar-pair j is given by

$$\psi_{kj} = \mu_0 \frac{I_j}{g'} \times \frac{\pi[(1-\sigma_j) - (1-\sigma_k)]RL_{stk}}{p}. \quad (11.113)$$

The mutual inductance L_{kj} is obtained as $2p\psi_{kj}/I_j$, and the self inductance is again obtained with $k = j$.

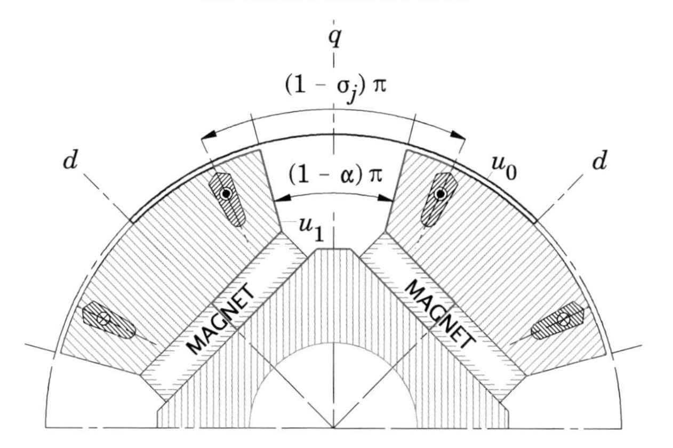

Fig. 11.31 q-axis bar-pair

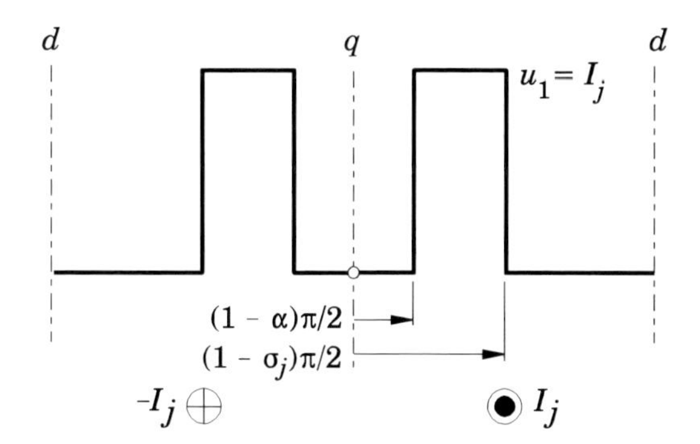

Fig. 11.32 Magnetic potential distribution; q-axis bar-pair

It remains only to determine the mutual inductance between the bar-pair and a single coil of $k_{w1}T_{ph}$ turns representing the stator winding and aligned with the q-axis. For this we use Fourier analysis of Fig. 11.32 to obtain the fundamental flux/pole produced by the jth set of bar-pairs: thus

$$\Phi_{j1} = \frac{8RL_{stk}}{\pi p} B_g \left[\sin \frac{(1-\sigma_j)\pi}{2} - \sin \frac{(1-\alpha)\pi}{2} \right]; \quad \sigma_j \leq \alpha . \quad (11.114)$$

The fundamental mutual flux-linkage with the stator coil is then $\psi_{j1q} = k_{w1}T_{ph}\Phi_{j1}$, so the mutual inductance is ψ_{j1q}/I_j. This completes the inductances required for the q-axis partition of the L-matrix.

L_d	L_{dd1}	L_{dd2}	L_{dd3}	L_{dd4}	L_{dd5}	L_{dd6}							
	L_{d11}	L_{d12}	L_{d13}	L_{d14}	L_{d15}	L_{d16}							
		L_{d22}	L_{d23}	L_{d24}	L_{d25}	L_{d26}							
			L_{d33}	L_{d34}	L_{d35}	L_{d36}				0			
				L_{d44}	L_{d45}	L_{d46}							
					L_{d55}	L_{d56}							
						L_{d66}							
							L_q	L_{qq6}	L_{qq5}	L_{qq4}	L_{qq3}	L_{qq2}	L_{qq1}
								L_{q66}	L_{q65}	L_{q64}	L_{q63}	L_{q62}	L_{q61}
									L_{q55}	L_{q54}	L_{q53}	L_{q52}	L_{q51}
			0							L_{q44}	L_{q43}	L_{q42}	L_{q41}
											L_{q33}	L_{q32}	L_{q31}
												L_{q22}	L_{q21}
													L_{q11}

The L-matrix $[L]$ has a d-axis partition $[L_d]$ and a q-axis partition $[L_q]$, with no cross-coupling. Each partition is symmetric, and only the upper triangle is shown populated, with the first row assigned to the stator circuit (L_d or L_q). The matrix is shown for a cage with 6 bar-pairs in each axis. The reverse numbering in the q-axis partition reflects the diminishing span from left to right.

Corresponding to the L-matrix is a square resistancc matrix of the same dimension. The resistance of a single bar-pair circuit can be calculated from the dimensions of the bars and end-rings shown in Fig. 11.33. Note that the current can flow in two parallel paths through each end-ring. A complication arises in that sections of end-ring are common to multiple bar-pair circuits, so the resistance matrix $[R]$ has many off-diagonal elements. It may be necessary to make an approximate allowance for skin-effect especially if the slip frequency is high, and more especially in larger machines.

The ultimate objective of the bar-pair-by-bar-pair model is to calculate the frequency-dependent synchronous inductances $L_d(js\omega)$ and $L_q(js\omega)$ that were used in eqn. (11.56) on p. 528 and subsequently to calculate the cage torque at any slip s.

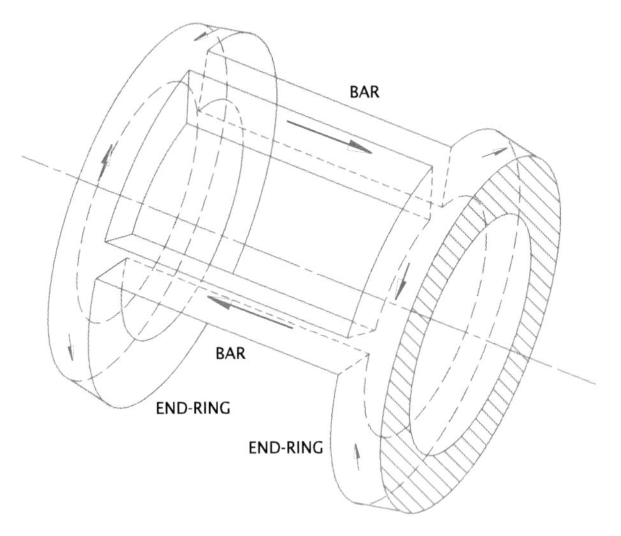

Fig. 11.33 Bar circuit, for calculating resistance

This is achieved by means of the elimination process used in eqn. (11.61) on p. 529 with only a single rotor circuit in each axis, generalized for any number of rotor circuits in each axis.

The voltage equation for the kth bar-pair circuit in the d-axis is

$$0 = \mathrm{j}s\omega\,\psi_{dk} + R_{d1k}i_{d1} \ldots + R_{dkk}i_{dk} \ldots + R_{dNk}i_{dN} \quad (11.115)$$

where R_{djk} is the mutual resistance between the kth and j^{th} bar-pair circuits and i_{dj} is the current in the jth bar-pair circuit, $j = 1 \ldots N$, and N is the number of d-axis bar-pair circuits (including the kth). We also have

$$\psi_{dk} = L_{ddk}i_{d} + L_{d1k}i_{d1} \,.. + L_{dkk}i_{dk} \,.. + L_{dNk}i_{dN}. \quad (11.116)$$

These two equations can be combined to solve for the current i_{dk}:

$$i_{dk} = \frac{-\mathrm{j}s\omega}{R_{dkk} + \mathrm{j}s\omega L_{dkk}}\left[L_{ddk}i_{d} + L_{d1k}i_{d1} \ldots + L_{dNk}i_{dN}\right] \quad (11.117)$$

This equation can be used to eliminate i_{dk} from all the other d-axis bar-pair circuit equations. The process is repeated systematically until the flux-linkage equation for the stator circuit reduces to

$$\psi_{d} = L_{d}(\mathrm{j}s\omega)\,i_{d}. \quad (11.118)$$

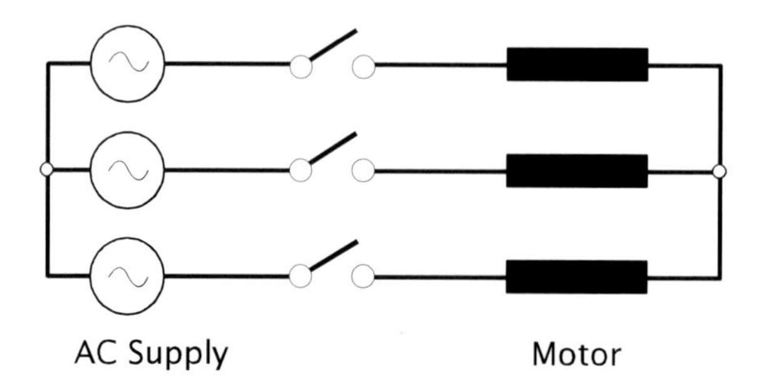

Fig. 11.34 3-phase AC circuit connection

11.5.3 Connection circuits

Fig. 11.34 shows the connection of a 3-phase line-start PM motor direct to the AC mains through a switch. The switch as well as the protective elements (not shown) may need to be rated for the sustained inrush current (Fig. 11.16), although this must be decided according to the particular load and service requirements.

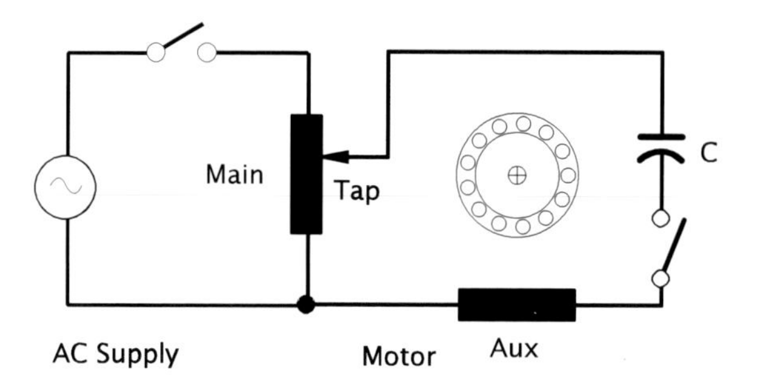

Fig. 11.35 Single-phase motor connection

Fig. 11.35 shows the connection of a single-phase line-start PM motor to the single-phase AC mains through a switch. In principle the auxiliary winding can be switched out once the motor is running, but in most cases the motor is likely to run at full load for an extended period, preferably at the maximum possible efficiency, and so there is no advantage in pure single-phase running. Fig. 11.35 also shows the possibility of a tapped-winding connection, not for variable speed (as in the induction motor), but for final adjustments "on site".

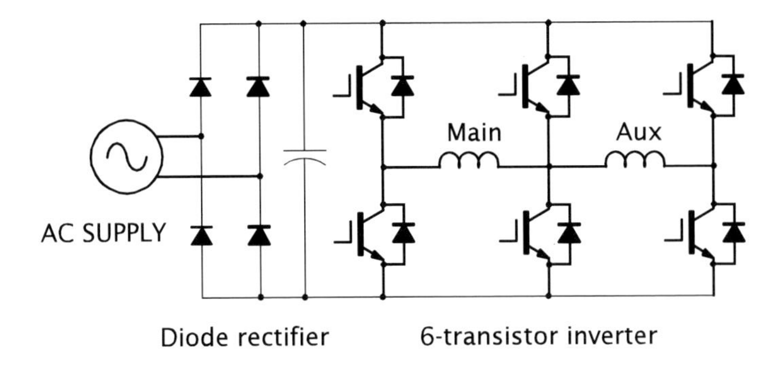

Fig. 11.36 Split-phase motor with 6-transistor inverter

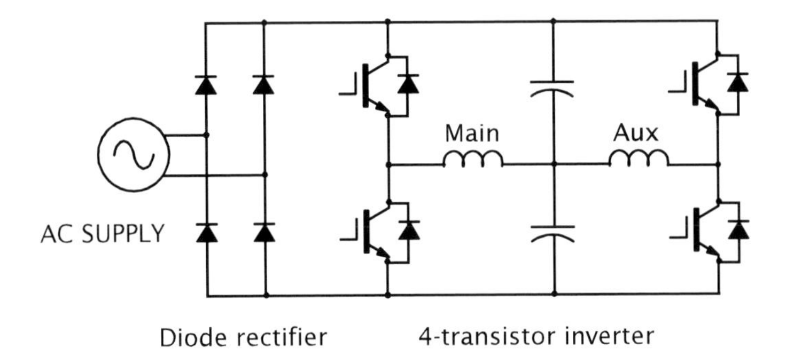

Fig. 11.37 Split-phase motor with 4-transistor inverter (H-bridge)

The line-start PM motor can be operated in open-loop "constant Volts/Hz" mode with an inverter, as already mentioned on p. 499. PWM voltage inverters can also be used, as in Fig. 6.1 (3-phase); or Figs. 11.36 and 11.37 (split-phase).[99,100] The inverter-fed motor will generally have lower starting current *and torque*; longer time to synchronize; and higher efficiency.

---

[99] Popescu M., Miller T.J.E., Cossar C., McGilp M.I., Strappazzon G., Trivillin N. and Santarossa R., *Comparative Study of the Starting Methods for a Single-Phase Permanent Magnet Synchronous Motor*, EPE Journal, Vol. 15, No. 1, February 2005, pp. 48-56.

[100] Popescu M., Miller T.J.E., Cossar C., McGilp M.I., Strappazzon G., Trivillin N. and Santarossa R., *Torque behavior of one-phase permanent magnet AC motor*– IEEE Transactions on Energy Conversion, Vol. 21, No. 1, March 2006, pp. 19-26.

12 LOSSES and COOLING

12.1 Introduction

Power losses are important because they determine the efficiency and the temperature-rise of the machine. The two most important components of power loss are the Joule loss (I^2R loss) in the stator conductors and the iron loss (also known as core loss), most of which is in the stator laminations. The iron loss is roughly proportional to the square of (flux × frequency). Consequently it is relatively more significant at high speed and/or light load, whereas the Joule loss is often predominant at low speed.

It is fortunate that the two largest loss components arise almost entirely on the stator, and not on the rotor as they do in DC motors. Even in the AC induction motor a significant fraction of the Joule loss arises on the rotor, as well as a small proportion of the iron loss and various other parasitic losses. This feature means that the brushless PM machine is relatively easily cooled, although the totally enclosed construction (required to prevent the accumulation of magnetic dust) makes the cooling somewhat more difficult.

The predominance of stator losses over rotor losses has often given rise to the impression, even the claim, that the rotor loss is zero. It is often negligible, but whenever there are conducting paths on the rotor there is a definite risk of parasitic eddy-current losses. Since the rotor is usually not well cooled, these losses can easily cause an objectionable temperature rise in the magnets. The factors most conducive to rotor eddy-current loss include conductive magnets; metallic retaining cans; large physical size; and high frequency. The term "high frequency" includes the fundamental frequency, the slot-passing frequency, and the inverter switching frequency, all of which can be construed as having a separate influence on the rotor loss.

Windage and friction losses are similar to those in induction motors. To the extent that a PM machine may have a slightly larger airgap than a comparable induction motor, the windage loss will be lower. Induction motors often have shaft-mounted fans either inside or outside the housing, but the PM machine often does not need such a fan, in which case the associated "fan losses" will be avoided.

12.2 Joule losses in stator conductors

Joule losses are generally the largest component of power loss in brushless PM motors. They are generally calculated as $mI_{ph}^2R_{ph}$ where m is the number of phases; I_{ph} is the RMS phase current, and R_{ph} is the phase resistance.

The increase in winding temperature increases the resistivity of the windings: a 50°C rise by 20%, and a 135°C rise by 53%, increasing the I^2R losses by the same amount if the current remains the same. The resistance increase is used in test procedures to determine the actual temperature rise of the winding, but this is obviously an *average* temperature; hot-spot temperatures can be 10–20° higher. At any temperature T °C the resistivity of copper can be calculated from eqn. (3.32) :

$$\rho = \rho_{20}[1 + \alpha(T - 20)] \quad \text{ohm–m} \tag{12.1}$$

where $\rho_{20} = 1{\cdot}724 \times 10^{-8}$ ohm-m is the resistivity at 20°C; $\alpha =$ 0·00393 /°C; and $\rho_0\alpha$ is the temperature coefficient of resistivity.

A useful formula can be derived from eqn. (12.1) to scale the resistance from one temperature to another:

$$R_2 = R_1 \times \frac{234{\cdot}5 + T_2}{234{\cdot}5 + T_1}. \tag{12.2}$$

For example if $T_2 = 155$°C and $T_1 = 20$°C, $R_2 = 1{\cdot}53 \times R_1$. If T_1 and T_2 are in °F, 234·5 is replaced by 390 in this formula.

In high-speed machines and even in lower-speed machines operating with inverters having a high switching frequency, the effect of eddy-currents in the stator conductors must be taken into account, (§3.6.7.4). Usually the conventional skin-effect is limited by making the individual strands of wire small compared to the skin-depth, but this is not sufficient to suppress the *proximity effect*, in which the distribution of current is affected by the magnetic field of currents in neighbouring conductors, usually within the same slot. The use of Litz wire is helpful in suppressing proximity effect, but the layout of the conductors in the slots is also of critical importance, particularly when the winding has multiple parallel paths, and/or when it is fed by multiple inverters (Chapter 10).

12.3 Core losses

Core losses are generally the second largest component of power loss in the brushless motor. They arise from the time-variation of magnetic flux-density throughout the core, mainly on the stator.

We will survey the complexities of core-losses rather briefly, making reference to more advanced works. A simple formulation of the core-loss coefficients for laminated steel is explained, as well as the method for applying these coefficients in design calculations.

12.3.1 The nature of core losses

Core losses are distributed throughout the laminated steel core.[101] and they depend essentially on the flux-density waveform, which varies from point to point in the cross-section.

According to classical theory, core loss has a *hysteresis* component and an *eddy-current* loss component. Hysteresis loss results from the "unwillingness" of the steel to change its magnetic state. Through one electrical cycle the magnetic represented by the point (H,B) describes a closed loop in the B/H diagram, Fig. 12.1, discovered by Professor J.A. Ewing while working in Japan. The loss *per cycle* is proportional to the enclosed loop area, suggesting that the mean power loss due to hysteresis is proportional to the frequency f,

$$W_h = C_h B_{pk}^{\ n} \quad [\text{W/kg}]. \qquad (12.3)$$

This formula is due to C.P. Steinmetz. The exponent n depends on the type of material and typically falls in the range 1·6 – 2·2. It is not constant but varies with B_{pk} and f.

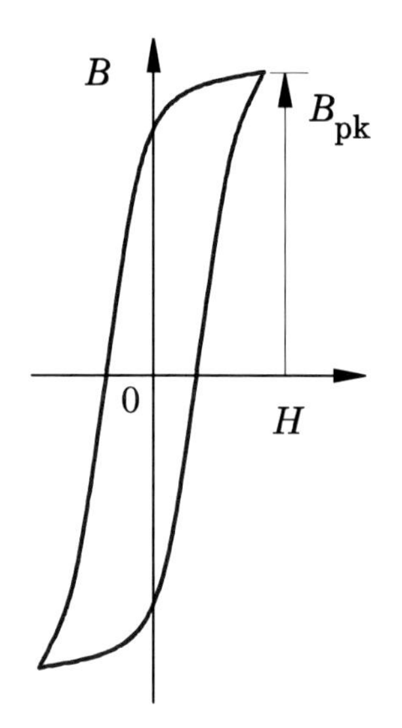

Fig. 12.1 Hysteresis loop

[101] We will confine attention to laminated steel cores, i.e., essentially the stator core. In the IPM, the rotor core is also laminated, and the methods for core-loss estimation are similar to those used for the stator. Surface-magnet motors may have non-laminated rotor cores, which are subject to bulk eddy-currents and are treated in §12.4 together with magnet losses and can losses.

The eddy-current component of core loss is generally held to vary with the square of the peak flux-density and the square of the frequency, as in the classical formula

$$W_e = C_e B_{pk}^2 f^2 \quad \text{[W/kg]}. \tag{12.4}$$

The coefficient C_e can be calculated from an idealized theory as[102]

$$C_e = \frac{\pi^2 t^2 \sigma}{6 \rho_m}, \tag{12.5}$$

where t is the lamination thickness, σ is the conductivity, and ρ_m is the mass density. Eddy-current losses can be reduced by using thinner lamination steels; for example, if t is reduced from 0·5mm to 0·35mm, C_e decreases by half. Lamination lengthens the conduction path of the eddy-currents, forcing them to flow in directions orthogonal to the EMF that drives them, while increasing the resistance that impedes them.

12.3.2 Core loss properties of practical materials

In practice the core losses of practical materials are measured using an Epstein frame or a "single-sheet tester" according to a standardized procedure.[103] These measurements may appear in the form of curves of total watts/kg plotted as a function of frequency f, with curves at different peak flux-density B_k; or conversely as curves of watts/kg vs. B_{pk} at different frequencies. Sometimes the loss data is limited to a single number, typically of so many watts/kg at 50 or 60 Hz, with B_{pk} equal to 1·5T or sometimes 1·0T. It is uncommon to find published loss data for any particular steel covering a comprehensive range of frequencies and flux-densities typical of the wide variation found in brushless PM motors. To the extent that this data exists, it is usually proprietary. This is hardly surprising, considering the cost of obtaining it and its value once measured.

---

[102] See, for example, Carter G.W., *The Electromagnetic Field in its Engineering Aspects*, 2nd edition, Longman, 1967.

[103] For example, *Standard Test Method for Alternating-Current Magnetic Properties of Materials at Power Frequencies using Wattmeter-Ammeter-Voltmeter Method and 25-cm Epstein Frame*, ASTM A343/A343M-03, 2003. Many other equivalent IEC and national standards are published.

Core loss is invariably measured with a sinusoidal flux-density waveform; and since it is always *total* loss, any decomposition into components requires a curve-fitting procedure as well as a mathematical model of the curves that are to be fitted. A simple and much-used model is

$$W_c = C_h f B_{pk}^{\,n} + C_e f^2 B_{pk}^{\,2} \quad \text{[W/kg] or [W/lb]}. \qquad (12.6)$$

Two procedures will be described for extracting the two coefficients C_h, C_e and the exponent n from sinewave loss data. The first is quite simple and is used when only a single value of W_c is available. There is not enough data to determine all three parameters, so we *assume* a typical value for n in eqn. (12.6), such as $n = 1{\cdot}7$. We must also assume the fraction h of the total loss that is attributable to hysteresis; for example, $h = 0{\cdot}6$. Then

$$C_e = \frac{W_c(1 - h)}{f^2 B_{pk}^{\,2}} \quad \text{and} \quad C_h = \frac{h W_c}{B_{pk}^{\,n} f}. \qquad (12.7)$$

Example — Suppose $W_c = 8$ W/kg at 50 Hz, $B_{pk} = 1{\cdot}5$ T. Calculate C_e and C_h.

Assume $n = 1{\cdot}7$ and $h = 0{\cdot}6$. Then $C_e = 8 \times (1{-}0{\cdot}6)/(50 \times 1{\cdot}5)^2 = 0{\cdot}57 \times 10^{-3}$ W/Hz^2/T^2. $C_h = 0{\cdot}6 \times 8/(1{\cdot}5^{1{\cdot}7} \times 50) = 0{\cdot}048$ W/Hz/T^n.

The more elaborate method requires a complete set of curves of core-loss vs. frequency at different flux-densities. First divide eqn. (12.6) by f :

$$\frac{W_c}{f} = C_h B_{pk}^{\,n} + C_e f B_{pk}^{\,2} = D + Ef, \qquad (12.8)$$

where $D = C_h B_{pk}$ and $E = C_e B_{pk}^{\,2}$. This represents a straight-line graph of W_c/f vs. f, which can be matched to the test data by a least-squares process. Using a single graph of W_c vs. f at a fixed B_{pk}, C_e can be determined immediately from the gradient E divided by $B_{pk}^{\,2}$. To determine C_h and n it is necessary to plot the intercept D obtained from at least two W_c/f-vs.f graphs against B_{pk} on log paper, giving two simultaneous linear equations to be solved for C_h and n: thus

$$\begin{aligned} \log D_1 &= \log C_h + n \log B_{pk1} \\ \log D_2 &= \log C_h + n \log B_{pk2}. \end{aligned} \qquad (12.9)$$

The model in eqn. (12.6) is functionally limited in its ability to represent W_c accurately over a wide range of flux-density and frequency. Particularly when the coefficients are constant (as they will be, if obtained from a single application of the fitting procedures just described), significant errors may arise in any core-loss values calculated from the formula using values of B_{pk} and/or f that are far from the original fitted data.

One approach to extend the useful domain of eqn. (12.6) is to add a further term called the anomalous loss or excess loss, proportional to $f^{1\cdot5} B_{pk}{}^{1\cdot5}$; but a much more effective method developed by Ionel and Popescu[104] is to allow the coefficients to vary, with polynomial fitting functions *for the coefficients themselves.*

Even when the sinewave core-loss data is fitted accurately, there is a difficulty when the flux-density waveforms in the machine are not sinusoidal. One method for such cases is the modified model

$$W_c \;=\; C_h\, f\, B_{pk}{}^n + K_e \overline{\left[\frac{dB}{dt}\right]^2}, \tag{12.10}$$

in which the eddy-current component is taken to be proportional to the mean squared value of dB/dt over one cycle of the fundamental frequency, while the hysteresis loss component is unchanged. Another method is to decompose the flux-density waveform into harmonics and to apply the sinewave loss eqn. (12.6) (with variable coefficients if available) to each harmonic in turn; see Ionel (*op. cit.*). Objections can be raised on the grounds that the nonlinearity of the magnetic circuit precludes the use of Fourier analysis, but with well-fitted variable coefficients the results should be no worse than those obtained with constant coefficients in eqn. (12.6) or (12.10).

---

[104] Ionel D.M., Popescu M., McGilp M., Miller T.J.E., Dellinger S.J. and Heidemann R.J., *Computation of Core Losses in Electrical Machines Using Improved Models for Laminated Steel*, IEEE Transactions on Industry Applications, Vol. 43, No. 6, November/December 2007, pp. 1554-1564. This paper gives a review and bibliography of earlier works). The variable-coefficient method produces accurate reconstituted values for sinewave loss over a wide range of B_{pk} and f (0·05–2 T and 20–400 Hz). However it requires a large amount of accurately measured loss data and sophisticated data-reduction procedures; and even with that, the more complex variants of eqn. (12.6) require greater sophistication in machine-design programs. Nevertheless, these methods are important in designing for high efficiency.

The eddy-current loss coefficient K_e in eqn. (12.10) can be derived from the sinewave coefficient C_e if we set $B = B_{pk} \sin(2\pi f t)$ in eqn. (12.4). Then $(dB/dt)^2 = 4\pi^2 f^2 B_{pk}^2 \cos^2(2\pi f t)$, the mean value of which is $2\pi^2 f^2 B_{pk}^2$. For sinewave flux-density, eqns. (12.6) and (12.10) give the same result if

$$K_e = \frac{C_e}{2\pi^2}. \tag{12.11}$$

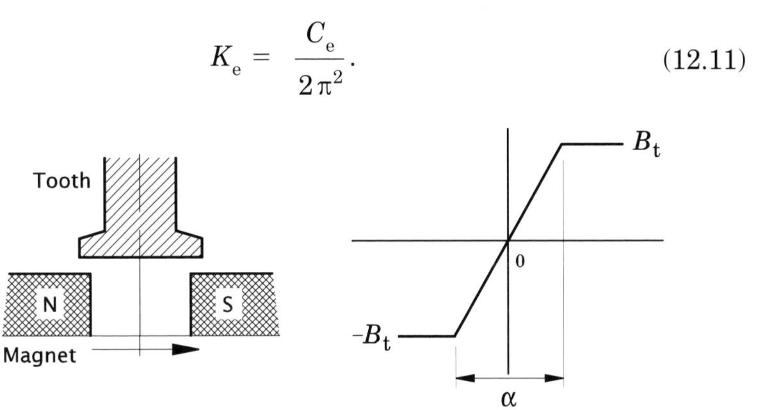

Fig. 12.2 Eddy-current loss in stator teeth

12.3.3 Calculation of core losses

A simple method for squarewave motors is to calculate dB/dt in the stator teeth assuming that the flux-reversals caused by the passing magnets are ramp-functions of extent α; Fig. 12.2. Then the eddy-current loss is calculated as

$$W_{Te} = \frac{4}{\pi} \frac{f^2 B_t^2 C_e}{\alpha} \quad \text{[W/kg]}, \tag{12.12}$$

Both B_t and α can be obtained from the tooth flux-density waveform (Chapter 4). The hysteresis loss in the teeth is computed using the peak flux-density B_t in eqn. (12.3). A similar process is used for the core losses in the yoke.[105] In this simple formulation only two flux-density waveforms are used; one for the teeth and one for the yoke.

[105] See Rabinovici R. and Miller T.J.E. *Eddy-current losses of surface-mounted permanent magnet motors*, IEE Proceedings, Electric Power Applications, Vol.144, Number 1, January 1997, pp.61-64; also Miller T.J.E. and Rabinovici R. *Back-EMF waveforms and core losses in brushless DC motors*. IEE Proceedings **141B,** 144-154. Also Slemon G.R. and Liu X., [1990].

A refinement is to obtain the flux-density waveforms in the teeth and yoke from search-coil measurements or finite-element calculations. If A_T is the cross-sectional area of a stator tooth and $\phi_T(\xi)$ is the waveform of the tooth flux as a function of rotor position ξ, the flux-density waveform in the stator teeth is given by

$$B_T(\xi) = \frac{\phi_T(\xi)}{A_T} \tag{12.13}$$

and if $e_T(\xi)$ is the EMF in a single-turn search-coil around the tooth,

$$\frac{dB_T}{dt} = \frac{e_T(\xi)}{A_T}. \tag{12.14}$$

Since $e_T(\xi)$ is often calculated as part of the process of calculating the phase EMF, it can be used at the same time for the eddy-current loss, and it is interesting to see the relationship between the EMF and the open-circuit core-loss. It follows from the instantaneous relationship in eqn. (12.14) that the eddy-current loss in the teeth is practically proportional to the mean squared phase EMF.

A similar relation is derived for the yoke, since

$$B_Y(\xi) = \frac{\phi_Y(\xi)}{A_Y} \quad \text{and} \quad \frac{dB_Y}{dt} = \frac{e_Y(\xi)}{A_Y} \tag{12.15}$$

where A_Y is the cross-section area of the yoke and e_Y is thc EMF waveform of a single-turn search coil wound around the yoke. Thus the mean squared value of e_Y can be used in the calculation of the yoke eddy-current losses.

All of these simple methods are very fast to calculate. Above them the next level of sophistication is to use the finite-element method to calculate the B-waveforms at thousands of points in the cross-section, one for each element, and to process each by means of eqn. (12.6) or (12.10). With a well-automated procedure this is not so time-consuming as might be expected, and gives a result of much better quality simply because the variation in the flux-density waveforms across the cross-section is taken into account. Even rotational losses can be allowed for by this method; see Ionel *et al*, (*op.cit.*).

12.4 Rotor eddy-current losses

12.4.1 Causes of rotor loss

In an ideal synchronous machine the field rotates in synchronism with the rotor, and the flux-density is time-invariant throughout the rotor cross-section. There is no tendency for eddy-currents to flow anywhere in the rotor. There are no losses in the magnets, the rotor body, or the shaft. Such ideal conditions would exist at constant speed in a machine with smooth cylindrical surfaces (no slotting); with sine-distributed windings; and with balanced polyphase sinusoidal currents.

Eddy-currents are induced in practice by imperfections or departures from the ideal synchronous machine. The main ones are introduced as follows.

Space-harmonics in the stator ampere-conductor distribution and **time-harmonics in the stator current waveform** (including **PWM-harmonics**) combine to produce asynchronous field components that rotate forwards or backwards relative to the rotor. In general the number of these asynchronous components can be several dozens. (See Tables 12.1–12.6).

For example in motors with squarewave drive, the stator ampere-conductor distribution remains fixed in space for successive intervals, typically of 60° duration. As the rotor moves relative to the fixed "armature reaction" field, EMFs and eddy-currents may be induced in it. Again, commutation of the current from one phase to another is, in effect, a voltage step at the stator terminals, inducing a "transformer" EMF in closed paths in the rotor. The resulting eddy-currents are transient but repetitive, resulting in a steady-state loss.

Even when the phase currents are sinusoidal, any **imbalance** can produce a **negative-sequence** component of the armature-reaction field, which rotates backwards and induces EMFs in the rotor at twice the fundamental frequency. This is akin to the harmonic losses.

The overall **permeance of the magnetic circuit may be modulated** at the **slot-passing frequency**. The **permeance harmonics** produce eddy-currents in the rotor, as well as cogging torque and "slot ripple" in the EMF waveform.

Stator slot-openings modulate the airgap flux-distribution by creating "dips" which rotate backwards at synchronous speed relative to the rotor. They produce pools of motion-induced eddy-currents that remain stationary in space, roughly opposite the slot openings.

The harmonic losses can be analyzed by solving the electromagnetic field excited by time-harmonics in the current waveform acting together with the space-harmonics in the winding distribution. If the induced currents are assumed not to affect the stator current waveform, the field and circuit analyses can be separated, simplifying matters greatly. This solution is called "current-forced", and is adopted throughout this chapter.

For surface-magnet machines, the solution for harmonic losses can be developed by solving the complex diffusion equation in a multi-layer cylindrical structure, including the shaft and any retaining sleeve.[106] A complete simulation of the machine and drive is required to obtain the time-harmonics of the current waveforms. Further, a harmonic analysis of the winding is required to obtain the space harmonics of the ampere-conductor distribution. This method is extended by means of an equivalent harmonic current sheet to give a unified treatment of losses due to the permeance harmonics and slot-opening modulation of the airgap field.[107] Approximate modifications are applied to the basic 2-dimensional result, to account for finite length and any segmentation of magnets in the axial and circumferential directions. Several original methods are described.

For interior-magnet machines the solution of the complex diffusion equation is too difficult, and a different approach is used, based on the frequency-response of the complex synchronous inductance in the d-axis. An important by-product of this analysis is the calculation of the subtransient reactance and time-constant, which are needed in the calculation of sudden short-circuit faults; (Chapter 9). The frequency-response method is also developed for surface-magnet machines from the complex diffusion equation.

---

[106] Miller TJE and Lawrenson PJ, *Penetration of transient magnetic fields through conducting cylindrical structures, with particular reference to superconducting A.C. machines*, Proc. IEE, Vol. 123, No. 5, May 1976, pp. 437-443.

[107] Lawrenson PJ, Reece P and Ralph MC, *Tooth-ripple losses in solid poles*, Proc. IEE., Vol. 113, No. 4, April 1966, pp. 657-662.

12.4.1.1 Loss mechanisms in the magnets themselves

Eddy-current losses are due to the variation of flux-density in the magnets.[108]

Dimensional analysis has been used to help understand the behaviour of eddy-currents, and the commonest example of this is to calculate the ratio between a key dimension h of the eddy-current conductor and the so-called skin-depth,

$$\delta = \sqrt{\frac{2}{\omega \mu \sigma}} \quad [\mathrm{m}]. \tag{12.16}$$

For example, consider a permanent magnet with a conductivity of $0{\cdot}6 \times 10^6$ S/m[109] and relative recoil permeability $\mu_{rec} = 1{\cdot}05$, operating in a field that alternates with a frequency 1 kHz, (which is typical of PWM ripple in the current waveform, or the slot-passing frequency at normal speeds). Then

$$\begin{aligned} \delta &= \sqrt{\frac{2}{2\pi \times 1000 \times 1{\cdot}05 \times 4\pi \times 10^{-7} \times 0{\cdot}6 \times 10^6}} \quad (12.17) \\ &= 0{\cdot}020 \ [\mathrm{m}] \end{aligned}$$

or 20 mm, i.e., approximately 0·8". It is tempting to compare δ with the length of the magnet in the direction of magnetization, L_m; but in many cases the magnet *width* and *axial length* are more appropriate "key dimensions"; (see p. 643). If the ratio h/δ is < 1, it is apt to say that the eddy-currents are *resistance-limited*. This important term is examined in detail.

---

[108] The basic theory is presented in several books (for example, Lammeraner and Štafl, or Stoll. The engineering analysis of eddy-currents is mathematically delicate even in idealized 2-dimensional models, and very few 3D effects can be fully analyzed by classical methods. 3D effects include the effects of "finite-length" and of shapes other than simple rectangular blocks or continuous cylinders. Of course finite-element methods can be used in such cases, but they are slow and expensive, and not easily verified.

[109] This conductivity can also be expressed as approximately 1% of the conductivity of OFHC copper. NDFEB magnets have typical conductivities in this range. Sm_2Co_{17} magnets have higher conductivities typically around 2% OFHC.

12.4.1.2 Resistance- or inductance-limited eddy-currents?

The essential properties of resistance-limited eddy-currents are that

1. they have negligible effect on the field, and
2. the associated losses decrease if the conductivity of the magnets decreases.

If the ratio h/δ is greater than 1, we are inclined to expect the eddy-currents in the magnets to be *inductance limited*. The essential properties are that

3. the eddy-currents produce a reaction field which tends to oppose the exciting field; and
4. the eddy-current losses increase if the conductivity of the magnets decreases;

The best way to prevent eddy-currents in magnets is to use magnets with zero or very low conductivity (such as polymer-bonded or ferrite magnets), but this may not be possible if other properties take precedence. This being so, it becomes important to understand the factors that cause the eddy-currents so that other aspects of the design can be adjusted to minimize them.

Inductance-limited eddy-currents have the effect of *screening*: in other words, they tend to oppose the penetration of flux, attenuating the field on the side of the conducting component that is remote from the high-frequency source of excitation.

The "rule-of-thumb" test using h/δ is an oversimplification. It was shown by Stoll and Hammond that the behaviour of eddy-currents depends on other dimensions and dimensionless ratios; for example, the pole-pitch and the permeability of the eddy-current conductor. In some cases it is not sufficient to compare a single key dimension with δ, and both widths of the magnet measured in a plane normal to the direction of the flux must be compared; (see p. 642).

It can be said that the determination of eddy-current loss requires a detailed calculation by the most powerful methods available, and it should not be left to rule-of-thumb approximations.

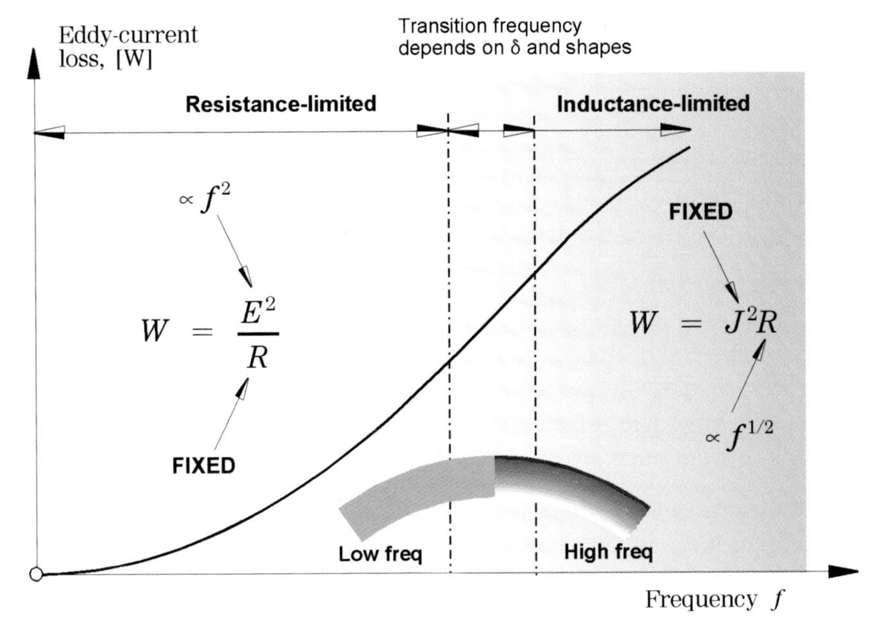

Fig. 12.3 Eddy-current loss vs. frequency

Resistance-limited eddy-currents arise at low frequency and are limited by the resistivity of the material. Although they may cause significant losses, they have little effect on the magnetic field that is driving them. As indicated in Fig. 12.3, they are driven by a dB/dt that is unaffected by the eddy-currents themselves, and the induced electric field E produces a current-density J that is inversely proportional to the resistivity of the conducting material.

At a specific frequency ω, dB/dt can be expressed as ωB, where B is the peak value of a sinusoidal variation at that frequency. Accordingly the losses produced by these eddy-currents can be characterized by a function of the form $(\omega B)^2/R$, where R expresses the resistance of the eddy-current path.

In short, resistance-limited eddy-current losses are proportional to the square of the exciting frequency, and they can be reduced by increasing the resistivity. If the resistivity cannot be increased, the resistance of the eddy-current paths can be increased by lamination or segmentation, as we shall see.

As the frequency increases, the eddy-currents increase in magnitude and their phase tends to shift such that at very high frequency they form a flux-screen that prevents the original B-field from penetrating into the conducting material. The total eddy-current required to perform this screening effect needs to be just sufficient to annul the internal field in the material, and it tends to become constant as the frequency increases.

At the same time the resistance of the eddy-current path increases with frequency as the eddy-currents are concentrated into a *skin depth* of the form stated in eqn. (12.16). If the path resistance is inversely proportional to δ, the inductance-limited eddy-current losses will have the form I^2R, where I is independent of frequency and R is proportional to $\sqrt{\omega}$, the square-root of frequency.

This implies that increasing the conductivity will decrease the losses, but this is true only if the eddy-currents are inductance-limited. Higher conductivity will tend to make them even more inductance-limited and will tend to shift the behaviour towards that of a perfectly conducting AC flux screen.

It can be said that the preferred means of limiting eddy-current losses is to use a high resistivity or a segmented structure to keep the eddy-currents resistance-limited, except that in components used specifically as flux-screens the resistivity should be minimized.

12.4.1.3 Hysteresis loss in magnets

Hysteresis losses are well known in electrical steels, but rarely mentioned in connection with permanent magnets. Yet in 2005 Fukuma *et al* published data in which they recorded hysteresis losses "twice as great" as the eddy-current loss in a permanent-magnet.[110]

Fukuma measured hysteresis losses of approximately 1·3 W/kg at 50 Hz with a field variation of 0·1 T in a fully magnetized sample of NEOMAX-44H.[111]

---

[110] Fukuma A., Kanazawa S., Miyagi D., and Takahashi N., *Investigation of AC Loss of Permanent Magnet of SPM Motor Considering Hysteresis and Eddy-Current Losses*, IEEE Trans. on Magnetics 41 No. 5, 2005, pp. 1964-1967.

[111] Fukuma gives the conductivity as $6{\cdot}9 \times 10^5$ S/m, that is, 1·2% of the conductivity of OFHC copper.

The density of the magnet was 7500 kg/m^3, so this corresponds to a minor loop area (Fig. 12.4) of

$$a = W_h \times \frac{\rho}{f} = 1{\cdot}3 \times \frac{7500}{50} = 195 \ \text{J/m}^3. \quad (12.18)$$

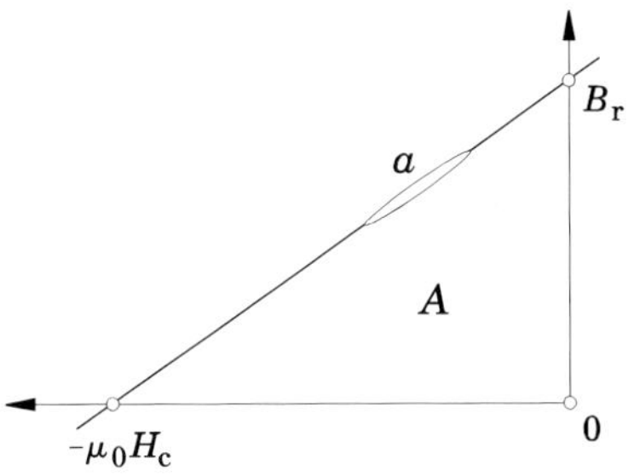

Fig. 12.4 Magnet hysteresis loss

With a remanence B_r of 1·26 T and relative recoil permeability μ_{rec} of 1·05, the area A under the demagnetization curve is given by

$$A = \frac{1}{2}\frac{B_r^2}{\mu_{rec}\mu_0} = \frac{1}{2}\frac{1{\cdot}26^2}{1{\cdot}05\mu_0} = 601{\cdot}6 \times 10^3 \ \text{J/m}^3. \quad (12.19)$$

The ratio $x = a/A$ gives an idea of the order of this effect:

$$\frac{a}{A} = \frac{195}{601{\cdot}6 \times 10^3} = 0{\cdot}00032. \quad (12.20)$$

In other words, a hysteresis loop of only 0·03% of the area under the demagnetization curve is enough to produce hysteresis losses of 1·3 W/kg at 50 Hz. In general we can write

$$W = x\frac{B_r^2 f}{2\mu_{rec}\mu_0\rho} \ \text{W/kg}. \quad (12.21)$$

Fukuma surmised that the hysteresis loss was proportional to the square of the variation in flux-density. In his measurement of 1·3 W/kg at 50 Hz, the flux-density variation was 0·1T throughout the magnet. In his test motor, such a large variation occurs only near the surface of the magnets and not through their entire volume.

These figures suggest that the hysteresis loss in the magnets will be generally small, but not completely negligible, and it will be as well to check it in cases where there is an appreciable variation in the magnet flux-density especially at high frequencies.

12.4.2 Harmonic losses in surface-magnet machines

The analysis begins with a purely 2-dimensional system along well established lines.[112] This includes exterior- and interior-rotor motors in which the magnet is a continuous cylinder. Interior-rotor machines may have a conductive retaining sleeve on the rotor; (see Fig. 12.6).

The eddy-currents are excited by space- and time-harmonics in the stator ampere-conductor distribution; or by negative-sequence currents flowing under unbalanced conditions. The excitation is represented by a current-sheet having an arbitrary number of pole-pairs and an arbitrary frequency of rotation.

Losses due to "permeance harmonics" caused by slotting are incorporated in the general analysis using the method of Lawrenson and Ralph [*op. cit.*], in which the modulation of the airgap field is represented by an equivalent harmonic current-sheet whose fundamental wavelength is equal to the slot-pitch; this current-sheet rotates backwards relative to the rotor at twice synchronous speed.

The conventional 2-dimensional solution is presented in detail for an exterior-rotor motor with 2 regions. The solution for an interior-rotor motor with 4 or 6 regions is similar.[113] The solutions is checked against independent Laplacian solutions for zero frequency.[114] Finite-element calculations are also used for this purpose.

Laminated steel components are assumed to have infinite permeability, as is normal in this type of analysis. This makes it possible to represent such regions (particularly the stator core) by surfaces at which the tangential field strength is defined by a current-sheet representing the stator ampere-conductors. Were this not so, the solution would require more regions and the algebraic complexity would increase with little improvement in the results.

---

[112] See Miller and Lawrenson, *op. cit.*

[113] Details of this solution (and the Cartesian solution) are given in *SPEED's Electric Machines*, Chapter 2.

[114] Hughes A. and Miller T.J.E., *Analysis of fields and inductances in air–cored and iron–cored synchronous machines*, Proceedings IEE, Vol. 124, No. 2, February 1977, pp. 121-131.

The screening effect of a conducting rotor sleeve is a by-product of the general analysis.

Methods are then introduced to deal with the effects of **finite axial length** and **segmentation** of the magnets in both the circumferential and axial directions.

The old method of **flux-dip-sweeping** published by Robinson et al and by Russell and Norsworthy in the 1950s is presented as an alternative to Lawrenson's method. Originally developed to calculate losses in a cylindrical can fixed to the stator bore or the rotor surface, this method assumes that the eddy-currents are resistance-limited. It is also limited in application to very *thin* cans, and is therefore of little use for calculating magnet losses. Nevertheless, the method is here improved as far as possible by introducing an improved method of calculating the flux dips.[115] The method is especially useful for the calculation of losses in rotor and stator cans.

A limitation of the approach described here is that the methods are applied independently, which means that any interaction of harmonics from difference sources is not taken into account. However, the methods can be studied separately, and in a computer calculation switched on or off, making it possible to assess the relative importance of the different loss-producing phenomena.

The geometry of the surface-magnet machine analyzed by these methods is shown in Fig. 12.5. The solution domain lies between r_S and r_B. If the rotor shell (3) is conductive, the solution domain can be extended to lie between r_S and r_H, giving a 3-region model.

Fig. 12.6 shows the geometry of a 4-region model of an interior-rotor machine that can be analyzed by a similar method. The magnet sits directly on the shaft, and both the magnet and the shaft may be conductive. The solution domain lies between r_H and r_S. Full details are given in *SPEED's Electric Machines*.

The general solution will be developed first, then applied to the model of Fig. 12.5 in detail.

---

[115] Zhu Z.Q., Ng K., Schofield N. and Howe D., *Improved analytical modelling of rotor eddy current loss in brushless machines equipped with surface-mounted permanent magnets*, IEE Proc.-Electr. Power Appl., Vol. 151, No. 6, November 2004, pp. 641-650.

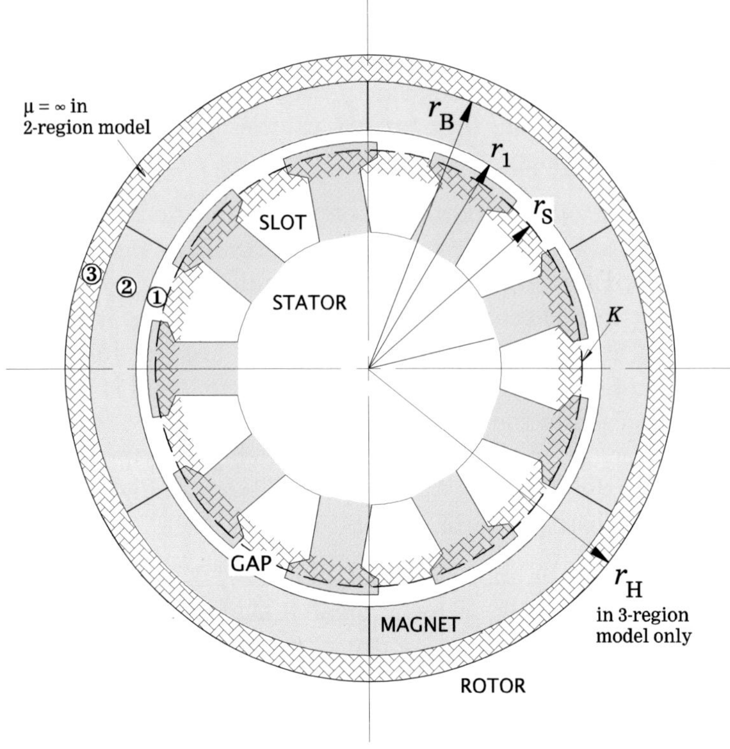

Fig. 12.5 2- or 3-region model of 9-slot 6-pole exterior-rotor motor

12.4.2.1 Solution of the Complex Diffusion Equation

Starting from the vector potential equation

$$\text{curl}\ \mathbf{A} = \mathbf{B} \tag{12.22}$$

and taking the curl of both sides, we get

$$\text{curl}\ \text{curl}\ \mathbf{A} = \text{curl}\ \mathbf{B}. \tag{12.23}$$

If $\mathbf{J}$ is current-density we have

$$\text{curl}\ \mathbf{H} = \mathbf{J} \tag{12.24}$$

and in linear materials $\mathbf{B} = \mu\mathbf{H}$, so curl $\mathbf{B} = \mu$ curl $\mathbf{H} = \mu\mathbf{J}$. Hence

$$\text{curl}\ \text{curl}\ \mathbf{A} = \mu\mathbf{J}. \tag{12.25}$$

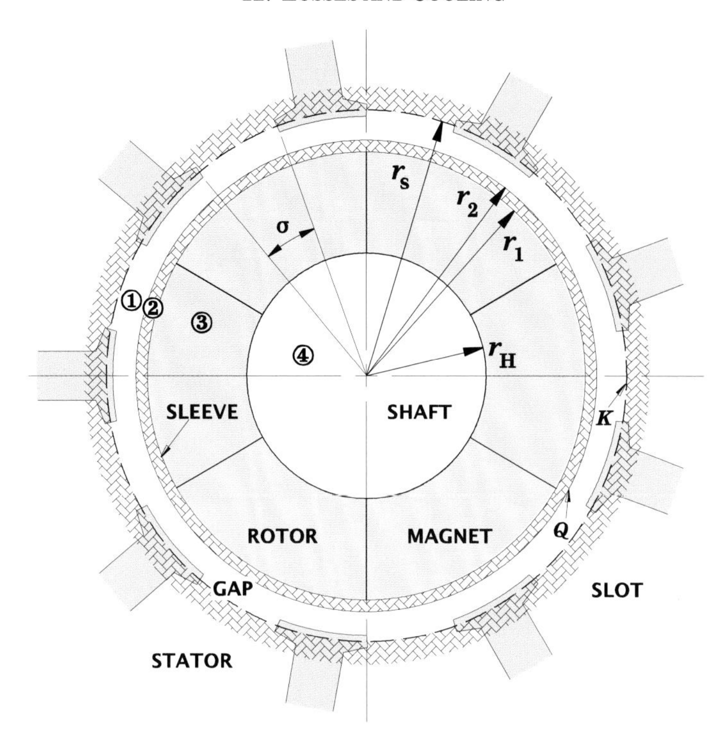

Fig. 12.6 4-region model of 9-slot 6-pole machine

The current can be forced from an external circuit, or it can be induced in closed loops as *eddy*-current. In the first case no change is needed in the curl curl **A** equation, but for eddy-currents we write

$$\mathbf{J} = \sigma \mathbf{E} = -\sigma \frac{\partial \mathbf{A}}{\partial t}. \tag{12.26}$$

Hence

$$\text{curl curl } \mathbf{A} = -\mu \sigma \frac{\partial \mathbf{A}}{\partial t}. \tag{12.27}$$

In cartesian coordinates we have

$$\text{curl curl } \mathbf{A} = \text{grad div } \mathbf{A} - \text{grad div } \mathbf{A} = -\nabla^2 \mathbf{A} \tag{12.28}$$

provided div $\mathbf{A} = 0$, which is normally assumed. Hence

$$\nabla^2 \mathbf{A} = \mu \sigma \frac{\partial \mathbf{A}}{\partial t}. \tag{12.29}$$

In cylindrical coordinates curl curl **A** is more complicated, but if it is assumed that **A** has only a z-component A, the equation simplifies to the so-called two-dimensional diffusion equation:

$$\frac{\partial^2 A}{\partial r^2} + \frac{1}{r}\frac{\partial A}{\partial r} + \frac{1}{r^2}\frac{\partial^2 A}{\partial \theta^2} = \mu \sigma \frac{\partial A}{\partial t}. \tag{12.30}$$

For regions carrying forced current-density **J**, the right-hand side is replaced by $-\mu\mathbf{J}$.

A well known solution (by separation of variables) takes the form:

$$A(r,\theta,t) = \mathbf{A}(r) \cos p\theta \, e^{j\omega t} \tag{12.31}$$

for stationary pulsating fields; or

$$A(r,\theta,t) = \mathbf{A}(r) \, e^{j(\omega t - p\theta)} \tag{12.32}$$

for rotating fields. In both cases **A** is complex and is written in boldface to indicate that it is essentially a phasor quantity, giving[116]

$$\frac{d^2\mathbf{A}}{dr^2} + \frac{1}{r}\frac{d\mathbf{A}}{dr} - \left[\frac{p^2}{r^2} + j\omega\mu\sigma\right]\mathbf{A} = 0. \tag{12.33}$$

This is the modified Bessel equation, with solution[117]

$$\mathbf{A} = \mathbf{c}_1 I_p(j^{1/2} r/d) + \mathbf{c}_2 K_p(j^{1/2} r/d) \quad \text{with} \quad d = \frac{1}{\sqrt{\omega\mu\sigma}}. \tag{12.34}$$

I_p and K_p are modified Bessel functions of the first and second kind respectively, while $\mathbf{c}_1$ and $\mathbf{c}_2$ are complex constants. The solution can also be written in terms of the Kelvin functions with real arguments defined by the identities described in *SPEED's Electric Machines*.

Note that the characteristic length d is equal to $1/\sqrt{2}$ times the conventional "skin depth".

---

[116] In some technical papers and books the coefficient of **A** in eqn. (12.33) appears as $(p^2/r^2 - j\omega\mu\sigma)$, owing to the use of $e^{-j\omega t}$ instead of $e^{+j\omega t}$.

[117] McLachlan N. W., *Bessel Functions for Engineers*, Oxford University Press, 1934.

In non-conducting regions $\sigma = 0$ and eqn. (12.33) degenerates to the Laplace equation

$$\frac{d^2\mathbf{A}}{dr^2} + \frac{1}{r}\frac{d\mathbf{A}}{dr} - \frac{p^2}{r^2}\mathbf{A} = 0 \qquad (12.35)$$

with solution

$$\mathbf{A} = \mathbf{c}_3 r^p + \mathbf{c}_4 r^{-p}. \qquad (12.36)$$

In regions carrying forced current the equation is Poisson's equation

$$\frac{d^2\mathbf{A}}{dr^2} + \frac{1}{r}\frac{d\mathbf{A}}{dr} - \frac{p^2}{r^2}\mathbf{A} = -\mu\mathbf{J}. \qquad (12.37)$$

The solution is then extended with an additional term in $\mu\mathbf{J}$: if $p = 2$,

$$\mathbf{A} = \mathbf{c}_3 r^p + \mathbf{c}_4 r^{-p} - \frac{\mu\mathbf{J}}{4} r^2 \ln r \; ; \qquad (12.38)$$

otherwise

$$\mathbf{A} = \mathbf{c}_3 r^p + \mathbf{c}_4 r^{-p} + \frac{\mu\mathbf{J}}{p^2 - 4} r^2. \qquad (12.39)$$

While the basic solution is expressed in terms of vector potential **A**, we also need expressions for the other field vectors **B**, **H**, **E** and **J**, which are needed to calculate practical quantities. Also, in a multiple-region problem, the boundary conditions between regions are expressed in terms of **B** and **H**. Thus

$$\overline{\mathbf{B}} = \text{curl}\ \overline{\mathbf{A}} \quad \text{or} \quad \mathbf{B}_r = \frac{1}{r}\frac{\partial \mathbf{A}}{\partial \theta}; \quad \mathbf{B}_\theta = -\frac{\partial \mathbf{A}}{\partial r} \qquad (12.40)$$

where the overline indicates a true vector and boldface continues to indicate a complex phasor component. Finally

$$\overline{\mathbf{E}} = -\frac{\partial \overline{\mathbf{A}}}{\partial t}; \quad \text{or} \quad \mathbf{E} = -\,j\omega\mathbf{A}. \qquad (12.41)$$

In conducting regions the eddy-current density is

$$\mathbf{J} = \sigma\mathbf{E} = -\,j\omega\sigma\mathbf{A}. \qquad (12.42)$$

The power loss in conducting regions can be determined by integrating J^2/σ or $\mathbf{EJ}^*$ over the region volume. For a continuous conducting cylinder with radii r_1 and r_2, this can be shown to be

$$W = \frac{2\pi}{2}\omega^2\sigma\int_{r_1}^{r_2}\mathbf{AA}^* r\,dr \qquad \text{W/m}_z \tag{12.43}$$

Alternatively the radial component of Poynting's vector $\overline{\mathbf{E}} \times \overline{\mathbf{H}}^*$ can be used to give the difference between the average power losses over the inner and outer surfaces of the cylinder,

$$W = \frac{1}{2}\,\mathrm{Re}\left[-\mathrm{j}\omega\mathbf{A}\mathbf{H}_\theta^*\right]_{r_1}^{r_2} \qquad \text{W/m}^2.$$

The sign of W indicates whether the power flow is radially inwards or outwards.

12.4.2.2 Exterior-rotor machine; 2-region model

The analysis is performed first for the exterior-rotor machine with a non-conducting rotor shell, Fig. 12.5. This is the simplest model, because it has only two regions.

In region 1 (the airgap),

$$\begin{aligned}\mathbf{A} &= \mathbf{c}_1 r^p + \mathbf{c}_2 r^{-p};\\ \mathbf{B}_r &= -\mathrm{j}\frac{p}{r}\left[\mathbf{c}_1 r^p + \mathbf{c}_2 r^{-p}\right];\\ \mathbf{H}_\theta &= -\frac{p}{\mu_0}\left[\mathbf{c}_1 r^{p-1} - \mathbf{c}_2 r^{-p-1}\right].\end{aligned} \tag{12.45}$$

The magnet may be conducting or non-conducting. If it is conducting, then in region 3 we have

$$\begin{aligned}\mathbf{A} &= \mathbf{c}_3 I_p(\mathbf{z}) + \mathbf{c}_4 K_p(\mathbf{z});\\ \mathbf{B}_r &= -\mathrm{j}\frac{p}{r}\left[\mathbf{c}_3 I_p(\mathbf{z}) + \mathbf{c}_4 K_p(\mathbf{z})\right];\\ \mathbf{H}_\theta &= -\frac{\mathrm{j}^{1/2}}{\mu_M d_M}\left[\mathbf{c}_3 I_p'(\mathbf{z}) + \mathbf{c}_4 K_p'(\mathbf{z})\right]\end{aligned} \tag{12.46}$$

where

$$\mathbf{z} = \mathrm{j}^{1/2}\frac{r}{d_\mathrm{M}} \quad \text{and} \quad d_\mathrm{M} = \frac{1}{\sqrt{\omega\mu_\mathrm{M}\sigma_\mathrm{M}}} = \frac{\delta_\mathrm{M}}{\sqrt{2}}. \tag{12.47}$$

δ_M is recognized as the skin depth in the magnet material at the radian frequency ω. μ_M is the magnet permeability in H/m and σ_M is the magnet conductivity in S/m. The functions I_p and K_p are modified Bessel functions of the first and second kinds respectively. When they are differentiated with respect to r, as is necessary to determine $\mathbf{H}_\theta = -(1/\mu)\,\partial\mathbf{A}/\partial r$, the additional factor $\mathrm{j}^{1/2}/d_\mathrm{M}$ emerges.

When the magnet is non-conducting we have the simpler Laplacian solution in region 2 :

$$\begin{aligned} \mathbf{A} &= \mathbf{c}_3 r^{p} + \mathbf{c}_4 r^{-p}; \\ \mathbf{B}_\mathrm{r} &= -\mathrm{j}\frac{p}{r}\left[\mathbf{c}_3 r^{p} + \mathbf{c}_4 r^{-p}\right]; \\ \mathbf{H}_\theta &= -\frac{p}{\mu_0}\left[\mathbf{c}_3 r^{p-1} - \mathbf{c}_4 r^{-p-1}\right]. \end{aligned} \tag{12.48}$$

The complex coefficients $\mathbf{c}_1$, $\mathbf{c}_2$, $\mathbf{c}_3$ and $\mathbf{c}_4$ must be found by solving four simultaneous algebraic equations obtained from the boundary conditions. These will be written for the case of a conducting magnet, but the results are formally applicable when the magnet is non-conducting, as will be seen.

At $r = r_\mathrm{s}$ we have a boundary with an infinitely permeable material, on which the current sheet K gives rise to a discontinuity in the tangential magnetic field $\mathbf{H}_\theta$. However, $\mathbf{H}_\theta = 0$ inside the stator, since its permeability is deemed to be infinite. Therefore the boundary condition is

$$-\frac{p}{\mu_0}\left[\mathbf{c}_1 r_\mathrm{s}^{\,p-1} - \mathbf{c}_2 r_\mathrm{s}^{\,-p-1}\right] = K. \tag{12.49}$$

Across the boundary at $r = r_1$, $\mathbf{H}_\theta$ and $\mathbf{B}_\mathrm{r}$ are both continuous. Thus if $\mathbf{z}_{1\mathrm{M}} = r_1/d_\mathrm{M}$ we have

$$-\frac{p}{\mu_0}\left[\mathbf{c}_1 r_1^{\,p-1} - \mathbf{c}_2 r_1^{\,-p-1}\right] = -\frac{\mathrm{j}^{1/2}}{\mu_\mathrm{M} d_\mathrm{M}}\left[\mathbf{c}_3 I_\mathrm{p}{}'(\mathbf{z}_{1\mathrm{M}}) + \mathbf{c}_4 K_\mathrm{p}{}'(\mathbf{z}_{1\mathrm{M}})\right];$$

and

$$-\frac{jp}{r_1}\left[\mathbf{c}_1 r_1^{\,p} + \mathbf{c}_2 r_1^{\,-p}\right] = -\frac{jp}{r_1}\left[\mathbf{c}_3 I_p(\mathbf{z}_{1M}) + \mathbf{c}_4 K_p(\mathbf{z}_{1M})\right]. \quad (12.51)$$

Finally at $r = r_B$ we have an infinitely permeable boundary at which $\mathbf{H}_\theta = 0$:

$$-\frac{j^{1/2}}{\mu_M d_M}\left[\mathbf{c}_3 I_p'(\mathbf{z}_{BM}) + \mathbf{c}_4 K_p'(\mathbf{z}_{BM})\right] = 0,$$

where $\mathbf{z}_{BM} = r_B/d_M$. Now let

$$\boldsymbol{a}_1 = -p r_s^{\,p-1}; \quad \boldsymbol{a}_2 = p r_s^{\,-p-1}; \quad \boldsymbol{a}_3 = p r_1^{\,p-1} \quad \boldsymbol{a}_4 = -p r_1^{\,-p-1};$$

$$\boldsymbol{a}_7 = r_1^{\,p}; \quad \boldsymbol{a}_8 = r_1^{\,-p};$$

and let

$$\boldsymbol{a}_5 = -\frac{j^{1/2}}{d_M}\frac{\mu_0}{\mu_M} I_p'(\mathbf{z}_{1M}); \quad \boldsymbol{a}_6 = -\frac{j^{1/2}}{d_M}\frac{\mu_0}{\mu_M} K_p'(\mathbf{z}_{1M});$$

$$\boldsymbol{a}_9 = -\, I_p(\mathbf{z}_{1M}); \quad \boldsymbol{a}_{10} = -\, K_p(\mathbf{z}_{1M});$$

$$\boldsymbol{a}_{11} = -\frac{j^{1/2}}{d_M} I_p'(\mathbf{z}_{BM}); \quad \boldsymbol{a}_{12} = -\frac{j^{1/2}}{d_M} K_p'(\mathbf{z}_{BM}).$$

When the magnet is non-conducting, we have instead

$$\boldsymbol{a}_5 = -p r_1^{\,p-1}\frac{\mu_0}{\mu_M}; \quad \boldsymbol{a}_6 = p r_1^{\,-p-1}\frac{\mu_0}{\mu_M}; \quad \boldsymbol{a}_9 = -r_1^{\,p};$$

$$\boldsymbol{a}_{10} = -r_1^{\,-p}; \quad \boldsymbol{a}_{11} = p r_B^{\,p-1}; \quad \boldsymbol{a}_{12} = -\, p r_B^{\,-p-1}.$$

The boundary conditions now become

$$\begin{aligned}
&\boldsymbol{a}_1\mathbf{c}_1 + \boldsymbol{a}_2\mathbf{c}_2 = \mu_0 K;\\
&\boldsymbol{a}_3\mathbf{c}_1 + \boldsymbol{a}_4\mathbf{c}_2 + \boldsymbol{a}_5\mathbf{c}_3 + \boldsymbol{a}_6\mathbf{c}_4 = 0;\\
&\boldsymbol{a}_7\mathbf{c}_1 + \boldsymbol{a}_8\mathbf{c}_2 + \boldsymbol{a}_9\mathbf{c}_3 + \boldsymbol{a}_{10}\mathbf{c}_4 = 0;\\
&\boldsymbol{a}_{11}\mathbf{c}_3 + \boldsymbol{a}_{12}\mathbf{c}_4 = 0.
\end{aligned}$$

The coefficients $\boldsymbol{a}$ being known, these complex boundary-condition equations can be solved for the unknown coefficients $\mathbf{c}$ by simple algebra. From the last equation,

$$\mathbf{c}_4 = -\boldsymbol{a}_{11}\mathbf{c}_3/\boldsymbol{a}_{12},$$

so the second and third equations become

$$\boldsymbol{a}_3\mathbf{c}_1 + \boldsymbol{a}_4\mathbf{c}_2 + \left[\boldsymbol{a}_5 - \boldsymbol{a}_6\boldsymbol{a}_{11}/\boldsymbol{a}_{12}\right]\mathbf{c}_3 = 0;$$

$$\boldsymbol{a}_7\mathbf{c}_1 + \boldsymbol{a}_8\mathbf{c}_2 + \left[\boldsymbol{a}_9 - \boldsymbol{a}_{10}\boldsymbol{a}_{11}/\boldsymbol{a}_{12}\right]\mathbf{c}_3 = 0.$$

Let

$$\boldsymbol{b}_1 = \left[\boldsymbol{a}_5 - \boldsymbol{a}_6\boldsymbol{a}_{11}/\boldsymbol{a}_{12}\right]; \qquad \boldsymbol{b}_2 = \left[\boldsymbol{a}_9 - \boldsymbol{a}_{10}\boldsymbol{a}_{11}/\boldsymbol{a}_{12}\right].$$

Then

$$\mathbf{c}_3 = -\boldsymbol{a}_7\mathbf{c}_1/\boldsymbol{b}_2 - \boldsymbol{a}_8\mathbf{c}_2/\boldsymbol{b}_2$$

with which

$$\left[\boldsymbol{a}_3 - \boldsymbol{b}_1\boldsymbol{a}_7/\boldsymbol{b}_2\right]\mathbf{c}_1 + \left[\boldsymbol{a}_4 - \boldsymbol{b}_1\boldsymbol{a}_8/\boldsymbol{b}_2\right]\mathbf{c}_2 = 0.$$

Now let

$$\boldsymbol{b}_3 = \left[\boldsymbol{a}_3 - \boldsymbol{b}_1\boldsymbol{a}_7/\boldsymbol{b}_2\right]; \qquad \boldsymbol{b}_4 = \left[\boldsymbol{a}_4 - \boldsymbol{b}_1\boldsymbol{a}_8/\boldsymbol{b}_2\right].$$

Then

$$\boldsymbol{b}_3\mathbf{c}_1 + \boldsymbol{b}_4\mathbf{c}_2 = 0.$$

This can be written

$$\mathbf{c}_2 = -\boldsymbol{b}_3\mathbf{c}_1/\boldsymbol{b}_4.$$

Hence the first boundary condition can be written

$$\left[\boldsymbol{a}_1 - \boldsymbol{a}_2\boldsymbol{b}_3/\boldsymbol{b}_4\right]\mathbf{c}_1 = \mu_0 K,$$

from which

$$\mathbf{c}_1 = \frac{\mu_0 K}{\left[\boldsymbol{a}_1 - \boldsymbol{a}_2\boldsymbol{b}_3/\boldsymbol{b}_4\right]}.$$

We can now work back through the formulas to calculate $\mathbf{c}_2$, $\mathbf{c}_3$ and $\mathbf{c}_4$, and this completes the solution.

Checking the solution under zero-frequency conditions—The solution for $\omega = 0$ can be checked by referring to the complete solution given by Hughes and Miller [*op. cit.*] for the Laplacian field. The excitation is in the form of a current sheet at the radius r_0 :

$$K = \frac{2T_{\mathrm{ph}}k_{\mathrm{w1}}}{\pi r_0} i \sin p\theta \qquad \mathrm{A/m} \tag{12.67}$$

where T_{ph} is the number of turns in series per phase, k_{w1} is the fundamental winding factor, and i is the instantaneous phase current. (Only one phase is active). In Fig. 12.7, a 4-pole exterior-rotor motor is represented by two regions with infinitely permeable boundaries at r_{S} and r_{B}, as in Fig. 12.5. The exciting current sheet is located on the stator surface; i.e., $r_0 = r_{\mathrm{S}}$. Then at any radius r in the magnet region 2, we have simplified expressions for B_{r} and B_θ :

$$\begin{aligned} B_{\mathrm{r}} &= \frac{\mu_0 K}{2}\left[\frac{r_{\mathrm{S}}}{r}\right]^{p+1} \times \frac{2\left[1 + (r/r_{\mathrm{B}})^{2p}\right]}{1 - (r_{\mathrm{S}}/r_{\mathrm{B}})^{2p}} \cos p\theta ; \\ B_\theta &= \frac{\mu_0 K}{2}\left[\frac{r_{\mathrm{S}}}{r}\right]^{p+1} \times \frac{2\left[1 - (r/r_{\mathrm{B}})^{2p}\right]}{1 - (r_{\mathrm{S}}/r_{\mathrm{B}})^{2p}} \sin p\theta . \end{aligned} \tag{12.68}$$

If $T_{\mathrm{ph}} = 36$, $k_{\mathrm{w1}} = 0{\cdot}866$, $i = 15$ A, $r_{\mathrm{S}} = 34$ mm, $r_1 = 35$ mm, $r_{\mathrm{B}} = 42$ mm, $r = 38{\cdot}5$ mm and $p = 2$, the result is $K = 8756$ A/m ; $B_{\mathrm{r}} = 0{\cdot}02265 \cos p\theta$ T (at **X**) ; and $B_\theta = 0{\cdot}00390 \sin p\theta$ T (at **Y**).

Fig. 12.8 shows a finite-element calculation of the same field, with spot values of B_{r} and B_θ which corroborate the analytical calculation. Interestingly, the analytical solution is more precise than the finite-element one.

These solutions are used to verify that the complete solution developed earlier is correct for the exterior-rotor case. That solution includes a true zero-frequency solution that does not use Bessel functions and corresponds exactly to the Laplacian solution given above. It is also verified that the Bessel-function solution converges towards the true zero-frequency solution when the frequency is reduced towards zero. This makes the skin-depth in the magnet region much larger than any of the magnet dimensions, so the Bessel functions must ultimately be evaluated with very small arguments.

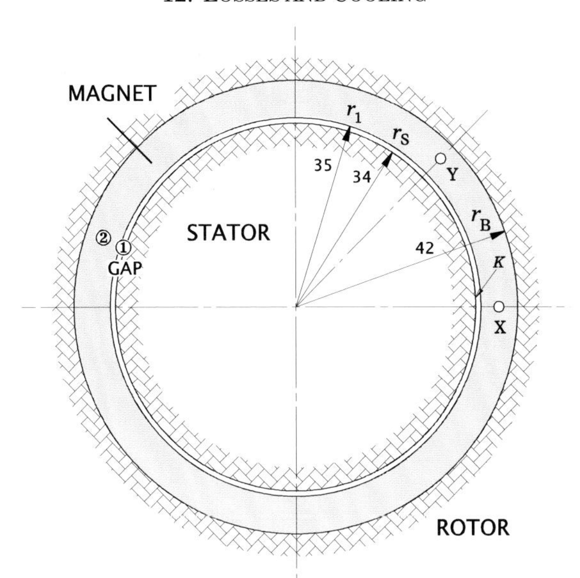

Fig. 12.7 Geometry for checking the solution

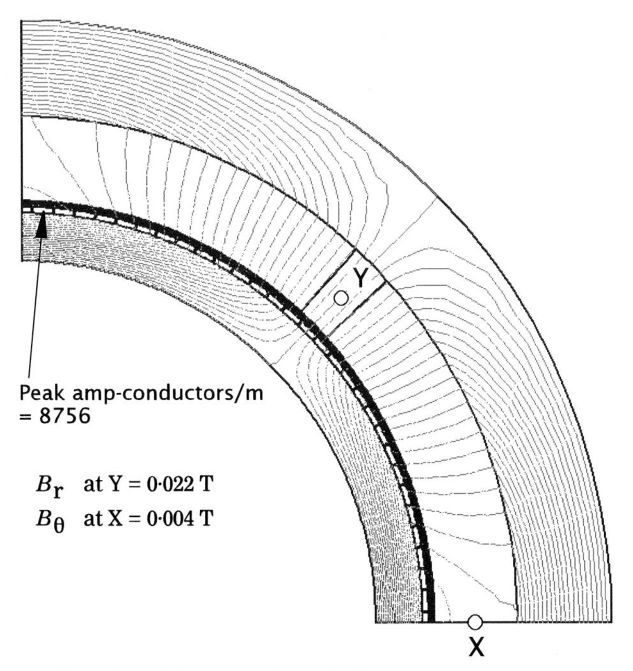

Fig. 12.8 Checking the solution at zero frequency

12.4.2.3 Evaluation of the Exciting Harmonic Current Sheets

The current waveform in phase k is assumed to be periodic although it is otherwise not restricted. It is therefore written in terms of the electrical angle $\omega_e t$, where ω_e is the fundamental electrical radian frequency $2\pi f$:

$$i_k = i_k(\omega_e t). \tag{12.69}$$

This current can be analyzed into time-harmonics: thus

$$\begin{aligned} i_k(\omega_e t) &= I_{k1}\cos(\omega_e t + \alpha_{k1}) + I_{k3}\cos(3\omega_e t + \alpha_{k3}) \\ &\quad + \ldots + I_{kn}\cos(n\omega_e t + \alpha_{kn}) + \ldots \end{aligned} \tag{12.70}$$

The harmonic coefficients are computed using

$$I_{kn} = \frac{2}{2\pi}\int_0^{2\pi/\omega_e} i_k(\omega_e t)\cos(n\omega_e t + \alpha_{kn})\, d(\omega_e t) \tag{12.71}$$

with $n = 1,3,5...$

Ampere-conductor distribution — Each phase has a fixed conductor distribution in the slots, which can be denoted C_k. C_k is called the slot conductor distribution for phase k. It is natural to think of C_k as an array of values denoted C_{kq} or $C_k[q]$, each of which means the number of conductors in slot q belonging to phase k. It is a signed quantity, depending on the direction of the conductors in the slots. When C_{kq} is plotted as a function of ϕ, the azimuthal angle around the stator bore, it is a series of impulse functions, as shown in Fig. 12.9. Alternatively it can be represented as a series of bars, each bar having the angular width of the slot opening, as shown in Fig. 12.10. The functions drawn in Figs. 12.9 and 12.10 are denoted $C_k(\phi)$, and the units of $C_k(\phi)$ are conductors per radian.

If we multiply C_{kq} by the phase current i_k, we have the slot *ampere*-conductor distribution A_{kq} which is simply a scaled replica of C_{kq}. For reasons which appear later, it is better to express the function $A_k(\phi)$ in ampere-conductors per metre around the periphery of the stator bore at radius R. Thus in mathematical notation,

$$A_k(\phi) = i_k C_k(\phi)/R \quad \text{Amp-conductors/m}. \tag{12.72}$$

The graph of $A_k(\phi)$ is similar to Fig. 12.9 or Fig. 12.10.

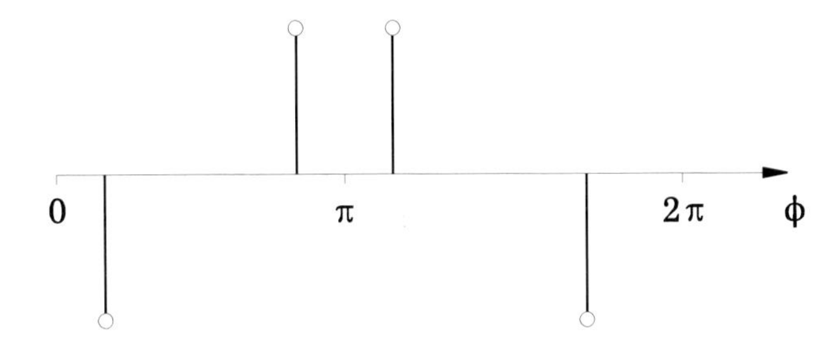

Fig. 12.9 Slot-conductor distribution (impulse functions)

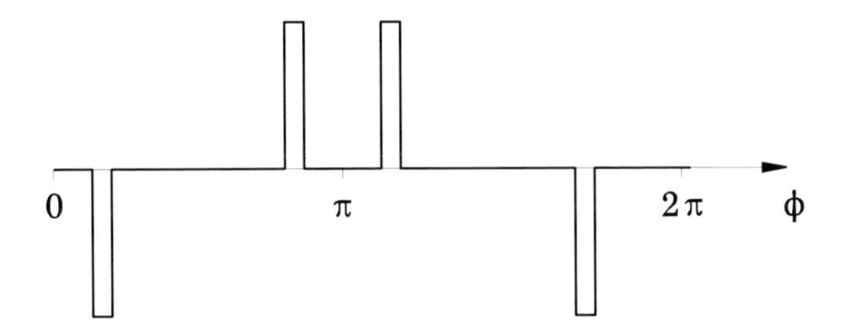

Fig. 12.10 Slot-conductor distribution (bars)

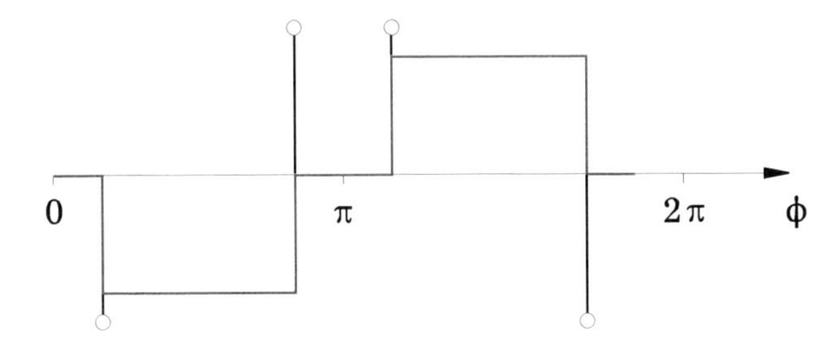

Fig. 12.11 MMF distribution (step functions)

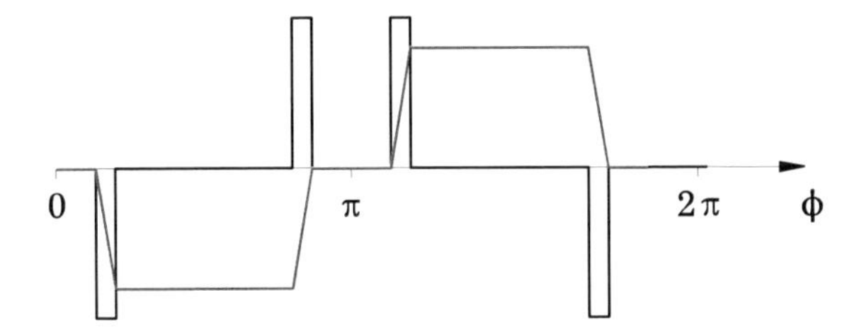

Fig. 12.12 MMF distribution (ramp functions)

The so-called MMF distribution $F_k(\phi)$ is the integral of the ampere-conductor distribution $A_k(\phi)$:

$$F_k(\phi) = \int A_k(\phi)\, R\, d\phi = \int i\, C_k(\phi)\, d\phi. \tag{12.73}$$

$F_k(\phi)$ is evaluated with a constant of integration so that its mean value over one period is zero. Examples corresponding to Figs. 12.9 and 12.10 are shown in Figs. 12.11 and 12.12. The units of F_k are ampere-conductors or just amperes. The MMF distribution is central to the classical theory of electric machines, particularly the theory of winding factors. It can be used to predict the flux distribution across a short airgap, when the iron is assumed to be infinitely permeable.

The MMF distribution is generally calculated together with its Fourier components or *space-harmonic* components. With $i_k = 1{\cdot}0$ A flowing in the winding this is written in boldface $\mathbf{F}_k(\phi)$; ϕ is measured in mechanical radians and since windings may have more than one pair of poles, the harmonic series includes both odd and even harmonics : thus

$$\begin{aligned}\mathbf{F}_k(\phi) &= \mathbf{F}_{k1} \sin\,(\phi + \beta_{k1}) + \mathbf{F}_{k2} \sin\,(2\phi + \beta_{k2}) \\ &\quad + \ldots + \mathbf{F}_{km} \sin\,(m\phi + \beta_{km}) + \ldots\end{aligned} \tag{12.74}$$

The corresponding space-harmonics of the ampere-conductor distribution are obtained by differentiation, that is, from the inverse of eqn. (12.73): thus with $i_k = 1{\cdot}0$ A

$$\begin{aligned}\mathbf{A}_k(\phi) &= [\mathbf{F}_{k1} \cos\,(\phi + \beta_{k1}) + 2\mathbf{F}_{k3} \cos\,(2\phi + \beta_{k2}) \\ &\quad + \ldots + m\mathbf{F}_{km} \cos\,(m\phi + \beta_{km}) + \ldots]/R\end{aligned} \tag{12.75}$$

From this we can isolate the mth space-harmonic of the ampere-conductor distribution

$$\mathbf{A}_{km}(\phi) = \frac{1}{R} m \mathbf{F}_{km} \cos\,(m\phi + \beta_{km}) \tag{12.76}$$

Now multiply this by the n'th time-harmonic in the current waveform $I_{kn} \cos\,(n\omega_e t + \alpha_{kn})$, to give

$$A_{kmn}(\phi,t) = \frac{1}{R} m I_{kn} \mathbf{F}_{km} \cos\,(m\phi + \beta_{km}) \cos\,(n\omega_e t + \alpha_{kn}). \tag{12.77}$$

This ampere-conductor distribution is sinusoidally distributed in space around the stator bore, with m pole-pairs, and it pulsates in time with frequency $n\omega_e$ rad/s. It can be resolved into a forward-rotating component

$$A_{\mathrm{kf}mn}(\phi,t) = \frac{1}{2R} m I_{\mathrm{k}n} \mathbf{F}_{\mathrm{k}m} \cos\left(m\phi - n\omega_e t + \beta_{\mathrm{k}m} - \alpha_{\mathrm{k}n}\right) \quad (12.78)$$

and a backward-rotating component

$$A_{\mathrm{kb}mn}(\phi,t) = \frac{1}{2R} m I_{\mathrm{k}n} \mathbf{F}_{\mathrm{k}m} \cos\left(m\phi + n\omega_e t + \beta_{\mathrm{k}m} + \alpha_{\mathrm{k}n}\right). \quad (12.79)$$

The forward component rotates in the positive direction at the angular velocity $(n/m)\,\omega_e$ rad/s. The backward component rotates in the negative with angular velocity $-(n/m)\,\omega_e$ rad/s. The velocity of the harmonics in either direction is proportional to the order n of the time harmonic in the current, and inversely proportional to the order m of the space-harmonic in the winding distribution.

Now consider these components in a frame of reference rotating synchronously with the rotor. Let θ be the azimuthal coordinate in the rotating frame, as distinct from ϕ which is the azimuthal coordinate in the stationary frame. They are related by

$$\theta = \phi - \omega_0 t, \quad (12.80)$$

where ω_0 is the angular velocity of the rotor in mechanical rad/s. If the number of *rotor* pole-pairs is P,

$$\omega_0 = \frac{\omega_e}{P}. \quad (12.81)$$

To express the forward and backward components of the stator ampere-conductor distribution in the rotating frame, substitute for ϕ using eqns. (12.80) and (12.81) in eqns. (12.78) and (12.79):

$$A_{\mathrm{kf}mn}(\phi,t) = \frac{1}{2R} m I_{\mathrm{k}n} \mathbf{F}_{\mathrm{k}m} \cos\left[m\theta + (m - nP)\,\omega_0 t + \beta_{\mathrm{k}m} - \alpha_{\mathrm{k}n}\right] \quad (12.82)$$

and

$$A_{\mathrm{kb}mn}(\phi,t) = \frac{1}{2R} m I_{\mathrm{k}n} \mathbf{F}_{\mathrm{k}m} \cos\left[m\theta + (m + nP)\,\omega_0 t + \beta_{\mathrm{k}m} + \alpha_{\mathrm{k}n}\right]. \quad (12.83)$$

The angular velocity of the ampere-conductor distribution relative to the rotor is

$$\Omega = -(m \mp nP)\frac{\omega_0}{m} \qquad \text{rad/s.} \tag{12.84}$$

For example, suppose we have a 4-pole rotor rotating at 1,000 rpm. Then $\omega_0 = 2\pi/60 \times 1000 = 104{\cdot}7$ rad/s and $P = 2$. Consider the 5th "electrical" space-harmonic of the winding distribution, with fundamental current flowing. In a 4-pole machine the 5th "electrical" harmonic is the 10th "mechanical" harmonic, so $m = 10$ and $n = 1$. The relative velocity of the forward component is $-(10 - 1 \times 2)/10 \times 104{\cdot}72 = -4/5 \times 104{\cdot}72 = -83{\cdot}76$ rad/s, and the relative velocity of the backward component is $-(10 + 1 \times 2)/10 \times 104{\cdot}72 = -12/10 \times 104{\cdot}72 = -125{\cdot}66$ rad/s. In the stationary frame the forward component rotates at $104{\cdot}72 - 83{\cdot}76 = 104{\cdot}72 \times (1 - 4/5) = 104{\cdot}72/5 = 20{\cdot}94$ rad/s, and the backward component at $104{\cdot}72 - 125{\cdot}66 = 104{\cdot}72 \times (1 - 1{\cdot}2) = -104{\cdot}72/5 = -20{\cdot}94$ rad/s.

As a second example, consider the same *space*-harmonic but with 5th *time*-harmonic current flowing in the windings. Then $m = 5 \times 2 = 10$ as before, while $n = 5$ instead of 1. Eqn. (12.84) shows that the forward component rotates at a velocity of $-(10 - 5 \times 2)\,\omega_0/10 = 0$ relative to the rotor, while the backward component rotates at $-(10 + 5 \times 2)\,\omega_0/10 = -2\,\omega_0 = -209{\cdot}44$ rad/s relative to the rotor. In the stationary frame the forward component rotates at $104{\cdot}72$ rad/s, synchronously with the rotor; while the backward component rotates at $104{\cdot}72 - 209{\cdot}44 = 104{\cdot}72 \times (1 - 2) = -104{\cdot}72$ rad/s.

Extracting the required amplitude, pole-number and frequency of the harmonic waves — For the analysis of harmonic losses we need all the space/time harmonic components of the stator ampere-conductor distribution expressed in the form

$$A\,\mathrm{e}^{\mathrm{j}(m\theta - \omega t)} \tag{12.85}$$

in a frame of reference rotating synchronously with the rotor. Such current sheets have already been used [for example in eqn. (12.49)], where they were used to introduce the excitation *via* a boundary condition at the stator bore.[118]

[118] In those cases the symbol K was used instead of A

The parameters A and ω are yet to be determined, but m is the number of harmonic pole-pairs, which depends only on the stator winding distribution. Thus m is the same in either the rotating or the stationary frame of reference: it is invariant.

The radian frequency ω must be chosen to give the correct angular velocity relative to the rotor. In terms of eqn. (12.85) this velocity is ω/m rad/s, and it must be equal to Ω from eqn. (12.84): thus

$$\omega = (-m \pm nP)\omega_0. \tag{12.86}$$

If we now define the "electrical" harmonic order as

$$m' = \frac{m}{P}, \tag{12.87}$$

and substitute this together with eqn. (12.81) in eqn. (12.86), we have

$$\omega = (-m' \pm n)\omega_e \quad \text{rad/s}. \tag{12.88}$$

Finally, the amplitudes of the forward and backward components are found directly from the amplitudes in eqns. (12.82) and (12.83).

Example — Consider a case where $m' = 19$ and $n = 1$. Then eqn. (12.88) gives $\omega = (-19 \pm 1)\,\omega_e$ which is $-20\,\omega_e$ or $-18\,\omega_e$. The 19th space-harmonic produces a forward component rotating at 1/19 of the synchronous speed in the forward direction. In a frame of reference rotating forwards at synchronous speed, this component appears to be rotating backwards at the relative speed $(1/19 - 1) = -18/19$ times the synchronous speed. The number of pole-pairs is 19, so the frequency is $-18/19 \times 19 = -18$ times the fundamental frequency ω_e.

The 19th space-harmonic also produces a backward component rotating at 1/19 of the synchronous speed in the backward direction. Again, in the rotor frame of reference the backward component is rotating backwards at the relative speed $(-1/19 - 1) = -20/19$ times the synchronous speed. The number of pole-pairs is 19, so the frequency is $-20/19 \times 19 = -20$ times the fundamental frequency ω_e.

In both cases the negative sign simply means that the field is rotating backwards relative to the rotor. When a negative value of $\omega = -18\,\omega_e$ is substituted in eqn. (12.85) along with $m' = 19 = 19P$, it becomes

$$A\mathrm{e}^{\mathrm{j}(19P\theta + 18\omega_e t)} = A\mathrm{e}^{\mathrm{j}(19P\theta + 18P\omega_0 t)}. \tag{12.89}$$

This represents a field of $38P$ poles rotating backwards at $-18/19$ times the rotor speed *relative to the rotor*. For a fixed supply frequency ω_e, all physical speeds are inversely proportional to P.

12.4.2.4 Balanced operation of 3-phase machines

In 3-phase machines with perfectly balanced windings and balanced 3-phase currents, roughly 2/3 of the possible harmonic fields vanish, as will now be shown. The analysis begins in the stationary frame of reference with eqns. (12.78) and (12.79). Considering first the forward component, I_{kn} and α_{kn} will be the same for all three phases $k = 1,2,3$, but $\omega_e t$ will be replaced by $\omega_e t - 2\pi/3$ in phase 2 and by $\omega_e t + 2\pi/3$ in phase 3. Similarly $\mathbf{F}_{km}$ and β_{km} will be the same for $k = 1,2,3$, while ϕ will be replaced by $\phi - 2\pi/3P$ in phase 2 and by $\phi + 2\pi/3P$ in phase 3. If we write γ_{mn} for $\beta_m - \alpha_n$ and $h = 2\pi/3$, the total forward component for the three phases becomes

$$\begin{aligned} A_{fmn}(\phi,t) = \frac{1}{2R} m I_n \mathbf{F}_m \{ & \cos[m\phi - n\omega_e t + \gamma_{mn}] \\ & + \cos[m(\phi - h/P) - n(\omega_e t - h) + \gamma_{mn}] \\ & + \cos[m(\phi + h/P) - n(\omega_e t + h) + \gamma_{mn}] \} \end{aligned} \tag{12.90}$$

Let $\zeta = m\phi - n\omega_e t + \gamma_{mn}$. Then with $m' = m/P$ this expression can be reduced to

$$A_{fmn}(\phi,t) = \frac{1}{2R} m I_n \mathbf{F}_m \cos\zeta \times \left[1 + 2\cos(m' - n)h\right] \tag{12.91}$$

Let $\xi = m\phi + n\omega_e t + \alpha_m + \beta_n$ for the backward component. Then

$$A_{bmn}(\phi,t) = \frac{1}{2R} m I_n \mathbf{F}_m \cos\xi \times \left[1 + 2\cos(m' + n)h\right] \tag{12.92}$$

The coefficient term $[1 + 2\cos(m' - n) \times 2\pi/3]$ in the forward component vanishes unless $(m' - n)$ is zero or a multiple of 3. Similarly the term $[1 + 2\cos(m' + n) \times 2\pi/3]$ in the backward component vanishes unless $(m' + n)$ is a multiple of 3.

Thus for example if $m' = 1$ and $n = 1$ we have the fundamental electrical space-harmonic of the winding distribution and the fundamental component of phase current, $m' - n = 0$, and

$$\begin{aligned} A_{f11}(\phi,t) &= \frac{3}{2R} I_1 \mathbf{F}_1 \cos\zeta \\ &= \frac{3}{2R} I_1 \mathbf{F}_1 \cos(P\phi - \omega_e t + \beta_1 - \alpha_1), \end{aligned} \tag{12.93}$$

while $A_{b11} = 0$. This represents a $2P$-pole field rotating at the angular velocity ω_e rad/s with a phase angle $\beta_1 - \alpha_1$. The frequency relative to the rotor is given by eqn. (12.88) as $(-1 + 1)\,\omega_e = 0$. Note that eqn. (12.88) also gives the frequency of the backward field relative to the rotor as $(-1 - 1)\,\omega_e = -2\,\omega_e$, but since the coefficient $A_{b11} = 0$, there is no backward field.

Next consider $m' = 5$ and $n = 7$. The coefficient term $[1 + 2\cos(m' - n) \times 2\pi/3]$ in the forward component is 0, so there is no forward field: $A_{f57} = 0$. The term $[1 + 2\cos(m' + n) \times 2\pi/3]$ in the backward component is equal to 3, so there is a backward field

$$\begin{aligned} A_{b57}(\phi,t) &= \frac{3}{2R}\, m I_7 \mathbf{F}_5 \cos\xi \\ &= \frac{3 \times 5}{2R} I_7 \mathbf{F}_5 \cos(5P\phi + 7\omega_e t + \beta_5 + \alpha_7). \end{aligned} \tag{12.94}$$

This represents a field with $5P$ pole-pairs rotating at the angular velocity $-(7/5)\,\omega_e t$ rad/s. Relative to the rotor, assuming $P = 1$, the angular velocity is $-(1 + 7/5)\,\omega_e t = -12/5\,\omega_e t$ and with 5 pole-pairs the frequency induced in the conductive components on the rotor is $5 \times (-12/5\,\omega_e) = -12\,\omega_e$ rad/s. Eqn. (12.88) gives $\omega = (-5 \times 1 - 7)\,\omega_e = -12\,\omega_e$, which checks the result.

The rotor frequencies given by eqn. (12.88) are displayed in Tables 12.1 and 12.2 for the forward and backward components respectively. In all cases the units are multiples of ω_e, and the space-harmonics are *electrical* (i.e, m' is the parameter in the left-hand column).

Counting only odd harmonics up to the 37th in m' and n, there are 102 forward harmonics in Table 12.1 and 120 non-zero backward harmonics in Table 12.2. Along the diagonal in Table 12.1 are the "synchronous" harmonics including the fundamental. The total number of field solutions required is 222.

Tables 12.3 and 12.4 show the rotor frequencies for an unbalanced machine. Both tables are full, except for the diagonal of Table 12.3 which again represents the synchronous harmonics. In this case there are 703 non-zero entries requiring 703 field solutions. The balanced machine thus has only 222/703 or approximately one-third the number of effective harmonics.

n ⇨

m	1	3	5	7	9	11	13	15	17	19	21	23	25	27	29	31	33	35	37
1	0			6			12			18			24			30			36
3		0			6			12			18			24			30		
5			0			6			12			18			24			30	
7	-6			0			6			12			18			24			30
9		-6			0			6			12			18			24		
11			-6			0			6			12			18			24	
13	-12			-6			0			6			12			18			24
15		-12			-6			0			6			12			18		
17			-12			-6			0			6			12			18	
19	-18			-12			-6			0			6			12			18
21		-18			-12			-6			0			6			12		
23			-18			-12			-6			0			6			12	
25	-24			-18			-12			-6			0			6			12
27		-24			-18			-12			-6			0			6		
29			-24			-18			-12			-6			0			6	
31	-30			-24			-18			-12			-6			0			6
33		-30			-24			-18			-12			-6			0		
35			-30			-24			-18			-12			-6			0	
37	-36			-30			-24			-18			-12			-6			0

TABLE 12.1
ROTOR FREQUENCIES FOR FORWARD FIELD COMPONENT
IN 3-PHASE BALANCED MACHINE

If we delete all triple-m space harmonics of the winding distribution and all triple-n time-harmonics from the current waveforms, Tables 12.1 and 12.2 for a balanced 3-phase machine reduce to Tables 12.5 and 12.6, with 72 and 85 non-zero entries respectively, making a total of 156 — only 22% of the original 703.

To achieve this "triple-n" reduction it is only necessary to connect the windings in wye (star) with a 3-wire connection, since the triple-n time harmonics only interact with triple-m space harmonics. Conversely the same effect can be achieved in a winding with all triple-m winding factors zero.

n ⇨

m'	1	3	5	7	9	11	13	15	17	19	21	23	25	27	29	31	33	35	37
1			-6			-12			-18			-24			-30			-36	
3		-6			-12			-18			-24			-30			-36		
5	-6			-12			-18			-24			-30			-36			-42
7			-12			-18			-24			-30			-36			-42	
9		-12			-18			-24			-30			-36			-42		
11	-12			-18			-24			-30			-36			-42			-48
13			-18			-24			-30			-36			-42			-48	
15		-18			-24			-30			-36			-42			-48		
17	-18			-24			-30			-36			-42			-48			-54
19			-24			-30			-36			-42			-48			-54	
21		-24			-30			-36			-42			-48			-54		
23	-24			-30			-36			-42			-48			-54			-60
25			-30			-36			-42			-48			-54			-60	
27		-30			-36			-42			-48			-54			-60		
29	-30			-36			-42			-48			-54			-60			-66
31			-36			-42			-48			-54			-60			-66	
33		-36			-42			-48			-54			-60			-66		
35	-36			-42			-48			-54			-60			-66			-72
37			-42			-48			-54			-60			-66			-72	

TABLE 12.2
ROTOR FREQUENCIES FOR BACKWARD FIELD COMPONENT
IN 3-PHASE BALANCED MACHINE

12.4.2.5 Unbalanced operation of 3-phase machines

Unbalanced operation, ("imbalance" for short), comes in many combinations: unbalanced currents may flow in balanced windings, or, conversely, balanced currents may flow in unbalanced windings. In the general case both the currents and the windings are unbalanced.

In spite of the mathematical complexity, the intuitive engineering notion of symmetry is all we need to define "balance".

n ⇨

m'	1	3	5	7	9	11	13	15	17	19	21	23	25	27	29	31	33	35	37
1	0	2	4	6	8	10	12	14	16	18	20	22	24	26	28	30	32	34	36
3	-2	0	2	4	6	8	10	12	14	16	18	20	22	24	26	28	30	32	34
5	-4	-2	0	2	4	6	8	10	12	14	16	18	20	22	24	26	28	30	32
7	-6	-4	-2	0	2	4	6	8	10	12	14	16	18	20	22	24	26	28	30
9	-8	-6	-4	-2	0	2	4	6	8	10	12	14	16	18	20	22	24	26	28
11	-10	-8	-6	-4	-2	0	2	4	6	8	10	12	14	16	18	20	22	24	26
13	-12	-10	-8	-6	-4	-2	0	2	4	6	8	10	12	14	16	18	20	22	24
15	-14	-12	-10	-8	-6	-4	-2	0	2	4	6	8	10	12	14	16	18	20	22
17	-16	-14	-12	-10	-8	-6	-4	-2	0	2	4	6	8	10	12	14	16	18	20
19	-18	-16	-14	-12	-10	-8	-6	-4	-2	0	2	4	6	8	10	12	14	16	18
21	-20	-18	-16	-14	-12	-10	-8	-6	-4	-2	0	2	4	6	8	10	12	14	16
23	-22	-20	-18	-16	-14	-12	-10	-8	-6	-4	-2	0	2	4	6	8	10	12	14
25	-24	-22	-20	-18	-16	-14	-12	-10	-8	-6	-4	-2	0	2	4	6	8	10	12
27	-26	-24	-22	-20	-18	-16	-14	-12	-10	-8	-6	-4	-2	0	2	4	6	8	10
29	-28	-26	-24	-22	-20	-18	-16	-14	-12	-10	-8	-6	-4	-2	0	2	4	6	8
31	-30	-28	-26	-24	-22	-20	-18	-16	-14	-12	-10	-8	-6	-4	-2	0	2	4	6
33	-32	-30	-28	-26	-24	-22	-20	-18	-16	-14	-12	-10	-8	-6	-4	-2	0	2	4
35	-34	-32	-30	-28	-26	-24	-22	-20	-18	-16	-14	-12	-10	-8	-6	-4	-2	0	2
37	-36	-34	-32	-30	-28	-26	-24	-22	-20	-18	-16	-14	-12	-10	-8	-6	-4	-2	0

TABLE 12.3
ROTOR FREQUENCIES FOR FORWARD FIELD COMPONENT
IN 3-PHASE UNBALANCED MACHINE

Thus balanced windings are symmetrical, and in a three-phase machine this means that the windings are physically identical, but displaced from one another in the circumferential direction around the stator by $2\pi/3P$ radians or $120/P°$, that is, 120 electrical degrees, (P being the fundamental number of rotor pole-pairs). Similarly, balanced currents have identical waveforms and are displaced from one another in time phase by 120° at the fundamental frequency, giving rise to a "star of phasors" displaced from one another by 120° as shown by the phasors $\mathbf{I}_1'$, $\mathbf{I}_2'$, $\mathbf{I}_3'$ in Fig. 12.13a.

n ⇨

m'	1	3	5	7	9	11	13	15	17	19	21	23	25	27	29	31	33	35	37
1	-2	-4	-6	-8	-10	-12	-14	-16	-18	-20	-22	-24	-26	-28	-30	-32	-34	-36	-38
3	-4	-6	-8	-10	-12	-14	-16	-18	-20	-22	-24	-26	-28	-30	-32	-34	-36	-38	-40
5	-6	-8	-10	-12	-14	-16	-18	-20	-22	-24	-26	-28	-30	-32	-34	-36	-38	-40	-42
7	-8	-10	-12	-14	-16	-18	-20	-22	-24	-26	-28	-30	-32	-34	-36	-38	-40	-42	-44
9	-10	-12	-14	-16	-18	-20	-22	-24	-26	-28	-30	-32	-34	-36	-38	-40	-42	-44	-46
11	-12	-14	-16	-18	-20	-22	-24	-26	-28	-30	-32	-34	-36	-38	-40	-42	-44	-46	-48
13	-14	-16	-18	-20	-22	-24	-26	-28	-30	-32	-34	-36	-38	-40	-42	-44	-46	-48	-50
15	-16	-18	-20	-22	-24	-26	-28	-30	-32	-34	-36	-38	-40	-42	-44	-46	-48	-50	-52
17	-18	-20	-22	-24	-26	-28	-30	-32	-34	-36	-38	-40	-42	-44	-46	-48	-50	-52	-54
19	-20	-22	-24	-26	-28	-30	-32	-34	36	-38	-40	-42	-44	-46	-48	-50	-52	-54	-56
21	-22	-24	-26	-28	-30	-32	-34	-36	-38	-40	-42	-44	-46	-48	-50	-52	-54	-56	-58
23	-24	-26	-28	-30	-32	-34	-36	-38	-40	-42	-44	-46	-48	-50	-52	-54	-56	-58	-60
25	-26	-28	-30	-32	-34	-36	-38	-40	-42	-44	-46	-48	-50	-52	-54	-56	-58	-60	-62
27	-28	-30	-32	-34	-36	-38	-40	-42	-44	-46	-48	-50	-52	-54	-56	-58	-60	-62	-64
29	-30	-32	-34	-36	-38	-40	-42	-44	-46	-48	-50	-52	-54	-56	-58	-60	-62	-64	-66
31	-32	-34	-36	-38	-40	-42	-44	-46	-48	-50	-52	-54	-56	-58	-60	-62	-64	-66	-68
33	-34	-36	-38	-40	-42	-44	-46	-48	-50	-52	-54	-56	-58	-60	-62	-64	-66	-68	-70
35	-36	-38	-40	-42	-44	-46	-48	-50	-52	-54	-56	-58	-60	-62	-64	-66	-68	-70	-72
37	-38	-40	-42	-44	-46	-48	-50	-52	-54	-56	-58	-60	-62	-64	-66	-68	-70	-72	-74

TABLE 12.4

ROTOR FREQUENCIES FOR BACKWARD FIELD COMPONENT IN 3-PHASE UNBALANCED MACHINE

The phasor diagram is familiar for the fundamental harmonic component of current. When there are harmonics, there is a phasor diagram for every harmonic. It is hardly practical to draw this diagram superimposed on the fundamental phasor diagram, because the phasor diagram for a harmonic does not rotate at the same speed as the fundamental, and it may not even have the same phase sequence. The geometric construction of the “star of phasors” can also be used to represent the windings in terms of the harmonic MMF vectors $\mathbf{F}_{km}$ considered earlier. The Görges diagram is based on this principle.

n ⇨

m'	1	5	7	11	13	17	19	23	25	29	31	35	37
1	0		6		12		18		24		30		36
5		0		6		12		18		24		30	
7	-6		0		6		12		18		24		30
11		-6		0		6		12		18		24	
13	-12		-6		0		6		12		18		24
17		-12		-6		0		6		12		18	
19	-18		-12		-6		0		6		12		18
23		-18		-12		-6		0		6		12	
25	-24		-18		-12		-6		0		6		12
29		-24		-18		-12		-6		0		6	
31	-30		-24		-18		-12		-6		0		6
35		-30		-24		-18		-12		-6		0	
37	-36		-30		-24		-18		-12		-6		0

TABLE 12.5

ROTOR FREQUENCIES : 3-PHASE, BALANCED, FORWARD, NO TRIPLE-M OR TRIPLE-N

n ⇨

m'	1	5	7	11	13	17	19	23	25	29	31	35	37
1		-6		-12		-18		-24		-30		-36	
5	-6		-12		-18		-24		-30		-36		-42
7		-12		-18		-24		-30		-36		-42	
11	-12		-18		-24		-30		-36		-42		-48
13		-18		-24		-30		-36		-42		-48	
17	-18		-24		-30		-36		-42		-48		-54
19		-24		-30		-36		-42		-48		-54	
23	-24		-30		-36		-42		-48		-54		-60
25		-30		-36		-42		-48		-54		-60	
29	-30		-36		-42		-48		-54		-60		-66
31		-36		-42		-48		-54		-60		-66	
35	-36		-42		-48		-54		-60		-66		-72
37		-42		-48		-54		-60		-66		-72	

TABLE 12.6

ROTOR FREQUENCIES : 3-PHASE, BALANCED, BACKWARD, NO TRIPLE-M OR TRIPLE-N

Every electrical engineer knows that *symmetrical components* are commonly used for the analysis of unbalanced operation, especially in power systems. When the imbalance is confined to the currents and the windings are balanced, this method (see below) is not only manageable but sufficiently general to deal with all cases of steady-state imbalance. However, in our case we have to deal with imbalance in the windings as well as in the currents, and we have already developed the mathematics to do this in the form of eqns. (12.88), (12.82) and (12.83). For this reason it is more useful to consider special simple cases of imbalance as simplifications or reductions of these equations, leaving the method of symmetrical components as a means of illustration and interpretation and not the main analytical tool. Indeed we have already considered two special cases of "no imbalance" and "no triplen harmonics", which are summarized in Tables 12.1, 12.2, 12.5 and 12.6.

Single-parameter imbalance — Two special simple cases of imbalance will be considered, each of which requires only a *single parameter* to define the amount of imbalance. The first has a negative-sequence component but no zero-sequence component, while the second has a zero-sequence component but no negative-sequence component. Both also have a positive-sequence component, in general. For more general cases of imbalance, it is necessary to revert to the general equations cited above.

Negative-sequence only — Fig. 12.13*a* shows a simple case of imbalance in which the current in phase 1 is increased by the factor $(1+u)$, while the currents in phases 2 and 3 remain unaltered from their normal balanced values; when $u = 0$ the currents are balanced. In Fig. 12.13*b* the phasors $\mathbf{I}_2$ and $\mathbf{I}_3$ are copied to form a closed triangle with $\mathbf{I}_1$, representing conditions in a machine with a 3-wire connection and no zero-sequence component:

$$\mathbf{I}_1 + \mathbf{I}_2 + \mathbf{I}_3 = 0. \tag{12.95}$$

With the constraint of eqn. (12.95), the increase in $\mathbf{I}_1$ drags the $\mathbf{I}_2$ and $\mathbf{I}_3$ phasors to the right in the closed triangle in Fig. 12.13*b*. They retain the same magnitude, but $\mathbf{I}_2$ is retarded in phase by η while $\mathbf{I}_3$ is advanced by the same angle η. These phase shifts can be seen more clearly in the star diagram in the left-hand part of Fig. 12.13*b*.

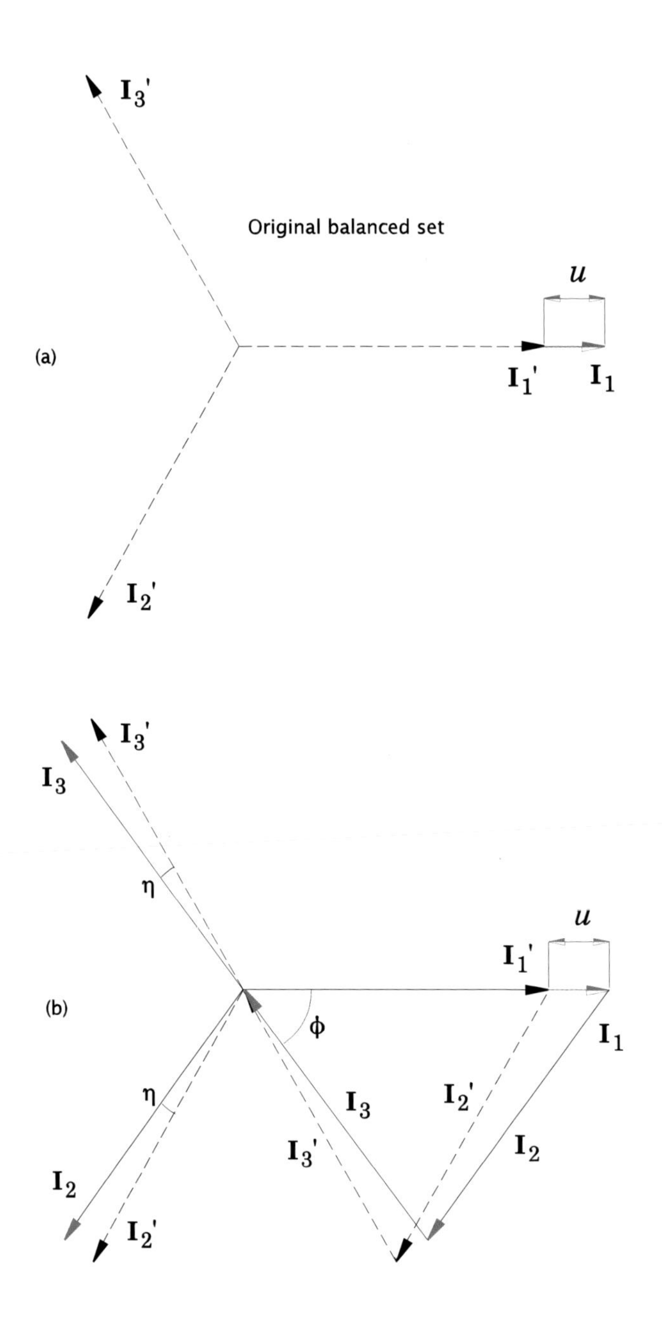

Fig. 12.13 Negative-sequence imbalance with no zero-sequence component

With unchanged magnitudes $I_2 = I_3 = 1$, it appears from the closed triangle $\mathbf{I}_1\mathbf{I}_2\mathbf{I}_3$ in Fig. 12.13*b* that

$$I_2 = I_3 = 1 = \frac{1+u}{2\cos\phi} = \frac{1+u}{2\cos(\pi/3-\eta)}. \qquad (12.96)$$

The phase-shift angle η can be solved from this equation, giving

$$\eta = \frac{\pi}{3} - \cos^{-1}\frac{1+u}{2}. \qquad (12.97)$$

Hence

$$\mathbf{I}_1 = 1 + u; \qquad \mathbf{I}_2 = 1\,\mathrm{e}^{-\mathrm{j}(2\pi/3+\eta)}; \qquad \mathbf{I}_3 = 1\,\mathrm{e}^{\mathrm{j}(2\pi/3+\eta)}. \qquad (12.98)$$

The fundamental components of the instantaneous currents are given by

$$\begin{aligned} i_1 &= (1+u)I_1\sqrt{2}\cos\omega t \\ i_2 &= I_1\sqrt{2}\cos[\omega t - (2\pi/3+\eta)] \\ i_3 &= I_1\sqrt{2}\cos[\omega t + (2\pi/3+\eta)], \end{aligned} \qquad (12.99)$$

and from this the nth harmonic can be inferred as

$$\begin{aligned} i_1 &= (1+u)I_n\sqrt{2}\cos n\omega t \\ i_2 &= I_n\sqrt{2}\cos n[\omega t - (2\pi/3+\eta)] \\ i_3 &= I_n\sqrt{2}\cos n[\omega t + (2\pi/3+\eta)]. \end{aligned} \qquad (12.100)$$

These currents can be substituted in eqns. (12.78) and (12.79) to give an equation similar to eqn. (12.90), which can then be reduced to the following equations for the forward and backward components, similar to eqns. (12.91) and (12.92):

$$A_{\mathrm{f}mn}(\phi,t) = \frac{1}{2R}mI_n\mathbf{F}_m\cos\zeta \times \{1+u+2\cos[(m'-n)h-n\eta]\}; \qquad (12.101)$$

$$A_{\mathrm{b}mn}(\phi,t) = \frac{1}{2R}mI_n\mathbf{F}_m\cos\xi \times \{1+u+2\cos[(m'+n)h+n\eta]\}. \qquad (12.102)$$

If $u = 0$ these equations reduce to eqns. (12.91) and (12.92) for balanced operation.

We have already seen that for balanced operation the forward component vanishes unless $(m' - n)$ is zero or a multiple of 3; but for unbalanced operation it is generally non-zero for all values of m' and n; hence the fullness of Tables 12.3 and 12.4. For example if $m' = 1$ and $n = 1$, with $u = 0$ we have already seen that the coefficient of the forward component is $3I_1\mathbf{F}_1/2R$. With $u = 0{\cdot}1$ we have $\eta = 3{\cdot}367°$ and

$$A_{f11}(\phi,t) = \frac{1}{2R} I_1 \mathbf{F}_1 \cos\zeta \times \{1 + 0{\cdot}1 + 2\cos[-3{\cdot}367°]\}$$
$$= \frac{1}{2R} I_1 \mathbf{F}_1 \cos\zeta \times 3{\cdot}09655; \qquad (12.103)$$

$$A_{b11}(\phi,t) = \frac{1}{2R} I_1 \mathbf{F}_1 \cos\xi \times \{1 + 0{\cdot}1 + 2\cos[2 \times 120° + 3{\cdot}367°]\}$$
$$= \frac{1}{2R} I_1 \mathbf{F}_1 \cos\xi \times 0{\cdot}20345. \qquad (12.104)$$

The forward component A_{f11}, which is synchronous with the rotor, is increased by approximately 3·2%. The backward component A_{b11}, which has a frequency of $-2\omega_e$ relative to the rotor, and which was zero under balanced operation, has magnitude 0·20345/3·09655 = 0·0657 compared to the forward component.

Again consider $m' = 5$ and $n = 7$. Previously with balanced operation $A_{f57} = 0$, but with $u = 0{\cdot}1$ we get

$$A_{f57}(\phi,t) = \frac{5I_7\mathbf{F}_5}{2R} \cos\zeta \times \{1 + 0{\cdot}1 + 2\cos[(5-7) \times 120° - 7 \times 3{\cdot}367°$$
$$= \frac{5I_7\mathbf{F}_5}{2R} \cos\zeta \times 0{\cdot}87599.$$

The backward component is

$$A_{b57}(\phi,t) = \frac{5I_7\mathbf{F}_5}{2R} \cos\xi \times \{1 + 0{\cdot}1 + 2\cos[(5+7) \times 120° + 7 \times 3{\cdot}367°$$
$$= \frac{5I_7\mathbf{F}_5}{2R} \cos\xi \times 2{\cdot}93316,$$

which is reduced in the ratio 2·93316/3 = 0·97772 compared with the balanced case.

The imbalance characterized by Fig. 12.13 is represented by a single imbalance parameter u that refers to the currents; the *winding* is assumed to be balanced. The imbalance produces a negative-sequence component but no zero-sequence component. While it is convenient to work with only a single imbalance parameter and a graphical interpretation, it is also important to associate the imbalance parameter u with the negative-sequence current, and with its effect on the positive-sequence component, at least for the fundamental time-harmonic of the current.

The symmetrical-component transformation can be written

$$\begin{bmatrix} \mathbf{I}_p \\ \mathbf{I}_n \\ \mathbf{I}_0 \end{bmatrix} = \frac{1}{3} \begin{bmatrix} 1 & \mathbf{h} & \mathbf{h}^2 \\ 1 & \mathbf{h}^2 & \mathbf{h} \\ 1 & 1 & 1 \end{bmatrix} \begin{bmatrix} \mathbf{I}_1 \\ \mathbf{I}_2 \\ \mathbf{I}_3 \end{bmatrix} \qquad (12.107)$$

where $\mathbf{h} = e^{j2\pi/3}$. Substituting from eqns. (12.98), and simplifying,

$$\begin{aligned} \mathbf{I}_p &= \frac{1}{3}\left[1 + u + 2\cos\eta\right]; \\ \mathbf{I}_n &= \frac{1}{3}\left[1 + u + 2\cos(2\pi/3 - \eta)\right]; \\ \mathbf{I}_0 &= \frac{1}{3}\left[1 + u + 2\cos(2\pi/3 + \eta)\right]. \end{aligned} \qquad (12.108)$$

For example with $u = 0{\cdot}1$, $\eta = 3{\cdot}367^\circ$,

$$\begin{aligned} \mathbf{I}_p &= \frac{1}{3}[1 + 0{\cdot}1 + 2\cos 3{\cdot}367^\circ] = 1{\cdot}03218; \\ \mathbf{I}_n &= \frac{1}{3}[1 + 0{\cdot}1 + 2\cos(120^\circ - 3{\cdot}367^\circ)] = 0{\cdot}06782; \\ \mathbf{I}_0 &= \frac{1}{3}[1 + 0{\cdot}1 + 2\cos(120^\circ + 3{\cdot}367^\circ)] = 0. \end{aligned} \qquad (12.109)$$

Note that $I_n/I_p = 0{\cdot}06782/1{\cdot}03218 = 0{\cdot}06571$, which is the same ratio found between A_{b11} and A_{f11} above.

The converse problem is also of interest : that is, to find the value of u when the sequence components are given. However this requires an iterative solution.

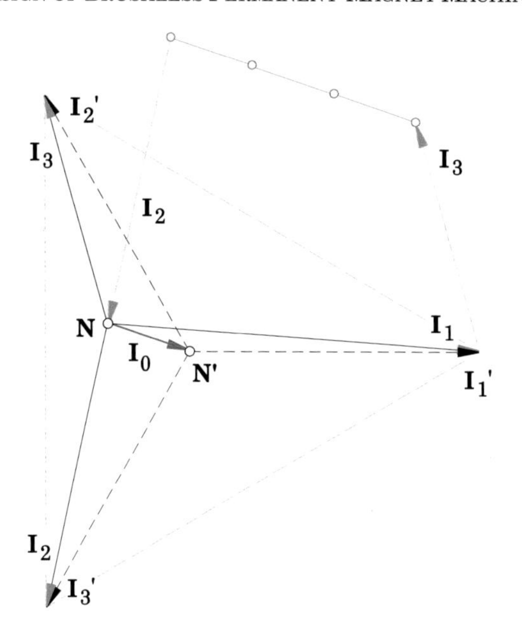

Fig. 12.14 Zero-sequence imbalance but no negative-sequence

Zero-sequence only — A second example of "single-parameter" imbalance is shown in Fig. 12.14. In this case there is a zero-sequence component $\mathbf{I}_0 = \mathbf{NN}'$, but no negative-sequence component. It is characteristic of such systems that the vertices of the unbalanced current phasors $\mathbf{I}_1$, $\mathbf{I}_2$ and $\mathbf{I}_3$ form an equilateral triangle, but the neutral point **N** is displaced from the centroid **N**', and $\mathbf{NN}' = \mathbf{I}_0$. In Fig. 12.14 $\mathbf{I}_2$ and $\mathbf{I}_3$ are copied and translated to try to form a closed triangle, but it cannot be done : instead there is formed a quadrilateral whose sides are $\mathbf{I}_1$, $\mathbf{I}_2$, $\mathbf{I}_3$, and 3**NN**'. Only if $\mathbf{NN}' = 0$ does the triangle close.

The unbalanced system in Fig. 12.14 is equivalent to the sum of the balanced system $\mathbf{I}_1'$, $\mathbf{I}_2'$, $\mathbf{I}_3'$ and the zero-sequence component $\mathbf{I}_0$. Evidently

$$\mathbf{I}_1 = \mathbf{I}_1' + \mathbf{I}_0; \qquad \mathbf{I}_2 = \mathbf{I}_2' + \mathbf{I}_0; \qquad \mathbf{I}_3 = \mathbf{I}_3' + \mathbf{I}_0. \qquad (12.110)$$

The balanced system and its harmonics obey the rules already worked out in relation to eqns. (12.91) and (12.92). So it remains to add the zero-sequence component in the rotor frame of reference.

Starting with eqn. (12.90), the zero-sequence component $uI_n \cos(\zeta + \psi)$ is added to each phase, where ψ is the phase angle between $\mathbf{I}_0$ and $\mathbf{I}_1$. With $\zeta = m\phi - n\omega_e t + \gamma_{mn}$, the forward component becomes

$$A_{fmn}(\phi,t) = \frac{1}{2R} m I_n \mathbf{F}_m \Big[\cos\zeta + \cos(\zeta - m'h) + \cos(\zeta + m'h) + 3u\cos(\zeta + \psi) \Big]$$

$$= \frac{1}{2R} m I_n \mathbf{F}_m \Big\{ \cos\zeta \times \Big[1 + 3u\cos\psi + 2\cos(m' - n)h \Big] - 3u\sin\psi\sin\zeta \Big\}.$$

This simplifies if $\psi = 0$, which is not unduly restrictive for loss calculations: thus

$$A_{fmn}(\phi,t) = \frac{1}{2R} m I_n \mathbf{F}_m \cos\zeta \times \Big[1 + 2\cos(m' - n)h + 3u \Big]. \quad (12.112)$$

The frequency relative to the rotor is given as $-(m' - n)\omega_e$ electrical rad/s by eqn. (12.88). The backward component has a frequency $-(m' - n)\omega_e$ relative to the rotor, and

$$A_{bmn}(\phi,t) = \frac{1}{2R} m I_n \mathbf{F}_m \cos\zeta \times \Big[1 + 2\cos(m' + n)h + 3u \Big]. \quad (12.113)$$

If $u = 0$ these equations again reduce to eqns. (12.91) and (12.92) for balanced operation. Otherwise both components are generally nonzero even when $(m' \pm n)$ is zero or a multiple of 3; hence again the fullness of Tables 12.3 and 12.4.

The idea of forward and backward zero-sequence components perhaps seems strange, because the co-phasal zero-sequence phasors seem to have had all sense of rotation knocked out of them, so an example may be helpful. First notice that A_{fmn} and A_{bmn} are both zero for non-triplen values of the electrical space-harmonic m'. This helps to explain the common association (and even confusion) of "zero sequence" with "third harmonic". So consider first the case $m' = 3$ and $n = 1$. According to eqn. (12.88) the frequency relative to the rotor is $-2\omega_e$ for the forward component and $-4\omega_e$ for the backward component, just as they appear in Tables 12.3 and 12.4 respectively.

Remembering that the zero-sequence components of current in the three phases are in phase with one another, they produce a stationary armature-reaction field with $3P$ pole-pairs pulsating or alternating at the fundamental frequency. This is resolved into a forward component rotating at $\omega_e/3$ electrical rad/s or $\omega_e/3P$ mechanical rad/s; and a backward component rotating at $-\omega_e/3$ electrical rad/s or $-\omega_e/3P$ mechanical rad/s. Both components have $3P$ pole-pairs. Relative to the rotor, the angular velocity of the forward component is $\omega_e/3 - \omega_e = -2/3\ \omega_e$ electrical rad/s or $\omega_e/3P - \omega_e/P = -2/3\ \omega_e/P$ mechanical rad/s. Since there are $3P$ pole-pairs, the electrical frequency generated in the rotor is $3P \times [-2/3\ \omega_e/P] = -2\omega_e$ rad/s.

Relative to the rotor, the angular velocity of the backward component is $-\omega_e/3 - \omega_e = -4/3\ \omega_e$ electrical rad/s or $-\omega_e/3P - \omega_e/P = -4/3\ \omega_e/P$ mechanical rad/s. Since there are $3P$ pole-pairs, the frequency generated in the rotor is $3P \times [-4/3\ \omega_e/P] = -4\omega_e$ rad/s.

For a wye-connected machine with no neutral connection there can be no zero-sequence currents under normal operating conditions, but in the closed delta connection there is nothing to restrict them. According to our theory and eqns. (12.111) and (12.112) in particular, they can be completely suppressed in windings whose triplen-harmonic winding factors are all zero, even when the winding is otherwise unbalanced. If this is not the case, one must try to eliminate triplen-harmonic EMFs from the phases by profiling the airgap flux-density due to the magnets. The former method is surer.

An alternative model of negative-sequence imbalance is shown in Fig. 12.15*a*. The unbalanced phasors $\mathbf{I}_1$, $\mathbf{I}_2$, $\mathbf{I}_3$ form a closed triangle, so that there is no zero-sequence component and the neutral point is at the centroid in the star diagram, Fig. 12.15*b*. The balanced set $\mathbf{I}_1'$, $\mathbf{I}_2'$, $\mathbf{I}_3'$ forms an isosceles triangle, with $\mathbf{I}_1' = \mathbf{I}_1$. The imbalance is formed by disturbing $\mathbf{I}_2$ and $\mathbf{I}_3$ by displacing the top vertex of the triangle by $\mathbf{I}_N$.[119]

The resultant MMF of the unbalanced set $\mathbf{I}_1$, $\mathbf{I}_2$, $\mathbf{I}_3$ is equal to the sum of the resultant MMF of the balanced set $\mathbf{I}_1'$, $\mathbf{I}_2'$, $\mathbf{I}_3'$ and the MMF of the single-phase current $\mathbf{I}_N$ flowing in phases 2 and 3.

---

[119] Neumann R., *Symmetrical Component Analysis of Unsymmetrical Polyphase Systems*, Pitman, London, 1939.

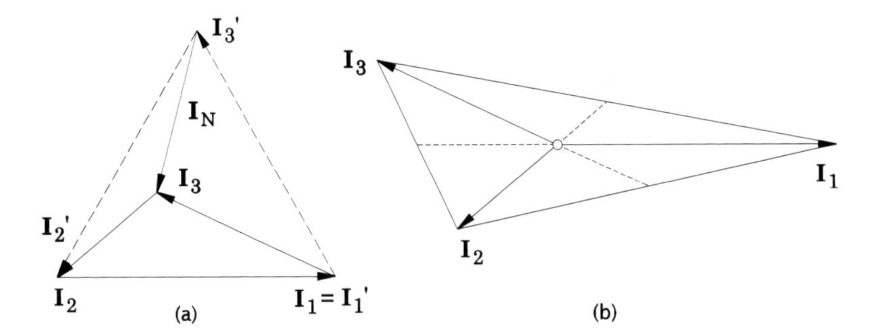

Fig. 12.15 Single-parameter imbalance, with no zero-sequence component.

From Fig. 12.15,

$$\mathbf{I}_1 = \mathbf{I}_1'; \qquad \mathbf{I}_2 = \mathbf{I}_2' - \mathbf{I}_N; \qquad \mathbf{I}_3 = \mathbf{I}_3' + \mathbf{I}_N. \tag{12.114}$$

These equations can be solved to find $\mathbf{I}_N$:

$$\mathbf{I}_N = \left[(\mathbf{I}_3 - \mathbf{I}_3') - (\mathbf{I}_2 - \mathbf{I}_2')\right]/2 = I_N e^{-j\theta_N}. \tag{12.115}$$

The forward MMF component due to $\mathbf{I}_N$ at the fundamental frequency is

$$A_{fmn} = \frac{m I_N \mathbf{F}_m}{2R}\Big\{-\cos\left[m(\phi - h/P) - (\omega_e t - \theta_N) + \gamma_{mn}\right] + \cos\left[m(\phi + h/P) - (\omega_e t - \theta_N) + \gamma_{mn}\right]\Big\}, \tag{12.116}$$

a messy expression that shows this method of "parameterizing" the imbalance to be unpromising.

To summarize, the purpose of all this analysis is to provide a basis for defining imbalance in terms of a single parameter, accompanied by a statement that the imbalance contains "only negative sequence" or "only zero sequence" in addition to the main positive sequence component. By this means we can attach a precise mathematical definition to a description such as "10% imbalance" without the need for a symmetrical component analysis. The equations for the rotating ampere-conductor distributions A_{fmn} and A_{bmn} are equally precisely defined and can be used as excitation terms in the calculation of rotor eddy-current losses caused by imbalance.

Fig. 12.16 Rotor with segmented magnets

12.4.3 Segmented magnets and finite-length effects

Magnets are often divided into blocks which are isolated from one another electrically; see Fig. 12.16. They are nearly always divided in the circumferential direction with at least one block per pole. Further division in the circumferential direction is common, especially in larger machines. Segmentation in the axial direction is also common, even in small machines. A basic reason for the segmentation is to keep the individual blocks of magnets small, for obvious manufacturing reasons. But segmentation also divides the eddy-current paths into smaller loops, increasing the effective resistance. Provided that the eddy-currents are *resistance-limited*, this will decrease the associated power loss.

The analysis of the effects of segmentation falls outside the scope of 2-dimensional analysis, while full 3-dimensional analysis is generally not feasible except by numerical methods. For rapid calculation there is no alternative other than to use approximate estimates, and a number of methods are developed below. Suffice it to say that these methods generally do not rigorously obey Maxwell's equations. Unless tested or calibrated, they are fraught with risk, and their practical usefulness is their only justification. Nevertheless, approximate estimates are inevitable in engineering, and valuable when used with proper care.

Circumferential segmentation can in principle be included in a conventional 2-dimensional formulation, solving the complex Helmholtz equation by separation of variables, but it is necessary to subdivide the magnet regions into isolated segments, with air in the "interpolar" regions between them. Such solutions are difficult and rare, the best (and possibly the only) published example being that of Deng. Zhu embarked on a similar analytical path but he represented the magnets by a single region, a continuous ring, and subsequently integrated the eddy-current loss density only over the actual magnet material. He did, however, include a continuous conductive sleeve.

The main method developed here is based on the 2-dimensional solution for a continuous ring, which is then segmented and subjected to "residual current suppression" in each segment. This approach can be justified only for eddy-currents that are approximately resistance-limited.

Axial segmentation and finite length. Eddy currents which are induced to flow in the axial direction must close their paths at the ends of the machine. If the ratio of the magnet axial length to the harmonic pole-pitch is small, the additional impedance of the "closure" sections may not be negligible.

Axial segmentation could, in theory, be analyzed by postulating a harmonic variation of the field in the z-direction. This very old idea (Wood and Concordia; Angst; Preston and Reece) was first formulated to deal with finite-length effects, which are approximated by postulating a series of rotors stacked end-to-end, possibly with a gap between each pair. If it works for finite-length effect it must also work for multiply-segmented magnets. The basic notion can be expressed in terms of an extended solution for the vector potential in the form of an infinite series of axial harmonics m,

$$A(r,\theta,t) = \mathbf{A}(r) \cos p\theta \sin mz \, e^{j\omega t} \qquad (12.117)$$

in which m is an axial wavenumber. The idea was used recently by Kirtley *et al*, but a much more detailed development was given 20 years earlier by Ralph.[120]

[120] Lawrenson P.J. and Ralph M.C., *The general 3-dimensional solution of eddy-current and Laplacian fields in cylindrical structures*, Proc. IEE, Vol. 117, pp. 469-472 (1970).

Ralph discovered previously unknown terms in the solution of the complex diffusion equation, including one with linear variation with z. This raises questions about the rigour of simplified approaches such as the one in eqn. (12.117). Lawrenson commented (modestly but somewhat prophetically) that

> "the complexity of the solutions probably leaves the reader sharing the view . . . that contemplation of anything more algebraically complex is unlikely to be worthwhile and purely numerical approaches must be taken up"

Numerical approaches certainly have been "taken up".

The methods developed here for axial end-effects and axial segmentation are based on postulated eddy-current paths at the ends of the magnets (or magnet segments). These paths have a predefined shape which makes it possible to estimate not only the change in the path resistance but also the change in the path EMF which results from finite length and segmentation. A similar approach used by Russell and Norsworthy is also summarized later. But first we consider circumferential segmentation.

12.4.3.1 Circumferential segmentation

Fig. 12.17 shows a magnet of width β in the circumferential direction. It is shown without curvature, to clarify the analysis. Also shown is a wave of the current-density that *would* be induced by a harmonic field component rotating relative to the magnet, *if* the magnet were a complete unbroken ring. This wave is labelled J, and it can be calculated using the methods of earlier sections. The diagram is drawn for one instant in time, and end-effects are neglected so that the model is 2-dimensional and invariant in the axial (z) direction. The eddy-currents are not necessarily assumed to be resistance-limited.

The position of the magnet relative to the J-wave can be defined as the *phase* ξ of the centre-line of the magnet relative to the J-wave: thus

$$\xi = \frac{\theta_1 + \theta_2}{2} \quad \text{and} \quad \beta = \theta_2 - \theta_1 \tag{12.118}$$

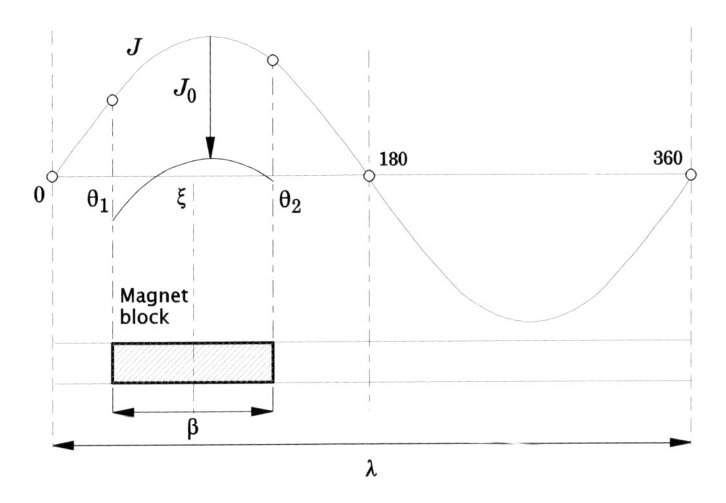

Fig. 12.17 Magnet segmentation in the circumferential direction

or

$$\theta_1 = \xi - \frac{\beta}{2}; \qquad \theta_2 = \xi + \frac{\beta}{2}. \tag{12.119}$$

The angles θ_1, θ_2, ξ and β are all measured here in electrical degrees or radians relative to the harmonic wavelength λ. Thus if β_m is the magnet width in actual mechanical radians, $\beta = \beta_m \times 2\pi/\lambda$.

If the J-wave is represented as $J_1 \sin\theta$, the integral

$$\int_{\theta_1}^{\theta_2} J_1 \sin\theta \, d\theta \tag{12.120}$$

represents the net current that would flow in a *section of a complete ring* of magnet between the angles θ_1 and θ_2. This integral is not in general zero. However, the net current in a magnet block of finite width β must be zero, because there is no connection by which it can be routed to a return path in another magnet carrying current in the opposite direction. In fact the net current must return through the magnet block itself. The *distribution* of return current-density across the cross-section of the magnet block is not known *a priori*; but it can be supposed to be uniform on the grounds that any non-uniformity would imply that there were loops in the return current path containing induced EMFs, when the induced EMFs have in fact already been accounted for by the solution of the field equations leading to the J-wave.[121]

Thus with a uniformly-distributed return current density J_0,

$$\int_{\theta_1}^{\theta_2} (J_0 + J_1 \sin\theta)\, d\theta = 0, \qquad (12.121)$$

from which

$$J_0 = J_1 \frac{\cos\theta_2 - \cos\theta_1}{\theta_2 - \theta_1} = -J_1 \sin\xi \frac{\sin(\beta/2)}{\beta/2}. \qquad (12.122)$$

The loss in the magnet block is proportional to $(J_0 + J_1 \sin\theta)^2$ integrated over β : thus if $q = J_0/J_1$

$$\begin{aligned} \Lambda &= J_1^2 \int_{\theta_1}^{\theta_2} (q + \sin\theta)^2 d\theta \\ &= J_1^2 \left[(q^2 + \frac{1}{2})\beta + 4q \sin\frac{\beta}{2} \sin\xi - \frac{1}{2}\cos 2\xi \sin\beta \right]. \end{aligned} \qquad (12.123)$$

When $\beta = 360k^\circ$ (for integer k), the magnet width is an integral multiple of the wavelength λ of the harmonic field component, and eqn. (12.121) is automatically satisfied, with $J_0 = 0$, regardless of the phase or position of the J-wave relative to the magnet. The harmonic loss in a magnet whose width is equal to an integral multiple of the harmonic wavelength is therefore the same as would be calculated in a segment of a complete ring according to the theory described earlier using Bessel functions. The integral Λ in eqn. (12.123) then degenerates to

$$\Lambda_0 = J_1^2 \frac{1}{2}\beta. \qquad (12.124)$$

and so it becomes possible to characterize the effect of circumferential segmentation of the magnets by the loss reduction factor

---

[121] In 2D finite-element programs the imposition of zero net current is sometimes achieved by a related process (often without proof), in which the end-faces of the conducting regions are shorted together.

$$\frac{\Lambda}{\Lambda_0} = \frac{2}{\beta}\left[(q^2+\frac{1}{2})\beta + 4q\sin\frac{\beta}{2}\sin\xi - \frac{1}{2}\cos 2\xi\sin\beta\right]. \quad (12.125)$$

An example helps to illustrate the effect. In Fig. 12.17 the magnet width is $\beta = 90^\circ$ relative to the harmonic wavelength, and its phase position is $\xi = 80^\circ$. Thus $\theta_1 = 80 - 90/2 = 35^\circ$ and $\theta_2 = 80 + 90/2 = 125^\circ$. Eqn. (12.122) gives $q = J_0/J_1 = -0{\cdot}88664$; then with $\beta = \pi/2$ eqn. (12.125) gives the loss reduction factor $\Lambda/\Lambda_0 = 0{\cdot}0207$. This seems a substantial reduction, but it needs further comment.

First, this value applies only at one instant corresponding to the phase angle $\xi = 80^\circ$. As the cycle progresses and the harmonic wave moves relative to the magnet, Λ/Λ_0 varies and there are instants when it is equal to 1. Therefore we can expect the average value of the loss reduction factor will be markedly greater than 0·0207.

Secondly, a magnet width of $\beta = 90^\circ$ means that the width of the magnet segment is one-quarter of the harmonic wavelength. If we consider, say, the 5th space-harmonic of the stator winding, it has a wavelength at fundamental frequency equal to $1/5^{th}$ of a pole-pitch. Consequently $\beta = 90^\circ$ for this harmonic implies that the magnet is segmented into 20 blocks per pole — rather a large number. A magnet with 180° arc *not segmented* would have $\beta = 5 \times 90 = 450^\circ$, and it can be verified from eqn. (12.125) that the loss reduction factor does not fall much below 1. A magnet with 80%pole-arc (144°) would have $\beta = 360^\circ$ relative to the 5th winding space-harmonic, and in this case the loss reduction factor would be 1. Of course the magnet "region" is only 80% filled with magnet, so there is a reduction of 0·8 relative to a full-ring magnet; but there is no reduction due to the "residual current suppression" effect.

The example with $\beta = 90^\circ$ and $\xi = 80^\circ$ is shown graphically in Fig. 12.18. The graph J_1 is the "original" current distribution and the graph J is the net current distribution with "residual suppression". Also shown are the squares of these two graphs. At this phase position the reduction in squared current-density is substantial.

Fig. 12.19 shows the same magnet and the same harmonic wave at a different phase position, $\xi = 0$. At this instant the net current in the magnet block is *naturally* zero; J_0 is not necessary and is zero.

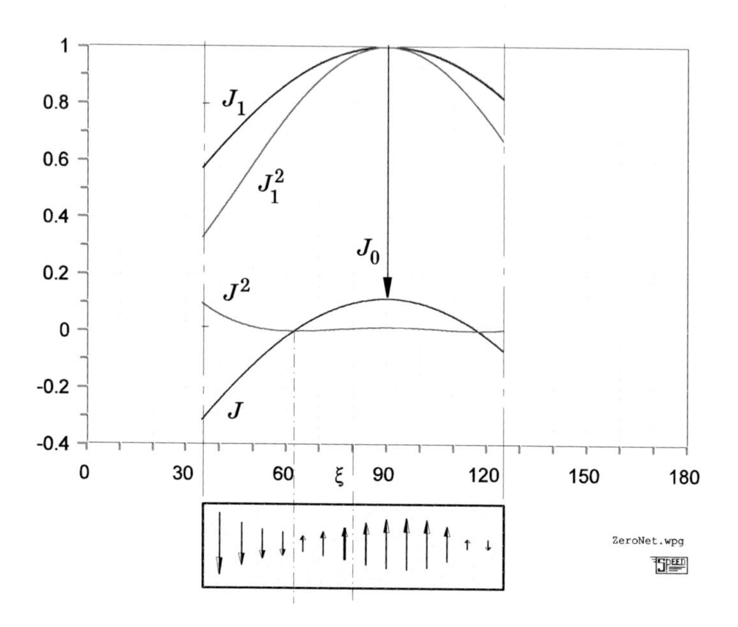

Fig. 12.18 Example of current distribution with "residual suppression"

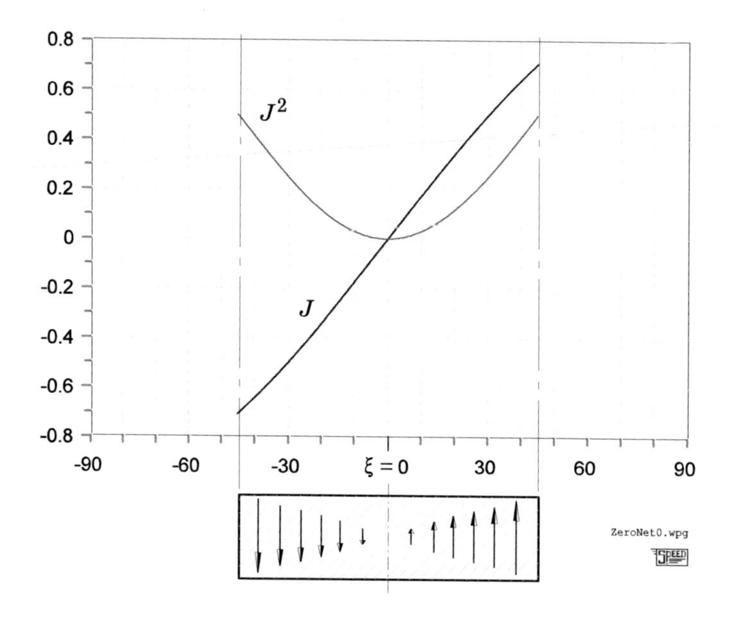

Fig. 12.19 An instant when the residual suppression current is zero

The arrows in Figs. 12.18 and 12.19 show schematically the direction and magnitude of the current density in the magnet block, "seen from above". At the instant $\xi = 0$ in Fig. 12.19 the distribution is momentarily symmetrical with positive current in one half of the block, and negative in the other half. But at the instant $\xi = 80°$ in Fig. 12.18, it is asymmetrical. When β is an integral multiple of the harmonic wavelength, the distribution is similar to the one in Fig. 12.19, except that as ξ advances the arrows at one end leave the block *and re-appear at the other end*, while J_0 remains zero at all times.

The loss reduction factor eqn. (12.125) and the diagrams in Figs. 12.18 and 12.19 are specific to one field harmonic. This means that simplified methods of allowing for segmentation (such as equivalent resistivity) are hardly likely to be successful. Moreover, eqn. (12.125) cannot be used to introduce the effect of segmentation into the results of a 2-dimensional finite-element calculation.

Average loss reduction factor over a complete harmonic cycle — The loss reduction factor Λ/Λ_0 in eqn. (12.125) must be integrated over one harmonic cycle to get the average value. With q expressed in terms of ξ from eqn. (12.122) and $a = -2/\beta \times \sin(\beta/2)$, Λ/Λ_0 can be expressed as

$$\begin{aligned} u &= \frac{\Lambda}{\Lambda_0} \\ &= 1 - \frac{\sin\beta}{\beta} + \frac{2}{\beta}\left[\beta a^2 + 4a\sin\frac{\beta}{2} + \sin\beta\right]\sin^2\xi \end{aligned} \tag{12.126}$$

Then the average value of Λ/Λ_0 is given by

$$U = \frac{1}{2\pi}\int_0^{2\pi} u(\xi)\,d\xi = 1 - \left[\frac{\sin(\beta/2)}{\beta/2}\right]^2. \tag{12.127}$$

..a remarkably simple function.

For the example considered earlier with $\beta = 90°$ or $\pi/2$, we get $U = 0{\cdot}18943$. When $\beta = 2\pi$ or a multiple thereof, $U = 1$ as expected.

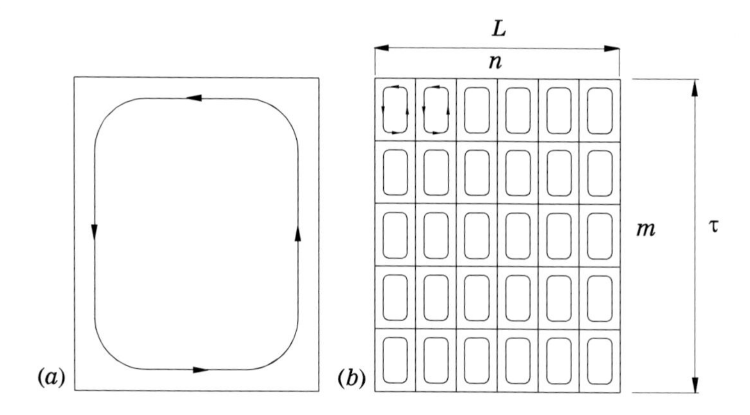

Fig. 12.20 Eddy-current break-up

12.4.3.2 Simplified analysis of double segmentation

Fig. 12.20 shows one eddy-current pole or loop in a magnet of axial length L. In (b) the magnet is divided into $n \times m$ segments. If the driving E-field is unaffected by the segmentation, only the effect on the resistance of the eddy-current path needs to be considered.

The path length of eddy-currents in the monolithic magnet is of the order $2(L + \tau)$, where τ is the pole-pitch of the exciting space-harmonic. If the induced EMF this loop is E, the driving EMF in one element of the segmented magnet will be of the order of E/mn and the path length will be of the order of $2(L_{stk}/n + \tau/m)$. Therefore the total losses will be changed in the ratio

$$\frac{W_{\text{segmented}}}{W_{\text{monolithic}}} = \frac{mn \dfrac{(E/mn)^2}{2(L/n + \tau/m)}}{\dfrac{E^2}{2(L + \tau)}} = \frac{L + \tau}{mL + n\tau}. \tag{12.128}$$

For example if L is approximately equal to the pole-pitch τ,

$$\frac{W_{\text{segmented}}}{W_{\text{monolithic}}} = \frac{2}{m + n}. \tag{12.129}$$

Thus if the magnet is segmented in both directions with $m = n = 10$, the losses should be reduced by a factor of $2/(10 + 10) = 0{\cdot}1$.

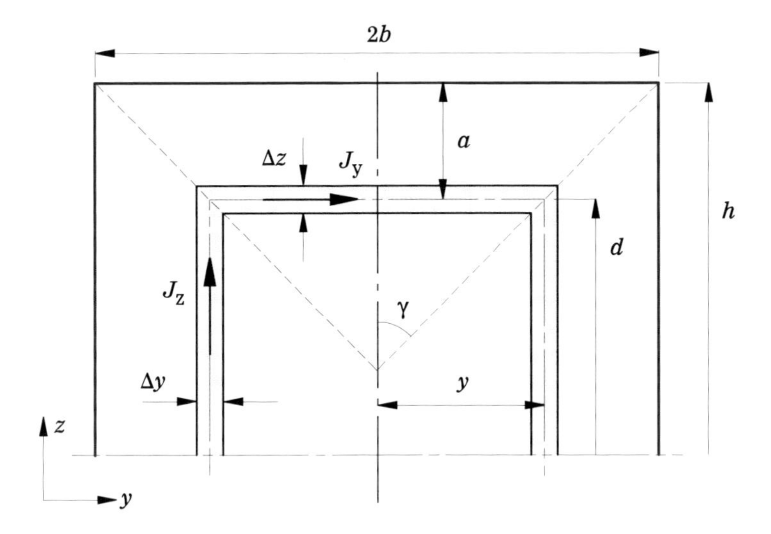

Fig. 12.21 Approximate calculation of end-effect

12.4.3.3 End-effect; segmentation in the axial direction

Fig. 12.21 shows half a block of magnet in rectangular coordinates. The direction of rotation is in the y direction and z is the axial coordinate. The axial length of the block is $2h$ and its width in the circumferential direction is $2b$. This width can be taken as the wavelength of the exciting harmonic.

Consider a filamentary loop of eddy-current. If the block was infinitely long in the axial direction, the current density in the filament would be $\mathbf{J}_{z0} = \sigma\mathbf{E} = \mathrm{j}\omega\sigma\mathbf{A}$, where $\mathbf{A}$ is the solution of the 2-dimensional field at the circumferential position y.

The cut edge of the magnet at $z = h$ forces all the current to veer into the circumferential direction and rejoin its return path. In Fig. 12.21 the current is assumed to be symmetrical about the centre-line of the block. It is further assumed that the current in the filament Δy turns abruptly into the circumferential direction and flows in a circumferential filament of width Δz such that

$$\mathbf{J}_{\mathrm{y}}\,\Delta z = \mathbf{J}_{\mathrm{z}}\,\Delta y. \tag{12.130}$$

The filament widths are further assumed to be related by

$$\frac{\Delta y}{\Delta z} = \tan \gamma = m, \tag{12.131}$$

where γ is an arbitrary angle defining the slope of the “break” line shown dashed in Fig. 12.21. Hence

$$\mathbf{J}_y = m\mathbf{J}_z. \tag{12.132}$$

Considering just one quadrant of the loop, the driving EMF can be identified as $\mathbf{E}d$. In the case where the magnet is infinitely long in the z direction we have $\mathbf{E}d = \rho\mathbf{J}_{z0}h$, where $\rho = 1/\sigma$ is the resistivity. When the length is finite, the filament acquires a second segment of length y in the y-direction, while the segment in the z-direction is shortened from h to d, where

$$d = h - a = h - \frac{b - y}{m}. \tag{12.133}$$

The shortening of the axial length reduces the EMF proportionally, while the addition of the second segment increases the total resistance. This is expressed by the equation

$$\mathbf{E}d = \rho\left[\mathbf{J}_z d + \mathbf{J}_y y\right] \tag{12.134}$$

which can be expanded as

$$\begin{aligned}\mathbf{E} &= \rho\mathbf{J}_z\left[1 + m\frac{y}{d}\right] = \rho\mathbf{J}_z\left[1 + \frac{my}{h - \dfrac{b - y}{m}}\right] \\ &= \rho\mathbf{J}_z\left[1 + \frac{m^2 y}{mh - (b - y)}\right],\end{aligned} \tag{12.135}$$

and so

$$\mathbf{J}_z = \frac{\mathbf{E}}{\rho\left[1 + \dfrac{m^2 y}{mh - (b - y)}\right]} \quad \text{with} \quad \mathbf{J}_y = m\mathbf{J}_z. \tag{12.136}$$

The current-density $\mathbf{J}_z$ is decreased by the factor in brackets.

However, the losses are proportional to

$$w = \rho(\mathbf{J}_z^2 d\Delta y + \mathbf{J}_y^2 y\Delta z) \tag{12.137}$$

and this can be expanded as

$$\begin{aligned} w &= \rho\mathbf{J}_z^2\left[d\Delta y + m^2 y\Delta z\right] \\ &= \rho\mathbf{J}_z^2\left[(mh - (b - y) + m^2 y\right]\frac{\Delta y}{m} \end{aligned} \tag{12.138}$$

Substituting for $\mathbf{J}_z$ from eqn. (12.136), and simplifying, we get

$$w = \frac{\mathbf{E}^2}{\rho}\frac{[mh - (b - y)]^2}{m[mh - (b - y) + m^2 y]}\Delta y. \tag{12.139}$$

If there is no end-effect we have simply

$$w_0 = \frac{\mathbf{E}^2}{\rho}h\,\Delta y. \tag{12.140}$$

Hence it is possible to define a loss reduction factor λ for the filament at y :

$$\lambda(y) = \frac{w}{w_0} = \frac{[mh - (b - y)]^2}{mh[mh - (b - y) + m^2 y]}. \tag{12.141}$$

If we normalize h and y to b by writing $\mathbf{h} = h/b$ and $\mathbf{y} = y/b$, this can be written

$$\lambda(\mathbf{y}) = \frac{w}{w_0} = \frac{[m\mathbf{h} - (1 - \mathbf{y})]^2}{m\mathbf{h}[m\mathbf{h} - (1 - \mathbf{y}) + m^2\mathbf{y}]}. \tag{12.142}$$

If $\gamma = 45^\circ$, $m = 1$ and the expression simplifies further:

$$\lambda(\mathbf{y}) = \frac{w}{w_0} = \frac{[\mathbf{h} - (1 - \mathbf{y})]^2}{\mathbf{h}[\mathbf{h} - 1 + 2\mathbf{y}]}. \tag{12.143}$$

A magnet which is long in the axial direction has $\mathbf{h} >> 1$, so that $\lambda(\mathbf{y}) \to 1$ for all values of y. For such long magnets the value of γ is not critical: see Fig. 12.22. However, in short magnets γ will have a minimum value. For example a "square" magnet has $\mathbf{h} = 1$ or $h = b$. In this case γ must not be less than 45°, giving $m > 1$.

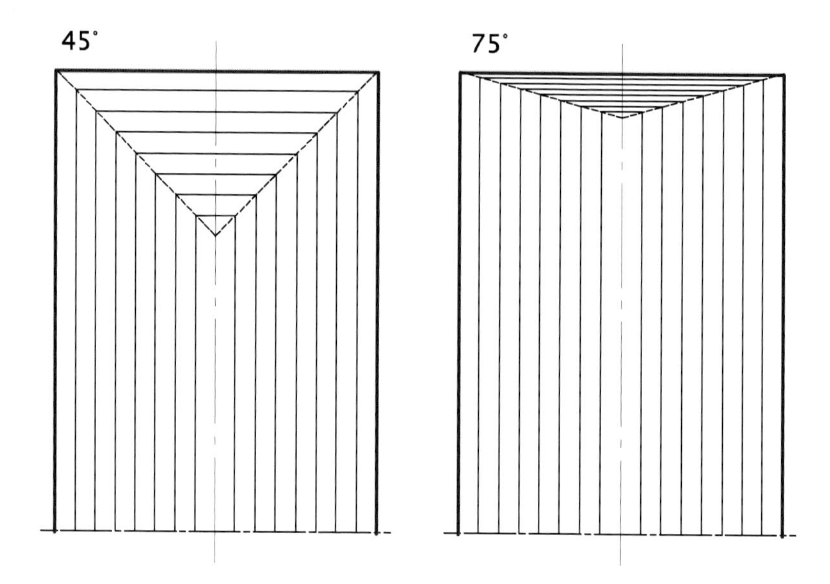

Fig. 12.22 "Long" magnet with two values of γ, 45° and 75°

A magnet for which $\mathbf{h}$ = 0·5 (or $h = b/2$) restricts γ to values greater than arc tan(2) = 63·4°. These limits of course have no physical basis, but are constraints imposed by the modelling assumptions.

The loss reduction factor for the whole block is obtained as the average of $\lambda(\mathbf{y})$ for all the filaments, or

$$\Lambda = \frac{1}{1}\int_0^1 \lambda(y)\,dy. \tag{12.144}$$

This can be integrated numerically or formally, giving

$$\Lambda(\mathbf{h}) = \frac{(AC - B + 1/C)\ln(1+C) + (B+1/2)C - 1}{C^2 k(k-1)} \tag{12.145}$$

where $k = m\mathbf{h}$, $A = (k-1)^2$; $B = 2(k-1)$; and $C = (1+m^2)/(k-1)$.

Fig. 12.23 shows examples of $\Lambda(\mathbf{h})$ calculated by eqn. (12.145) for various values of the magnet length/width ratio, $\mathbf{h}$. The parameter k is arbitrary and should be adjusted to match test data.

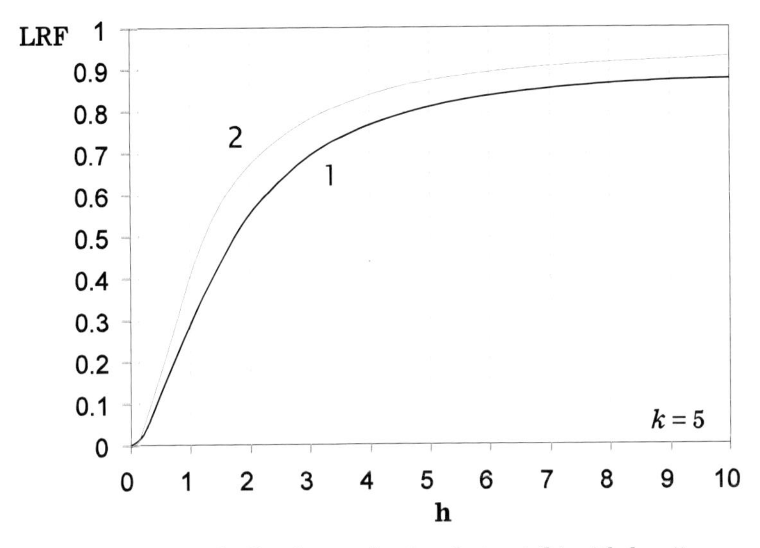

Fig. 12.23 End-effect loss reduction factor $\Lambda(\mathbf{h})$ with $k = 5$
1 — Eqn. (12.145); 2 — Russell & Norsworthy

The overall factor Λ in eqn. (12.145) is so far simply an end-effect factor for the losses in magnets of different length/width ratio **h**. Now suppose we start with a full-length magnet with a certain value of length/width ratio $\mathbf{h}_1$ and an end-effect factor Λ_1. If this magnet is divided into n segments in the axial direction, the end-effect factor for each segment becomes Λ_n, calculated with $\mathbf{h}_n = \mathbf{h}_1/n$. Although Λ_n operates on only $(1/n)$ of the losses, there are now n segments, so the overall effect is that the end-effect factor is Λ_n for the whole array, instead of Λ_1.

As an example, suppose we start with a full-length magnet having $\mathbf{h} = 3$, and divide it into 3 segments. The end-effect factor with $\gamma = 60°$ is 0·699 for the undivided magnet, and 0·2935 for the divided magnet. Thus the division into 3 segments reduces the loss by a factor of 0·2935/0·699 = 0·419.

It should be said that this end-effect analysis is a rough-and-ready estimate, and by no means "analytical" in the sense of conforming with Maxwell's equations.

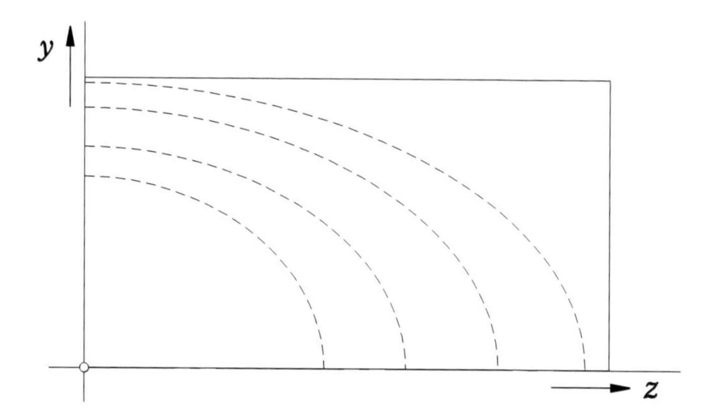

Fig. 12.24 Russell and Norsworthy's eddy-current flow-lines

12.4.3.4 Russell and Norsworthy's method

Russell and Norsworthy studied the stator can losses in a screened-rotor induction motor.[122] Their analysis included the effect of finite axial length. It also included the effect of overhangs in the axial direction (that is, where the can is longer than the axial length of the stack). The overhangs could have different thicknesses and conductivities from those of the central section of the can.

Fig. 12.24 shows the essential concept in Russell and Norsworthy's finite-length analysis. They solved a form of Laplace's equation in the plane of a rolled-out can in cartesian coordinates, to establish flow-lines for the eddy-currents in the can. Fig. 12.24 shows one quadrant of this model. Russell and Norsworthy measured these flow-lines (using a pair of point-contact probes with a high-impedance voltmeter, under conditions of single-phase excitation), and showed good agreement with the calculated lines. The solution included the current-density, from which the loss is calculated. They presented the result in terms of a coefficient K_s to be used with the power loss calculated by eqn. (12.173) on p. 625.

K_s is equivalent to Λ in the previous section, and a comparison is shown in Fig. 12.23.

[122]Russell RL and Norsworthy KH, *Eddy currents and wall losses in screened-rotor induction motors*, Proc. IEE, Vol. 105A, pp. 163-175, 1958.

Russell and Norsworthy's formula for K_s is

$$K_s = 1 - \frac{\tanh\left[\dfrac{pl}{a}\right]}{\dfrac{pl}{a}(1 + \lambda)} \tag{12.146}$$

where $2l$ is the length of the can (i.e., L_{stk}); a is its mean radius; and p is the number of pole-pairs. For an open-ended can,

$$\lambda = \tanh\left[\frac{pl}{a}\right]\tanh\left[\alpha\frac{pl}{a}\right] \tag{12.147}$$

where α is the per-unit overhang, that is, the overhang length at one end divided by l. If the overhang lengths are different, K_s can be calculated separately for the two ends and then averaged. For a can with zero-resistance end-rings, tanh $[\alpha pl/a]$ is simply replaced by its inverse, coth $[\alpha pl/a]$.

Fig. 12.23 shows K_s compared with the loss reduction factor calculated by eqn. (12.145) for various values of the magnet length/width ratio, **h**. The equivalence is based on

$$\frac{pl}{a} = \frac{\pi}{2}\frac{h}{b} = \frac{\pi}{2}\mathbf{h}. \tag{12.148}$$

The difference between curves 1 and 2 in Fig. 12.23 is partly due to the explicit way in which eqn. (12.145) allows for the reduction of driving EMF in the eddy-current loops. In Russell and Norsworthy this allowance appears to be implicit in the shape of the current flow-lines. They achieved good agreement with test data, and their work has since been used elsewhere with satisfactory results for the calculation of stator can- loss. Russell and Norsworthy's analysis is based on the fundamental harmonic of the main field (2-pole in their test), using a formal but approximate solution of Laplace's equation for the flow lines. In contrast, the method leading up to eqn. (12.145) is relatively arbitrary.

In the absence of much more expensive methods based on 3D finite-elements, there is some merit in comparing these approximate methods, but of course the only certainty is that obtained by test.

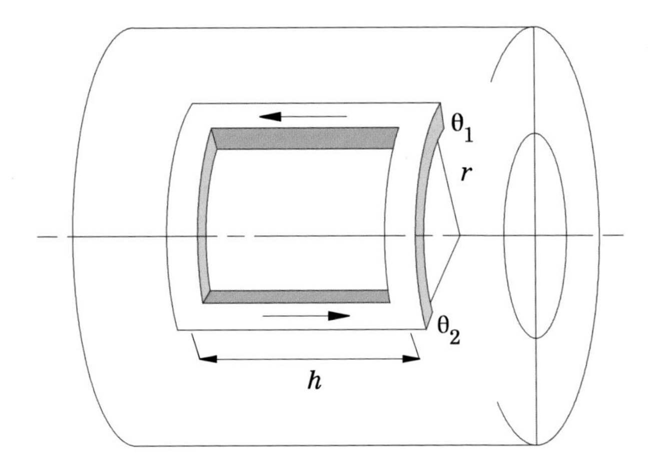

Fig. 12.25 Filamentary "coil" inside a conductive cylindrical region

12.4.3.5 Alternative analysis of segmented magnets

When the eddy-currents in the magnets are resistance-limited, they can be postulated to flow in predefined physical circuits, Fig. 12.25. The resistance of each filamentary loop can be calculated from its dimensions, while the EMF induced in it can be calculated from the 2-dimensional field solution developed earlier. In terms of this solution, the magnets will be found in a non-conducting region since, by the definition of resistance-limited, the eddy-currents in the magnets have negligible effect on the magnetic field. By the same token, the inductance of the filamentary loops can be ignored.[123]

Consider a filamentary coil embedded in a conductive cylindrical region representing a segmented magnet, Fig. 12.25. It lies on a cylinder of radius r whose thickness t is much less than r.

[123] Although this model of the eddy-current paths in the magnets is crude and arbitrary, its merit is that it deals directly with the effects of segmentation in both directions. More complex methods such as the finite-element method or the use of quasi-3D solutions employing infinite series of analytic functions such as eqn. (12.117) have not delivered calculation procedures that are fast enough for the initial stages of design, and their formulations give very limited physical interpretation. It is possible that in future refinements, the shapes of the eddy-current paths could be made more "analytical", and that the inductances and mutual inductances of the filamentary loops could be calculated and introduced into the calculation.

The straight sides of the filament are located at angles θ_1 and θ_2, and they subtend an angle β at the axis, so that

$$\beta = \theta_2 - \theta_1. \tag{12.149}$$

The straight sides are, in effect, strips of length h, width w_b, and thickness t, giving a cross-sectional area $w_b t$ for current flow. The curved sides are strips of length $r\beta$, width w_a and cross-sectional area $w_a t$. The resistance of the loop is

$$R = \frac{2h}{\sigma w_b t} + \frac{2r\beta}{\sigma w_a t} = \frac{2}{\sigma t}\left[\frac{h}{w_b} + \frac{r\beta}{w_a}\right]. \tag{12.150}$$

The flux ϕ linking the loop is given in general by the line-integral of vector potential $\mathbf{A}$ around the circumference, $2(h + r\beta)$; but if $\mathbf{A}$ has only a z-component the integral degenerates to

$$\phi = h(\mathbf{A}_2 - \mathbf{A}_1) \tag{12.151}$$

where $\mathbf{A}_1$ is the value at θ_1 and $\mathbf{A}_2$ is the value at θ_2. If we reintroduce the common factor $e^{j(\omega t - p\theta)}$,

$$\phi = h\mathbf{A}(r)\left[e^{j(\omega t - p\theta_2)} - e^{j(\omega t - p\theta_1)}\right] \tag{12.152}$$

If we write $\theta_0 = (\theta_1 + \theta_2)/2$, the θ-coordinate of the centres of the curved sides, this reduces to

$$\phi = 2h\mathbf{A}(r)\sin p\frac{\beta}{2}\, e^{j(\omega t - p\theta_0 - \pi/2)}. \tag{12.153}$$

The EMF induced in the loop is $d\phi/dt$ or

$$\mathbf{e} = j\omega \times 2h\mathbf{A}(r)\sin p\frac{\beta}{2}\, e^{j(\omega t - p\theta_0 - \pi/2)} \tag{12.154}$$

and the (peak) phasor value is

$$\mathbf{E} = j\omega \times 2h\mathbf{A}(r)\sin p\frac{\beta}{2}. \tag{12.155}$$

Finally the power loss in the filamentary coil is calculated as

$$W = \frac{1}{2}\mathrm{Re}\,\frac{\mathbf{E}\mathbf{E}^*}{R} = \frac{2\,\omega^2 h^2 \sin^2(p\beta/2)\,\mathrm{Re}[\mathbf{A}\mathbf{A}^*]}{R}. \tag{12.156}$$

12.4.4 Slot ripple

Slot ripple (also known as tooth ripple) refers to the modulation of the airgap flux-density distribution (B_{gap}) caused by the stator slot-openings. The modulation causes surface losses in the rotor, due to eddy-currents which are excited by the rotation of the rotor past the stationary "dips" in the flux wave. Calculation of the slot modulation and its effects is an old topic in electrical machine theory; Carter's coefficient is well-known example of it. Freeman used a sophisticated procedure involving elliptic integrals to determine the harmonics in the flux-density. The method of Zhu and Howe described below is a modern development adapted for brushless PM machines. Of course the finite-element method is also a powerful and flexible method for calculating the slot modulation.

The simplest method for calculating slot-ripple loss in a thin sleeve is "flux-dip-sweeping".[124] This method uses the calculated magnetostatic slot-modulation in the B_{gap} distribution. It is closely related to the calculation of losses in *stator* cans due to the rotation of the main field. Its main limitation is the assumption that the eddy-currents are resistance-limited. It is also not suited for calculating magnet loss, because the slot-modulation tends to vary significantly through the thickness of the magnets.

The eddy-current reaction (skin effect) is important in high-speed PM machines, and in these cases the thickness of the conductive components must be taken into account. Lawrenson *et al* developed the analysis of the surface losses to include the reaction effect of the eddy-currents, pointing out the limitation of previous works which dismissed or ignored it.[125] They used an equivalent AC current-sheet on the bore of the stator, whose wavelength was equal to the tooth-pitch, and whose magnitude was just sufficient to establish a flux variation equal to the variation calculated without eddy-currents or rotation by an earlier method based on conformal transformation.

---

[124] The term "flux-dip-sweeping" is meant to describe the movement of the rotor as it sweeps past fixed dips in the flux.

[125] Lawrenson PJ, Reece P and Ralph MC, *Tooth-ripple losses in solid poles*, Proc. IEE., Vol. 113, No. 4, April 1966, pp. 657-662 See also Oberretl K, *Eddy Current Losses in Solid Poles of Synchronous Machines at No-Load and On Load*, IEEE Transactions, Vol. PAS-91, 1972, pp. 152-160.

The AC current-sheet was then used to calculate the resulting field distribution in a simple 3-region cartesian solution of the complex diffusion equation.[126] Lawrenson limited his analysis to the fundamental slot-harmonic, allowing for saturation by means of saturated permeabilities in an otherwise linear analysis.

Lawrenson's method is implemented by first determining the slot modulation in the B_{gap} distribution by the method of Weber, as described by Heller and Hamata and subsequently extended by Zhu and Howe.[127] The modulated B_{gap} distribution is Fourier-analyzed to determine its harmonic components. In rotor coordinates, the typical n^{th} harmonic in the B_{gap} distribution is of the form

$$B_n \cos n(\theta - \omega t) \qquad (12.157)$$

which represents a field with n pole-pairs rotating past the rotor at the relative angular velocity ω, the synchronous speed. For the fundamental slot-ripple harmonic, n is equal to the number of slots, and generally only the fundamental (and possibly the 2nd harmonic) is significant. For each harmonic current-sheet $K_n \sin n\theta$, K_n can be determined from the equations in Hughes and Miller [*op. cit.*]. From here the calculation of the slot-ripple field and losses proceeds in the same way as for stator MMF and time harmonics, as described earlier.

Slot-ripple is related to the concept of *permeance harmonics*. As the rotor rotates past the stator slots, the overall permeance is modulated at the slot-passing frequency, causing the main flux to pulsate at this frequency. However, permeance is a lumped-circuit concept rather than a distributed-field concept, and so the calculation of permeance variations or flux variations is useful only in the context of a lumped-parameter magnetic circuit model. This approach is used later for the IPM. For surface-magnet machines, where the magnets (and any cans) are located in the distributed and time-varying field, a field-theory approach is more appropriate.

---

[126] When the skin-depth is small enough, it is even possible to treat the magnets as infinitely thick, on the grounds that the skin effect (and also the natural $\beta(r)$ attenuation) tends to limit the eddy-current to a layer near the surface. Nothing happens beneath that layer, so its depth ceases to affect the losses.

[127] Zhu Z.Q., Ng K., Schofield N. and Howe D., *Improved analytical modelling of rotor eddy current loss in brushless machines equipped with surface-mounted permanent magnets*, IEE Proc.-Electr. Power Appl., Vol. 151, No. 6, November 2004, pp. 641-650.

Determination of the slot-modulation — For surface-magnet machines the effective airgap is given by

$$g' = k_C g + \frac{L_m}{\mu_{rec}} \qquad (12.158)$$

where k_C is Carter's coefficient. g' is generally much larger than the physical airgap g. Furthermore, PM machines are often designed with a small number of slots/pole, so that the ratio of slot-opening s to slot-pitch τ is often relatively small. It is common to find that the ratios s/g and s/τ are at the extremes of the classical analysis, necessitating a revised field analysis to be sure of a method that is appropriate for PM machines.[128] Here we use Weber's method extended by Zhu [*op. cit.*], in which the modulation in the B_{gap} wave is given by

$$\begin{aligned} B(r,\alpha) &= B_m \left[1 - \beta(r) \left(1 + \cos \pi\alpha/\alpha_s \right) \right], \quad 0 < |\alpha| < \alpha_s; \\ B(r,\alpha) &= B_m, \quad \alpha_s < |\alpha| < \gamma_s/2. \end{aligned} \qquad (12.159)$$

where α is the angle measured from the slot centre-line, γ_s is the slot-pitch angle corresponding to the linear tooth-pitch τ, and B_m is the maximum flux-density that would be obtained without slotting. Also

$$\alpha_s = 0{\cdot}8\,\alpha_o = 1{\cdot}6 \times \alpha_o/2 \qquad (12.160)$$

where α_o is the slot-opening angle s/r_S, and r_S is the stator bore radius. Thus the angle α_s is extended 60% beyond the edges of the slot ($\alpha_o/2$) to account for the observed fact that the slot modulation "dip" is wider than the slot opening. $\beta(r)$ is half the maximum relative "dip" in the B_{gap} wave at the centre-line of the slot, so if B_d is the actual maximum dip, we have $\beta = B_d/B_m \times ½$.

Whereas Heller and Hamata provide a graph of β vs. s/g without derivation at a single radius (the rotor surface radius), Zhu re-calculates $\beta(r)$ as a function of r from first-principles using conformal transformation, and validates the calculation with finite-elements. (The same has been done with the equations reproduced below).

---

[128] Freeman's method could also be used, [1962]. The approach described here is quicker but more approximate, although it can easily be checked (or even substituted) by finite-element analysis which was not available in 1962.

It is shown that $\beta(r)$ varies across the airgap and right through the magnet, as shown in Fig. 12.26. Zhu's equation for $\beta(r)$ is

$$\beta(r) = \frac{1}{2}\left[1 - \frac{1}{\sqrt{1 + (1 + v^2)/u^2}}\right] \tag{12.161}$$

where v is the solution of

$$y\frac{\pi}{s} = \frac{1}{2}\ln\left[\frac{\sqrt{a^2 + v^2} + v}{\sqrt{a^2 + v^2} - v}\right] + u\arctan\frac{uv}{\sqrt{a^2 + v^2}} \tag{12.162}$$

with

$$u = \frac{2g'}{s} \quad \text{and} \quad a^2 = 1 + u^2. \tag{12.163}$$

and

$$y = r - r_S + g' \qquad \text{interior rotor} \tag{12.164}$$

$$y = r_S - r + g' \qquad \text{exterior rotor} \tag{12.165}$$

For surface-magnet machines B_m is taken as the mean flux-density at the rotor surface. Then $B(r,\alpha)$ is determined from eqn. (12.159).

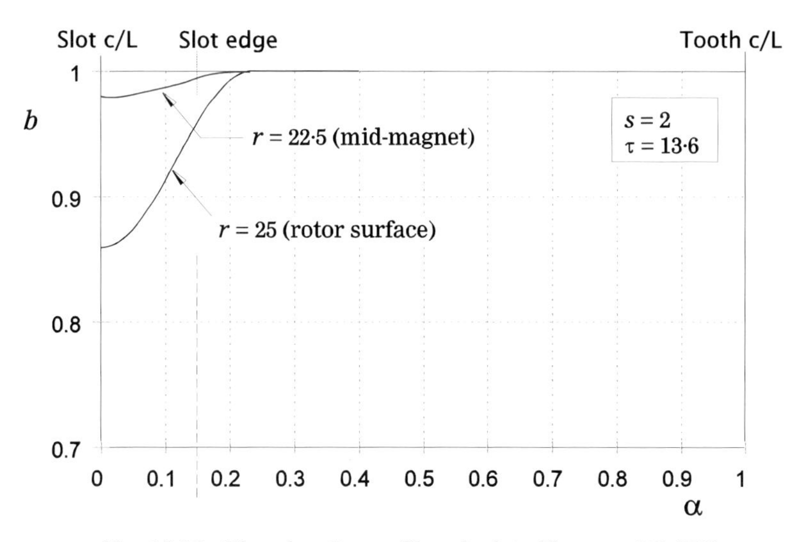

Fig. 12.26 Flux-density profile calculated by eqn. (12.159)

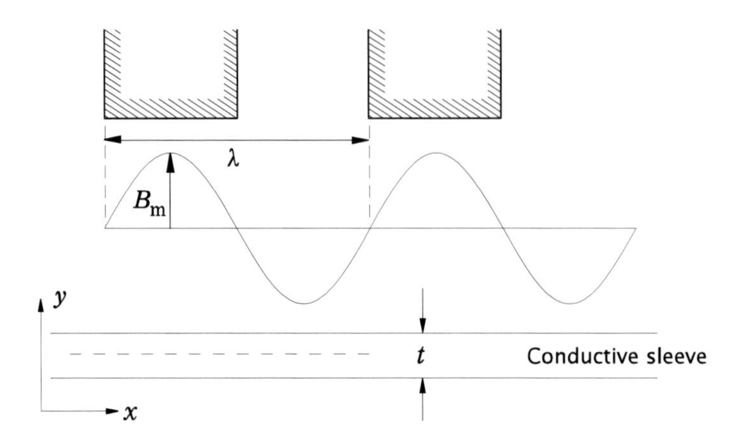

Fig. 12.27 Slot-ripple analysis with a thin conductive sleeve

12.4.4.1 Flux-dip-sweeping analysis of losses in thin can

Fig. 12.27 shows the parameters of a simple analysis of slot-ripple in a thin conductive can or sleeve.[129]

The "flux-dip-sweeping" analysis assumes resistance-limited eddy-currents in the can, so the eddy-current reaction on the field is neglected. Moreover there is no variation of flux-density through the thickness of the can. Cartesian coordinates are used for simplicity, since the wavelength λ of the slot-ripple is assumed to be small compared with the radius.

The central plane of the rolled-out conductive sleeve is shown by a dotted line in Fig. 12.27. This line represents a constant radius $r = D/2$, where D is the diameter. The linear coordinate x is given by

$$x = r\theta, \tag{12.166}$$

where θ is angular distance in the circumferential direction. Along this line the flux-density is assumed to have a sinusoidal variation

$$B_y = B_m \sin p\theta, \tag{12.167}$$

[129] Examples of this analysis are given by Robinson *et al*, Russell & Norsworthy, and Takahashi *et al*. Here the method will be derived from first principles because of some uncertainties in the original papers.

where p is the number of pole-pairs. For a *stator* can, B_m is the peak airgap flux-density of the main flux, assumed sinusoidal, while p is the number of fundamental pole-pairs. Only the y-component is assumed to generate eddy-currents in the can.

The relative linear velocity between the field and the stator can at diameter D is given by

$$v = \omega r = \frac{2\pi N}{60} \times \frac{D}{2}; \tag{12.168}$$

where N is the speed in rev/min and ω is the angular velocity in mechanical rad/s. The motion-induced EMF per metre of axial length (normal to the page) is given by

$$E_z = vB_y = vB_m \sin p\theta, \tag{12.169}$$

and the resistance-limited current-density is

$$J_z = \sigma E_z = \sigma v B_m \sin p\theta. \tag{12.170}$$

where σ is the conductivity of the can in S/m. The power loss per unit volume is

$$\rho J_z^2 = \sigma v^2 B_m^2 \sin^2 p\theta, \tag{12.171}$$

where $\rho = 1/\sigma$ is the resistivity in ohm-m. The sine^2 function has a time-averaged value of 0·5 *at every point in the can, regardless of its position*. Therefore the total power loss in the can is

$$P = \rho J_z^2 V = \frac{1}{2}\frac{v^2 B_m^2}{\rho} \times 2\pi r t L \quad \text{W}, \tag{12.172}$$

where $V = 2\pi r t L$ is the volume of the can and L is its axial length. End-effects are ignored, on the grounds that λ is generally much shorter than L. This equation can be written in terms of the speed N in rpm, and the sleeve diameter $D = 2r$, if we substitute from eqn. (12.168): thus

$$P = \frac{\pi^3}{2}\frac{B_m^2 N^2 D^3 t L}{3600\rho} \quad \text{W}. \tag{12.173}$$

The loss P is independent of the number of pole-pairs p, because all elements of EMF are induced by relative motion at the common velocity v, which is independent of p or indeed of any aspect of the spatial variation of the field; see eqn. (12.169). Still, the pattern of eddy-currents induced in the can is sinusoidal and has $2p$ poles.

12.4.4.2 Rotor can losses

Robinson *et al* deduced a formula for *rotor* can loss from eqn. (12.173), by exchanging the source of excitation from the main field to the slot-ripple *modulation* of the main field. Similar processes can be found in Russell & Norsworthy and in Takahashi et al.[130] The dimensions and resistivity in eqn. (12.173) are substituted by those of the rotor can, while N remains the same, because the relative velocity between the slot-ripple field and the rotor is that same as the relative velocity between the main field and the stator. The number of slots does not appear, for the same reason that the number of main-field poles does not appear in eqn. (12.173).

A difficulty in using eqn. (12.173) is the determination of the effective value of B_m for the slot-modulation. The modulation is not sinusoidal and it should be treated harmonic-by-harmonic according to the assumptions on which the formulas are derived.

---

[130] Takahashi's analysis appears to have been derived independently. It does not refer to Robinson or to Russell & Norsworthy, but uses a similar equation

$$P = \frac{\pi^3}{1800\,\rho} B_o^{\,2} N^2 D^3 t L \quad \text{W}, \tag{12.174}$$

which gives *four times* the loss of eqn. (12.173) when $B_o = B_m$. To investigate this further, eqn. (12.174) in the original Japanese [Obaraki *et al*, 1991] is derived from an equation

$$W_{eff} = \frac{\text{P}}{2\rho}\left[\frac{B_m \omega}{\pi}\right]^2 \tau^3 t L \tag{12.175}$$

where P is the number of poles. This can be shown to be identical to eqn. (12.173) if

$$\omega = \frac{2\pi N}{60} \times \frac{\text{P}}{2} \quad \text{and} \quad \tau = \frac{\pi D}{\text{P}}. \tag{12.176}$$

Thus $\omega = 2\pi f$ and τ is the pole-pitch. Next, Takahashi substitutes P by N_s, the number of slots; τ by $\pi D/N_s$; ω by $2\pi N/60 \times N_s$; and B_m by B_o, giving eqn. (12.174). However, it appears that P should be substituted by $2N_s$ instead of N_s, and τ should be substituted by $\pi D/2N_s$ instead of $\pi D/N_s$. If this is done, the result is eqn. (12.173). Even when these "corrections" are applied to Takahashi's eqn. (12.174), uncertainties remain. Takahashi's slot-modulation is about half the finite-element value, appearing to compensate for the apparent error of 4 in eqn. (12.174); but it remains unclear how the formula is to be used.

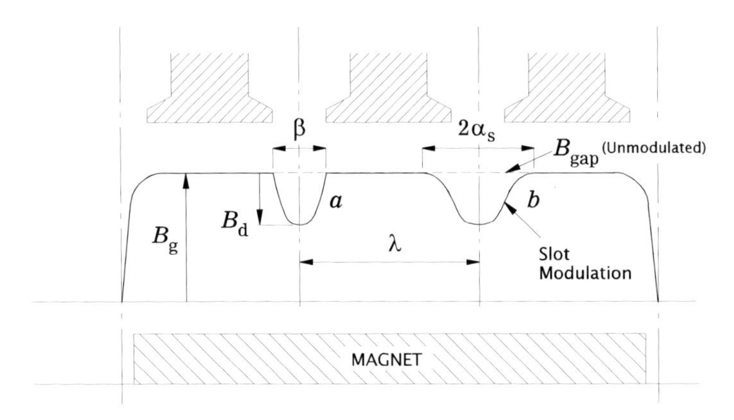

Fig. 12.28 Slot modulation of the open-circuit airgap flux distribution

The can loss equation (12.173) is rewritten in terms of the RMS value of the slot-ripple field:

$$W = \pi^3 \times \frac{B_{rms}{}^2 N^2 D^3 t L}{3600 \rho} \qquad (12.174)$$

where B_{rms} is determined from the dips in the flux-density wave in the rotor can, caused by the slot modulation. B_{rms} would be equal to $B_m/\surd 2$ for a sinusoidal slot-ripple wave of peak value B_m. The single application of eqn. (12.174) is deemed to include all harmonics.

In method *a* in Fig. 12.28, each dip has the shape of a half-sinewave of peak value B_d and width β radians, corresponding to the slot-opening augmented by $2g$ to allow for the fact that the dip is somewhat wider than the slot-opening s. The period of the slot-modulation is equal to the slot-pitch $\lambda = 2\pi/N_s$. Assuming an uninterrupted series of dips, the RMS value of the modulation is

$$B_{rms} = \frac{B_d}{\sqrt{2}} \times \sqrt{\frac{\beta}{\lambda}}. \qquad (12.175)$$

If the airgap flux distribution is substantially flat, a further scale factor $\surd(\beta_M/180)$ may be applied to account for the finite magnet arc β_M (in electrical degrees). If it is sinusoidal, B_{rms} should be calculated from B_d at the peak, and then multiplied by a further factor of $1/\surd 2$.

In general it can be scaled by the ratio of the RMS value of the unslotted B_{gap} waveform to the peak value. It can also be calculated as the RMS value of the difference between the modulated and unmodulated B_{gap} distributions (Fig. 12.28).

An alternative shape given by Heller and Hamata is shown as *b* in Fig. 12.28. In this case the RMS value of the dip is calculated as

$$B_{rms} = \sqrt{\frac{2}{\lambda}\frac{B_d^2}{4}\int_0^{\alpha_s}\left[1+\cos\pi\frac{\alpha}{\alpha_s}\right]^2 d\alpha} = \frac{B_d}{\sqrt{2}} \times \sqrt{\frac{3}{2}\frac{\alpha_s}{\lambda}} \qquad (12.176)$$

12.4.5 Harmonic losses in the IPM

The solution of the complex diffusion equation is too difficult for interior-magnet machines because of the complex shape of the rotor lamination. The eddy-current losses in the magnets are therefore analyzed by an approximate method based on the frequency-dependent synchronous inductance in the *d*-axis, $L_d(j\omega)$. We have already met this idea in the calculation of rotor losses in the line-start motor in Chapter 9, where the frequency-dependence of L_d was due to the cage. Here it is due to the induced currents in the magnets.

12.4.5.1 Losses caused by time-harmonics in the current

The frequency-dependent synchronous inductance $L_d(j\omega)$ can be written

$$L_d(j\omega) = L_{dR} - jL_{dX}, \qquad (12.177)$$

where the real and imaginary components L_{dR} and L_{dX} are both functions of the frequency ω in the rotor frame of reference. The phase angle of $L_d(j\omega)$ is always negative.

A *d*-axis current $\mathbf{I}_d(j\omega)$ which alternates at the radian frequency ω produces a voltage

$$\mathbf{V}_d(j\omega) = [R_d + j\omega L_d(j\omega)]\,\mathbf{I}_d(j\omega) \qquad (12.178)$$

where R_d is the stator resistance. Substituting the real and imaginary components of $L_d(j\omega)$,

$$\mathbf{V}_{\mathrm{d}}(\mathrm{j}\omega) = \left[(R_{\mathrm{d}} + \omega L_{\mathrm{dX}}) + \mathrm{j}\omega L_{\mathrm{dR}}\right]\mathbf{I}_{\mathrm{d}}(\mathrm{j}\omega). \tag{12.179}$$

The term ωL_{dX} represents the resistance of the conductive elements on the rotor, referred to the d-axis circuit of the stator. Generally these elements are just the magnets. The losses in the magnets are therefore given by

$$W_{\mathrm{m(d)}} = \omega L_{\mathrm{dX}} I_{\mathrm{d}}^2, \tag{12.180}$$

where I_{d} is the RMS value of the current at the harmonic frequency ω. In a balanced 3-phase machine the simplest cases of such a current arise from the $(6k \pm 1)^{\mathrm{th}}$ time-harmonics interacting with the fundamental electrical space-harmonic of the winding distribution. For example the 5th harmonic produces a rotating ampere-conductor distribution rotating backwards relative to the rotor at six times the fundamental synchronous speed, and this can be resolved into d- and q-axis components which are stationary with respect to the rotor, but which pulsate at six times the fundamental frequency. (See Tables 12.1-12.6).

The analysis for higher-order space-harmonics is more complex, but these should be attenuated relative to the fundamental. Losses of this type can in principle also occur in the q-axis, but here they are ignored on the grounds that the q-axis armature-reaction flux does not pass through the magnets, and in any case the circuits formed by induced currents in the magnets will be far less effective in the q-axis.

12.4.5.2 Losses caused by flux-pulsations (slotting)

The flux Φ_{m} through the magnet can be seen as the integral of the airgap flux modulated by slotting, as shown in Fig. 12.29. Suppose the d-axis is at an angle ξ relative to a fixed point on the stator (such as the axis of phase 1). If the pole-arc is β, then the limits of integration are $\theta_1 = \xi - \beta/2$ and $\theta_2 = \xi + \beta/2$. Ignoring leakage, and taking R as the mean radius in the airgap, and L_{stk} as the axial length, we have

$$\Phi_{\mathrm{m}}(\xi) = R L_{\mathrm{stk}} \int_{\xi - \beta/2}^{\xi + \beta/2} B_{\mathrm{g}}(\theta)\, d\theta. \tag{12.181}$$

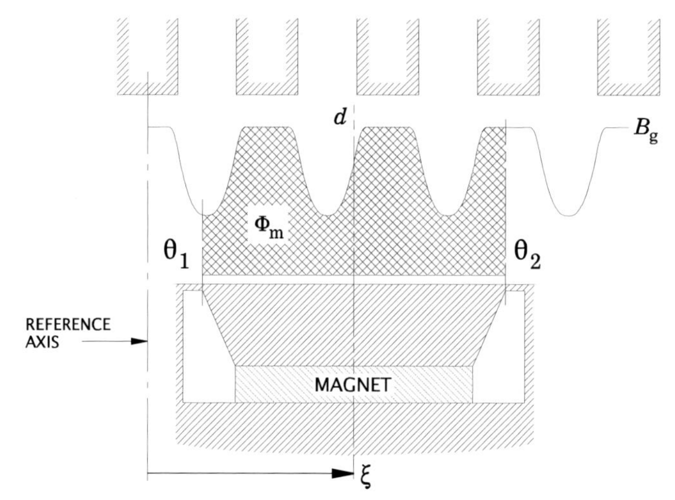

Fig. 12.29 Integration of airgap flux distribution modulated by slotting

The fundamental time-harmonic component of $\Phi_m(\omega t)$ can be represented as a phasor $\mathbf{\Phi}_m(j\omega)$ if we write $\xi = \omega t$, where $\omega/2\pi$ is the slot-passing frequency; the harmonics can be treated likewise. The harmonic flux per pole $\mathbf{\Phi}_m(j\omega)$ is now assumed to link a fictitious N-turn coil wrapped around each magnet, and if all the poles are assumed to be in series it will produce a total flux-linkage per phase equal to $\mathbf{\Psi}_m(j\omega) = 2pN\,\mathbf{\Phi}_m(j\omega)$. The induced voltage will be $j\omega\mathbf{\Psi}_m(j\omega)$ at the harmonic frequency, and this is "applied" to a circuit whose inductance is L_R. The resistance of this circuit is equal to L_R/T_{do}'', where T_{do}'' is the open-circuit d-axis subtransient time-constant (calculated later), so the impedance at the harmonic frequency is

$$\mathbf{Z}(j\omega) = \frac{L_R}{T_{d0}''}(1 + j\omega T_{d0}''). \tag{12.182}$$

The current is

$$\mathbf{I}(j\omega) = \frac{j\omega\mathbf{\Psi}_m(j\omega)}{\mathbf{Z}(j\omega)} \tag{12.183}$$

and the associated losses are

$$W_{m[\text{slot mod}]} = \frac{I^2 L_R}{T_{d0}''}. \tag{12.184}$$

12.4.6 Subtransient inductance and time-constant

During transients, rapid changes of current occur, and currents induced in the rotor are "reflected" in the phase impedances of the stator. Fig. 12.30 shows the underlying physical principle in terms of two coupled circuits. The primary (1) represents the stator; more particularly it will be used to represent the synchronous inductances L_d and L_q. The secondary (2) represents the rotor, and it includes all components in which induced currents may flow. That includes the magnets, the shaft, and any retaining sleeve. The induced currents in these components are "distributed" and not in fixed wiring, so their representation by a single circuit is an oversimplification. An exact equivalent circuit would need an infinite number of coupled circuits, like a transmission line. Nevertheless, an analysis with only a "first-order" equivalent circuit is instructive and useful for approximate calculations.

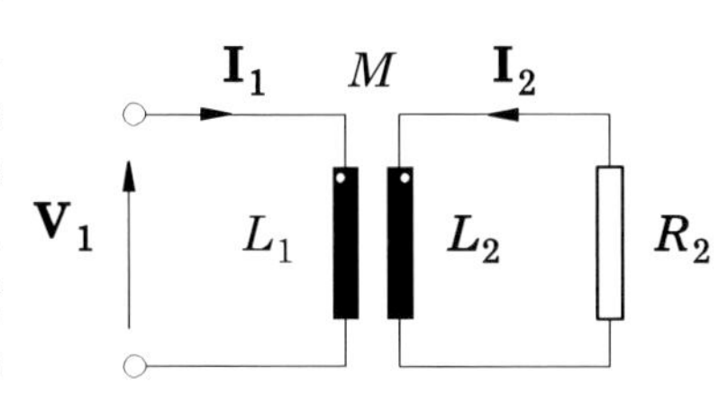

Fig. 12.30 Coupled circuits

The voltage equations for the two circuits in Fig. 12.30 are

$$\begin{aligned} \mathbf{V}_1 &= \mathrm{j}\omega L_1 \mathbf{I}_1 + \mathrm{j}\omega M\, \mathbf{I}_2; \\ 0 &= \mathrm{j}\omega M\, \mathbf{I}_1 + (R_2 + \mathrm{j}\omega L_2)\, \mathbf{I}_2. \end{aligned} \tag{12.185}$$

The secondary voltage is zero because the rotor circuit is short-circuited, and the primary resistance R_1 is omitted because it is not needed for the present. If the second equation is used to eliminate $\mathbf{I}_2$,

$$\mathbf{V}_1 = \mathrm{j}\omega L_1 \left[1 - \frac{\mathrm{j}\omega M^2/L_1}{R_2 + \mathrm{j}\omega L_2} \right] \mathbf{I}_1 . \tag{12.186}$$

Thus the primary inductance appears complex, and if we write L_d instead of L_1, we get

$$L_d(\mathrm{j}\omega) = L_d \left[\frac{1 + \mathrm{j}\omega T_d (1 - k^2)}{1 + \mathrm{j}\omega T_d} \right] = L_d \left[\frac{1 + \mathrm{j}\omega T_d''}{1 + \mathrm{j}\omega T_{d0}''} \right], \tag{12.187}$$

where

$$T_{d0}'' = \frac{L_2}{R_2} \qquad (12.188)$$

and

$$T_d'' = T_{d0}''(1 - k^2). \qquad (12.189)$$

Here L_d has been written instead of L_1, and R_d instead of R_1. k is the coupling coefficient $M/\surd(L_1L_2)$. These substitutions yield a result which is recognizable in the classical theory of synchronous machines, where L_d is the synchronous inductance, T_{d0}'' is the open-circuit subtransient time-constant, and T_d'' is the short-circuit subtransient time-constant. The resistance R_2 is the referred resistance of the conductive circuits on the rotor in the d-axis, and the inductance L_2 is the referred self-inductance of these circuits.[131]

If ω is very large, we get

$$L_d(j\omega) \approx L_d \frac{T_d''}{T_{d0}''} = L_d(1 - k^2) = L_d'', \qquad (12.190)$$

where L_d'' is the *subtransient inductance.* Similar equations apply to the q-axis.

In the PM machine there is no field winding, and therefore the *transient* reactance and its associated time-constants T_{d0}' and T_d' do not exist. For surface-magnet machines, we can expect the d- and q-axis reactances and time-constants to be practically the same.

The parameters T_d'', T_{d0}'', L_d and L_d'' are all essential to the analysis of sudden short-circuits, which is treated in Chapter 9. The synchronous inductance L_d is associated with conditions in which there are no induced currents on the rotor, and we can assume that it is already known. What follows is a method of estimating the subtransient parameters using a frequency-response approach based on the earlier solution of the complex diffusion equation.

From eqn. (12.187) we can see that the phase angle of $L_d(j\omega)$ is

$$\alpha = \mathrm{ArcTan}(\omega T_d'') - \mathrm{ArcTan}(\omega T_{d0}''). \qquad (12.191)$$

[131] This analysis does not require explicit values for L_2 or R_2.

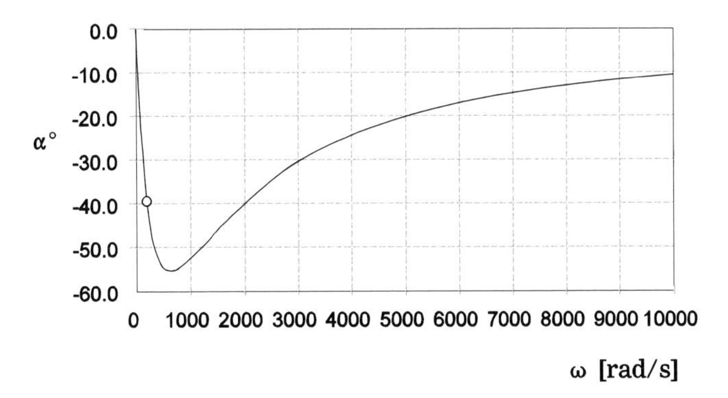

Fig. 12.31 Variation of phase angle of $L_d(j\omega)$ with frequency ω

When $\omega T_{d0}'' = 1$, we have a phase angle of 45° in the denominator of eqn. (12.187) and ArcTan $(1 - k^2)$ in the numerator, and the overall phase angle can be written

$$\alpha_1 = \mathrm{ArcTan}\,(1 - k^2) - \frac{\pi}{4} \quad [\mathrm{rad}]. \tag{12.192}$$

Fig. 12.31 shows an example of the variation of α with frequency ω, with $k = 0{\cdot}95$ and $T_{d0}'' = 5$ ms. The short-circuit time-constant is $T_d'' = (1 - 0{\cdot}95^2) \times 5 = 0{\cdot}4875$ ms, roughly ten times shorter. There is always a minimum phase angle. At frequencies below the frequency of minimum phase, the induced currents are resistance-limited; at frequencies well above it, they are inductance-limited.

Suppose k is known. Then if we calculate $L_d(j\omega)$ and find the frequency ω_1 at which $\alpha = \alpha_1$, it follows that

$$T_{d0}'' = \frac{1}{\omega_1}. \tag{12.193}$$

Then T_d'' can be found from eqn. (12.189). In the example, α_1 = ArcTan$(1 - 0{\cdot}95^2) - 45° = -39{\cdot}43°$. This is marked in Fig. 12.31. It occurs at 200 rad/s, so that from eqn. (12.193), $T_{d0}'' = 1/200$ or 5 ms.

In general k is not known *a priori*, even when the frequency-response in Fig. 12.31 is available. In principle it is possible to determine $(1 - k^2)$ from the asymptotic value of the magnitude $|L_d(j\omega)|$ at very high frequency, but extremely high frequencies are generally needed to reach this condition and the calculation of Bessel functions with very large arguments (inversely proportional to the skin depth) then becomes problematic. A simpler approach is to begin with an estimate of the coupling coefficient k' for the fundamental space-harmonic, which can be calculated using Hughes and Miller [*op. cit.*]. In terms of the dimensions in Fig. 12.6 on p. 571, for a winding at radius r_0,

$$k = \left[\frac{r_0}{r_S}\right]^p \sqrt{\frac{2\left[1 + (r_H/r_0)^{2p}\right]}{\left[1 + (r_H/r_S)^{2p}\right]\left[1 + (r_0/r_S)^{2p}\right]}}. \qquad (12.194)$$

The "winding" at radius r_0 is a fictitious sine-distributed current-sheet with p pole-pairs and zero radial thickness. In this context it represents the thin layer of eddy-currents induced in the rotor at very high frequency, so r_0 should be taken as very slightly less than the rotor radius. Now it is the fundamental magnetizing inductance L_{md} that is modified by $(1 - k^2)$: the total subtransient inductance is obtained by adding the leakage inductance L_σ, which includes the end-turn leakage, the slot leakage, and the differential leakage:

$$L_d'' = (1 - k^2)L_{md} + L_\sigma. \qquad (12.195)$$

The leakage inductance L_σ is obtained from

$$L_\sigma = L_d - L_{md}. \qquad (12.196)$$

We need to find the *overall* coupling coefficient k' that makes

$$L_d'' = (1 - k'^2)L_d, \qquad (12.197)$$

and this can be obtained by solving the above equations, giving

$$k' = k\left[1 - \frac{L_\sigma}{L_d}\right]. \qquad (12.198)$$

The frequency response in Fig. 12.31 is calculated from the solution of the complex diffusion equation by means of a frequency scan to obtain the phase angle of the vector potential **A** at the stator bore, with a current sheet of constant amplitude.

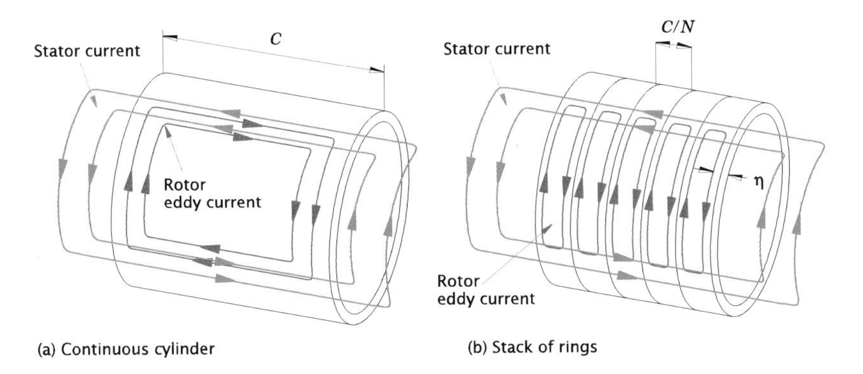

Fig. 12.32 Effect of segmentation on the subtransient reactance

12.4.6.1 Effect of segmentation on subtransient reactance

Fig. 12.32(a) shows the eddy-currents in a continuous rotor can, together with a representation of the stator ampere-conductor distribution. When the stator and rotor are both infinitely long, the coupling coefficient between the stator and the rotor "circuits" is given by the 2D formula (12.194), and here it will be denoted k_{d}.

We have already seen that when the rotor is represented by a single circuit, the short-circuit inductance of the stator is given by an equation of the form

$$L'' = L_0(1 - k_{\mathrm{d}}^2) \tag{12.199}$$

where L_0 has been identified as the magnetizing inductance L_{md} and L'' as the subtransient inductance (ignoring L_σ for the moment). Here, L'' is viewed as the primary inductance of a set of coupled circuits; so in Fig. 12.32(a) there is only one secondary circuit. In Fig. 12.32(b) there is a stack of N secondary circuits, each one corresponding to one ring or segment.

Let m be the mutual inductance between the primary and *each* secondary, and let l be the self-inductance of *each* secondary. The problem is simplified very drastically by assuming that l and m are identical for all the secondaries; moreover, it is assumed that there is no mutual coupling between any pair of secondaries. (In practice they are small and may even be negative).

With these provisions we can write a primitive inductance matrix

L_0	m	m	m	m
m	l			
m		l		
m			l	
m				l

It is easy to show that when the secondaries are all short-circuited, the matrix can be reduced to a 1 × 1 matrix representing the short-circuit inductance,

$$L'' = L(1 - Nk_m^2) \tag{12.200}$$

— an exceedingly simple result, with

$$k_m = \frac{m}{\sqrt{L_0 l}}. \tag{12.201}$$

Unfortunately the calculation of m and l is practically impossible because of the difficulty of identifying definite circuits in which the eddy-currents flow, and also because the eddy-current circuits are short-circuited. Indeed it is questionable whether a circuit-based approach is justifiable at all : the problem is really a distributed field problem. However, what is most needed is an estimate of the relationship between k_m and N, and a crude estimate can be made by the concept of "loss of effectively coupled length".

The inductances l and m are considered to be proportional to an area that is basically defined by the pole-pitch in the circumferential direction and the length C/N in the axial direction, where C is the overall length of the unsegmented can. However, because the eddy-currents must turn to flow in the circumferential direction, there is a loss of "effectively coupled length" with the stator. This loss of length is denoted η, and since it applies at both ends, the effectively coupled length of each section is reduced from C/N to $C/N - 2\eta$. Even when $N = 1$, the effectively coupled length is $C - 2\eta < C$.

Both m and l are proportional to the effectively coupled length in each section, that is, $C/N - 2\eta$, whereas L_0 is constant and proportional to C. So when the can is divided into N rings, we can write

$$k_m = \frac{C/N - 2\eta}{\sqrt{C(C/N - 2\eta)}} \times k_d = k_d\sqrt{\frac{1}{N} - \frac{2\eta}{C}}. \quad (12.202)$$

The number of turns in each secondary circuit is not needed, because when the secondaries are short-circuited the impedance referred to the primary is independent of the number of secondary turns.

If eqn. (12.202) is substituted in eqn. (12.200), the result is

$$L'' = L_0\left[1 - k_d^2\left\{1 - \frac{2\eta}{C/N}\right\}\right]. \quad (12.203)$$

Suppose η is taken as $\tau/6$, where τ is the pole-pitch, and let $\tau = 0{\cdot}6\,C$, and $k_d = 0{\cdot}96$. Then if $N = 1$ we get

$$L''/L_0 = \left[1 - 0{\cdot}96^2\left\{1 - \frac{2 \times \tau/6}{\tau/0{\cdot}6/1}\right\}\right] = 0{\cdot}2627. \quad (12.204)$$

If $N = 4$ we get a much higher inductance:

$$L''/L_0 = \left[1 - 0{\cdot}96^2\left\{1 - \frac{2 \times \tau/6}{\tau/0{\cdot}6/4}\right\}\right] = 0{\cdot}8157. \quad (12.205)$$

If $N = 5$ the factor in curly brackets is zero, so the effective coupling coefficient is zero and $L''/L_0 = 1$. For any higher value of N, the coupling coefficient is taken to remain zero, giving $L''/L_0 = 1$. The value of N that reduces the coupling coefficient to zero clearly depends on η. A general rule for the value of η cannot be given, but of course it can be chosen to match the results of finite-element analysis or measurement. η has an important influence on the peak short-circuit current, so its value should be chosen judiciously. A value of 0·1 is probably a reasonable starter.

For any given number of rings N, the most pessimistic value of η is 0, since this has the effect of ignoring the segmentation altogether, which minimizes L'' and the subtransient inductance, and so produces the maximum short-circuit current. The most optimistic value of η is $C/2N$, since this always leaves $L'' = L_0$, so the subtransient reactance will be equal to the steady-state synchronous reactance and the peak short-circuit current will be minimized.

In practice when N is increased, the self-inductance l will not decrease as fast as the mutual m, because of the additional "leakage inductance" associated with the flow of currents in the circumferential direction at the ends. This tends to reduce the effective coupling coefficient more rapidly with increasing N, and although the effect can be calculated it is not included here.

When the machine has no can, eddy-currents may arise in the magnets, but the above method is applied only when the magnet forms a complete ring with no segmentation whatsoever. In all other cases the eddy-currents in the magnet are assumed to be uncoupled to the stator.

12.4.6.2 Coupling coefficient of the IPM

For IPM machines the complex diffusion equation is not applicable and a different approach is needed.

Fig. 12.33 shows one pole of an IPM. The magnet in each pole is divided into two sections, each of width $w/2$, which are electrically isolated from each other. The airgap g is shown wider than normal for clarity in the drawing, and the effective airgap length is $g' = k_C g$, where k_C is Carter's coefficient. The magnet length is h in the direction of magnetization, and the stator bore radius is R. The pole-pitch is $\tau = \pi/p$ mechanical radians, and p is the number of pole-pairs.

During fast transients, induced currents tend to flow at the edges of the magnets as indicated by the hatching. Let the induced currents be represented by currents flowing in two coils of wire, one wrapped all the way around each block. Each of these coils has N turns. The flux/pole produced by the rotor current is practically identical in form to the open-circuit magnet flux, and the resulting airgap flux can be written

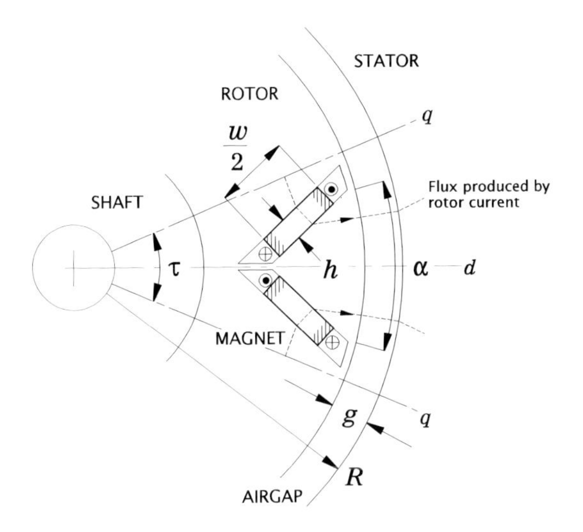

Fig. 12.33 Calculation of coupling coefficient — d-axis

$$\Phi_g = \frac{F_m}{R_m + R_g'}, \tag{12.206}$$

where F_m is the number of ampere-turns in one of the rotor coils, equal to N times the current in each coil. R_m is the reluctance of the two magnet blocks in parallel, and R_g' is the reluctance of a section of airgap of arcuate extent α mechanical radians, modified to account for rotor leakage flux that passes from pole-to-pole without crossing the airgap. Thus

$$R_g' = \frac{R_g}{1 + P_L R_g} = \lambda R_g, \tag{12.207}$$

where P_L is the pole-to-pole leakage permeance per pole and λ is a leakage coefficient which is introduced at this stage to simplify the algebra. The bridges and centre web are assumed to be completely saturated and are omitted from the calculation at this stage. In terms of the dimensions in Fig. 12.33, if L is the axial length,

$$R_m = \frac{h}{\mu_0 \mu_{rec} w L}, \tag{12.208}$$

and

$$R_g{}' = \frac{g'\lambda}{\mu_0 R\alpha L}. \tag{12.209}$$

Substituting for R_m and $R_g{}'$, we get

$$\Phi_g = \frac{\mu_0 L F_m}{\dfrac{h}{\mu_{rec} w} + \dfrac{g'\lambda}{R\alpha}}. \tag{12.210}$$

The distribution of this flux in the airgap is a rectangular block of arcuate extent α, so the peak flux-density is given by $\Phi_g/(R\alpha L)$ or

$$B_g = \frac{1}{R\alpha}\frac{\mu_0 F_m}{\dfrac{h}{\mu_{rec} w} + \dfrac{g'\lambda}{R\alpha}} = \frac{\mu_0 F_m}{\dfrac{hR\alpha}{\mu_{rec} w} + g'\lambda} \quad [\mathrm{T}]. \tag{12.211}$$

The fundamental component is easily determined by Fourier analysis of the rectangular block, giving

$$B_1 = \frac{\mu_0 F_m}{\dfrac{hR\alpha}{\mu_{rec} w} + g'\lambda} \times \frac{4}{\pi} \sin\frac{p\alpha}{2} \quad [\mathrm{T}]. \tag{12.212}$$

The fundamental flux associated with B_1 is

$$\Phi_1 = \frac{DL}{p}B_1 = \frac{DL}{p} \times \frac{\mu_0 F_m}{\dfrac{hR\alpha}{\mu_{rec} w} + g'\lambda} \times \frac{4}{\pi} \sin\frac{p\alpha}{2}, \tag{12.213}$$

where $D = 2R$. Now suppose the rotor current is sinusoidal, with frequency f. The EMF generated in one phase of the stator winding is

$$E = \frac{2\pi}{\sqrt{2}} k_{w1} T_{ph} \Phi_1 f \quad \mathrm{V_{rms}} \tag{12.214}$$

where k_{w1} is the fundamental winding factor and T_{ph} is the number of turns in series per phase.

The peak flux-linkage per phase is $\surd 2E/(2\pi f)$ or

$$\Psi_1 = k_{w1}T_{ph}\Phi_1 \qquad \mathrm{Vs_{rms}}. \tag{12.215}$$

With 1·0 A peak current flowing in the rotor coils, the mutual inductance is equal to $\Psi_1/1{\cdot}0$ or just Ψ_1. If we set $N = 1$ and retain 1·0 A rotor current, $F_m = 1$ and we can write the mutual inductance as

$$M = \frac{3}{2}k_{w1}T_{ph} \times \frac{DL}{p} \times \frac{\mu_0}{\dfrac{hR\alpha}{\mu_{rec}w} + g'\lambda} \times \frac{4}{\pi}\sin\frac{p\alpha}{2}, \tag{12.216}$$

The 3/2 factor anticipates a switch to dq axes which is necessary so that the effects of saliency can be taken into account. So M is the apparent mutual inductance between the rotor winding and one phase, under conditions of symmetrical operation with currents in all three phases.

To obtain the coupling coefficient we need the self-inductance of both windings. From eqn. (5.87) the d- and q-axis magnetizing inductances are

$$L_{md} = \Gamma_d L_{m0}; \qquad L_{mq} = \Gamma_q L_{m0}, \tag{12.217}$$

where L_{m0} is the airgap component of the synchronous inductance of a nonsalient pole machine having an effective airgap g', eqn. (5.88).

L_{m0}, L_{md} and L_{mq} are all associated with the fundamental flux produced by the stator winding; they do not include the space-harmonic fluxes. For the moment we will content ourselves with L_{md} and L_{mq}, and add the leakage inductances (including the harmonic leakage inductance) later.

The self-inductance of the rotor coils is given simply by the self flux-linkage divided by the current. The total airgap flux/pole produced by the rotor current has already been calculated as Φ_g, so if all the poles are in series the total flux-linkage of the complete rotor "winding" is $N \times \Phi_g \times 2p$. With a current of 1·0 A the self-inductance is equal to $2pN\Phi_g$. Again if $N = 1$ and the rotor current is 1·0 A, $F_m = 1$ and we can write the rotor self-inductance as

$$L_{\mathrm{R}} = \frac{2p\mu_0 L}{\dfrac{h}{\mu_{\mathrm{rec}} w} + \dfrac{g'\lambda}{R\alpha}}. \qquad (12.218)$$

The coupling coefficient follows as

$$k_{\mathrm{d}} = \frac{M}{\sqrt{L_{\mathrm{d}} L_{\mathrm{R}}}} \qquad (12.219)$$

in the d-axis. A similar process can be developed for L_{q}.

12.4.6.3 Rotor time-constant

The essential time-constant of the conductive components of the rotor is the open-circuit time-constant T_{d0}'', which can be identified as the diffusion time-constant of eddy-currents in these components.

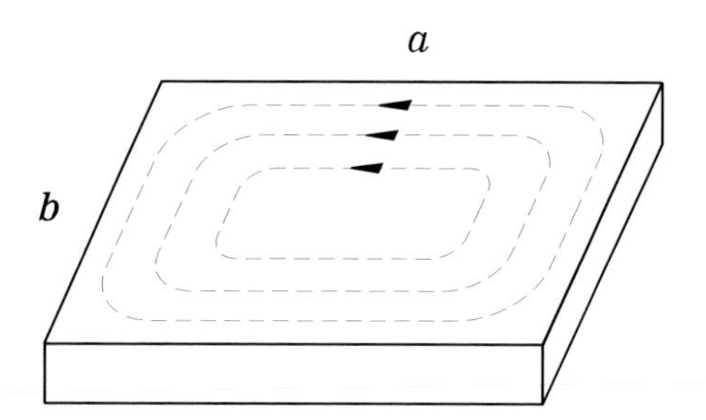

Fig. 12.34 Eddy-currents in a magnet block

A related problem analyzed by Lammeraner and Štafl[132] can be brought to bear on this calculation. Fig. 12.34 shows a rectangular block of magnet with sides a in the x-direction and b in the y-direction, in which eddy-currents are flowing in planes parallel to the xy-plane. The flux-density vector in the magnet obeys the diffusion equation

$$\frac{\partial^2 \mathbf{B}}{\partial x^2} + \frac{\partial^2 \mathbf{B}}{\partial y^2} = \mu\sigma \frac{\partial \mathbf{B}}{\partial t}. \qquad (12.220)$$

[132] Lammeraner J and Štafl M, *Eddy currents*, Iliffe Books Ltd., London, 1966

The flux-density is postulated to have only a z-component and the direction of magnetization is also in the orthogonal z-direction, that is, vertical. Lammeraner and Štafl state that since for symmetry reasons the dependence of flux density **B** in the direction of the x and y axes must be an even function, the solution can be assumed to be of the form

$$\mathbf{B} = B_0 \cos \alpha x \cos \beta y \, e^{-t/\tau} \tag{12.221}$$

where τ denotes the time-constant. Substituting in the differential diffusion equation we obtain a condition relating the so far unknown quantities α, β and τ :

$$\alpha^2 + \beta^2 = \frac{\mu\sigma}{\tau}. \tag{12.222}$$

They then apply the boundary condition to eqn. (12.221) at $t = 0$, $x = \pm a/2$, $y = \pm b/2$, to obtain

$$B_0 \cos(\alpha a/2) \cos(\beta b/2) = 0. \tag{12.223}$$

This equation is satisfied if

$$\alpha = (2n + 1)\pi/a; \quad \beta = (2m + 1)\pi/b, \tag{12.224}$$

where n and m are integers. From eqn. (12.222) the time-constant is then obtained as

$$\tau_{m,n} = \frac{\mu\sigma}{[(2n + 1)\pi/a]^2 + [(2m + 1)\pi/b]^2}. \tag{12.225}$$

Although the complete solution involves an infinite series of terms for all non-negative integer values of n and m, Lammeraner and Štafl point out that the duration of the transient only requires finding the greatest time-constant which is obtained with $n = 0$ and $m = 0$, so we get, finally,

$$T_{d0}'' = \tau_{0,0} = \frac{\mu\sigma}{\pi^2} \frac{ab}{a/b + b/a}. \tag{12.226}$$

Lammeraner and Štafl also consider the effect of an airgap in series with the magnet, but in a typical IPM this effect will be small.

The time-constant T_{d0}'' is recognizable as a diffusion time-constant and it is interesting to note that the characteristic dimension $ab/(a/b + b/a)$, which has the dimensions of [length], is determined entirely by dimensions parallel to the xy plane. The "diffusion" is in fact lateral, in the sense that the current starts in a concentrated layer at the edges and progressively fills the block by diffusing in the x and y directions. There is no variation or diffusion in the z-direction.

The dimensions a and b have so far been tacitly assumed to be those of a monolithic magnet block, Fig. 12.34. Suppose the block is divided into M segments in the x-direction such that $a = Mu$, and N segments in the y-direction such that $b = Nv$. Then it can be argued that a should be replaced by $u = a/M$ and that b should be replaced by $v = b/N$ in eqn. (12.226). Segmentation of the magnets has no effect on the inductive effect of the eddy-currents (cf. Fig. 12.20 on p. 610), but it has a marked effect on the resistance impeding the eddy-currents. As a further example of this, in Fig. 12.33 the positive and negative "wired" eddy-currents cancel in the centre, but yet the eddy-currents must pass through those paths and in doing so they meet considerable additional resistance. Again in Fig. 12.33, the dimensions to be used in eqn. (12.226) are $w/2$ and L (assuming the magnets are not segmented in the axial direction).

12.4.7 Finite-element calculation of losses

The finite-element method is held to produce results of assured accuracy, but it is also the slowest and most expensive method in terms of engineering time. 3D alculations may take days, yet what is often needed is *adequate* accuracy in seconds or minutes. 2D finite-elements may be used in eddy-current problems, in which the *zero net current condition*

$$\int \mathbf{J}\, dS = 0 \tag{12.227}$$

is imposed (usually without proof) individually across each conducting region by means of a fictional external circuit connection with a high resistance shorting the two ends.

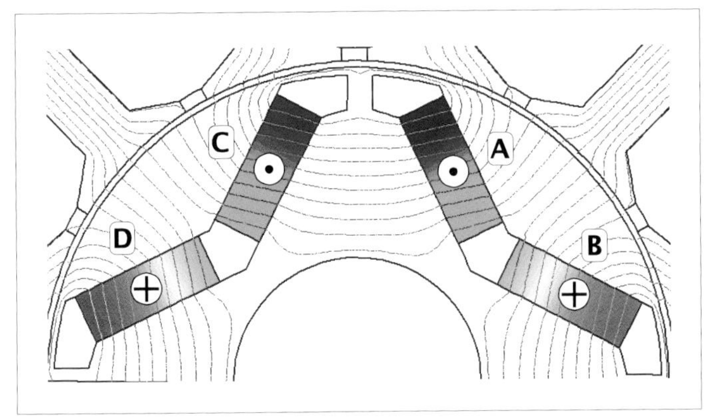

Fig. 12.35 Incorrect eddy-current calculation

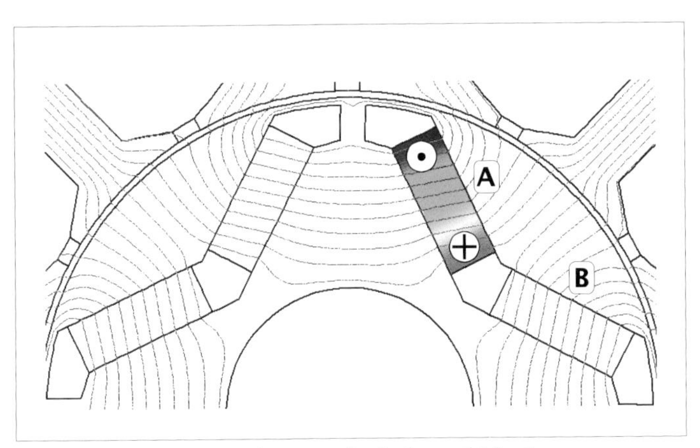

Fig. 12.36 Approximate calculation : 1 block

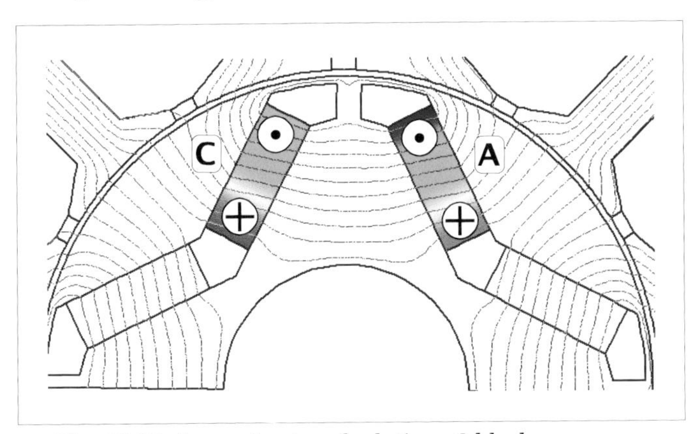

Fig. 12.37 Approximate calculation : 2 blocks

This technique requires a voltage-driven solution and a special formulation in which the circuit equations are incorporated in the field-solution matrix. Although there is excellent mathematical literature on the finite-element method, a review of several books on finite-elements in electrical engineering fails to provide any practical reassurance of the validity of this method.

Fig. 12.35 shows the calculation of eddy-currents with a conventional 2D solver using current excitation (and no external circuit connection). The problem is to calculate the no-load eddy-current losses in the magnets at high speed. The example in Fig. 12.35 uses the time-stepping algorithm of Crank-Nicholson, and predicts a total loss of 2·06 W, but this result is incorrect because the "infinite length" assumption permits induced current in magnet **A** to return in magnet **B**, and likewise current in magnet **C** to return in magnet **D**. Since there is no electrical connection between the magnets, this is a false result.

The simple finite-element formulation satisfies eqn. (12.227) over the whole solution domain, but not individually in each magnet region. An improved result can be obtained by suppressing the conductivity of, say, magnets **B**, **C**, and **D**, and simply calculating the loss in magnet **A**. In a situation where the losses must be equal in all magnet blocks, the final result is obtained by multiplying the result for one block by 8. When this is done in Fig. 12.36, the total calculated loss is 0·97 W when scaled up to include all magnets. This is slightly less than half the incorrect first estimate. The method can be described as a crude form of residual current suppression without using external circuits.

This method of single-region eddy-current calculation obviously relies on the assumption that the eddy-currents in any magnet do not affect the eddy-currents in any other magnet. One could assume that this is characteristic of "resistance-limited" eddy-currents, but it is more correct to describe it as the neglect of proximity effect.

A "refinement", so to speak, is to suppress the conductivity judiciously in pairs or patterns of magnets which are not expected to form a circuit. Thus Fig. 12.37 shows an example in which magnets **A** and **C** are conductive, but magnets **B** and **D** are not.

The total loss calculated in this case is 1·02 W, again scaled up to include all magnets. This is reasonably close to the 0·97 W calculated using the single-block approximation, and the difference may give some idea of the accuracy of the method. The only way to be sure is to measure it, although some confidence might be obtained through more sophisticated calculation tools.

An interesting observation in Figs. 12.35, 12.36 and 12.37 is the "lateral" diffusion of the eddy-currents towards the edges of the magnets, with little variation in current density in a direction parallel to the flux. This property was used in the formulation of simplified loss calculations for the IPM, and the related calculation of the frequency-dependent synchronous inductance mentioned earlier. With reference to the skin-depth criterion discussed on p. 563, in this example the "key dimension" to be compared with the skin depth is the width of the magnet and not its length in the direction of magnetization.

12.5 Windage, friction and bearing losses

Except in high-speed machines, losses caused by friction and windage are very low in PM brushless machines, typically accounting for less than 1 or 2% of the total losses.

The variation of windage loss with speed is typically expressed as a scaling formula

$$W_{WF} = W_{f0} \times \left[\frac{N}{N_0}\right]^{n+1} \tag{12.228}$$

where W_{WF} is the windage loss power at the speed N, W_{f0} is the windage loss power at the reference speed N_0, and n is an exponent representing the variation of the windage *torque* with speed. Typically $n = 2$. When the rotor is running in a fluid, specialist works on fluid dynamics are required to determine the drag losses.

Bearing loss is treated similarly. Most importantly, the bearing manufacturers provide excellent and detailed guidance on the calculation of drag losses, and these should be consulted in particular cases. Note that seals can sometimes produce more drag torque than the bearings themselves.

12.6 Thermal analysis and cooling

12.6.1 The need for cooling

There are two major aspects to the thermal problem in electrical machines:

1. heat removal; and
2. temperature distribution within the motor.

The main reasons for limiting the temperature rise of the windings and frame of a motor are:

1. to preserve the life of the insulation and bearings;
2. to prevent excessive heating of the surroundings; and
3. to prevent injury caused by touching hot surfaces.

In PM motors the temperature of the magnets needs to be kept under control, in order to avoid demagnetization.

Insulation life. The life of electrical insulation is inversely related to the temperature. A sustained 10°C increase in temperature reduces the insulation life by approximately 50%. Similar considerations apply to bearings. Bearings may be filled with high-temperature grease for hot-running applications, but in aerospace machines the bearings are usually lubricated by separately-cooled oil or oil mist. The extent to which excessive temperatures can be tolerated depends on the duration and the actual temperatures reached.

Heating of the surroundings is obviously undesirable especially if the motor is heating the equipment it is driving. For this reason it is important to minimize rotor losses conducted along the shaft. PM brushless motors have cooler rotors than DC or induction motors. In some applications such as hermetic compressors used in air-conditioning, refrigeration, etc., the motor losses are removed by the working fluid, reducing the thermodynamic efficiency of the system. Very high efficiency is important in such systems.

To prevent injury or harm from touching, exposed surfaces must be kept below 50°C. In certain applications (e.g., under car bonnets), this requirement is impossible to meet because the "ambient" temperature under the bonnet may reach 100°C.

In industrial applications the ambient temperature is generally less than 50 °C, and NEMA ratings for electrical insulation assume an ambient temperature of 40 °C. In aerospace applications motors and generators may be directly cooled by oil or fuel and coolant temperatures can be as high as 100 °C.

The increase in winding temperature increases the resistivity of the windings, as described on p. 554.

12.6.2 Cooling and efficiency

The definition of efficiency is

$$\text{Efficiency } \eta = \frac{\text{Output power}}{\text{Input power}} \times 100\%. \qquad (12.229)$$

Also

$$\text{Watts loss} = \text{Output power} - \text{Input power}. \qquad (12.230)$$

Hence

$$\text{Watts loss} = \text{Output power} \times \left[\frac{1}{\eta} - 1\right]. \qquad (12.231)$$

Table 12.6 shows the result of eqn. (12.231) for different levels of efficiency. When the efficiency is 100%, obviously the watts loss is zero. When the efficiency falls to 90%, the watts loss is equal to 11% of the output power, and when it falls to 50%, the watts loss is equal to the output power.

Efficiency	$\frac{\text{Watts loss}}{\text{Output power}}$
100	0
90	0·11
75	0·33
50	1·0

TABLE 12.6
EFFICIENCY AND WATTS LOSS

Between 90% efficiency and 50% efficiency, the watts loss increases by a factor of 9; between 90% and 75%, it increases by a factor of 3. So although we might describe a small motor with 75% efficiency as "fairly efficient", its losses are *three times as high* as those of a motor with 90% efficiency and the same output power.

12.6.3 Responsibility for temperature rise

The designer of an electrical machine can more or less guarantee the efficiency of that machine when it is operated under specified conditions, but he cannot be held responsible for the temperature rise if the machine is used in abnormal conditions. It is the user who determines the actual power output, the ambient temperature, and in many cases the cooling. Failures are often caused by overheating, so it is wise to be clear about where these responsibilities lie.

In the factory, testing is an essential part of the product development process. Prototype testing normally takes place on a dynamometer, which measures speed, torque, power, and electrical quantities such as voltage, current, and power factor. Dynamometer testing is commonly used to verify design calculations, and temperature rise measurements are almost always included, not just at the frame surface, but throughout the machine. Thermocouples and resistance thermometers are used for this, and the flow rates of coolants are often measured as well — usually airflow. Temperature rise should ideally be measured in the final application under worst-case loaded conditions. With very large machines it is sometimes necessary to conduct "synthetic" load tests, such as back-to-back testing of two similar machines, or operation with a zero-power-factor load, in order to achieve full-load loss without having to load the machine to its normal power output.

Life testing may follow prototype testing, to identify defects in the design or the manufacturing process which were not anticipated at the design stage. Life testing is often "accelerated" by overloading the machine in order to shorten the time-to-failure so that the results may be obtained in a reasonable time.

12.6.4 Heat removal

A simple measure of the cooling capability of a motor is the "degrees C per watt". This is the ratio of the temperature rise to the total watts loss. The temperature rise can refer to the winding or to the frame surface, as in Fig. 12.38. It has the units of thermal resistance. As a single parameter characterizing the thermal resistance, it is useful in the analysis of intermittent operation in §12.6.6.

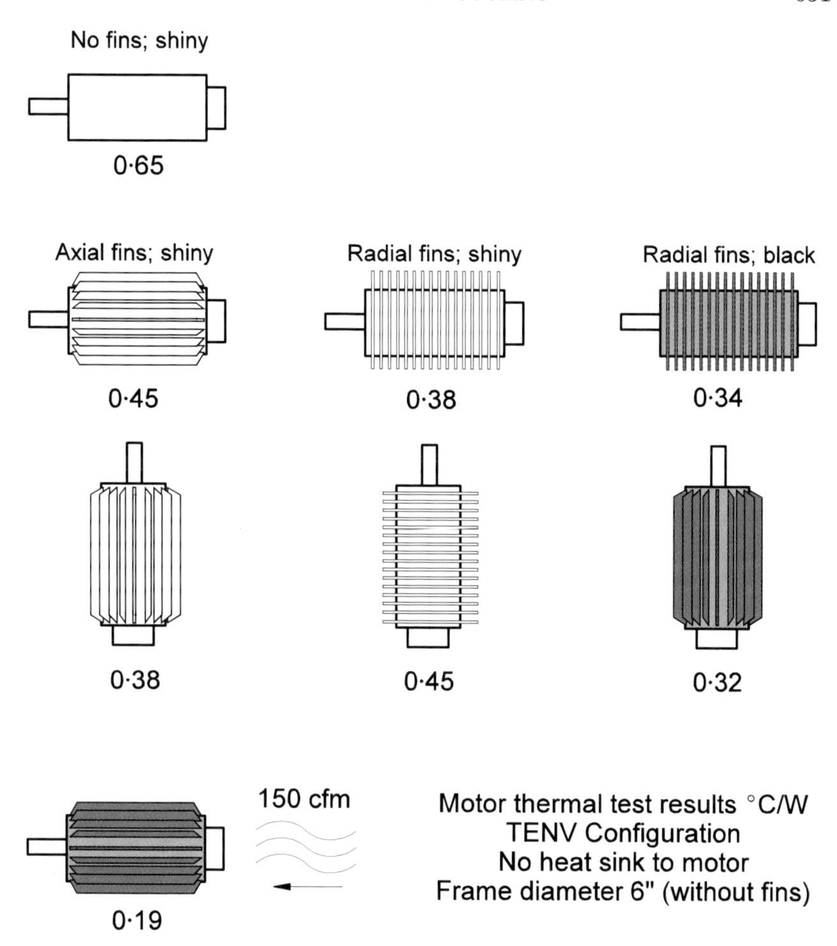

Fig. 12.38 "Degrees C per Watt" values measured on a small motor. (Data kindly supplied, with permission, by Erland Persson)

Fig. 12.38 shows some handy measured values of thermal resistance for a small motor. These values are specific to one size of motor. As the motor size increases, the "degrees C per watt" tends to decrease — indeed it *must* decrease: in large machines forced cooling, even forced internal cooling, is required to limit the temperature rise. The values in Fig. 12.38 include several different means of heat removal (mainly convection with a small amount of radiation). Note that the thermal resistance of servo motors is often quoted with the motor bolted to a plate of a standard size.

12.6.5 Detailed analysis of cooling

In most industrial and commercial motors, heat is removed by a combination of

1. conduction to the frame mountings;
2. air convection, which may be natural or forced; and
3. radiation.

In highly-rated machines direct cooling methods are used:

1. oil mist, especially in aerospace machines;
2. immersion in refrigerant, in "hermetic" motors used in refrigerator compressors; and
3. direct conductor cooling, with hydrogen, oil, or water forced through hollow conductors, especially in turbine-generators.

12.6.5.1 Conduction

The conduction equation for a block of thickness t and area A is

$$Q = k\,A\,\frac{dT}{dx} \approx k\,A\,\frac{\Delta T}{t} \quad \mathrm{W} \tag{12.232}$$

where ΔT is the temperature difference through the thickness t. The coefficient k is the *thermal conductivity*, with units (W/m^2) per (°C/m), i.e. W/°C-m. The thermal conductivity is a material property, and usually it is a function of temperature. Most metals have high thermal conductivities, especially those which are also good electrical conductors. On the other hand, electrical insulating materials and most fluids have low thermal conductivities.

Example—Consider the flow of heat along a conductor whose cross-section area is $A = 64$ mm^2 and length 50 mm, when the RMS current-density is 7 A/mm^2. The electrical resistivity of copper is $1{\cdot}7 \times 10^{-8}$ ohm-m, so heat is produced at the rate of $J^2\rho = (7 \times 10^6)^2 \times 1{\cdot}7 \times 10^{-8} = 833{,}000$ W/m^3 or 83·3 W/cm^3. In one conductor the I^2R loss is therefore $833{,}000 \times 64 \times 10^{-6} \times 50 \times 10^{-3} = 2{\cdot}7$ W. To take the most pessimistic estimate, assume that all of this heat is generated at the mid-point of the coil-side, half-way along the motor. The thermal conductivity of copper is 387 (W/m^2) per (°C/m). So the temperature gradient along the coil-side is given by eqn. (12.232) as

$$\frac{dT}{dx} = \frac{Q}{kA} = \frac{2{\cdot}7}{387 \times 64 \times 10^{-6}} = 108 \ \mathrm{^\circ C/m}. \tag{12.233}$$

Since the heat can flow in both directions, the temperature-gradient is only half this value, and the temperature rise between the ends of the stack and the centre is therefore $110/2 \times 50 \times 10^{-3}/2 = 1{\cdot}4$ °C, which is negligible. A more thorough analysis would have to consider the full *diffusion equation* along the length of the coil-side, but this quick calculation reveals that such sophistication is not needed in the example considered.

Thermal resistance and contact resistance — Eqn. (12.232) can be used to define *thermal resistance* as the ratio of temperature difference ΔT to heat flow rate Q : the symbol used for thermal resistance is R, with units °C/W. Thus

$$R = \frac{\Delta T}{Q} = \frac{t}{kA} \quad \text{°C/W.} \tag{12.234}$$

The thermal resistance can be used in a simple calculation of the conduction through a region or interface where the individual values of k, A, and t may be difficult to determine. The contact resistance between two surfaces is usually treated in this way, as, for example, between the frame and the stator core. The temperature drop across a thermal resistance is given by eqn. (12.232) as $\Delta T = QR$. For example, if the contact resistance between the motor flange and the mounting plate is 1°C/W, then with 40W flowing through it the temperature difference across the interface would be 40°C.

12.6.5.2 Radiation

Radiation is described by the *Stefan-Boltzmann* equation

$$\frac{Q}{A} = e\,\sigma\,(T_1^{\,4} - T_2^{\,4}) \quad \text{W/m}^2 \tag{12.235}$$

where σ is the *Stefan-Boltzmann* constant, $5{\cdot}67 \times 10^{-8}$ W/m²/K⁴ for a *black body*, T_1 is the absolute surface temperature of the radiating body in degrees Kelvin, and T_2 is the absolute temperature of the surroundings.[133] A black body is a perfect radiator, that is, one which reflects no radiated heat but absorbs all the heat radiated towards it. The radiative effectiveness of a real surface relative to that of a black body is called the *emissivity* e. A black matt surface can achieve an emissivity as high as 0·98, but 0·8–0·9 is typical for painted motor surfaces. e is sometimes modified with a "view factor".

[133] The absolute temperature in degrees Kelvin (K) is the temperature in °C plus 273·2.

For example, a surface with an emissivity of 0.9 that is 50°C above the surroundings at 50°C, has a net heat transfer rate of

$$0{\cdot}9 \times 5{\cdot}67 \times 10^{-8} \times ((50+50+273)^4 - (50+273)^4) \qquad (12.236)$$

which is 432 W/m^2 or 0·28 W/in^2. This is quite a useful component of the heat-removal capability.

12.6.5.3 Convection

Heat removal by convection is governed by *Newton's Law*:

$$\frac{Q}{A} = h \, \Delta T \quad \mathrm{W/m^2} \qquad (12.237)$$

where ΔT is the temperature difference between the cooling medium and the surface being cooled, and h is the *heat-transfer coefficient*. The units of h are W/m^2/°C. The value of h depends on the viscosity, thermal conductivity, specific heat, and other properties of the coolant, and also on its velocity. In *natural convection* the flow of coolant is not assisted by fans, blowers, pumps etc. In *forced convection* the flow is assisted by one of these external means.

The heat transfer coefficient for natural convection around a horizontally-mounted unfinned cylindrical motor can be roughly estimated as[134]

$$h \approx 7{\cdot}5 \left(\frac{\Delta T}{D} \right)^{1/4} \quad \mathrm{W/m^2/°C} \qquad (12.238)$$

where D is the diameter in mm. For example, for an unfinned cylinder of diameter 100 mm and a temperature rise of 50°C, the natural-convection heat-transfer coefficient is calculated as h = 6·3 W/m^2/°C. For a ΔT of 50°C, the heat transfer rate is then given by eqn. (12.237) as 6·3 × 50 = 315 W/m^2. As a first approximation this value can be applied to the whole surface including the ends, but if the motor is flange-mounted then only one end is available for convective cooling.

Forced convection (with a shaft-mounted fan or an external blower) increases the heat-transfer coefficient by as much as 5–6 times, depending on the air velocity.

---

[134] The origin of this formula is frankly obscure.

12.6.5.4 Some rules of thumb

In a water-immersed wire 1 m long, 1 mm diameter, a power loss of 22 W (0·022 W per mm length) is sufficient to *boil* the water at the wire surface. The wire surface temperature is 114°C and the heat transfer coefficient (see below) is 5000 W/m^2/°C. The heat flow at the wire surface is 0·07 W/mm^2 and the current-density in the wire is approximately 35 A/mm^2. In normal motors, the rate at which heat can be abstracted is *far less than this*, and current-densities over 30 A/mm^2 are achievable only for short bursts. 35 A/mm^2 is sufficient to fuse a copper wire in free air.

The maximum rate of heat removal by natural convection and radiation (with 40°C rise) is only about 800 W/m^2. With forced air convection the rate increases to about 3000 W/m^2, and with direct liquid cooling about 6000 W/m^2. A motor that generates more heat than can be removed at these rates must absorb the heat in its *thermal mass*, which permits the output power to be increased *for a short time*. These rates limit the heat generated *per unit volume* to about 0·012 W/cm^3 for natural convection, 0·3 W/cm^3 for metallic conduction or forced-air convection, and 0·6 W/cm^3 for direct liquid cooling.

The permissible current-density cannot be directly related to the temperature rise of the winding by a simple general equation, because the heat transfer rate depends on the shape of the conductors. As an example, 1 cm^3 of copper can be made into a stubby cylinder of 1 cm diameter and 1·27 cm length, or a long wire of 1 mm diameter and 1·27 m length. The short cylinder has a cylindrical surface area of 4 cm^2 while the long wire has a surface area of 40 cm^2. The loss density in the conductor is $J^2\rho$ where J is the current density and ρ is the resistivity. With ten times the surface area the long wire can dissipate ten times the heat, assuming the same heat transfer coefficient in both cases. This suggests that the permissible current-density in the long wire can be $\sqrt{10}$ times that in the short stubby cylinder.

If rated torque is required at very low speed, a shaft-mounted fan may not provide enough coolant flow to keep the motor cool. DC motors often have separate AC-driven fans, because they have to work for prolonged periods at low speed with high torque. Since most of the heat in a DC motor is generated on the rotor, good internal airflow is essential. In DC motors the external fan is usually mounted to one side of the motor, where it is easily accessible, and does not increase the overall length. As with vector-controlled induction motors, it is possible to mount an external fan in line with the motor at the non-drive end, and arrange it to blow air over the outside of the finned frame. The fan may increase the overall length by up to 60%. Brushless motors generally do not require external fans because of their high efficiency.

12.6.5.5 Internal temperature distribution

The steady-state temperature distribution within the motor is essentially a diffusion problem. The most important aspect of the problem is finding the hottest temperature in the motor, given a certain distribution of losses and a known rate of heat removal. It is difficult to solve precisely, because of three-dimensional effects and because some thermal resistances (such as the resistance between slot conductors and slot liner) are hard to calculate.

The differential equation for three-dimensional conduction of heat is the so-called diffusion equation:

$$\nabla^2 T + \frac{1}{k}\frac{\partial q}{\partial t} = \frac{1}{\alpha}\frac{\partial T}{\partial t} \tag{12.239}$$

where

$$\nabla^2 T = \frac{\partial^2 T}{\partial x^2} + \frac{\partial^2 T}{\partial y^2} + \frac{\partial^2 T}{\partial z^2} \tag{12.240}$$

and

$$\alpha = \frac{k}{\rho c} \quad \mathrm{m^2/s} \tag{12.241}$$

is the *diffusivity* in SI units. In SI units, k is the thermal conductivity in W/m°C; c is the specific heat in kJ/kg°C, and ρ is the density in kg/m^3. In a structure as complex as an electric motor the heat conduction equation is a complex boundary-value problem that is best solved by computer-based numerical methods.

In electric motors internal convection and radiation may be as important as conduction, and when the differential equation is extended to include them, matters become very complicated, even for steady-state calculations. During transients the temperature distribution can be very different from the steady-state distribution, and different methods of analysis may be needed for the two cases.

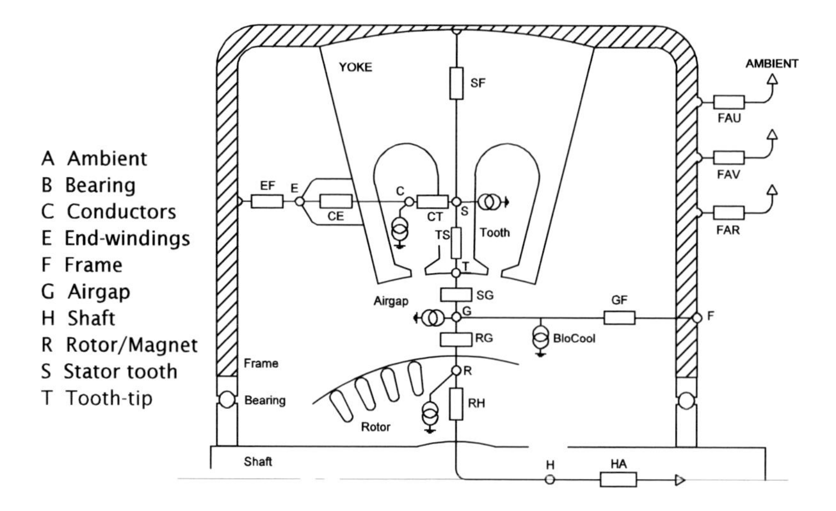

Fig. 12.39 Thermal equivalent circuit

12.6.5.6 Thermal equivalent circuit

For most purposes it is sufficient to use a *thermal equivalent circuit* of the interior of the motor, Fig. 12.39. This is analogous to an electric circuit, in that heat is generated by "current sources", while temperature is analogous to voltage. The rate of generation of heat in a source is measured in watts. The heat flow rate, which is also measured in watts, is analogous to current. Resistance is measured in °C/W. The copper losses, core losses, and windage & friction losses are represented by individual current sources at temperature nodes **C**, **E**, **S**, **T** etc., and the thermal resistances of the laminations, insulation, frame, etc. are represented as resistances between these nodes, for example R_{CS} for the thermal resistance between the stator conductors and the stator teeth. In the simplest possible model, all the losses are represented together as one total source, i.e. the individual sources are taken as being in parallel. The thermal equivalent circuit is really a lumped-parameter model of all the heat-flow processes within the motor as well as the heat removal processes discussed earlier.

The thermal equivalent circuit should ideally take anisotropy effects into account : for example, the effective thermal conductivity through a lamination stack is lower in the axial than the radial direction.

A more complex thermal equivalent circuit may include provision for direct cooling of the winding conductors, or for direct cooling of the rotor shaft. If it also includes the thermal masses or *capacities* of the winding, the rotor and stator laminations, the frame, the shaft, and other massive components, then it can be solved for transient as well as steady-state heat transfer.

The heat removal routes by conduction, radiation, and convection are represented by thermal resistances. For convection the appropriate resistance R_v is given by

$$R_v = \frac{1}{hA} \quad °C/W \qquad (12.242)$$

where A is the appropriate surface area for convective heat-transfer and the subscript "v" stands for convection. If h is a function of the temperature-difference, the equivalent circuit becomes non-linear and requires an iterative solution. For radiation the equivalent thermal resistance R_r is the ratio of the temperature difference $T_1 - T_2$ to the radiation heat exchange rate Q in eqn. (12.235).

12.6.5.7 Some useful tables

Motor type	Class **B**	Class **F**	Class **H**
1·15 Service Factor	90	115	140
1·00 Service Factor	85	110	135
TEFC	80	105	125
TENV	85	110	135

TABLE 12.7
TEMPERATURE RISE BY RESISTANCE AND INSULATION
(NEMA STANDARD MG-1), °C. ASSUMES 40°C AMBIENT TEMPERATURE.

Material	Emissivity	Material	Emissivity
Black body	1·0	Black lacquer	0·95
Polished Aluminium	0·04	Grey iron	0·3
Polished copper	0·025	Mild steel	0·25
Aluminium paint	0·5	Stainless steel	0·55

TABLE 12.8
SELECTED EMISSIVITIES

Material	$\rho(20°C)$ ohm-m × 10^{-8}	k (W/m K)	Sp. Heat kJ/kg/°C	Density kg/m^3
Copper	1·724	360	0·38	8950
Aluminium	2·8	220	0·90	2700
0·1% Carbon steel	14	52	0·45	7850
Silicon steel	30–50	20–30	0·49	7700
Cast iron	66	45	0·5	7900
Cobalt-iron	40	30	0·42	8000
Ceramic magnet	10^4	4·5	0·8	4900
RE-Co magnet	80	25	0·37	8400
NDFEB magnet	140	6·5	0·46	7600
Kapton®	303 V/μm*	0·12	1·1	1420
Teflon	260V/μm*	0·20	1·2	2150
Pressboard/Nomex	10kV/0·22mm*	0·13	—	1000
Epoxy resin	30kV/mm*	0·5	1·7	1400
Water (20°C)		0·0153	4·18	997·4
Freon		0·0019	0·966	1330
Ethylene Glycol		0·0063	2·38	1117
Engine oil		0·0037	1·88	888

TABLE 12.9
SELECTED MATERIAL PROPERTIES[135]
*Dielectric strength

Property	Units	Ceramic	RE-Co	NDFEB
Curie Point	°C	450	820	340
Temperature coefficient of B_r	%/°C	−0·2	−0·03	−0·1
Temperature coefficient of H_{cj}	%/°C	0·2–0·5	−0·17	-0·5
Coefficient of thermal expansion	°C^{-1}	14×10^{-6}	10×10^{-6}	Variable

TABLE 12.10
PHYSICAL TEMPERATURE PROPERTIES OF MAGNETS

[135] See Holman JP, *Heat Transfer*, McGraw-Hill, New York, 1992.

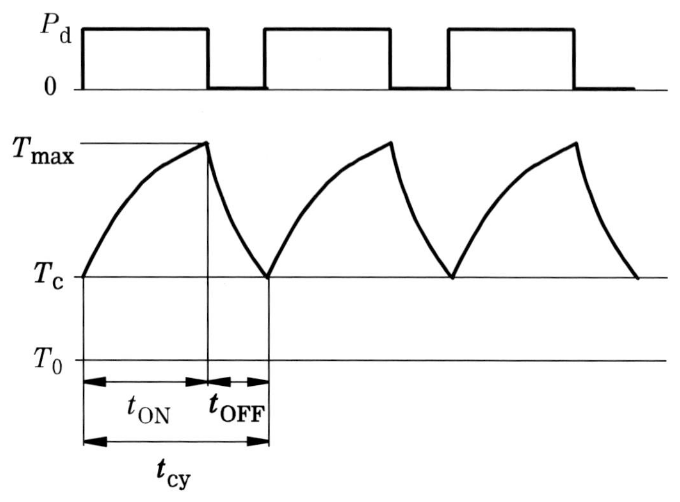

Fig. 12.40 Intermittent operation

12.6.6 Intermittent operation

Intermittent operation is normal for brushless PM motors, because most of the applications that use them are motion-control applications with programmed moves, accelerations, decelerations, stops, starts, and so on. Consequently the temperatures of the windings and magnets are constantly varying. A simple example is shown in Fig. 12.40, where the motor executes a simple on-off sequence: on for t_{ON} and off for t_{OFF}, after which the on/off cycle repeats indefinitely. The cycle time t_{cy} is

$$t_{cy} = t_{ON} + t_{OFF}. \tag{12.243}$$

The *duty-cycle d* is defined as

$$d = \frac{t_{ON}}{t_{cy}} = \frac{t_{ON}}{t_{ON} + t_{OFF}}. \tag{12.244}$$

The most efficient use of the thermal capability of the motor will be made if the maximum winding temperature T_{max} just reaches the rated value T_r at the end of each on-time. Because the power dissipation is interrupted with cool-down intervals t_{OFF}, the power P_d that can be dissipated during the on-times may exceed the steady-state continuous dissipation rating of the motor P_r. Therefore the motor may be permitted to exceed its steady-state power rating during the on-times.

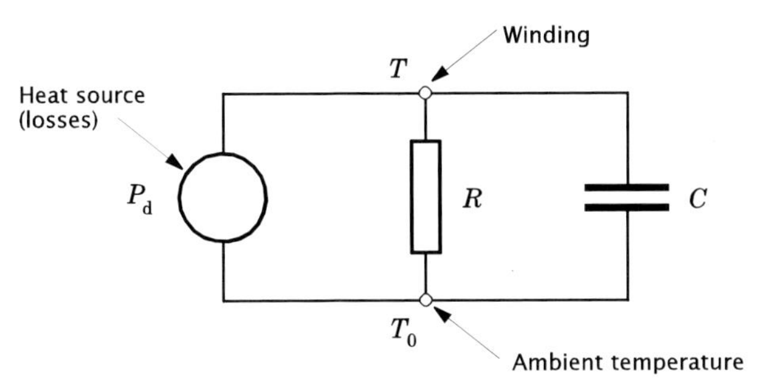

Fig. 12.41 Simple thermal equivalent circuit

The simplified thermal equivalent circuit model in Fig. 12.41 makes it possible to calculate the permissible overload factor as a function of the on-time t_{ON} and duty-cycle d for a given motor.

The thermal equivalent circuit is a parallel combination of thermal resistance R and thermal capacitance C. R represents the steady-state thermal resistance between the winding and the surroundings in °C/W. C represents the thermal capacity of the entire motor in J/°C. The thermal time-constant τ is given [in seconds] by

$$\tau = RC \tag{12.245}$$

The analysis proceeds by equating the temperature rise during the on-time with the temperature fall during the off-time. To do this we need the equations for the temperature rise and the temperature fall.

Temperature rise during ON-time — During the on-time t_{ON}, the power dissipation in the motor is P_d and the temperature rises according to the equation

$$T - T_0 = RP_d(1 - e^{-t/\tau}) + (T_c - T_0)e^{-t/\tau}. \tag{12.246}$$

The temperature rise is expressed relative to the ambient temperature T_0. The second term in eqn. (12.246) is due to the initial condition in which the temperature rise is $(T_c - T_0)$ at $t = 0$. At $t = t_{ON}$,

$$T_{max} - T_0 = RP_d(1 - e^{-t_{ON}/\tau}) + (T_c - T_0)e^{-t_{ON}/\tau}. \tag{12.247}$$

By definition, the steady-state rated temperature-rise $(T_r - T_0)$ is

$$T_r - T_0 = RP_r, \tag{12.248}$$

where P_r is the rated steady-state power dissipation in the motor, i.e., the continuous power dissipation that produces rated temperature rise. We can use this to "calibrate" P_d in eqns. (12.246) and (12.247), by defining the *dissipation overload factor* k^2, where

$$k^2 = \frac{P_d}{P_r}. \tag{12.249}$$

The reason for using k^2 instead of k is that in most types of brushless servomotor the losses are dominated by I^2R losses while the load torque is proportional to the current I. If the load is increased by a factor k, it means that the current and torque are increased by the factor k while the losses increase by k^2. Thus k is the overload factor for torque and current.

Substituting eqns. (12.248) and (12.249) in eqn. (12.247) and rearranging, and assuming that

$$T_{max} = T_r, \tag{12.250}$$

we obtain the following equation relating the temperature rise to the overload factor and the on-time:

$$(T_r - T_0)[1 - k^2(1 - e^{-t_{ON}/\tau})] = (T_c - T_0)e^{-t_{ON}/\tau} \tag{12.251}$$

Temperature fall during OFF-time — When the motor is switched off, the power dissipation falls to zero and the winding temperature falls according to the equation

$$T - T_0 = (T_r - T_0)e^{-t/\tau} \tag{12.252}$$

where t is measured from the end of the on-time, i.e. the beginning of the off-time. At t_{OFF},

$$T_c - T_0 = (T_r - T_0)e^{-t_{OFF}/\tau}. \tag{12.253}$$

Steady-state : equating the temperature rise and fall –First, multiply eqn. (12.253) by $e^{-t_{ON}/\tau}$:

$$(T_c - T_0)e^{-t_{ON}/\tau} = (T_r - T_0)e^{-(t_{ON} + t_{OFF})/\tau}. \tag{12.254}$$

The left-hand side of eqn. (12.254) is identical to the right-hand side of eqn. (12.251), so the right-hand side of eqn. (12.254) can be equated to the left-hand side of eqn. (12.251). With suitable rearrangement, the result can be expressed in different ways for different purposes.

Maximum overload factor — First, we get a solution for the dissipation overload factor k^2 in terms of the on-time and the duty-cycle. Writing t_{ON}/d instead of $t_{ON} + t_{OFF}$, i.e., instead of t_{cy},

$$k^2 = \frac{1 - e^{-t_{ON}/\tau d}}{1 - e^{-t_{ON}/\tau}} \tag{12.255}$$

For example, if the duty-cycle is 25% (d = 0·25) and $t_{ON} = 0{\cdot}2 \times \tau$, the dissipation overload factor is

$$k^2 = \frac{1 - e^{-0{\cdot}2/0{\cdot}25}}{1 - e^{-0{\cdot}2}} = 3{\cdot}04, \tag{12.256}$$

which means that the dissipation can be increased to 304% of its rated steady-state value for a period of $t_{ON} = 0{\cdot}2\tau$ in every cycle of length $t_{cy} = t_{ON}/d = (0{\cdot}2/0{\cdot}25)\tau = 0{\cdot}8\tau$. If τ = 40 min, the dissipation can be raised to 304% for 8 minutes followed by a cool-down period of 24 minutes. Increasing the dissipation to 304% corresponds to an increase in current and torque to $\sqrt{k} = \sqrt{3{\cdot}04} = 1{\cdot}74$ times their rated values.

If $t_{cy} << \tau$, then eqn. (1.46) simplifies so that

$$k^2 = \frac{1}{d}. \tag{12.257}$$

This means that when the on/off cycles are very short compared with the thermal time-constant of the motor, the mean dissipation will be equal to P_r when the peak dissipation $P_d = k^2 P_r$ is equal to P_r/d. This simple result is intuitive.

Maximum overload for a single pulse — Eqn. (12.255) can also be used to calculate the maximum dissipation overload factor for a single pulse, for which d = 0. In this case

$$k^2 = \frac{1}{1 - e^{-t_{ON}/\tau}}. \tag{12.258}$$

For example, if t_{ON} = 8 min and τ = 40 min, then the maximum dissipation overload factor k^2 is 5·5 or 550%, and the maximum overload factor k is 2·35 or 235%.

Required cool-down period for a given overload factor and on-time — The second result that arises from equating the temperature rise and temperature fall is an expression for the necessary cool-down time t_{OFF} as a function of the dissipation factor k^2 and the on-time t_{ON}. The expression is

$$t_{OFF} = -\tau \ln\left[k^2 - (k^2 - 1)e^{t_{ON}/\tau}\right]. \qquad (12.259)$$

Together with eqn. (12.244), this can be used to determine the maximum duty-cycle d that can be used with a given dissipation overload factor k^2 and a given on-time t_{ON}, for a motor of thermal time-constant τ. For example, if the dissipation is 200% of rated, and if t_{ON} = 8 min, τ = 40 min,

$$t_{OFF} = -40 \times \ln\left[2 - (2 - 1) \times e^{8/40}\right] = 10{\cdot}0 \text{ min}. \qquad (12.260)$$

The minimum cycle time is therefore 18 min and the maximum duty-cycle (with 8 minutes' on-time) is 8/18 = 0·44 or 44%.

Maximum on-time for a given overload factor and cool-down time — A third result obtained by equating the temperature rise and fall is an expression for the maximum on-time t_{ON} as a function of the dissipation overload factor k^2 and the off-time t_{OFF}. The expression is

$$t_{ON} = \tau \ln\left[\frac{k^2 - e^{-t_{OFF}/\tau}}{k^2 - 1}\right]. \qquad (12.261)$$

Maximum duration of single pulse — This expression can be used to calculate the maximum duration of a single pulse having a given dissipation overload factor k^2. For a single pulse, t_{OFF} is infinite and

$$t_{ON} = \tau \ln\left[\frac{k^2}{k^2 - 1}\right]. \qquad (12.262)$$

For example, if k^2 = 5·5 and τ = 40 min, then t_{ON} = 8 min.

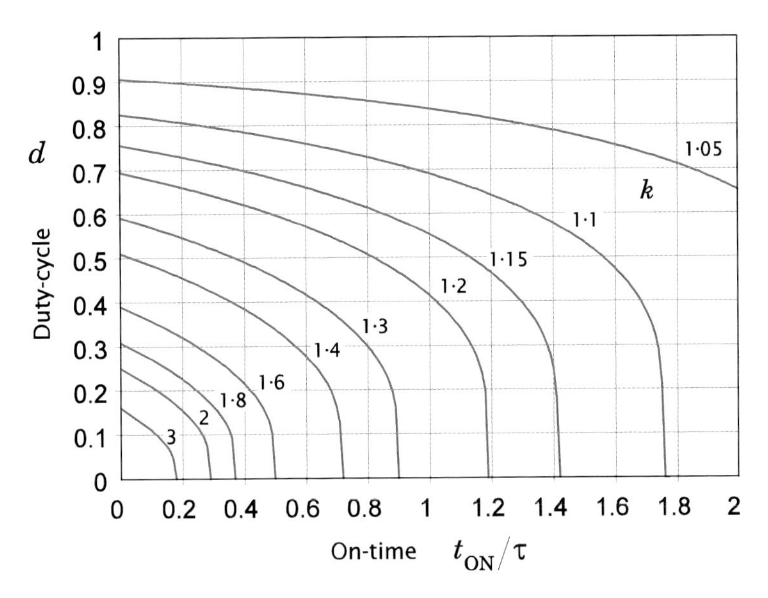

Fig. 12.42 Intermittent heating curves

Graphical transient heating curves — Fig. 12.42 shows the relationship expressed by eqn. (12.261) graphically in terms of the duty-cycle d, the on-time t_{ON} as a fraction of the time-constant τ, and the overload factor k.

This graph can be used in a number of ways. For example, to determine the maximum permissible duration of a single pulse with a given overload factor k, the duty-cycle d should be set to zero. Thus with $k = 1{\cdot}3$ the maximum pulse duration is $0{\cdot}9\tau$. With a time-constant of 40 min this is 36 min.

The graph shows the maximum duty-cycle that can be used with a given overload factor. For example, at 200% load the maximum duty-cycle is 0·25 or 25%, but in this limiting case the on-time must be vanishingly small. With an on-time of $0{\cdot}1\tau$ at 200% load, the maximum duty-cycle is approximately 0·2, which means that the cool-down period in each cycle must be $(1 - d)\tau = 0{\cdot}9\tau$. If τ is 40 min, this means a maximum operating time at 200% load of 4 min, followed by a cool-down period of 36 min before the cycle can be repeated. Operations that need a short on-time with a high duty-cycle must use a lower overload factor.

It must be emphasized that the curves in Fig. 12.42 represent an oversimplified thermal model. These curves were published originally by Welch and Kaufman [1991 and 1992]; (see also Noodleman, [1973]). Much more analysis of thermal performance has been undertaken in the last 20 years (see, for example, Boglietti *et al*, [2008, 2009]).

Improved "simple" models have also been developed for intermittent operation. In particular it has been recognized that the winding temperature is not necessarily accurately represented by the single temperature T in Fig. 12.41, and a 4-parameter model has been proposed that allows a more detailed model of the winding temperature separately from the frame temperature. [See Richard Welch, *Hotter than You Think*, Machine Design, February 4, 2010, pp. 58-61; also see Ref. 265].

13 TESTING

13.1 Introduction

The importance of physical testing is self-evident for all electrical machines. Effective testing is a matter of great engineering skill. It includes the design and assembly of dynamometers and other test fixtures; the acquisition and sometimes the design of measuring instruments; a knowledge of standards and standard procedures; a high standard of organization and record-keeping; and above all a meticulous attention to detail, both in the operation of the tests and in the observation of processes and results. The subject deserves a book of its own.

Here we have space for no more than a discussion of certain special topics pertinent to PM machines and drives.

13.2 Objectives of testing

In the factory the most basic tests are "quality control" tests intended to check that the product is fit for delivery to the customer. Obviously the complexity depends on the number of units being made: a standard motor manufactured in large numbers will need sample testing and type testing, but it may not be necessary to make comprehensive tests on every unit.

In the context of this book, laboratory testing is important as a means of verifying or disproving the methods of calculation used in design. Performance tests on prototypes serve this purpose to a certain extent, and are required in any case on prototype machines; but it is sometimes helpful to measure certain parameters that are of no interest to the end-user of the machine and may not be related to the quality-control tests that are important in the factory. For example, the end-winding leakage reactance is important in design calculations but impossible to measure on a single machine; it requires a series of special machines to be made with different stack-lengths, and even then the inductance measurement is a specialized test requiring skills and instrumentation that would often not be found in a standard test laboratory, and never in the factory.

13.3 Basic tests and measurements

Certain basic tests should be performed on prototype machines before any electrical connections are made. Certain measurements should be made even while the machine is being assembled. For example, the weight of one lamination, the weight of the stator core, the weight of the copper windings, and indeed the weight of every single component in the machine should be measured and recorded. These weights are often invaluable in the process of design verification, when the design calculations are being correlated with the performance test data. It is all too easy to forget to measure them, but once the machine is assembled it is too late.

Not only weights, but dimensions. For example, the overall length over the end-windings is a simple dimension to measure, but impossible to calculate precisely. The airgap length should be measured at both ends of the machine with feeler gauges at several rotor positions to test for uniformity and run-out.

It should be verified that the rotor is axially centred, both mechanically and magnetically. This may require a special bearing system with enough freedom of movement in the axial direction to allow the rotor to "float" to its equilibrium position.

Such dimensional checks help to eliminate uncertainties in design verification. Without them, the designer can be faced with discrepancies between test and calculation that cannot be resolved by head-scratching.

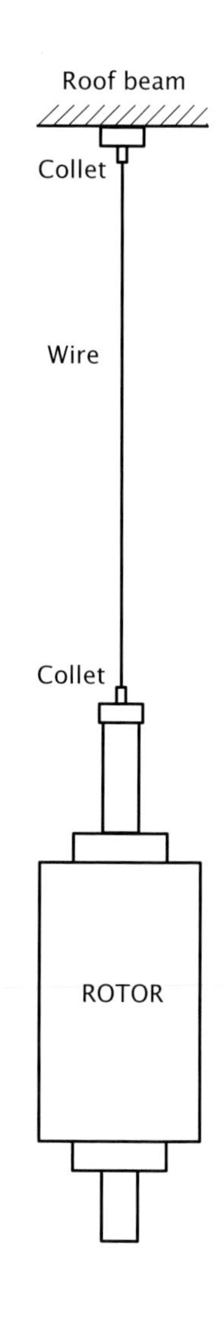

Fig. 13.1 Inertia

13.3.1 Inertia

In addition to the weight of the rotor, its inertia should be measured. The simplest method is the torsional pendulum, Fig. 13.1.

The rotor is suspended from the wire in a collet that clasps the end of the shaft. Care should be taken to machine and fit this collet so that the rotor axis is collinear with the line of the wire.

The number of torsional swings in a timed period gives the torsional oscillation frequency f. Then the rotor is replaced by a reference inertia J_0. If the frequency with J_0 is f_0, then the inertia of the test motor is given by

$$J = J_0 \times \left[\frac{f_0}{f} \right]^2 . \tag{13.1}$$

If J_0 is a simple cylinder of mass M and radius r,

$$J_0 = \frac{1}{2} M r^2 . \tag{13.2}$$

Corrections should be made for the inertia of the lower collet using this formula applied to each cylindrical "element" thereof.

13.4 Resistance

The simplest way to measure winding resistance is to use a multimeter with "4-terminal" resistance measurement, which is altogether the most accurate method. The winding temperature must be measured at the same time as the resistance, because the accuracy of the resistance measurement is only as good as the accuracy of the temperature. See Fig. 13.2.

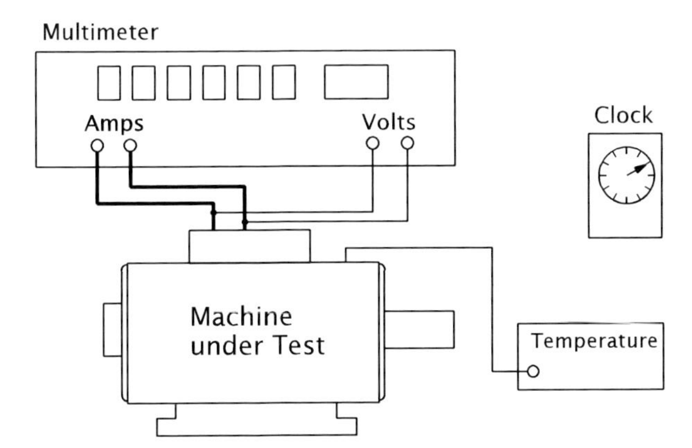

Fig. 13.2 Resistance measurement

Three-phase machines usually have a star- or delta-connected winding with only three terminals. It is important to measure the resistance between all pairs of terminals to check for any asymmetry. Any imbalance (more than 2 or 3%) between phases or between line-line values may be a symptom of an incorrect winding or connection.

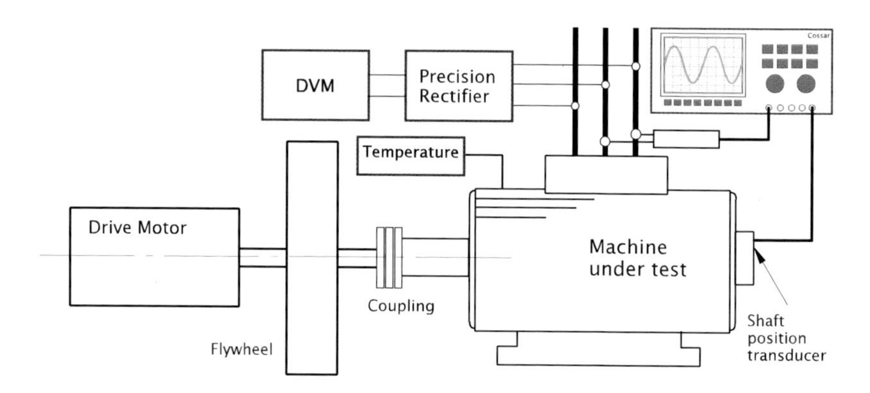

Fig. 13.3 EMF testing

13.5 EMF Testing

The EMF test shown in Fig. 13.3 is arguably the most important and useful test which can be performed on a brushless PM motor. In many cases it is the only performance test required on the production line for motor qualification, because the relationship between the EMF and the torque is so predictable. (See Chapter 8).

Fig. 13.3 shows the measurement of the mean rectified EMF using a precision rectifier, as well as the EMF waveform from which the peak line-line EMF is obtained. It thus provides for both the preferred methods of defining and measuring the EMF constant k_E.

If a simple brushless DC drive is available it can be used as an analog switch to connect the greatest line-line EMF at any instant to the oscilloscope, effectively functioning as a rectifier. If the signals from a Hall sensor or optical encoder are displayed at the same time, the alignment information is also available from this test. The flywheel inertia is not absolutely necessary, but the results are better if it is used, especially if the motor has any cogging torque.

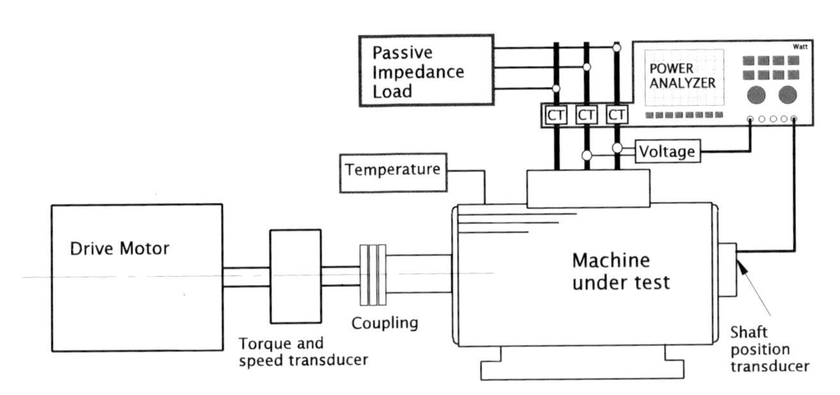

Fig. 13.4 Generator load testing

13.6 Generator load testing

Fig. 13.4 shows the configuration for testing a generator under load. The arrangement is developed from the EMF test in Fig. 13.3 but is more substantial. It requires a drive motor of at least the steady-state rating of the generator. The passive load impedance must be capable of dissipating the power of the generator, and there is a torque transducer. To achieve the best accuracy, the torque transducer should be sized so that the rated torque of the machine under test produces "full scale deflection". Torque transducers must be calibrated: a small error in the torque results in a much larger error in efficiency, if the efficiency is deduced from the difference between output power and input power.

A power analyzer is generally used to measure all the electrical quantities at the output terminals of the generator, especially if the load is a rectifier or a transistor inverter. In those cases, harmonics in the voltage and/or current waveforms must be included in the measurement, so the bandwidth of the power analyzer must be checked, as well as its accuracy in the power range of interest.

Sometimes the machine under test or even the drive motor is "gimballed", that is, mounted on low-friction bearings so that the reaction torque can be measured. This avoids the need for an in-line torque transducer which may be an advantage especially if torque transients (due to starting, for example) are more than 1·5 – 2 p.u. of the torque transducer full-scale rating.

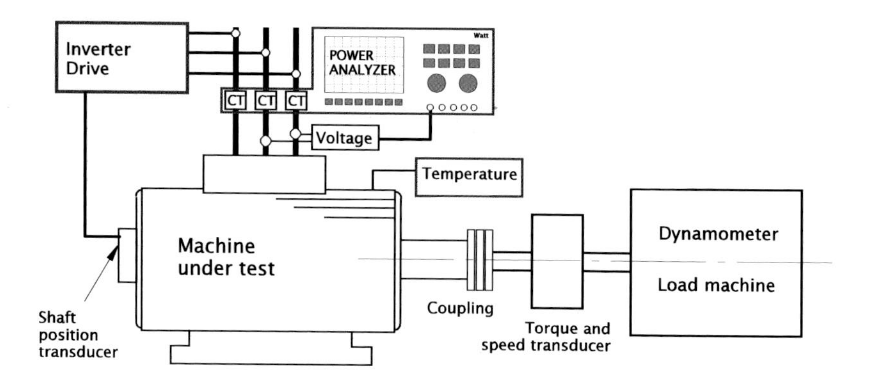

Fig. 13.5 Motor load testing

13.7 Motor load testing

Fig. 13.5 shows the general configuration of a dynamometer system for load testing of a motor fed by its own inverter drive. The same considerations as for generator testing apply to the torque transducer and the power analyzer, but with increased emphasis because motors are more likely to experience torque transients and an inverter produces more harmonics in the current and the voltage. Motors are more likely to experience wide variations in loading and they may even operate as generators part of the time, so the most advanced dynamometers have to be able to apply a programmed load.

13.8 Torque Testing

13.8.1 Torque constant kT

The torque linearity can be tested on a setup such as the one in Fig. 13.5, preferably with a load machine or brake that can be programmed with torque. A typical result is shown in Fig. 13.6. It is immediately clear that the "torque per ampere" is not fixed, but is subject to nonlinearities. The first of these is the friction, including the breakaway or static friction at zero speed. Once the machine is running the mechanical losses may vary with speed, so the speed at which the measurement is performed must be recorded. If core losses are included in the mechanical losses, they will vary to some extent with speed and torque.

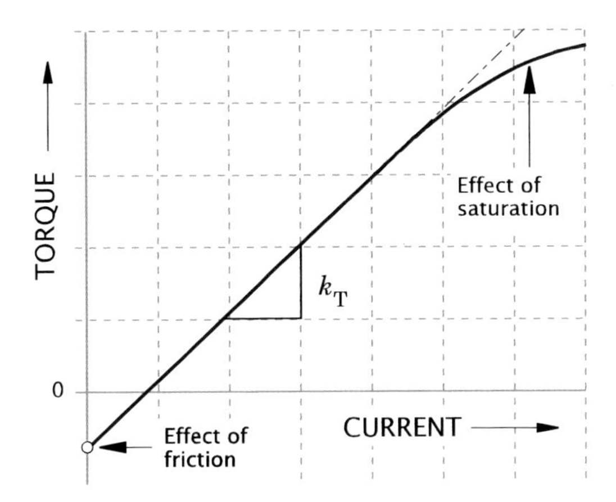

Fig. 13.6 Measurement of torque constant k_T

At high currents the effect of magnetic saturation causes a reduction in k_T. Even without saturation the inductance can influence the current waveform and this also affects the value of k_T. As with k_E, the temperature of the magnets also affects k_T.

The measurement of k_T is clearly a much more complex undertaking than the measurement of k_E, and even when the test is performed it does not and cannot produce a single value, even at one temperature. This helps to explain why the k_T quoted in catalogue data of servo motors is usually deduced from a measured value of k_E according to the relationships developed in Chapter 8.

13.8.2 Cogging torque

Cogging torque is by definition a *zero-current* property, since it is the torque produced by the magnets alone interacting with the slotted structure of the stator.[136] It requires the machine to be driven, typically by a gearmotor with a flywheel, Fig. 13.7. A bias torque is applied to the shaft (as depicted by the rope and bias weight). The motor is rotated in both directions to get an average cogging torque waveform.

---

[136] The test system of Fig. 13.5 can in principle measure the torque *ripple* when the machine is operating normally, provided that the speed can be held constant and the torque transducer is capable of following the torque variations. Even so, the measurement is susceptible to mechanical resonances.

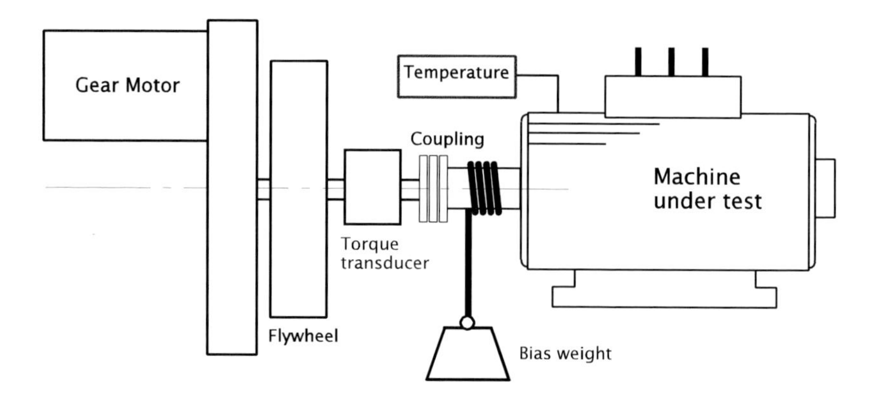

Fig. 13.7 Measurement of cogging torque

13.8.3 On-line estimation of torque using the i-psi loop

We have seen in §4.5 that the mean electromagnetic torque over one electrical cycle can be obtained from the area of the i-ψ loop, as in eqn. (4.116). Fig. 4.39 shows an example in which neither the current nor the voltage is sinusoidal, emphasizing the fact that eqn. (4.116) is not restricted to any particular waveform.

The i-ψ loop area W can be estimated digitally on-line from samples of the terminal voltage and current, both of which can be obtained from signals that are already available in the drive controller.[137] If the i-ψ loop is represented by a series of N samples, W can be calculated from the area of a polygon with N vertices,

$$W = \frac{1}{2}\sum_{1}^{N}(\psi_k i_{k-1} - i_k \psi_{k-1}) \quad [\mathrm{J}]. \tag{13.3}$$

The samples of phase flux-linkage ψ_k can be obtained from eqn. (4.51) with $e = v_k - Ri_k$, where v_k is the phase voltage. v_k is usually not available directly, but it can be estimated from a knowledge of the states of the inverter transistors by calculating $\mathbf{u}^*$ from eqn. (7.105) and then deducing v_k in any phase from Fig. 7.25 in conjunction with Figs. 7.23 and 7.24, with corrections for device voltage drops.

[137] See Cossar C., Popescu M., Miller T.J.E., McGilp M.I. and Olaru, M., *A General Magnetic-Energy-Based Torque Estimator: Validation via a Permanent-Magnet Motor Drive*, IEEE Transactions on Industry Applications, Vol. 44, No. 4, July/August 2008, pp. 1210-1217.

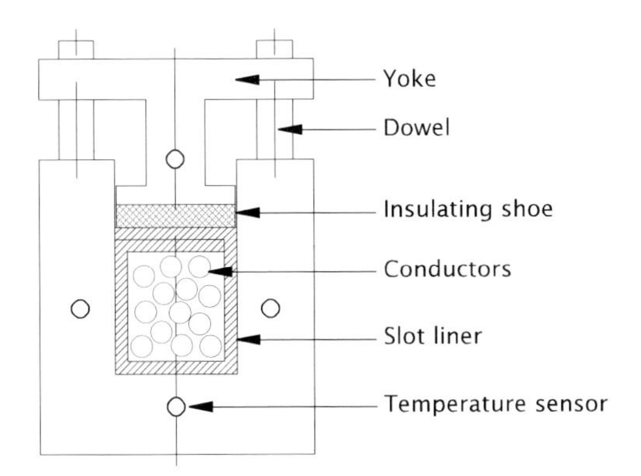

Fig. 13.8 Apparatus for measuring heat transfer in slots

13.9 Thermal Testing

13.9.1 Thermal equivalent-circuit parameters

The simplest thermal model of a PM machine is a single thermal resistance R in Fig. 12.41, examples of which are given in Fig. 12.38. In small totally-enclosed nonventilated motors R can be measured by passing DC through the windings with the rotor stationary, and deducing the final winding temperature rise from the resistance using eqn. (12.248). A reasonable idea of the thermal capacity C can be obtained from the same test, either from the initial rate of rise of the winding temperatures, or from an exponential function curve-fitted to the graph of winding temperature vs. time.

More complex cooling systems require more specialized tests, often involving measurements on the flow of coolant (air or liquid) inside and outside the machine. Because of the distributed nature of heat transfer, it can be difficult to identify parameter values for lumped-parameter thermal equivalent circuits, unless special test fixtures are used. These fixtures are generally designed to isolate one heat transfer path, and sometimes one or more heat sources, from all the others.[138]

---

[138] See, for example, Boglietti A., Cavagnino A., Staton D.A., Popescu M., Cossar C., and McGilp M., *End Space Heat Transfer Coefficient Determination for Different Induction Motor Enclosure Types*, IEEE Transactions on Industry Applications, Vol. 45, No. 3, May/June 2009, pp. 929-937.

Another (very simple) example of a specialized test fixture is shown in Fig. 13.8. A coilside wrapped in a slot liner is inserted in a slot cut in an aluminium block, and retained by a yoke guided by dowels or threaded studs so that pressure can be applied to adjust the degree of compression of the conductor array. The slot can be impregnated with varnish to give a more realistic simulation of conditions in a machine. Temperature sensors are embedded in holes in the aluminium block and in the yoke. Current is passed through the conductors to heat them, and the temperature rise of the conductors relative to the block is measured. Several useful parameters can be extracted from this test: for example, the effective thermal resistance across the slot-liner, and the effective thermal diffusion resistance through the array of conductors.

Although such specialized experimental rigs are useful only for lumped-parameter measurements, it must be said that analytical models of heat transfer in electrical machines have made significant progress in recent times.[139] This is important, because a full-scale numerical analysis of the heat transfer and coolant flow is complex and expensive, and does not yield parameters but only point values against which measurements on a large number of temperature sensors in a working machine can be correlated.

13.10 Inductance Testing

The so-called RLC bridge should never be used for inductance measurements on electrical machines.[140] The most reliable methods are those that rely on the simple fundamental principles of AC circuit theory together with Faraday's Law, (§5.1).

A very good example is the short-circuit test of a generator to measure X_d according to eqn. (9.1). This test requires nothing more than a voltmeter and an ammeter.

---

[139] See Boglietti A., Cavagnino A., and Staton D.A., *Determination of Critical Parameters in Electrical Machine Thermal Models*, IEEE Transactions on Industry Applications, Vol. 44, No. 4, July/August 2008, pp. 1150-1159.

[140] Sadly, it frequently is. The problems are that (1) the excitation level is much too low; (2) the excitation frequency is much too high; and (3) the indicated inductance is an *incremental* inductance which, even if correct, would be of little practical use. Inductance is too important to be measured with a push-button black box.

With a power analyzer, which is now not only a common instrument but a very accurate one, it is a simple matter to measure voltage, current, and phase angles. As long as the phase angles can be related to the rotor position, the phasor diagram can be reconstructed, and from it the reactances X_d and X_q can be deduced. Although this method works only for sinewave motor/drives, it has the huge advantage of measuring X_d and X_q in operation and not in some synthetic laboratory situation.

For squarewave drives there are many opportunities to measure the line-line inductance from the current waveform when the EMF and the terminal voltage and the resistance are known. Eqn. (6.3) is an example: if the rate of change of current $p_1 = di_1/dt$ is measured (for example, using an oscilloscope), the line-line inductance $(L - M)$ can be readily estimated.

It is generally not necessary for inductance measurements to be extremely accurate. What is more important is to have reliable measurements that represent the actual operation of the machine. It is also important to differentiate between total inductance (the ratio of flux-linkage and current) and incremental inductance (the differential coefficient of flux-linkage with respect to current). The total inductance is relevant to the production of torque and the voltage-drop produced by armature reaction, whereas the incremental inductance is of interest only to electronics engineers concerned with the relationship between switching frequency and current-ripple.

Even so, the accurate scientific measurement of inductance is very important. Because of resistance and parasitic induced currents in conductive components in the neighbourhood of the circuit whose inductance is to be measured, AC measurements are of questionable value, as are methods based on exponential decay of DC transients. It is therefore recommended to use the DC inductance bridge described by Jones,[141] which measures DC flux-linkage independently of any induced currents and with negligible errors arising from resistance. The circuit is shown in Fig. 13.9.

---

[141] An excellent account is given in Jones C.V., *The Unified Theory of Electrical Machines,* Butterworths, London 1967. Jones cites earlier work by Prescott J.C. and El-Karashi A.K: e.g., *A method of measuring self-inductances applicable to large electrical machines*, Proc. Inst. Electr. Engrs., Vol. 106, Part A, April 1959, p. 169ff.

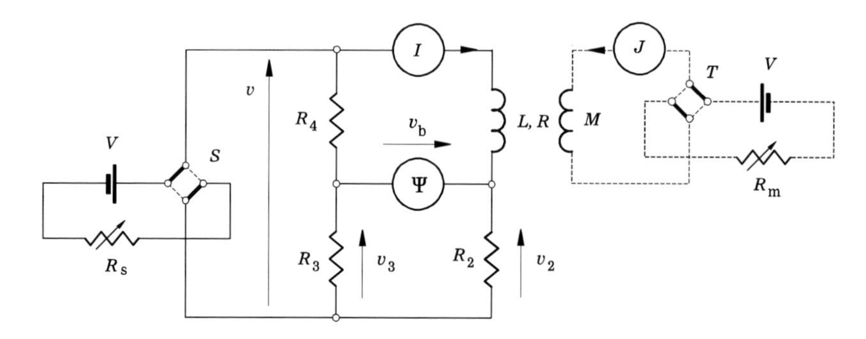

Fig. 13.9 DC inductance bridge for measuring flux-linkage and inductance

Self inductance — The inductance to be measured is L, and R is its internal resistance. It is connected in a bridge circuit which is supplied with DC current *via* a reversing switch S. The detector is an integrating voltmeter or fluxmeter. The bridge is balanced for DC, and then the switch S is opened (or reversed). For the right-hand branch of the bridge circuit we have

$$v = (R + R_2)i + L\frac{di}{dt} \tag{13.4}$$

and the voltage across R_2 is therefore

$$v_2 = R_2 i = \frac{R_2}{R + R_2}\left[v - L\frac{di}{dt}\right]. \tag{13.5}$$

Across R_3 we have

$$v_3 = vR_3/(R_3 + R_4) \tag{13.6}$$

and the voltage across the detector is

$$v_b = v_2 - v_3. \tag{13.7}$$

If the bridge is balanced we have

$$\frac{R_3}{R_3 + R_4} = \frac{R_2}{R + R_2}. \tag{13.8}$$

Hence

$$v_b = -\frac{R_2}{R + R_2}L\frac{di}{dt}. \tag{13.9}$$

The integrating voltmeter therefore reads

$$\Psi = \int_0^\infty v_b \, dt = -\frac{R_2}{R + R_2} L \int_I^0 di = \frac{R_2}{R + R_2} L I, \qquad (13.10)$$

whence

$$L = \left[1 + \frac{R}{R_2}\right] \frac{\Psi}{I}. \qquad (13.11)$$

The inductance L is the total inductance, that is, the ratio of flux-linkage to current Ψ/I. Induced currents in shorted circuits coupled to the inductance L contribute nothing to the voltage integral in eqn. (13.10), so the method measures the true DC inductance without having to remove or decouple these coupled circuits (even if that were possible). This is extremely useful in electrical machines where coupled short-circuited loops exist in the laminations, frame, etc.

Mutual inductance — The bridge is balanced with the desired current I in the "primary" and an independent current J in the "secondary". When J is switched off, the voltage in the primary is induced by mutual coupling instead of self-coupling and so by analogy with eqn. (13.11), M is given by

$$M = \left[1 + \frac{R}{R_2}\right] \frac{\Psi}{J}. \qquad (13.12)$$

In both the L and M measurements, the switches S and T can be reversed instead of being simply opened, and in that case Ψ should be replaced by $\Psi/2$ in eqns. (13.11) and (13.12).

Static measurement of L_d and L_q — The DC bridge method can be used to measure L_d and L_q directly using the connections shown in Fig. 5.22 on p. 246, with the rotor locked in the appropriate position.

14 APPENDIX

14.1 Frequently asked questions

14.1.1 Machine Design Questions

14.1.1.1 How do I decide the shape and size of the machine?

For *completely new* machines, use the **sizing** methods in §3.3. Table 3.7 should be used as a guide to the TRV or torque per unit rotor volume, which depends on the intensity of the losses and the method of cooling. The losses depend on the electric loading and the flux-density level combined with the magnetic frequency. All these quantities are interrelated as explained in §3.3.

The sizing equations are almost always constrained by **space limits** which set the maximum overall length and diameter. Sometimes the proportions of the machine are heavily influenced by the application requirements. For example, motors for electric screwdrivers have a small diameter/length ratio, while torque motors for rotating very large turntables at low speed have a ring-like structure.

For machines that are *derived from existing machines*, the design process is usually a question of making **many small changes**. Each of these may influence the performance only very slightly, but when they are all added together the improvement can be substantial. It is relatively unusual to see huge factors of improvement: 10–20% is generally a fine achievement in an already-mature product line. Claims of 2:1 improvement should be treated with healthy scepticism; this level of improvement is not unknown, but it usually comes at a price — for example, a complete re-tooling, or much higher cost.

The small changes needed to improve existing products are very diverse, and could fill a whole book. Many of them are based on common-sense interpretation of the theory (especially Chapter 3), but inventive developments often run ahead of the theory.

The role of "optimization" tools should be carefully considered.

Since they depend on mathematical or logical algorithms, they can only work on problems that are precisely posed. In the most advanced applications of optimization tools, the problems *are* precisely posed — even very complex problems — and they may be tightly constrained by limits on manufacturing processes and parameters. Although optimization tools cannot invent new solutions to problems, they can assist in improving designs while taking into account much detailed "factory" data. When this is done effectively, the result is highly proprietary (not easy to follow), and therefore commercially valuable.

14.1.1.2 How do I choose the number of slots and poles?

The number of poles is one of the most fundamental design decisions. It is discussed in detail in §3.2.2. With conventional AC or DC motors, 4 poles is a common choice because of the general compromise between such factors as the speed and frequency, the number of coils to be wound and inserted, the length of the end-windings, and the effectiveness of the magnetic circuit. 6- and 8-pole AC motors are also common, and the general tendency to favour these pole-numbers applies more or less equally to the brushless permanent-magnet machine, especially in larger sizes when material utilization is important. 2-pole machines are also used in high-speed applications, but they tend to have long end-windings and they are more sensitive to imbalance and bearing problems.

Brushless permanent-magnet machines often use fractional slots/pole to reduce cogging torque and to get the advantages of single-tooth concentrated windings with short end-turns.

The slots/pole ratio and the number of slots are discussed in §3.2.2, §3.5.8, and §3.6.

14.1.1.3 How do I design the stator teeth and slots?

In large machines that use form-wound coils, it is normal to use open slots with a nonmetallic wedge (Fig. 3.22). Occasionally this wedge is made of a special magnetic material to reduce the cogging torque; this also increases the slot-leakage inductance.

The more common case is that of smaller machines with semi-closed slots, Figs. 3.13, 3.21, 3.25, 3.26. Semi-closed and even closed slots are occasionally used even with form-wound coils inserted in the form of "hairpins" with end-turns welded at one end to complete the coil. This is done in order to achieve a very high slot-fill factor without the disadvantage of cogging that arises with open slots. It requires re-insulation of the conductors and is feasible only when the number of turns per coil is small (for example, 1 – 5).

It will often be the case that the geometry is constrained to that of a previous design, by the availability of tooling — punching dies — or to a standard catalogue shape. Several well-established specialist companies supply laminations or even complete stator cores, wound or unwound, and they not only have a comprehensive library of well established shapes, but in some cases they also provide a design service for custom laminations.[142]

The *number* of stator slots was addressed earlier. The relative widths of the stator teeth and slots is a fundamental design question; see the ratio $\tau = t/\lambda$ in Fig. 3.13. This ratio was discussed in §3.3.1 in connection with the relative flux-densities in the airgap and the teeth. Roughly speaking, it is common for τ to be about 0·5 so that the airgap flux-density is about half the tooth flux-density. If the teeth are working safely below the saturation density, say at 1·8T (peak), the airgap flux-density will be of the order of 0·9T (peak). In practice there is considerable variation on these values, depending on the choice of magnet and the type of machine.

What has not yet been emphasized is the importance of the ratio τ in balancing the magnetic loading and the electric loading; this relates also to the balance between core loss and Joule loss. If the teeth are made narrow (making τ smaller), the slot area increases, permitting an increase in the wire size, so the Joule loss can be reduced; but the flux-density in the teeth will increase, resulting in increased core loss. Saturation of the teeth is undesirable not only because of losses, but also because it indicates a waste of precious magnetization and magnet material.

---

[142] A good place to see them is at the C.W.I.E.M.E. "Coil Winding" Exhibition in Berlin and elsewhere; they also advertise in the Coil Winding International & Electrical Insulation Magazine, Poole, Dorset, UK.

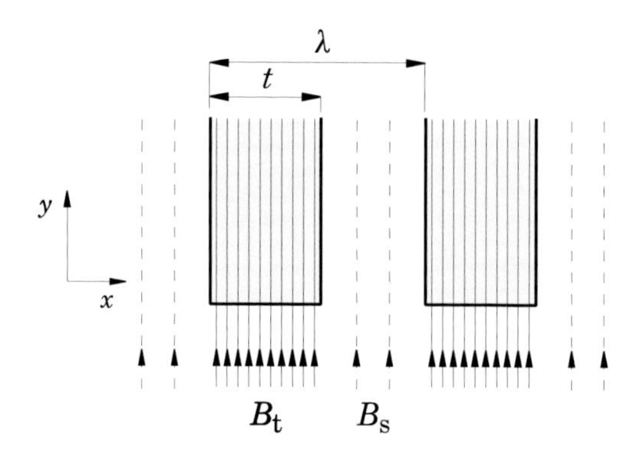

Fig. 14.1 Slot flux

It might be thought that the slot area can be increased by using deeper slots. Increasing the slot-depth decreases the thickness of the stator yoke and increases the yoke flux-density, which is undesirable for the same reasons as in the case of the tooth flux-density. It also increases the slot-leakage inductance and the AC resistance, and it may make the winding more difficult to manufacture.

In extreme cases of highly saturated teeth, some of the main flux begins to pass through the slot. In Fig. 14.1 the magnetizing force H in the teeth is in the y-direction and it is continuous across the boundary formed by the slot wall. At normal levels of flux-density, H is very small because of the high permeability of the steel, and the resulting flux-density $\mu_0 H$ in the slot is negligible. But when the teeth saturate, H increases rapidly, and flux appears in the slot. The slots act as a safety-valve that relieves the "pressure" of high flux-density in the teeth. It is for this reason that the tooth flux-density on open-circuit cannot normally rise far above the saturation flux-density (of about 2·1 T), no matter how much MMF is applied by the magnet. The same is not true when there is a high current in the slot, however.

14.1.1.4 How do I decide the number of turns?

The number of turns in series per phase T_{ph} must be adjusted to get the correct EMF at a given speed, or EMF constant k_E. For sinewave machines the key equation is eqn. (3.7), but several other equations for sinewave and squarewave machines are given in §4.2.

In practice it is common to use a design program and to search for the most suitable number of turns by an iterative process or even by trial-and-error.

The number of turns in each individual coil is determined to make T_{ph} "come out right", in consideration with the number of parallel paths and the total number of coils. The number of coils is most commonly equal to the number of slots, giving a 2-layer winding with 2 coil-sides per slot. Several examples can be found in §3.6.

14.1.1.5 How do I decide the type of stator winding?

For machines with slots/pole $\leq 1{\cdot}5$ the coils will be wound around single teeth, using a needle winder to wind in place, or pre-winding on a segmented core as in Figs. 2.18 or 2.48. Windings with higher slots/pole ratios can be made as lap windings or concentric windings, Figs. 2.46 and 2.47. Lap windings are used with form-wound coils inserted into open slots; this method is suitable for large machines, and in certain cases rectangular conductors are used to obtain a high slot-fill factor. See Fig. 3.10. Concentric windings require special machinery in which the coils are wound on "sheds" and inserted all at once; this method is common in the manufacture of induction motors and can be used with small to medium-size brushless permanent-magnet machines. For more detail see §3.5 and §3.6.

14.1.1.6 How can I get a fractional number of turns/coil?

A fractional value of the turns per coil is sometimes needed to adjust or fine-tune the EMF constant k_E. It can be obtained by using different numbers of turns in different coils connected in series, as described in §14.3.

14.1.1.7 How can I reduce the wire size?

It is often required to reduce the wire size in order to obtain a more flexible winding, without decreasing the slot-fill factor or the amount of copper in a slot. The two main methods are to use *parallel paths* and/or *multiple strands-in-hand*; see §3.6.1.

14.1.1.8 How can I reduce the inductance?

It is sometimes required to reduce the inductance in order to make better use of the available voltage, or to reduce the electrical time-constant. The most obvious way is to reduce the turns in series per phase. This also reduces the EMF, which can be restored only to a limited extent by adding magnet material or by using a higher grade of magnet — at greater cost. Better ways of reducing the inductance can be found by examining the individual components discussed in Chapter 5. For example, the airgap component can be decreased by increasing the physical airgap or magnet thickness, or both; the ultimate is attained by using a completely slotless stator core with an airgap winding. Similar considerations apply to the harmonic or differential leakage inductance, but this component also depends on the winding design and the number of slots/pole. The slot-leakage inductance can be decreased by using wider slot-openings, although this tends to increase the cogging torque and also to reduce the EMF slightly. The slot-leakage component will be decreased if the conductors are located closer to the slot-openings. End-turn inductance is usually small and cannot be easily controlled, but it is worth noting that shorter end-turns have smaller inductance. Also, the end-turn inductance will be lower if the conductors are spaced apart from one another, rather than being tightly bunched.

14.1.1.9 How can I increase the inductance?

It is sometimes required to increase the inductance to get a flux-weakening effect or to reduce the current-ripple when using a PWM current-regulator with a limited switching frequency. All of the above methods for reducing the inductance can also be used to increase it, by making converse alterations.

14.1.1.10 How do I choose between SPM and IPM?

Possibly the easiest way to answer this question is to look at the types of applications that use SPM and the IPM. Small machines used in disk-drives and motion-control servos are almost always of the SPM type, where the *torque linearity* is important and where it is acceptable to use arc or ring-shaped magnets. The IPM is altogether less common, and although it is used in certain high-quality servo-type products it is more likely to be found in electric or hybrid vehicle traction motors such as in Fig. 2.4. In both these examples the torque linearity might be thought to be important, but the IPM configuration is preferred for a variety of reasons and the electronic control is programmed to deal with variation of k_T as the load varies. The reasons include the ability to use rectangular magnets and the advantages of higher inductance and reluctance torque. The IPM can also be designed to have a wide speed range at constant power without recourse to an oversized inverter (see Chapter 7). The IPM is also used in small high-efficiency products such as air-conditioning compressors, where the torque linearity is not as important as the cost advantage of rectangular magnets.

In choosing between the SPM and the IPM, an engineering manager faced with a new product development must balance the requirements of the machine and the electronic controller, while optimizing the combination from the point of view of the customer. It is often the case that companies are set up to manufacture one or the other (occasionally both); for this reason there is some overlap between the SPM and the IPM in serving the same applications.

JRH writes : "The rotor must be of sufficient diameter to allow internal magnet placement, particularly if the magnets are in a V shape for each pole. Then after this requirement is met there are several important reasons to use IPM rotor as follows:

1. Lowest-cost PM rotor construction as compared to a robust surface-magnet design requiring magnet retainment.
2. Lower mass of magnet per unit of torque than surface-magnet machine.
3. Rectangular shape of magnet is less expensive than shaped surface magnets.
4. The laminated rotor core is almost free if stamped from the same blank as the stator; otherwise this material is wasted.
5. Magnet retainment is almost free with magnet slabs inside the laminated rotor core with appropriate support webs, etc."

14.1.1.11 How do I choose between exterior or interior rotor?

This choice is often decided by the packaging requirements of the application. The exterior rotor is a convenient rotating platform for the load, whether it be a stack of computer disks or a ring of fan blades. It clearly lends itself to highly integrated products such as the pan-and-tilt camera-positioning mechanism cited in Chapter 2. In contrast, the interior-rotor motor is always coupled to the load by a shaft extension, so it lends itself to general-purpose applications as well as applications where the motor is integrated *together with its housing* into the driven system. The packaging flexibility of the interior-rotor machine comes from the design of the housing and/or end-caps, with an almost infinite variety of mounting arrangements. It is fair to say that the choice between exterior and interior rotor is never made on the basis of performance characteristics.

JRH writes : "I have always treated this question with respect to two factors — single speed and low cost. If the application requires a single direction of rotation and nearly constant-speed, I would always consider an outside rotor first, like Fig 2.6, 2.38, or 2.44, due to its low cost advantage: low-cost ceramic or bonded NdFeB rings can be used with plenty of flux on the outside, while the stator can be wound using DC motor automation. Magnet retention is also quite easy if not for free; for example 150 m/s is common for these machines with only the rotor yoke for magnet support.

14.1.1.12 When should I consider an axial-flux machine?

Only when you are prepared to undertake a custom mechanical design in all its detail. Some illustrations are provided in Chapter 2, while Gieras [2004] gives a comprehensive account of them, with commercial examples. One reason to contemplate an axial-flux configuration is to achieve a short axial length. However, when the entire machine is assembled it is not necessarily shorter than a radial-flux machine of equivalent performance; (see Fig. 2.43).

JRH writes: "Just about every study ever conducted claims that the axial-flux PM brushless machines produce higher torque density than radial-flux machines. I would suggest we propose that the designer check the validity of any such claim himself or herself, if high densities are important to his or her application."

14.1.1.13 How do I decide the rotor geometry?

For exterior-rotor machines and interior-rotor surface-magnet machines this is a relatively simple matter, since the magnet is in the form of a ring or a set of arcs, with only a small number of dimensions to be determined according to the principles set out in Chapters 3 and 4. Some SPM machines use bread-loaf magnets which have slightly more dimensioning requirements, but the same principles apply. In broad terms the magnet length (thickness in the direction of magnetization) must be chosen to give a reasonably high permeance coefficient, so as to minimize the risk of demagnetization and to ensure a satisfactory airgap flux-density. The length in the axial direction is fixed by the overall machine sizing. The magnet arc can be adjusted: for maximum flux/pole a wide arc is used, even approaching 180°elec; but a shorter pole-arc is often used in order to reduce the harmonics in the B_{gap} waveform and the EMF. Magnet profiling is used in some cases to achieve a more sinusoidal distribution of airgap flux (Fig. 4.18); and even Halbach magnets for the same reason. Halbach magnets are capable of producing a stronger magnetic field than plain profiled magnets, and they can even be designed to work with an air-cored rotor hub: that is, with no rotor yoke or "back-iron".

For IPM machines there is scope for more variety in mechanical design, much of it intended to maximize the flux/pole by maximizing the magnet pole area while minimizing the pole-to-pole leakage flux in the rotor, at the same time retaining sufficient mechanical strength to withstand the forces experienced during manufacture and subsequently due to rotation. These requirements lead to the use of thin webs and saturating bridges, examples of which can be seen in Figs. 2.35, 4.7, 5.25, 5.27, and several others in Chapter 11.

Specialized examples of IPM are sometimes seen with multiple nested layers of magnet, as in Fig. 2.50 and Fig. 14.2. The reason for adopting such intricate geometry is to maximize the saliency ratio X_q/X_d, in order to maximize the reluctance torque. (It was shown by Soong[143] that for any saliency ratio there is an optimum level of magnet flux that maximizes the speed range at constant power).

[143] Soong W.L. and Miller T.J.E., *Field-weakening performance of brushless synchronous AC motor drives*, IEE Proc.-Electr. Power Appl., Vol. 141, No. 6, Nov. 1994, pp. 331–340.

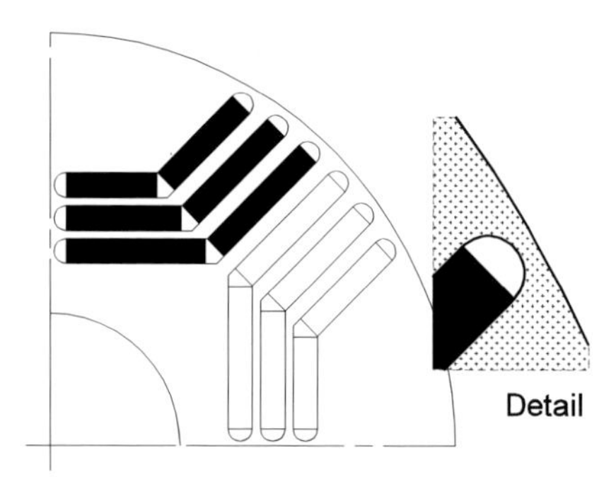

Fig. 14.2 Multiple-layer IPM

High-speed machines — JRH writes: "Experience with a large number of high-speed machine designs suggests that the rotor diameter is one of the main issues. I usually try to maximize the rotor diameter and minimize its length, to keep the bearings close together. I solve for a peak rotor 'tip speed' that allows the surface-mounted magnets to be held in place with whatever retaining-sleeve materials can be used. I have developed a chart of approximate rotor tip speeds for use with different sleeve materials, Table 14.1. If an excellent magnet adhesive is properly used to hold surface magnets in place (such as Loctite® #331 & activator #7387) the maximum safe tip speed is about 75 m/s assuming the rotor temperature never exceeds 125°C. If the tip speed is higher then some type of magnet retention is required. A sleeve design would be based on §3.7. After the rotor diameter I decide on the cooling method and then solve for the rotor dimensions based upon the expected torque density."

Tip speed (m/s)	Retaining material
50 – 100	Fibreglass or Kevlar®
75 – 125	Work-hardened 304-series stainless steel
100 – 200	Inconel 718®, aged and work-hardened
150 – 250	MP35H® Alloy
100 – 500	Pre-stressed Carbon Fiber / PEEK

TABLE 14.1
TIP SPEEDS USED WITH DIFFERENT RETAINING-SLEEVE MATERIALS

14.1.1.14 How can I reduce the inertia?

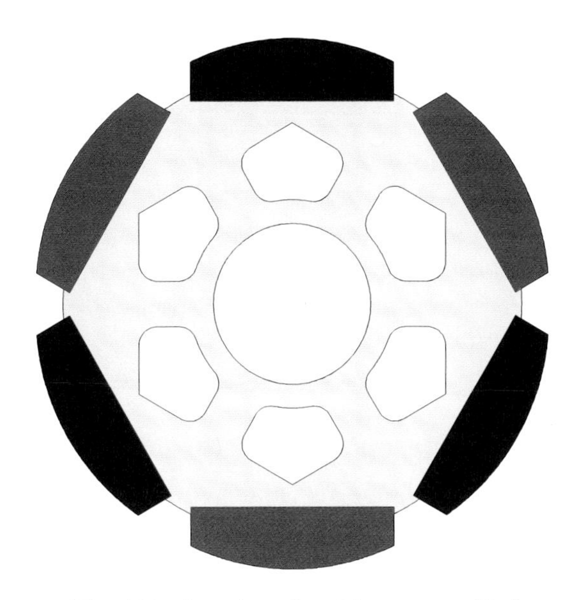

Fig. 14.3 Inertia reduced by means of holes

The inertia of a homogeneous cylinder increases with the fourth power of its diameter, so the obvious implication is to design for small diameter. To achieve the same torque, the length may well need to be increased more than proportionally. Even if this is possible within the available space, it may be undesirable for other reasons: the distance between bearings increases, and cooling becomes more difficult.

To reduce inertia without sacrificing diameter, the obvious strategy is to remove unwanted mass, particularly at larger radii. Fig. 14.3 shows an example in which the space between magnets is left open, or possibly filled with a lightweight material. In addition, this rotor shows the use of carefully shaped holes that remove mass without materially increasing the reluctance of the magnetic circuit through the rotor yoke.[144]

[144] See Mhango, L., *New Design Techniques for Low Inertia PM Brushless DC Motor Suitable for Fuel Pumping in Aerospace Drives*, International Conference on Electrical Machines, Manchester, 1992, pp. 185-189.

14.1.1.15 How can I improve the torque linearity?

Use a SPM. Avoid saturation by avoiding high flux-densities. Avoid current-regulator saturation by ensuring that the drive has sufficient voltage, especially at higher speeds.

14.1.1.16 How can I reduce torque ripple?

Torque ripple includes cogging (§3.5.12) and electromagnetic torque ripple. To reduce the electromagnetic torque ripple, the waveforms of EMF and current should approach the ideal forms introduced in Chapter 1. (See also §4.3). A speed-control feedback loop with sufficient bandwidth can also reduce torque ripple.

14.1.1.17 How do I design a PM synchronous generator?

— more or less the same way as for a motor; but see Chapter 9.

14.1.1.18 How do I test a PM synchronous machine?

See Chapter 13.

14.1.1.19 Why isn't my measured kE equal to kT?

"$k_E = k_T$" is a theoretical ideal, attained only in "consistent units", with no saturation and no friction. It also depends on the definition of k_E and k_T. In most cases, even the theoretically ideal ones, there is a conversion ratio between them. See Chapter 8.

14.1.1.20 How do I calculate the machine temperature?

The losses must be calculated first, and used as input data for a thermal model, as described in §12.6. It is essential to take account of worst-case conditions — usually the highest ambient temperature (or coolant temperature in direct-cooled machines). It is also essential to calculate the effects of intermittent or continuous duty, or overloads. "Soak-back" is another factor to consider. If the machine is mounted on a hot engine, for example, its temperature can continue to increase after the engine and the electrical machine have both been switched off, by conduction from the hot engine.

14.1.1.21 What are the main effects of temperature?

Concerning the **magnet**, an increase in temperature generally results in a decrease in the remanent flux-density B_r. The effect is approximately linear,

$$B_{rT} = B_{r20}[1 + C_{Br}(T - 20)], \tag{14.1}$$

where B_{rT} is the remanence at temperature T (°C), B_{r20} is the remanence at 20°C, T is the temperature in °C, and C_{Br} is the temperature coefficient of remanence, which can be found on the manufacturer's data sheet and usually has a negative value (around $-0{\cdot}1$ % per °C for NDFEB magnets). The coercivity of magnets also decreases with increasing temperature (except for ferrite magnets, in which it may decrease or increase depending on the temperature range).

An increase in temperature initially produces a linear reduction in B_r and therefore in the generated EMF. Within the normal operating range of the machine this variation is reversible, but as soon as the operating point of the magnet falls below the knee in the "demag" curve (Fig. 14.4), there will be an irreversible partial loss of magnetization. As long as we focus attention in design calculations on the avoidance of this loss, the behaviour of the coercivity can be ignored. This statement may seem bold and even reckless, but it should be kept in mind that machines must be designed so that the magnet does not go anywhere near the point $-H_c$.

The winding resistance also increases with temperature (§3.6.7), and the core loss also. Consequently temperature has a strong effect on efficiency. If a motor is controlled to make a constant torque, then at a higher temperature it must draw more current to compensate for the reduction in EMF. The Joule loss increases with the square of the current, which is flowing through a higher resistance. The temperature is one of the few parameters over which the user has any control, once the machine is purchased and installed.

High temperature also accelerates the aging of insulation. It can cause lubricants to degrade and to flow out of bearings. It smells. It is dangerous to touch. It discolours paint and embrittles nonmetallic components. It is possibly the most important indication that things are not going well in the machine.

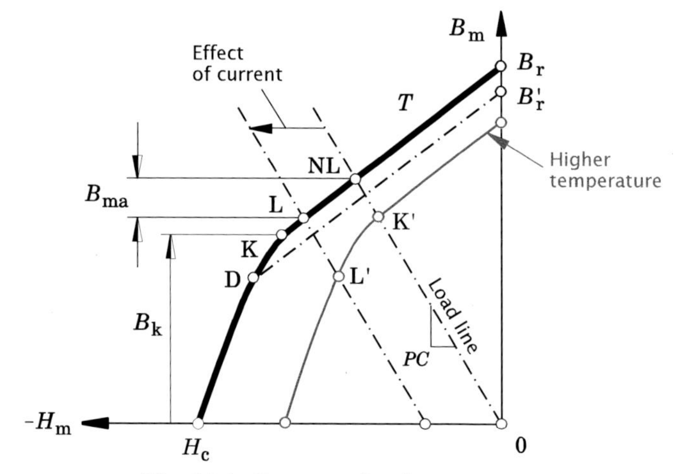

Fig. 14.4 Demagnetization curves

14.1.1.22 How can I prevent demagnetization?

Design for a high permeance coefficient at no-load [eqn. (4.13)]; and avoid excessive demagnetizing current, while taking into account the effect of temperature. Fig. 14.4 shows this characteristic for a NDFEB magnet at temperature T and at a higher temperature. The no-load operating point NL at temperature T is defined by the intersection of the zero-current load line and the demagnetization characteristic. As NL lies above the **knee-point** K, the magnet is safe. A demagnetizing component of load current shifts the load line to the left, moving the operating point to L; the flux-density in the magnet has been reduced by the amount B_{ma}, §5.14. At temperature T the magnet is still safe because L lies above K.

A higher current would shift the operating point further down the demagnetization curve. If it goes below the "knee" K, there will be an irreversible loss of some of the magnetization. For example, if the operating point is driven as low as D, the remanence will fall from B_r to B_r' and it will not recover.

At the higher temperature the knee-point K′ is higher up the curve, and the same load that was safe at temperature T will now cause irreversible loss, since L′ is below K′. It can be stated another way: at the higher temperature, it takes less current to cause demagnetization.

14.1.1.23 How can I reduce the noise level?

The noise of electrical machines is a complex subject; (see, for example, Tímár [1989]; Gieras *et al* [2006]). Some noise comes from vibratory movement of the magnetic core, due to variations in flux at the pole- and slot-passing frequencies and combinations thereof. Noise at PWM frequencies can be particularly annoying in the audible range. Magnetic forces are roughly proportional to B^2, so the noise tends to be greater in highly-rated machines. It is best to shape the magnets and the stator teeth to avoid sharp changes in the magnitude or the direction of the field as the rotor rotates, and to try to obtain balanced forces on the rotor at all positions.

Another component of magnetic noise is magnetostriction of the laminations, which depends on the core plate and the type of insulation. Fans and bearings are additional sources of noise that can be eased by mechanical design. These noises are worse at high speed. Noise can be exacerbated by resonance of the machine itself, or of the combined structure formed by the machine and its mounting.

14.1.1.24 How can I reduce the motor cost?

This complex question does not lend itself to glib generalizations, but one important point is not to over-design or over-specify the machine (or to under-design it!). Designers have the difficult task of including a safety margin in their designs, while avoiding waste. As cost-savings tend to impact safety margins, so it helps to be clear about tolerances and precise in specifications. In designing new products, manufacturing and even marketing aspects should be incorporated in the design specification as far as possible.

Aluminium conductors are sometimes considered and occasionally used when the cost of copper is high. The conductivity of aluminium is only about 60% of that of copper, but its mass density is much lower and the methods of insulating and terminating conductors are not quite the same. The use of aluminium conductors is not a matter of 1:1 substitution, but is likely to involve a complete re-design.

JRH writes: "IPM designs like Figs 2.3 and 2.33 can reduce cost significantly, and so can the single-tooth windings shown, for example, in Figs 2.18, 2.40, and 3.19".

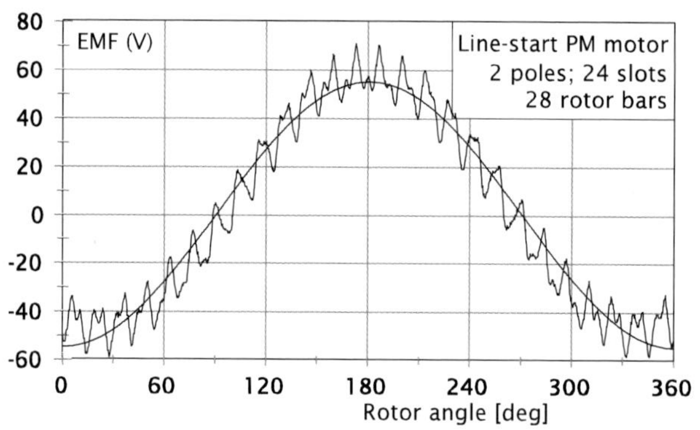

Fig. 14.5 EMF ripple caused by permeance harmonics

14.1.1.25 How about EMF ripple?

Fig. 14.5 shows an example of EMF ripple caused by **permeance harmonics**. As the rotor rotates, the permeance of the magnetic circuit varies at the slot-passing frequency, causing the magnet flux to vary. This is called *slot ripple*, or *slot-modulation of the flux*. The variation in the flux may be quite small, but the ripple in the EMF is amplified by the slot-passing frequency as a result of differentiating the flux with respect to time (Faraday's law). When the EMF ripple is compared with the *rotational* EMF, its size can be startling, as in Fig. 14.5 which shows the additional modulation caused by the rotor bars in a 24-slot, 2-pole line-start motor.

The methods used to reduce EMF ripple are similar to those used to reduce cogging torque; see §3.5.1.2.

14.1.1.26 How about a sine-EMF motor with squarewave drive?

With servo-motors a sine-EMF motor is simetimes used with a squarewave drive to reduce cost. We can see from Tables 8.1 and 8.2 that the torque per *peak* ampere will *increase* in the ratio 1/0·90690 = 1·10266; but the torque per RMS ampere will *decrease* in the ratio 1·22474/1·28255 = 0·9549.

As mentioned on p. 422, and in Fig. 6.29, the torque ripple will increase markedly with the squarewave drive, and it becomes sensitive to any phase shift in the current. With sinewave EMF and sinewave drive it is theoretically zero, regardless of the phase shift.

14.1.2 Performance and Control Questions

14.1.2.1 How can I increase efficiency?

The first point to make is that machines with variable load and/or speed should ideally be designed to maximize the effective or average efficiency over their normal operating cycles. This is not the same as maximizing the efficiency at one operating point; compromises may be necessary. For example, a high magnetic loading may help to reduce the requirement for current at full load, thus reducing the copper loss. But at light load the high flux-density may give rise to disproportionate iron loss. If the machine spends most of its time at light load, the overall efficiency may well be less than it could be.

Increasing efficiency is synonymous with reducing losses: more precisely, the sum total of all the losses. As machines are driven to higher and higher levels of efficiency, the losses become more complex and more difficult to calculate, because the second-order parasitic effects come into play.

The most basic guidelines for loss reduction include the use of the lowest possible current-density in the conductors and the lowest possible flux-density in the core, consistent with the required power and speed. The current-density can be reduced by packing as much copper as possible into the slots, and by using the largest possible slot area consistent with satisfactory tooth dimensions. If the teeth are too narrow, the core losses in the teeth may become excessive, and if the slots are too deep, the slot-leakage inductance may become too great. These considerations must be seen in the context of all the related manufacturability issues.

Core losses depend strongly on frequency and flux-density, so it pays to design with the lowest feasible pole-number for a given speed of operation. Likewise the number of slots/pole affects the magnetic frequency and the winding harmonics, both of which affect the core losses. There is also a wide choice of core materials, and it is probably true to say that it is a *critical* choice requiring a thorough understanding of the properties of the steel and the way in which they are utilized in the design.

Especially since the introduction of NDFEB magnets, eddy-current losses in the rotors of brushless permanent-magnet machines have become quite critical. Although these losses are present with Samarium-Cobalt magnets, NDFEB is much more sensitive to the resulting temperature rise, and it is often necessary to segment the magnets in both the axial and circumferential directions, and to use a laminated rotor core. Even conductive shields have been studied as a means of reducing these losses (Shah and Lee, [2006]).

Further improvements can be obtained by the use of multiple phases to increase the fundamental winding factor and reduce the effects of space-harmonics (including rotor eddy-current losses).

14.1.2.2 How can I increase power-factor?

The power-factor is clearly defined for AC machines operating from a sinusoidal supply, but for inverter-fed machines it is more useful to think of the volt-ampere requirement for a given power. This directly relates to the size and cost of the inverter. Volt-ampere requirement can be expressed as the peak or RMS current multiplied by the peak line-line voltage and the number of phases. The peak quantities are considered because the cost of power transistors is more closely related to them than to the RMS values, (particularly the voltage).

Increasing the power-factor then becomes a question of minimizing the volt-ampere requirement or the kVA/kW, and this has to do with the *matching* of the machine to the inverter. As we have seen in Chapter 7 for sinewave drives, this is a somewhat complex subject that can be tackled using the voltage locus diagram, Fig. 7.6. A simple guiding principle is that the maximum voltage required by the motor should be the same as the maximum voltage available from the inverter, while both have the same maximum current. Achieving this requires careful use of phase advance in the controller, as well as the correct values of k_E and inductance.

14.1.2.3 How can I get smooth rotation at low speed?

This would not be difficult if the load had a very large inertia. But in practical cases the attainment of true constant speed requires that the electromagnetic motor torque be varied to compensate for spurious variations in torque caused by cogging, by variations in the EMF and current waveforms, and by the load itself.

Compensation implies a speed-feedback control loop with a sufficient bandwidth. At low speed this demands a high-resolution shaft position encoder or resolver.[145]

14.1.2.4 How can I make the motor go faster?

Brushless permanent-magnet machines are said to be "self-commutated", "auto-commutated", or "auto-synchronous" — all of which mean that the speed and the supply frequency are automatically locked together. Consequently it is the voltage that really limits the maximum speed, as we have seen in Chapter 7 for sinewave drives. The voltage must always be sufficient to drive the required current, which in turn is determined by the torque requirement. The required voltage is determined by the EMF and the inductive voltage drop (neglecting resistance). Since the EMF increases in proportion to the speed, and so does the inductive voltage drop (if the current is fixed), the terminal voltage must increase with speed. When it approaches the maximum voltage available from the inverter, the speed cannot increase any further.

A reduction in the number of turns will decrease both the EMF and the inductive voltage, permitting a higher speed to be attained, but only at the expense of a higher current to maintain the same torque.

The machine can also be designed with a lower inductance to minimize the inductive voltage drop; or it can be designed with sufficient inductance to use flux-weakening. Both methods can be used to attain higher speeds, and success is often judged by the "speed range at constant power". This approach makes sense only if the power required by the *load* is not increasing with speed. Only certain types of load meet this criterion. Many others require ever-increasing power as the speed increases, and in these cases there is no alternative but to use a larger inverter that can deliver more kW with more kVA. These kVA will be obtained at higher voltage or higher current, depending on the choice of the number of turns.

---

[145] At zero speed such feedback transducers cannot provide a speed signal. In his Ph.D. thesis at Leeds University in the early 1970s, J.M. Stephenson developed an optical speed transducer with two coaxial slotted disks, one of which was driven at a constant speed, so that there would be a differentiable pulse rate even when the other one was stationary. It is not known if this method has been used commercially.

14.1.2.5 How can I get a more sinusoidal EMF waveform?

It is worth remembering that a perfectly sinusoidally-distributed winding will always have a pure sinewave EMF, no matter what is the shape of the airgap flux-distribution. Conversely, a purely sinusoidal distribution of airgap flux will generate a pure sinewave EMF, no matter what is the winding distribution.

Since neither of these ideals is attainable, a combination is usually employed. The winding distribution can be arranged to minimize the 5th and 7th harmonics, which are generally the most troublesome low-order harmonics. The third harmonic does not appear in the line-line EMF waveform and this is often used as an "excuse" for not trying to remove it from the airgap flux distribution. The residual harmonics can never be reduced to the lowest levels by means of the winding distribution alone. Machines that are designed with the best quality sinusoidal EMF waveforms generally have profiled magnets, or profiled magnetization such as Halbach magnetization. Slot-order harmonics can be reduced by skewing the rotor or the stator.

14.1.2.6 How can I get a more sinusoidal current waveform?

In sinewave drives it is the job of the current regulator to maintain a sinusoidal current waveform. To do this it must have sufficient voltage from the DC supply, and a sufficiently high switching frequency to minimize the current ripple, while the machine must have sufficient inductance. Much depends on the control algorithms in the drive, especially at higher speeds, as described in §7.2.

14.1.2.7 How do I avoid first-turn insulation failure?

"First-turn failure" is the common term used to refer to insulation failures attributed to voltage overshoot associated with the use of PWM inverters having fast-switching IGBT transistors. The rise-time of each voltage pulse from the inverter can be in the range 50–200 ns, fast enough to cause an oscillatory voltage overshoot at the motor terminals as a result of the transient response of the cable inductance together with the motor capacitance. The voltage overshoot can be significantly increased when the length of the cable is such that the propagation time of the voltage wavefront between the inverter and the motor is longer than the voltage rise-time. In such cases reflections of the wavefront can combine to step up the total voltage at the motor by a factor approaching 2 (and in some cases even higher). The voltage overshoots are of course repetitive at the inverter switching frequency. The main concern is with progressive degradation of the winding insulation caused by partial discharge, when the overshoots exceed the "corona inception voltage" of the insulation system.

This issue has been mainly confined to "low-voltage" induction motors designed for operation at 460 — 690V, especially those with random or "mush" windings. The propagation of the voltage overshoot through the winding is a complex matter, but in many cases it is the first turn of the winding that sustains most of the overvoltage and is most likely to fail by a discharge to a coil further down the winding. Machines wound for higher voltages tend to have form-wound coils with more substantial insulation and an ordered disposition of conductors which alleviates the problem. At lower voltages the problem has not arisen to nearly the same degree.

Several methods are well established for avoiding failures from this cause, including the use of "inverter-grade" magnet wire, additional layers of interturn insulation, series reactors and LCR dV/dt filters.[146]

JRH writes :

1. Locate the PWM inverter close to the machine so the leads to the machine do not exceed 20m.
2. Use inverter-duty magnet wire, such as Ultra Shield™ Plus by Superior Essex, or equivalent.
3. Insulate the first turn of the first coil connected to the line with Teflon® sleeving.
4. Vacuum-encapsulate the entire stator in epoxy.

---

[146] See for example GAMBICA/REMA Technical Report No. 1, 2001, which provides a comparison of methods and an excellent physical explanation of the causes and effects. Other valuable references include Langhorst and Hancock [1997]; Melfi, Sung, Bell and Skibinski [1998]; Persson [1992]; and Stranges *et al*, [2009]. Others abound.

14.1.2.8 How do I avoid bearing currents?

Bearings can be damaged by pitting or fluting caused by discharge currents that break down the insulating film of lubrication. With fast-switching IGBT inverters any *common-mode* voltage that is impressed at the motor terminals is communicated through the capacitance C_w between the stator winding and the rotor. The airgap forms the dielectric of this capacitor, while a second capacitor C_r between the rotor and the stator core returns the circuit to ground. The normally-insulating film of bearing lubricant is in parallel with C_r, and if the potential difference across it is allowed to exceed the breakdown voltage there will be a discharge.

Over time the discharges erode the bearing surfaces, causing eventual failure. Preventive measures include the insulation of the bearings; the use of conductive grease, or ceramic-coated balls or rollers; and the use of a brush which bears on the shaft and short-circuits it to ground. It is even possible to use a conductive screen between the rotor and stator, to by pass C_g.

Undesirable bearing currents can be induced by magnetic asymmetry, or by common-mode voltages imposed by an inverter. (See Langhorst and Hancock, *op. cit.*; also Schiferl and Melfi [2006]).

14.1.2.9 What causes machines to fail?

Premature failure — failure occurring before the design life-span — can be caused by power supply problems: excessive harmonics or imbalance in the current cause overheating, while overvoltage (sustained or repetitive) degrades the insulation. Insulation can also be mechanically damaged, for example by fretting (small rubbing movements under vibration); this can be exacerbated by abrasive or corrosive particles in a contaminated atmosphere. In motors stored below the dew-point, condensation will reduce the dielectric strength unless they are warmed before use.

Insufficient, excess, or unsuitable lubrication can lead to bearing failure. Mechanical misalignment in couplings, mountings, and even internally in the machine can cause abormal stress that will lead to eventual failure.

14.2 Saliency

Saliency is an important property of electrical machines. It is necessary for the production of reluctance torque, and it determines the ability to produce smooth torque. Saliency is often expressed in terms of the "saliency ratio" $\xi = L_d/L_q$. In brushless permanent-magnet machines such as the IPM, generally $L_q > L_d$, and ξ is expressed as L_q/L_d. This is called "inverse saliency". Saliency ratios greater than 2 or 3 are hard to achieve in a fully loaded IPM.

The basic concept of "saliency" is the presence or absence of *projections* or *saliencies* from the surface of the stator or rotor. The field poles of a universal motor provide a common example, as represented in Fig. 14.6D. Another well-known example is the field poles of a synchronous machine, Fig. 14.6A.

The IPM has a salient-pole rotor and belongs to type A in Fig. 14.6: the saliencies, so to speak, do not project outwards from the rotor surface, but are buried inside it. Nevertheless, they confer the same 2-axis symmetry as in Fig. 14.6A.

The machines in Fig. 14.6 are all 2-pole machines, but the concept of saliency applies to machines of any pole-number. The axes of high inductance and the axes of low inductance simply repeat $2p$ times per revolution in a machine with p pole-pairs.

Slotting is normally neglected when saliency is being considered. It is true that the teeth in a slotted surface are "saliencies", and they are even associated with a form of reluctance torque known as *cogging torque*. However, this is normally regarded as a parasitic, second-order effect. Unlike the normal reluctance torque found in salient-pole machines, the cogging torque is zero when averaged over one revolution, and it serves no useful purpose.

Fig. 14.6 shows the four possible combinations of salient-pole or nonsalient-pole rotors and stators. Thus Fig. 14.6A shows a nonsalient-pole stator with a salient-pole rotor (wound-field synchronous machine or synchronous reluctance machine); B shows a machine with no saliency (induction machine); C shows a machine with "double saliency"(switched reluctance machine); and D shows a salient-pole stator with a nonsalient-pole rotor (wound-field DC commutator motor or universal motor).

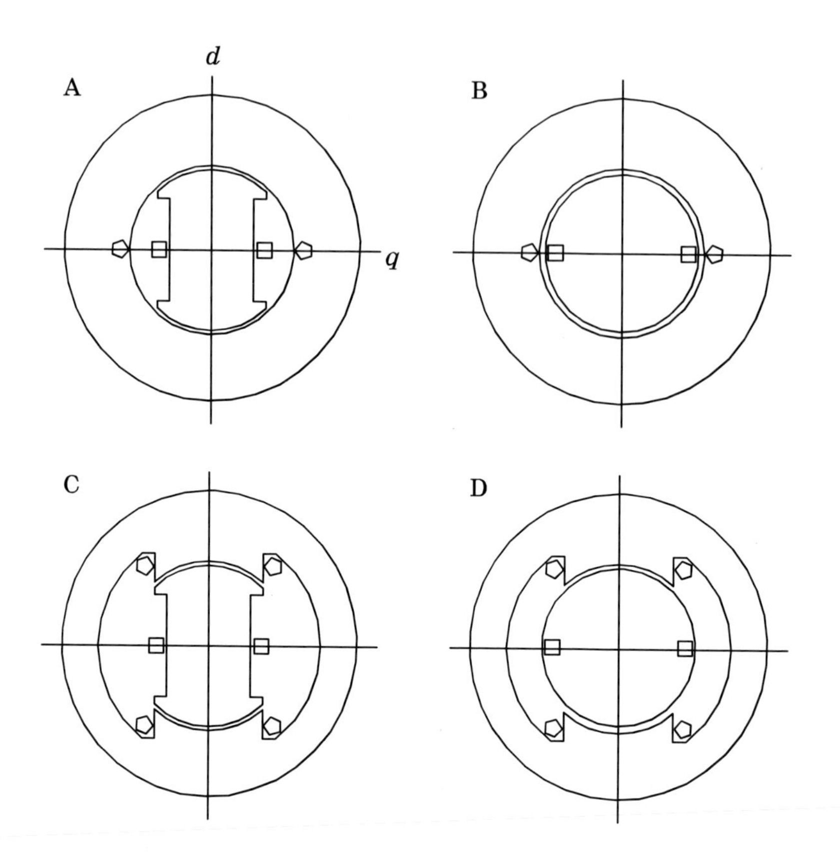

Fig. 14.6 Saliency. A. Salient-pole rotor, nonsalient-pole stator. B. Nonsalient-pole rotor and stator. C. Salient-pole stator and rotor. D. Nonsalient-pole rotor, salient-pole stator.

Test for saliency — In each case in Fig. 14.6 there is a single coil on the stator and a single coil on the rotor to represent the windings. An electrical test for saliency is the variation in *self*-inductance of one of these coils when the opposite member is rotated. For example, if the rotor of A is rotated, the inductance of the stator coil will vary, and so the rotor is deemed to have saliency. If the rotor of D is rotated, the inductance of the stator coil remains constant. Therefore the rotor in Fig. 14.6D has no saliency. On the other hand, if the stator is rotated, the self-inductance of the rotor coil varies, so the stator is deemed to have saliency.

The generalized machine theory shows that if a machine has at least one member with no saliency, then there is a form of that machine that can produce constant, ripple-free torque when excited with pure sinusoidal AC or pure DC. The practical importance of this is profound. For example, machine A can produce smooth torque when the stator has a polyphase distributed winding fed with balanced polyphase sinusoidal AC current, when the rotor is either unexcited or fed with pure DC. Machine D can produce smooth torque when the stator is fed with pure DC and the rotor is fed with pure DC through brushes and a commutator that has a sufficiently large number of segments.

Machine B (the induction motor) can produce smooth torque when the stator has a polyphase distributed winding fed with balanced polyphase sinusoidal AC current, while the rotor has a similar winding or a cage winding with a similar AC current distribution induced by slippage. Machine C (the switched reluctance machine) cannot produce smooth torque with either a pure DC or pure sinusoidal AC current waveform. To achieve smooth torque, it requires a specially profiled current waveform.

In machine types with windings on both the stator and the rotor the torque is produced as a result of the variation of *mutual* inductance between stator and rotor windings. These machines are sometimes called *doubly-fed*. The PM brushless machine can be seen as being of this type, especially if the magnet is represented as a set of current-carrying filaments along its edges.

The variation of *self*-inductance associated with saliency can be used to produce reluctance torque, and in reluctance motors this is the only available component of torque. Such machines are sometimes called *singly-fed*. Curiously, the PM brushless machine can be treated as though it were of this type: if the flux produced by the magnet is treated as being produced by the d-axis component of stator current (in a rotating frame of reference), the machine appears to have the attribute of saliency and its torque can be calculated as reluctance torque. However, the saliency ratio will be variable because the magnet flux remains more or less fixed while the stator current varies. Consequently the designer will find little advantage in this rather academic viewpoint.

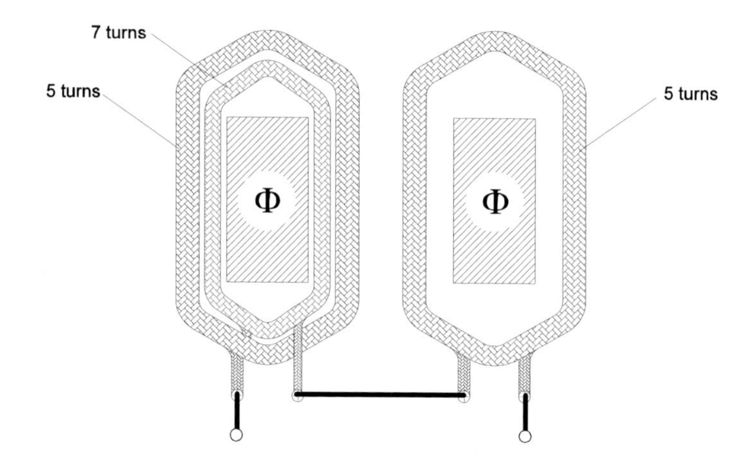

Fig. 14.7 A circuit comprising coils with different numbers of turns

14.3 Half turns

The question of "half turns" sometimes arises in electric machine design. The concept of a "half-turn" challenges both Faraday's and Ampère's laws, which are respectively associated with the concepts of flux-linkage and MMF :

$$\psi = \oint \mathbf{A} \cdot d\boldsymbol{l} \quad \text{and} \quad F = \oint \mathbf{H} \cdot d\boldsymbol{l} \tag{14.2}$$

In both cases the integral is round an *entire* loop, which must be *closed*. In the process of counting turns, it is impossible to count a fractional number of turns: the result is always an integer. A fractional turn is not a complete circuit.

However, suppose we have a winding on two poles, as in Fig. 14.7. On the left-hand pole there are 2 coils, one with 5 complete turns and the other with 7. The right-hand pole has only one coil, with 5 turns. All three coils link the same amount of flux Φ, so the total flux-linkage is $\psi = (5 + 7 + 5)\ \Phi = 17\Phi$ Wb-turns or volt-seconds. For the purpose of calculating the EMF $d\psi/dt$, it is common to work with the number of turns per pole, and in this case with 2 poles in series the flux-linkage per pole is $17\Phi/2 = 8{\cdot}5\Phi$ Vs. So we have the *appearance* of a fractional number of turns per pole, even though the number of turns in every coil in the winding is clearly an integer.

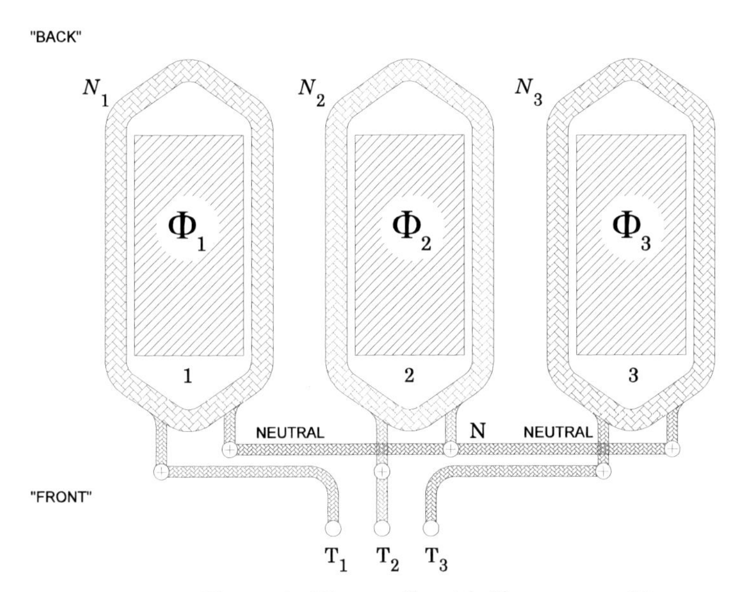

Fig. 14.8 Three coils with "front neutral"

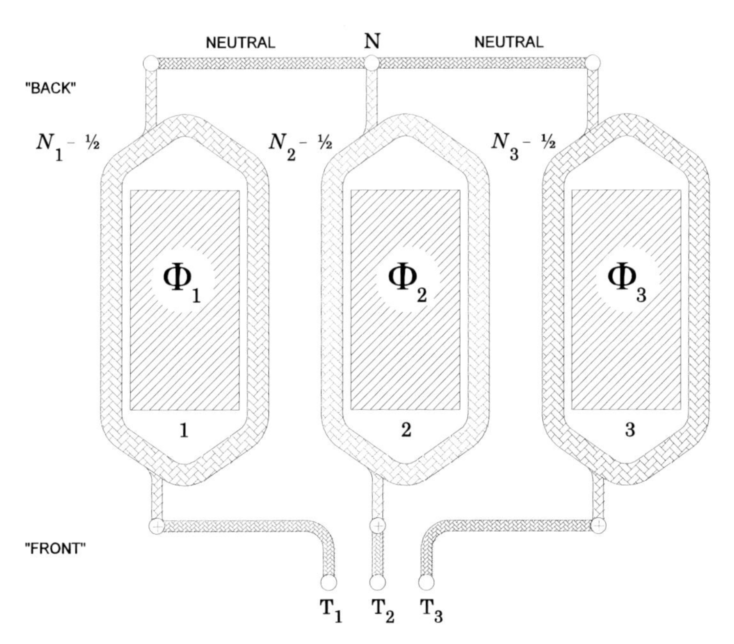

Fig. 14.9 Three coils with "back neutral"

Likewise it is common to work with the MMF per pole, and if the current I flows through all the coils in series, the MMF per pole is $8{\cdot}5I$ ampere-turns, giving the impression of a fractional number of turns. Whenever we see a fractional number of turns, it must be expected to mean an average taken over more than one coil; moreover, for the purpose of calculating EMF, all the relevant coils must link the same amount of flux Φ, while for the purpose of calculating MMF, all the relevant coils must have an equivalent disposition in the magnetic circuit, meaning that they must all be similarly positioned relative to the nearest magnetic pole.

The position of the neutral — In polyphase machines another misconception can arise in relation to half-turns, depending on the position of the neutral connection between the phases. Fig. 14.8 shows a simple 3-phase winding with 1 coil per phase. The neutral point is connected at the *front* of the machine, that is, at the same end as the phase terminals. Thus each coil has an integer number of turns wrapped completely around its respective pole. A circuit from T_1 to T_2 is necessarily *closed*, since T_1 and T_2 are practically at the same position, and the flux-linkage of this circuit is $N_1\Phi_1 + N_2\Phi_2$.

In Fig. 14.9, however, the neutral point is connected at the "back", remote from the terminal connections. This makes the coils *appear* to be one-half turn short : coil 1 appears to have only $N_1 - \frac{1}{2}$ turns, coil 2 $N_2 - \frac{1}{2}$, etc. The half-turns are misconceived, because they belong to incomplete circuits. In passing through a complete circuit from terminal T_1 to T_2 pole 1 is encircled N_1 times, not $N_1 - \frac{1}{2}$ times; the final half-turn being completed through coil 2. Likewise pole 2 is encircled $N_2 - \frac{1}{2}$ times by the turns of coil 2, plus ½ turn completed through coil 1. If we neglect the stray flux in the region between pole 1 and pole 2, the total flux-linkage in circuit $T_1 - T_2$ remains equal to $N_1\Phi_1 + N_2\Phi_2$, as in Fig. 14.8.

The stray flux between poles will tend to offset the potential of the neutral point, creating a slight imbalance between phases. The degree of imbalance will be small — of the same order as that which is caused by differences in the physical shapes of the coils and their positions in the slots. It will be insignificant unless the number of turns per coil is small; even then it should be possible to reduce it by making the neutral a complete ring to minimize any asymmetry.

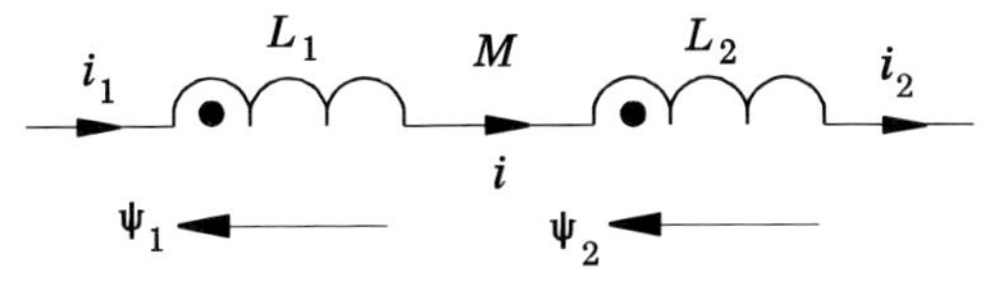

(*a*) Series aiding

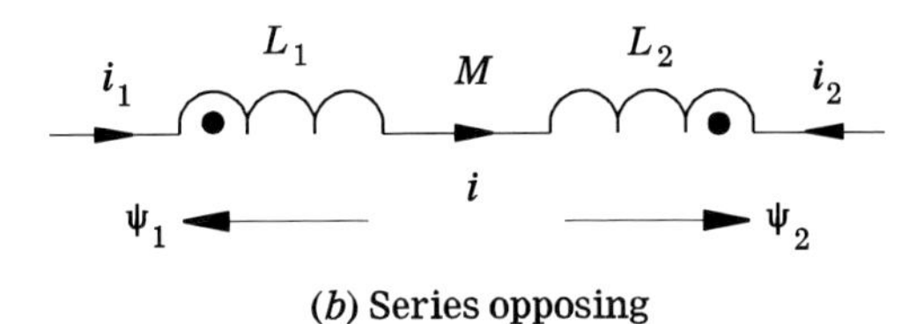

(*b*) Series opposing

Fig. 14.10 Series inductance

14.4 Series and parallel inductances

In the analysis of electrical machines it is often necessary to consider inductances in series or in parallel, or in more complex circuit configurations. In Fig. 14.10(*a*), two inductances L_1 and L_2 are in series with a common current $i = i_1 = i_2$. The arrows show the directions of positive current and flux-linkage. For each coil, positive current flows into the dotted end and produces a positive component of flux-linkage in that coil: by definition, this component (the *self* flux-linkage) is always positive and in fact it defines the direction of positive flux-linkage in that coil. The flux-linkages ψ_1 and ψ_2 also include mutual flux-linkages and are given by

$$\begin{aligned} \psi_1 &= L_1 i_1 + M i_2; \\ \psi_2 &= L_2 i_2 + M i_1. \end{aligned} \tag{14.3}$$

so the total flux-linkage of the series combination is

$$\psi = \psi_1 + \psi_2 = (L_1 + L_2 + 2M)i. \tag{14.4}$$

The series inductance is the ratio of flux-linkage to current ψ/i:

$$L_{\text{series}} = L_1 + L_2 + 2M. \tag{14.5}$$

M can be positive or negative in this equation, according to the direction of the flux produced by coil 1 in coil 2, and *vice versa*. This depends on the physical arrangement *and* the connection of the coils.

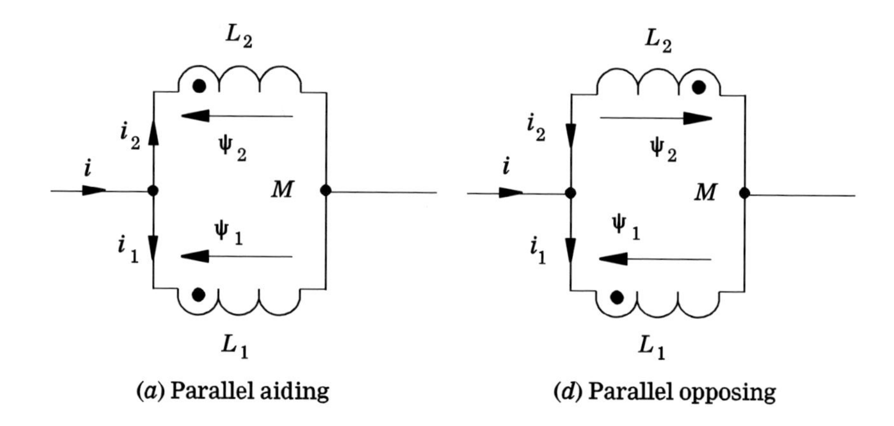

Fig. 14.11 Parallel inductances

In Fig. 14.10(a) the connection is such that $i_1 = i_2 = i$. But in Fig. 14.10(b) the connections to coil 2 have been reversed, so that $i_2 = -i$. The argument leading to eqn. (14.5) now gives

$$L_{\text{series}} = L_1 + L_2 - 2M. \tag{14.6}$$

This might represent two phases of a wye-connected motor connected in series, the positive directions of i_1 and i_2 having already been defined with respect to the start and finish of each winding before the connection is made. (See Fig. 14.13). In a balanced winding $L_1 = L_2 = L_3 = L$, and $M_{12} = M_{23} = M_{31} = M$. The resulting line-line inductance is $L_{LL} = 2(L - M)$, with the third phase open-circuited. M is usually negative because the winding axes are at 120°elec relative to one another, so that if L_{ph} is the phase self-inductance and M_{ph} is the *absolute* value of the mutual inductance between phases, we can write $L_{LL} = 2(L_{ph} + M_{ph})$. Care is necessary to incorporate the mutual flux-linkage with the correct sign.

In Fig. 14.11(a), the same two inductances L_1 and L_2 are in parallel with a common flux-linkage ψ and respective currents i_1 and i_2, with $i = i_1 + i_2$. It must be the case that

$$\psi_1 = \psi_2 = \psi = L_1 i_1 + M i_2 = L_2 i_2 + M i_1, \tag{14.7}$$

which amounts to a constraint on i_1 and i_2. Rearranging, we have

$$(L_1 + M) i_1 = (L_2 + M) i_2. \tag{14.8}$$

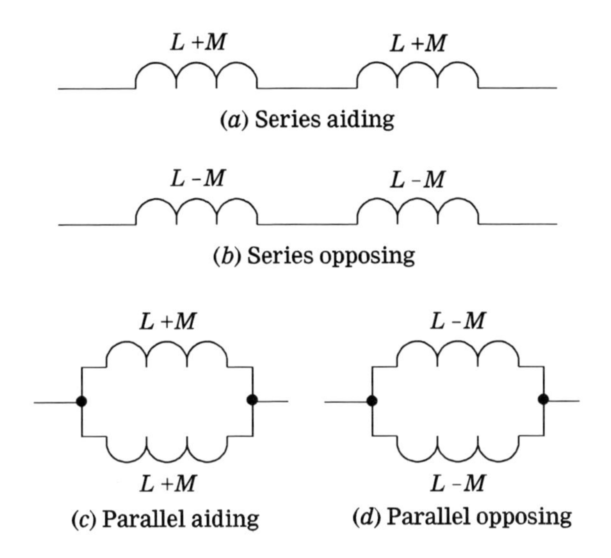

Fig. 14.12 Equivalent circuits when $L_1 = L_2 = L$

This can be substituted in the preceding equation for ψ, and also into the constraint $i = i_1 + i_2$, so that the effective inductance ψ/i becomes

$$L = \frac{L_1 L_2 - M^2}{L_1 + L_2 - 2M}. \tag{14.9}$$

If the connections to coil 2 are reversed, the effect is the same as if the sign of the mutual inductance were reversed, giving

$$L = \frac{L_1 L_2 - M^2}{L_1 + L_2 + 2M}. \tag{14.10}$$

Note that if $L_1 = L_2 = L$, eqn. (14.9) simplifies to $(L + M)/2$, and eqn. (14.10) simplifies to $(L - M)/2$, suggesting the equivalent circuits in Fig. 14.12(*c*) and (*d*) with the mutual inductance absorbed into two separate self-inductances. Likewise for the series connection, eqn. (14.5) simplifies to $2(L + M)$ and eqn. (14.6) to $2(L - M)$, suggesting the equivalent circuits in Fig. 14.12(*a*) and (*b*).

A *bifilar* winding can be regarded as a pair of identical parallel inductors, so tightly coupled that M is very nearly equal to L. If the connection is "aiding" as in Fig. 14.11(*a*) or Fig. 14.12(*c*), the inductance becomes $(L + M)/2 = L$, which is essentially the same as if two "strands in hand" were wound together in one coil. On the other hand, if the connection between the two strands is "opposing", as in Fig. 14.11(*b*) or Fig. 14.12(*d*), the inductance becomes $(L - M)/2 = 0$. This principle is used to make a "coil" of zero or very small inductance: for example, in resistance-start split-phase motors some of the turns may be "bifilar wound" in this way to increase the resistance of the auxiliary winding without changing its inductance, thus providing an inexpensive way to change the resistance/reactance ratio to provide starting torque at speeds near zero.

Another interesting property of the equivalent circuits in Fig. 14.12 is the change in inductance when two inductors in series are reconnected in parallel. For example, if the series circuit of Fig. 14.12(*a*) is reconnected as the parallel circuit of Fig. 14.12(*c*), the inductance changes from $2(L+M)$ to $(L+M)/2$, which is the same change of 4:1 that would be obtained with plain resistors. The necessary conditions are that the two self inductances be equal, and likewise the two mutual inductances; furthermore, the value and sign of the mutual inductance must not be changed by the reconnection. In an electrical machine or transformer, this will tend to be the case because the physical position of the coils is fixed and not altered by reconnection. Moreover, the necessary equality of the respective self and mutual inductances will usually be assured by symmetry; if this were not so, the parallel connection would be liable to circulating current within the loop formed by the parallel inductors. In such cases the inductance can be expressed as

$$L = \frac{L_{series}}{a^2} \tag{14.11}$$

where L_{series} is the inductance with all the turns in series and a is the number of parallel paths. If all the turns are in series, $a = 1$, but if there are two parallel circuits, each with half the total number of turns, $a = 2$. If the conditions pertaining to Fig. 14.12 are satisfied, eqn. (14.11) can be generalized to any number of parallel circuits.

Eqn. (14.11) is often used in machine calculations. The inductance of n coils per phase is simpler to calculate if they are all in series than if they are in a parallel paths each having n/a coils in series.

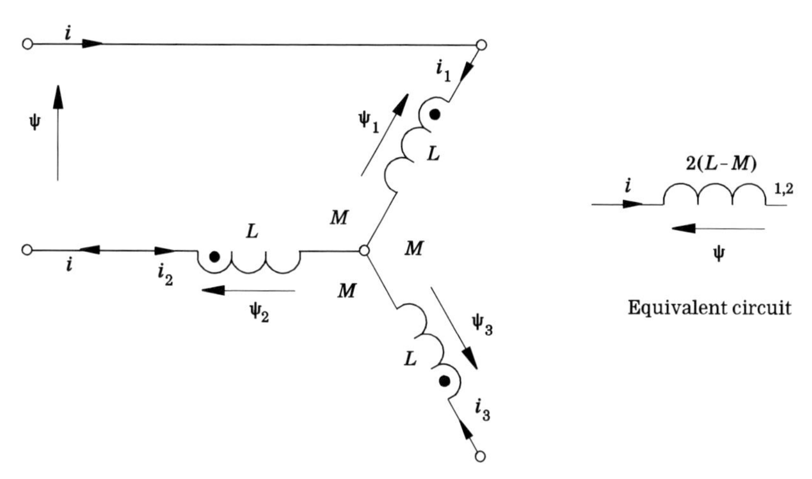

Fig. 14.13 Wye connection; line-line inductance

Inductances of wye and delta connections — Fig. 14.13 shows a wye-connected winding with equal self-inductances L in each phase, and equal mutual inductances M between each pair of phases; that is to say, a balanced winding. As we have seen earlier, the line-line inductance is $2(L - M)$, and if $M < 0$ we have $M_{ph} = |M|$, $L_{ph} = L$, and

$$L_{LL} = 2(L_{ph} + M_{ph}). \tag{14.12}$$

Fig. 14.14 shows the line-line connection with a delta-connected balanced winding. This is slightly more complicated than the wye connection because it forms a parallel circuit in which the two branches are dissimilar. The equations will be written out, because it shows the method of analysis for the more general case of an unbalanced winding, even though the result for a balanced winding is simple. First, the individual phase flux-linkages are given by

$$\begin{aligned} \psi_1 &= Li_1 + M(i_2 + i_3) \\ \psi_2 &= Li_2 + M(i_3 + i_1) \\ \psi_3 &= Li_3 + M(i_1 + i_2). \end{aligned} \tag{14.13}$$

The connection contrains these flux-linkages such that

$$\psi = \psi_1 = -(\psi_2 + \psi_3), \tag{14.14}$$

while the currents are constrained by the relation

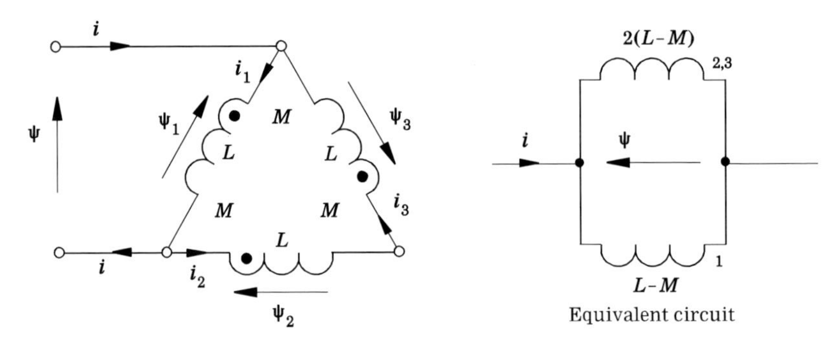

Fig. 14.14 Delta connection : line-line inductance

$$\begin{aligned} i_2 &= i_3 \\ i &= i_1 - i_3 = i_1 - i_2. \end{aligned} \tag{14.15}$$

If ψ_1, ψ_2, ψ_3 and i_1, i_2 and i_3 are eliminated from these equations, the result is

$$\psi = \frac{2}{3}(L - M)i, \tag{14.16}$$

which gives the required inductance as $2(L - M)/3$. This is 1/3 the value of the line-line inductance for the wye connection, showing another instance where the mutual inductance is "eliminated" by incorporating it in a modified self-inductance (in this case $L - M$).

14.5 Gearing

The torque density (TRV) in electric machines is low relative to what engineers would like to achieve, and in order to minimize the size and the amount of material used for a given power output, machines are frequently designed to run at speeds higher than the load requires. This situation can be characterized as a mismatch between the speed/torque characteristic of the motor and that of the load. The same situation arises in generating systems. A good example is the wind turbine, which produces a huge torque at only a few tens of rpm. An electrical generator "matched" to this combination of torque and speed would need a large number of poles and would be far too large to install in the available space. Consequently a gearbox is used, with a speed ratio of the order of 50.

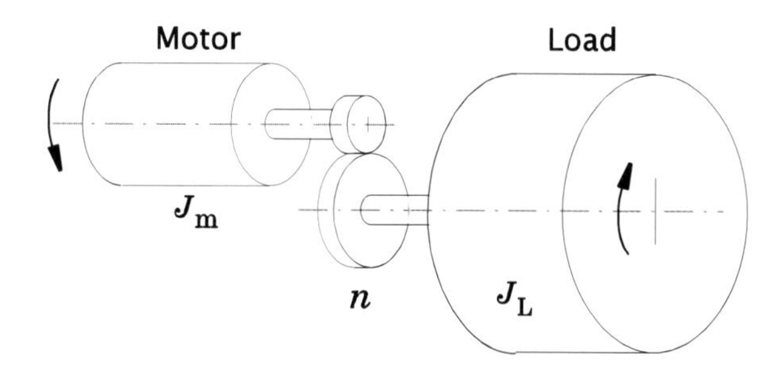

Fig. 14.15 Gear ratio

If the gear ratio is $n > 1$, and T_m is the motor torque, the torque applied to the load is nT_m. The motor speed ω_m is increased over the load speed ω_L by the same ratio. Thus

$$T_L = nT_m \qquad \text{and} \qquad \omega_m = n\omega_L. \tag{14.17}$$

If the gearbox efficiency is 100%, the output power of the motor is equal to the power applied to the load, since $\omega_m T_m = \omega_L T_L$. In practice the gearbox efficiency is less than 100%, and $T_L < nT_m$. For a generator, if T_L is the torque delivered to the gearbox by the prime mover, and T_m is the torque received by the electric machine, the inequality is $T_L > nT_m$.

Eqn. (14.17) can be written

$$\frac{T_L}{T_m} = n \qquad \text{and} \qquad \frac{\omega_L}{\omega_m} = \frac{1}{n}. \tag{14.18}$$

This is formally the same pair of equations relating the primary and secondary voltages and currents of an ideal transformer, showing that the "load-matching" discussed above is analogous to the impedance-matching function of a transformer.

The gear ratio used with motors depends on the operational requirements. If the speed is constant it can be chosen simply to match the load torque T_L to the rated continuous motor torque T_{mc}:

$$n = \frac{T_L}{T_{mc}}. \tag{14.19}$$

Simple acceleration of pure inertia load — Referring to Fig. 14.15, if we use the peak torque T_{mp} available from the motor, the acceleration of the load is given by

$$\alpha = \frac{T_{mp}}{n\left(J_m + \dfrac{J_L}{n^2}\right)} \quad \text{rad/s}^2. \tag{14.20}$$

The term in brackets is the combined inertia of the motor and load, referred to the motor shaft. If n is large, J_m is predominant.

If n is small, the referred load inertia is large, and this limits the acceleration. Between the extremes of large and small n, there is an optimal value that gives maximum acceleration for fixed values of T_{mp} and the inertias. This value can be determined by equating the differential coefficient $d\alpha/dn$ to zero, giving the well-known result

$$n = \sqrt{\frac{J_L}{J_m}} \tag{14.21}$$

This value of n makes the referred load inertia equal to the motor inertia, and is analogous to impedance-matching in a transformer. The maximum acceleration of the load is therefore

$$\alpha_{max} = \frac{1}{2}\frac{T_{mp}}{J_m}\frac{1}{n} \quad \text{rad/s}^2. \tag{14.22}$$

The corresponding acceleration of the motor is n times this value. In this analysis, the inertias of the gearwheels have been ignored.

14.6 Units of inertia

Several different units of inertia are used in engineering. While conversion factors are readily available from various sources, it is rare to find a rigorous explanation of their origin or meaning, especially in a form that is appropriate for electrical machine calculations.

The equation of rotary acceleration is Newton's second law,

$$T = J\alpha \tag{14.23}$$

where T = torque, J = inertia, and α = acceleration [rad/s^2]. This can be rearranged to give a "torque-based" definition of inertia as

$$J = \frac{T}{\alpha}. \tag{14.24}$$

The torque-based definition is suitable for determining inertia from measured torque and acceleration. It is "performance-oriented" in the sense that it tells how much torque is required to achieve a certain acceleration. The units implied by eqn. (14.24) are units of torque divided by units of acceleration, for example, [lbf-ft]/[rad/s^2].

There is also a "mass-based" definition

$$J = M k^2 \tag{14.25}$$

where M is the rotating mass and k is the so-called *radius of gyration*. The mass-based definition is suitable for design calculations because it is expressed in terms of physical dimensions, so it can be said to be "design-oriented". The units implied by eqn. (14.25) are units of mass multiplied by units of [length]^2, for example [lb]×[ft^2].

Inertia units defined in terms of eqn. (14.24) are not necessarily consistent with eqn. (14.25). Already this is true for the quoted examples of [lbf-ft]/[rad/s^2] and [lb]×[ft^2], because the [lbf] in the torque-based unit is force, whereas the [lb] in the mass-based unit is mass. These are not the same, being related by g, the acceleration due to gravity. When [lb] is force, it should be written [lbf], but laziness often prevails and the f is frequently lost.

Only the so-called *fundamental units* are simultaneously valid in both equations. In the S.I. system, the fundamental units are [kg] for mass M, [m] for radius k, and [kg-m^2] for inertia J.

In the imperial system, the fundamental units are [slug] for mass M; [lbf] for force; [ft] for radius k, and [slug-ft^2] for inertia J. A slug is the mass that will accelerate at [1 ft/sec^2] when a force of 1 [lbf] is applied to it; it is approximately 32·2 lb (mass). The slug is rarely used; but if fundamental units are *not* used, a conversion factor will appear in eqn. (14.24) or eqn. (14.25), or both, depending on the units chosen. [See eqn. (14.37), below].

If T is in [lbf-in], the units of J in eqn. (14.24) are [lbf-in]/[rad/s^2]. This is commonly abbreviated as [lb-in-s^2]. Now

$$1 \ \ [\text{lb–in}] \ \ = \ \ 0{\cdot}11298 \ \ [\text{N–m}]. \qquad (14.26)$$

Therefore in "eqn. (14.24) units",

$$1 \ [\text{lb–in–s}^2] = 0{\cdot}11298 \ [\text{N–m–s}^2] \text{ or } 0{\cdot}11298 \ [\text{N–m}]/[\text{rad/s}^2].$$

The [N], the [m] and the [s] are all fundamental units in the S.I. system: 1 [N]/[m/s^2] = 1 [kg] (linear motion), and 1 [N-m]/[rad/s^2] = 1 [N]/[m/s^2] × 1 [m^2] = 1 [kg-m^2]. These units can be used in eqn. (14.25) because they are fundamental units. Hence the conversion

$$1 \ \ [\text{lb–in–s}^2] \ \ = \ \ 0{\cdot}11298 \ \ [\text{kg–m}^2] \qquad (14.28)$$

where the left-hand side is in "eqn. (14.24) units" and the right-hand side is in in "eqn. (14.25) units".

Now we can make a further conversion of the right-hand side, using 1 [kg] = 10^3 [g], 1 [m] = 10^2 cm :

$$\begin{aligned} 1 \ [\text{lb–in–s}^2] &= 0{\cdot}11298 \, [\text{kg–m}^2] \times 10^3 \, [\text{g/kg}] \times (10^2 \, [\text{cm/m}])^2 \\ &= \ 1{\cdot}1298 \ \times \ 10^6 \ \ [\text{g–cm}^2] \end{aligned} \qquad (14.29)$$

where the left-hand side is in "torque-based" units and the right-hand side is in "mass-based" units.

Consider a further conversion of the right-hand side into [lb-in^2], all in "mass-based" units:

$$\begin{aligned} 1 \ \ [\text{lb–in–s}^2] &= 0{\cdot}11298 \, [\text{kg–m}^2] \\ &= 0{\cdot}11298 \times 2{\cdot}2046 \ \ [\text{lb/kg}] \times (39{\cdot}37 \ \ [\text{in/m}])^2 \\ &= \ \ 386{\cdot}1 \ \ \ [\text{lb–in}^2]. \end{aligned} \qquad (14.30)$$

Clearly we have to be careful with units: not only is 1 [lb-in-s^2] equal to 386·1 [lb-in^2], but they are not really compatible because the first is consistent with eqn. (14.24) (with T in [lbf-in]), while the second is not. It would be better to write [lbf-in-s^2] and [lbm-in^2], where 1 [lbm] is 1 pound *mass* to distinguish it from 1 [lbf] (*force*).

Now consider an inertia expressed as 1 [lb-in^2] in terms of the "mass-based" definition eqn. (14.25). In fundamental units compatible with eqn. (14.25) this inertia is

$$1 \ [\text{lbm–in}^2] \ = \ \frac{1}{32{\cdot}2} \times \frac{1}{12^2} \ = \ \frac{1}{4637} \ [\text{slug–ft}^2]. \qquad (14.31)$$

Now 1 [slug] = 14·593 [kg] and 1 [ft] = 0·3048 [m]. We can use these to convert directly to S.I. units:

$$\begin{aligned} 1 \ [\text{lbm–in}^2] \ &= \ \frac{1}{4637} \times 14{\cdot}593\,[\text{kg/slug}] \times (0{\cdot}3048\,[\text{m/ft}])^2 \\ &= 0{\cdot}000292\,[\text{kg–m}^2]. \end{aligned} \qquad (14.32)$$

Both sides of this equation are in "mass-based" units. It can be converted into [g-cm^2] as before :

$$1 \ [\text{lbm–in}^2] = 0{\cdot}000292 \times 10^3 \times (10^2)^2 = 2{,}923 \ [\text{g–cm}^2]. \qquad (14.33)$$

Provided that we convert consistently according to eqn. (14.24) or eqn. (14.25), unit conversions can be done directly without going through the intermediate steps. The confusion arises when we convert from torque-based units consistent with eqn. (14.24) to mass-based units consistent with eqn. (14.25), or *vice versa*.

Finally consider what happens if inertia is defined as Wk^2 — the "weight-based" definition

$$J \ = \ Wk^2, \qquad (14.34)$$

where W is the *weight*, not the mass. If weight is expressed in [kg], it is numerically equal to the mass M, and J calculated from eqn. (14.34) is then consistent with both eqns. (14.24) and (14.25). It can also be used in eqn. (14.23) to calculate acceleration. Strictly speaking, weight is a force and should be expressed in [N], but if we did that we would need to introduce g in eqn. (14.23).

In the imperial system, W is normally expressed in [lb] (really [lbf]). So if Wk^2 is calculated in [lbf-ft^2] it is not consistent with either eqn. (14.24) or eqn. (14.25) and cannot be used in eqn. (14.23) to calculate acceleration. When the f is omitted and the unit is written [lb-ft^2], as is common, it has the *appearance* of a mass-based definition, but the acceleration equation must now be written

$$\alpha = \frac{T}{J} = \frac{T}{Wk^2/g} \quad \text{or} \quad [\text{rad/s}^2] = \frac{[\text{lb–ft}]}{[\text{lb–ft}^2]/32{\cdot}2\ [\text{ft/s}^2]} \qquad (14.35)$$

or

$$\alpha = \frac{T}{J} \times 32{\cdot}2. \tag{14.36}$$

If W is replaced by the mass M in [slug] , using

$$M \;\; [\text{slug}] = \frac{W \;\; [\text{lbf}]}{g \;\; [\text{ft/s}^2]} = \frac{W}{32{\cdot}2}, \tag{14.37}$$

then all of eqns. (14.23), (14.24) and (14.25) can be used without further modification provided that T is in [lbf-ft]. But the slug is generally eschewed even by diehard users of the imperial system, who must therefore use eqn. (14.36) with the conversion factor g.

This inconvenience is quite possibly why engineers using the English or imperial system sometimes define inertia in terms of eqn. (14.24) instead of eqn. (14.25). However, both equations are needed: eqn. (14.24) for consistency with eqn. (14.23) in dynamic calculations, and eqn. (14.25) for design calculations. Therefore in the imperial system there is no way of escaping the conversion factor g completely. The S.I. system escapes it by expressing weight [force] in [kg] instead of [N], and torque in [N-m].

In giving examples of the inertias of different solid shapes, *Machinery's Handbook* [1948 edn.] gives examples in terms of dimensions, naturally using the "mass-based" definition of eqn. (14.25). The equations are given without units, implying that fundamental units are assumed (in either system) — laudable and worthy of note. But *practical formulas* for calculating acceleration are quoted in English units only — with inevitable conversion factors that are recognizable as g (i.e., 32·2 ft/s^2!).

Example — Consider a solid cylinder of diameter 2", axial length 1·5", and mass density 0·28 [lb/in^3]. The mass is

$$M = \frac{\pi}{4} D^2 L \rho = \frac{\pi}{4} \times 2^2 \times 1{\cdot}5 \times 0{\cdot}28 = 1{\cdot}319 \text{ [lb]}$$

$$\text{or} \quad \frac{1{\cdot}319}{32{\cdot}2} = 0{\cdot}0410 \text{ [slug]}$$

According to eqn. (14.25) the inertia in fundamental "eqn. (14.25) units" is calculated with $k = D/(2\sqrt{2})$ [ft]:

$$J = Mk^2 = 0{\cdot}0410 \times \left[\frac{2{\cdot}0/2}{12\sqrt{2}}\right]^2 = 0{\cdot}0001423 \text{ [slug–ft}^2\text{]}.$$

Since 1 [slug-ft^2] = 1 [lbf-ft]/[rad/s^2] or 1 [lbf-ft-s^2] in fundamental units, we get

$$J = 0{\cdot}0001423 \text{ [lbf–ft–s}^2\text{]}$$

and this can be directly converted in terms of "eqn. (14.24) units" to [lbf-in-s^2]:

$$J = 0{\cdot}0001423 \times 12 = 0{\cdot}001707 \text{ [lbf–in–s}^2\text{]}.$$

To convert to [g-cm^2], however, we must go back to "eqn. (14.25) units" and convert 0·0001423 [slug-ft^2] : thus

$$J = 0{\cdot}0001423 \times (32{\cdot}2 \times 0{\cdot}4536 \times 10^3) \times (12 \times 2{\cdot}54)^2 = 1931 \text{ [g–cm}^2\text{]}.$$

This can be directly converted to [lb-in^2]:

$$J = 1931 \times \frac{1}{453{\cdot}6} \times \frac{1}{2{\cdot}54^2} = 0{\cdot}660 \text{ [lb–in}^2\text{]}.$$

Note that we get this same result (much more simply) by multiplying the mass 1·319 [lb] by k^2 = ½ [in^2].

If we use the S.I. system we have M = 1·319 × 0·4536 = 0·599 [kg], and k^2 = ½ × 0·0254^2 = 0.0003226 [m^2]. Then

$$J = 0{\cdot}599 \times 0{\cdot}0003226 = 0{\cdot}0001931 \text{ [kg–m}^2\text{]}.$$

This is in "eqn. (14.25) units" and can be directly converted to [g-cm^2] : thus

$$J = 0{\cdot}0001931 \times 10^3 \times (10^2)^2 = 1931 \text{ [g–cm}^2\text{]},$$

which checks the earlier value.

14.7 Calculation of inertia

Fig. 14.16 shows a right-angled triangle with base c and height h. The second moment of area about O is

$$A_2 = \frac{hc}{4}\left[c^2 + \frac{h^2}{3}\right], \qquad (14.46)$$

If the triangle is the cross-section of an element of a rotor of length L and density δ, its contribution to the inertia is

$$J = A_2 L\delta \text{ [kg m}^2\text{]}. \qquad (14.47)$$

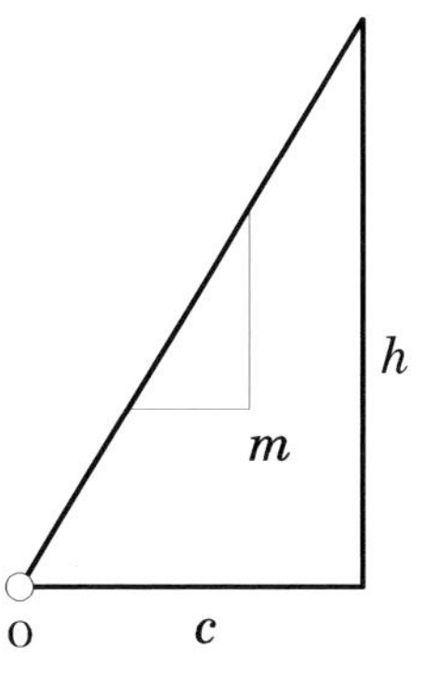

Fig. 14.16 Triangle

The second moment of area of the rectangle in Fig. 14.17 is

$$A_2 = \frac{4}{3} hc\,(c^2 + h^2). \tag{14.48}$$

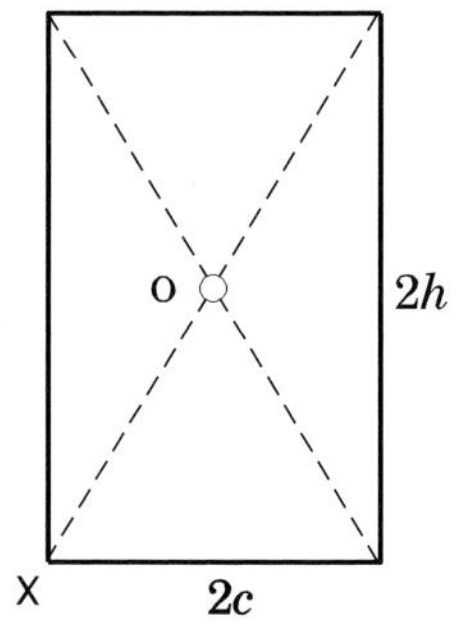

Fig. 14.17 Rectangle

In general an inertia can be expressed as the product of the mass and the radius of gyration k: if A is the cross section and M is the mass,

$$J = Mk^2 = AL\delta k^2. \tag{14.49}$$

It follows that

$$A_2 = Ak^2. \tag{14.50}$$

An inertia can be "translated" from one axis of rotation to another, by using the formula

$$J' = J + Mr^2, \tag{14.51}$$

where r is the distance of the new axis from the old one. The inertia of the rectangle about one corner **X** can be obtained by this formula. If we write $H = 2h$ and $C = 2c$, the result is

$$J_X = \frac{HC}{3}(C^2 + H^2). \tag{14.52}$$

For a sector of radius r and arc β (Fig. 14.18), the second moment of area about O is

$$A_2 = \frac{\beta}{4} r^4. \tag{14.53}$$

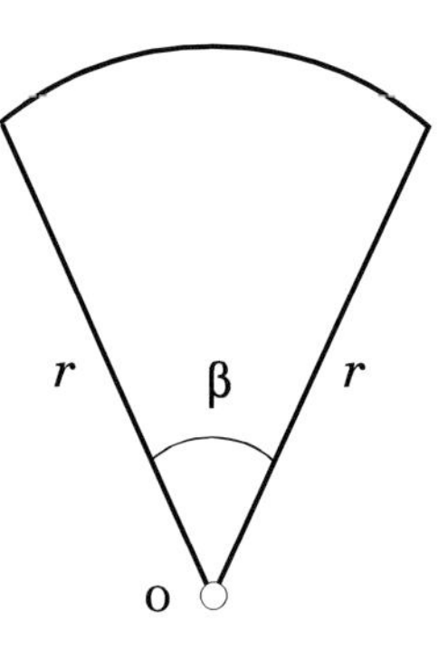

Fig. 14.18 Sector

Given that second moments and inertias about a common axis can be added and subtracted, the basic formulas for simple shapes, together with the shifting formula (14.51), can be used to calculate the exact inertia of a rotor whose cross-section is defined in terms of lines and circular arcs. If more complex shapes are involved, they can be approximated using smaller elements.

Symbols, Abbreviations, and Explanatory Notes

Capital italic letters generally signify DC or RMS AC quantities. Boldface capital letters generally signify phasors, and are complex.

Lower-case letters generally signify instantaneous quantities, as in i, ψ, etc. Subscripts make the meaning more specific: e.g., i_{Lpk} (peak line current), i_1 (instantaneous current in phase 1). In Chapter 7, lower-case letters are used for per-unit quantities in the analysis of speed/torque characteristics of the IPM.

Not all instantantaneous quantities are lower-case, particularly magnetic parameters such as A, B, F, H. These tend to have upper-case symbols because they are generally met in magnetostatic calculations, even when they may be time-variable. P is used for power, T for torque, and F for MMF : these have to be upper-case to distinguish them from p (pole-pairs), t (time), and f (frequency).

Not all symbols are listed, and there are many local variations for which we must ask the reader to rely on the context.

---

a	No. of parallel paths in stator phase winding.
a	Per-unit tooth span of auxiliary tooth; §3.6.5 only.
A	Area, [mm^2] or [in^2] or [m^2].
A	Vector potential, [Wb/m].
A	Electric loading; (Ch. 3).
A_{m}	Magnet area, generally per pole, and measured perpendicular to the D.o.M.
A_{g}	Airgap area per pole, through which the magnet flux flows.
A_{slot}	Slot area; see Fig. 3.21.
A_{slotLL}	Slot area, less liner and other bits of insulation; see p. 101.
B	Flux-density, [T] (occasionally [kl/in^2]).
B_{g}	Airgap flux-density.
B_{m}	Magnet flux-density.
B_{r}	Remanent flux-density, [T]. Sometimes *radial component* of B.
B_{t}	Tooth flux-density.
B_{y}	Yoke flux-density.
C	Coils per phase; §3.6.4.
C	Conductor distribution [conductors/radian].
C_1	Fundamental distribution of conductors per radian; §5.8.
d	Wire strand diameter; Ch. 3.
d	Switching duty-cycle; Ch. 6.
D	Diameter, [m or mm] (occasionally [in]). (In Ch. 5, D is the mean airgap diameter, but we might be sloppy in one or two approximate calculations and use the stator bore diameter or the rotor OD with the same meaning).
e	Instantaneous EMF; that is, generated EMF or back-EMF.
e	Emissivity; Ch. 12.

E	DC or RMS AC EMF.
E	Young's modulus; p. 155.
$\mathbf{E}$	Electric field strength; Ch. 12.
e_1	Instantaneous EMF in phase 1.
E_d	Mean rectified EMF, (mostly the line-line EMF). Also, in Ch. 8, the EMF of the ideal equivalent DC motor.
e_{LL}	Instantaneous line-line EMF, [V].
e_{LLpk}	Peak instantaneous line-line EMF, [V].
e_{ph}	Phase EMF, [V].
e_{pk}	Peak phase EMF.
E_{q1}	RMS value of open-circuit fundamental phase EMF, [V].
$\mathbf{E}_{q1}$	Phasor values of open-circuit fundamental phase EMF, [V].
f	Fundamental frequency, [Hz].
F	Magnetomotive force, [A].
f_{LKG}	Leakage factor; p. 160.
F_{slot}	Slot-fill factor (pp. 89-90); the same as SFg (p. 102).
g	Airgap length.
g'	Effective airgap length, $k_c g$; §5.4.1.
g''	Effective airgap length, eqn. (5.9); includes the magnet.
$\mathbf{h}$	The 120° complex rotation operator.
h	Slot depth; p. 230.
h	Hysteresis coefficient; §12.3.2.
H	Magnetic field strength, [A/m].
H_c	Coercivity, [A/m] or [kA/m]; (sometimes [Oe] or [kOe]).
H_{cJ}	Intrinsic coercivity, [A/m] or [kA/m].
i	Instantaneous current, [A].
I	DC or RMS AC current.
I_d	DC current associated with energy conversion, [A].
I_d	d-axis current; d-axis component of phasor current $\mathbf{I}$; Ch. 7.
i_{Lpk}	Peak line current, [A].
I_{Lrms}	RMS line current, [A]
I_m	Maximum fundamental current available from inverter; Ch. 7.
i_{pk}	Peak phase current, [A].
I_q	q-axis current; q-axis component of phasor current $\mathbf{I}$; Ch. 7.
I_{sp}	Set-point or reference current of current-regulator, [A pk].
j	$\sqrt{(-1)}$. The 90° complex rotation operator.
j	General counter, number, integer or index.
J	Current-density (usually RMS), [A/mm^2] or [A/in^2].
J	Polar moment of inertia, [kg m^2]; (see §§14.6, 14.7).
k	General counter, number, integer or index.
k	Thermal conductivity; Ch. 12.
k	Radius of gyration; §§14.6, 14.7.
$\mathbf{k}$	EMF or torque constant of ideal DC motor.
K	AC/DC resistance ratio; §3.6.7.4.
$k_{\alpha d}$	Armature-reaction flux coefficient; p. 254.
k_{1ad}, k_{1aq}	Fundamental armature-reaction flux coefficients; p. 255.

k_c Carter's coefficient; pp. 215-216.
k_d Differential leakage coefficient; p. 225.
k_{d1} Fundamental distribution factor (spread factor).
k_{dn} Distribution factor (spread factor) for n^{th} harmonic.
k_E EMF constant in Vs/rad; (Chs. 1, 4 and 8).
K_E EMF constant in V/krpm.
$k_{E[LLpk]}$ Peak line-line EMF per rad/s.
$k_{E[pk]}$ Peak phase EMF per rad/s.
K_m Motor constant, [Nm/A/√ohm]; (Ch. 8).
k_{p1} Fundamental pitch factor (chording factor).
k_{pn} Pitch factor (chording factor) for n^{th} harmonic.
$k_{\sigma 1}$ Fundamental skew factor.
$k_{\sigma n}$ Skew factor for n^{th} harmonic.
k_T Torque constant; torque per ampere, [Nm/A]; (Chs. 1,4 and 8).
$k_{T[pk]}$ Torque per peak ampere of motor line current.
$k_{T[rms]}$ Torque per RMS ampere of motor line current.
$k'_{T[pk]}$ Equivalent to $k_{T[pk]}$: the prime is used to denote a sinewave-EMF motor coupled to a squarewave drive. Likewise $k''_{T[pk]}$ is used for a squarewave motor coupled to a sinewave drive. The primes are used in the same way with $k_{T[rms]}$. See Ch. 8.
k_w Winding factor used with squarewave motors; p. 179.
k_w Winding factor used in airgap inductance, §5.4.
k_{w1} Fundamental winding factor. This is the ratio of the fundamental space-harmonic MMF produced by the actual winding, to the fundamental space-harmonic MMF produced by an ideal winding having the same number of turns, all of which have full 180° pitch, with no distribution (spread) and no skew. It is also the ratio of the fundamental EMF generated in the actual winding by a rotating magnetic field, to the EMF generated in the ideal full-pitch concentrated unskewed winding. In using winding factors we are effectively relating the performance of the actual winding to the performance of the ideal full-pitch winding.
k_{wn} Winding factor for n^{th} harmonic. The description given for k_{w1} applies equally to k_{wn}, but for the nth harmonic rather than the fundamental.
L Length, [m].
L_m Magnet length in the direction of magnetization.
L_{stk} Stack length, i.e. the length of the lamination stack in the axial direction.
L Inductance, [H] or [mH].
L_0 Constant component of variable phase inductance; see p. 191.
L_2 Second-harmonic component of phase inductnace; see p. 191.
L_d Synchronous inductance, d-axis.
L_{diff} Differential leakage inductance.
L_{end} End-turn leakage component of L_{ph}.

L_g	Airgap component of L_{ph}.
L_{LL}	Line-line inductance.
L_{md}	Magnetizing component of L_d.
L_{mq}	Magnetizing component of L_q.
L_{ph}	Phase self-inductance.
L_q	Synchronous inductance, q-axis.
L_{slot}	Slot-leakage component of L_{ph}.
L_σ	Total leakage inductance; p. 250.
m	No. of phases.
m	Per-unit tooth span of main (wound) tooth; §3.6.5 only.
m	No. of winding layers; §3.6.7.4 only.
m	Reciprocal or Poisson's ratio; §3.7 only.
m	Modulation index; Ch. 7.
m	Mechanical harmonic order; §12.4.2.3.
m'	Electrical harmonic order; §12.4.2.3.
M	Mutual inductance, [H] or [mH].
M	Mass, [kg] or [lb] or [slug].
M_0	Constant component of variable mutual inductance; see p. 191.
M_2	Second-harmonic component of mutual inductance; see p. 191.
M_{end}	End-turn leakage component of M_{ph}.
M_g	Airgap component of M_{ph}.
M_{ph}	Phase-phase mutual inductance.
M_{slot}	Slot-leakage component of M_{ph}.
M_σ	Total leakage component of mutual inductance; p. 250.
n, N	General counter, number, integer or index.
n	Order of harmonic, as in "n^{th} harmonic" or k_{wn}.
n	Gear ratio.
n	Time harmonic order; §12.4.2.3.
N	Speed, [rev/min]; [rev/min] is also denoted [rpm].
N	Number of turns.
N_c	Coils per phase; §3.6.7.1.
N_c	Turns per coil; §5.4.
N_S	Number of sections in a phase winding; §3.6.4.
p	No. of pole-*pairs*.[1]
$\mathbf{p}$	Differential operator d/dt.
P	Power, [W] or [kW].
P	Permeance; usually with a subscript, [Wb/A].
P_e	Time-averaged electromagnetic power.
P_{elec}	Electrical power, usually at machine terminals, [W].
P_m or P_{mech}	Mechanical power, [W] or [kW].
p_{rl}	Rotor leakage permeance (normalized to P_{m0}); p. 159.
P_{shaft}	Shaft power, [W] or [kW].

[1] In §12.4.2.3 and §12.4.2.4 we use P for the number of **rotor** pole-pairs. These sections deal with the harmonic ampere-conductor distributions of the stator, which generally do not have the same number of pole-pairs as the rotor.

P_{m0}	Magnet internal permeance, [Wb/A].
P_{slot}	Slot permeance coefficient; p. 231.
q	Slots per pole per phase, or coil-sides per phase-belt; p. 77.
Q	Reactive power, [VA]; Ch. 9.
Q	Heat flow rate; Ch. 12.
Q_1, Q_2,	Labels used for transistors.
r,R	Radius, [m]; (occasionally [in]).
R	Resistance, [ohm]. In analytical work it is generally the phase resistance, but when used with figures of merit (Ch.8) it is usually the line-line resistance.
R	Magnetic reluctance, particularly in Chs. 4 and 12. [A/Wb].
R	Magnetic reluctance; usually with a subscript, [A/Wb].
R	Geometric mean radius; §5.6.
R_g	Airgap reluctance per pole, [A/Wb].
R_{LL}	Line-line resistance, [ohm].
R_{ph}	Phase resistance, [ohm].
R_q	Resistance of one transistor; Ch. 6.
s	Slip, defined as 1 − Actual speed/Synchronous speed. The speeds in this expression can be measured in any units: rpm, rad/s, elec. rad/s, etc. Slip is used mainly with line-start motors, in which the asynchronous torque is important.
s	Slot-opening; §5.4.1.
s	Complex frequency used with Laplace transform; §8.4.
S	No. of stator slots; Ch. 3.
S	Steepness of torque/speed characteristic; (Ch.1).
S_1	Slots per winding section; §3.6.4.
S_F	"Slots forward"; §3.6.4.
s_{Q1}	Switching state of transistor Q_1; also used as a real variable in state-space averaging; Ch. 6.
t	Time, [s].
t_{on}	On-time of switching transistor.
t_s	Switching period.
T	Temperature, [°C].
T	Torque, [Nm] or [lb-in]; many other units are used.
$\mathbf{T}$	*dq*-axis transform matrix, §4.4.2 and §5.10.
T_1	Torque produced by current i_1 in phase 1.
T_a	Armature time-constant; Ch. 9.
T_A	Average alignment torque; Ch. 7.
T_c	Turns per coil.
T_d''	Short-circuit subtransient time-constant; Chs. 9, 12.
T_{d0}''	Open-circuit subtransient time-constant; Chs. 9, 12.
T_e	Electromagnetic torque.
T_{ei}	Alignment torque.
T_{LR}	Locked-rotor torque or stall torque, [Nm].
T_{ph}	Turns in series per phase.
T_R	Average reluctance torque; Ch. 7.

T_{rel}	Reluctance torque.
u	Magnetic potential; Ch. 5.
$\mathbf{u}$	Voltage space-vector; Ch. 7.
U	Kinetic energy, [J].
$\mathbf{U}$	Phasor of inductive voltage; Fig. 7.2.
v, V	Voltage, [V].
V_{bld}	Applied voltage in "building" circuit; Ch. 6.
V_d	DC voltage associated with energy conversion, [V].
V_d	d-axis voltage; d-axis component of phasor voltage **V**; Ch. 7.
V_{fwh}	Applied voltage in "freewheeling" circuit; Ch. 6.
V_{LL1}	Fundamental RMS line-line voltage.
V_m	Maximum fundamental voltage available from inverter; Ch. 7.
V_q	q-axis voltage; q-axis component of phasor voltage **V**; Ch. 7.
V_q	Voltage drop across one transistor; Ch. 6.
V_r	Rotor volume, [m^3].
V_s	Supply voltage, [V]. May be DC or AC, depending on context.
w	Slot width; p. 230.
W_{2R}	Rotor loss (in line-start motor).
W_c	Coenergy, [J].
W_{Cu}	Weight of copper; §3.6.7.2.
W_e	Eddy-current component of core loss, [W].
W_h	Hysteresis loss, [W].
W_{WF}	Windage and friction loss, [W].
x	Multiplicitiy or "plex"; Ch.10.
X	Reactance (= ωL); meaningful only at frequency ω; [ohm].
X_d	Synchronous reactance, d-axis.
X_d''	Subtransient reactance, d-axis.
X_q	Synchronous reactance, q-axis.
X_q''	Subtransient reactance, q-axis.
X_{md}, X_{mq}	Magnetizing components of X_d and X_q.
$\mathbf{Z}$	Complex impedance, [ohm].
$\mathbf{Z}_1$	Positive-sequence impedance.
$\mathbf{Z}_2$	Negative-sequence impedance.

Greek

α	Phase-control angle, [rad or °].
α	Temperature coefficient, [/°C]; §3.6.7.3.
α	General angular dimension, [°].
α	Angular acceleration, [rad/s^2].
α	Coil-pitch, [elec° or per-unit of pole-pitch]. In §3.6.4 it is used once or twice interchangeably with coil-span, which is the same thing measured in slot-pitches.
α	General phase-shift angle [° or rad].
α	Coefficient of linear expansion; p. 155.
α	Per-unit pole-arc; p. 179.
β	Arc dimension, [°].

β	Phase angle; Fig. 4.37.
β	Turns ratio, main/auxiliary; Ch. 11.
β_M	Magnet pole-arc, [° or rad, usually electrical].
γ	Phase control angle, [°]. Especially the orientation of the current phasor **I** relative to the q-axis EMF $\mathbf{E}_{q1}$ in the phasor diagram, or the instantaneous phase current i_1 relative to the instantaneous EMF e_1.
γ	Slot-pitch angle; Fig. 3.8 and eqn. (3.4).
γ_{Tmax}	Phase angle γ for maximum torque; "optimum gamma".
Γ_d, Γ_q	Synchronous inductance coefficients; Ch. 5.
δ	Torque angle, [°]. Used with line-start motors. The phase angle between the EMF phasor **E** and the terminal voltage phasor **V**. In a generator, δ is defined so that it is positive when **E** leads **V**. In a motor, it is the other way round.
δ	Small angle, [°].
δ	Skin depth; Ch. 12.
δ_m	Mass density; p. 154.
∂	Partial derivative.
Δ	A change in something; an increment.
ΔT	Temperature change, [°C].
ε	Short-pitch or chording angle, equal to $\pi - \alpha$ elec. rad., where α is the coil-pitch; (Ch.3).
ε	Strain; p. 155.
ε	Unbalance factor; p. 188.
ζ	Damping ratio; §8.4.
η	Efficiency.
θ	Rotor position, [rad or °] (usually electrical).
θ	General azimuthal or circumferential coordinate, [°].
μ_0	Permeability of space, $4\pi \times 10^{-7}$ H/m or $3{\cdot}19 \times 10^{-8}$ A/in.
μ_{rec}	Relative recoil permeability; p. 161.
ξ	Rotor position, [rad or °]; (occasional)
ξ	General phase angle; Ch.1.
ξ	Saliency ratio (usually L_q/L_d for IPM machines).
ρ	Resistivity, [ohm-m].
σ	Airgap shear stress; p. 89. As a subscript, it means *skew*.
σ	Coil-span. Usually σ is in [slot-pitches], but sometimes it is used interchangeably with the coil-pitch α, as in §3.6.4.
σ	Conductivity, [S/m].
σ	Stfan-Boltzmann constant; p. 653.
σ_t	Hoop or tangential stress; §3.7.
τ	Time-constant, [s or ms].
τ	Ratio of tooth-width to slot-width; Fig. 3.13.
τ_e	Electrical time-constant; Ch. 8.
τ_m	Mechanical time-constant; Ch. 8.
ϕ	Power-factor angle; phase angle between voltage and current (usually at the machine terminals).

ϕ, Φ	Flux, [Wb].
Φ_g	Airgap flux.
Φ_{m1}	Fundamental airgap flux/pole produced by the magnet on open-circuit.
Φ_r	Remanent flux, [Wb].
χ	Magnetic susceptibility; p. 170.
ψ, Ψ	Flux-linkage, [Vs].
ψ_1	Instantaneous flux-linkage in phase 1.
Ψ_{1Md}	Fundamental flux-linkage per phase produced by the magnet on open-circuit, [Vs].
ω	Radian frequency, $2\pi f$.
ω_m	Angular velocity in mechanical rad/s.
ω_n	Undamped natural frequency; §8.4.
ω_{NL}	No-load angular velocity, [rad/s].
Ω	Per-unit angular velocity; Ch. 7.
Ω	Angular velocity of ampere-conductor distribution; Ch. 12.
Ω_Q	Per-unit corner-point speed; Ch. 7.

Subscripts

0	Zero-sequence.
0	Reference value (depending on context).
1	Phase 1.
1	Positive-sequence.
1	Fundamental.
2	Phase 2.
2	Negative-sequence.
3	Phase 3.
a	Phase *a* (same as phase 1).
b	Phase *b* (same as phase 2).
c	Phase *c* (same as phase 3).
A	Line A.
B	Line C.
C	Line C.
pk	Peak (usually of sinewave).

Abbreviations[2]

°elec.	Electrical degrees (= mechanical degrees × p)
12s14p	12-slot, 14-pole. Other examples abound.
2D	Two-dimensional
3D	Three-dimensional
AC	Alternating current. We use AC in the same "autonomous" way we use DC; *viz*. "AC current". In its most general form, "alternating" refers to a waveform that has positive and negative segments, (usually assumed equal). AC does not necessarily mean "sinusoidal": a squarewave or a triangular wave can be "alternating". The sinewave is a special case of an alternating waveform. In this book we have many *alternating* waveforms of current, EMF, voltage and flux-linkage; a few that are sinusoidal; and some that would like to be sinusoidal but can't quite manage it (as, for example, when current regulators saturate). So we keep the term AC quite general, and when we mean sinusoidal, we say sinusoidal.
BH	Characteristic of flux-density vs. magnetizing force: a material property of steels and magnets. Usually we mean a single-valued curve and not the whole hysteresis loop.
BLAC	Brushless AC. Not used in this text; we use the term "sinewave" to refer to motors with sinewave drive. See also "synchronous AC" and "PM synchronous AC" in the Index.
BLDC	Brushless DC. Not used in this text; we use the term "squarewave" to refer to motors with squarewave drive, but sometimes we refer to the "classical brushless DC" motor.
BLV	EMF calculation method; see p. 182.
BPM	Brushless permanent-magnet. Not used in this text.
CAD	Computer-aided design.
CCW	counter-clockwise (= anti-clockwise); this is the positive direction of rotation, as in mathematics.
DC	Although this is technically an abbreviation of "direct current", it is used autonomously to describe (and ascribe) the properties of direct current and direct-current devices, as in the term "DC current".
D.o.M.	Direction of magnetization.
EMC	Electromagnetic compatibility. Also EMI : electromagnetic interference.
EMF	Electro-motive force: the open-circuit rate of change of flux-linkage caused by the rotation of magnets.
DBPMM94	*Design of Brushless Permanent Magnet Motors*, by J.R. Hendershot and T.J.E. Miller, Magna Physics Publishing/O.U.P., 1994.

[2] SMALL CAPS are used mainly for abbreviations of general electrical engineering terms used frequently throughout the book. This is not done with abbreviations of particular types of motor: thus IPM is not in small caps, neither is SPM.

F&K-II *Electric Machinery*, by A.E. Fitzgerald and C. Kingsley Jr., SECOND EDITION, McGraw-Hill, 1961.

FET Field-effect transistor.

HCF Highest common factor.

ID Inside diameter.

IEC International Electro-Technical Commission.

IGBT Insulated-gate bipolar transistor.

IPM Interior permanent-magnet machine.

LCM Least common multiple.

LHS Left-hand side.

M-19 A grade of silicon steel; likewise M-36, M-43 etc.

MMF Magneto-motive force. This is used widely to mean *magnetic potential drop*, that is, the line integral of the field strength **H** between two points, and particularly across the airgap. When the MMF F is known in the airgap, the flux-density follows from $\mathbf{B} = \mu_0 \mathbf{H} = \mu_0 F/g$. F can be produced by the magnets or the winding ampere-conductors; or a combination of both.

MS Military standard (US only).

NDFEB a general descriptor used to refer to a member of the Neodymium Iron Boron family of magnets.

NEMA National Electrical Manufacturers' Association (USA).

OD Outside diameter.

OFHC Oxygen-free high-conductivity copper. See p. 142.

PLC Programmable logic controller.

PM Permanent magnet.

PR Power rate; Ch. 8.

PWM Pulse-width modulation.

RHS Right-hand side.

RMS Root-mean-square, or effective value.

SFg Gross slot-fill factor; p. 102. Same as F_{slot} on pp. 89-90.

SFn Net slot-fill factor; p. 102.

SMC Soft magnetic composite or pressed-core material.

SPM Surface-permanent-magnet machine.

SR Speed rate; Ch. 8.

TRV Torque per unit of rotor volume.

Other terms and conventions

Armature reaction is the magnetic effect of the stator current.

Dots and crosses are used to denote the direction of current or EMF. They are also used to denote the direction of conductors, even when there is no EMF and no current.

Phase refers to a physical section of winding, not one of the main supply terminals or one of the main phases of the supply. *Phase voltage* means the voltage across that section of winding; it does *not* mean the line-line voltage. In a 3-phase wye connection, the phase voltage is a line-neutral voltage. In a 3-phase delta connection, the phase voltage is a line-line voltage.

Servo-motor means a motor that is designed to operate in a motion-control system, which is characterized by closed-loop control of velocity or position.

Sinewave is a general term referring to brushless AC motors which operate in the steady-state with sinusoidal currents.

Sinewound refers to a machine that is wound for the lowest possible level of harmonics in the EMF and the winding distribution, i.e., for sinewave operation. It has, ideally, a sinusoidal EMF waveform and a sinusoidal variation of inductance with rotor position.

Sink convention : induced voltage is generally treated as a "back EMF"; we do not have a minus sign in Faraday's law. This is convenient for analysing motors, but perhaps less so for generators. However, most of the generator material uses phasors with generator sign convention (source convention).

Six-step is used only with the classical voltage-source inverter. For brushless DC drives with 60° commutation of the line currents, we use the term "squarewave".

Space vector (Also known as space *phasor* [Räumzeiger]). A complex number representing the instantaneous state of three-phase currents or voltages in a stationary reference frame. Space vectors can also be identified as instantaneous symmetrical components [Ku, 1959].[3]

---

[3] The space vector is probably the most compact form for expressing the performance equations of sinewound AC machines. Space vectors of flux, flux-linkage, current, MMF, EMF, and voltage are complex numbers that represent the magnitude and direction of the spatial distribution of these quantities in a polyphase machine with a rotating field. They usually represent the combined effect of all three phases acting simultaneously. They are analogous to *time phasors* which represent the magnitude and phase of individual phase currents, voltages, etc., that vary sinusoidally in time; space vectors are based on quantities that vary sinusoidally around the airgap, and they include quantities derived by integration or differentiation. They are related to the *d,q-axis* and α,β components which are widely used in classical AC machine theory. Space vectors, dq-axis and α,β quantities can be calculated formally from instantaneous quantities by means of reference-frame transformations. Space vectors have a long history, but they are important and popular today because of the widespread use of *vector control, field-oriented control* and *Direct Torque Control* ; see Chapter 7. Many modern PWM control strategies are best understood and analysed in terms of space vectors.

Span, **throw**, and **pitch** are sometimes used interchangeably in relation to the arc subtended by a coil. *Span* is usually expressed in slot-pitches. It is often *signed*, the sign indicating polarity. *Throw* is similar to *span*, being measured in slot-pitches, usually without a sign. Sometimes it is expressed as the relative slot-numbers of the "go" and "return" coil-sides: e.g., a *throw* of "1 and 6" represents a coil with a *span* of 5 slot-pitches. *Throw* would not be expressed as "6 and 1"; but a *span* of −5 means a coil with opposite polarity to one with a *span* of 5. *Pitch* is usually reserved for mathematical analysis of harmonics and winding factors. It is usually expressed in °elec, or fractions of a pole-pitch.

Squarewave refers to brushless DC drives which have a flat-topped current waveform obtained from a DC source that is switched or commutated to the phases in turn. The terms SQUAREWAVE and TRAPEZOIDAL are often used interchangeably. In this book, the term squarewave is preferred for both the motor and the drive, because it represents the ideal brushless DC motor and its drive. It is impossible to achieve a perfectly square-edged waveform of current or emf. It is equally impossible to achieve pure trapezoidal waveforms.

Trapezoidal is a general term referring to brushless DC motors which have a flat-topped EMF waveform.

Triplen *Lit.*, *triple-n* describes harmonics of order 3 or a multiple thereof.

Yoke means the same as **back-iron**.

Labelling of phases : sorry, but this is not quite consistent throughout the book. Where we are concerned with physical quantities we have tended to use 1,2,3; thus in Chapter 6 the phases are labelled 1,2,3 to distinguish them from the lines A,B,C. But where we are dealing with the *dq*-axis transformation we tend to label the phases *a,b,c*, in line with the main references F&K-II; Concordia; and Y.H. Ku. Both sets of labels appear in Chapter 5, which could be confusing except that the physical 1,2,3 inductances are to be calculated on the spot, whereas the *a,b,c* inductances are rather abstract and vanish into L_d and L_q. Elsewhere, subscript 1 is used for the fundamental component, as in E_{q1} or k_{w1}; and again 1 and 2 are used for symmetrical components. Local context should make it clear which is which. Perhaps we should have used *u,v,w* or *r,s,t* or *R,Y,B* (red, yellow, blue), but no system is free of conflicts and we decided to leave it as it is.

Lit.	*Literally*.
ff.	*Following*: p. 530ff. means "page 530 and following pages".
i.e.	*id est* (that is).
e.g.	*Exempli gratia* (for example).
op. cit.	*In the work cited* (or *previously cited*).
§	Section number.
#	Ordinal number, e.g., #26 means No. 26 (as in gauges).
via	"by way of" or "through the action of". (*Lit.*, "road" or "way").
viz.	*Visually*, meaning "look at this, for example".
vs.	*Versus*; (in graph plotting or in comparisons it means *against*).

CARBON DATING

'You are old, commutator..', the young man said,
'And your segments exceedingly thin.
Your brushes are worn and your braids are quite frayed;
Don't you think you should just pack it in?'

'—In my youth' flashed the old man, crackling to life,
'I was warned to make way for induction.
When Silicon came, they thought me quite lame;
But you see I am still in production.'

'But you need to be dressed, and your sparking suppressed,
And you take up much space between bearings.
You're costly and noisy and gulp your amps neat;
Isn't this the right time for retiring?'

'—It's true I indulge in some old-fashioned ways,
But I start every time and keep spinning.
With your magnets, encoders, transistors and CAD,
Do you honestly think you are winning?'

TJEM 22-Apr-88

BIBLIOGRAPHY[4]

1. Hendershot J.R. and Miller T.J.E., *Design of Brushless Permanent-Magnet Motors*, Magna Physics Publications/Oxford Science Publications, 1994.
2. *SPEED's Electric Machines*, the theory text that is used with the *SPEED* training courses.
3. Miller T.J.E., *Brushless permanent-magnet and reluctance motor drives*, Clarendon Press, Oxford, 1989, ISBN 0-19-859369-4.
4. Miller T.J.E. (Ed.), *Reactive power control in electric systems*, John Wiley & Sons, 1982. ISBN 0-471-86933-3.
5. Hague B. : *Electromagnetic Problems in Electrical Engineering*, Oxford University Press, 1929. Reprinted as *The Principles of Electromagnetism Applied to Electrical Machines*, Dover Publications Inc., N.Y., 1962.
6. Fitzgerald A.E and Kingsley C. Jr., *Electric Machinery*, McGraw-Hill, 2nd Edition, 1961.[5]
7. Adkins B., *The General Theory of Electrical Machines*, Chapman & Hall, 1957.
8. Say M.G., *The Performance and Design of Alternating Current Machines*, Pitman, London, Second Edition, 1948. (First edition, 1936).

---

[4] The bibliography contains more than 300 references including about 60 books. We have not used numbered references in the text. In some cases where we have simply named an author, the appropriate reference will be clear from the Bibliography; (books take precedence over papers). References to Veinott or Alger are of this type, except where reference to specific papers are made by including the date in brackets [ ]. Some references are given in full in footnotes, where we wanted to draw the reader's attention to them immediately.
Except in one or two cases we have not provided references to web-sites. Although the internet is a rich source of information, individual web-sites are unstable. They can change or disappear without warning, and so the internet cannot be regarded as *archival*. Modern search engines are so powerful that specific material can often be found with only a few key-words even when the exact citation is unknown; but the internet *provides access only to material that has been specifically published on it*. In electrical engineering there is a vast reserve of material published in archival journals before about 1980, that is simply not available on the internet. To study these resources there is no alternative but to visit a good library.
The Bibliography contains practically all the works that were most helpful to us in our own work and in writing this book. It is compiled with reverence and appreciation for the authors, including many of our contemporaries. It must also be said that it represents only a tiny fraction of the publications in the field; with vast numbers of new ones appearing at a dozen international conferences every year, it is difficult to keep up without narrowing one's interests.

[5] The second edition is specifially cited, as later editions were diluted of the material for which this remarkable work is listed. In the text we sometimes refer to this work by the abbreviated reference F&K-II.

9. Jones C.V., *The Unified Theory of Electrical Machines,* Butterworths, 1967.
10. Ku Y.H., *Electric Energy Conversion*, The Ronald Press Company, New York, 1959.
11. Roters H.C., *Electromagnetic Devices*, John Wiley & Sons, New York, 1941.
12. Veinott C.G., *Theory and design of small induction motors*, McGraw-Hill, 1959.
13. Kimbark, E.W., *Power System Stability*, Wiley, New York, 1948.
14. Kostenko M. and Piotrovsky L., *Electric Machines*, MIR Publishers, 1974.
15. Alger P.L., *Induction Machines*, Gordon & Breach, New York, 2nd edn., 1970.
16. Concordia C., *Synchronous Machines, Theory and Performance*, John Wiley and Sons, New York, 1951.
17. Croft T., *Alternating-Current Armature Winding*, McGraw-Hill, New York, 1924.
18. Liwschitz-Garik M. and Gentilini C., *Winding Alternating Current Machines*, Litton Educational Publishing, 1950.
19. Srb N., *Winding Technique of Electrical Motors*, Tehnička Knija, Zagreb, 1990.
20. Heller B. and Hamata V., *Harmonic Effects in Induction Machines*, Elsevier Scientific Publishing Company, Amsterdam, 1977.
21. Lipo T.A., *Introduction to AC Machine Design*, Wisconsin, 1996.
22. Clayton A.E and Hancock N.N., *The Performance and Design of Direct Current Machines*, 3rd edn., Pitman, London, 1959-66.
23. Hanselman D., *Brushless Permanent Magnet Motor Design*, 2nd edition, The Writers' Collective.
24. Kenjo T. and Nagamori S., *Brushless Motors, Advanced Theory and Modern Applications*, Sogo Electronics Press, 2003.
25. Matsui N., Takeda Y., Morimoto S., and Honda Y., *Design of Interior Permanent Magnet Synchronous Motors and Their Control*, Ohmsha Publishing , Tokyo, [in Japanese] 2003.
26. Mohan N., Undeland T.M. and Robbins W.P., *Power Electronics: Converters, Applications, and Design*, John Wiley & Sons, 1989, 1995 [2nd edition].
27. Murphy J.M.D. and Turnbull F.G., *Power Electronic Control of AC Motors*, Pergamon Press, 1988.
28. Harris M.R., Stephenson J.M. and Lawrenson P.J., *Per-unit Systems*, Cambridge University Press, 1970.
29. Neumann R., *Symmetrical Component Analysis of Unsymmetrical Polyphase Systems*, Pitman, London, 1939.
30. Binns K.J., Lawrenson P.J. and Trowbridge C.W., *The analytical and numerical solution of electric and magnetic fields*, John Wiley & Sons., Chichester, 1992.
31. McLachlan N. W., *Bessel Functions for Engineers*, Oxford University Press, 1934.
32. Stoll R., *The Analysis of Eddy Currents*, Clarendon Press, Oxford, 1974.
33. Lammeraner J. and Štafl M., *Eddy currents*, Iliffe Books Ltd., London, 1966.
34. Štafl M., *Electrodynamics of Electrical Machines*, Iliffe Books Ltd., London, 1967.
35. Davies E.J., *Conduction and Induction Heating*, Peter Peregrinus Ltd., UK.
36. Perry M., *Low Frequency Electromagnetic Design*, Marcel Dekker, N.Y., 1985.
37. Reliance Motion Control Inc., *DC Motors, SPEED Controls, Servo Systems: The Electro-Craft Engineering Handbook*, 6th edn.
38. Abramowitz M. and Stegun I. A., *Handbook of Mathematical Functions*, Dover Publications Inc., New York, 1965.
39. Rissik H., *The Fundamental Theory of Arc Convertors*, Chapman & Hall, 1939.

40. Stölting H.-D., Kallenbach E., and Amrhein W. (Eds.), *Handbook of Fractional-Horsepower Drives*, Springer, 2006.

41. Leonhard W., *Control of Electrical Drives*, 2nd Edition, Springer-Verlag, Berlin, 1996.

42. Moczala H., Draeger J., Krauß H., Schock H. and Tillner S., *Electrische Kleinmotoren*, Expert Verlag, 1987.

43. Agrawal K.C., *Industrial Power Engineering Applications Handbook*, Newnes, 2001.

44. Shepherd J., Morton A.H. and Spence L.F., *Higher Electrical Engineering*, Pitman, 1970.

45. Bumby J.R., *Superconducting rotating electrical machines*, Oxford, 1983.

46. Dote Y., *Servo Motor and Motion Control Using Digital Signal Processors*, Texas Instruments/Prentice Hall, 1990.

47. Dote Y. and Kinoshita S. (Eds.), *Brushless Servomotors, Fundamentals and Applications*, Clarendon Press, Oxford, 1990.

48. Boldea I., *Variable Speed Generators*, Taylor & Francis, 2006.

49. Boldea I. and Nasar S., *Electric Drives*, CRC Press, 1999.

50. Compter J.C., *Electrical Drives for Precision Engineering Designs*, specAmotor, 2007

51. Subrahmanyam V., *Electric Drives*, McGraw-Hill, New York, 1996.

52. Krawczyk A. and Tegopoulos J. A., *Numerical modelling of eddy currents*, Monographs in Electrical & Electronic Engineering, Clarendon Press, Oxford, 1993.

53. Gieras J.F. and Wing M., *Permanent Magnet Motor Technology*, Marcel Dekker, 1997

54. Gieras J.F., Wang R.J., and Kamper M.J., *Axial Flux Permanent Magnet Brushless Machines*, Kluwer Academic Publishers, 2004

55. Gieras J.F., Wang C. and Cho Lai J., *Noise of Polyphase Electric Motors*, Taylor & Francis, 2006.

56. Tímár P.L. [Ed.], *Noise and Vibration of Electrical Machines*, Elsevier, 1989.

57. Ivanov-Smolensky A., *Electrical Machines*, MIR Publishers, Moscow, 1982.

58. Morley A., *Strength of Materials*, Longmans, Green and Co., 1908; 9th edn., 1940.

59. Pyrhönen J., Jokinen T. and Hrabovcová V., *Design of Rotating Electrical Machines*, John Wiley, 2008.

60. Bedford B.D. and Hoft R.G., *Principles of Inverter Circuits*, John Wiley & Sons, 1964.

61. Hanitsch R. (Ch.10) and Howe D. (Ch.11) in Coey J.M.D. [Ed], *Rare-Earth Iron Permanent Magnets*, Clarendon Press, Oxford, 1996.

62. Campbell P., *Permanent Magnet Materials and their Application*, Cambridge University Press, 1994.

63. Parker R.J., *Advances in Permanent Magnetism*, John Wiley & Sons, 1990.

64. Vas P., *Electrical Machines and Drives; A Space-Vector Theory Approach*, Clarendon Press, Oxford, 1992.

---

65. IEEE Standard 115 : *Test Procedures for Synchronous Machines*, 1994

66. Bolton H., *Transverse edge effect in sheet-rotor induction motors*, Proceedings IEE, **116**, No. 5, May 1969, pp. 725-731.

67. Arnold F. and Floresta J.G., *Power Rate — A Most Important Figure-of-Merit for the Incremental Motion Designer*, Incremental Motion Control Systems Society, Proceedings of the 13th Annual Symposium, Champaign, Illinois; Prof. B.C. Kuo, Editor, May 1984, pp. 11-18.

68. Arnold F., *Understanding Motion Control Figures-of-Merit*, Incremental Motion Control Systems Society, Proceedings of the 17th Annual Symposium, Champaign, Illinois; Prof. B.C. Kuo, Editor, June 1988, pp. 1-12.

69. Taft C.K., *Brushless DC Motor Figure of Merit Relationships*, Incremental Motion Control Systems Society, Proceedings of the 23rd Annual Symposium, Champaign, Illinois; Prof. B.C. Kuo, Editor, June 1994, pp. 179-199.

70. Hanselman D., *Figure of Merit*; Motor Constant Indicates Brushless Motor Performance, PCIM, December 1998, pp. 32-39.

71. Boules N., *Prediction of no-load flux-density distribution in permanent magnet machines*, IEEE Transactions on Industry Applications, Vol. IA-21, No. 4, May/June 1985, pp. 633-643.

72. Jahns, T.M.: *Torque production in PM synchronous motor drives with rectangular current excitation*, IEEE Transactions, IA-20, pp 803-813, 1984.

73. Demerdash, N.A. with Arkadan, A., Nehl, T., Vaidya, J. and others: papers on brushless DC and AC motors and drives, published in IEEE Transactions, including EC-3, Sept 88, 722-732; EC-2, March 87, 86-92; PAS-104, Aug 85, 2206-2213; 2214-2222; 2223-2231; PAS-103, July 84, 1829-1836; PAS-102, Jan 83, 104-112; PAS-101, Dec 82, 4502-4506; PAS-100, Sept 81, 4125-4135; EC-3, Sept 88, 714-721; EC-3, Dec 88, 880-889; 890-898.

74. Rasmussen K.F., Davies J.H., Miller T.J.E., McGilp M.I. and Olaru M., *Analytical and Numerical Computation of Airgap Magnetic Fields in Brushless Motors with Surface Permanent-Magnets*, IEEE Transactions on Industry Applications. Vol. 36, No. 6, November/December 2000, pp. 1547-1554.

75. Hughes A. and Miller T.J.E., *Analysis of fields and inductances in air-cored and iron-cored synchronous machines*, Proceedings IEE, Vol. 124, No. 2, February 1977, pp. 121-131.

76. Rasmussen K.F., *Analytical prediction of magnetic field from surface mounted permanent magnet motor,* IEEE IEMDC Conference, pp. 34-36, May 9-12, 1999.

77. Kenjo T. and Nagamori S., *Permanent magnet and brushless DC motors*, Sogo Electronics Publishing Company, Tokyo, 1984.

78. Rosa E.B. and Grover F.W., *Formulas and tables for the calculation of mutual and self-inductance*, Department of Commerce and Labor, Bureau of Standards, Bulletin Vol. 8, No. 1, January 1, 1911.

79. Soong W.L. and Miller T.J.E., *Field-weakening performance of brushless synchronous AC motor drives*, IEE Proc.-Electr. Power Appl., Vol. 141, No. 6, 1994, pp. 331-340.

80. Soong W.L. and Miller T.J.E., *Theoretical limitations to the field-weakening performance of the five classes of brushless AC motor drive*. IEE International Conference on Electrical Machines and Drives (**EMD**), University of Oxford, 8-10 September 1993, Conf. Publication No. 376, pp.127-132.

81. Hershberger D.D., *Design considerations of fractional horsepower size permanent-magnet motors and generators*, AIEE Transactions, pp. 581-584, June 1953.

82. Soong W.L. and Miller T.J.E., *Practical field-weakening performance of the five classes of brushless synchronous AC drive*. European Power Electronics Conference (**EPE-93**) Brighton, 1993, pp. 303-310.

83. Soong W.L., Staton D.A. and Miller T.J.E., *Design of a new axially-laminated interior permanent-magnet motor*. IEEE Transactions on Industry Applications, Vol.31, No.2, March/April 1995, pp. 358-367.

84. Strauss F., *Synchronous machines with rotating permanent-magnet fields*, AIEE Transactions, Vol. 71, Pt. II, pp. 887-893, October 1952.

85. Deodhar R.P., Staton D.A. and Miller T.J.E., *Prediction of cogging torque using the flux-MMF diagram technique*, IEEE Industry Applications Society Annual Meeting, Vol.1, Orlando, FL, 8-12 October 1995, pp. 693-700.

86. Jahns T.M., Kliman G.B. and Neumann T.A., *Interior permanent magnet motors for adjustable speed drives*, IEEE Transactions, Vol. IA-22, No. 4, pp. 738-747, July/August 1986.

87. Merrill F.W., *Permanent-magnet excited synchronous motors*, Transactions AIEE, Vol. 74, pp. 1754 1760, 1955.

88. Hanrahan D.J. and Toffolo D.S., *Permanent Magnet Generators. Part I — Theory*, AIEE Transactions, Vol. 76, December 1957, pp. 1098-1103.

89. Saunders R.M. and Weakley R.H., *Design of Permanent-Magnet Alternators*, AIEE Transactions, Vol. 70, 1951, pp. 1578-1581.

90. Ginsberg D. and Misenheimer L.J., *Design Calculations for Permanent-Magnet Generators*, Transactions AIEE, April 1953, Vol. 72, pp. 96-103.

91. Lajoie-Mazenc M., Foch H. and Villanueva C., *Feeding permanent-magnet machines by a transistorized inverter*, PCI/MOTORCON, pp. 558-570, 1983.

92. Lajoie-Mazenc M., Mathieu P. and Davat B., *Utilisation des Aimants Permanents dans les Machines à Commutation Électronique*, Revue Générale de l'Électricité, October 1984, pp. 695-612.

93. Davat B., Rezine H. and Lajoie-Mazenc M., *Modeling of a Brushless DC Motor with Solid Parts Involving Eddy-Currents*, IEEE Transactions on Industry Applications, Vol. IA-21, No. 1, January/February 1985, pp. 202-206.

94. Jahns T.M., *Flux-Weakening Regime Operation of an Interior Permanent-Magnet Synchronous Motor Drive*, IEEE Transactions on Industry Applications, Vol. IA-23, No. 4, July/August 1987, pp. 681-689.

95. Rahman M.A. and Osheiba A.M, *Effect of Parameter Variations on the Performance of Permanent Magnet Motors*, IEEE Industry Applications Society Annual Meeting, 1986, pp. 787-793.

96. Rahman M.A. and Osheiba A.M, *Performance of Large Line-Start Permanent Magnet Synchronous Motors*, IEEE Transactions on Energy Conversion, Vol. 5, No. 1, March 1990, pp. 211-217

97. Ionel D.M., Eastham J.F., Miller T.J.E. and Demeter E., *Design Considerations for Permanent Magnet Synchronous Motors for Flux Weakening Applications*, IEE Proceedings, Electr. Power Appl., Vol. 145, No. 5, September 1998, pp. 435-440.

98. Popescu M., Ionel D.M., Miller T.J.E., Dellinger S.J. and McGilp M.I., *Improved finite element computations of torque in brushless permanent magnet motors,* IEE Proc-Electr. Power Appl., Vol. 152, No 2, March/April 2005, pp. 271-276.

99. Ionel D.M., Popescu M., McGilp M.I., Miller T.J.E., and Dellinger S.J., *Assessment of torque components in brushless permanent-magnet machines through numerical analysis of the electromagnetic field*, IEEE Transactions on Industry Applications, Vol. 41, No. 5, September/October 2005, pp. 1149-1158.

100. Popescu M., Ionel D.M., Miller T.J.E., Dellinger S.J. and McGilp M.I., *Improved finite element computations of torque in brushless permanent magnet motors,* IEE Proc-Electr. Power Appl., Vol. 152, No 2, March/April 2005, pp. 271-276.

101. Ionel D.M., Popescu M., Dellinger S.J., Miller T.J.E., Heideman R.J. and McGilp M.I., *On the Variation with Flux and Frequency of the Core Loss Coefficients in Electrical Machines*, IEEE Transactions on Industry Applications, Vol. 42, No. 3, May/June 2006, pp. 658-668.

102. Ionel D.M., Popescu M., McGilp M.I., Miller T.J.E., Dellinger S.J., snd Heideman R.J., *Computation of Core Losses in Electrical Machines Using Improved Models for Laminated Steel*, IEEE Transactions on IndustryApplications, Vol. 43, No. 6, Nov/Dec 2007, pp.1554-1564.

103. Popescu M., Miller T.J.E., McGilp M.I., Kalluf F.J.H., da Silva C.A., von Dokonal L., *Effect of winding harmonics on the asynchronous torque of a single-phase line-start permanent-magnet motor*, IEEE Transactions on Industry Applications, Vol. 42, No. 4, July/August 2006, pp. 1014-1024.

104. Miller T.J.E., Popescu M., Cossar C., McGilp M.I., *Performance Estimation of Interior Permanent-Magnet Brushless Motors Using the Voltage-Driven Flux-MMF Diagram*, IEEE Transactions on Magnetics , Vol. 42, No. 7, July 2006, pp. 1867-1873.

105. Miller T.J.E., Popescu M., Cossar C., McGilp M.I., Olaru M., Davies A., Sturgess J., Sitzia A., *Embedded Finite-Element Solver for Computation of Brushless Permanent-Magnet Motors*, IEEE Transactions on IndustryApplications, Vol. 44, No. 4, July/August 2008, pp. 1124-1133.

106. Cossar C., Popescu M., Miller T.J.E., McGilp M.I. and Olaru, M., *A General Magnetic-Energy-Based Torque Estimator: Validation via a Permanent-Magnet Motor Drive*, IEEE Transactions on Industry Applications, Vol. 44, No. 4, July/August 2008, pp. 1210-1217.

107. Walker J. A., Cossar C. and Miller T.J.E., *Simulation and Analysis of Magnetization Characteristics of Interior Permanent Magnet Motors*, Acta Polytechnica, Vol. 45, No. 4, 2005, pp. 25-32.

108. Cahill D.P.M. and Adkins B., *The permanent-magnet synchronous motor*, Proc. IEE, Vol. 109, Part A, No. 48, December 1962, pp. 483-491.

109. Volkrodt W., Elektrotech. Z., **82**, p. 524, 1961; and *ibid*, **83**, p. 522, 1962.

110. Volkrodt W., *Excitation des machines électriques moyennes par aimants en ferrite*, Rev. Siemens **34**, 1976.

111. Honsinger V.B., *The Steady-State Performance of Reluctance Machines*, IEEE Transactions, Vol. PAS-90, No. 1, 1971, pp. 305-317. See also Honsinger VB., *Synchronous Reluctance Motor* (Allis-Chalmers Manufacturing Co., Milwaukee), United States Patent No. 3,652,885, Mar. 28; 1972 and Jorgensen MV, Albertson B.E, Michaels E and Turner GE, *Synchronous Induction Machine* (Louis Allis Co., Milwaukee), United States Patent No. 3,210,584, Oct. 5, 1965; and Honsinger VB., *Permanent Magnet Motor* (Allis-Chalmers Manufacturing Co,. Milwaukee), United States Patent No. 3,126,493, Mar. 24, 1964.

112. Kostko J.K., *Polyphase Reaction Synchronous Motor*, Journal AIEE, Vol. 42, pp. 1162-1169, 1923.

113. Binns K.J. and Jabbar M.A., *High-field self-starting permanent-magnet synchronous motor*, IEE Proc., Vol. 128, Pt. B, No. 3, May 1984, pp. 157-160.

114. Binns K.J. and Kurdali A., *Permanent-magnet a.c. generators*, Proc. IEE, Vol. 126, No. 7, July 1979, pp. 690-696.

115. Reichert K., *The Calculation of Magnetic Circuits with Permanent Magnets by Digital Computers*, IEEE Transactions on Magnetics., June 1979, pp. 283-288.

116. Laronze J., *Eine neue Generation von bürstenlosen Synchronmotoren*, Aktuelle Technik, Feb. 1978, pp. 9-12.

117. Miyashita K. et al, *Development of a high speed 2-pole permanent-magnet synchronous motor*, IEEE Trans., Vol. PAS-99, No. 6, Nov/Dec 1980, pp. 2175-2183. See also Miyashita K., Yamashita S., Watanabe H. and Tanabe S., *Permanent Magnet Rotor* (Hitachi Ltd), U.S. Patent No. 4,403,161, 6 September 1983.

118. Steen C.R., *Direct Axis Aiding Permanent Magnets For a Laminated Synchronous Motor Rotor*, United States Patent No. 4,139,790, February 13, 1979.

119. Siemens Aktiengesellschaft, *An Electric Machine Having Permanent Magnets Mounted in the Rotor between its Pole Segments*, U.K. Patent No, 1,166,247, 7 January 1970.

120. Baumann F.W. and Rosenberry G.M., *Low Flux Density Permanent Magnet Field Configuration*, United States Patent No. 3,840,763, 8 October 1974.

121. Kober W., *Dynamoelectric Machine*, US Patent No. 3,334,254, 1 August 1967.

122. Binns K.J., Barnard W.R. and Jabbar M.A., *Hybrid permanent-magnet synchronous motors*, IEE Proc., Vol. 125, No. 3, March 1978, pp. 203-208.

123. Miller T.J.E., Popescu M., Cossar C., McGilp M.I., Strappazzon G., Trivillin N., and Santarossa R., *Line-Start Permanent-Magnet Motor Single-Phase Steady State Performance Analysis*, IEEE Transactions on Industry Applications, Vol. 40, No. 2, March/April 2004, pp. 516-525.

124. Popescu M., Miller T.J.E., McGilp M.I, Strappazzon G., Trivillin N., and Santarossa R., *Line Start Permanent Magnet Motor: Single Phase Starting Performance Analysis*, IEEE Transactions on Industry Applications, Vol. 39, No. 4, July/August 2003, pp. 1021-1030

125. Popescu M., Miller T.J.E., McGilp M.I., Strappazzon G., Trivillin N., and Santarossa R., *Asynchronous Performance Analysis of a Single-Phase Capacitor-Start, Capacitor-Run Permanent Magnet Motor*, IEEE Transactions on Energy Conversion, Vol. 20, No. 1, March 2005, pp. 142-150

126. Popescu M., Miller T.J.E., Cossar C. McGilp M.I., Strappazzon G., Trivillin N. and Santarossa R., *Comparative Study of the Starting Methods for a Single-Phase Permanent Magnet Synchronous Motor*, EPE Journal Vol. 15, No. 1, February 2005, pp. 48-56.

127. Popescu M., Miller T.J.E., Cossar C. McGilp M.I., Strappazzon G., Trivillin N. and Santarossa R., *Torque Behavior of One-phase Permanent Magnet AC Motor*, IEEE Transactions on Energy Conversion, Vol. 21, No. 1, March 2006, pp. 19-26.

128. Staton D. A., Miller T.J.E. and Wood S. E., *Maximising the saliency ratio of the synchronous reluctance motor*, IEE Proceedings-B, Vol.140, No.4, 1993, pp. 249-259.

129. Betz R.E., Lagerquist R.L., Jovanovic M., Miller T.J.E. and Middleton R.H., *Control of synchronous reluctance machines*. Transactions IEEE **IA-29** Nov/Dec 1993, No. 6, pp. 1110-1122.

130. Miller T.J.E. and Rabinovici R., *Back-EMF waveforms and core losses in brushless DC motors*. IEE Proceedings **141B,** 1994, pp. 144-154.

131. Rabinovici R. and Miller T.J.E., *Eddy-current losses of surface-mounted permanent magnet motors*, IEE Proceedings, Electric Power Applications, Vol.144, Number 1, January 1997, pp.61-64.

132. Miller T.J.E., *Single-phase permanent-magnet motor analysis*, IEEE Transactions on Industry Applications, Vol. **IA-21**, No. 4, May/June 1985, pp. 651-658.

133. Miller T.J.E. *Synchronization of line-start permanent-magnet AC motors*. Transactions IEEE, Vol. **PAS-103**, 1822-1828, 1984.

134. Honsinger V.B., *Permanent-magnet machines: asynchronous operation*, Transactions IEEE, Vol. **PAS-99**, No. 4, July/August 1980, pp. 1503-1509.

135. Honsinger V.B., *The Fields and Parameters of Interior Type AC Permanent Magnet Machines*, IEEE Transactions on Power Apparatus and Systems, Vol. PAS-101, No. 4, April 1982, pp. 867-876.

136. Honsinger V.B., *Performance of Polyphase Permanent Magnet Machines*, Transactions IEEE, Vol. **PAS-99**, No. 4, July/August 1980, pp. 1510-1518.

137. Consoli A. and Abela A., *Transient Performance of Permanent Magnet AC Motor Drives*, IEEE Transactions on Industry Applications, Vol. IA-22, No. 1, January/February 1986, pp. 32-41.

138. Consoli A. and Renna G., *Interior Type Permanent Magnet Synchronous Motor Analysis by Equivalent Circuits*, IEEE Transactions on Energy Conversion, Vol. 4, No. 4, December 1989, pp. 681-689.

139. Consoli A. and Raciti A., *Analysis of Permanent Magnet Synchronous Motors*, IEEE Transactions on Industry Applications, Vol. 27, No. 2, March/April 1991, pp. 350-354.

140. Schiferl R., Colby R.S. and Lipo T.A., *Efficiency Considerations in Permanent Magnet Synchronous Motor Drives*, Electric Energy Conference (eecon'87), Institute of Electrical Engineers, Adelaide, Australia, October 1987, pp. 330-335.

141. Colby R.S. and Novotny D.W., *Efficient Operation of Surface Mounted PM Synchronous Motors*, IEEE IAS Conference, 1986, pp. 806-813.

142. Schiferl R. and Lipo T.A., *Core Loss in Buried Magnet Permanent Magnet Synchronous Motors*, IEEE Transactions on Energy Conversion, Vol. 4, No. 2, June 1989, pp. 279-284.

143. Schiferl R. and Lipo T.A., *Power Capability of Salient-Pole Permanent Magnet Synchronous Motors in Variable Speed Drive Applications*, IEEE Industry Applications Society Annual Meeting, 1988, pp. 23-31.

144. Chalmers B.J. and Baines G.D., *Synchronous Motors with Nd-Fe-B Magnets*, International Conference on the Evolution and Modern Aspects of Synchronous Machines, Zurich, 27-29 August 1992.

145. Chalmers B.J., Baines G.D. and Williamson A.C., *Performance of a Line-Start Single-Phase Permanent-Magnet Synchronous Motor*, Electrical Machines and Drives Conference, IEE Conference Publication No. 412, September 1995, pp. 413-417.

146. Bermond G. and Flynn J.B., *The Isosyn Motor, a New Generation of Permanent-Magnet Synchronous Motors*, IEE Conf. Publication No. 202, 1081, pp. 119-124.

147. Gieras J.F. and Wing M., *Calculation of Synchronous Reactances of Small Permanent-Magnet Alternating-Current Motors: Comparison of Analytical Approach and Finite Element Methos with Measurements*, IEEE Transactions on Magnetics, Vol. 34, No. 5, September 1998, pp. 3712-3720.

148. Stephens C.M., Kliman G.B. and Boyd J., *A Line-Start Permanent Magnet Motor with Gentle Starting Behavior*, IEEE Industry Applications Society Annual Meeting, pp. 371-379.

149. Hanitsch R., *Electromagnetic Machines with Nd-Fe-B Magnets*, Journal of Magnetism and Magnetic Materials, Vol. 80, 1989, pp. 119-130.

150. Maggetto G., Sneyers B. and Van Eck J.L., *Permanent Magnet Motor Used for Traction Purposes*, MOTORCON Proceedings, September 1982, pp. 61-68.

151. Sneyers B., Novotny D.W., and Lipo T.A., *Field Weakening in Buried Permanent Magnet AC Motor Drives*, IEEE Industry Applications Society Annual Meeting (**IAS**), Mexico City, October 1983, pp. 462-468.

152. Cornell E.P., *Permanent Magnet AC Motors*, Drives, Motors, Controls Conference, Harrogate, U.K., 1983, pp. 102-102.

153. Miller T.J.E., Richter E. and Neumann T.W., *A Permanent-Magnet Excited High-Efficiency Synchronous Motor with Line-Start Capability*. IEEE Industry Applications Society Annual Meeting (**IAS**), Mexico City, October 1983, pp. 1-7.

154. Richter E. and Neumann T.W., *Line Start Permanent Magnet Motors with Different Materials*, International Conference on Electrical Machines, Lausanne, Switzerland, 1984; also Intermag Conference, Hamburg, Germany, 1984.

155. Richter E. and Neumann T.W., *Saturation Effects in Salient Pole Synchronous Motors with Permanent Magnet Excitation*, International Conference on Electrical Machines, Lausanne, Switzerland, 1984.

156. Richter E., Miller T.J.E., Neumann T.W. and Hudson T.L., *The Ferrite Permanent-Magnet AC Motor: a Technical and Economical Assessment*, Transactions IEEE **IA-21**, 644-650.

157. Shanliang Y. et al, *Large Capacity Generators Using Rare Earth-Cobalt Permanent-Magnet*, Proceedings of the Seventh International Workshop on Rare Earth-Cobalt Permanent Magnets and their Applications, Beijing, China, September 16-18, 1983, pp. 21-28.

158. Amaratunga G.A.J., Acarnley P.P. and McLaren P.G., *Optimum Magnetic Circuit Configurations for Permanent Magnet Aerospace Generators*, IEEE Transactions on Aerospace and Electronic Systems, Vol. AES-21, No. 2, March 1985, pp. 230-255.

159. Douglas J.F.H. and Rautimo P., *Synchronous induction motor* (Louis Allis Company, Milwaukee), U.S. Patent No. 2,913,607, 17 November 1959.

160. Binns K.J., U.K. Patent No. 1,359,548, 9 December 1971; Binns K.J. and Barnard WR, U.K. Patent No. 1,324,147, 7 May 1971.

161. Finch J.W. and Lawrenson P.J., *Synchronous performance of single-phase reluctance motors*, Proceedings IEE, Vol. 125, No. 12, pp. 1350-1356, 1978.

162. Magnussen F. and Lendenmann H., *Parasitic effects in PM machines With Concentrated Windings*, Transactions IEEE, Vol. 43, No. 5, September/October 2007, pp. 1123-1232.

163. Magnussen F. and Sadarangani C., *Winding Factors and Joule Losses of Permanent Magnet Machines with Concentrated Windings*, Proceedings IEMDC Conference , Madison, WI, June 1-4, 2003, pp. 333-339.

164. Miller T.J.E. and Hughes A., *Comparative design and performance analysis of air-cored and iron-cored synchronous machines*, Proc. IEE, Vol. 124, No. 2, February 1977, pp. 127-132.

165. Carter F.W., *Pole-face losses*, J. IEE, 1916, Vol. 54, p. 168

166. Freeman E.M., *The calculation of harmonics, due to slotting, in the flux-density waveform of a dynamo-electric machine*, Proc. IEE, Vol. 109C, p. 581, 1962

167. Lawrenson P.J., Reece P. and Ralph M.C., *Tooth-ripple losses in solid poles*, Proc. IEE., Vol. 113, No. 4, April 1966, pp. 657-662

168. Oberretl K., *Eddy Current Losses in Solid Poles of Synchronous Machines at No-Load and On Load*, IEEE Transactions, Vol. PAS-91, 1972, pp. 152-160

169. Stoll R.L. and Hammond P., *Calculation of the magnetic field of rotating machines, Part 4. Approximate determination of the field and the losses associated with eddy currents in conducting surfaces*, Proc. IEE, Vol. 112, No. 11, November 1965, pp. 2083-2094.

170. Lawrenson P.J. and Ralph M.C., *The general 3-dimensional solution of eddy-current and Laplacian fields in cylindrical structures*, Proc. IEE, Vol. 117, pp. 469-472 (1970)

171. Preston T. and Reece A.B.J., *Transverse edge effects in linear induction motors*, Proc. IEE, Vol. 116, 1969, pp. 973-979.

172. Angst G., *Polyphase induction motor with solid rotor : effects of saturation and finite length*, Trans. AIEE, Vol. 80, pp. 902-909.

173. Wood A.J. and Concordia C., *Analysis of solid rotor induction machines: Pt. III — finite length effects*, Trans. AIEE, Vol. 79, pp. 21-26, 1960.

174. Kirtley J.L. et al, *Rotor loss models for high-speed PM motor-generators*, ICEM., Istanbul, 1998, pp. 1832-1837.

175. Ishak D., Zhu Z.Q. and Howe D., Eddy-Current Loss in the Rotor Magnets of Permanent-Magnet Brushless Machines Having a Fractional Number of Slots Per Pole, IEEE Trans. on Magnetics, Vol. 41, No. 9, September 2005, pp. 2462-2469.

176. Zhu Z.Q. and Howe D., *Instantaneous Magnetic Field Distribution in Brushless Permanent Magnet DC Motors, Part III : Effect of Stator Slotting*, IEEE Transactions on Magnetics, Vol. 29, No. 1, January 1993, pp. 143-151.

177. Zhu Z.Q., Ng K., Schofield N. and Howe D., *Improved analytical modelling of rotor eddy current loss in brushless machines equipped with surface-mounted permanent magnets*, IEE Proc.-Electr. Power Appl., Vol. 151, No. 6, 2004, pp. 641-650.

178. Shah M.R. and Lee S.B., *Rapid Analytical Optimization of Eddy Current Shield Thickness for Associated Loss Minimization in Electrical Machines*, IEEE Trans. Industry Applications, Vol. 42, No. 3, May/June 2006, pp. 642-649.

179. Shah M.R. and Lee S.B., *Optimization of Shield Thickness of Finite Length Rotors for Eddy Current Loss Minimization*, 41st Industry Applications Conference, Tampa, Florida, 8-12 October 2006, pp. 2368-2373.

180. Miller T.J.E. and Lawrenson P.J., *Penetration of transient magnetic fields through conducting cylindrical structures, with particular reference to superconducting A.C. machines*, Proc. IEE, Vol. 123, No. 5, May 1976, pp. 437-443.

181. Miller T.J.E., *Transient magnetic fields in the superconducting alternator*. Archiv für Elektrotechnik **62**, pp. 131-140, 1980.

182. Miller T.J.E. *Transient magnetic fields in the superconducting alternator*, PhD Thesis, University of Leeds, 1977.

183. Russell R.L. and Norsworthy K.H., *Eddy currents and wall losses in screened-rotor induction motors*, Proc. IEE, Vol. 105A, pp. 163-175, 1958.

184. Robinson R.C.. Rowe I. and Donelan L.E. : *The calculation of can losses in canned motors*, Trans. AIEE, June 1957, pp. 312-315.

185. Takahashi I. et al, *A Super High-Speed PM Motor Drive System by a Quasi-Current Source Inverter*, IEEE Transactions on Industry Applications, Vol. 30, No. 3, May/June 1994, pp. 683-690.

186. Takahashi I. et al, *A super high speed PM motor drive system by a quasi-current source inverter*, IEEE Industry Applications Society Annual Meeting, Toronto, 1993, Conf. Rec. pp. 657-662.

187. Obaraki H., Tawara K., Endo T., Takahashi I., Toyoshima H. and Ishii Y., *Characteristics evaluation of a high-speed brushless motor*, in Rec. JIEE Conf. Rotary Machine, June 1991, RM-91-21, pp. 59-66. [In Japanese]

188. Deng F., *Commutation-Caused Eddy-Current Losses in Permanent-Magnet Brushless DC Motors*, IEEE Trans. on Magnetics, Vol. 33, No. 5, September 1997, pp. 4310-4318

189. Deng F., *Analytical Modeling of Commutation-Caused Eddy-Current Losses in Permanent-Magnet Brushless Direct-Current Motors*, IEEE Trans. on Magnetics, Vol. 33, September 1997, pp. 4310-4318.

190. Deng F. and Nehl T.W., *Analytical Modeling of Eddy-Current Losses Caused by Pulse-Width Modulation Switching in Permanent-Magnet Brushless Direct-Current Motors*, IEEE Trans. on Magnetics, Vol. 34, No. 5, September 1998, pp. 3728-3736.

191. Nagarkatti A.K, Mohammed O.A. and Demerdash N.A., *Special Losses in Rotors of Electronically Commutated Brushless DC Motors Induced by Non-Uniformly Rotating Armature MMFs*, IEEE Transactions on Power Apparatus and Systems, Vol. PAS-101, No. 12, December 1982, pp. 4502-4506.

192. Abu Sharkh S.M., Harris M.R. and Irenji N.T., *Calculation of rotor eddy-current loss in high-speed PM alternators*, Electric Machines and Drives Conference, Cambridge, UK, September 1997, pp. 170-174.

193. Irenji N.T., Abu-Sharkh S.M., and Harris M.R., *Effect of rotor sleeve conductivity on rotor eddy-current loss in high-speed PM machines*, ICEM 2000, Espoo, Finland, August 2000, pp. 645-648.

194. Fukuma A., Kanazawa S., Miyagi D., and Takahashi N., *Investigation of AC Loss of Permanent Magnet of SPM Motor Considering Hysteresis and Eddy-Current Losses*, IEEE Trans. on Magnetics 41 No. 5, 2005, pp. 1964-1967.

195. Nakano M., Kometani H., Kawamura M. and Ikeda Y., *Permanent magnet type dynamo-electric machine and permanent magnet synchronous generator for wind power generation*, U.S. patent application US 2004/0155537 A1, August 12, 2004.

196. Saban D.M. et al, *Experimental evaluation of a high-speed permanent-magnet machine*, 55th IEEE Petroleum and Chemical Industry Technical Conference (PCIC), Cincinnati, Ohio, 22-24 September 2008, pp. 1-9.

197. Amos D.E. (Sandia National Laboratories), *Algorithm 644 : A Portable Package for Bessel Functions of a Complex Argument and Nonnegative Order*, ACM Transactions on Mathematical Software, Vol. 12, No. 3, September 1986, pp. 265-273.

198. Maver A., CERN, Computer program C303, 600 Series Library, June 1969.

199. Cooley J.W., Lewis P.A.W. and Welch P.D., *Application of the Fast Fourier Transform to Computation of Fourier Integrals, Fourier Series, and Convolution Integrals*, IEEE Trans., 1967, Vol. AU-15, pp. 79-84.

200. Carter F.W., *AirGap Induction*, Electrical World and Engineer, Vol. 38, 1901, pp. 884-888.

201. Carter F.W., *The Magnetic Field of the Dynamo-Electric Machine*, J.I.E.E., Vol. 64, 1926, p. 1115.

202. Gibbs W.J., *Tooth-Ripple Losses in Unwound Pole Shoes*, J.I.E.E., Vol. 94, 1947, Pt. II, p. 2.

203. Ralph M.C., *Eddy-current effects in the cylindrical members of rotating electrical machinery*, PhD thesis, University of Leeds, 1968.

204. Miller T.J.E., *Methods for testing permanent-magnet AC motors*. IEEE Industry Applications Society Annual Meeting (**IAS**), Toronto, October 1981, pp. 494-499.

205. Miller T.J.E., *Transient performance of permanent-magnet AC machines*. IEEE Industry Applications Society Annual Meeting (**IAS**), Toronto, October 1981, pp. 500-503.

206. Miller T.J.E., *Definition of kT and kE for Brushless DC Motors*, 27th Annual Symposium on Incremental Motion Control Systems and Devices (**IMCSS**), San Jose, California, 1992, pp. 87-96.

207. Miller T.J.E., McGilp M.I., and Klontz K.W., *Approximate Methods for Calculating Rotor Loss in Permanent-Magnet Brushless Machines*, IEEE IEMDC Conference, Miami, FL, May 2009

208. Klontz K.W., Miller T.J.E., McGilp M.I., Karmaker H., Zhong P., *Short-Circuit Analysis of Permanent-Magnet Generators*, IEEE IEMDC Conference, Miami, FL, May 2009.

209. Miller T.J.E. and McGilp M.I., *Unified Theory of Superconducting and PM Synchronous Machines*, ICEMS-2009, Tokyo, Japan, 15-18 November, 2009.

210. Miller T.J.E. and McGilp M.I., *Analysis of Multi-Phase Permanent-Magnet Synchronous Machines*, ICEMS-2009, Tokyo, Japan, 15-18 November, 2009.

211. Saban D.M., Bailey C., Gonzalez-Lopez, D., and Luca L., *Experimental Evaluation of a High-Speed Permanent-Magnet Machine*, 55th IEEE Petroleum and Chemical Industry Technical Conference (PCIC), Cincinnati, 22-24 September 2008, pp. 1-9.

212. Boglietti A., Cavagnino A., and Staton D.A., *Determination of Critical Parameters in Electrical Machine Thermal Models*, IEEE Transactions on Industry Applications, Vol. 44, No. 4, July/August 2008, pp. 1150-1159.

213. Boglietti A., Cavagnino A., Staton D.A., Popescu M., Cossar C., and McGilp M.I., *End Space Heat Transfer Coefficient Determination for Different Induction Motor Enclosure Types*, IEEE Transactions on Industry Applications, Vol. 45, No. 3, May/June 2009, pp. 929-937.

214. Sebastian T. and Slemon G.R., *Operating Limits of Inverter-Driven Permanent Magnet Motor Drives*, IEEE Transactions on Industry Applications , Vol. IA-23, No. 2, March/April 1987, pp. 327-333.

215. Slemon G.R. and Gumaste A.V., *Steady-State Analysis of a Permanent-Magnet Synchronous Motor Drive with Current Source Inverter*, IEEE Transactions on Industry Applications, Vol. IA-19, No. 2, March/April 1983, pp. 190-197.

216. Rowan T.M. and Kerkman R.J. : *Operation of naturally sampled current regulators in the transition mode*, IEEE Trans., Vol. IA-23, No. 4, July/August 1987, pp. 586-596

217. Rowan T.M. and Kerkman R.J., *A new synchronous current regulator and an analysis of current regulated PWM inverters*, Conf. Rec. 1985 IEEE-IAS Annual Meeting, pp. 487-495; and in IEEE Trans., Vol. IA-22, No. 4, 1986, pp. 678-690.

218. Krah J.-O. and Holtz J., *High-performance current regulation for low-inductance servo motors*", Conf. Rec. 1998 IEEE-IAS Annual Meeting, St. Louis, pp. 490-499, published also as *High-performance current regulation and efficient PWM implementation for low inductance servo motors*, IEEE Trans. Ind. Appl., Vol. IA-35, Sept/Oct. 1999, pp. 1039-1049.

219. Holtz J., Lammert P. and Lotzkat W., *High-speed drive system with ultrasonic MOSFET PWM inverter and single-chop microprocessor control*, IEEE Trans., Vol. IA-23, No. 6, Nov/Dec 1987, pp. 1010-1015.

220. Rahman M.F., Zhong L. and Lim K.W., *A Direct Torque-Controlled Interior Permanent Magnet Synchronous Motor Drive Incorporating Field Weakening*, IEEE Transactions on Industry Applications, Vol. 34, No. 6, November/December 1998, pp. 1246-1253.

221. Takahashi I. and Noguchi T., *A new quick-response and high-efficiency control strategy of an induction motor*, IEEE Transactions on Industry Applications, Vol. 22, No. 5, September/October 1986, pp. 820-827.

222. Depenbrock M., *Direct Self-Control(DSC) of Inverter-Fed Induction Machine*, IEEE Transactions on Power Electronics, Vol. 3, 1988, pp. 420-429.

223. Luukko J., *Direct Torque Control of Permanent Magnet Synchronous Machines — Analysis and Implementation*, Ph.D. thesis, Acta Universitatis Lappeenrantaensis (Finland), June, 2000.

224. *Technical Guide No. 1 - Direct Torque Control*, ABB Industry Oy, http://www.abb.fi/vsd/index.htm, June 1999.

225. Holling G.H. and Pershall A., *The Technique of Phase Advancing for Brushless Motors*, MOTOR-CON Proceedings, October 1985, pp. 9-19.

226. Idris N.R.N., Toh C.L. and Elbuluk M.E., *A New Torque and Flux Controller for Direct Torque Control of Induction Machines*, IEEE Trans. on Industry Applications, Vol. 42, No. 6, November/December 2006, pp. 1358-1366.

227. Stefanutti W. and Mattavelli P., *Fully Digital Hysteresis Modulation with Switching-Time Prediction*, IEEE Transactions on Industry Applications, Vol. 42, No. 3, May/June 2006, pp. 763-769.

228. Comstock R.H., *Trends in Brushless PM Drive and Motor Technology Overview*, MOTOR-CON Proceedings, October 1986, pp. 1-15.

229. Steuer M., *Extended Speed/Torque Profile Operation of Permanent Magnet Synchronous Motors*, MOTOR-CON Proceedings, October 1985, pp. 179-183.

230. Koch Th. and Binder A., *Permanent Magnet Machines with Fractional Slot Winding For Electric Traction*, International Conference on Electric Machines, Brugge, Belgium, 2002.

231. Cros J. and Viarouge P., *Synthesis of High Performance PM Motors with Concentrated Windings*, IEEE Transactions on Energy Conversion, Vol. 17, No. 2, June 2002, pp. 248-253.

232. Ishak D., Zhu Z.Q.. and Howe D., *Permanent-Magnet Brushless Machines with Unequal Tooth Widths and Similar Slot and Pole Numbers*, IEEE Transactions on Industry Applications, Vol. 41, No. 2, March/April 2005, pp. 584-590.

233. Dutta R. and Rahman M.F., *A Comparative Analysis of Two Test Methods of Measuring d- and q-Axes Inductances of Interior Permanent-Magnet Machine*, IEEE Transactions on Magnetics, Vol. 42, No. 11, November 2006, pp. 3712-3718.

234. Fratta A., Vagati A. and Villata F., *Design Criteria of an IPM Machine Suitable for Field-Weakened Operation*, International Conference on Electrcal Machines, 13-15 August 1990, Mass. Institute of Technology, Cambridge, MA, USA, pp. 1059-1065.

235. Fratta A., Vagati A. and Villata F., *On the Evolution of AC Machines for Spindle Drive Applications*, IEEE Transactions on Industry Applications, Vol. 28, No. 5, September/October 1992, pp. 1081-1086.

236. Ostović V., *Computation of Saturated Permanent-Magnet AC Motor Performance By Means of Magnetic Circuits*, IEEE Transactions on Industry Applications, Vol. IA-23, No. 5, September/October 1987, pp. 836-841.

237. Kusko A. and Peeran S., *Brushless DC Motors Using Unsymmetrical Field Magnetization*, IEEE Transactions on Industry Applications, Vol. IA-23, No. 2, March/April 1987, pp. 319-326.

238. Viarouge P., Lajoie-Mazenc M. and Andrieux C., *Design and Construction of a Brushless Permanent Magnet Servomotor for Direct-Drive Applications*, IEEE Trans. on Industry Applications, Vol. IA-23, No. 3, May/June 1987, pp. 526-531.

239. Soong W.L. and Ertugrul N., *Inverterless High-Power Interior Permanent-Magnet Automotive Alternator*, IEEE Transactions on Industry Applications, Vol. 40, No. 4, July/August 2004, pp. 1083-1091.

240. Morimoto S., Takeda Y. and Hirasa T., *Flux-Weakening Control Method for Surface Permanent Magnet Synchronous Motors*, Proceedings of the International Power Electronics Conference (IPEC), April 2-6, 1990, Tokyo, Japan, pp. 942-949.

241. Morimoto S., Takeda Y., Hirasa T. and Taniguchi K., *Expansion of Operating Limits for Permanent-Magnet Motor by Current Vector Control Considering Inverter Capacity*, IEEE Transactions on Industry Applications, Vol. 26, No. 5, September/October 1990, pp. 866-871.

242. Kirtley J.L., *Air-Core Armature Shape: A Comparison of Helical and Straight-With-End-Turns Windings*, Elect. Machines & Power Systems, Vol. 23, 1985, pp. 263-278.

243. Morimoto S., Sanada M. and Takeda Y., *Wide-Speed Operation of Interior Permanent Magnet Synchronous Motors with High Performance Current Regulator*, IEEE Transactions on Industry Applications, Vol. 30, No. 4, July/August 1994, pp. 920-926.

244. Sanada M., Kishi T., Morimoto S. and Takeda Y., *Torque Improvement for Interior Permanent Magnet Synchronous Motor with Concentrated Winding using Asymmetruc Flux Barriers*, International Power Electronics Conference, Niigata, Japan, April 4-8, 2005.

245. Hiwaki H., Murakami H., Honda Y., Sanada M., Morimoto S. and Takeda Y., *Reducing Iron Loss by Decreasing Stress in Stator Core of Permanent Magnet Synchronous Motor*, International Power Electronics Conference, Niigata, Japan, April 4-8, 2005.

246. Sudhoff S.D., Corzine K.A. and Hegner H.J., *A Flux-Weakening Strategy for Current-Regulated Surface-Mounted Permanent-Magnet Machine Drives*, IEEE Transactions on Energy Conversion, Vol. 10, No. 3, September 1995, pp. 431-437.

247. Anderson A.F., Bumby J.R. and Hassall B.I., *Analysis of helical armature windings with particular reference to superconducting a.c. generators*, IEE Proceedings, Vol. 127, Part C, No. 3, May 1980, pp. 129-144.

248. Bailey M.R., Bumby J.R., Hassall B.I. and Anderson A.F., *Magnetic Fields and Inductances of Helical Windings with 120° Phasebands*, Electric Machines and Electromechanics, Vol. 6, 1981, pp. 323-325.

249. Ross J.S.H., Anderson A.F. and MacNab R.B., *Alternating Current Dynamo-Electric Machine Windings*, U.K. Patent No. 1,395,152, 1 February 1971.

250. Lawrenson P.J., *Calculation of machine end-winding inductances with special reference to turbogenerators*, Proc. IEE, Vol. 117, No. 6, June 1970, pp. 1129-1134.

251. Stemme O. and Wolf P., *Principles and Properties of Highly Dynamic DC Miniature Motors*, Interelectric AG, Switzerland, 1994.

252. Cassat A. and Williams M.W., *Eccentricity Analysis in Brushless DC Motors*, Proceedings of the 23rd Annual Symposium, Incremental Motion Control Systems and Devices, 14 June 1994, pp. 201-216.

253. Williams M.W. and MacLeod D.J., *Performance Characteristics of Brushless Motor Slot/Pole Configurations*, Proceedings of the 23rd Annual Symposium, Incremental Motion Control Systems and Devices, 14 June 1994, pp. 145-153.

254. Daikoku A. and Yamaguchi S., *Cogging torque investigation of PM motors resulting from asymmetry property of magnetic poles: Influence of performance variation between permanent magnets*, Elect. Engng. in Japan, Vol. 163, No. 3, 2008, pp. 57-67.

255. Libert F. and Soulard J., *Investigation of the Pole-Slot Combinations for Permanent-Magnet Machines with Concentrated Windings*, International Conference on Electrical Machines, Paper 530, Cracow, Poland, September 2004.

256. Skaar S.E., Krøvel, Ø., and Nilssen R., *Distribution, coil-span and winding factors for PM machines with concentrated windings*, International Conference on Electrical Machines, Paper PSA1-18, Crete, 2-5 September 2006.

257. Tampion, A.A., Optimisation of the Design of Transposed Windings, International Conference on Electrical Machines, Manchester, 1992, pp. 49-53.

258. Field A.B., *Eddy Currents in Large Slot-Wound Conductors*, 22nd Annual Convention of the American Institute of Electrical Engineers, Asheville, N.C., U.S.A., June 19-23, 1905, pp. 761-788.

259. Lyon W.V., *Heat Losses in the Conductors of Alternating Current Machines*, Annual Convention of the American Institute of Electrical Engineers, Salt Lake City, Utah, U.S.A., 1921, pp. 1361-1395.

260. Noodleman S. and Patel B.R., *Duty Cycle Characteristics for DC Servo Motors*, IEEE Transactions on Industry Applications, Vol. IA-9, No. 5, September/October 1973, pp. 563-569.

261. Welch R. and Kaufman G., *Performance of a Three Phase Sinusoidal Ke Motor using a Sinusoidal Amplifier and a Trapezoidal Amplifier*, Proceedings of the First Annual Motion Control Technology Conference West, Los Angeles, CA, U.S.A., October 1990.

262. Welch R. and Kaufman G., *Advantages of Sinusoidal Ke Motor Over the Quasi-Sinusoidal Ke Motor when Operated with a Trapezoidal Drive,* Proceedings of the Third Annual Motion Control East Conference, Boston, MA, U.S.A., April 1991.

263. Welch R. and Kaufman G., *Design and Application Considerations of Permanent Magnet Sinusoidal Ke Brushless Servo Motors*, Proceedings of the Second Annual Motion Control Technology West Conference, Long Beach, CA, U.S.A., October 1991.

264. Welch R. and Kaufman G., *Dynamic Thermal Model for a Three Phase Sinusoidal Ke Brushless Motor*, 4th Annual Motion Control East Conference, Philadelphia, April 1992.

265. Welch R., *Continuous, Dynamic and Intermittent Thermal Operation in Electric Motors,* SMMA Motor & Motion College Tutorial, (www.smma.org); copies available from the author, welch022@tc.umn.edu).

266. Shah M.J., Kopp N.M. and Vaidya J.G., *Stall Torque Analysis of Brushless DC PM Motors*, MOTOR-CON '86, Proceedings of the Ninth International SATECH Conference, Boston, MA, U.S.A., October 27-31, 1986, pp. 30-40.

267. Alberkrack J.A., *A New Brushless Motor Controller*, MOTOR-CON '86, Proceedings of the Ninth International SATECH Conference, Boston, MA, U.S.A., October 27-31, 1986, pp. 269-282.

268. Staton D.A. and So E., *Computer Aided Design of Brushless Servo Motors*, U.K. Magnetics Society, One Day Seminar on Electromagnetic CAD for Industrial Applications, 28 February 2001, R.I.B.A, London.

269. Persson E. and Meshkat S., *Brushless Servo System withn Expanded Torque-Speed Operating Range*, MOTOR-CON Proceedings, Hannover, April 1985, pp. 96-106.

270. Brentani G., *Considerations on the Locked Rotor Torque Characteristics of Brushless DC Motors*, MOTOR-CON Proceedings, Hannover, April 22-24 1985, pp. 107-114.

271. Bahout Y. and Rault P., *Universal Motor Speed Constroller*, MOTOR-CON Proceedings, Hannover, April 22-24 1985, pp. 214-227.

272. Greig J. and Freeman E.M., *Travelling wave problem in electrical machines*, Proc. IEE, Vol. 114, No. 11, 1967, pp. 1681-1683

273. Pipes, L.A., *Matric theory of skin effect in laminations*, Journal of the Franklin Institute, 1956, Vol. 262, pp. 127-138.

274. Jufer M., *Starting Optimization of Synchronous Permanent Magnets Motors*, MOTOR-CON Proceedings, Geneva, September 28-30, 1982, pp. 366-374.

275. Bruchmann K., *A Performance Comparison Between D.C. Disc-Armature Motors and A.C. Disc-Rotor Motors Employing Sinusoidal Current*, MOTOR-CON Proceedings, Hannover, April 1-3 1987, pp. 30-39.

276. Fratta A., Vagati A. and Villata F., *A.C. Spindle Drives: A Unified Approach to the Field-Weakening Behaviour*, MOTOR-CON Proceedings, Munich, 1988, pp. 44-56.

277. Melfi M.J., Evon S. and McElveen R., *Induction Versus Permanent Magnet Motors*, IEEE Industry Applications Magazine, Vol. 15, No. 6, pp. 28-35, November/December 2009.

278. *Axial-Airgap Motor*, Electrical Engineering, 1947, p. 670ff.

279. Campbell P, *Performance of a permanent-magnet axial-field d.c. machine*, Electric Power Applications, August 1979, Vol. 2, No. 4, pp. 139-144.

280. Campbell P, Rosenberg DJ and Stanton DP, *The Computer Design and Optimization of Axial-Field Permanent Magnet Motors*, Paper 80 SM 630-4, IEEE PES Summer Meeting, Minneapolis, July 13-18, 1980.

281. Boules N and Weh H, *Machine Constants and Design Considerations of a High-Power, High-Speed Permanent-Magnet Disc Type Synchronous Machine*, Electric Machines and Electromechanics, Vol. 5, 1980, pp. 113-123.

282. Leung WS and Chan JCC, *A New Design Approach for Axial-Field Electrical Machines*, Paper F 80 209-7, IEEE PES Winter Meeting, New York, Feb. 3-8, 1980.

283. Bumby JR, Martin R, Mueller MA, Spooner E, Brown NL and Chalmers BJ, *Electromagnetic design of axial-flux permanent magnet machines*, IEE Proc.-Electr. Power Appl., Vol. 151, No. 2, March 2004, 151-160.

284. Spooner E and Chalmers BJ, '*TORUS*': *A slotless, toroidal-stator permanent-magnet generator*, IEE Proceedings-B, Vol. 139, No. 6, November 1992, pp. 497-506.

285. Qu R and Lipo TA, *Dual-Rotor Radial-Flux Toroidally Wound Permanent-Magnet Machines*, IEEE Trans. Industry Applications, Vol. 39, No. 6, November/December 2003, pp. 1665-1673.

286. Qu R and Lipo TA, *Design and Parameter Effect Analysis of Dual-Rotor Radial-Flux Toroidally Wound Permanent-Magnet Machines*, IEEE Trans. Industry Applications, Vol. 40, No. 3, May/June 2004, pp. 771-779.

287. Carrichi F, Crescimbini F, Honorati O, Di Napoli A and Santini E, *Compact Wheel Direct Drive for EVs*, IEEE Industry Applications Magazine, November/December 1996, pp. 25-32.

288. Carrichi F, Crescimbini F, Fedeli E and Noia G, *Design and Construction of a Wheel-Directly-Coupled-Axial-Flux PM Motor Prototype for EVs*, IEEE Trans. Industry Applications, Vol. 28, No. 3, May/June 1992, pp. 646-651.

289. Carrichi F, Capponi FG, Crescimbini F and Solero L, *Experimental Study on Reducing Cogging Torque and No-Load Power Loss in Axial-Flux Permanent-Magnet Machines with Slotted Winding*, IEEE Trans. Industry Applications, Vol. 40, No. 4, July/August 2004, pp. 1066-1075.

290. Carrichi F, Crescimbini F, Honorati O, Lo Bianco GL and Santini E, *Performance of Coreless-Winding Axial-Flux Permanent-Magnet Generator with Power Output at 400 Hz, 3000 r/min*, IEEE Trans. Industry Applications, Vol. 34, No. 6, November/December 1998, pp. 1263-1269.

291. Carrichi F, Crescimbini F, Honorati O, *Modular Axial-Flux Permanent-Magnet Motor for Ship Propulsion Drives*, IEEE Trans. Energy Conversion, Vol. 14, No. 3, September 1999, pp. 673-679.

292. Carrichi F, Crescimbini F, Mezzetti F and Santini E, *Multistage Axial-Flux PM Machine for Wheel Direct Drive*, IEEE Trans. Industry Applications, Vol. 32, No. 4, July/August 1996, pp. 882-888.

293. Marignetti F, Delli Colli V, Cancelliere P, Scarano M, Boldea I, and Topor M, *A Fractional Slot Axial Flux PM Direct Drive*, IEEE 2005.

294. Marignetti F, Tomassi T and Bumby JR, *Electromagnetic Modelling of Permanent Magnet Axial Flux Motors and Generators*, Electr Machines & Electromechanics.

295. Marignetti F and Scarano M, *Mathematical Modelling of an Axial-Flux PM Motor Wheel*, International Conf. Electric Machines (ICEM'2000) Vol. 3, Espoo, Finland, pp. 1275-1279.

296. Cavagnino A, Lazzari M, Profumo F, and Tenconi A, *Axial Flux Interior PM Synchronous Motor: Parameters Identification and Steady-State Performance Measurements*, IEEE Trans. Industry Applications, Vol. 6, November/December 2000, pp. 1581-1588.

297. Profumo F, Zhang Z and Tenconi A, *Axial Flux Machines Drives*, IEEE Trans. Industrial Electronics, Vol. 44, No. 1, February 1997, pp. 39-45.

298. Yoshikawa Y, Li H and Murakami H, *Design of Ultra Low Acoustic Noise and High Power Density Direct Drive Machines with Double Rotor and Toroidally Wound Structure*, IEEE 2006.

299. Del Ferraro L, Capponi FG, Terrigi R, and Honorati O, *Ironless Axial Flux PM Machine with Active Mechanical Flux Weakening for Automotive Applications*, IEEE 2006

300. Marignetti F, Tomassi G, Cancelliere P, Delli Colli V, Di Stefano R and Scarano M, *Electromagnetic and Mechanical Design of a Fractional-Slot-Windings Axial-Flux PM Synchronous Machine with Soft Magnetic Compound Stator*, IEEE 2006

301. Jang S.-M., Jeong S.-S., Ryu D.-W., and Choi S.-K., *Design and Analysis of High-Speed Slotless Machine with Halbach Array*, IEEE Transactions on Magnetics, Vol. 37, No. 4, July 2001, pp. 2827-2830.

302. Ofori-Tenkorang J. and Lang J.H., *A comparative analysis of torque production in Halbach and conventional surface-mounted permanentmagnet synchronous motors*," IEEE IAS Annual Meeting, Orlando, Oct. 1995, p. 657.

303. Lai, S. and Abu-Sharkh, S., *Structurally Integrated Slotless PM Brushless Motor with Spiral Wound Laminations for Marine Thrusters*, 3rd IET International Conference on Power Electronics, Machines and Drives (PEMD), Dublin, Ireland, 4-6 April 2006, pp. 106-110.

304. Jack A.G., *Experience with the use of soft magnetic composites in electrical machines*, International Conference on Electrical Machines, September 1998, pp. 1441-1448.

305. Jack A.G., *et al*, *Permanent-Magnet Machines with Powdered Iron Cores and Prepressed Windings*, IEEE Transactions on Industry Applications, Vol. 36, No. 4, July/August 2000, pp. 1077-1084.

306. Jack A.G., Mecrow B.C. and Dickinson P.G., *Iron Loss in Machines with Powdered Iron Cores*, Proceedings IEMDC Conference, May 1999, pp. 48-50.

307. Jack A.G., Mecrow B.C. and Haylock J.A., *A Comparative Study of Permanent Magnet and Switched Reluctance Motors for High-Performance Fault-Tolerant Applications*, IEEE Transactions on Industry Applications, Vo. 32, No. 4, July/August 1996, pp. 889-895.

308. Chalmers B.J., Musaba L. and Gosden D.A., *Variable-Frequency Synchronous Motor Drives for Electric Vehicles*, IEEE Transactions on Industry Applications, Vol. 32, No. 4, July/August 1996, pp. 896-903.

309. Persson E., *Transient Effects in Application of PWM Inverters to Induction Motors*, IEEE Transactions on Industry Applications, Vol. 28, No. 5, September/October 1992, pp. 1095-1101.

310. Tang Y., *Analysis of Steep-Fronted Voltage Distribution and Turn Insulation Failure in Inverter-Fed Form-Wound AC Motor*, IEEE Transactions on Industry Applications, Vol. 34, No. 5, September/October 1998, pp. 1088-1096.

311. Langhorst P. and Hancock C., *Solutions for Preventing VFD-Driven Motor Failures*, PCIM Maagazine, December 1997, pp. 26-38.

312. Fenger M., Campbell S.R. and Pederesen J., *Motor Winding Problems Caused by Inverter Drives*, IEEE Industry Applications Magazine, July/August 2003, pp. 22-30.

313. Timperley J.E., *Root Cause Analysis of Machine Stator Failures*, 73rd Annual International Doble Conference, Doble Engineering Company, 2006, pp. 1-13.

314. GAMBICA/REMA Working Group Technical Report No. 1, *Motor Insulation Voltage Stresses Under PWM Inverter Operation*, 2nd edition, 2001. (16 pp.)

315. Melfi M., Sung A.M.J., Bell S., and Skibinski G.L., *Effect of Surge Voltage Risetime on the Insulation of Low-Voltage Machines Fed by PWM Converters*, IEEE Trans. on Industry Applications, Vol. IA-34, No. 4, July/August 1998, pp. 776-775.

316. Schiferl R.F. and Melfi M.J., *Bearing Current Remediation Options*, IEEE Industry Applications Magazine, July/August 2004, pp. 40-50.

317. Richter E., *Power Density Considerations for Permanent Magnet Machines*, Electric Power Components and Systems, Volume 4, Issue 1, July 1979, pp. 21-32.

318. Li Y., Walls T., Lloyd J.D. and Skinner J.L., *A Novel Two-Phase BPM Drive System with High Power Density and Low Cost*, IEEE Transactions on Industry Applications, Vol. 34, No. 5, September/October 1998, pp. 1072-1080.

319. Žarko D., Ban D. and Lipo T.A., *Analytical Calculation of Magnetic Field Distribution in the Slotted Air Gap of a Surface Permanent-Magnet Motor Using Complex Relative Air-Gap Permeance*, IEEE Transactions on Magnetics, Vol. 42, No. 7, July 2006, pp. 1828-1837.

320. Mhango, L., *New Design Techniques for Low Inertia PM Brushless DC Motor Suitable for Fuel Pumping in Aerospace Drives*, International Conference on Electrical Machines, Manchester, 1992, pp. 185-189.

321. Stanges M.K.W., Stone G.C. and Bogh D.L., *Voltage Endurance Testing; Stator insulation systems for inverter-fed machines*, IEEE Industry Applications Magazine, November/December 2009, pp. 12-18.

322. Jang, D.-H., *PWM Methods for Two-Phase Inverters*, IEEE Industry Applications Magazine, March/April 2007, pp. 50-61.

323. Price A. and Fakley M., *Motor Magnet Bonding — Technology Review, Recent Advances & Future Trends*, Coil Winding International & Electrical Insulation Magazine, Vol. 25, Issue 2, 2002, pp. 34-38.

324. Yoshikawa Y., Hiwaki H., Tamamura T. and Funatsu T., *Highly Efficient Technology of Concentrated Winding Interior Permanent Magnet Motor*, Matsushita Technical Journal, Vol. 51, No. 1, February 2005, pp. 65-69.

325. Kadowaki K., Yasohara M., and Murakami H., *Small DC Brushless Motor for PPC and Laser Beam Printer Applications*, Matsushita Technical Journal, Vol. 51, No. 1, February 2005, pp. 43-47.

326. Kai T. and Ikami T., *Direct Drive Brushless Motor for Electric Drum-Type Washer Dryer Applications*, Matsushita Technical Journal, Vol. 51, No. 1, 2005, pp. 30-33.

327. Tamamura T., Funatsu T. and Hiwaki H., *High Efficiency DC Brushless Motor for Compressor Applications*, Matsushita Tech. Journal, Vol. 51, No. 1, 2005, pp. 26-29

328. Tamura S., Nishiyama M. and Tazawa T., *MINAS™ A4 Series AC Servo Motor and Amplifier*, Matsushita Technical Journal, Vol. 51, No. 1, February 2005, pp. 13-16.

329. Slemon G.R. and Liu X., *Core losses in Permanent Magnet Motors*, IEEE Transactions on Magnetics, Vol. 26, No. 5, September 1990, pp. 1653-1655.

330. Drury B, *The Control Techniques Drives & Controls Handbook*, IET, 2009.

331. Görges H., *Über Drehstrommotoren mit Verminderter Tourenzahl*, Elektr. Zeitschrift, Vol. 17, 1896, pp. 517-518. (See also Electrical Review, Vol. 39, 1896, pp. 689-90).

332. Wieseman R.W., *Graphical Determination of Magnetic Fields*, Trans. AIEE, Vol. 46, 1927, pp. 141-154.

INDEX

1.5 slots/pole ... 85, 86, 135, 136, 685
Croft 1924 ... 135
1- and 2-phase unipolar drives ... 315
12/10 motor
alternative windings ... 124
1·5 slots/pole ... 138
Abandon inductance! ... 214
ABB ... 502
AC resistance ... 554
and deep slots ... 683
and stranded conductors ... 144
example ... 150
practical considerations ... 151
proximity effect ... 102, 143
redistribution of current in a slot ... 146
Roebel transposition ... 102
AC synchronous
see Brushless AC ... 28
Acceleration of pure inertia load ... 716
Accumulations for mean and RMS currents ... 288
Active rectification ... 467
ADC (analog/digital converter) ... 323
Adhesives ... 156
Adkins B ... 468, 500
Airgap
tapered ... 316
Airgap flux distribution ... 157, 164
Airgap flux-density ... 161
Airgap inductance ... 215
calculation examples ... 217
general case ... 221
mutual between phases ... 217
Airgap length ... 92, 115
and Carter's coefficient ... 182, 252, 257, 622
and cogging ... 107
and EMF waveform ... 116
and inductance ... 226
effective (synchronous inductance) ... 256
relative to magnet length ... 93
Airgap shear stress ... 88, 89
Airgap winding ... 108, 686
inductance ... 238
Alignment torque ... 70, 190, 309, 329, 335, 347, 367, 492, 501
and reluctance torque ... 190, 332, 335
in line-start motor ... 501, 503, 504, 514, 534
Alnico ... 451, 453, 455, 501
Alstom high-speed train (AGV) ... 208
Aluminium conductors ... 695
Ampere-conductor distribution ... 18, 19, 69, 77, 82, 169, 239, 250, 255, 476, 482, 510,

525, 528, 580, 582-584, 601, 635
and six-step . . . 375
balanced operation . . . 586
in squarewave motor . . . 273
rotating . . . 2, 18, 371
sinewave motor . . . 325
space harmonics . . . 561, 562, 568, 580, 629
AO Smith . . . 53, 498
APPLICATIONS . . . 25
aerospace . . . 97, 649
checklist of requirements . . . 66
for brushless permanent-magnet machines . . . 25
general-purpose . . . 688
high torque . . . 82
high-precision motion-control . . . 241
high-speed . . . 682
high-volume . . . 97
light-duty fan . . . 71
low-powered fans or blowers . . . 316
of permanent-magnet generators . . . 451
single-phase line-start . . . 503
with intermittent duty . . . 660
Arc magnets . . . 170, 687
effective dimensions . . . 93
Arçelik Turkey . . . 56, 64
Armadillo (Panasonic)
see "roll-up stator" . . . 57
Armature reaction . . 77, 162, 168, 178, 192, 203, 212, 213, 253, 256, 268-271, 346, 397, 561, 677
Armature time-constant . . . 469-472
Asynchronous operation and starting
of line-start motor . . . 506
of single-phase line-start motor . . . 537
Auto-commutated
see self-commutated . . . 699
Auto-synchronous . . . 2
see self-commutated . . . 699
Automatic winding machinery . . . 36, 103
Auxiliary winding . . . 519-522, 526, 527, 532-534, 536, 539, 540, 550, 712
axis . . . 520
bifilar wound . . . 712
Average torque . . . 157, 185, 186, 188, 190, 197, 200, 520
Axial-flux machines . . . 37
configurations of . . . 41
stator coils . . . 37
when to consider . . . 688
Back iron
see yoke . . . 96
Back-EMF sensing . . . 69, 312
Harms H and Erdman D . . . 314
Balanced operation . . . 21, 110, 188, 198, 596, 629, 705
and multiple-phase machines . . . 475

and ripple-free torque 16, 192
and synchronous inductance 243
current waveforms 17
forward and backward components 76
i-psi loop 199
of 2-phase machines 74, 188
of 3-phase machines 74, 188, 586
of line-start motor 503
rotor loss 561
short-circuit 244

Balanced winding 74, 76, 84, 110, 127, 245
and parallel paths 151, 152
equivalent in single-phase line-start motor 520
multi-phase 476, 484, 485
necessary conditions 137
slot-numbers divisible by 3 134

Baldor Advanced Technology 51, 55
Base impedance 343
Base interval 288, 289, 295, 296, 300, 301, 308, 309, 312
Base speed 12, 69, 213, 282
for normalization 351
see corner speed 339, 352

Bearing currents 702
Bearing loss 647, 648
Bernard Hague 169
Bessel functions 572
BH characteristic
importance 98
magnet 94, 162
steel 98, 158, 555

Bifilar winding 71, 315-317, 319, 320, 711, 712
Bifurcated teeth
see dummy slots 108

Binder A
fractional-slot winding 131

Binns KJ 502
Block diagram
current control 369
DTC 400
FC-IV flexible controller system 323
Lajoie-Mazenc I-gamma 372
of field-oriented dq controller 372, 373

Blondel 248, 331
BLV waveform method
EMF calculation 181

Boules N 169
Bracing bridges 167, 503
Braking 15, 24, 66, 449
Braking torque
in line-start motor 507

Bridge
for inductance measurement 677, 678

inverter circuit; 3-phase brushless DC . . . 8
inverter circuit; 3-phase delta . . . 276, 297
inverter circuit; 3-phase wye . . . 275, 279, 285, 292, 299, 383
inverter circuit; back-EMF sensing . . . 312
inverter circuit; H-bridge . . . 315
inverter circuits; 1, 2 and 3 phases . . . 80
Bridge
saturable . . . 160, 167, 168, 254-256, 268, 270, 503, 544, 546, 639, 689
Brown Boveri . . . 371, 502
Brushless AC
also known as PM AC synchronous . . . 2, 28
basic operation . . . 16, 327, 368
control . . . 325
Brushless DC
and brushless AC (distinction between) . . . 2, 28
control . . . 273
Brushless DC motor . . . 1
basic operation . . . 5
control-system model including inductance . . . 445
EMF waveform . . . 7
operating waveforms . . . 6
Brushless motor
as a synchronous machine . . . 1
definition . . . 1
Brushless permanent-magnet machines
applications . . . 25
Brushless PM motor
in control systems . . . 442
Building current . . . 283
Bumby JR . . . 241
C 120 Q1 . . . 287
C 60 Q1 . . . 286, 307
dwell control . . . 308
C 60 Q6 . . . 286
dwell control . . . 308
Cable length . . . 700
Cahill and Adkins . . . 500
Calculation of inertia . . . 721
Carbon fibre . . . 26, 49, 156, 690
Carrier frequency . . . 383, 385
Carter's coefficient . . . 182, 215, 220, 252, 257, 259, 545, 620, 622, 638
approximate formula . . . 216
CEM . . . 502
Centrifugal stress
in retaining sleeve . . . 155
Ceramic bearings . . . 59, 702
Ceramic magnet . . . 212, 659, 688
Ceramic shaft . . . 45
Chart of machine configurations . . . 28
Checklist of application requirements . . . 66
Chopping
and back-EMF sensing . . . 314

and PWM losses . . . 24
and torque ripple . . . 24
current regulation . . . 67, 198, 274, 279-289, 292, 294, 297, 301, 306-309
duty-cycle . . . 280
in bifilar circuit . . . 320
in squarewave drive . . . 279
sinewave controllers . . . 373

Chopping diode . . . 289

Chopping frequency
and inductance . . . 213, 284
to minimize current ripple . . . 69

Chopping transistor . . . 282-284, 286, 289, 292, 294, 297, 301, 308

Circle and ellipse diagrams . . . 338

Circle diagram
nonsalient-pole motor . . . 340
oversized inverter . . . 345

Circle tracking . . . 394

Circuit
inverter : see Bridge; inverter circuit . . . 8
see Equivalent circuit . . . 10

Circuit-breaker . . . 213

Circulating currents . . . 143, 145

Circulator pump . . . 45

Classification of machines . . . 27

Clearance gap
and equivalent magnet . . . 165

Closed slots . . . 229

Closed-loop feedback system . . . 446

Coating
of metallic magnets . . . 94

Coenergy . . . 185

Cogging . . . 24, 698
and integral slots/pole . . . 107
and skew . . . 107
as a reluctance torque . . . 107
calculation . . . 107
frequency . . . 134, 137
minimization of . . . 107

Cogging frequency . . . 108, 134, 135, 137

Cogging torque
measurement . . . 673
not included in i-ψ loop calculation . . . 200

Cogging-torque reduction
and closed slots . . . 683
large airgap . . . 107
magnetic slot wedges . . . 682
other methods . . . 108
skew . . . 108
slotless stator . . . 108
small slot-openings . . . 107

Coil
chorded . . . 110

definition 110
short-pitched 110
Coil List 125
Coil span 110, 111, 116, 118-120, 122, 123, 125, 126, 129, 130, 136, 184
and airgap inductance 222
and End-winding leakage inductance 233
and Hague's method 170
in concentric winding 113
in squarewave motor 180
lowest possible 0·5 84
of rotor bar-pair 544
of slotless winding 238, 239
Table 86
Coil Winding Exhibition 683
Coil-shooting 104
Coil-sides per slot 105
Coil-span table
and slots/pole 86
Coils per pole 111
Coilside 110
Common-mode voltage 702
Communication protocols 66
Commutating diode 289
Commutating inductance 464
Commutating transistor 289
Commutation 2, 4, 273, 282
in dc commutator motor 4
overcurrents during 289
Commutation frequency 287
Commutation interval 273
Comparator 370
Complex diffusion equation (eddy-currents) 570
Compressor 648
Concentrated winding 67, 68, 133, 134, 137, 138, 180, 217, 242, 273, 682
high winding factor 86, 133, 138
Concentric winding 104, 111-113, 685
winding factor 113
Condensation
and dielectric strength 702
Conductive grease 702
Conductive shield 698
Conductor
AC resistance 143
aluminium 695
and end-turn inductance 686
current distribution in 146
current-density 697
definition 110
fretting 104
go and return 110, 221, 232
hollow 90
inductance of bunched 218

position in slot . . . 226, 686
rectangular . . . 100, 102, 109, 685
sinusoidal distribution . . . 130
stranded . . . 104, 105, 110, 139, 144-146, 151, 152, 685, 712
temperature . . . 23
temperature hot-spot . . . 105
total area . . . 72
varnishing . . . 104
Conductor distribution
see Ampere-conductor distribution; see Winding . . . 18
Constant-power operation . . . 70, 213, 339
speed range . . . 343
Constant-power speed-range
see Speed range at constant power . . . 68
Constant-speed operation . . . 15
Contact resistance . . . 653
Continuous operation . . . 14, 23, 66, 89, 90, 437, 439, 499, 662, 692, 715
Control block diagram
see Block diagram . . . 369
Control chart
IPM . . . 348
synchronous reluctance motor . . . 363
Control strategies
3-phase sinewave . . . 325
3-phase squarewave . . . 286
Control system model . . . 442
Control Techniques Drives and Controls Handbook . . . 66
Controller architecture . . . 321
Cooling . . . 23, 87-93, 648-658, 675, 681, 690, 691
and efficiency . . . 649
Conduction . . . 652
Convection . . . 654
Radiation . . . 653
thermal analysis and cooling . . . 648
Copper
resistivity . . . 142
Core losses . . . 24, 90, 97, 553-559, 657, 672, 697
eddy-current component . . . 555
hysteresis component . . . 555
simple method for squarewave motors . . . 559
Core plate
see Laminations . . . 97
Corner point . . . 282
Corner speed . . . 339
Corona inception voltage . . . 701
Corrosion . . . 94
Coupling coefficient . . . 634
between bifilar windings . . . 320
d-axis . . . 529, 639, 641, 642
in end-turns . . . 235
subtransient . . . 632, 635, 637, 638
Croft T . . . 86, 135

Cros J . . . 133, 138
Cross-magnetizing current . . . 268
Cross-saturation . . . 268
Cuffed slot-liner . . . 99, 100
Current
reference or set-point . . 281-284, 296, 300, 304, 305, 308, 370, 372, 379, 381, 467
Current error . . . 383
Current regulation . . . 279
need for . . . 369
SINEWAVE DRIVE . . . 325, 370
SQUAREWAVE DRIVE . . . 273
torque control . . . 369
Current ripple
and inductance . . . 280
inductance . . . 213
Current sensor
single . . . 276
Current waveform
how to make sinusoidal . . . 700
Current-density . . . 87, 89, 90, 143, 144, 227, 652, 655, 697
typical values . . . 90
Current-density (eddy-currents) . . . 565, 570, 572, 604-612, 616, 625, 647
Current-limit circle . . . 338
Current-limited maximum torque . . . 332
Custom laminations . . . 683
CWIEME Exhibition . . . 683
Cycle hub dynamo
Sturmey-Archer DYNOHUB . . . 452
Cycloconverter . . . 80
d-axis . . . 5
magnet flux defines the d-axis . . . 5
d-axis synchronous inductance . . . 247
Damping curves . . . 449
Damping ratio . . . 448
DC motor . . . 1, 9, 11, 13, 67, 179, 553, 655, 682, 688
ideal . . . 405, 407, 408, 411-415, 422, 423, 427
Definition
of brushless motor or generator . . . 1
Degrees C per watt . . . 651
delta
for maximum torque . . . 334
Delta connection . . . 9, 17, 21, 72, 75, 116, 117, 122, 180, 181, 186, 251, 274, 289, 291, 293, 317, 413, 670
analysis of squarewave drive . . . 296-301, 309, 310
inductance . . . 713, 714
inverter circuit . . . 276
reconnection from Wye . . . 189
waveforms (squarewave drive) . . . 278
wye/Delta combination . . . 479, 480
zero-sequence . . . 600
Demagnetization . . 24, 93, 162, 166, 268-270, 349, 351, 439, 455, 471, 499, 501, 648, 689

at higher temperature . . . 694
how to prevent . . . 694
in IPM . . . 33
Deng F . . . 603
Design procedure . . . 65
di/dt
and inductance . . . 213
Dialogue
between motor engineer and control engineer . . . 337
Dielectric strength and condensation . . . 702
Differential inductance . . . 131, 134, 214, 225, 226, 250, 258, 482, 487, 490, 634, 686
Diode rectifier . . . 464
Direct axis . . . 5
Direct calculation of synchronous inductance . . . 253
Direct cooling . . . 649
Direct torque control (DTC) . . . 396
Direct-drive motor . . . 57
Distribution factor . . . 77, 126
harmonic . . . 122, 240
of concentric winding . . . 113
spread factor . . . 111
Double-layer winding . . . 105
Doubly-fed machines . . . 705
dq axes . . . 193
dq transformation . . . 193, 194, 247-249, 485
reference-frame diagram . . . 193
salient-pole machines . . . 193
dq-axis inductances from Park's transform . . . 248
dq-axis model . . . 247
dq_VV_CR . . . 381
and DTC . . . 381
Drive
3-phase bridge inverter circuit . . . 275
sinewave . . . 325
squarewave . . . 273
Drive circuit . . . 8
1-phase . . . 81
2-phase . . . 81
3-phase . . . 81
DSP (digital signal processor) . . . 323
DTC . . . 374, 381, 396
and dq_VV_CR . . . 381
Dummy slots (bifurcated teeth) . . . 108
Duplex winding . . . 478
phasor diagram . . . 494
Duty-cycle
and peak mean and RMS currents . . . 289
chopping . . . 280
precision . . . 323
Dwell control . . . 306
Dynamic braking . . . 449
Eccentricity . . . 137

Eddy-current core loss . . . 555
and lamination thickness . . . 556
Eddy-current losses . . . 94
and segmented magnets . . . 602
in rotor . . . 561
see AC resistance . . . 143
Eddy-currents
inductance-limited . . . 564
resistance-limited . . . 563
Effective airgap . . . 252, 622, 641
Efficiency . . . 23, 92, 97, 113, 117, 317, 320, 366, 422, 423, 437, 453, 463, 499, 503, 550, 551, 558, 648, 656, 671, 687, 697
and cooling . . . 650
and power factor . . . 436
and watts loss . . . 650
as a figure of merit . . . 436
effect of temperature . . . 693
gearbox . . . 715
how to increase . . . 697
Electric loading . . . 87, 681
Electro-discharge machining (wire-erosion) . . . 97
Electronic control of Sinewave drive . . . 368
Ellipse diagram . . . 22, 326, 338
IPM . . . 348
synchronous reluctance motor . . . 363
EMF . . . 178
basic concept . . . 178
BLV calculation . . . 181
brushless DC . . . 7
by formula . . . 179
flat-top, for squarewave drive . . . 115
fundamental EMF/phase Eq1 . . . 19, 181
measurement . . . 670
per-unit . . . 341
sinusoidal . . . 131, 700
slot ripple (permeance harmonics) . . . 108, 131, 456, 696
standard equation for sinewaves . . . 88
toothflux calculation . . . 183
waveform . . . 6, 7, 157, 179, 187, 188, 277, 278
waveform, squarewave motor . . . 7, 277, 278
waveform, with harmonics . . . 201, 700
waveform; how to make sinusoidal . . . 700
EMF constant kE . . . 10, 157, 179, 684
measurement . . . 456, 670
of sinewave motor . . . 181
of squarewave motor . . . 179, 180
see Chapter 8 . . . 405
Encoder . . . 323, 371
End turns
see End-windings . . . 109

End-windings
in 2-pole machines . . . 682
laced . . . 62, 101, 104
leakage inductance . . . 214, 233-237
leakage inductance (Lawrenson's method) . . . 241
"blocking" or "forming" . . . 109
"knuckle" . . . 109
Energy conversion equation
ideal . . . 7, 185, 187, 188, 407, 411-421, 427-433
Energy-conversion loop
see i-ψ loop . . . 197
Epstein frame . . . 556
Equality of kT and kE . . . 692
Equivalent circuit
diode rectifier . . . 464
electrical . . . 10, 190, 192, 198-202, 209, 232, 243, 408, 494
generator . . . 457
line-start motor . . . 517, 518
magnetic . . . 157-159, 164, 168, 173
series/parallel inductances . . . 711, 712
subtransient . . . 631
thermal . . . 657, 658, 661, 675
Equivalent sine-distributed windings . . . 242
Erland Persson . . . 651
Euler . . . 266
Ewing . . . 555
Exterior-rotor machine . . . 35, 688
characteristics . . . 35
cooling . . . 37
exterior-rotor . . . 3
in pan-and-tilt mechanism . . . 60
inertia . . . 36
rotor cup . . . 35
rotor yoke . . . 96
split ratio . . . 91
stator coils . . . 36
External (series) inductance
and flux-weakening . . . 344
F1 dynamometer, MTS Systems . . . 48
Failure
premature . . . 702
Fan (cooling) . . . 89, 90, 553, 654-656
Fan-drive applications . . . 28, 71, 688
Fanuc . . . 28
Faraday's law . . . 210
Faulhaber . . . 59
Fault-tolerant machines . . . 100, 480
FC-IV Controller . . . 321
Feedback . . . 445
Fibre-optic gate drive connections . . . 323
Field AB . . . 146
Field-oriented dq control . . . 372, 373

Fieldbus ... 66
Figures of merit ... 436
  Efficiency and power factor ... 436
  kT and kE ... 436
  Mechanical time-constant ... 439
  Motor Constant ... 440
  Power rate ... 437
  Speed rate ... 439
  Torque/Inertia ratio ... 437
Finite-element method ... 53, 157, 158, 164, 168, 174-178, 229
  and inductance ... 262
  calculation of cogging torque ... 107
  calculation of i-ψ loop ... 199
  calculation of i-ψ loop from known current waveform ... 200, 496
  calculation of i-ψ loop with only a few points ... 207
  calculation of saturated synchronous inductance ... 267, 268, 496
  calculation of slot-leakage inductance ... 226
  calculation of torque from i-ψ loop with known current waveform .. 200, 496
  calculation of yoke flux distribution ... 106
  does not protect the unwary ... 210
  flux-plot ... 53
  good with toothflux method ... 183
  identification of leakage flux ... 211
  magnet flux distribution ... 183
  mesh ... 53
  not good with BLV method ... 182
  requires foreknowledge of current waveform ... 199
  torque calculation from one solution ... 206
  uncertainties with inductance calculation ... 192
  used to calculate T-gamma curves ... 196
  using flux-linkage (abandon inductance!) ... 214, 248
First-order system (control-system model) ... 444
First-turn insulation failure ... 109, 700
Flux
  airgap ... 159
  alternating polarity ... 1
  and Magnet overhang ... 95
  and yoke dimensions ... 96
  calculation of magnet flux ... 162
  concentration ... 161
  confined to the stator teeth ... 3
  distribution of airgap flux ... 164
  effect of airgap on waveshape ... 115
  effect of clearance gap ... 165
  effect of phase advance ... 70
  effect of temperature ... 23
  forward and backward rotating components ... 75
  fringing and pole-to-pole leakage ... 113, 116, 158
  fundamental component ... 19
  fundamental magnet flux/pole ... 164
  fundamental space-harmonic ... 113
  harmonic components of armature reaction ... 129

in bracing bridges ... 167
in shaft ... 82
in stator yoke ... 105
in teeth ... 183
in yoke ... 105, 184
magnet ... 160
magnet flux calculation ... 157
magnet flux defines the d-axis ... 5
methods for calculating ... 157
nonlinear ... 192
of armature reaction ... 77
of Halbach magnet ... 131
of rotating magnet ... 19, 185
rectangular distribution ... 113
remanent ... 158
rotating ... 75
sinusoidal distribution ... 79, 88
space-harmonic ... 71
through the magnet ... 158
torque equals current × flux ... 87, 88
variation due to slotting ... 106, 108

Flux times turns
(as an approximate definition of flux-linkage) ... 5, 211
and inductance ... 211

Flux-concentration
in exterior-rotor machine ... 36
in IPM ... 34
in spoke-type machine ... 28
reduction of permeance coefficient ... 161

Flux-dip-sweeping ... 624
Robinson Rowe and Donelan ... 569
Russell and Norsworthy ... 569

Flux-linkage
and Faraday's law ... 210
and inductance ... 209, 210
and magnetization curves ... 263-267
calculation using line-integral of vector potential ... 262
demagnetizing component ... 328
measurement ... 210
rate of change equals EMF ... 178, 264
real-time measurement using FC-IV controller ... 674
waveform ... 5-9, 116, 178, 200, 203, 206, 207

Flux-plot
open-circuit ... 106, 183

Flux-spreading
in rotor cup of exterior-rotor motor ... 36, 96

Flux-weakening .. 69, 70, 92, 134, 213, 304, 326-328, 337, 341, 346, 349, 353-355, 358-360, 369, 383, 686, 699
and external inductance ... 344
and inductance ... 33
extreme case ... 328
inverter size required ... 345

Flux/pole 93, 96, 116, 117, 158, 160, 179, 638, 641, 689
fundamental 87, 164, 176, 181, 423, 526, 546, 547
of armature reaction 216, 630
Fong W 500
Form factor 90
Form-wound coils 100, 102, 105, 109, 111, 682, 685, 701
Forward and backward rotating fields 75, 518
Four quadrants of operation 23, 24
Fourier Transform 472
FPGA (field-programmable gate array) 323
Fractional number of turns/coil 685, 706
Fractional slots/pole 67, 68, 84-86, 107, 108, 682
Fractional-slot windings 118
Frame
allowable temperature 648
contact thermal resistance 653
cooling 90, 652, 657
finned 656
short-circuited current paths in 679
temperature in 4-parameter model 666
temperature measurement 650
thermal capacity 658
totally enclosed aluminium 30
Freewheel circuit 279, 291, 319, 391
Freewheel diodes 274, 301, 304, 317, 319
Freewheeling current 279, 283, 285, 288, 291-297, 306, 308, 312, 382
Frequency
and eddy-current loss . . . 104, 555, 563-566, 575, 580, 583-587, 590, 599, 600, 629, 630, 634, 640
and AC resistance 104, 143, 144, 151
and core-loss 553, 554, 556-558
and pole-pairs 1
and speed 1
base 361
carrier 383, 385
cogging 108, 134, 135, 137
commutation 287
complex 443, 529, 530, 548, 562, 628
corner 339
fundamental . . 1, 2, 4, 82, 88, 110, 180, 243, 269, 325, 339, 340, 350, 361, 366, 369, 385, 386, 456, 457, 464, 499, 514, 542, 601, 607, 699
magnetic 82, 681, 697
maximum possible switching 382
negative-sequence 561, 587, 596
Nyquist 473
of harmonic variation of inductance 191, 249, 250, 315
of supply 66
of torsional oscillation (inertia measurement) 669
pulsating torque 187, 188, 517
sampling 381, 387, 401
slip 528
slot-passing 108, 553, 561, 563, 621

swing . . . 472
switching in DTC . . . 402
switching or chopping . 22, 69, 213, 279-281, 284, 323, 368, 373, 377-380, 382, 383, 387, 402, 553, 554, 677, 686, 700, 701
undamped natural . . . 448
Frequency-dependent synchronous inductance . . . 543, 548, 562, 628, 632-634, 647
Frequency-response test . . . 543, 562
Frequently asked questions:
How about a sine-EMF motor with squarewave drive? . . . 696
How about EMF ripple? . . . 696
How can I get a fractional number of turns/coil? . . . 685
How can I get a more sinusoidal current waveform? . . . 700
How can I get a more sinusoidal EMF waveform? . . . 700
How can I get smooth rotation at low speed? . . . 698
How can I improve the torque linearity? . . . 692
How can I increase efficiency? . . . 697
How can I increase power-factor? . . . 698
How can I increase the inductance? . . . 686
How can I make the motor go faster? . . . 699
How can I prevent demagnetization? . . . 693
How can I reduce the inductance? . . . 686
How can I reduce the inertia? . . . 691
How can I reduce the motor cost? . . . 695
How can I reduce the noise level? . . . 695
How can I reduce the wire size? . . . 685
How can I reduce torque ripple? . . . 692
How do I avoid bearing currents? . . . 702
How do I avoid first-turn insulation failure? . . . 700
How do I calculate the machine temperature? . . . 692
How do I choose between exterior or interior rotor? . . . 688
How do I choose between SPM and IPM? . . . 686
How do I choose the number of slots and poles? . . . 682
How do I decide the number of turns? . . . 684
How do I decide the rotor geometry? . . . 689
How do I decide the shape and size of the machine? . . . 681
How do I decide the type of stator winding? . . . 685
How do I design a PM synchronous generator? . . . 692
How do I design the stator teeth and slots? . . . 682
How do I test a PM synchronous machine? . . . 692
What are the main effects of temperature? . . . 693
What causes machines to fail? . . . 702
When should I consider an axial-flux machine? . . . 688
Why isn't my measured kE equal to kT? . . . 692
Fretting . . . 104, 702
Frozen rotor . . . 63
Full-pitch coil . . . 116, 128, 179, 180, 215, 217, 220, 222
Full-pitch winding . . . 115, 116, 130
Full-ring magnet . . . 107, 607
GAMBICA/REMA . . . 701
gamma
optimum phase advance . . . 333
Gate drives . . . 323

GE
back-EMF sensing scheme 314
Gearing 714
GENERATING
see Permanent-magnet generator 451
Generic second-order system 448
Gieras 41, 688
Görges diagram ("star of phasors") 125, 130, 591
Görges effect
dip in speed/torque characteristic 542
Gramme ring 37
Greens Mower
John Deere 50
Grover F 234
Grundfos 45
Hague B 169
Hague's method
and inductance 225
Hague-Boules method 172
Hairpin coils 683
Halbach magnet 59
and nonmagnetic rotor yoke 3, 96
sinusoidal EMF 131, 689, 700
Half turns 706
Hall-effect sensor 71, 100, 323
Hancock 702
Hand tools 61
Hanrahan and Toffolo 451
Harmonic current-sheet 580
Harmonic leakage (differential) inductance . 131, 134, 214, 225, 226, 258, 482, 487, 490, 686
Harmonic losses 82, 96, 467, 561, 562, 568-647
in surface-magnet machines 568
in the IPM 628
see AC resistance 143
Harmonic pole-pitch 603
Harmonic wavelength 609
Harmonic winding factor 77, 88, 108, 122, 129-131, 172, 240, 242, 267, 700
Harmonics 16, 66
and back-EMF sensing 314
and i-ψ loop 192
and imbalance 595, 599
and kE 413
and rotor losses 580-592
and slots/pole 82, 697
as cause of failure 702
axial 603
current-sheet 169, 171, 172
effect on current-density 90
effect on torque 190, 192, 198-202
elimination by pitch-factor 129, 278
even 315

fundamental component . . . 113, 125, 164, 175, 225, 242, 250, 258
ignoring higher-order . . . 131
in airgap inductance . . . 217, 225, 259, 261
in current waveform . . . 70
in current waveform examples . . . 376, 378, 382, 384, 388, 390
in current waveform examples (squarewave drive) . . 290, 295, 303, 305, 307, 308, 311
in EMF . . . 93, 108, 113, 131, 315, 387, 456, 561, 620, 621, 689, 700
in flux-density waveform . . . 558
in line-start motor . . . 542, 543
in power measurement . . . 671, 672
in rotor flux . . . 131
in squarewave current (effect on RMS) . . . 419, 421
in squarewave motors . . . 79, 116
inductance components not available from finite-element method . . . 263
inverter . . . 386, 394, 419
one of the nasty things that goes on in machines . . . 326
permeance/slot-modulation . . . 108, 131, 456, 561
series representation of magnetization . . . 169, 171, 172, 225
slot-order . . . 700
space . . . 131, 217, 250
space harmonics used to start single-phase motor . . . 71
third harmonic and zero-sequence . . . 599, 600, 700
third-harmonic injection . . . 387, 404
triple-n . . . 116, 117, 278, 593, 599, 600
variation of inductance with rotor position . 191, 249, 251, 259, 261, 314, 489, 490

Head-scratching
caused by failure to measure things . . . 668
Heat removal . . . 650
Heat transfer
see Cooling . . . 648
Helical windings . . . 241
Heller B and Hamata V . . . 628
Hermetic compressors . . . 648
Hexagon tracking . . . 394
and Third-harmonic injection . . . 387
High-speed machines . . . 92, 96, 105, 151, 156, 366, 554, 620, 647, 682, 690
Historical development of sinewave drive . . . 371
Hitachi . . . 502
Höganäs . . . 26
Holes (to reduce inertia) . . . 691
Holtz . . . 374, 394
Space-vector controller . . . 391
Honeywell . . . 43
Honsinger . . . 499, 500, 507
Hoop stress
in retaining sleeve . . . 154
Howe D . . . 569
Hughes A . . . 169, 242
Hybrid vehicles . . . 451
Hysteresis loss . . . 555

Hysteresis loss in magnets . . . 566
Hysteresis-band current regulator . . . 377
  leakage outside the hysteresis band . . . 377
I-γ controller . . . 372
i-ψ loop . . . 192, 196
  and cogging torque . . . 200
  calculation of saturated synchronous inductance . . . 268, 496
  elliptical . . . 203
  examples . . . 200-202
  properties . . . 203-207
  theory of average torque production . . . 197-200
  torque per ampere . . . 206
  with six-step drive . . . 207
i-psi loop
  see i-ψ loop . . . 197
IEC . . . 43
IGBT transistors . . . 700
Imbalance . . . 561
  single-parameter . . . 593
Impedance protection . . . 100
Inconel® . . . 26
INDUCTANCE . . . 209
  abandon! . . . 214
  airgap component . . . 214, 215
  and airgap length . . . 226
  and ceramic or bonded NdFeB magnets . . . 36
  and closed slots . . . 229
  and current regulation . . . 33
  and current ripple . . . 33, 213, 280
  and di/dt . . . 213
  and finite-element calculations . . . 262
  and flux-linkage . . . 210
  and flux-weakening . . . 33, 344
  and Hague's method . . . 225
  and parallel paths . . . 216
  and phase shift . . . 213
  and power factor . . . 213
  and short-circuit faults . . . 213
  and skew . . . 250
  and speed range . . . 213
  and switching frequency . . . 213
  and type of magnet . . . 212
  chopping frequency . . . 213
  components . . . 214
  definition . . . 209
  di/dt . . . 211
  differential . . . 131, 134, 214, 225, 226, 258, 482, 487, 490, 686
  effect of slot shape . . . 231
  effect of tooth overhangs . . . 231
  end-turn component . . . 214
  Faraday's law . . . 210
  flux times turns . . . 211

general case of airgap inductance . . . 221
harmonic . . . 131, 134, 214, 225, 226, 258, 482, 487, 490, 686
in salient-pole machines . . . 247
in torque calculations . . . 190
incremental . . . 263
link between static and dynamic calculations . . . 209
magnetizing . . . 225
measurement . . . 260, 676
mutual . . . 210
of end-winding . . . 233
of slotless (airgap) windings . . . 238
per-unit . . . 212
phase . . . 214
position of conductors in slot . . . 230
practical effects . . . 213
Prescott and El-Karashi inductance bridge . . . 677
self . . . 210
series and parallel . . . 709
slot-leakage . . . 226
slot-leakage and magnetic slot-wedges . . . 682
slot-leakage component . . . 214
subtransient . . . 631
synchronous . . . 243
how to increase . . . 686
how to reduce . . . 686
turns squared . . . 212
variation with rotor position . . . 191, 249, 251, 259, 261, 314, 489, 490
wye and delta connections . . . 713
Inductive voltage drop . . . 213
Inertia
acceleration of . . . 716
calculation . . . 721
measurement . . . 668
of exterior-rotor machine . . . 36
how to reduce . . . 691
units . . . 716
Infinite bus . . . 462
Infinite maximum speed . . . 341
Insulation life
related to temperature . . . 648
Integral gain compensation . . . 447
Integral-slot windings . . . 111
Integrated frequency converter . . . 45
Interior rotor . . . 3, 688
Interior-rotor machine
split ratio . . . 91
Interlocking laminations . . . 98
Intermittent operation . . . 660
Inverse saliency . . . 249, 251, 505
Inverter
available current . . . 328
oversized required for flux-weakening . . . 345

sinewave : see Chapter 7 . . . 325
squarewave : see Chapter 6 . . . 273
Inverter circuit
see bridge; inverter circuit . . . 8
Inverter-grade magnet-wire . . . 26, 701
Ionel DM . . . 558
IPM . . . 28, 32
airgap comparable to that of an induction motor . . . 33
and demagnetization . . . 33
and torque linearity . . . 33
control complexity . . . 33
control mode diagram . . . 348
essential features . . . 32
multiple-layer . . . 690
reasons to use . . . 687
reluctance torque . . . 32
saturation in . . . 34
speed range . . . 33
V-shaped magnets . . . 53
with squarewave drive . . . 309
Iron losses
see Core losses . . . 555
Irregular slotting . . . 131, 132
Irreversible loss of magnetization . . . 694
Isosyn motor . . . 371, 501, 509
j
rotate phasor by 90° . . . 19
Jack A
fault-tolerant machine . . . 100
powdered-iron core . . . 100
prepressed windings . . . 100
Jahns TM . . . 373
John Deere . . . 50
Jones bridge
see Prescott and El-Karashi inductance bridge . . . 677
Jones CV . . . 677
Joule losses . . . 143, 554
Kalluf . . . 542
kE
see EMF constant kE . . . 157
Keeper . . . 455
Kelvin functions . . . 572
Knee-point
on magnet demagnetization curve . . . 161, 693, 694
Koch Th . . . 131
kT
see Torque constant kT . . . 157
kT & kE
2-phase sinewave motor and drive . . . 428
2-phase sinewave motor with squarewave drive . . . 430
2-phase squarewave and sinewave systems compared . . . 435
2-phase squarewave motor and drive . . . 426

2-phase squarewave motor with sinewave drive 432
3-phase sinewave motor and drive 415
3-phase sinewave motor with squarewave drive 417
3-phase squarewave and sinewave systems compared 422
3-phase squarewave motor and drive 411
3-phase squarewave motor with sinewave drive 419
as Figures of merit 436
DC commutator motor and drive 407
detailed analysis : see Chapter 8 405
Tables; 2-phase 434
Tables; 3-phase 422
when are they equal and when are they not equal? 11, 406, 692
Laced end-turns 62
Lajoie-Mazenc M 371, 372
Laminations
choice of steel 97
custom designs 683
improvements in electrical steels 26
insulating coatings 97
insulation 26
punching 97
self-cleating 99
skewing 99
stacking 98
suppliers 683
thickness and eddy-current core loss 556
thin 97
Lammeraner and Štafl 146, 563, 642, 643
Langhorst 702
Lap winding 77, 78, 100, 104, 109-113, 120, 685
inductance calculation 217
Laplace/Poisson equations 157, 169
Laronze J 501
Lateral deflection and whirling 96
Lawrenson PJ 473, 562, 568, 569
end-winding inductance calculation 241
pull-in criterion 514
synchronous reluctance motor 500
Layers
in winding 77, 110, 111, 138, 238, 240
LCM
least common multiple of slots and poles 135
Ld
see Synchronous inductance 243
Ldiff
see harmonic or differential inductance 226
Leakage factor 160
Leakage flux (in rotor bridges) 167
Leakage flux (pole-to-pole or "rotor leakage") 113, 116, 158-160, 167, 183, 211, 257, 270, 639, 689
Length/diameter ratio 92
Libert F 138

Line-start motor
- advantages . . . 499
- analysis of polyphase . . . 503
- analysis of synchronization . . . 510
- asynchronous operation and starting . . . 506
- bar-pair-by-bar-pair model of the rotor cage . . . 543
- Chapter 11 . . . 497
- connection circuits . . . 550
- history . . . 500
- magnet braking torque . . . 507, 509, 516, 543
- non-orthogonal windings . . . 536
- phasor diagram . . . 533
- pull-up torque . . . 507
- saliency braking torque . . . 507
- single-phase . . . 517
- torque reversals . . . 509
- winding harmonics . . . 542

Linear motor . . . 42
Linear power amplifier . . . 323
Linearity
- from a control viewpoint . . . 11
- see Torque linearity . . . 11

Liquid coolant . . . 31
Litz wire . . . 144, 151, 554
Load
- speed/torque characteristic . . . 12

Load angle
- power angle . . . 461

Load-line . . . 161
- out-of-stator . . . 455

Locked-rotor / stall . . . 13, 14, 270, 436, 439-441, 543
Loctite . . . 98, 690
Losses
- AC resistance . . . 554
- and cooling . . . 553
- and finite-length effects . . . 602
- and multiple phases . . . 698
- bearing loss . . . 647
- core losses . . . 555
- due to imbalance . . . 561
- due to MMF Space-harmonics . . . 561
- due to permeance harmonics . . . 561
- due to time-harmonics . . . 561
- effect of temperature on resistance . . . 554
- finite-element calculation . . . 644
- in Segmented magnets . . . 602
- in the IPM rotor . . . 628
- in thin can . . . 624
- Joule (copper) . . . 554
- proximity effect . . . 554
- rotor eddy-current . . . 561
- slot ripple . . . 620

windage and friction ... 553, 647
Lq
see Synchronous inductance ... 243
Lubrication ... 702
M-19 ... 97
Machine configuration
chart ... 28
variety of ... 25
Machine Design Questions ... 681
Machine temperature
How to calculate ... 692
MAGNA circulator pump
Grundfos ... 46
Magnet
alignment torque ... 32
arc ... 93
effect of temperature ... 23
effect on inductance ... 212
energy product ... 94
ferrite ... 26
flux calculation ... 162
full-ring ... 107, 607
grade of ... 94
initial dimensioning ... 93
knee-point ... 161
knee-point and its variation with temperature ... 693, 694
length ... 93
load-line calculation ... 162
Neodymium-Iron-Boron ... 26
operating point calculation ... 162
overhang ... 95
permeance coefficient calculation ... 162
polymer-bonded ... 45
profiling ... 689
retention ... 31, 153, 690
rotating ... 1
Samarium-Cobalt ... 26
segmented ... 93
thickness ... 93
width ... 93
Magnet braking torque ... 507, 509, 516, 543
Magnet flux-linkage ... 5
Magnet-wire
inverter-grade ... 26
Magnetic equivalent-circuit method ... 157, 158
Magnetic frequency ... 82, 681, 697
Magnetic loading B ... 87
Magnetic slot-wedge ... 682
Magnetization curves ... 263-267
in dq-axes ... 266
Magnetizing fixture
with skewed poles ... 107

Magnetizing inductance 225
Magnussen F 138
Manual winding 61
Maximum speed
    and inductive voltage drop 213
    attainable with a given supply voltage 33, 282, 699
    infinite 341
    of nonsalient-pole motor 341
Maximum torque
    Current-limited 332
    Voltage-limited 334
Maxon
    slotless motor 59
McLachlan N W 572
Mean rectified EMF 407, 410
Measurement
    airgap length 668
    cogging torque 673
    EMF 670
    EMF constant 456
    flux-linkage 210
    inductance 260, 676
    inertia 668
    mutual inductance 679
    on-line estimation of torque using the i-psi loop 674
    resistance 669
    synchronous inductance 246
    thermal resistance 675
    torque 672
    torque constant 673
Mechanical time-constant
    as a Figure of merit 439
Melfi M 702
Merrill FW 500
Mhango L 691
Miller TJE
    Rotor eddy-currents 473
MINAS® servo-motor
    Panasonic 99, 101
Misalignment 702
Miyashita 502
MMF distribution
    see Ampere-conductor distribution 582
Mode diagram
    IPM control 348
    synchronous reluctance motor 363
Modular winding 134
Modulation index 386
Morley A 153
Motor constant
    Figure of merit 440
Motor load testing 672

Motorcycle alternator
Triumph Bonneville . . . 57
Moulded plastic insulator . . . 100
Mounting flange . . . 43
MS-TECH Japan . . . 53, 63
MTS Systems Inc . . . 48
Multi-level converter . . . 80
Multiple phases
used to increase efficiency . . . 475
Multiple-layer IPM . . . 690
MULTIPLE-PHASE MACHINES . . . 475
Multiple-strand conductor
see Conductor; stranded . . . 104, 685
Multiplex windings . . . 478
reasons for using . . . 479
Mutual inductance
airgap component . . . 217-225
and differential inductance . . . 258
between phases . . . 191, 198, 209, 214, 225, 232, 243-250, 258, 259, 265, 280, 291, 313, 314, 319
components . . . 214
definition . . . 210
end-winding component . . . 234
in bifilar winding . . . 316
in line-start rotor . . . 529, 543-548
in multi-phase winding . . . 478, 481-491, 495
in rotor loss calculation . . . 635, 638, 641
in series/parallel connections . . . 709-714
in slotless machine . . . 238-240
measurement . . . 679
saliency and torque-production . . . 705
slot-leakage component . . . 229-231
turns-square rule modified . . . 212
Mylar . . . 156
Natural frequency . . . 448
Natural symmetrical components . . . 530
NEMA . . . 43
Neutral connection
insulated . . . 152
Ng K . . . 569
No-load speed . . . 13
and losses . . . 646
and Motor Constant . . . 440
and regulation . . . 458
and voltage . . . 15, 443
effect of temperature . . . 23
example calculation . . . 424, 425
generator on open-circuit . . . 455
open-circuit condition . . . 157, 455
precise determination . . . 301-303
No-load test . . . 455
Noguchi T . . . 401

Noise : causes ... 695
Non-orthogonal windings
in line-start motor ... 520, 536
Non-overlapping winding
see Concentrated winding ... 86
Non-uniqueness of reluctance torque ... 335
Nonsalient-pole machines ... 68
Number of phases
in electrical machines ... 75
in electrical systems ... 72
in inverters and rectifiers ... 80
multiple phases used to increase efficiency ... 698
practical considerations ... 71
Number of poles ... 82, 682
Number of stator slots ... 82, 105, 682
Offset
winding ... 127
ohms per 1000ft ... 140
ohms/km or ohms/1000ft ... 140
On-line estimation of torque using the i-psi loop ... 674
Open slots ... 100, 105
and form-wound coils ... 105, 682
slot-fill factor ... 102
Open-circuit test ... 456, 670
Operating point
of the magnets ... 157
Operation of salient-pole motor/generator (IPM) ... 347, 348
Optimization tools ... 681
Optimum gamma ... 333, 347, 348
Oriental Motor Co Ltd ... 52
planetary gearmotor ... 52
Output equation ... 87
Outside rotor
see Exterior rotor ... 688
Overcurrent circuit-breaker ... 213
Overcurrents during commutation ... 289
Overexcited generator ... 330
Overmodulation ... 386, 394
Oversized inverter ... 345
Overview Ltd UK ... 60
Overview of controllers
Sinewave drive ... 373
Pacific Scientific ... 28, 51
Pan-and-tilt mechanism
Overview Ltd ... 60
Panasonic Japan ... 58
Pancake coils ... 37
Parallel paths
and bifilar winding ... 316
and circulating currents ... 145, 146
and Litz wire ... 151, 554
and turns in series per phase ... 216, 240

defining conductor current 110
effect on EMF constant kE 180
effect on inductance 216, 232, 712
effect on resistance 139
not balanced 151
used to adjust wire size 685
used to get correct turns/coil or turns in series per phase 152, 685
Parallel-sided slots
see open slots 105, 682
Park's equations 195
Park's transform 193, 194, 247-249, 326, 485
and inductance 248
Peak, mean and RMS currents
versus duty-cycle (squarewave) 289
Per-unit EMF 341
Per-unit inductance 212
Per-unit short-circuit current 343
Per-unit synchronous reactance 343
Performance and Control Questions 697
Peripheral velocity 154
Permanent-magnet generator
sign conventions 453
active rectification 467
applications 451
armature time-constant 469
as a motor with the direction of power flow reversed 453
connected to infinite bus 462
diode rectifier load 464
load testing 671
no-load (open-circuit) 455
open-circuit test 456
over-running of squarewave drive 301
overexcited 330
passive impedance load 457
pull-out torque 461
regulation 458
self-regulating 453
short-circuit fault 468
short-circuit ratio 456
steady-state short-circuit 456
steady-state stability limit 461
subtransient reactance 469
subtransient time-constant 469
types of load 454
underexcited 331
voltage regulation curves 459
Permasyn motor 500
Permeance coefficient
of magnetic circuit 93, 161
of slot 230
Permeance harmonics
and cogging torque 108

and EMF ripple 108, 456, 696
and rotor losses 561, 562, 620-630
Phase advance 18, 70
and flux-weakening 304, 344
effect on torque constant 333
in squarewave drive 304
increase in torque ripple 305, 696
uncontrolled rectification 304
Phase separator 101
Phase shift 371
and inductance 213
Phasor diagram 22, 203, 327, 329, 332
definition 19
does not apply to squarewave drive 273
duplex winding 494
flux-linkages 328
generating 330
including space phasor diagram of flux-linkages 203, 329
motor operation 327
of split-phase line-start PM motor 533
Pitch (coil)
see coil span 86, 126
Pitch factor 113, 122, 126, 128, 129, 134, 136
definition 129
for a general winding 130
harmonic 240
PM alignment torque
see Alignment torque 70
PM generator
see permanent-magnet generator 451
PM synchronous AC
see Brushless AC 28
PM-assisted synchronous reluctance motor 64, 364
Pole-group 111-113
Pole-pairs
and frequency 1
and speed 1
Poles
number of 82, 682
Polifibra 156
Position of the neutral 708
Powdered-metal materials 26
Power factor
and double-frequency pulsating component of power 187
and flux-weakening 358, 364
and inductance 213, 314
and phase advance 67
and volt-ampere requirement 213, 698
as a Figure of merit 436
auxiliary capacitor as a power-factor correction capacitor 534
example 342
how to increase 698

importance as a performance criterion . . . 367
in line-start motor . . . 497, 503, 534
in testing . . . 650
internal . . . 205
leading . . . 497, 503
maximization as a control strategy . . . 366
of generator . . . 330, 331, 459-463
variation with speed . . . 341, 359, 365
zero-power-factor load . . . 650
Power per volt-ampere . . . 213
Power rate
Figure of merit . . . 437
Premature failure . . . 702
Prescott and El-Karashi inductance bridge . . . 677
Pressed-core
see powdered-metal materials . . . 26
Printed-circuit board . . . 100
Prius
Toyota Prius . . . 34
Profibus
see Fieldbus . . . 66
Proximity effect . . . 102, 109, 143, 144, 150, 554, 646
Pull-out torque
of permanent-magnet generator . . . 461
Pull-up torque
in line-start motor . . . 506, 507
Punching
see Lamination . . . 683
Punching die . . . 683
PWM (pulse-width modulation)
see Chopping . . . 370
q-axis synchronous inductance
see synchronous inductance . . . 247
q-axis web
effect on inductance . . . 258
Quadrants of operation . . . 24
Quadrature control . . . 329, 353
Rabinovici R . . . 164, 559
Radial-flux machines . . . 30, 31
Ramp comparison . . . 383
Rasmussen KF . . . 169
Ratio of reluctance torque to alignment torque . . . 335
REA Magnet Wire Co USA . . . 102
Recoil permeability
and saliency . . . 94
generally of little significance . . . 94
Rectangular conductors . . . 100, 102, 109, 145, 685
Rectifier . . . 80
12- or 24-pulse . . . 79, 80
action of transistor bridge diodes in over-running . . . 301
as load on a PM generator . . . 2, 18, 22, 453, 454, 458, 464-467, 671
in Lajoie-Mazenc's I-γ controller . . . 372

mean rectified EMF . . . 407, 410
phase-controlled SCR . . . 13, 372, 454
precision . . . 456, 670
transistor inverter operating as active rectifier . . . 453, 454, 458, 467
waveforms . . . 410
Reference current
see Set-point current . . . 370
Reference-frame transformations
of single-phase line-start motor . . . 520
see Park's transform . . . 193
Reflection of voltage wave . . . 701
Regeneration . . . 301
Regulation
of permanent-magnet generator . . . 458, 459
Reliance Electric . . . 371, 497, 502
Reluctance torque . . . 68, 190-192, 329, 332, 335, 346, 347, 350, 351, 361, 705
and saliency . . . 68-70, 256, 703
and squarewave drive . . . 273, 310, 371
and torque linearity . . . 423
and torque ripple . . . 191, 192, 309, 310
cogging as a form of reluctance torque . . . 107, 703
concept undermined by saturation . . . 335, 367
in IPM . . . 32, 92, 687
in line-start motor . . . 501-504, 514, 515
in multi-phase machine . . . 492
included in i-ψ loop . . . 197, 198
IPM . . . 32
maximizing using multiple-layer IPM . . . 689
non-uniqueness . . . 335
small effect due to recoil permeability . . . 94
Remanence . . . 158, 160, 161
variation with temperature . . . 693, 694
Renewable energy . . . 451
Resistance . . . 12
AC resistance . . . 104, 143-151
and copper weight . . . 140
and Figures of merit . . . 405, 406, 439, 441
and Joule loss . . . 554, 693
and Litz wire . . . 144
and locked-rotor current . . . 13, 14
and magnet braking torque . . . 507
and ohms/km or ohms/1000ft . . . 140
and parallel paths . . . 139
and saliency braking torque . . . 507
and short end-windings . . . 133
and slot-fill factor . . . 101
calculation of winding resistance . . . 139
effect on measurement of inductance . . . 677, 678
equivalent DC impedance and commutating inductance . . . 464
in armature time-constant . . . 471
in complex synchronous inductance . . . 632
in electrical and mechanical time-constants . . . 443-445

increased using bifilar winding 712
load on generator 457
measurement 669, 670
must be known in DTC controller 402
of eddy-current paths 604, 610, 612, 618, 619, 629, 630, 632, 644
of laminations 556
of magnets in subtransient time-constant 470
of multi-strand conductor 104
of rotor cage in line-start motor 516, 524, 543, 548, 549
per-unit, and scaling laws 509
ratio formula for temperature variation 142
temperature rise by resistance 658, 675
thermal : see Thermal resistance 99
variation with temperature 140-142, 554, 693
X/R ratio of split-phase line-start motor 712
Resistance thermometer 650
Resistance-limited eddy-currents 563-566, 569, 602, 603, 618, 620, 625, 633, 646
Resistance-start line-start motor 712
Resistivity
of copper 142
temperature coefficient 140
Resolver 323
Retaining sleeve 26
carbon fibre 49
effect of thermal expansion 155
fitting 63
loss calculations 561
material 156
tangential or hoop stress 153
Rhombic windings 241
Richter 28
Ring magnet 31, 68, 83, 107, 607, 687
Rise-time
of voltage pulse from the inverter 700
Roebel transposition 102, 145
Roll-up stator (Panasonic Armadillo) 57
Rosa and Grover 234
Rotating field
forward and backward components 75
production with two phases 75
Rotor
can loss 561, 626
diameter 87
eccentricity 137
eddy-current loss 107, 561, 626
exterior 35
inertia 668, 717
interior 3, 30
interpolar axis (q-axis) 5
IPM 32
line-start 499-503
nonsalient-pole 68, 69

of DC motor 4
permanent-magnet 5
reference axis (d-axis) 5, 19
retaining sleeve 156
salient-pole 69, 70
skew 107
split-ratio 91
switching of transistors in synchronism 1, 2, 16
thermal expansion 155
torque at rest position 71
yoke 82
Rotor can losses 561
Rotor cup
flux-density 96
Rotor design 92-96
Rotor frequencies 588-592
rotor leakage
in IPM 160
permeance 159
see Leakage flux (pole-to-pole) 113
Rotor time-constant 642
Rotor volume 87, 88, 91
Rotor yoke
dimensions 96
solid steel 96
Rowan and Kerkman 384, 386, 389
RS232 66
RS485 66
Russell and Norsworthy 616
Saliency 68-70, 190, 248, 249, 350, 458, 509, 517, 518, 542, 543, 641, 703-705
and 2-pole rotor 256
and double-frequency inductance variation 250
and effective airgap 252
and magnetization curves 265
and optimum delta 334
and optimum gamma 333
and power factor 367
and recoil permeability 94
and saturation 256, 334, 335
and torque linearity 333, 369
braking torque in line-start motor 507
in IPM 326, 367
inverse 249, 251, 505
ratio of reluctance torque to alignment torque 335
test for 69, 704
undesirable with squarewave drive 273, 371
Saliency ratio 335
Salient-pole and nonsalient-pole machines 68
Salient-pole machines 69, 248
dq transformation 193
inductance 247
with squarewave drive 309

Sampling 378, 381
Sampling frequency 378, 387, 401
Saturable bridges 167, 168, 254-256, 268, 270, 503, 544, 546, 639, 689
Saturation 70
    and energy partition 262
    and Finite-element analysis 70
    and i-ψ diagram 190-192, 205, 207
    and inductance 212, 214, 229, 245
    and losses 346, 368
    and magnet operating point 157
    and magnetization curves 266, 267
    and narrow airgap 248
    and q-axis web 258
    and reluctance torque 367
    and short-circuit ratio 456
    and speed/torque curve 24, 333, 334
    and torque linearity 333, 369, 414, 423, 673, 692
    cross-saturation 268
    finite-element method 158
    in dq-axis model 267, 268
    in IPM 326
    in salient-pole machines 248, 249, 458
    in single-phase bifilar motor 71
    in stator teeth and yoke 683
    in the dq-axis model 267
    local 174
    non-uniqueness of reluctance torque 335
    of bridges 167
    of current-regulator 370, 383, 390, 692
    of Ld and Lq 266-270, 496
    of rotor yoke 96
    of stator tooth-tips 107
    on open-circuit 157
Schiferl R 702
Schofield N 569
Second-order system 448
Segmented magnets 93, 94, 566, 602, 603, 610, 618
Segmented rotor sleeve 618
Segmented stator 45, 63, 98, 99, 685
Self-cleating lamination stack 98
Self-commutated 699
Self-inductance 210, 214
Self-synchronous 2, 371
Sensorless control
    back-EMF sensing 312
    sinewave drive 370
Series and parallel inductances 709
Servomotor 43, 51, 52, 89, 662
Set-point current 281-284, 296, 300, 304, 305, 308, 370, 372, 379, 381, 467
Shaft position transducer 323
Shaft-mounted fan 553
Shear stress in airgap 88

Shin-Etsu Chemical Co Ltd Japan ... 162
Short-circuit current ... 338
Short-circuit faults ... 213, 468
Short-circuit ratio ... 456
Short-time operating region ... 23
Siemens ... 500
Sign conventions (permanent-magnet generator) ... 453
Sine-distributed flux ... 88
Sine-distributed magnetization
    see Halbach magnet ... 173
Sine-distributed windings . 75, 76, 217, 242, 252, 259, 261, 266, 270, 371, 520, 561, 634
    and space-vectors ... 273
Sine/triangle ramp comparison ... 383
SINEWAVE DRIVE ... 325
    basic concept ... 2
    Chapter 7 ... 381
    circle tracking ... 394
    design consideration ... 68
    electronic control ... 368
    ellipse diagram ... 326
    flux-weakening ... 326
    hexagon tracking ... 394
    hysteresis-band ... 377
    historical development ... 371
    overview of controllers ... 373
    phasor diagram — motor operation ... 327
    PWM control algorithms ... 326
    quadrature control ... 329
    six-step ... 375
    space-vector controller ... 391
    synchronous regulator ... 389
    voltage PWM (sine/triangle) ... 385
    voltage-locus diagram ... 326
Sinewave motors and generators
    basic concepts ... 16
Sinewound machine ... 325
Single-layer winding ... 105
Single-parameter imbalance ... 593
Single-phase bifilar motor ... 71
Single-phase line-start motor ... 517
    reference-frame transformations ... 520
    symmetrical components ... 519
Single-sheet tester ... 556
Single-tooth winding
    see Concentrated winding ... 133
Singly-fed machines ... 705
Sinusoidal EMF ... 131, 700
Sinusoidally-magnetized rotor ... 88, 131, 173
Six-step ... 370, 375
Sizing ... 65, 87, 681
Skew ... 113, 114, 700
    and airgap flux density ... 164

and differential inductance 250
excessive loss of EMF 108, 134
harmonic skew factor 172, 240
in squarewave motor 180
skew factor 108
skewed lamination pack 99
skewed magnetization pattern 107
to minimize cogging 107

Skin effect 143
Skin-depth 563
Sleeve
see Retaining sleeve 156
Slemon GR 559
Slot depth 683
Slot flux 683
Slot permeance 231
Slot ripple 106, 696
see Permeance harmonics 620
Slot shape
effect on inductance 231
Slot-fill factor 89, 101
and hairpin coils 683
examples 102
with rectangular conductors 100
"gross" 102
"net" 101
Slot-leakage inductance 226
and magnetic slot-wedges 682
Slot-liners
3M® fluidized-bed epoxy coating system 100
cuffed 99, 100
hand-cut 100
Slot-passing frequency 108, 553, 561, 563, 621
Slot-wedge
magnetic 682
Slot/pole ratio
minimum value 0·5 136
systematic analysis 133
Slotless winding
EMF : see §4.1.2 169
inductance 238
Maxon 59
Slots
number of 82, 105, 682
Slots forward 124
Slots/pole 82
2-phase table 83
3-phase table 84, 85
and windings 137
coil-span table 86
systematic analysis : see §3.6.6 682
SMC

see powdered-metal materials 26
Smooth rotation 698
Soak-back 692
Soft magnetic composite (SMC)
see powdered-metal materials 26
Solid steel rotor yoke
forms a stiff hub 96
Soong WL 64, 689
Soulard J 138
Space harmonics 131, 217, 250
attenuation of 225
Space limits 681
Space Station 43
Space vectors 76, 325, 375
and sine-distributed winding 242
Space-vector controller 391
Holtz 391
overmodulation 394
Span
see coil span 110
Speed
and frequency 1
and pole-pairs 1
Speed range
and inductance 213
attainable with a given supply voltage 33
of IPM 33
Speed range at constant power 68, 343, 344, 357-360, 687, 689, 699
Speed rate
Figure of merit 439
Speed-feedback control loop
to reduce torque ripple 699
Speed/torque characteristic 11, 12, 14, 15, 357-360, 365
effect of voltage 13
of the load 11
Split ratio 91
Spoke-type interior-magnet rotor 28
Spread factor
distribution factor 111
see distribution factor 77
SQUAREWAVE DRIVE 5-15, 273
and salient-pole machines 309
basic concept 2
design consideration 67
phase advance 304
Stabilization 455
Stack length 87, 92, 220, 226, 257, 423, 509, 667
Stacking
laminations 98
Staggered magnets 51
Stall / locked-rotor 13, 14, 270, 436, 439-441, 543
Standardized parts 31

Star connection
  see Wye . . . 9
Starter/generator system . . . 451
State-space averaging . . . 284
Stationary regulator . . . 374
Staton DA . . . 64
Stator
  coils (in axial-flux machine) . . . 37
  coils (in exterior-rotor machine) . . . 36
  cooling . . . 31
  core dimensions . . . 105
  design . . . 97-109, 682-685
  Gramme ring . . . 37
  laminated construction . . . 31
  laminations . . . 97
  number of slots . . . 105
  segmented . . . 45, 63
  slot depth . . . 683
  slot flux . . . 683
  tooth flux-density . . . 683
  tooth-tips . . . 106, 107
  tooth-width . . . 683
  volume (in relation to rotor volume) . . . 91
  yoke flux-density . . . 105
  yoke iron loss . . . 105
  yoke radial thickness . . . 105
Steady-state stability limit
  of permanent-magnet generator . . . 461
Steady-state stability margin . . . 504
Steen CR . . . 497, 502
Steepness
  of torque/speed characteristic . . . 14
Stefan-Boltzmann constant . . . 653
Steinmetz CP . . . 555
Step skew . . . 51
Step-response . . . 444
Stephenson JM . . . 699
Stoll and Hammond . . . 564
Stoll RL . . . 563
Stranded conductor
  see Conductor; stranded . . . 104
Strands-in-hand . . . 104, 110, 685
Strap conductors . . . 100
Sturmey-Archer Dynohub . . . 453
  Cycle hub dynamo . . . 452
Subtransient inductance and time-constant . . . 631
  effect of segmentation . . . 635
  subtransient reactance . . . 469
Summary of inverter voltage capabilities . . . 404
Superconducting machines
  related to permanent-magnet machines . . . 169, 241
Superior Essex . . . 701

Supply frequency . . . 66
Suppression circuit . . . 319
Susceptibility . . . 169
Switching duty-cycle . . . 280
Switching frequency . . . 280, 323, 368, 373, 377-383, 387, 402, 553, 554, 677, 686, 700, 701
    and inductance . . . 213
Switching representation by voltage vectors . . . 374
Switching strategy
    3-phase squarewave . . . 289
Symmetrical components . . . 21, 326, 518-522, 530-534, 539, 593
Synchronization
    of line-start motor . . . 510
Synchronous AC
    see Brushless AC . . . 28
Synchronous inductance . . . 168, 209, 243, 396, 464
    3/2 times the phase self-inductance . . . 245
    airgap component . . . 225, 240, 641
    and finite-element method . . . 263
    coefficients . . . 252
    direct calculation . . . 253, 256
    frequency-dependent . . . 529, 548, 562, 628, 631, 632, 647
    from circuit theory . . . 251
    in demagnetization calculation . . . 269
    Ld and Lq . . . 247
    magnetizing component . . . 225
    measurement . . . 246
    not applicable with nonsinusoidal current . . . 243
    saturation factors from i-psi loop calculation . . . 267, 268, 496
    static measurement . . . 246
    vector-potential method . . . 263
Synchronous regulator . . . 374, 389
Synchronous reluctance motor . . . 32, 361-363, 365-367, 371, 703
    control . . . 361
    control chart . . . 363
    line-start . . . 500-502, 509
    mode diagram . . . 363
    PM-assisted . . . 64, 364
Synchronous speed . . . 1
Synduction motor (Honsinger) . . . 499, 502
Takahashi
    Direct torque control (DTC) . . . 401
    losses in high-speed rotor . . . 626
Tapered airgap . . . 316
Teflon™ . . . 701
Temperature
    effect on efficiency . . . 693
    effect on remanence . . . 693
    important effects . . . 693
Temperature coefficient of remanence . . . 693
Temperature distribution . . . 648, 656
Temperature rise

hot-spot ... 105
importance in sizing ... 87
responsibility for ... 650
Temperature rise by resistance ... 658, 675
Terminology ... 28
Test for saliency ... 69, 704
TESTING ... 667
Thermal
analysis and cooling ... 648
diffusion equation ... 656
equivalent circuit ... 657
expansion ... 155, 659
protector ... 100
testing ... 675
Thermal resistance ... 99-101, 440-442, 650-653, 656-658, 661, 675, 676
Thin magnets
difficult to manufacture ... 93
ThinGap Motor Technologies ... 59
Third-harmonic injection ... 387, 404
Three-phase bipolar drives ... 274
Throw
see Coil span ... 86, 103
Tip speed
peripheral velocity ... 690
Tooth-width ... 683
Toothflux waveform method
EMF calculation ... 183
Toroidal stator
see Gramme-ring stator ... 41
Torque
alignment; see Alignment torque ... 190, 329
and inductance ... 190
current-limited ... 332
from coenergy ... 185
from i-ψ loop ... 197
measurement ... 672, 674
of Sinewave motors ... 187
reluctance ... 190, 329
voltage-limited ... 334
Torque constant ... 157
3-phase sinewave motor ... 189
3-phase squarewave motor ... 10, 186
and EMF constant kT & kE: see Chapter 8 ... 405
and saturation ... 213, 333
effect of phase advance ... 333
measurement ... 673
Torque linearity ... 686, 687, 692
and reluctance torque ... 423
of IPM ... 33, 333
Torque motor ... 14
Torque per unit of rotor volume
TRV ... 87, 89, 92, 681, 714

typical values (TRV) 89
Torque reversals
in line-start motor 509
Torque ripple 16, 192, 692, 696
Torque transducer 323
Torque/angle curve 333
of line-start motor 505
saturated 333
Torque/inertia ratio 31
as a Figure of merit 437
Torque/speed characteristic 282
calculation 349
see Speed/torque characteristic 11
Totally-enclosed aluminium frame 30
Toyota Prius 34, 58
Train, Alstom high-speed 208
Transfer function
between voltage and speed 443
Transient analysis
Computer simulation 291
Transient Magnetic Field by Fourier Transform 472
Triplex winding 478
Triumph Bonneville 57
Truth table (commutation table) 274
TRV
see Torque per unit of rotor volume 87
Turbogenerator 89
Turns 110
and parallel paths 152, 180, 216, 232, 240
fractional turns/coil 152, 685
high inductance in ferrite-magnet motors 212
how to decide the number of turns 684
in equivalent sine-distributed winding 242
multiple-strand 104
one turn comprises two conductors 110
related winding definitions 110
short-circuited 104
turns in series per phase 87, 139, 179, 216, 240, 684
turns per coil 110, 152
turns squared and inductance 212
Ultra Shield™ Plus (Superior Essex) 701
Unbalance
see Imbalance 593
Unbalanced operation of 3-phase machines 589
Unbalanced radial force 137
Uncontrolled rectification 304
Undamped natural frequency 448
Underexcited generator 331
Unipolar drives 315
Unipolar motors 71
Units of inertia 716
V 120 Q1 287

V 60 Q1
    dwell control ... 308
V 60 Q6 ... 286
V-shaped magnets
    in IPM ... 53
Varnishing ... 104
Vector control
    see field-oriented control ... 70
Vector potential
    and inductance ... 262
Veinott CG ... 216
Viarouge P ... 133
Vibration ... 702
Volkrodt W (Siemens) ... 500
Voltage ... 22
    capabilities of sinewave controllers ... 404
    effect on speed/torque characteristic ... 12
    inductive voltage drop ... 213
    overshoot at the motor terminals ... 700
Voltage PWM (sinewave drive) ... 326, 370, 373, 385-390, 404, 700
Voltage PWM (squarewave drive) ... 276, 286-289, 295, 306-308
Voltage regulation curves
    of permanent-magnet generator ... 459
Voltage vector ... 374
Voltage-limit ellipse ... 338
Voltage-limited maximum torque ... 334
Voltage-locus diagram ... 22, 326, 336
Walmsley ... 40
Waveforms
    3-phase delta connection; squarewave drive ... 277, 278, 283
    3-phase sinewave currents ... 17
    3-phase wye connection; squarewave drive ... 277
    basic 3-phase brushless DC ... 6
    C 60 Q6 and C 120 Q1 squarewave drive modes ... 290
    chopping ... 281
    commutation ... 283, 285, 295
    dq_VV_CR ... 382
    dwell control ... 306-308
    e,i,ψ and i-ψ loop ... 201, 202
    EMF ripple due to permeance harmonics (slot ripple) ... 696
    for accumulating current and current-squared ... 288
    hysteresis-band controller ... 378
    ideal rectifier waveforms for defining kE and kT ... 410
    ideal waveforms for defining kE and kT ... 409, 411, 420, 427
    no-load ... 303
    phase advance ... 305
    ramp-comparison controller ... 384
    regeneration ... 303
    sine/triangle voltage PWM ... 385, 388
    single-phase and 2-phase bifilar ... 315
    six-step current ... 376
    six-step voltage ... 375

space-vector modulator 395
squarewave drive with IPM 311
starting of line-start motor 508
switching of C 60Q6 and V 60 Q6 modes 287
synchronization of line-start motor 513
synchronous regulator in saturation 390
WEG Brazil 32, 55, 62, 103
Wet runner 45
Whirling 96
Wind power 451
Windage and friction 553, 647
Winding 685
AC resistance 143
balanced 110
bifilar 71, 315-317, 319, 320, 711, 712
concentrated 67, 68, 133, 134, 137, 138, 180, 217, 242, 273, 682
concentric 104, 111-113, 685
definitions 110
double-layer 105
duplex 478
electrical design 110
for squarewave drive 115
fractional-slot 118
integral-slot 111
manual 61
multiplex 478
non-overlapping 86
offset 127
resistance 139
single-layer 105
slot/pole combination 137
triplex 478
winding and inserting the phase coils 103
wire size 685
with multiple-strand conductors 104
Winding factor 218
12s10p example 126
18s8p example 122
and Hague's method 225
and magnetization curves 267
and mmf distribution 582
and synchronous inductance 252
for general winding 120
fundamental 88
harmonic 129, 131
harmonic suppression 117
of 12-slot machines 136
of concentrated winding 86, 133
of concentric winding 113
of duplex winding 479
of equivalent sine-distributed winding 242
of promising slot/pole combinations 138

of sinewave and squarewave motors 130
of squarewave motor 179, 180
shown by coil EMF diagram 130
skew 108
with irregular slotting 132

Wire
3-wire connection 21, 74, 75, 131, 194, 247, 276, 293, 307, 309, 317, 376, 380, 540, 588, 593
4-wire connection 21, 274
and conductor 110
auxiliary winding 519
connection/termination 100
current-carrying capacity 655
how to reduce wire size 685
insulation 104
inverter-grade 26, 701
length 139
Litz 144, 151, 554
mass density 140
multiple-strand 104
rectangular 102, 111
silver soldering 152
skin-effect 554
variation of diameter 140
weight 140

Wire size 685
Wire-EDM (electro-discharge machining) 97
Wood WS 509
Wye (3-phase star) connection 17, 21, 72, 116, 317, 353, 356, 361, 366, 411, 413
6-phase duplex 479-481, 484
EMF constant 180, 181, 289-293
inductance 251
inverter circuit 274, 275
line-line inductance 713
only 2 phases conducting 9, 10, 186
reconnection in Delta 189
salient-pole motor with squarewave drive 309, 310
series/parallel inductances 710
triple-n harmonic suppression 588
waveforms (squarewave drive) 277, 278
zero-sequence 600

Yoke
core losses 559
effect of pole-number on flux-density 96, 106
flux calculation 184
flux-density 106
flux-density waveform 184, 560
in exterior-rotor machines 96
nonmagnetic 96, 689
saturation 96
search-coil measurements 560
solid steel rotor 96

thickness 82, 96, 105, 106
Zener diode 318-320
Zero steady-state error 383
Zero-sequence 247
Zero-voltage states 382
Zhu ZQ 134, 169, 172, 569, 603, 620-623
Zig-zag leakage inductance 106